BUSINESS STATISTICS
A Logical Approach

Theory, Models, Procedures, and Applications
Including Computer (Minitab®) Solutions

Athanasios Vasilopoulos
St. John's University

PEARSON
Custom Publishing

Printed in the United States of America

5   17

ISBN 0-536-29714-2

2006160139

CS/KL

Please visit our web site at *www.pearsoncustom.com*

PEARSON CUSTOM PUBLISHING
75 Arlington Street, Suite 300, Boston, MA 02116
A Pearson Education Company

This book is dedicated to my family: Paraskevi, Basil John, Katherine, Panagiota, Anastasia, Thomas Athanasios V., Nicholas, Electra, Paraskevi (Pia), Peter, Melina, Thomas Athanasios F., Anysia, Alexios, Theodoros, and Steven, and to all my other relatives and friends in Mavranei and Grevena, Greece, whose support and encouragement greatly contributed to the completion of this book.

"*της παιδει΄ας αι μεν ρι΄ζαι πικραι΄,
οι δε καρποι΄ ηδει΄ς*".

"The roots of education are bitter,
but the fruit is sweet".

In Diogenes Laertius
Lives of Philosophers:
Aristotle, V, 20

Brief Contents

Contents

Part II—Probability and Random Variables   101

Chapter 4—Elements of Probability Theory   103

Chapter 5—Random Variables and Probability Functions   143

Chapter 6—The Binomial and Other Discrete Variables   197

Chapter 9—Estimation Theory   315

Chapter 10—Classical Theory of Testing   369

Chapter 11—Inferential Statistics for Small Samples   415

Part IV—Analysis of Variance   467

Chapter 12—Analysis of Variance (ANOVA)   469

Part V—Regression and Correlation Analysis   533

Chapter 13—Bivariate Analysis   535

Chapter 14—Non-Linear Regression   585

Chapter 15—Generalized Regression (Multivariate)   605

Preface

On the door of the office of one of my colleagues at St. John's University hangs the sign: "Be the teacher you always wanted to have." I have tried to be such a teacher, and over the years I have developed a set of notes which, I believe, have helped me "write the Statistics book you always wanted to read."

The ever-increasing development of highly quantitative and scientific methods in such fields as business and economic, and the social, behavioral, and administrative sciences created a strong interest in statistical methods to solve many of their problems. As a result statistics is undergoing continuous adaptation and development. However, the basic elements which are common to such fields have not changed and are needed for an understanding of the more sophisticated techniques which are being developed. It is the objective of this book to explain these basic ideas and provide the background for understanding the more advanced methods.

The underlying philosophical approach to the text is that every statistical tool presented has some business application. Even though the book is written with some mathematical rigor, it is written in such a way that the student can readily see that the proper application of statistics in the business world goes hand-in-hand with good decision-making. Mathematical rigor is used only when it is absolutely necessary to explain and understand concepts which require such treatment, such as probability, statistical inference, and regression analysis.

Statistics is presented as a means of converting data into useful information, which can then be used as the basis for more thoughtful and information-based decisions. Emphasis is placed on problem solving (and this book has over 300 solved problems) to help the student understand not only the theory and concepts but also how the statistical techniques presented and analyzed can be applied in solving real world problems.

The material covered is sufficient for a two-semester course in basic and advanced statistical concepts and applications. After a thorough discussion of Descriptive Statistics (Unit I), the book discusses six additional units which together can be used to form the following possible two-semester course in statistics:

1. Semester One
   a) Unit I—Descriptive Statistics
   b) Unit II—Probability and Random Variables
   c) Unit III—Inferential Statistics
      i) Large Sample Statistics
      ii) Small Sample Statistics

2. Semester Two
   a) Unit IV—ANalysis Of VAriance (ANOVA)
   b) Unit V—Regression Analysis
      i) Linear Regression and Correlation
      ii) Coefficient of Determination
      iii) Non-Linear Regression
      iv) Multivariate Regression

3. Unit VI—Time Series Analysis
   a) Forecasting Methods
   b) Index Numbers

4. Units VII and VIII—Special Topics
   a) Non-Parametric Statistics

The book also includes the following six (6) book Appendices, which provide sufficient background for the complete understanding of each topic:

1. Appendix A—Elements of Set Theory
2. Appendix B—Elements of Differential and Integral Calculus
3. Appendix C—Elements of Matrix Algebra
4. Appendix D—Elements of Summation Theory
5. Appendix E—Statistical Symbols and the Greek Alphabet
6. Appendix F—Elements of Sampling and Sampling Techniques

Also included are several chapters Appendices, namely:

In Chapter 16:

1. Appendix 16A—Derivation of the normal equations for a Quadratic Model
2. Appendix 16B—Barometric Methods of Forecasting
3. Appendix 16C—Analytical Methods of Forecasting

in which more advanced concepts of the chapters in questions are further discussed and analyzed.

I am grateful to many individuals who over the years, have played a direct or indirect role in making this book possible, such as: Dr. Bernardi, my undergraduate mathematics teacher at New York University, Dr. Roellofs and Dr. Cacoullos who taught me Probability and Statistics during my graduate studies at New York University, and Dr. Ya-Lun Chou, my late colleague at St. John's University whose book "Statistical Analysis" contributed greatly to my love of statistics and inspired me to write my own statistics book, but with a different emphasis.

I also want to acknowledge greatly the assistance given to me by the former Associate Dean for Academic Affairs, Tobin College of Business, St. John's University, Dr. Nejdet Delener who, over the years of writing this book, provided me with some excellent Graduate Assistants who helped me greatly in the preparation and review of the material of this book, and especially the solved problems at the end of the chapters of this book. Jie Gu, Rui (Grace) Gong, Lu Huang, Li (Gloria) Shen-Li, Timothy Kirwan, Bin (Betty) Zhao, Grigory Shterin, Li Ping Zheng, and Christala Katopodis.

I thank them all very much for their contributions. I also wish to express my gratitude to Christala Katopodis for her invaluable assistance in integrating the many pieces of this work into one unified entity.

Also, I wish to thank the editorial staff of Pearson Publishing: Delia Uherec, Erin Williams, Janice Hackenberg, Donald Golini, and Chanda Fortuna.

Finally, I wish to thank my family for their patience, understanding, and encouragement while the book was written.

A. Vasilopoulos
Commack, New York

1 Introduction to Statistics

Statistics is the science which tells us how to generate, collect, classify, present and interpret numerical data.

It is a branch of Applied Mathematics and it is used in all aspects of decision-making.

In this chapter, we introduce a number of basic terms and definitions, establish the connection between probability and statistics, and introduce a five-step procedure which is used in every statistical investigation.

Also introduced are the concepts of random and representative sampling and the resulting sampling studies which are compared and contrasted to a census study.

1.1   What Is Statistics?

Statistics is the science of generating, collecting, classifying, presenting, and interpreting numerical data.

Statistics is divided into 2 main branches:

1. Descriptive statistics, which deals with the generation, collection, classification, and presentation of numerical data.
2. Inferential statistics, which deals with the interpretation of numerical data.

Statistics is used in every field of human endeavor and it includes Education, Sciences, Government, and every form of Industry.

Some times statistics is misused, either intentionally or un-intentionally and the only safe way to avoid the misuse of statistics is to learn the basic tenets of statistics thoroughly!

The misusing of statistics usually takes the following forms:

1. Employing "tricky graphs" (*i.e.*, graphs in which the scale is omitted) to purposely confuse the issue.
2. Employing insufficient information for decision-making. As we will show shortly, a data set requires 4 different types of descriptive measures to be completely defined and all 4 of these are needed in making an informed decision.

   These 4 descriptive measures are:
   a) Measure of Central Tendency.
   b) Measure of Dispersion (or data spread).
   c) Measure of Skewness, which measures symmetry or non-symmetry.
   d) Measure of Peakedness (or Kurtosis) which measures the "narrowness" or "wideness" of the data set.

   As a minimum, measures a) and b) are absolutely essential in any meaningful decision, and yet, people continue to use either only a) or only b) in their decision-making.
3. Employing descriptive measures (such as $\overline{x}$, $\hat{s}$, etc.) in situations where they do not apply.

1.2   Basic Terms Used in Statistics

Every field of human activity has its own vocabulary and statistics, being such a field, also has its vocabulary.

Below we list a few of the most important words, making up this vocabulary, and a brief definition of each. As we progress with the development of statistical thought and methodology, more terms will be added to this list.

1. **Population** is the complete collection of all the objects or items we wish to study and which have at least one common characteristic (usually they have more) which is (are) the objectives of our interest.

   Note: In the Set Theory terminology the population is referred to as the Universal set.

   Examples of populations are the following: The planets of our solar system, the cars in a parking lot, the students taking a particular course, the particular stocks making up the portfolio of a number of investors, etc.

Populations are usually grouped in 2 major types: Infinite and Finite.

a) Infinite populations are those which include an immeasurable number of elements (such as the number of stars).

b) Finite populations are those with a measurable number of elements, such as the cars in a parking lot.

2. **Elementary Units** are the individual items which make up the population. For example, if the population of interest is "The planets of our solar system", then the elements of this population are the 8 planets: Mercury, Venus, Earth, Mars, Jupiter, Saturn, Uranus, Neptune.

On the other hand, if the population is "students taking a particular course" then every student registered in this course is an element of this population.

3. **Sample** is a portion of the population. This portion can be large or small, and in some cases can be equal to the population. In the Set Theory terminology the sample is called a subset. If the population of interest is "the planets of our solar system" then an example of a sample (or of a subset) will be the inner planets (Mercury, Venus, Earth, Mars).

4. **Variable** is a characteristic found in each individual element of the population and being different from element to element. Because the elements have many characteristics we can define many variables each of which is represented by a capital letter of the English alphabet, such as: $A, B, C, \ldots, X, Y, Z$ (or with the same letter with a different subscript such as: $X_1, X_2, \ldots$).

Let us assume, as an example, that the population of interest is "students taking a course in statistics". Then the students, being the elements of this population, have many different characteristics (as shown by the table below) such as: Height, Weight, Age, IQ, Distance to drive to SJU, etc. which can be represented by the variables: H, W, A, Q, D, etc.

CHARACTERISTICS OF THE ELEMENTS					
Individual elements	H: Height	W: Weight	A: Age	Q: IQ	D: Distance to SJU
Student 1	h_1	w_1	a_1	q_1	d_1
Student 2	h_2	w_2	a_2	q_2	d_2
Student 3	h_3	w_3	a_3	q_3	d_3
...	...	...	...	...	...
Student n	h_n	w_n	a_n	q_n	d_n

If our interest is in studying only one of the characteristics of the elements (such as H = Height) then the individual measurements of this characteristic in the different elements of the population (given in this example by $h_1, h_2, h_3, \ldots, h_n$) constitute a Univariate data set. If, on the other hand, we are interested in studying 2 characteristics of the elements jointly (such as H = Height, and W = Weight) then the data set consisting of the ordered pairs: $(h_1, w_1), (h_2, w_2), (h_3, w_3), \ldots, (h_n, w_n)$ constitute a Bivariate data set. To study 3 (or more) characteristics of the elements jointly (such as H = Height, W = Weight, and A = Age, then the data set consisting of the ordered triplets: $(h_1, w_1, a_1), (h_2, w_2, a_2), \ldots, (h_n, w_n, a_n)$ constitute a Multivariate data set. Univariate, Bivariate, and Multivariate data sets are analyzed by separate and distinct methods (as we will see later). As an example, the Multivariate case is best analyzed using matrix methods.

The many different variables we encounter in statistical analysis are grouped into 2 distinct types: Discrete and Continuous variables. Every variable, whether Discrete or Continuous, has an "Interval of Variation" associated with it. This interval defines the possible range of values for the variable of interest, from the smallest possible value to the highest possible value.

For example, if the variable of interest is H = Height of human beings, then, assuming that life begins at conception, the interval of variation for the variable H may be stated as:

$$0 \leq H = \text{Height} \leq 8^* \text{ feet} \tag{1.1}$$

Note: We assume that 8 feet is the maximum human height.

Similar intervals of variation can be stated for any other variable. Now we can use the interval of variation for each variable to make the distinction between Discrete and Continuous variables:

a) A variable is said to be discrete if it can only assume a measurable number of specific values in the interval of its variation. Discrete variables are analyzed, as we will show in our discussion of random variables, in terms of summations.

b) A variable is said to be continuous, if it can assume every value (*i.e.*, an immeasurable number of values) in its interval of definition. Continuous variables are analyzed, as we will show in our discussion of Random Variables, in terms of Integration.

5. **Data** is the set of numerical values assigned to each variable. Using the table above, the data for the variable H is given by $h_1, h_2, \ldots, h_n$ which may consist of the numerical values: $h_1 = 65$ in., $h_2 = 68$ in., $h_3 = 70$ in.,..., $h_n = 67$ in.

Similar comments can be made about numerical data of each of the variables and the data can then be classified as: Univariate, Bivariate or Multivariate, depending on whether we are analyzing one, two or more characteristics.

The data we will be called upon to analyze can have several properties which can be summarized as follows.

■ Cross-Sectional or Time-Series

Cross-Sectional data is data which is generated at essentially the same instant of time and the values obtained are *independent* of each other (*i.e.*, one value does not depend on any of the other values). An example of a Cross-Sectional data set is the grades on a test of a statistics class, generated at essentially the same time, without any cheating.

Time-Series data, on the other hand, is data generated over a period of time. An example of a Time-Series data is the time history of, say, the IBM stock. Such data are dependent because each value depends on at least one or more previous values.

■ Numerical or Categorical

Numerical data are numbers (such as the grades on a test: 78, 83, ..., 95) while Categorical data are data forming classes of data (such as the letter grade assigned to students at the end of the courses: *A, B, C, D, F*).

■ Univariate or Bivariate or Multivariate

As explained earlier Univariate data is capable of examining only one characteristic of the elements of a population, Bivariate data is capable of examining simultaneously 2 characteristics of the elements of a population, while Multivariate data is capable of examining 3 or more characteristics of the elements of the population.

In the early part of our development of statistics we will be dealing exclusively with data which is Cross-Sectional, Numerical, and Univariate.

Later on, after we develop an understanding of statistical analysis and methodology, we will discuss data which is Cross-Sectional, Numerical and Bivariate or Multivariate, while much later we will discuss time-series data.

6. **Experiment** is any planned activity which generates a set of data. An experiment can consist of a number of direct observations (such as the waiting service time of bank customers), a number of phone calls to obtain answers to pre-designed questions, personal interviews, mail questionnaires, etc.

   An experiment can be either: Deterministic (if the outcome of the experiment is known in advance and therefore there is no need to perform the experiment: it is stated here only for the purpose of forming a contrast with the other type of experiment, *i.e.*, the Stochastic experiment) or Stochastic (if the possible outcomes, which are 2 or more are known, but we do not know which of these outcomes will occur the next time the experiment is performed; Note: if the possible number of outcomes is one, the experiment is Deterministic).

   An example of a Deterministic experiment is the flipping of a specially designed coin which has 2 faces of "heads" (therefore only one outcome, heads, is possible when flipping such a coin) while an example of a Stochastic experiment is the flipping of a regular coin, with one face being a "Head" and the other a "Tail". Since there are 2 possible outcomes to this experiment (Head and Tail), the experiment is Stochastic.

7. **Parameter** is a measurable characteristic of a population, such as the population mean, represented by the lower case Greek letter μ, the population standard deviation represented by σ, the variance represented by σ^2, etc.

8. **Sample Statistic** is a measurable characteristic of a sample, such as the sample mean, represented by $\overline{x}$, the unbiased sample standard deviation represented by $\hat{s}$, the unbiased sample variance represented by $\hat{s}^2$, etc.

Note: Population parameters are always represented by lower case letters of the Greek alphabet, while sample statistics are represented by lower case letters of the English alphabet.

To better understand the difference between parameters and sample statistics, consider the diagram below, where the population is represented by the large rectangle with the population parameters listed within the rectangle, while the corresponding sample information, drawn from the population, is listed below the rectangle.

$$
\boxed{
\begin{array}{l}
\textbf{Population} \\
N \ = \text{Number of Elements in the Population} \\
\mu \ = \text{Population Mean} \\
\sigma \ = \text{Population Standard Deviation} \\
\sigma^2 \ = \text{Population Variance}
\end{array}
}
$$

$\downarrow$

Let $X_1, X_2, X_3, \ldots, X_n$ be n Sample Observations drawn from the population and

n = Sample Size

$\overline{x}$ = Sample Mean

$\hat{s}$ = Unbiased Sample Standard Deviation

$\hat{s}^2$ = Unbiased Sample Variance

The population parameters are usually unknown and in order to obtain estimates for them, we draw a sample of size n from the population (where $n \leq N$) and from the observations: $X_1, X_2, X_3, \ldots, X_n$ we calculate (as we will learn shortly) $\overline{x}, \hat{s}, \hat{s}^2$, etc. Then we use statistical theory to connect the population parameters to the sample statistics.

1.3   Impact of Digital Computers on Statistics

Before the advent of computers (the first computer became commercially available in 1954) most statistical analysis was performed by hand, with the aid of some gear-driven mechanical calculators which were very slow, noisy, and not very accurate.

The availability of digital computers in the processing of statistical data affected statistics in both positive and negative ways.

The positive effects consist of the following:

1. Increase in the Speed of Calculations.
2. Increase in the Accuracy of Calculations.
3. Increase in Storage Capability of Data.
4. Increase in Retrieval Capability of Data.

The main negative effects are the problems related to the theft of proprietary information and other security considerations. Therefore, digital computers have been a mixed blessing so far in the field of statistics because the positive effects have been counterbalanced by the very serious security problems.

1.4   Relationship Between Probability and Statistics

Probability and statistics are separate but related fields of mathematics. Probability does not depend on statistics but, without probability, statistics is not possible. Probability is the "vehicle" of statistics. The difference between probability and statistics can be summarized as follows:

1. In probability, we are interested in the chances that something will happen, when we know the possibilities.
2. In statistics, we are interested in the possibilities which gave rise to a result, when we know the result.

1.5   The 5 Stages of a Statistical Investigation

Now, after we have introduced some useful statistical background, we are ready to answer the question: how do you analyze a statistical problem? The answer to this question is: Follow the 5 step procedure below but, first let us repeat the definitions of Descriptive and Inferential statistics because they will be needed in the procedure which follows:

Descriptive Statistics: The Generation, Collection, Classification and

Presentation of Numerical data.

Inferential Statistics: The Interpretation of Numerical data.

The 5 steps of a Statistical Investigation are the following:

1. Define the problem to be solved.

   This is a very important step because you can not hope to solve a problem unless you know what it is. Do not attempt to apply possible existing data to a yet undefined problem. Instead, first define accurately the problem to be solved and then use step 2 below, to generate the data needed to solve the problem.

2. Design an appropriate experiment to generate the data to solve the problem.

   To accomplish this we need to make a number of decisions here:

   a) Define the population which contains the elements of interest

   b) Then, we need to answer the following questions:

      i) Are we going to measure every element in the population (*i.e.*, are we going to perform a Census study?)

         A Census study is more accurate but it is also more expensive and time consuming.

         (Sometimes a Census study is also destructive; For example, if we have a large number of items to sell and we need an accurate estimate of their life expectancy, in our effort to obtain it we may end up destroying all of the items.)

      ii) Are we going to select a sample* from the population and measure only the elements of the sample and then use statistical methods to make the connection between population parameters and sample calculations (*i.e.*, are we going to perform a sampling study?).

         A sampling study is less accurate (*i.e.*, it introduces some uncertainty) but it is also less expensive and less time consuming.

         (A sampling study eliminates the possible destructiveness of a Census study measuring only the elements of a small subset from the population and thus retaining the integrity of the bulk of the product.)

         If we decide to perform a sampling study we need to make certain that the following are true; otherwise the results will not be valid.

         A) The selected sample must be Random, which means that every element of the population has an equal chance of being selected in the sample.

         B) The selected sample must be Representative of the entire population we want to study and not only a portion of it. A classical example of this is the 1936 presidential election between FDR and Alfred Landon. Based on a telephone sampling the day before the election, the pollsters predicted an overwhelming victory for Landon, but the election was a triumph for FDR. Why such a discrepancy in the results? Remember, in 1936, we were in the middle of a depression, and only Republicans had telephones. The telephone sampling, even though correctly done, represented only the Republican and not all of the voters.

            Today a sales manager of a large firm, who wants to establish goal guidelines, should not select a random sample from among his top sales achievers but, rather, from the entire sales staff because a random sample from the top sales stars will produce an overstated average. Similarly, if the manager of a cafeteria in a large company wants to get an estimate of the "average price of lunch", he should not randomly sample only among

---

*See also Appendix F (Sampling and Sampling Techniques) for a more detailed discussion of sampling methods.

the company's low-level workers, nor only among his executive lunch room customers but he should sample among all of the company's employees.

Also a professor who is assigning group projects should select the groups randomly from the entire class rather than first use some means of stratification (such as Grade-Point Average) and then sample within the strata.

In each of these cases even though the sample is random within its smaller context, it is not representative of the entire group.

C) The selected sample must be large enough to get the desired accuracy in the results (We will show later, under our discussion of Estimation theory, that the sample size n and the maximum error we are willing to accept, e_{max}, are inversely proportional of each other).

3. Collect the generated data.

After the appropriate experiment has been designed to generate the required data, how is such data collected?

The usual methods are:

a) By direct observation, especially in traffic studies.

b) By questioning people through: personal interviews, telephone interviews, mail questionnaires, etc.

But we need to be careful! We must make sure that the data collected comes from objects chosen at random for this study and not from any "innocent bystanders". The people chosen represent many other people which are "similar" to them and "replacing" him/her by some one else, entirely different from them, will invalidate the conclusions of the study.

Note: A statistical study consists of the 5 steps outlined here of which we have already discussed 3. At this point we have a set of data which can be: Cross-Sectional, Numerical and Univariate and we will represent it by: $X_1, X_2, X_3, \ldots, X_n$.

Defining statistical problems, designing appropriate experiments and collecting the generated data require special skills that a student of introductory statistics does not usually have. Therefore, we will assume that someone else, more experienced and skilled in statistical analysis, has performed the first 3 steps of this procedure and our task, presented with a data set, is how to properly analyze such a data set. Therefore, steps 4 and 5 below are the main steps of interest to us, without of course minimizing the importance of the previous 3 steps.

4. Organization and Description of the Data.

Given the data set: $X_1, X_2, X_3, \ldots, X_n$, we proceed as follows:

a) Arrange the collected data into readable form. This may consist of tables, graphs, or both.

b) Calculate Descriptive measures (such as: mean, variance, etc) from the data.

Recall that earlier we defined N to be the number of elements of the population and n to be the number of elements of the sample.

If we performed a Census study (*i.e.*, if $n = N$), the calculations of the sample and of the populations produce identical results and the statistical study ends here.

However, if we performed a Sampling study (*i.e.*, if $n < N$), the sample and population calculations are not the same and the next step, step 5, is very important because, using the sample results, we want to answer questions regarding the characteristics of the entire population.

5. Final Decision or Inference

If our study is a sampling study we want to use the sample results and statistical methodology to infer (*i.e.*, to extract) the characteristics of the population. For example:

a) We may want to estimate the parameters of a distribution.

For example: In the normal (*i.e.*, bell-shaped) distribution, described by the density function:

$$f(x) = \frac{1}{\sqrt{2\pi}} \frac{1}{\sigma} e^{-\frac{1}{2\sigma^2}(x-\mu)^2} \qquad\qquad -\infty < x < \infty \qquad (1.2)$$

where μ, σ and σ^2 are the parameters of this population, we would like to obtain the "best" possible values for them and see how they are related to the sample values: $\bar{x}$, $\hat{s}$ and $\hat{s}^2$.

■ ■ ■

or   b) We may want to test a Hypothesis (*i.e.*, the validity of a claim) regarding the values of the population parameters.

For example: We may want to know if $\mu = 100$. To accomplish this we formulate the Hypotheses:

$$H_0: \mu = 100 \text{ vs } H_1: \mu \neq 100 \qquad (1.3)$$

and follow a 7-step procedure (as we will show later, in our coverage of Hypothesis testing) and there we will see how the sample calculations $\bar{x}$ and $\hat{s}$ affect certain steps of this procedure.

■ ■ ■

1.6 Mathematics Needed for the Study of Statistics

As we have stated earlier, statistics is a branch of mathematics and as such it utilizes certain mathematical tools in its analysis. The mathematics needed in the study of statistics can be summarized as in the following list:

1. Mathematical background you already have
   a) Arithmetic and Algebra
   b) Differential and Integral Calculus
2. New mathematical background (See appropriate Appendices)
   a) Summation theory (To be used in Descriptive Statistics)
   b) Set Theory (To be used in Probability theory)
3. Statistical symbols and Greek alphabet (used to represent population parameters)
   As we have already stated, sample statistics are represented by lower case letters of the English alphabet (for example $\bar{x}$ and $\hat{s}$) while population parameters are represented by lower case letters of the Greek alphabet (μ and σ).

1.7 References

Berenson, Marc, L., Levine, David, M., and Krehbiel, Timothy, C., 2004. *Basic Business Statistics*. 9th Edition. Pearson-Prentice Hall.

Black, Ken, 2004. *Business Statistics*. 4th Edition. Wiley.

Canavos, George, C., 1984. *Applied Probability and Statistical Methods*. Little, Brown.

Carlson, William, L., and Thorne, Betty, 1997. *Applied Statistical Methods*. Prentice Hall.

Chou, Ya-lun, 1992. *Statistical Analysis for Business and Economics*. Elsevier.

Freund, John, E., and Williams, Frank, J., 1969. *Modern Business Statistics*. Revised by: Perles, Benjamin and Sullivan, Charles. Prentice-hall.

Freund, John, E., and Williams, Frank, J., 1982. *Elementary Business Statistics: The Modern approach*. Prentice-Hall.

Johnson, Robert, 1973. *Elementary Statistics*. Duxbury Press.

McClave, James, T., Benson, George, P., and Sinich, Terry, 2001. *Statistics for Business and Economics*. 8th Edition. Prentice Hall.

Salvatore, Dominick, *Theory and Problems of Statistics and Econometrics*. SCHAUM'S OUTLINE SERIES, McGraw-Hill.

Steel, Robert, G.D., and Torrie, James, H., 1976. *Introduction to Statistics*. McGraw-Hill.

1.8 PROBLEMS

1. What is Statistics?

2. What are the Main branches of Statistics? What does each branch deal with?

3. Who uses Statistics?

4. What are some misuses of Statistics?

5. Define the basic statistical terms: Population, Elementary Units, Sample, Variable, Data, Stochastic Experiment, Parameter, Sample Statistic.

6. What are the types of Populations?

7. What are the types of Variables? What is the interval of variation of a variable and how is it used to distinguish between the types of variables?

8. What are the types of data to be analyzed?

   a) What is the difference between Cross-Sectional and Time-Series data?

   b) What is the difference among Univariate, Bivariate and Multivariate data?

9. What is the effect of computers on Statistics?

10. What is the relationship between probability and statistics?

11. What are the five (5) stages of statistical analysis?

   a) What is the difference between a Census and a Sampling study?

   b) When performing a Sampling study, what is meant by:
      i) a Random Sample?
      ii) a Representative Sample?

   c) When collecting the data what should we be watching for?

   d) What does Organization and Description of data consist of?

   e) What does the Final decision or Inference consist of?

DESCRIPTIVE STATISTICS

2 Data Organization and Presentation

For a given data set to provide important information for decision making it must be organized and presented in meaningful forms, such as tables and graphs, from which then useful information is obtained about the population from which the data set came from.

In this chapter we learn how to construct a data array and plot a line diagram (appropriate for the analysis of an ungrouped data set) and how to construct a frequency distribution and plot a histogram, a frequency polygon, and an ogive (appropriate for the analysis of a grouped data set).

These tables will also be used in the next chapter to calculate useful characteristics for the data set (such as arithmetic mean, median, standard deviation, etc.) while the plots help us derive the shape information of the population from which the sample data being analyzed came from.

2.1　Types of Data Collected

In the previous chapter, one of the many new terms that were introduced was that of a population which we defined as a "complete collection of items that we wish to study" (or as the *Universal Set*, if we wish to use the set theory terminology. See also Appendix A, Elements of Set Theory).

The items that make up a given population have many common properties or characteristics. For example if the students of a particular class in statistics are the items (elements) of a population, each of the students has a weight (W_i), Height (H_i), *IQ* level (IQ_i), etc. and these characteristics are measurable.

Since we can safely assume that a given population may include a very large number of elements, even though intuitively we know that each element has these characteristics which can be measured, the particular characteristic of interest, which represents the over-all population level is, in general, unknown. Statistics, then, can be considered as the science of generating, collecting, and analyzing appropriate data for the purpose of estimating the appropriate population characteristic(s).

If we are interested in estimating only one of the many elemental characteristics of a population, we measure only this characteristic in the elements of the population we select for measurement. The data thus generated is called UNIVARIATE data and the method of analysis is called UNIVARIATE analysis.

When we measure two characteristics of the elements of a population, the data thus generated is called BIVARIATE data and the method of analysis is called BIVARIATE analysis.

When we measure three or more characteristics of the elements of a population the data thus generated is, in general, called MULTIVARIATE data and the method of analysis is referred to as MULTIVARIATE analysis.

The conclusion that one should draw, from this type of reasoning, is that the data generated should conform to the objectives of the study. We should know well in advance what we wish to study or measure and then design the appropriate experiment to generate precisely the data needed for the successful completion of the study.

Therefore, based on our desire to learn something about a population and depending on the objectives of the study, the data collected for the study may be:

1. **Cross-Sectional**, which is data collected at, essentially, the same instant of time. (Example: grades in a test)
2. **Time-Series**, which is data collected over a period of time. (Example: daily values of the IBM stock)
3. **Quantitative**, which is data consisting of Numerical values. (Example: 59, 64, 73, 82, 95, 106, 121)

4. **Qualitative**, which is data consisting of categories. (Example: Pass, Fail on a test)
5. **Univariate**, which is data measuring a single characteristic of the elements of a population. (Example: If the elements of a population are the students of a statistics class, **Height** is one such characteristic.)
6. **Bivariate**, which is data measuring two characteristics of the elements of a population. (Example: Measure *Height* and *Weight* in the above example.)
7. **Multivariate**, which is data measuring three or more characteristics of the elements of a population. (Example: Measure *Height*, *Weight*, and *IQ* in the example of (5) above.)

Traditionally data which is Cross-Sectional, Quantitative and Univariate is discussed and analyzed in the first semester of a two semester Business Statistics Course.

Bivariate, Multivariate, and Time-Series data is discussed in the second semester of such a course which also includes an elementary discussion of Analysis of Variance and Industrial Experimentation.

2.2 Frequency Distribution of Data

Recall that our main objective for collecting data is to learn something about the characteristics of the population under study. If we are interested in accurately measuring a single characteristic of this population, the following three items must be evaluated:

1. The **Shape of the population**, which refers to whether the population is symmetrical or not symmetrical, thin or wide, of equal or different height, etc. regarding the characteristic of interest.
2. The **Mean Value of the population**, which refers to the average value or central location of the population concerning the characteristic of interest.
3. The **Standard Deviation of the population**, which refers to the dispersion or data spread of the population concerning the characteristic of interest.

Even though the mean and the standard deviation of the population characteristic can be determined from the *Raw Data* (*i.e.*, the data recorded in the order they are collected), such data is hard to interpret and not very helpful in determining the shape of the population characteristic. For these reasons the Raw Data is *Ranked* (*i.e.*, it is organized (arranged) according to magnitude). The ranking of the data can be either ascending (lowest to highest) or descending (highest to lowest).

The main advantages of ranked data are:

1. The shape (or distribution pattern) of the data set can be obtained with some additional effort (the actual procedure will be discussed shortly).
2. The range of the data set (which is a measure of data spread or dispersion) can be found by inspection of the ranked data set.
3. The greatest concentration of data values (equivalent to the Central Location of the population) can be found by inspection of the ranked data set.

To further pursue our analysis of a given data set, it is advantageous to classify the given data set as either "Ungrouped" data or "Grouped" data.

"Ungrouped" data is a data set which consists of *few* distinct values, but each of these values occurs *many* times. Such a data set is typical of a data set represented by a discrete random variable.

"Grouped" data is a data set which consists of many distinct values, but each of these values occurs few times. Such data sets are typical of data sets represented by continuous random variables.

The reason for making this distinction is the fact that the methods of analysis (in particular the construction of the data frequency distribution) is quite different as is the time required for the analysis.

2.2.1 Frequency Distribution of an "Ungrouped" data set

Suppose we are given a data set for analysis which, after ranking of the raw data, appears to meet the definition of an "Ungrouped" data set.

If we let X be a random variable representing the population characteristic under study, and X_1, X_2, ..., X_n the distinct values of X which occur with frequencies of repetition f_1, f_2, ..., f_n respectively, then the frequency distribution of the data set, which we collected to study the population characteristic represented by the random variable X, is:

Table 2.1 An Array							
X	X_1	X_2	X_3	X_4	X_5	...	X_n
f	f_1	f_2	f_3	f_4	f_5	...	f_n

Such a summary of the data set is also referred to as an *Array*. Then, using this data array, we can plot a "line diagram" which is a graphical representation plotting f on the vertical axis and X on the horizontal axis. The line diagram is an approximation of the "shape" or data distribution of the population characteristic under study.

This array or frequency distribution will also be used to derive many single-value descriptive measures which uniquely characterize the pattern of data distribution of the random variable X, using methods which will be discussed in the next chapter.

2.2.2 Frequency Distribution of a "Grouped" Data Set

Suppose the given data set, after ranking of the data, appears to meet the definition of a "Grouped" data set. Constructing an array for such a data set, and then plotting a line diagram from it, will not reveal the desired "shape" or data-distribution information on the population characteristic under study because, the very few data values associated with each distinct X value will give the appearance of a noise pattern rather than a data-distribution data pattern (or useful information pattern).

To analyze such a data set we need to arrange the individual data in "classes" or "groups" of data by devising a method of classification which tells us that every data value between, say, V_1 and V_2 will be in class 1, between $V_2 + \delta$ and V_3 in class 2, etc. We do this to condense the data and force it to yield the data-distribution or "shape" information but without losing too much accuracy.

The basic assumption in arriving at such a data arrangement is the "Mid-Point Assumption" which defines the middle point of each class as the representative value for all X values falling in that class.

To arrive at the frequency distribution of a "Grouped" data set we need to follow a somewhat lengthy procedure which, for convenience of discussion, is divided into: I) General Rules and II) Specific Rules.

To facilitate the discussion and introduce more visibility in the understanding of the procedure, refer to the diagram below, which shows a number of classes superimposed on the real line which is imagined to extend from $-\infty$ to $+\infty$.

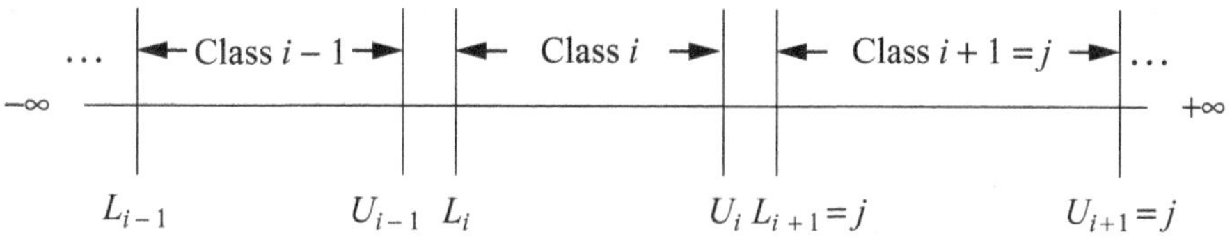

Figure 2.1 Specifying the classes of a Grouped Data Set

I. General Rules

a) Each class (Class i as an example) is defined by its Lower Class limit (L_i) and Upper Class Limit (U_i).

b) The difference between two successive Lower Class Limits or two successive Upper Class Limits is referred to as the "class interval". For class i and j, the class interval $C = C_{ij}$ is given by:

$$\text{Class Interval} = C = C_{ij} = L_j - L_i = U_j - U_i \tag{2.1}$$

If the class interval is constant throughout the classification design, then C_{ij} is replaced by C. In this case we speak of a uniform class interval. The class interval represents the portion of the real live allocated to each class.

c) The number of classes or groups, which is represented by m, should be between 5 and 15 (*i.e.*, $5 \le m \le 15$), depending on the accuracy of representation that is desired. More accuracy requires more classes. The usual number chosen for m is 10 which is the midpoint of the interval of variation for m.

A method exists, called *Sturge's Rule*, which determines a "ball-park" value for m, as a function of the sample size n, from the formula:

$$m = 1 + 3.322 \log_{10} n \tag{2.2}$$

As an example, when $n = 50$, $\log_{10} n = 1.69897$, and
$$\begin{aligned}
m &= 1 + 3.322(1.69897) \\
&= 1 + 5.64 \\
&= 6.64 \\
&= 7 \quad \text{(since we cannot have a "fractional" class)}
\end{aligned}$$

The interpretation that should be assigned to the value of m obtained from Sturge's Rule is that the selected value for m should be at least as large as the m calculated by the Sturge's Rule, or

$$m \ge 1 + 3.322 \log_{10} n. \tag{2.3}$$

d) To facilitate calculations, make the class intervals whole numbers, by rounding up to the next higher whole number. This is dictated by the requirement that the classes be "Collectively Exhaustive" (as discussed in (g) below).

e) If L is the smallest value in the ranked data set, start the class design at a value lower than L (to be specified under the *Specific Rules*).

f) If H is the highest value in the ranked data set, end the class design at a value higher than H (to be specified under the *Specific Rules*).

g) Use classes which are both "Mutually Exclusive" (that is non-overlapping), and "Collectively Exhaustive", (that is, they cover all possibilities).

One way to accomplish "Mutual Exclusiveness" is to use the following heading:

"From"	and	*"Up to but not including"*
5		10
10		15

etc.

"Collectively exhaustive" classes can be obtained, as discussed in (d) above, by starting with a value less than L and ending the design with a value higher than H.

II. Specific Rules

To completely classify a given "Grouped" data set we must do the following:

a) Rank the data and identify L = the lowest data value and H = the highest data value.

b) Find the range of the data set R, where:

$$R = H - L \tag{2.4}$$

c) Choose the number of classes (*i.e.*, specify the value of m) either arbitrarily or by using Sturge's Rule.

d) Then, to make certain that the classes will be Collectively Exhaustive, let:

$$C \geq \frac{R}{m} \quad \text{(or } Cm \geq R) \tag{2.5}$$

By taking $C > \dfrac{R}{m}$ we will insure that the design will start at a value lower than L and end at a value higher than H (see step (e) below).

e) Define the starting point (*S.P.*) of the class design as:

$$S.P. = L - \left(\frac{Cm - R}{2}\right) \tag{2.6}$$

Thus the starting point is lower than L and the ending point will be higher than H (when the design is completed (see step (g) below)).

f) Then the lower class limits of the design are given by:

$$L_i = S.P. + (i - 1)C \quad \text{where } i = 1, 2, \ldots, m \tag{2.7}$$

g) Before we give a similar formula to define the Upper Class Limits of the design, we must stress a requirement that must be satisfied, namely that the Upper Class Limit of any class must be less than the Lower Class limit of the next class limit. In terms of the symbols used in the diagram above, this requirement can be stated mathematically as:

$$U_i < L_{i+1} \tag{2.8}$$

In particular we are interested in the value of U_1, in terms of which the other U_i will be defined.

The actual value of U_1 depends on the "granularity" of the data (that is, it depends on the number of decimal places in the data. If the data are all whole numbers U_1 will be a whole number and it is obtained from:

$$U_1 = L_2 - 1 \tag{2.9}$$

If the data has one decimal place, then U_1 will also have one decimal place and it is obtained from:

$$U_1 = L_2 - 0.1 \tag{2.10}$$

In general, if the data has k decimal places, the value of U_1 is obtained from:

$$U_1 = L_2 - \frac{1}{10^k}, \text{ where } k = 0, 1, 2, 3, \ldots \tag{2.11}$$

Then the other Upper Class Limits of the design can be found from the equation:

$$U_i = U_1 + (i - 1)C \text{ where } i = 1, 2, \ldots, m \tag{2.12}$$

h) The mid-point or "class mark" of each class, needed to represent the value of each data point falling in this class in accordance with the "Mid-Point" assumption, is given by m_i, where:

$$m_i = \frac{L_i + U_i}{2} \tag{2.13}$$

i) The mid point between one class's Upper Class Limit and the next class's Lower Class Limit is referred to as "Class Boundary".

Then the class boundary between classes i and j is:

$$Cb_{ij} = \frac{U_i + L_j}{2} \tag{2.14}$$

Note that each class has a class boundary on each of its two sides, except for the first and last classes which have only one class boundary.

It is clear from the above definitions that if U_i is very close to L_j, the distance $L_j - U_i$ can be made arbitrarily small and Cb_{ij} can be made to almost coincide with U_i and L_j.

j) For a class design with a uniform class interval C, we have:

$$C = L_j - L_i = U_j - U_i = m_j - m_i = Cb_{ij} - Cb_{i-1, i} \tag{2.15}$$

This property is maintained throughout the design and can be used to test the accuracy and validity of the design at arbitrary points of the data frequency distribution table we are about to construct.

2.2.3 Frequency Distribution Table and Plots which can be made from the Frequency Distribution of a Grouped Data Set

The information generated by following the class design procedure discussed above can be summarized in a table similar to the one shown below.

Table 2.2 A Frequency Distribution of a Grouped Data Set						
Column 1	Column 2		Column 3	Column 4	Column 5	Column 6	Column 7
Class Number	Class Limits		Frequency	Class Mark	Class Boundaries	Relative Frequency $\dfrac{f_i}{n}$	Cumulative Relative Frequency
	L_i	U_i	f_i	m_i	Cb_{ij}		
0	L_0	U_0	$f_0 = 0$	m_0	$Cb_{0,1}$	0	0
1	L_1	U_1	f_1	m_1	$Cb_{1,2}$	$\dfrac{f_1}{n}$	$\dfrac{f_1}{n}$
2	L_2	U_2	f_2	m_2	$Cb_{2,3}$	$\dfrac{f_2}{n}$	$\dfrac{f_1}{n} + \dfrac{f_2}{n}$
...	...	...	...	...	...	...	
m	L_m	U_m	f_m	m_m	$Cb_{m, m+1}$	$\dfrac{f_m}{n}$	$\dfrac{f_1 + f_2 + \cdots + f_n}{n}$
$(m + 1)$	L_{m+1}	U_{m+1}	$f_{m+1} = 0$	m_{m+1}		0	1

Note: Classes (0) and $(m + 1)$ do not really exist. They are shown to justify the calculation of the class boundaries $cb_{0,1}$ and $cb_{m, m+1}$.

The frequency column (column 3) in the above table is obtained from the ranked data set by counting the number of data values that fall between L_1 and U_1 to obtain f_1, between L_2 and U_2 to obtain f_2, etc.

Another column that should be included in the table above and is very useful is "Cumulative Frequency" whose values are obtained from column 3 and are given by:

$$f_0, f_0 + f_1, f_0 + f_1 + f_2, \ldots, f_0 + f_1 + f_2 + \cdots + f_m.$$

For calculations purposes we should also calculate: $\sum_{i=1}^{m} f_i m_i$ and $\sum_{i=1}^{m} f_i m_i^2$.

The derivation of the other columns is self-explanatory. Columns 3 and 4 contain information which is equivalent to the information contained in the data array discussed under "Frequency Distribution of an Ungrouped Data Set" with the class mark m_i taking the place of X_i, while f_i remains unchanged.

Note that the entries of column 5 are almost on the line separating two successive classes. This is done intentionally to emphasize the point that class boundaries are values separating two classes and are not associated with a single class only.

Just as the data array will be used to calculate single value descriptive measures for the Ungrouped Data Set, so the Frequency Distribution table will be used to calculate single value descriptive measures for the Grouped Data Set.

But, in addition to that which will be demonstrated later, the frequency distribution will be used to make the following plots:

1. Histogram
2. Frequency Polygon
3. Ogive

From these plots the desired "shape" or data distribution information can be extracted, for the population characteristic under evaluation.

Generally speaking the Histogram is a bar chart which plots Absolute or Relative frequency against Class Boundaries, the Frequency Polygon is a line diagram which plots Absolute or Relative Frequency against Class Marks, while the Ogive is a line chart which plots Cumulative Absolute or Relative Frequency against Class Boundaries.

The actual way by which these plots are made will be demonstrated by an example which will also illustrate the methodology used in the design of the classification scheme.

Example 1

Considering the following set of Raw data as a Grouped data set, derive the Frequency Distribution table and from it construct the Histogram, Frequency Polygon and Ogive plots.

Raw Data:

75	97	74	120	71
97	58	73	94	106
71	94	68	79	86
65	43	54	80	108
84	116	50	83	84
27	123	49	71	93
108	91	81	88	77
91	120	128	88	107
122	94	103	47	44
84	43	76	73	127

Re-arranging this data set from smallest to highest and identifying the smallest and highest values in the set by L and H respectively, we obtain the ranked Data Set shown below.

1. Ranked Data

$L = 27$	68	79	91	107
43	71	80	91	108
43	71	81	93	108
44	71	83	94	116
47	73	84	94	120
49	73	84	94	120
50	74	84	97	122
54	75	86	97	123
58	76	88	103	127
65	77	88	106	$128 = H$

2. From the ranked data, $R = H - L = 128 - 27 = 101$
3. Selection of m:

   Since $n = 50$, and Sturge's Rule produces $m \geq 7$, we will choose $m = 10$, for greater accuracy.
4. Then, from $C > \dfrac{R}{m}$ we obtain: $C > \dfrac{101}{10}$ or $C > 10.1$. We select $C = 11$, to make computations easier.
5. Starting point $= S.P. = L - \left(\dfrac{mC - R}{2} \right) = 27 - \left(\dfrac{110 - 101}{2} \right) = 27 - 4.5 = 22.5$

   ≈ 22 (To make computations easier)
6. Lower Class Limits: $L_i = S.P. + (i - 1)C$

   $$L_i = 22 + (i - 1)(11) \quad \text{for } i = 1, 2, \ldots, 10$$

   Therefore, the Lower Class Limits are $L_1 = 22$, $L_2 = 33$, $L_3 = 44$, $L_4 = 55$, $\ldots$, $L_{10} = 121$.
7. Upper Class Limits:

   Since $U_1 < L_2$, obviously $U_1 < 33$; therefore, many values less than 33 are suitable. Because the data consists of whole numbers, the best choice for U_1 is 32 (We could have chosen 32.9, 32.5, 32.2, etc.)

   Then $\quad U_i = U_1 + (i - 1)C$

   $$U_i = 32 + (i - 1)(11) \quad \text{for } \quad i = 1, 2, \ldots, 10$$

   Therefore, the Upper Class Limits are:

   $U_1 = 32, 43, 54, 65, 76, 78, 98, 109, 120, U_{10} = 131$
8. Now that the L_i and U_i have been defined, the mid-point or class mark for each class can be calculated from:

   $$m_i = \frac{L_i + U_i}{2}$$

   The results are: $m_1 = 27, 38, 49, 60, 71, 82, 93, 104, 115, m_{10} = 126$.

   We can also calculate the class marks of the hypothetical classes 0 and $m + 1$ which are needed for the Frequency Polygon plot and obtain: $m_0 = 16$, and $m_{11} = 137$
9. The class boundaries, $Cb_{i, j}$, are calculated from:

   $$Cb_{i, j} = \frac{U_i + L_j}{2}$$

Using the values obtained for L_i and U_i above, we calculate:

$$Cb_{0,1} = 21.5, 32.5, 43.5, 54.5, 65.5, 76.5, 87.5, 98.5, 109.5, 120.5, Cb_{10,11} = 131.5$$

10. Clearly for this design

$$C = 11 = L_j - L_i = U_j - U_i = m_j - m_i = Cb_{i,j} - Cb_{i-1,i} \quad \text{for all } i, j$$

The derived Frequency Distribution is shown in the table below:

Column 1	Column 2		Column 3	Column 4	Column 5	Column 6	Column 7
Class Number	Class Limits L_i	U_i	Frequency f_i	Class Mark m_i	Class Boundaries cb_{ij}	Relative Frequency $\dfrac{f_i}{n}$	Cumulative Relative Frequency
(0)	11	21	0	(16)	21.5	0	0
1	22	32	1	27	32.5	0.02	0.02
2	33	43	2	38	43.5	0.04	0.06
3	44	54	5	49	54.5	0.10	0.16
4	55	65	2	60	65.5	0.04	0.20
5	66	76	9	71	76.5	0.18	0.38
6	77	87	9	82	87.5	0.18	0.56
7	88	98	10	93	98.5	0.20	0.76
8	99	109	5	104	109.5	0.10	0.86
9	110	120	3	115	120.5	0.06	0.92
10	121	131	4	126	131.5	0.08	1.00
(11)	132	142	0	(137)		0	1.00

The entries for the Cumulative Frequency column are: 0, 1, 3, 8, 10, 19, 28, 38, 43, 46, 50, and 50, and $\sum_{i=1}^{10} f_i m_i = 4{,}144$ and $\sum_{i=1}^{10} f_i m_i^2 = 372{,}456$.

From this table the Histogram, Frequency Polygon, and Ogive are plotted as shown on figures 2.1, 2.2, and 2.3.

Figures 2.1a and 2.1b show the Histogram in bar chart form with the vertical scale consisting of both Absolute and Relative frequency while the horizontal axis is the class boundaries. Therefore, the Histogram plots column 3 and/or 6 against column 5.

HISTOGRAM

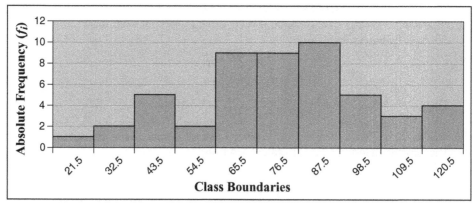

Figure 2.1a Histogram: Bar Graph Representation of an entire set of data (Absolute)

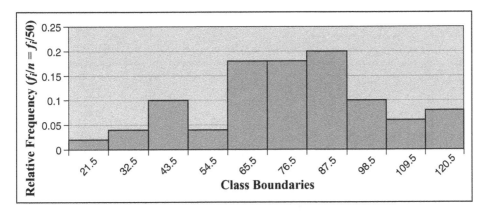

Figure 2.1b Histogram: Bar Graph Representation of an entire set of data (Relative)

Notice that the resulting shape is almost symmetrical, with large concentration of values in the center which then taper off at the ends. To increase the accuracy of the distribution we could: a) Choose more classes and b) Increase the sample size, or c) do both simultaneously.

Notes:
1. The Shape of the population, from which the sample was drawn, is very similar to the shape of the histogram
2. For more accuracy:
   a) Choose more classes
   b) Increase the sample size
3. Types of Distributions which may emerge from a histogram:
   a) Symmetrical
   b) Rectangular
   c) Skewed
   d) J-Shaped
   e) Bi-Modal
4. Notes:
   a) Mode: Singular most common piece of data (Not unique in this example!) 71, 84, 94 each occurs 3 times!
   b) Modal Class: Most populous Class (class 7 here)

Figures 2a and 2b show the Frequency Polygon as a line graph. It plots Frequency (either Absolute or Relative or both) against Class Marks. The resulting shape, in its limiting form, is similar to the shape of the population from which the sample came from. It is useful in comparing alternate design classifications on the same distribution or when comparing several distributions. It is much clearer to draw and compare Frequency Polygons than Histograms.

FREQUENCY POLYGON
It plots Absolute or Relative Frequency or both versus Class Marks.

1. A dot is placed at the appropriate frequency level for each class midpoint.
2. Use a line to connect adjacent dots.
3. Starts at zero.
4. Ends at zero.
5. It is useful when comparing several distributions (or different classification designs on the same distribution). It is much clearer to use Frequency Polygons than Histograms for such comparisons.

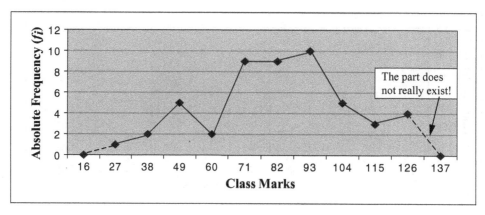

Figure 2.2a Frequency Polygon: Line Graph Representation (Absolute)

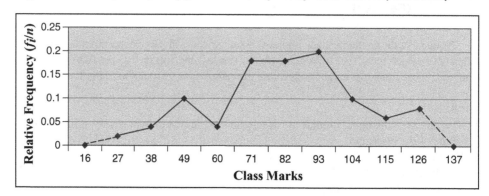

Figure 2.2b Frequency Polygon: Line Graph Representation (Relative)

Figures 3a and 3b shows a plot of the Ogive which plots Cumulative Absolute or Relative Frequency (column 4 or 7) against Class Boundaries (column 5). It is a very useful graph, and unique for each distinct population. It can be used to calculate approximately all the Quartiles and Percentiles as shown on Figure 3 and discussed, in greater detail, in the next Chapter.

OGIVE

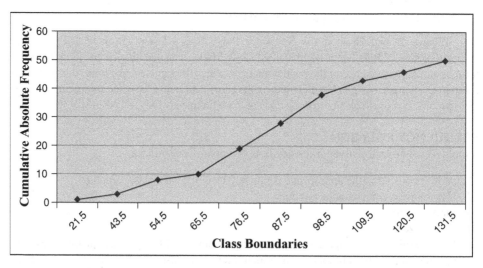

Figure 2.3a Ogive Cumulative Absolute Frequency Diagram

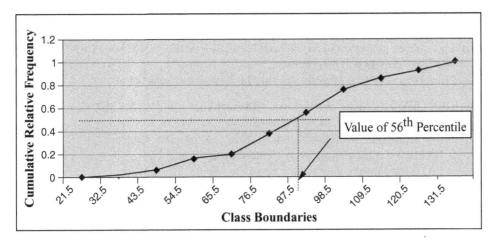

Figure 2.3b Ogive Cumulative Relative Frequency Diagram

Notes:
1. Starts at zero.
2. Ends at 1.
3. It is a very useful graph. It can be used to calculate approximately all the quartiles and percentiles.

Method: On the vertical scale locate the item of interest; say 56th percentile; Draw a line parallel to the horizontal axis until it intersects the Ogive; then drop a line perpendicular to the horizontal axis. The point of intersection on the horizontal axis is the desired value.

Note: The accuracy of these calculations depends on the accuracy of the scales used.

2.3   MINITAB Computer Solutions

Most of the analysis we have done by hand can also be done by a computer. Many statistical analysis tools are commercially available and, when properly exercised, produce correct results.

In fact, when the given data set is very large, the computer solution is the preferred method of analysis. When the sample size is relatively small, both hand and computer solutions should be obtained and the two results be compared. After confidence is gained through such comparisons that hand and computer solutions are equivalent, one can move to an exclusive computer solution. But it is important to first learn how to interpret the computer-generated solution.

One of the best known and widely used statistical tools is the MINITAB which, in its latest version: MINITAB Release 14.1+, in addition to other tasks, performs analysis of DESCRIPTIVE STATISTICS (*i.e.*, Data Organization and Calculation of Descriptive Measures) in 2 different ways, which manifest themselves when one is linked to MINITAB. The first screen one obtains is a Split Screen, with the upper half titled "SESSION" window and the lower "WORKSHEET 1" window. Each of these 2 windows is exercised differently, as shown on the next page:

■ The "SESSION" Window

To use this window the MINITAB prompt, MTB> must be shown on the session window. If it is not shown, go to the "EDITOR" and "ENABLE THE COMMAND LANGUAGE", and the MTB> prompt will be generated.

To solve a statistical problem, you need to follow the steps below:

1. IDENTIFY the column in which you will enter your data (MTB> SET C1)
2. ENTER your numerical data (DATA> 50, 60 ...)
3. ISSUE appropriate MTB commands to solve your problem, such as:
   a) NAME the column in which you entered your data.
   b) SAVE the named column (once saved the data can be recalled).
   c) RETRIEVE the named column of data.
   d) SORT the named column of data (it arranges data in order of Magnitude).
   e) PRINT the column of data you typed.

Note: Press "Print Screen" key to get copy of what the screen shows.

1. DOTPLOT the column. (This is a plot similar to the LINE diagram of Ungrouped Data.)
2. HISTOGRAM the column. (To obtain a Histogram of the Grouped Data Set.)
3. DESCRIBE the column. (To obtain Numerical values for a number of selected DESCRIPTIVE STATISTICS. See Chapter 3)

Note: There are many more MINITAB commands but the ones listed above represent a minimum set to perform the data organization and computation analysis discussed in Chapters 2 and 3 respectively. Their actual usage is shown below. Additional MINITAB commands will be introduced, as needed in future chapters.

To apply this procedure to the example of section 2.2, 2.3, we must do the following:

MTB>	SET C1
DATA>	75 97 71 65 84 27 108 91 122 84
DATA>	97 58 94 43 116 123 91 120 94 43
DATA>	74 73 68 54 50 49 81 128 103 76
DATA>	120 94 79 80 83 71 88 88 47 73
DATA>	71 106 86 108 84 93 77 107 44 127
DATA>	END
MTB>	NAME C1 'DSTAT'
MTB>	PRINT C1
MTB>	DOTPLOT C1
MTB>	HISTOGRAM 'DSTAT';
SUBC>	MIDPOINT 27:126/11;
SUBC>	BAR.

This is the entire histogram command and consists of the main and 2 subcommands. The ";" indicates continuation of the command, while "." indicates termination of the command.

Note: MIDPOINT 27 is the midpoint of the FIRST CLASS and 126 is the MIDPOINT of the LAST CLASS, while C is the CLASS width which, in our example, is C = 11.

The Histogram command is rather complicated but, in this form, it allows us to specify the midpoint of the FIRST and LAST classes, and also the classwidth.

There is also a simpler HISTOGRAM Command (MTB> HISTOGRAM 'DSTAT') without the 2 subcommands but, in this case, we obtain the "Default" Histogram allowed by the tool, and not the one we want to specify.

MTB >   DESCRIBE C1

After the data is entered as shown above, and we issue the commands numbered (1), (2), and (3) above, the resulting computer output is given by Figures 2.4, 2.5, and 2.6, respectively. At this point it is instructive to compare the computer results with the hand computations (both for Ungrouped and Grouped data), where possible, and identify any differences that may exist. These differences should be analyzed properly and the reasons for their occurrence should be documented and corrected if necessary.

■ The "WORKSHEET 1" WINDOW

1. Type all of the given data, one by one, in the FIRST column of the worksheet.
2. Go to the EDITOR and "ENABLE THE COMMAND LANGUAGE".
3. TO OBTAIN THE DOTPLOT, do the following:
   a) Go to Graph.
   b) Click "DOTPLOT", when the window appears.
   c) DOUBLE CLICK "C1".
   d) Then CLICK "OK".

Note: You can also add a title to the graph, by following directions.

4. TO OBTAIN THE HISTOGRAM, do the following:
   a) Go to Graph.
   b) Click "HISTOGRAM", when the window appears.
   c) DOUBLE CLICK "C1".
   d) Then CLICK "OK".

Note: YOU MAY ALSO NEED TO CLICK "OPTION" TO DEFINE WHETHER YOU WANT TO CREATE A HISTOGRAM ABOUT:
   a) FREQUENCY
   b) PERCENT
   c) DENSITY
   d) CUMULATIVE FREQUENCY
   e) CUMULATIVE PERCENT
   f) CUMULATIVE DENSITY
   g) DEFINE THE "TYPES OF INTERVAL" OR "DEFINITION OF INTERVAL"

5. TO OBTAIN MEASURES OF DESCRIPTIVE STATISTICS, do the following:
   a) Go to "STAT"
   b) CLICK "DESCRIPTIVE STATISTICS" and obtain values for:
      MEAN, MEDIAN, STANDARD DEVIATION, MAXIMUM VALUE, MINIMUM VALUE, Q_1 VALUE, Q_3 VALUE

DOTPLOT OF C1

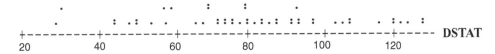

Figure 2.4 Dotplot for Example 1

HISTOGRAM OF C1

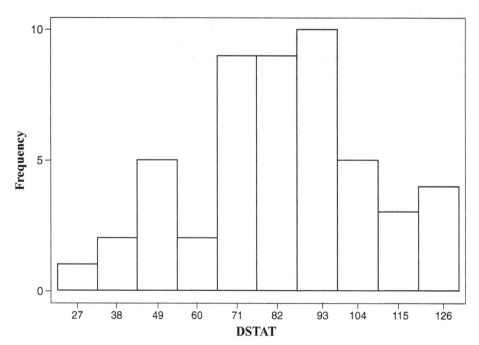

Figure 2.5 Histogram for Example 1

MTB> Describe C1;

Descriptive Statistics: C1

Variable	N	Mean	Median	TrMean	StDev	SE Mean
C1	50	83.70	84.00	83.95	24.32	3.44

Variable	Minimum	Maximum	Q1	Q3
C1	27.00	128.00	71.00	98.50

Figure 2.6 Selected Descriptive Measures

2.4 References

Berenson, Marc, L., Levine, David, M., and Krehbiel, Timothy, C., 2004. *Basic Business Statistics*. 9th Edition. Pearson-Prentice Hall.

Black, Ken, 2004. *Business Statistics*. 4th Edition. Wiley.

Canavos, George, C., 1984. *Applied Probability and Statistical Methods*. Little, Brown.

Carlson, William, L., and Thorne, Betty, 1997. *Applied Statistical Methods*. Prentice Hall.

Chou, Ya-lun, 1992. *Statistical Analysis for Business and Economics*. Elsevier.

Freund, John, E., and Williams, Frank, J., 1969. *Modern Business Statistics*. Revised by: Perles, Benjamin and Sullivan, Charles. Prentice-Hall.

Freund, John, E., and Williams, Frank, J., 1982. *Elementary Business Statistics: The Modern approach*. Prentice-Hall.

Johnson, Robert, 1973. *Elementary Statistics*. Duxbury Press.

McClave, James, T., Benson, George, P., and Sincich, Terry, 2001. *Statistics for Business and Economics*. 8th Edition. Prentice Hall.

Salvatore, Dominick, *Theory and Problems of Statistics and Econometrics*. SCHAUM'S OUTLINE SERIES, McGraw-Hill.

Steel, Robert, G.D., and Torrie, James, H., 1976. *Introduction to Statistics*. McGraw-Hill.

2.5 PROBLEMS

The following set of data represents final Grades of 50 students in Statistics, selected at random from among all students taking the course at a given university, in a given year:

66	47	93	70	34
61	81	95	65	86
67	42	34	65	75
53	62	98	67	76
87	92	67	62	55
58	40	74	56	66
72	42	78	74	44
79	82	67	60	85
36	56	68	44	88
51	49	89	78	76

We wish to analyze this data set both as an Ungrouped and Grouped data set.

1. Considering this data set as an Ungrouped data set:
   a) Construct an appropriate data Array.
   b) Plot the corresponding Line diagram.
   c) Use MINITAB to obtain the "DOTPLOT".
   d) Compare the hand-drawn Line Diagram and the computer-drawn "DOTPLOT".

2. Considering this data set as a Grouped data set:
   a) Construct a Frequency Distribution for this data set, using 31 as the Starting Point, and with a class width $C = 10$
   b) Construct a Histogram, with both Absolute and Relative frequency scales.
   c) Construct a Frequency Polygon, with both Absolute and Relative frequency scales.
   d) Construct an Ogive, with both Absolute and Relative frequency scales.
   e) Use MINITAB to obtain the "HISTOGRAM"
   f) Compare the hand-drawn histogram and the computer-drawn "HISTOGRAM".

3. Construct a Frequency distribution of the Area of the States, using a class width of $c = 10,000$ square miles.
   a) Plot the Histogram of this Frequency distribution. What does the "shape" of the "smooth" curve fitted to this Histogram look like?
   b) How many states have an area of under 10,000 square miles?
   c) How many states have an area of over 100,000 square miles?

4. Construct a Frequency distribution of the Population of the States, using a class width of $c = 1,000,000$. Plot the Histogram of this Frequency distribution. What does the "shape" of the "smooth" curve fitted to this Histogram look like?
   a) How many states have a Population of under 1,000,000?
   b) What is the modal class and what is the frequency of the modal class?
   c) How many states have a Population of over 10,000,000?

5. Using as the distinct values of X the letters of the alphabet with which each state begins:

   a) Construct a data array in which frequency represents the number of states which begin with a given letter of the alphabet.

   b) Plot a line diagram of f (frequency) on the vertical scale versus X (the letters of the alphabet) on the horizontal line.

   c) Which letters of the alphabet are the most popular (*i.e.*, which letters of the alphabet begin the names of more states)?

   d) Which letters of the alphabet are the least popular?

6. For the partially given frequency distribution given below:

Class Number	Class Limits		Absolute Frequency (f_i)	Cumulative Frequency (F_i)	Class Marks (m_i)	$m_i f_i$	$m_i^2 f_i$
	L	U					
1	15	19	3				
2	20	24	12				
3	25	29	19				
4	30	34	6				
5	35	39	5				
6	40	44	2				
7	45	49	2				
8	50	54	1				

   a) Complete the frequency distribution so that the required plots of histogram, frequency polygon, and ogive, can be made (need the columns of cumulative frequency, class marks, and class boundaries).

   b) Plot the histogram. It plots frequency (on the vertical axis) versus class boundaries (on the Horizontal axis).

   c) Plot the frequency polygon. It plots frequency (on the vertical axis) versus class marks (on the Horizontal axis).

   d) Plot the ogive. It plots cumulative frequency (on the vertical axis) versus class boundaries (on the Horizontal axis).

7. The cans in a sample of 20 cans of fruit contain net weights of fruit from 19.3 to 20.9 oz, as shown in the table below:

   19.9, 19.7, 20.1, 19.5, 20.9, 20.2, 19.9, 20.3, 20.8, 20.0, 20.6, 19.9, 20.0, 19.3, 20.4, 20.6, 19.9, 19.9, 19.8, 20.3.

   Treating this data set as an ungrouped data set, a) Construct a data array, and b) Plot the corresponding line diagram.

8. Treating the data of problem 7 as a grouped data set,

   a) Construct a frequency distribution.

   b) Plot the histogram.

   c) Plot the frequency polygon.

   d) Plot the ogive.

9. A student received the following grades (measured from 0 to 10) on the 10 quizzes he took during a semester in a statistics class: 7, 8, 7, 9, 6, 8, 7, 9, 10, 6. Construct:

   a) An array of these grades.

   b) Plot a Line Diagram.

10. A sample of 25 workers in a plant received the hourly wages shown below: 3.65, 3.60, 3.88, 3.78, 3.90, 3.95, 3.85, 4.26, 4.06, 3.95, 3.75, 4.18, 4.00, 3.95, 4.05, 4.10, 4.05, 4.25, 4.08, 3.55, 4.15, 3.85, 3.80, 3.96, 4.05.

a) Construct a Frequency distribution.

b) Present the data in the form of a Histogram.

c) Present the data in the form of a Frequency Polygon.

d) Present the data in the form of an Ogive.

11. Suppose in a given data set, $H = 109.6$ and $L = 92.3$. Explain why in such a data set the class interval of a frequency distribution could reasonably be 2 units.

12. The wages paid to the piecework employees of a firm in a given week varied from $165.20 to $266.60.

a) Derive the Lower and Upper limits of six classes into which these wages can be grouped.

b) Are these six classes mutually exclusive and collectively exhaustive? Justify your answer.

13. To group sales invoices ranging from $15.00 to $40.00, a clerk uses the following classes: $15.00 to $19.99, $20.00 to $25.99, $25.00 to $29.99, $30.00 to $34.90, and $35.00 to $39.99. Are these classes mutually exclusive and collectively exhausted? Justify your answers, because the values from $34.91 to $34.99 and the value of $40.00 are not accommodated.

14. The class marks of a frequency distribution of the daily number of cameras brought into a repair shop are: 4, 11, 18, 25 and 32. If it is known that $L_1 = 1$, find:

a) The class limits;

b) The class boundaries.

15. A customs official groups the declared values of a number of packages mailed from a foreign country into a frequency distribution with the classes: $0.00–9.99, $10.00–19.99, $20.00–29.99, $30.00–39.99, $40.00–49.99, $50.00–59.99, and $60.00 and over. Is it possible to determine from this distribution the number of packages valued at:

a) less than $40.00;

b) $40.00 or less;

c) more than $30.00;

d) $30.00 or more?

16. The number of empty seats on flights from New York to Tampa are grouped into a table with the classes: 0–9, 10–19, 20–29, 30–39, and 40 or more. Is it possible to determine from this table the number of flights on which there were:

a) At least 30 empty seats?

b) More than 30 empty seats?

c) At least 19 empty seats?

d) At least 10 empty seats?

17. The year-end executive bonuses paid by a firm range from $8,600 to 32,500. Derive the class limits and the class boundaries of a frequency distribution with 10 equal classes into which these bonuses can be grouped.

18. A meteorologist uses the classes: 0–5, 6–10, 12–17, 18–23, and 23–30 to group data showing the number of rainy days reported by a weather station for the month of September, during the last 60 years. Are these classes Mutually Exclusive and Collectively Exhaustive? Justify your answers.

19. A set of measurements of the lengths of a large number of manufactured parts are grouped into a frequency distribution table whose classes have the class boundaries: 4.9, 6.9, 8.9, 10.9 and 12.9. If $L_2 = 5$, determine

   a) Lower and Upper limits of each class;

   b) Determine the class marks for each class.

20. The class marks of the frequency distribution of the daily number of calls received by a landscaping service are: 2, 7, 12, 17, and 22. If $U_5 = 24$:

   a) What are the class limits of this distribution?

   b) What are the class boundaries of this distribution?

21. The table below presents a partial frequency distribution for gasoline prices at 50 stations in a town.

Price	$2.00–2.04	$2.05–2.09	$2.10–2.14	$2.15–2.19	$2.20–2.24	$2.25–2.29
Frequency	4	6	10	17	8	5

   a) Complete the frequency distribution by computing the columns for cumulative frequency, class marks, and class boundaries.

   b) Plot the Histogram.

   c) Plot the Frequency Polygon.

   d) Plot the Ogive.

22. The table below presents a partial frequency distribution of family incomes for a sample of 100 families in a city.

Family Income	Frequency
$10,000–14,999	10
15,000–19,999	14
20,000–24,999	24
25,000–29,999	15
30,000–34,999	10
35,000–39,999	7
40,000–44,999	6
45,000–49,999	4
50,000–54,999	5
55,000–59,999	5

   a) Complete the frequency distribution by computing the columns for cumulative frequency, class marks, and class boundaries.

   b) Plot the Histogram.

   c) Plot the Frequency Polygon.

   d) Plot the Ogive.

23. The table below gives the grades on a quiz for a class of 40 students:

7	5	6	2	8	7	6	7	3	9
10	6	7	5	3	6	7	4	10	5
4	4	5	7	9	6	7	9	7	2
3	5	6	8	4	8	2	4	8	9

a) Treating this data as an ungrouped data set,
    i) Construct a data array.
    ii) Plot a line diagram.

b) Treating this data as a grouped data set,
    i) Construct the frequency distribution.
    ii) Plot the Histogram.
    iii) Plot the Frequency Polygon.
    iv) Plot the Ogive.

24. The lengths of X-ray treatments, given at a local hospital, were recorded in milliseconds and given below:

0.2	0.8	1.1	1.7	1.5	0.7	0.9	1.2
0.7	1.1	1.2	0.2	1.7	0.3	0.7	0.8
1.1	1.4	0.9	0.9	0.8	0.5	1.2	1.6
0.3	1.2	0.7	0.8	0.9	1.2	1.3	1.3
1.5	0.8	0.6	1.2	0.5	1.4	1.7	1.2

a) Treating this data as an ungrouped data set,
    i) Construct a data array.
    ii) Plot a line diagram.

b) Treating this data as a grouped data set,
    i) Construct the frequency distribution.
    ii) Plot the Histogram.
    iii) Plot the Frequency Polygon.
    iv) Plot the Ogive.

25. Prior to constructing a dam on the Colorado River, the U.S. Army Corps of engineers measured the water flow past the proposed location of the dam. The measurements were used to construct the following partial frequency distribution.

River Flow Thousands of Gallons/minute	Frequency
1 0 0 1–1 0 5 0	12
1 0 5 1–1 1 0 0	20
1 1 0 1–1 1 5 0	35
1 1 5 1–1 2 0 0	45
1 2 0 1–1 2 5 0	53
1 2 5 1–1 3 0 0	40
1 3 0 1–1 3 5 0	30
1 3 5 1–1 4 0 0	15
Total	250

a) Complete the frequency distribution by computing columns for cumulative frequency, class marks, and class boundaries.

b) Plot the Histogram.

c) Plot the Frequency polygon.

d) Plot the Ogive.

26. The shipping manager of a food processing plant has compiled the following data on the pounds of beans (expressed in 100-pound units) loaded into refrigerated trucks over a 40-day period:

a) Construct the frequency distribution for this data set.

b) Plot the Histogram.

c) Plot the Frequency polygon.

d) Plot the Ogive.

7	10	8	9	12	12	6	5	10	12	8	9
11	7	5	6	8	6	9	10	15	8	9	14
6	7	5	10	8	12	9	8	8	6	9	15
6	5	10	15								

27. The price-earnings ratios of a selected set of stocks on the New York Stock Exchange were as follows:

14.5	25.4	12.3	9.4	20.4	7.7	13.4	9.6	14.7	25.3
13.7	10.2	11.9	18.8	8.6	12.3	14.8	8.4	11.8	18.7
12.8	16.2	12.1	14.2	15.4	27.5	30.2	16.1	16.6	11.5
9.7	21.2	12.9	9.8	30.4	13.3	11.7	8.7	19.5	8.3

a) Construct the frequency distribution for this data set.

b) Plot the Histogram.

c) Plot the Frequency Polygon.

d) Plot the Ogive.

28. The following data show the traveling time to and from school per day, for a group of college students:

Time	Under 1 hour	1 up to 2	2 up to 3	3 up to 4	4 up to 5	5 up to 6
Frequency	80	40	10	5	3	2

a) Construct the frequency distribution for this data set.

b) Plot the Histogram.

c) Plot the Frequency Polygon.

d) Plot the Ogive.

29. The following data give the number of students who obtained the corresponding scores on a Graduate Management Admissions Test (GMAT):

Score	Frequency
200–249	1
250–299	2
300–349	8
350–399	13
400–449	16
450–499	20
500–549	18
550–559	13
600–649	7
650–699	2

a) Construct the frequency distribution for this data set.

b) Plot the Histogram.

c) Plot the Frequency Polygon.

d) Plot the Ogive.

30. A sample of 200 outstanding balances is grouped into a frequency distribution having the classes: $0.00–24.99, $25.00–49.99, $50.00–74.99, $75.00–99.99, and $100.00–124.99, with corresponding frequencies: 20, 40, 80, 50, 10.

a) Complete the frequency distribution by computing columns for cumulative frequency, class marks, and class boundaries.

b) Plot the Histogram.

c) Plot the Frequency Polygon.

d) Plot the Ogive.

SOLUTIONS

1 and **2** Since we need MINITAB solutions for these problems, we will obtain them, as follows:

MTB> set C1									
DATA> 66	58	47	40	93	74	70	56	34	66
DATA> 61	72	81	42	95	78	65	74	86	44
DATA> 67	79	42	82	34	67	65	60	75	85
DATA> 53	36	62	56	98	68	67	44	76	88
DATA> 87	51	92	49	67	89	62	78	55	76
DATA> end									

Then, using MTB > SORT C1, we obtain the ranked data set:
34, 34, 36, 40, 42, 42, 44, 44, 47, 49, 51, 53, 55, 56, 56, 58, 60, 61, 62, 62, 65, 65, 66, 66, 67, 67, 67, 67, 68, 70, 72, 74, 74, 75, 76, 76, 78, 78, 79, 81, 82, 85, 86, 87, 88, 89, 92, 93, 95, 98

To obtain the MINITAB–generated line diagram, we use the command:

MTB> Dotplot C1,

while to obtain the MINITAB–generated Histogram, we use the command:

MTB> Histogram C1;

SUBC> Midpoint 35.5: 95.5/10;

SUBC> BAR.

Note: The mid-point values of 35.5 and 95.5 will be derived below, when we construct the frequency distribution.

1. a) Data Array

X	34	36	40	42	44	47	49	51	53	55	56	58	60	61	62	65	66	67	68	70	72	74	75	76	78	79	81	82	85
f	2	1	1	2	2	1	1	1	1	1	2	1	1	1	2	2	2	4	1	1	1	2	1	2	2	1	1	1	1

X	86	87	88	89	92	93	95	98
f	1	1	1	1	1	1	1	1

b) Line Diagram

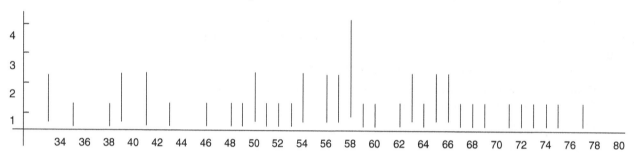

c) MINITAB Solution to problem 1:

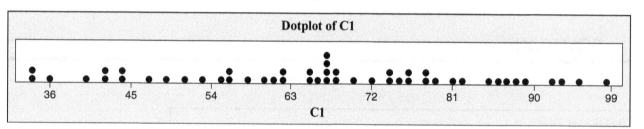

d) The hand drawn line diagram and the MINITAB–derived Dotplot are identical.

2. a) Since $R = H - L = 98 - 34 = 64$ and $c = 10$ (given),

$$m > \frac{R}{c} = \frac{64}{10} = 6.4 \text{ or } m = 7, \text{ and because}$$

the starting Point $= SP = 31$, we define:

$L_i = SP + (i - 1) C$ or L_i: 31, 41, 51, 61, 71, 81, 91

for $i = 1, 2, 3, \ldots, 7$ and $U_i = U_1 + (i - 1) C$, or

$U_i = 40 + (i - 1) C$ (because $U_1 = L_2 - 1$),

and U_i: 40, 50, 60, 70, 80, 90, 100 for $i = 1, 2, \ldots, 7$. Then:

class marks $= m_i = \dfrac{L_i + U_i}{2}$, or: 35.5, 45.5, 55.5, 65.5,

75.5, 85.5, 95.5 for $i = 1, 2, \dots, 7$ and class boundaries

$= cb_{ij} = \dfrac{U_i + L_j}{2}$, or: 40.5, 50.5, 60.5, 70.5, 80.5, 90.5

$i = 1, 2, \dots, 7$. Also absolute frequency, f_i; 4, 6, 7, 13, 9, 7, 4, and cumulative frequency, F_i; 4, 10, 17, 30, 39, 46, 50. Then, the frequency distribution for this data set becomes:

Class Number	Class Limits L_i	U_i	f_i = Absolute Frequency	F_i = Cumulative Absolute Frequency	m_i = Class Marks	cb_{ij} = Class Boundaries for classes i and j	$\dfrac{f_1}{n} = \dfrac{f_i}{50}$	$\dfrac{F_i}{n} = \dfrac{F_i}{50}$
(0)	21	30	0	0	25.5	(30.5)	0	0
1	31	40	4	4	35.5	40.5	0.08	0.08
2	41	50	6	10	45.5	50.5	0.12	0.20
3	51	60	7	17	55.5	60.5	0.14	0.34
4	61	70	13	30	65.5	70.5	0.26	0.60
5	71	80	9	39	75.5	80.5	0.18	0.78
6	81	90	7	46	85.5	90.5	0.14	0.92
7	91	100	4	50	95.5	(100.5)	0.18	1.00
(8)	101	110	0	50	105.5		0	1.00
			$\Sigma f_i = n$ $= 50$				$\Sigma f_i / n$ $= 1$	

MINITAB Solution to problem 2:

b) Histogram

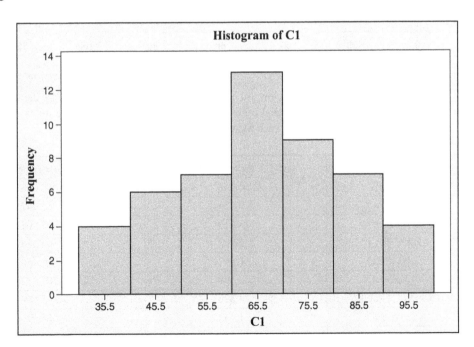

c) Frequency Polygon

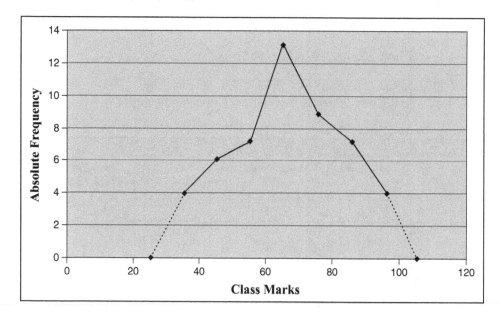

d) Ogive

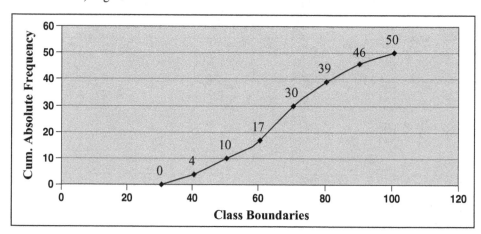

Use the Table of data below for Problems 3, 4, and 5. The Table lists the 50 States of the United States in alphabetical order, and also gives the Area (in square miles) of each State as well as the Population of each State (according to the 1990 CENSUS).

Number	STATE	AREA (Square Miles)	POPULATION (1990 CENSUS)
1	ALABAMA	50,766	4,062,608
2	ALASKA	570,833	551,947
3	ARIZONA	113,510	3,677,965
4	ARKANSAS	52,082	2,362,239
5	CALIFORNIA	156,297	29,839,250
6	COLORADO	103,598	3,307,912
7	CONNECTICUT	4,872	3,295,669
8	DELAWARE	1,933	668,696
9	FLORIDA	54,157	13,003,362

Number	STATE	AREA (Square Miles)	POPULATION (1990 CENSUS)
10	GEORGIA	58,060	6,508,419
11	HAWAII	6,427	1,115,274
12	IDAHO	82,413	1,011,986
13	ILLINOIS	55,646	11,466,682
14	INDIANA	35,936	5,564,228
15	IOWA	55,965	2,787,424
16	KANSAS	81,783	2,485,600
17	KENTUCKY	39,674	3,698,969
18	LOUISIANA	44,520	4,238,216
19	MAINE	30,995	1,233,223
20	MARYLAND	9,838	4,798,622
21	MASSACHUSETTS	7,826	6,029,051
22	MICHIGAN	56,959	9,328,784
23	MINNESOTA	79,548	4,387,029
24	MISSISSIPPI	47,234	2,586,443
25	MISSOURI	68,945	5,137,804
26	MONTANA	145,388	803,655
27	NEBRASKA	76,639	1,584,617
28	NEVADA	109,895	1,206,152
29	NEW HAMPSHIRE	8,992	1,113,915
30	NEW JERSEY	7,468	7,748,634
31	NEW MEXICO	121,336	1,521,779
32	NEW YORK	47,379	18,044,505
33	NORTH CAROLINA	48,843	6,657,630
34	NORTH DAKOTA	69,299	641,364
35	OHIO	41,004	10,887,325
36	OKLAHOMA	68,656	3,157,604
37	OREGON	96,187	2,853,733
38	PENNSYLVANIA	44,892	11,924,710
39	RHODE ISLAND	1,054	1,005,984
40	SOUTH CAROLINA	30,207	3,505,707
41	SOUTH DAKOTA	75,956	699,999
42	TENNESSEE	41,154	4,896,641
43	TEXAS	262,015	17,059,805
44	UTAH	82,076	1,727,784
45	VERMONT	9,273	564,964
46	VIRGINIA	39,700	6,216,568
47	WASHINGTON	66,512	4,887,941
48	WEST VIRGINIA	24,124	1,801,625
49	WISCONSIN	54,424	4,906,745
50	WYOMING	96,988	455,975
	DISTRICT OF COLUMBIA (WASHINGTON DC)	69	609,909

Since $N = n = 50$, the analysis below pertains to the entire Population of States.

3. If we let X = Area and f = frequency, then the Frequency distribution becomes:

$X < 10$	$10 \leq X < 20$	$20 \leq X < 30$	$30 \leq X < 40$	$40 \leq X < 50$	$50 \leq X < 60$	$60 \leq X < 70$	$70 \leq X < 80$
$f_1 = 9$	$f_2 = 0$	$f_3 = 1$	$f_4 = 5$	$f_5 = 7$	$f_6 = 8$	$f_7 = 4$	$f_8 = 3$

$80 \leq X < 90$	$90 \leq X < 100$	$100 \leq X < 110$	$110 \leq X < 120$	$120 \leq X < 130$	$130 \leq X <140$	$X > 140,000$
$f_9 = 3$	$f_{10} = 2$	$f_{11} = 2$	$f_{12} = 1$	$f_{13} = 1$	$f_{14} = 0$	4

a) For $20 \leq X \leq 130$, the "smooth" curve looks like a "chi-square" distribution, but there is also a bar of height 9 for $X < 10,000$, and also there are 4 states with Area greater than 140,000 square miles.

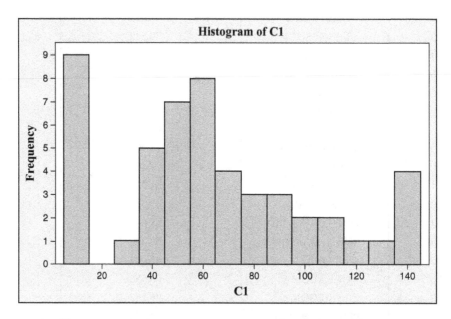

b) There are 9 states with square area under 10,000 square miles (Rhode Island, Delaware, Connecticut, Hawaii, New Jersey, Massachusetts, New Hampshire, Vermont, Maryland).

c) There are 8 states with square area over 100,000 square miles (Colorado, Nevada, Arizona, New Mexico, Montana, California, Texas, Alaska).

4. a) If we let X = Population (in millions) and f = frequency, then the frequency distribution becomes:

The "smooth" curve, fitted to the resulting Histogram will be a "decreasing" exponential.

X	f
$X < 1\,M$	7
$1\,M \leq X < 2\,M$	10
$2\,M \leq X < 3\,M$	5
$3\,M \leq X < 4\,M$	6
$4\,M \leq X < 5\,M$	7
$5\,M \leq X < 6\,M$	2

X	f
6 M ≤ X < 7 M	4
7 M ≤ X < 8 M	1
8 M ≤ X < 9 M	0
9 M ≤ X < 10 M	1
10 M ≤ X < 11 M	1
11 M ≤ X < 12 M	2
12 M ≤ X < 13 M	1
13 M ≤ X < 14 M	1
14 M ≤ X < 15 M	0
15 M ≤ X < 16 M	0
16 M ≤ X < 17 M	0
17 M ≤ X < 18 M	1
18 M ≤ X < 19 M	1
19 M ≤ X ≤ 29 M	0
X > 29 M	1

b) Histogram

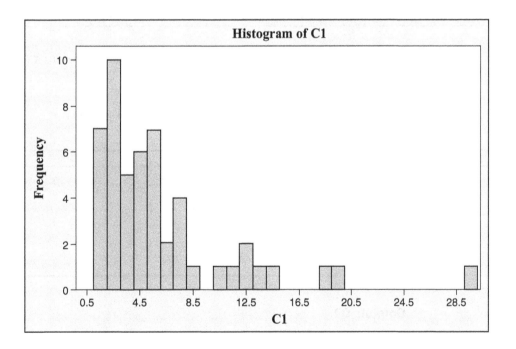

c) There are 7 states with Population under 1,000,000 (Wyoming, Alaska, Vermont, North Dakota, Delaware, South Dakota, Montana)

d) The Modal Class is the class for which $1 M \leq X < 2M$, and its frequency = 10 (Rhode Island, Idaho, New Hampshire, Hawaii, Nevada, Maine, New Mexico, Nebraska, Utah, West Virginia)

e) There are 7 states with Population over 10,000,000 (Ohio, Illinois, Pennsylvania, Florida, Texas, New York, California)

5. a) A: Alabama, Alaska, Arizona, Arkansas
C: California, Colorado, Connecticut
D: Delaware
F: Florida
G: Georgia
H: Hawaii
I: Idaho, Illinois, Indiana, Iowa
K: Kansas, Kentucky
L: Louisiana
M: Maine, Maryland, Massachusetts, Michigan, Minnesota, Mississippi, Missouri, Montana
N: Nebraska, Nevada, New Hampshire, New Jersey, New Mexico, New York, North Carolina, North Dakota
O: Ohio, Oklahoma, Oregon
P: Pennsylvania
R: Rhode Island
S: South Carolina, South Dakota
T: Tennessee, Texas
U: Utah
V: Vermont, Virginia
W: Washington, West Virginia, Wisconsin, Wyoming

X	A	B	C	D	E	F	G	H	I	J	K	L	M	N	O	P	Q	R	S	T	U	V	W	X	Y	Z
f	4	0	3	1	0	1	1	1	4	0	2	1	8	8	3	1	0	1	2	2	1	2	4	0	0	0

b) Plot a line diagram of f (frequency) on the vertical scale versus X (the letters of the alphabet) on the horizontal line

c) M and N (each begins the names of 8 states)

d) B, E, J, Q, X, Y, Z (No State's name begins with these letters)

```
MTB>    set C2
DATA>    1    2    3    4    5    6    7    8    9    10    11    12    13    14    15    16    17    18
        19   20   21   22   23   24   25   26
DATA>    4    0    3    1    0    1    1    1    4     0     2     1     8     8     3     1     0     1
         2   21    2    4    0    0    0
DATA> end
MTB>    Dotplot c2
```

Dotplot: C2

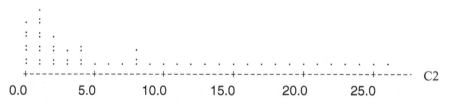

6. a)
   i) Cumulative frequency: 3, 15, 34, 40, 45, 47, 49, 50
   ii) Class marks (m_i): 17, 22, 27, 32, 37, 42, 47, 52
   iii) Class Boundaries: 19.5, 24.5, 29.5, 34.5, 39.5, 44.5, 49.5

b)

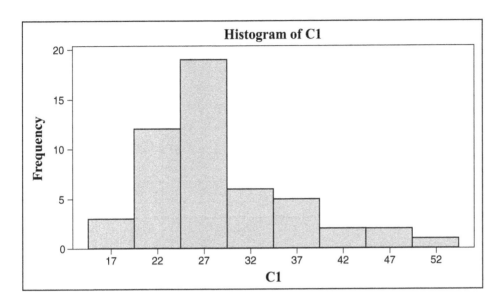

c)

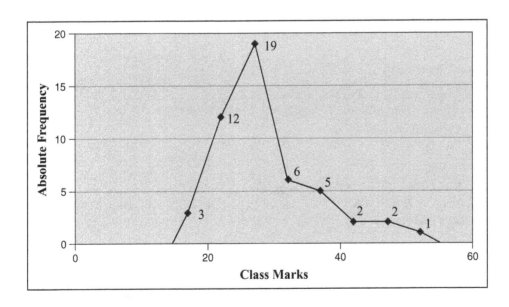

d)

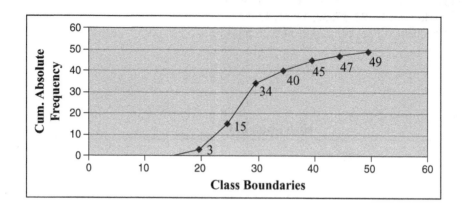

7. a)

X	19.3	19.5	19.7	19.8	19.9	20.0	20.1	20.2	20.3	20.4	20.6	20.8	20.9
f	1	1	1	1	5	2	1	1	2	1	2	1	1

b) Line Diagram

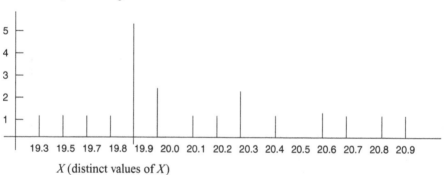

X (distinct values of X)

8. $R = 20.9 - 19.3 = 1.6.$ If we choose $m = 5(5 \leq m \leq 15) = $ number of classes, then $c > R/m = 1.6/5 = 0.32$, and we let $c = $ class width $= 0.4$. Then our starting point becomes:

$$SP = L - \frac{m \cdot c - R}{2} = 19.3 - \left[\frac{(5 \times 0.4) - 1.6}{2} \right] = 19.3 - 0.2 = 19.1,$$

and $L_i = SP + (i - 1)c$ or: 19.1, 19.5, 19.9, 20.3, 20.7, and $U_i = U_1 + (i - 1)c$, or $U_i = 19.4 + (i - 1)c$ because $U_1 = L_2 - 0.1 = 19.5 - 0.1 = 19.4$. Then, U_i: 19.4, 19.8, 20.2, 20.6, 21.0.

a) Frequency distribution

Class Number	Class Limits L_i	U_i	Absolute Frequency f_i	Cumulative Absolute Frequency F_i	Class Marks m_i	Class Boundaries cb_{ij}
(0)	(18.7	19.0)	0	0	(18.85)	(19.05)
1	19.1	19.4	1	1	19.25	19.45
2	19.5	19.8	3	4	19.65	19.85
3	19.9	20.2	9	13	20.05	20.25
4	20.3	20.6	5	18	20.45	20.65
5	20.7	21.0	2	20	20.85	(21.05)
(6)	(21.1	21.4)	0	20	(21.25)	

b) Histogram

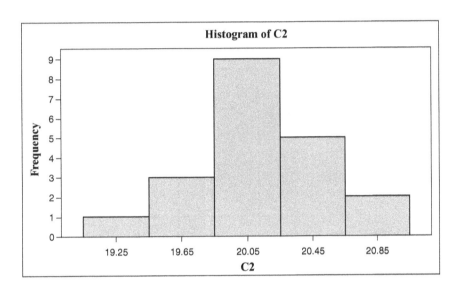

c) Frequency Polygon

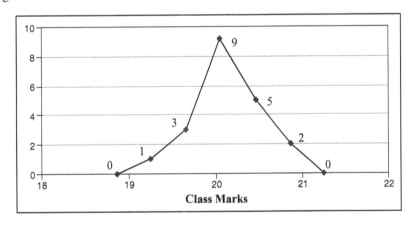

d) Ogive

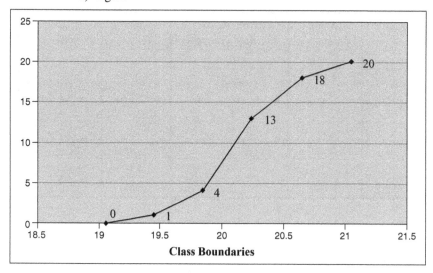

Class Boundaries

9. a)

X	6	7	8	9	10
f	2	3	2	2	1

b)

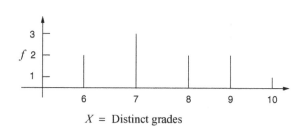

$X = $ Distinct grades

10. a) Ranking the data we obtain:

3.55, 3.60, 3.65, 3.75, 3.78, 3.80, 3.85, 3.85, 3.88, 3.90, 3.95, 3.95, 3.95, 3.96, 4.00, 4.05, 4.05, 4.05, 4.06, 4.08, 4.10, 4.15, 4.18, 4.25, 4.26

Then, $R = H - L = 4.26 - 3.55 = 0.71$; Since $5 \le m \le 15$, we can chose $m \ge 6$ because Sturge's rule ($m \ge 1 + 3.322 \log_{10} n$, with $n = 25$) requires that $m = 6$ or higher.

Suppose we choose $m = 8$; Then $c > \dfrac{R}{m} = \dfrac{0.71}{8} = 0.09$, and, for convenience we let $c = $ class width $= 0.1$.

Then, the starting point $= SP = L - \dfrac{(m \cdot c - R)}{2}$

$= 3.55 - \left[\dfrac{(8 \times 0.1) - 0.71}{2} \right] = 3.55 - \dfrac{0.09}{2}$

$= 3.550 - 0.045 = 3.51 \approx 3.50$.

Then $L_i = SP + (i - 1)c$

$= 3.50 + (i - 1) 0.1$, and L_i: 3.50, 3.60, 3.70, 3.80, 3.90, 4.00, 4.10, 4.20; $U_i := U_1 + (i - 1)c = 3.59 + (i - 1)0.1$, because $U_1 = L_2 - 0.01 = 3.60 - 0.01 = 3.59$, and U_i: 3.59, 3.69, 3.79, 3.89, 3.99, 4.09, 4.19, 4.29.

Class Number	Class Limits		Absolute Frequency	Cumulative Absolute Frequency	Class Marks	Class Boundaries
	L_i	U_i	f_i	F_i	m_i	cb_{ij}
(0)	(3.40	3.49)	0	0	(3.445)	(3.495)
1	3.50	3.59	1	1	3.545	3.595
2	3.60	3.69	2	3	3.645	3.695
3	3.70	3.79	2	5	3.745	3.795
4	3.80	3.89	4	9	3.845	3.895
5	3.90	3.99	5	14	3.945	3.995
6	4.00	4.09	6	20	4.045	4.095
7	4.10	4.19	3	23	4.145	4.195
8	4.20	4.29	2	25	4.245	(4.295)
(9)	(4.30	4.39)	0	25	(4.345)	

b) Histogram

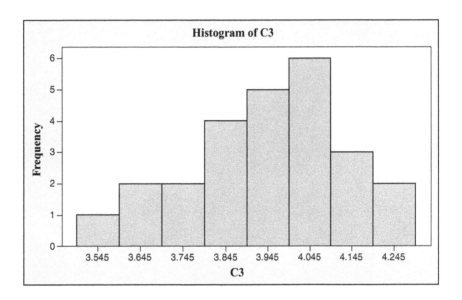

c) Frequency Polygon

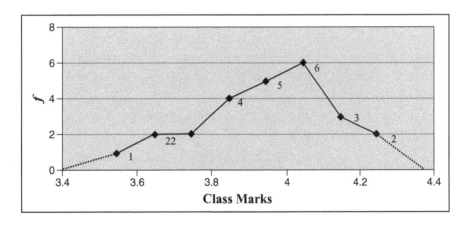

d) Ogive

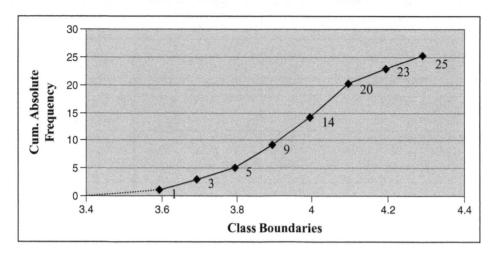

3

Calculation of Descriptive Measures for Univariate Data

Data sets can be completely characterized in terms of the following four categories of measures which define four very significant properties of the data set, namely:

1. **Measures of Central Tendency** which attempt to locate the center of the data set. The most important measures of this category are: The sample mean $(\bar{x})$ the sample median $(x_{0.5})$, and the sample mode (x_m).
2. **Measures of Dispersion (or Data spread)** which attempt to determine the proportion of the data set to be found within a certain distance from the location of the center of the distribution. The most important measures of this category are: The sample range (R), the sample unbiased variance $(\hat{s}^2)$ and the sample standard deviation $(\hat{s})$.
3. **Measures of Skewness** which attempt to determine whether the data set (and the population from which the sample came from) is symmetrical or non-symmetrical. The most important measure of this type is Pearson's coefficient of Skewness (S_{Kp}).
4. **Measures of Kurtosis (or Peakedness)** which attempt to determine whether the data set (and the population form which the sample came from) is narrow or wide, or somewhere in between. The most import measure of this category is the coefficient of Kurtoris (K).

Statisticians believe that a set of measures, consisting of the "best" measure from each category, is sufficient to completely define the data set (and the population form which the data sample came from).

In future chapters (and more specifically in Chapter 9) we will outline a procedure which will determine the "best" measure of each category and, therefore, the set consisting of the "best" measures from each category.

In this chapter we learn how to calculate the individual measures identified above (and other additional measures) for both ungrouped and grouped data sets.

3.1   Introduction

In the previous chapter, we learned how to reduce a data set into a compact form, by obtaining either its array or its frequency distribution, depending on whether the data set was identified either as Ungrouped or Grouped respectively.

The array or frequency distribution not only organizes the data, but it can also provide the capability of calculating descriptive measures which characterize the pattern of the distribution of the random variable of interest.

In this chapter, we will learn how to calculate measures which are given by a single number. We will calculate four different groups of measures, namely:

1. Measures of Central Tendency, which attempt to locate the center of the data set.
2. Measures of Dispersion (or Data Spread).
3. Measures of Skewness, which measure the symmetry or non-symmetry of the data set.
4. Measures of Peakedness (or Kurtosis), which measure how thin or wide is the data distribution.

and then select a set of four measures, consisting of the "best" measure in each group. Such a set is believed to be sufficient to completely characterize the frequency distribution of a univariate data set.

These groups of measures will be derived for both ungrouped and grouped data sets. (*See Chapter 2 for the distinction between ungrouped and grouped data and for the difference in the method of constructing the corresponding frequency distribution.*)

Selecting the "best" measure in each group of measures requires the development of a set of "criteria of goodness" against which each of the different measures of a group will be evaluated and then compared with each other. The measure which satisfies all, or most of these "criteria of goodness" will be considered the "best" in each group. However, the development of such "criteria of goodness" will have to wait until we first discuss "estimation theory" and the desirable properties of "good" estimators for the population parameters of interest. In this chapter we simply learn how to calculate the several different measures which belong to each group of measures, given the sample data set $X_1, X_2, X_3, \ldots, X_n$.

3.2 Descriptive Measures for Ungrouped Data

At this point we should recall the definition of ungrouped data and the frequency distribution (or array) which resulted when the raw data is transformed into an array. This is important because, while some measures (as for example the mean) can be computed directly from the raw data, other measures, (such as the median) can only be calculated from ranked data. (*See Section 2.2.1 for the definition and the appropriate frequency distribution table.*)

3.2.1 Measures of Central Tendency

For many distributions the observations tend to cluster about or be near a central value that can be said to "locate" the distribution. In this section we will discuss the most important "distribution-locating" measures, the formulas from which these measures are derived, and some of their most important properties. Specifically we will discuss the following measures of central tendency of a data set:

- **"Median"** value of a data set
- **"Mode"** value of a data set
- **"Arithmetic Mean"** value of a data set
- **"Weighted Arithmetic Mean"** value of a data set
- **"Mid-range"** value of a data set
- **"Geometric mean"** value of a data set
- **"Harmonic Mean"** value of a data set

3.2.1.1 Median

The median value of a data set, usually designated by $X_{0.5}$, is a value which separates a ranked data set into 2 equal parts.

To completely define the median we must define both its **location** and its **value**, both of which depend on the sample size (n) and on whether n is an odd number or even number of observations.

When n is odd:

The location of the median is always at

$$\frac{n+1}{2} \qquad \left(\text{where } \frac{n+1}{2} \text{ is a whole number}\right) \tag{3.1}$$

The value of the median is the value of the observation occupying the $\dfrac{n+1}{2}$ location in the ranked data set.

Clearly then, when n is odd, the median is the middle value of the ranked data set.

When n is even:

The location of the median is at

$\dfrac{n+1}{2}$ (where $\dfrac{n+1}{2}$ is not a whole number)

Since $\dfrac{n+1}{2}$ is not a whole number, the location of the median falls half-way between two observations, namely the $\dfrac{n}{2}$ and the $\dfrac{n}{2}+1$ observations, and the value of the median is obtained as the arithmetic average of the two adjacent values, namely:

$$X_{0.5} = \frac{V_{\frac{n}{2}}^* + V_{\frac{n}{2}+1}^*}{2} \tag{3.2}$$

* **The data set $X_1, X_2, X_3, \ldots, X_n$ is the Raw data while the data set $V_1, V_2, V_3, \ldots, V_n$ is the ranked data set.**

Example 1

Find the median of the data set: 5, 7, 3, 2, 9.

Note: For this data set: $X_1 = 5$, $X_2 = 7$, $X_3 = 3$, $X_4 = 2$, and, $X_5 = 9$, while $V_1 = 2$, $V_2 = 3$, $V_3 = 5$, $V_4 = 7$, and $V_5 = 9$.

First we rank the data set to obtain:

V_1 = 1st	V_2 = 2nd	V_3 = 3rd	V_4 = 4th	V_5 = 5th
2	3	5	7	9

We note that $n = 5$, which is an odd number.

Then the location of the median $= \dfrac{n+1}{2} = 3$, and the value of the median is the observation occupying the 3rd location which, in this case, is equal to 5.

■ ■ ■

Example 2

Find the median of the data set: 5, 7, 3, 2, 9, 12.

Ranking the data set, we obtain:

V_1 = 1st	V_2 = 2nd	V_3 = 3rd	V_4 = 4th	V_5 = 5th	V_6 = 6th
2	3	5	7	9	12

We now note that $n = 6$, which is an even number.

Then the location of the median $= \dfrac{n+1}{2} = \dfrac{6+1}{2} = 3.5$, and the value of the median is equal to:

Value of $X_{0.5} = \dfrac{V_{\frac{n}{2}} + V_{\frac{n}{2}+1}}{2} = \dfrac{5+7}{2} = 6$

According to our definition, there is always exactly one median. Since its value depends on "central" values, it is not affected by extreme values as the arithmetic mean is. However, medians are less stable than means (*i.e.*, medians vary more in repeated sampling than means) and an overall median cannot be obtained (without the availability of the original data) from a set of medians as an overall arithmetic mean can be obtained from a set of means by a weighted average.

Note: Once the Location of the Median has been found (using (3.1)) the value of the Median can also be obtained from the following Linear Interpolation formula:

$$\text{Median Value} = V_{\frac{n}{2}} + 0.5\left(V_{\frac{n}{2}+1} - V_{\frac{n}{2}}\right) \tag{3.3}$$

which can be shown to be equivalent to (3.2).

3.2.1.2 Mode

The mode is the observation (value) which occurs most frequently in the data set, and is represented by X_m. A mode does not always exist, and if it does, it may not be unique. But the mode is not affected by extreme values in the data set as the mean is.

Example 3

Consider the 3 data sets below:

1. $3, 5, 7, 7, 7, 8, 8$
2. $3, 5, 7, 7, 8, 8, 9$
3. $3, 3, 6, 6, 9, 9, 12, 12$

Set (1) above has one mode (namely the value 7), set (2) has two modes (namely the values 7 and 8), while set (3) has no mode (because each value in the set occurs an equal number of times).

Because of these undesirable properties the mode is not considered a satisfactory measure of central tendency when analyzing ungrouped data sets.

3.2.1.3 The Arithmetic Mean

The arithmetic mean or arithmetic average or, simply, mean of a data set is the most commonly used measure of central location because it is easy to calculate and it possesses a number of desirable properties, as we will discover in our discussion of Estimation Theory.

The population mean is usually represented by the lower case Greek letter mu (*i.e.*, μ), while the sample mean is represented by $\overline{X}$ (read "X" bar). The population mean is a parameter and once its value is determined it remains constant.

The sample mean, on the other hand (and this is true with all sample measures), can change its value from sample to sample such that all the possible values form a distribution of values for $\overline{X}$, and this leads to the "Sampling Distribution" of $\overline{X}$ as we will discuss in a later chapter.

The sample mean ($\overline{X}$) is calculated from the formula:

$$\overline{X} = \frac{X_1 + X_2 + \cdots + X_n}{n} = \frac{\sum_{i=1}^{n} X_i}{n} \tag{3.4}$$

Notice that all of the values of the sample enter in the calculation of $\overline{X}$, unlike the calculation of the median ($X_{0.5}$) and the mode (X_m) which depend only on few "central" values. Because of this definition, the sample mean is affected by extreme values in the data set, while the median and the mode are not!

In cases in which many observations are identical, it is more convenient to first prepare a frequency distribution before performing the calculation for the mean.

For example, if observation X_1 occurs f_1 times, observation X_2 occurs f_2 times, ..., and observation X_k occurs f_k times, we can re-write the above equation as:

$$\overline{X} = \frac{f_1 X_1 + f_2 X_2 + \cdots + f_k X_k}{f_1 + f_2 + \cdots + f_k} = \frac{\sum_{i=1}^{k} f_i X_i}{\sum_{i=1}^{k} f_i} = \frac{\sum_{i=1}^{k} f_i X_i}{n} \tag{3.5}$$

Some of the more important properties of the sample mean are the following:

1. Several means from the same population $(\overline{X}_1, \overline{X}_2, \ldots, \overline{X}_k)$ can be combined readily to give an overall mean by using appropriate weights.

   For example, suppose $\overline{X}_1$ is based on n_1 values, and $\overline{X}_2$ is based on n_2 values, where both $\overline{X}_1$ and $\overline{X}_2$ are sample means calculated to estimate the population mean μ.

   We can then compute a "pooled" mean by combining the observations as follows:

   Since $\overline{X}_1 = \dfrac{\sum_{i=1}^{n_1} X_i}{n_1}$, we may write $\sum_{i=1}^{n_1} X_i = n_1 \overline{X}_1$,

   and similarly for X_2, namely: $\sum_{i=1}^{n_2} X_i = n_2 \overline{X}_2$

   Then $\overline{X} = \dfrac{n_1 \overline{X}_1 + n_2 \overline{X}_2}{n_1 + n_2} = \left(\dfrac{n_1}{n_1 + n_2}\right)\overline{X}_1 + \left(\dfrac{n_2}{n_1 + n_2}\right)\overline{X}_2 \tag{3.6}$

2. The sample mean $(\overline{X})$ may be substituted for the value of each item, without affecting the total value. This can be seen directly from the definition of $\overline{X}$, which can be written as:

$$n\overline{X} = \sum_{i=1}^{n} X_i$$

   Clearly, if each X_i is replaced by $\overline{X}$, $n\overline{X} = \sum_{i=1}^{n} \overline{X}_i$ and the total value is not affected.

3. If we form the deviations $(X_i - \overline{X})$ for each observation X_i, and then sum up these deviations, this sum is always equal to 0, regardless of what the individual X_i values are.

   Mathematically we write this as $\sum_{i=1}^{n}\left(X - \overline{X}\right) = 0 \tag{3.7}$

   This can be demonstrated easily, by expanding the summation, simplifying, and applying the definition of $\overline{X}$:

$$\sum_{i=1}^{n} \left(X_i - \overline{X} \right) = \left(X_i - \overline{X} \right) + \left(X_2 - \overline{X} \right) + \cdots + \left(X_n - \overline{X} \right)$$

$$= \left(X_1 + X_2 + \cdots + X_n \right) - n\overline{X}$$

$$= \sum_{i=1}^{n} X_i - n\overline{X} = 0,$$

since $n\overline{X} = \sum_{i=1}^{n} X_i$ (from the definition of $\overline{X}$)

4. The summation $Y = \sum_{i=1}^{n} \left(X_i - C \right)^2$ $\qquad\qquad\qquad$ (3.8)

attains the smallest possible value when $C = \overline{X}$. This property is used in the definition of the variance of a data set and can be proved easily by utilizing the optimization methodology of differential calculus (*see also Appendix B*).

$$Y = \sum_{i=1}^{n} \left(X_i - C \right)^2 = \left(X_1 - C \right)^2 + \left(X_2 - C \right)^2 + \cdots + \left(X_n - C \right)^2$$

Let $\quad Y = \left(X_1^2 - 2X_1C + C^2 \right) + \left(X_2^2 - 2X_2C + C^2 \right) + \cdots$

$$+ \left(X_n^2 - 2X_n + C^2 \right)$$

$$Y = \left(X_1^2 + X_2^2 + \cdots + X_n^2 \right) - 2C \left(X_1 + X_2 + \cdots + X_n \right)$$

$$+ \left(C^2 + C^2 + \cdots + C^2 \right)$$

$$Y = \sum_{i=1}^{n} X_i^2 - 2C \sum_{i=1}^{n} X_i + nC^2 \qquad\qquad\qquad (3.9)$$

Differentiating Y with respect to C, we find

$$\frac{dY}{dC} = 0 - 2 \sum_{i=1}^{n} X_i + 2nC = -2 \sum_{i=1}^{n} X_i + 2nC \qquad\qquad (3.10)$$

Setting $\dfrac{dY}{dC} = 0$ and solving the resulting equation

$$-2 \sum_{i=1}^{n} X_i + 2nC = 0 \qquad\qquad\qquad (3.11)$$

for C, we find the critical point of the function, defined by (3.8), to be

$$C = \frac{\sum_{i=1}^{n} X_i}{n} = \overline{X} \qquad\qquad\qquad (3.12)$$

Since $\qquad\qquad\qquad \dfrac{d^2Y}{d^2C} = 2n > 0, \qquad\qquad\qquad (3.13)$

the function $Y = \sum_{i=1}^{n} \left(X_i - C \right)^2$ has a minimum at the critical point $C = \overline{X}$.

3.2.1.4 The Weighted Arithmetic Mean

A weighted mean is used when the separate observations have differing amounts of information.

To define a weighted mean, suppose $X_1, X_2, \ldots, X_n$ are observed values and $W_1, W_2, \ldots, W_n$ are appropriate respective weights. Then the weighted mean is defined as:

$$\overline{X}_W = \frac{\sum_{i=1}^{n} W_i X_i}{\sum_{i=1}^{n} W_i} \tag{3.14}$$

Example 4

Consider a firm which pays a wage of $6 per hour to its 40 unskilled workers, $8 to its 20 semiskilled workers, and $10 to its 15 skilled workers. What is the weighted average and how does it compare with the simple arithmetic average?

The weights in this problem are the number of workers in each wage group, and $\sum_{i=1}^{3} W_i = 40 + 20 + 15 = 75$ is equal to the total number of workers in the firm. Then

$$\overline{X}_W = \frac{40 \times 6 + 20 \times 8 + 15 \times 10}{40 + 20 + 15} = \frac{550}{75} = \frac{25 \times 22}{75} = \frac{22}{3} = \$7.33, \text{ while the}$$

simple arithmetic average is

$$\overline{X} = \frac{6 + 8 + 10}{3} = \frac{24}{3} = \$8$$

3.2.1.5 The Midrange

The sample midrange is another measure of central tendency of a population and is defined as

$$X_{\text{midrange}} = \frac{(L + H)}{2}, \tag{3.15}$$

where L and H are, respectively, the low and high values in a ranked data set.

3.2.1.6 The Geometric Mean

The geometric mean, $\overline{X}_g$, of a set of numbers $X_1, X_2, \ldots, X_n$ is defined by:

$$\overline{X}_g = \sqrt[n]{X_1 \times X_2 \times \cdots \times X_n} = \left(X_1 \times X_2 \times \cdots \times X_n\right)^{1/n} \tag{3.16}$$

It is used with numbers which tend to increase geometrically (*i.e.*, each number is the same multiple of the preceding one) rather than arithmetically. Using an arithmetic mean in such cases to define the average will be misleading.

Example 5

Given the observations: $X_1 = 1, X_2 = 3$, and $X_3 = 9$, find the Geometric and Arithmetic averages.

The Geometric average of these observations is $\overline{X}_g = \sqrt[3]{1 \times 3 \times 9} = \sqrt[3]{27} = (27)^{1/3} = (3^3)^{1/3} = 3$, while their arithmetic average $\overline{X}$ is $\overline{X} = (1 + 3 + 9) \div 3 = 13 \div 3 = 4.33$.

■■■

Note: The Geometric mean is used in the "mathematics of finance" to average percentages, as the following example shows.

Example 6

If a nation faces inflation rates of 2% for year 1, 5% for year 2, and 6.4% for year 3, what is the (Geometric) Mean of the inflation rates, and how does it compare with the Arithmetic Mean?

Then $\overline{X}_g = (2 \times 5 \times 6.4)^{1/3} = (64)^{1/3} = (4^3)^{1/3} = 4,$

and $\overline{X} = \dfrac{2 + 5 + 6.4}{3} = \dfrac{13.4}{3} = 4.4667$

■ ■ ■

3.2.1.7 The Harmonic Mean

The harmonic mean $\overline{X}_h$, of a set of numbers $X_1, X_2, \ldots, X_n$ is defined by:

$$\overline{X}_h = \frac{1}{\dfrac{\dfrac{1}{X_1} + \dfrac{1}{X_2} + \cdots + \dfrac{1}{X_n}}{n}} = \frac{1}{\dfrac{\displaystyle\sum_{i=1}^{n} \dfrac{1}{X_i}}{n}} = \frac{n}{\displaystyle\sum_{i=1}^{n} \dfrac{1}{X_i}} \tag{3.17}$$

The harmonic mean is primarily used to average ratios.

Example 7

Consider a commuter who drives 10 miles on a highway at 60 miles/hour and 10 miles on local streets at 15 miles/hour. What is his average speed?

Solving this problem as a problem in physics first, we obtain

$$\text{Average Speed} = \frac{(\text{Total Distance Traveled} = D_1 + D_2)}{(\text{Total Time} = t_1 + t_2)}$$

$$= \frac{10 + 10}{\dfrac{10}{60} + \dfrac{10}{15}} = \frac{20}{\dfrac{50}{60}} = 24 \text{ miles/hour}$$

where $D_1 = 10$ miles, $D_2 = 10$ miles, and $D = D_1 + D_2 = 20$ miles;

$$t_1 = \frac{10 \text{ miles}}{60 \text{ miles/hour}} = \frac{10}{60} \text{ hours and } t_2 = \frac{10 \text{ miles}}{15 \text{ miles/hours}} = \frac{10}{15} \text{ hours} = \frac{40}{60} \text{ hours,}$$

and

$$T = t_1 + t_2 = \frac{10}{60} + \frac{40}{60} = \frac{50}{60} \text{ hours}$$

The arithmetic average, $\overline{X}$, is $\overline{X} = (60 + 15)/2 = 75/2 = 37.5$ miles/hour. But, at this average speed, it would have taken the commuter $t_{\text{average}} = \text{Distance/Speed} = (20/37.5) \times 60$ (minutes/hour) = 32 minutes, when in fact it took the commuter 50 minutes. Clearly the arithmetic average is not the appropriate measure to use here. Calculating the harmonic average of the values, however, we obtain:

$$\overline{X}_h = \frac{1}{\left(\dfrac{1}{60} + \dfrac{1}{15}\right) \div 2} = \frac{2}{\dfrac{1}{60} + \dfrac{1}{15}} = \frac{2}{\dfrac{1}{60} + \dfrac{4}{60}} = \frac{2}{\dfrac{5}{60}} = \frac{120}{5} = 24 \text{ miles/hour,}$$

which agrees with the answer obtained, when using Physics to obtain the solution to the problem. Clearly in this case the harmonic is the appropriate mean to use.

■ ■ ■

Note: If the observations $X_1, X_2, \ldots, X_n$ are all positive and the arithmetic, geometric, and harmonic means are all calculated for the same data set, we would obtain:

$$\overline{X}_h < \overline{X}_g < \overline{X} \qquad (3.18)$$

For the data set $X_1 = 1$, $X_2 = 3$, and $X_3 = 9$,

$$\overline{X} = \frac{1 + 3 + 9}{3} = \frac{13}{3} = 4.33..., $$

$$\overline{X}_g = \sqrt[3]{1 \times 3 \times 9} = \sqrt[3]{27} = 3,$$

while
$$\overline{X}_h = \frac{1}{\dfrac{\dfrac{1}{1} + \dfrac{1}{3} + \dfrac{1}{9}}{3}} = \frac{3}{9 + 3 + 1} = \frac{27}{13} = 2.077,$$

and the above relationship is clearly satisfied.

3.2.1.8 Summary of Properties for The Measures of Central Location

Of the seven measures of Central Location that we discussed above, the mean $(\overline{X})$, median $(X_{0.5})$, and mode (X_m) are usually the most important ones.

Depending on the numerical values we obtain for these three measures for a given data set, we can draw the following conclusions about the data set and, by deduction, of the population from which the data set came from.

1. If $\overline{X} = X_m = X_{0.5}$, the distribution is symmetric.

   Note: Similarly, if the data set $X_1, X_2, X_3, \dots, X_n$ is given and $\overline{X}$, $X_{0.5}$ and X_m are calculated for it then, if $\overline{X} = X_{0.5} = X_m$, we conclude that the given data set and, by extension, the Population from which the data set was obtained, is symmetrical.

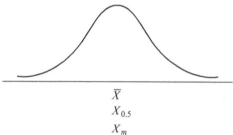

2. If $\overline{X} < X_{0.5} < X_m$, the distribution has a long left tail and is called "Negatively Skewed".

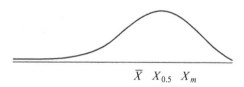

3. If $X_m < X_{0.5} < \overline{X}$, the distribution has a long right tail and is called "Positively Skewed".

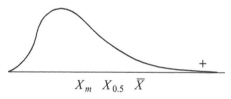

Note: Later, when we define measures of skewness, one of these measures is defined in terms of the difference $\overline{X} - X_m$. However, if you recall our discussion on the sample mode (X_m) of a data set (in section mode), the sample mode is not always unique. Because of this an equivalent expression is needed for the difference $\overline{X} - X_m$ which will be always defined.

It can be shown that

$$\overline{X} - X_m \approx 3\left(\overline{X} - X_{0.5}\right) \tag{3.19}$$

which is always defined and will be used in place of $\overline{X} - X_m$ in our future discussion.

3.2.2 Measures of Dispersion (or Data Spread)

Calculating the central location of a distribution is not sufficient to characterize the distribution because the combination of values that produced the central location measures is not unique.

Consider, for example, the definition of the midrange, where $X_{\mathrm{midrange}} = (L + H)/2$, where L and H are respectively, the lowest and highest values in a ranked data set.

It is clear from the above definition that an infinite number of (L_i, H_i) pairs of values exist such that the midrange remains a constant value, say 50. For example, $L_1 = 40$ and $H_1 = 60$ is such a pair while $L_2 = 30$ and $H_2 = 70$ is another.

It is obvious from this observation that, since the measures of central location (of which the midrange is but one of them), are not sufficient to characterize a data set, as a minimum, another type of measure is needed to measure the "spread" or the "Dispersion" of the data. As was the case with the measures of Central Tendency, there are many measures of data spread. In this section we will discuss the most important such measures, present the formulas from which these measures are calculated, and discuss some of their most important properties. Specifically we will discuss the following measures of Dispersion of a data set.

- Range = R
- Interquartile Range = IQR
- Interpercentile Range = IPR
- Average Deviation = AD
- Average Absolute Deviation = AAD
- Variance
    Biased = s^2
    Unbiased = $\hat{s}^2$
- Standard Deviation = $\sqrt{Variance}$
    Biased = s
    Unbiased = $\hat{s}$
- Coefficient of Variation = COV

After the discussion of these basic dispersion measures, we will explain the use of the standard deviation (which emerges as the "best" measure of data spread when the theory of Estimation is considered) as a measure of dispersion and present three very important rules (namely: a) The Empirical Rule; b) Chebychev's Inequality; and c) The Standard Score) which make the interpretation and application of the standard deviation very clear.

3.2.2.1 The Range, R

The Range for an ungrouped data set is defined by:

$$R = H - L \tag{3.20}$$

where H = Largest observation in a ranked data set
and L = Smallest observation in a ranked data set

As can be seen from this definition the range is very easy to calculate and understand. Stock market reports are usually stated in terms of the range (High and Low daily values are reported). Similarly the variation in the daily temperature is stated in terms of the range. Its main disadvantage is the fact that it uses only two data points (the lowest and highest) in a data set and disregards all the other data points, regardless of the size of n. Also it is greatly affected by extreme values. Because of these disadvantages, the range has only the limited uses mentioned above and it is also used in quality control where the range is used as a "surrogate" for the standard deviation.

3.2.2.2 Interquartile Range, IQR

The Interquartile Range is defined as:

$$IQR = Q_3 - Q_1 \tag{3.21}$$

where Q_1 and Q_3 are the first and third Quartiles of a ranked data set respectively, and as such they are themselves additional measures of location of a distribution. Their difference, however, is a measure of spread and includes only the middle 50% of the distribution. Because of this, the IQR is not affected by extreme values. Thus it is better than the range, but it is not as widely used as other measures of dispersion, as the standard deviation for example.

To divide a ranked data set into quartiles (*i.e.*, four equal parts, each containing 25% of the data distribution), we need to define three numbers: Q_1, Q_2, Q_3, such that:

1. 25% of the data is less than or equal to Q_1.
2. 25% of the data is between Q_1 and Q_2, with the end points included.
3. 25% of the data is between Q_2 and Q_3, with the end points included.
4. 25% of the data is greater than or equal to Q_3.

We note that Q_2 divides a ranked data set into 2 equal parts, each containing 50% of the data distribution and as such is identical with the median of a data set discussed earlier under measures of Central tendency. Therefore, we will not discuss further the derivation of Q_2.

In addition to needing Q_1 and Q_3 to obtain the IQR, these two Quartiles are also used in the definition of the coefficient of Peakedness, which will be discussed later. To find Q_1 and Q_3, we need to define both the position and value of each, just as we did with the median earlier.

1. Q_1 Calculations

$$\text{Location of } Q_1 = (n + 1)/4 \tag{3.22}$$

If $(n + 1)$ is exactly divisible by 4, then the value of Q_1 is the value in the ranked data set occupying the $(n + 1)/4$th location (for example, if $n = 19$, then $(n + 1)/4 = 5$ and the value of Q_1 is the observation occupying the 5th location in the ranked data set).

If $(n + 1)$ is not exactly divisible by 4, then the value of Q_1 is to be interpolated linearly by using the two adjacent observation values straddling the Q_1 location.

Example 8
If $n = 18$, $(n + 1)/4 = 19/4 = 4.75$, and

$$Q_1 = \text{Value in location 4} + 0.75 \begin{bmatrix} \text{Value in} \\ \text{Location 5} \end{bmatrix} - \begin{bmatrix} \text{Value in} \\ \text{Location 4} \end{bmatrix}$$

If $n = 17$, $(n + 1)/4 = 18/4 = 4.50$, and

$$Q_1 = \text{Value in location 4} + 0.50 \begin{bmatrix} \text{Value in} \\ \\ \text{Location 5} \end{bmatrix} - \begin{matrix} \text{Value in} \\ \\ \text{Location 4} \end{matrix}$$

If $n = 16$, $(n + 1)/4 = 17/4 = 4.25$, and

$$Q_1 = \text{Value in location 4} + 0.25 \begin{bmatrix} \text{Value in} \\ \\ \text{Location 5} \end{bmatrix} - \begin{matrix} \text{Value in} \\ \\ \text{Location 4} \end{matrix} \qquad (3.23)$$

■ ■ ■

2. **Q_3 calculations**

$$\text{Location of } Q_3 = \frac{3(n + 1)}{4} \qquad (3.24)$$

The value of Q_3 is calculated similarly to the value of Q_1. If $3(n + 1)$ is exactly divisible by 4 (as for example when $n = 3, 7, 11, 15, 19, \ldots$), the Q_3 value is the data observation occupying the $3(n + 1)/4^{\text{th}}$ location of the ranked data set. If $3(n + 1)$ is not exactly divisible by 4, the Q_3 value will be found by Linear Interpolation of two adjacent values as explained in our discussion of Q_1.

Once the Q_1 and Q_3 values have been found the IQR is calculated by subtraction, namely:

$$\text{IQR} = Q_{3\text{value}} - Q_{1\text{value}} \qquad (3.25)$$

3.2.2.3 Interpercentile Range, IPR, and Interdecile Range, IDR

Percentiles are 99 values, $P_1, P_2, \ldots, P_{99}$, which divide a ranked data set into 100 equal parts, each containing 1% of the observations.

The IPR is defined by:

$$\text{IPR} = P_{75} - P_{25} \qquad (3.26)$$

and it is identical to the *IQR* because $P_{75} = Q_3$ and $P_{25} = Q_1$.

However, because percentiles are regularly used with student's scores on standard aptitude tests, graduate record examinations and similar other examinations and because the Coefficient of Peakedness includes the 90th and 10th percentile (*i.e.*, P_{90} and P_{10}), we show below how the *i*-th percentile can be computed for a data set consisting of n sample observations.

The Location of the *i*-th percentile in a ranked data set is at:

$$\text{Location of } i\text{-th percentile} = \frac{i(n + 1)}{100} \qquad (3.27)$$

The value of the *i*-th percentile will, in general, be found by linear interpolation between two adjacent values, as was done earlier for Q_1 and Q_3, except for those special cases when $i(n + 1)$ is exactly divisible by 100 (for example when $n = 99, 199, 299, \ldots$) when the *i*-th percentile will have as its value the observation occupying the appropriate location in the ranked data set. Because we will need P_{10} and P_{90} later, we demonstrate their calculation below:

Assume, for example, that $n = 200$ in a given data set. Then

a) Location of the 10th percentile $P_{10} = \dfrac{10(n+1)}{100} = \dfrac{10(201)}{100} = 20.1,$ (3.28)

and the value of P_{10} is

$P_{10} = (\text{Value at location 20}) + 0.1(\text{Value at location 21} - \text{Value at location 20})$ (3.29)

b) Location of the 90th percentile $P_{90} = \dfrac{90(n+1)}{100} = \dfrac{90(201)}{100} = 180.9$ (3.30)

and the value of P_{90} is $P_{90} = (\text{Value at location 180})$
$+ 0.9(\text{Value at location 181} - \text{Value at location 180})$ (3.31)

In a similar manner we can find any percentile, including P_{75} and P_{25}, and then we find the IPR from:

$$\text{IPR} = P_{75\text{value}} - P_{25\text{value}}$$ (3.32)

Having found Q_1, Q_3, P_{75} and P_{25} it appears reasonable to redefine the midrange as:

$$\textbf{Midrange} = \frac{Q_1 + Q_3}{2} = \frac{P_{25} + P_{75}}{2}$$ (3.33)

Clearly this modified definition of the midrange will produce a central value for the data set of interest.

The Interdecile Range, IDR, is defined as:

$$\text{IDR} = P_{90} - P_{10}$$ (3.34)

and includes the Central 80% of the data distribution. It is used in the definition of the Coefficient of Peakedness or Kurtosis (K), as we will show later.

3.2.2.4 Average Deviation, AD

If, from each observation of a data set X_i, we subtract the sample mean, $\overline{X}$, we obtain the difference $X_i - \overline{X}$, which is called a "deviation" from the mean.

Then, by the Average Deviation, AD, we mean

$$\text{AD} = \frac{1}{n}\sum_{i=1}^{n}\left(X_i - \overline{X}\right)$$ (3.35)

However,   since $\displaystyle\sum_{i=1}^{n}\left(X_i - \overline{X}\right) = \sum_{i=1}^{n}X_i - \sum_{i=1}^{n}\overline{X} = \sum_{i=1}^{n}X_i - n\overline{X} = 0$ always,
regardless of the individual X_i values, AD $= 0$.

Clearly, since AD $= 0$ always, it provides no useful information. But the reason we are discussing it here is the fact that the concept of "deviations" from the mean is used in the definitions of the Average Absolute Deviation (AAD) and the Variance which are discussed below.

3.2.2.5 Average Absolute Deviation, AAD

The reason the Average Deviation of any data set is always equal to zero is the fact that the sum of the negative deviations exactly equals the sum of the positive deviations, while some of the deviations may be equal to zero.

Realizing that a negative deviation of, say 2 units, is the same as a positive deviation of 2 units, and that what we have is a total of 2 deviations of 2 units each rather than a zero deviation, it becomes obvious that to avoid getting a zero Average Deviation, we must change the effect that negative deviations have on the positive ones. This can be accomplished by either

a)   Taking the Absolute value of the Deviations, before summing them up, or
b)   Squaring each deviation before summing up.

Using the Absolute value of the deviations defines the Average Absolute Deviation (AAD) as a measure of the data spread while the squaring of the deviations defines the variance as a different measure of data spread.

Then
$$\text{AAD} = \frac{1}{n} \sum_{i=1}^{n} \left| X_i - \overline{X} \right| \tag{3.36}$$

where $|\ \ |$ indicates Absolute Value

Since the $|\ \ |$ is always positive, the AAD will, in general, be different than zero, except in the special case in which all the X_i are equal to each other when the AAD $= 0$ as it should, since all of the values are concentrated on one point and, therefore, there is no data spread.

Therefore, the AAD is a useful measure of data spread and, for a normal data distribution, about 58% of the data are included in the interval: $\overline{X} - \text{AAD}$ and $\overline{X} + \text{AAD}$.

From its definition it is apparent that it takes every observation into account. However, because it is easier to square numbers than to take absolute values of the numbers (this is at least true in a computer), the AAD is not used very much. The variance is used instead, which involves squaring the differences.

3.2.2.6 Variance

When the individual deviations are squared, the resulting measure of dispersion is called variance and is defined by

$$\text{Variance} = \frac{1}{R} \sum_{i=1}^{n} \left(X_i - \overline{X} \right)^2, \qquad \text{where } R = \begin{cases} n, & \text{or} \\ n-1 \end{cases} \tag{3.37}$$

as we discuss below.

Intuitively, it appears that the value of R should be n.

However, as will be discussed in detail in our treatment of Estimation Theory, in order for the sample variance to be a good estimator of the population variance (σ^2), it must possess a desirable property for an estimator called "unbiasedness" and this requires that R is assigned the value of $n - 1$. The explanation for this hinges on the concept of "degrees of freedom" associated with a "sum of squares" as we will discuss later (when we discuss "small sample" theory). There, it will become clear that the sum of squares:

$$Y = \sum_{i=1}^{n} (X_i - \overline{X})^2 \tag{3.38}$$

which, under normal circumstances should have n degrees of freedom, because of the presence of $\overline{X}$ which must be estimated from the observations, loses one degree of freedom and now has $n - 1$, which is the appropriate value which should be assigned to R.

Because of the two possible values of R, it is necessary to define two different expressions for the variance which differ only in the value of R. The difference in the values of the two expressions is significant only for small values of n. As n becomes larger and larger, the two expressions get closer and closer to each other and, in the Limit (*i.e.*, when $n \rightarrow \infty$), the two expressions are identical.

The expression for the variance which uses $R = n$ is called "Biased Variance" and is represented by the symbol s^2, while the expression using $R = n - 1$ is called "Unbiased Variance" and is represented by $\hat{s}^2$. The meaning behind "Biased" and "Unbiased" variance will become clear after our "Estimated Theory" discussion.

$$\text{Biased Variance} = s^2 = \frac{1}{n}\sum_{i=1}^{n}(X_i - \overline{X})^2 \tag{3.39}$$

$$\text{Unbiased Variance} = \hat{s}^2 = \frac{1}{n-1}\sum_{i=1}^{n}(X_i - \overline{X})^2 \tag{3.40}$$

The two expressions above are the "definitional" formulas for the Biased and Unbiased Variance, but they are not very convenient for the actual calculation of variances. This is especially true if the values of the X_i are fractional numbers and the value of $\overline{X}$ also becomes fractional. By applying the rules of summation theory on

$$Y = \sum_{i=1}^{n}(X_i - \overline{X})^2 \tag{3.41}$$

we can rewrite it as:

$$\sum_{i=1}^{n}(X_i - \overline{X})^2 = \sum_{i=1}^{n}\left(X_i^2 - 2\overline{X}X_i + \overline{X}^2\right) = \sum_{i=1}^{n}X_i^2 - 2\overline{X}\sum_{i=1}^{n}X_i + \overline{X}^2\sum_{i=1}^{n}(1)$$

$$= \sum_{i=1}^{n}X_i^2 - 2\overline{X}\left(n\overline{X}\right) + n\overline{X}^2$$

$$= \sum_{i=1}^{n}X_i^2 - n\overline{X}^2$$

$$= \sum_{i=1}^{n}X_i^2 - n\left(\frac{\sum_{i=1}^{n}X_i^2}{n}\right)^2$$

$$= \sum_{i=1}^{n}X_i^2 - \frac{1}{n}\left(\sum_{i=1}^{n}X_i\right)^2$$

$$= \frac{n\sum_{i=1}^{n}X_i^2 - \left(\sum_{i=1}^{n}X_i\right)^2}{n}$$

$$= \frac{n\left(X_1^2 + X_2^2 + \cdots + X_n^2\right) - \left(X_1 + X_2 + \cdots + X_n\right)^2}{n} \tag{3.42}$$

This later expression tells us that to calculate either variance for a data set $X_1, X_2, \ldots, X_n$, all we have to do is calculate the sum of the values of the observations (*i.e.*, $X_1 + X_2 + \cdots + X_n$) and the sum of the squares of the observations (*i.e.*, $X_1^2 + X_2^2 + \cdots + X_n^2$) and then apply the above formula in order to evaluate

$\sum\limits_{i=1}^{n}\left(X_i - \overline{X}\right)^2$. We note at this point that both: $\sum\limits_{i=1}^{n} X_i^2$ and $\sum\limits_{i=1}^{n} X_i$ can be very easily programmed in a digital computer (as the following program in Basic shows) and can also be obtained very easily using a hand calculator, by using the appropriate keys.

PROGRAM IN BASIC TO CALCULATE
THE MEAN AND VARIANCE OF A DATA SET

```
 10  LET A = 0
 20  LET B = 0
 20  LET N = 0
 40  READ X
 50  DATA X₁, X₂,..., Xₙ   (← The Actual Data Values)
 60  LET S₁ = A + X   (← Calculates ∑ᵢ₌₁ⁿ Xᵢ)
 70  LET S₂ = B + X ↑ 2   (← Calculates ∑ᵢ₌₁ⁿ Xᵢ²)
 80  LET N = N + 1   (← Calculates N )
 90  GO TO 40   (← Make Sure All Values of X are Included)
100  LET S₃ = N × S₂ − S₁↑ 2(← Calculates Numerator of Variance Expression)
110  LET K₁ = N↑ 2
120  LET K₂ = N × (N − 1)
130  LET M = S₁/N   (← Calculates X̄)
140  LET S = S₃/K₁   (← Calculates S²)
150  LET T = S₃/K₂   (← Calculates Ŝ²)
160  PRINT M, S, T
170  END
```

where in the above program we have used the following "computational" formulas for the two variances.

$$s^2 = \text{Biased Variance} = \frac{n\sum\limits_{i=1}^{n} X_i^2 - \left(\sum\limits_{i=1}^{n} X_i\right)^2}{n^2} \tag{3.43}$$

$$\hat{s}^2 = \text{Unbiased Variance} = \frac{n\sum\limits_{i=1}^{n} X_i^2 - \left(\sum\limits_{i=1}^{n} X_i\right)^2}{n(n-1)} \tag{3.44}$$

If one insists on using the "definitional" formulas for the calculation of variance, the easiest way to proceed is by means of the following table:

Individual Observations X_i	$(X_i - \overline{X})$	$(X_i - \overline{X})^2$
X_1	$X_1 - \overline{X}$	$(X_1 - \overline{X})$
X_2	$X_2 - \overline{X}$	$(X_1 - \overline{X})^2$
$\ldots$	$\ldots$	$\ldots$
X_n	$X_n - \overline{X}$	$(X_n - \overline{X})^2$
$\sum\limits_{i=1}^{n} X_i = X_1 + X_2 + \cdots + X_n$	$\sum\limits_{i=1}^{n}(X_i - \overline{X}) = 0$	$\sum\limits_{i=1}^{n}(X_i - \overline{X})^2$

Then

$$\overline{X} = \frac{\sum_{i=1}^{n} X_i}{n} , \tag{3.45}$$

$$s^2 = \frac{\sum_{i=1}^{n} (X_i - \overline{X})^2}{n} , \quad \text{and} \tag{3.46}$$

$$\hat{s}^2 = \frac{\sum_{i=1}^{n} (X_i - \overline{X})^2}{n - 1} \tag{3.47}$$

3.2.2.7 Standard Deviation

Even though the variance is a well defined and clearly understood measure is it not appropriate to use as a measure of data spread because it does not have the same units as the original data. This happens because when we square the deviations, the units are also squared. What is needed is a measure which has the same units as the original data. Such a measure is the standard deviation which is defined as the positive square root of the variance, namely:

$$\text{Standard Deviation} = \sqrt{\text{Variance}} \tag{3.48}$$

Since we "differentiated" between "Biased" and "Unbiased" variance, we will maintain this distinction and define:

$$s = \text{Biased Standard Deviation} = \sqrt{\text{Biased Variance}} = \sqrt{s^2} \tag{3.49}$$

and $\quad \hat{s} = \text{Unbiased Standard Deviation} = \sqrt{\text{Unbiased Variance}} = \sqrt{\hat{s}^2}, \tag{3.50}$

even though it is not true that $E(\hat{s}) = \sigma$ (as is the case with $E(\hat{s}^2) = \sigma^2$)

Actually $\qquad\qquad\qquad E(\hat{s}) = C_2\sigma, \tag{3.51}$

where $\qquad\qquad\qquad C_2 = \sqrt{\frac{2}{n}} \times \frac{\left(\frac{n-2}{2}\right)!}{\left(\frac{n-3}{2}\right)!} \tag{3.52}$

For $\hat{s}$ to be an Unbiased Estimator C_2 would have to be equal to 1, for all values of n, something that is not True, as one can find in any Quality Control book.

The Standard Deviation has the correct units and is an appropriate measure to use. In section 3.2.2.10 (below) we will interpret and apply the standard deviation.

3.2.2.8 Coefficient of Variation, COV

On many occasions it is necessary to compare the spread of two data sets.

If the units of measurement in the two sets of observations are the same and the corresponding means are approximately the same then the standard deviation (either s or $\hat{s}$) is used for the comparison.

However, when the units of measurement are not the same and/or the corresponding means are not approximately the same, the standard deviation is not the appropriate measure of comparison. For example, it is meaningless to compare the variation in the weekly income of a neighborhood store (measured in dollars) and IBM (measured in Billions of dollars).

What is needed in such cases is a measure which does not depend on the units used and takes the mean (average) value into consideration. Such a measure is provided by the Coefficient of Variation, which is defined by

$$\text{Coefficient of Variation} = COV = \frac{\hat{s}}{\overline{X}} \tag{3.53}$$

To use this measure, we compute $\hat{s}$ and $\overline{X}$ for each data set and then form the ratio $\frac{\hat{s}}{\overline{X}}$. The set with the higher ratio $\frac{\hat{s}}{\overline{X}}$ has the highest relative variation.

3.2.2.9 Calculation of Total Mean and Variance When Additional Information Becomes Available

Suppose a data set $X_1, X_2, \ldots, X_n$ is given and we calculate $\overline{X}$ and $\hat{s}$ (or s) for this data set.

Also suppose that after $\overline{X}$ and $\hat{s}$ have been calculated an additional observation, X_{n+1}, becomes available.

Obviously, we can calculate a new $\overline{X}$ and $\hat{s}$ based on $n + 1$ observations. However, the question we wish to address is the following: Can we modify $\overline{X}$ and $\hat{s}$, based on n observations, to include the effect of the additional observation without starting from scratch? The answer is a "definite" yes, and we proceed as follows:

Using $\overline{X}_n$, $\overline{X}_{n+1}$, $\hat{s}_n$, and $\hat{s}_{n+1}$ to represent the appropriate sample means and variances based on n and $n + 1$ observations respectively, we write

$$\overline{X}_n = \frac{\sum_{i=1}^{n} X_i}{n} \tag{3.54}$$

$$\overline{X}_{n+1} = \frac{\sum_{i=1}^{n+1} X_i}{n + 1} = \frac{\sum_{i=1}^{n} X_i + X_{n+1}}{n + 1} \tag{3.55}$$

But since

$$\sum_{i=1}^{n} X_i = n\overline{X}_n, \tag{3.56}$$

we can write

$$\overline{X}_{n+1} = \frac{n\overline{X}_n + X_{n+1}}{n + 1} = \left(\frac{n}{n + 1}\right)\overline{X}_n + \left(\frac{1}{n + 1}\right)X_{n+1} \tag{3.57}$$

This is clearly a recursive formula, which allows a new $\overline{X}$ to be calculated from the previous one, as a new observation becomes available, and can be repeated for any number of new observations that may become available.

Let us now derive a similar formula to relate $\hat{s}_{n+1}$ and $\hat{s}_n$.

From the definition of variance we have

$$\hat{s}_n^2 = \frac{n\sum_{i=1}^{n} X_i^2 - \left(\sum_{i=1}^{n} X_i\right)^2}{n(n - 1)} \tag{3.58}$$

and
$$\hat{s}_{n+1}^2 = \frac{(n+1)\sum_{i=1}^{n+1} X_i^2 - \left(\sum_{i=1}^{n+1} X_i\right)^2}{(n+1)n}$$

$$= \frac{(n+1)\left[\sum_{i=1}^{n} X_i^2 + X_{n+1}^2\right] - \left[\sum_{i=1}^{n} X_i + X_{n+1}\right]^2}{n(n+1)} \tag{3.59}$$

But because $\sum_{i=1}^{n} X_i^2 = \frac{1}{n}\left[n(n-1)\hat{s}_n^2 + \left(\sum_{i=1}^{n} X_i\right)^2\right] = (n-1)\hat{s}_n^2 + \frac{1}{n}\left[n\overline{X}_n\right]^2$ (3.60)

$$= (n-1)\hat{s}_n^2 + n\overline{X}_n^2, \tag{3.61}$$

we can rewrite $\hat{s}_{n+1}^2$ as

$$\hat{s}_{n+1}^2 = \frac{1}{n(n+1)}\left\{(n+1)\left[(n-1)\hat{s}_n^2 + n\overline{X}_n^2 + X_{n+1}^2\right]\right.$$

$$\left. - \left[\left(\sum_{i=1}^{n} X_i\right)^2 + 2X_{n+1}\sum_{i=1}^{n} X_i + X_{n+1}^2\right]\right\} \tag{3.62}$$

$$= \frac{n-1}{n}\hat{s}_n^2 + \overline{X}_n^2 + \frac{1}{n}X_{n+1}^2 - \frac{\left[n^2\overline{X}_n^2 + 2n\overline{X}X_{n+1} + X_{n+1}^2\right]}{n(n+1)}$$

$$= \frac{n-1}{n}\hat{s}_n^2 + \overline{X}_n^2 + \frac{1}{n}X_{n+1}^2 - \frac{n}{n+1}\overline{X}_n^2 - \frac{2\overline{X}_n X_{n+1}}{n+1} - \frac{X_{n+1}^2}{n(n+1)}$$

$$= \frac{n-1}{n}\hat{s}_n^2 + \left(1 - \frac{n}{n+1}\right)\overline{X}_n^2 + \frac{1}{n}\left(1 - \frac{1}{n+1}\right)X_{n+1}^2 - \frac{2\overline{X}_n}{n+1}X_{n+1}$$

$$= \frac{n-1}{n}\hat{s}_n^2 + \left(\frac{1}{n+1}\right)\overline{X}_n^2 + \left(\frac{1}{n+1}\right)X_{n+1}^2 - \left(\frac{1}{n+1}\right)2\overline{X}_n X_{n+1}$$

$$= \frac{n-1}{n}\hat{s}_n^2 + \frac{1}{n+1}\left[\overline{X}_n^2 + X_{n+1}^2 - 2\overline{X}_n X_{n+1}\right]$$

$$= \frac{n-1}{n}\hat{s}_n^2 + \frac{1}{n+1}\left(\overline{X}_n - \overline{X}_{n+1}\right)^2 \tag{3.63}$$

Example 9

Suppose we have the observations $X_1 = 2$, $X_2 = 3$, $X_3 = 3$, $X_4 = 4$, $X_5 = 5$, $X_6 = 6$, $X_7 = 2$, $X_8 = 7$, and $X_9 = 4$.

Then
$$\overline{X}_n = \overline{X}_9 = \frac{\sum_{i=1}^{9} X_i}{n} = \frac{36}{9} = 4$$

and
$$\hat{s}_n^2 = \hat{s}_9^2 = \frac{9(168) - (36)^2}{9(8)} = \frac{1512 - 1296}{72} = \frac{216}{72} = \frac{54}{18} = 3$$

If now another observation, $X_{10} = 6$, became available we can re-calculate $\overline{X}$ and $\hat{s}^2$ now based on 10 observations and obtain:

$$\overline{X}_{10} = \frac{\sum_{i=1}^{10} X_i}{10} = \frac{36 + 6}{10} = 4.2$$

and

$$\hat{s}_{10}^2 = \frac{10 \sum_{i=1}^{10} X_i^2 - \left(\sum_{i=1}^{10} X_i\right)^2}{10(9)} = \frac{10(204) - (42)^2}{10(4)} = \frac{2040 - 1764}{90} = \frac{276}{90} = \frac{46}{15}$$

$$= 3\frac{1}{15} = 3.066667$$

■ ■ ■

The question now becomes: Do we get the values above for $\overline{X}_{10}$ and $\hat{s}_{10}^2$ when we use the recursive formulas below?

$$\overline{X}_{n+1} = \left(\frac{n}{n+1}\right)\overline{X}_n + \left(\frac{1}{n+1}\right)X_{n+1}$$

$$\hat{s}_{n+1}^2 = \left(\frac{n-1}{n}\right)\hat{s}_n^2 + \left(\frac{1}{n+1}\right)\left(\overline{X}_n - X_{n+1}\right)^2$$

Since the original value of $n = 9$ (in this example), we have:

$$\overline{X}_{10} = \left(\frac{9}{10}\right)\overline{X}_9 + \frac{X_{10}}{10} = \frac{9}{10}(4) + \frac{1}{10}(6) = \frac{36 + 6}{10} = 4.2, \text{ and}$$

$$\hat{s}_{10}^2 = \frac{8}{9}\left(\hat{s}_9^2\right) + \frac{1}{10}\left(\overline{X}_9 - X_{10}\right)^2 = \frac{8}{9}(3) + \frac{1}{10}(4-6)^2 = \frac{8}{3} + \frac{2}{5} = \frac{46}{15} = 3\frac{1}{15}$$

Clearly the two methods produce the same results and we conclude that the two recursive formulas:

$$\overline{X}_{n+1} = \left(\frac{n}{n+1}\right)\overline{X}_n + \left(\frac{1}{n+1}\right)X_{n+1} \tag{3.64}$$

$$\hat{s}_{n+1}^2 = \left(\frac{n-1}{n}\right)\hat{s}_n^2 + \left(\frac{1}{n+1}\right)\left(\overline{X}_n - X_{n+1}\right)^2 \tag{3.65}$$

are correct and produce the desired results.

Using a similar approach, we can extend these formulas to cover the case when we have 2 sets of data, one of n_1 samples which produces $\overline{X}_1$ and $\hat{s}_1^2$, and the other of n_2 samples which produces $\overline{X}_2$ and $\hat{s}_2^2$ respectively.

Then, the overall sample mean and variance can be expressed as:

$$\overline{X} = \left(\frac{n_1}{n_1 + n_2}\right)\overline{X}_1 + \left(\frac{n_2}{n_1 + n_2}\right)\overline{X}_2 \tag{3.66}$$

$$\hat{s}_{n+1}^2 = \left(\frac{n_1 - 1}{n-1}\right)\hat{s}_1^2 + \left(\frac{n_2 - 1}{n-1}\right)\hat{s}_2^2 + \frac{n_1 n_2}{n(n-1)}\left(\overline{X}_1 - \overline{X}_2\right)^2 \tag{3.67}$$

where $n = n_1 + n_2$

Example 10

Let Set 1 consist of the observations $X_1 = 2$, $X_2 = 3$, $X_3 = 3$, and $X_4 = 4$, from which

$$\overline{X}_1 = \frac{\sum_{i=1}^{4} X_i}{4} = \frac{12}{4} = 3$$

$$\hat{s}_1^2 = \frac{4\sum_{i=1}^{4} X_i^2 - (12)^2}{4(3)} = \frac{4(38) - 144}{12} = \frac{152 - 144}{12} = \frac{2}{3}$$

and let set 2 consist of the observations $X_5 = 5$, $X_6 = 6$, $X_7 = 2$, $X_8 = 7$, $X_9 = 4$ and $X_{10} = 6$ from which $\overline{X}_2 = 30/6 = 5$ and $\hat{s}_2^2 = 96/30 = 3.2$.

If we combine the observations into one data set, direct calculations give

$$\overline{X} = 42/10 = 4.2, \text{ and } \hat{s}^2 = 46/15 = 3 \ 1/15$$

■■■

Question: Do the above formulas give the same results?

By direct substitution we obtain

$$\overline{X} = (4/10)3 + (6/10)5 = (12 + 30)/10 = 4.2$$

$$\hat{s}^2 = \left(\frac{3}{9}\right)\left(\frac{2}{3}\right) + \left(\frac{5}{9}\right)\left(\frac{16}{5}\right) + \frac{(4)(6)}{10(9)}(3 - 5)^2 = \frac{2}{9} + \frac{16}{9} + \frac{24}{90} \ (4)$$

$$= \frac{18}{9} + \frac{96}{90} = \frac{180 + 96}{90} = \frac{46}{15} = 3\frac{1}{15},$$

and the results are identical.

3.2.2.10 Interpretation and some Applications of the Standard Deviation

The standard deviation is a useful measure which gives us an idea as to how the observations are spread about the mean. This spreading of the observations about the mean depends on the type of distribution from which the samples came from and we will present two useful rules (the Empirical Rule and Chebychev's Rule) to illustrate this point, but first we state and illustrate two theorems which are very important and very useful in the future development of this course.

1. **Theorem 1**   Adding the same constant to a set of observations, increases the mean by that constant, but the standard deviation remains the same.

   Proof   Let $X_1, X_2, \ldots, X_n$ be n observations with a given $\overline{X}$ and $\hat{s}_x$.
   Let us now define a new set $y_1, y_2, \ldots, y_n$ in which

$$y_i = X_i + C \tag{3.68}$$

   where C is any constant

Then $\overline{y} = \dfrac{\sum_{i=1}^{n} y_i}{n} = \dfrac{\sum_{i=1}^{n}\left(X_i + C\right)}{n} = \dfrac{\sum_{i=1}^{n} X_i}{n} + \dfrac{\sum_{i=1}^{n} C}{n} = \overline{X} + \dfrac{nC}{n} = \overline{X} + C \tag{3.69}$

Also

$$\hat{s}_y^2 = \frac{\sum_{i=1}^{n}(y_i - \bar{y})^2}{n - 1} = \frac{\sum_{i=1}^{n}[(X_i + C) - (\bar{X} + C)]^2}{n - 1} = \frac{\sum_{i=1}^{n}(X_i + C - \bar{X} - C)^2}{n - 1}$$

$$= \frac{\sum_{i=1}^{n}(X_i + C - \bar{X} - C)^2}{n - 1} = \frac{\sum_{i=1}^{n}(X_i - \bar{X})^2}{n - 1} = \hat{s}_x^2, \tag{3.70}$$

and $\hat{s}_y = \hat{s}_x$ $\qquad$ (3.71)

2. **Theorem 2** Multiplying each observation in a set by the same constant C, gives a new set in which both the mean and the standard deviation are multiplied by C.

Proof: Let $X_1, X_2, \ldots, X_n$ be n observations with a given $\bar{X}$ and $\hat{s}_x$.
Let us also define a new set $y_1, y_2, \ldots, y_n$ in which

$$y_i = CX_i \tag{3.72}$$

where C is any constant

Then $\qquad \bar{y} = \dfrac{\sum_{i=1}^{n}y_i}{n} = \dfrac{\sum_{i=1}^{n}CX_i}{n} = \dfrac{C\sum_{i=1}^{n}X_i}{n} = C\left(\dfrac{\sum_{i=1}^{n}X_i}{n}\right) = C\bar{X}$ $\qquad$ (3.73)

Also $\hat{s}_y^2 = \dfrac{\sum_{i=1}^{n}(y_i - \bar{y})^2}{n - 1} = \dfrac{\sum_{i=1}^{n}[(CX_i) - (C\bar{X})]^2}{n - 1} = \dfrac{\sum_{i=1}^{n}[C(X_i - \bar{X})]^2}{n - 1}$

$$= \frac{\sum_{i=1}^{n}C^2(X_i - \bar{X})^2}{n - 1} = C^2\frac{\sum_{i=1}^{n}(X_i - \bar{X})^2}{n - 1} = C^2\hat{s}_x^2 \tag{3.74}$$

and $\qquad\qquad\qquad\qquad \hat{s}_y = C\hat{s}_x$ $\qquad$ (3.75)

These two theorems will be very useful in determining the properties of one set of random variables from a second set of random variables when the two sets are linearly related, *i.e.*, when

$$y_i = a + bX_i \tag{3.76}$$

Note that the above linear relationship includes both of the above discussed relationships (*i.e.*, $y_i = X_i + C$ and $y_i = CX_i$) by appropriate value assignment to the constants a and b.

And now we state without proof the Empirical and Chebychev rules which make clear the usefulness of the standard deviation as a measure of data spread. Illustration of the validity of both of these rules would have to be postponed until we first discuss probability theory and random variables.

The Empirical Rule applies only to a set of data obtained from a population which is normally distributed and states:

1. The proportion of the distribution between $\bar{X} - \hat{s}$ and $\bar{X} + \hat{s}$ is approximately 68%.
2. The proportion of the distribution between $\bar{X} - 2\hat{s}$ and $\bar{X} + 2\hat{s}$ is approximately 95%.
3. The proportion of the distribution between $\bar{X} - 3\hat{s}$ and $\bar{X} + 3\hat{s}$ is approximately 99.7% (or practically all of the distribution).

This rule can also be applied in reverse, as follows:

Suppose we have a data set $X_1, X_2, \ldots, X_n$ and we do not know whether it came from a normal distribution or not. If we calculate $\overline{X}$ and $\hat{s}_x$, rank the data and then count the number of observations to be found within one, two, and three standard deviations of the mean and compare these proportions where by proportion we mean:

The Number of Observations Within One, Two, or Three Standard Deviations

Total Number of Observations

to the proportions above (0.68, 0.95, 0.997), we can determine the closeness of this data set to a normal distribution.

The Chebychev Rule, on the other hand, applies to any data set, whether normal or not, and states: "The proportion of any distribution which lies within K standard deviations of the mean (where K is a positive number greater than or equal to one), is at least

$$1 - \frac{1}{K^2} \tag{3.77}$$

When $K = 1$, $1 - \frac{1}{K^2} = 0$ and this rule is not very informative.

When $K = 2$, $1 - \frac{1}{K^2} = 0.75$, while when $K = 3$, $1 - \frac{1}{K^2} \approx 0.89$.

Note that in this case the proportion of the population within two or three standard deviations of the mean is much smaller than the corresponding proportions of the Empirical rule, but this is to be expected because this is a general rule which applies to all distributions while the Empirical rule which applies to only one distribution and, therefore, can be made to specify these proportions more accurately.

The "standardized" or "Z" score is another useful device, involving the standard deviation, which allows us to transform a set of observations $X_1, X_2, \ldots, X_n$, with any mean $\overline{X}$ and standard deviation $\hat{s}_x$ to another set $Z_1, Z_2, \ldots, Z_n$ in which $\overline{Z} = 0$ and $\hat{s}_z = 1$.

To accomplish this, all that is needed is to define Z_i as

$$Z_i = \frac{X_i - \overline{X}}{\hat{s}_X} \tag{3.78}$$

It is obvious from the definition of Z_i, that the transformed observations $Z_1, Z_2, \ldots, Z_n$ do not depend on the units (because the units of $X_i - \overline{X}$ and $\hat{s}_X$ are the same and cancel out). This fact suggests the following potential use of the standard score, in finding the *relative* standing of elements on different populations.

Suppose professor A gives a statistics exam to his class and calculates the mean $\left(\overline{X}_A\right)$ and standard deviation $\left(\hat{s}_A\right)$ of the grades in his class while Professor B also gives a statistics exam to his class and calculates the mean and standard deviation of his class as $\overline{X}_B$ and $\hat{s}_B$. If a student in professor A's class obtained a grade X_A while a second student, in professor B's class, obtained a grade X_B, which of the two students scored higher in the exam?

The standard score allows us to find the relative standing of the two students by computing their respective Z-scores, thus eliminating any differences that may exist between the two professors.

We have

$$\text{For student } A: Z_A = \frac{X_A - \overline{X}_A}{\hat{s}_A} \tag{3.79}$$

$$\text{For student } B: Z_B = \frac{X_B - \overline{X}_B}{\hat{s}_B} \tag{3.80}$$

The student with the higher Z-score scored higher in the exam.

If we had wanted to transform the observations $X_1, X_2, \ldots, X_n$ (with mean $\overline{X}$ and standard deviation $\hat{s}_X$) to another set $y_1, y_2, \ldots, y_n$ with mean $\overline{y}$ and standard deviation $\hat{s}_Y$ (for example a professor may wish to "curve" the grades of the exam $X_1, X_2, \ldots, X_n$ with mean $\overline{X}$ and standard deviation $\hat{s}_X$ to another set of grades with mean $\overline{y}$ and standard deviation $\hat{s}_Y$) the required transformation is:

$$y_i = \left(\frac{X_i - \overline{X}}{\hat{s}_X} \right) \hat{s}_Y + \overline{y} \tag{3.81}$$

One can prove the validity of this relationship by using the definition of the Z-score and theorems 1 and 2 that we discussed earlier in this section.

3.2.3 Measures of Skewness

In addition to central location and spread of data distributions are characterized by the "shape" of the distribution which is described by its symmetry or lack of symmetry (or Skewness) and its thinness or thickness which in statistics is known as "Peakedness" or "Kurtosis".

A distribution has zero skewness if it is symmetrical relative to its mean. We stated earlier that for a distribution which is symmetrical

$$\text{Mean} = \text{Median} = \text{Mode} \tag{3.82}$$

Also we have defined a "positively skewed" distribution to be one in which the right tail is long and in which

$$\text{Mean} > \text{Median} > \text{Mode} \tag{3.83}$$

while a distribution was called "negatively skewed" if it had a long left tail and

$$\text{Mean} < \text{Median} < \text{Mode} \tag{3.84}$$

These observations are summarized in "Pearson's Coefficient of Skewness" which is defined by

$$\hat{S}_{kp} = \frac{\overline{X} - X_m}{\hat{s}} \tag{3.85}$$

$$\approx \frac{3\left(\overline{X} - X_{0.5} \right)}{\hat{s}} \quad \text{(because the mode is not unique)} \tag{3.86}$$

and has the following interpretation:

1. If $S_{kp} > 0$, then $\overline{X} > X_{0.5}$, and the distribution is Positively Skewed.
2. If $S_{kp} = 0$, then $\overline{X} = X_{0.5}$, and the distribution is Symmetric. $\qquad$ (3.87)
3. If $S_{kp} < 0$, then $\overline{X} < X_{0.5}$, and the distribution is Negatively Skewed.

3.2.4 Measures of Peakedness or Kurtosis

A distribution which is very narrow (or thin) is called "Leptokurtic" while one which is wide (or thick) is called "Platykurtic". Between these two extremes is another type of distribution which is neither very thin nor very wide and is called "Mesokurtic".

These properties are encompassed in the "Coefficient of Peakedness" which is defined as

$$K = \frac{1/2(Q_3 - Q_1)}{P_{90} - P_{10}} = \frac{1/2(\text{IQR})}{P_{90} - P_{10}} = \frac{1/2(\text{IQR})}{\text{IDR}}, \tag{3.88}$$

where Q_3, Q_1, P_{90}, and P_{10} are Quartiles and Percentiles defined previously.

Depending on the calculated value of K, we attach the following interpretation:

1. If $K \approx 0.5$, the distribution is Leptokurtic.
2. If $K \approx 0.25$, the distribution is Mesokurtic.   (3.89)
3. If $K \approx 0$, the distribution is Platykurtic.

After we discuss the normal distribution in later chapters we will be in a position to perform calculations with it and show that:

$$\begin{aligned} Q_3 &\approx 0.675 & P_{90} &= 1.28 \\ Q_1 &\approx -0.675 & P_{10} &= -1.28 \end{aligned} \tag{3.90}$$

When these values are substituted in the definition of K above, we obtain $K = 0.263$.

Therefore, the normal distribution is approximately Mesokurtic (because $K = 0.263 \approx 0.25$) and also symmetric because $S_{kp} = 0$, since $\overline{X} = X_{0.5} = X_m$.

3.3 Descriptive Measures for Grouped Data

In Chapter 2 we learned how to summarize a grouped data set by designing an appropriate set of classes and then constructing the corresponding frequency distribution for the set. We should recall at this point that each observation falling in a given class is represented by the midpoint of the class which we defined as the class mark. For a given frequency distribution we define the following two classes which will make our discussion below easier:

(1)	(2)	(3)	(4)	(5)	(6)	(7)	(8)	(9)	(10)
	$L_i \quad U_i$	f_i	F_i	m_i	$m_i f_i$	$m_i^2 f_i$	U_i	$U_i f_i$	$U_i^2 f_i$
Class #	Class Limits	Absolute Frequency	Cumulative Frequency	Class Mark					
1	22–32	1	1	27	27	729	−5	−5	25
2	33–43	2	3	38	76	2,888	−4	−8	32
3	44–54	5	8	49	245	12,005	−3	−15	45
4	55–65	2	10	60	120	7,200	−2	−4	8
5	66–76	9	19	71	639	45,369	−1	−9	9
6	77–87	9	28	82	738	60,516	0	0	0
7	88–98	10	38	93	930	86,590	1	10	10
8	99–109	5	43	104	520	54,080	2	10	20
9	110–120	3	46	115	345	39,675	3	9	27
10	121–131	4	50	126	504	63,504	4	16	64
Sums of Columns: ⟶					4,144	372,456		4	240

1. Median Class is the class in which the Cumulative Frequency first exceeds the value of $(n + 1)/2$ (Example: When $n = 50$ the median class is the class in which the cumulative frequency first exceeds the value of 25.5).
2. Modal Class is the class with the highest absolute frequency.

We will again need four different types of measures to completely characterize a grouped data set and these types are the same four we used to describe an ungrouped data set. However the methods and formulas needed to calculate these measures are different and their values depend largely on the actual frequency distribution under consideration. For this reason we reproduce here most of the frequency distribution table we constructed in Chapter 2 and extend it to include several more columns which are needed in our discussion.

3.3.1 Measures of Central Tendency

Even though all of the central tendency measures we defined under the ungrouped data case can also be defined for the grouped data case (by recognizing that our data set now is: 27, 38, 38, 49, 49, 49, 49, ..., 126, 126, 126, 126), we will discuss only the Median, Mode, and the Mean because they are the most important ones.

3.3.1.1 Median

There are two methods for calculating the median of a grouped data set, using the frequency distribution.

One is a "Graphic Method" and uses the Ogive, as was discussed in Chapter 2. The other is an "Algebraic Interpolation Method" and uses an equation.

1. **Graphic Method**

   This method can be used to calculate approximately not only the median but also all the Quartiles and Percentiles.

   The method consists of first plotting the Ogive from the frequency distribution, and then drawing a horizontal line, parallel to the X-axis, starting at 0.5 in the vertical scale (to calculate Q_1 start at 0.25 in the vertical scale, to calculate P_{90} start at 0.9 in the vertical scale, etc.), until it intersects the Ogive. Then, from this point of intersection we drop a line perpendicular to the X-axis. The value of the median is the X value where the perpendicular line crosses the X-axis. This method is only approximate, but the approximation can be made quite accurate by being careful with the data and the scales on the two perpendicular axes.

2. **Algebraic Interpolation Method**

   If the accuracy provided by the graphic method is not acceptable, then we use the algebraic interpolation formula:

   $$X_{0.5} = L_{0.5} + \left[\frac{\left(\dfrac{n + 1}{2}\right) - F_{P_{X_{0.5}}}}{f_{0.5}} \right] C \tag{3.91}$$

   which requires that we first identify the "Median Class" of the frequency distribution (defined above) and then from it, and adjacent classes, specify the values for

   $$
   \begin{aligned}
   L_{0.5} &= \text{Lower Class Limit of the Median Class} \\
   f_{0.5} &= \text{Absolute Frequency of the Median Class} \\
   n &= \text{Number of Data Points in the Set} \\
   F_{P_{X_{0.5}}} &= \text{Cumulative Absolute Frequency in the Class Immediately} \\
   &\quad\ \text{Preceding the Median Class} \\
   C &= \text{Class Width in the Frequency Distribution}
   \end{aligned}
   $$

For the data set of our example, for which the frequency distribution appears in the table above, the median class is the sixth (because $(n + 1)/2 = 25.5$ and $F_{sixth} = 28$ which exceeds 25.5 for the first time). Then the values needed for the algebraic interpolation formula are:

$$L_{0.5} = 77$$
$$f_{0.5} = 9$$
$$F_{px_{0.5}} = F_{5th}\ \text{class} = 19$$
$$C = 11$$

Therefore $X_{0.5} = 77 + \left[\dfrac{25.5 - 19}{9}\right](11) = 77 + \left(\dfrac{6.5}{9}\right)(11) = 77 + 7.92 = 84.92$.

3.3.1.2 Mode

There are also two methods to calculate the mode. One is an "approximate method", which depends on the value of the absolute frequencies in the two classes adjacent to the mode class while the second one is an "algebraic interpolation method" and uses an appropriate equation. Both these methods require the identification of the Modal Class, which has been previously defined as the class with the highest absolute frequency.

1. **Approximate Method**

   After the modal class is identified as the class with the highest absolute frequency (f_{modal}), we need to examine the absolute frequencies of the two classes adjacent to the modal class (one on each side of the modal class); i.e., the frequency of the pre-modal class ($f_{pre-modal}$) and the frequency of the post-modal class ($f_{post-modal}$).

   This method approximates the mode by the class mark (mid-point) of the modal class if $f_{pre-modal}$ and $f_{post-modal}$ are "approximately" equal. We will assume that these two frequencies are approximately equal, if:

$$|f_{pre-modal} - f_{post-modal}| \leq 2 \tag{3.92}$$

2. **Algebraic Interpolation Method**

   If the approximate method is not acceptable, we use the interpolation formula below to calculate the mode

$$X_M = L_M + \left(\frac{\Delta_1}{\Delta_1 + \Delta_2}\right)C \tag{3.93}$$

   where

   L_m = Lower Class Limit of Modal Class

   $\Delta_1 = f_{modal} - f_{pre-modal}$

   $\Delta_2 = f_{modal} - f_{post-modal}$

   C = Class Width

   In our example the modal class is the seventh class since $f_{7th} = 10$, which is the highest absolute frequency in the classification design.

   Since $f_{pre-modal} = f_{6th} = 9$ and $f_{post-modal} = f_{8th} = 5$, and their difference is greater than 2, the approximate method is not acceptable.

From the Frequency Distribution table above we obtain:

$$L_m = L_{7\text{th}} = 88$$
$$\Delta_1 = f_{7\text{th}} - f_{6\text{th}} = 10 - 9 = 1$$
$$\Delta_2 = f_{7\text{th}} - f_{8\text{th}} = 10 - 5 = 5$$
$$\Delta_1 + \Delta_2 = 1 + 5 = 6$$
$$C = 11$$

Therefore
$$X_m = 88 + (1/6) \times 11 = 88 + 1.83 = 89.83$$

3.3.1.3 Mean

Starting with the basic definition for the arithmetic mean:

$$\overline{X} = \frac{X_1 + X_2 + \cdots + X_n}{n} = \frac{\sum_{i=1}^{n} X_i}{n} \tag{3.94}$$

and observing that, in a grouped data set, the mid-point value of the i-th class is m_i and occurs f_i times, the above definition of the mean can be modified to read:

$$\overline{X} = \frac{m_1 f_1 + m_2 f_2 + \cdots + m_m f_m}{f_1 + f_2 + \cdots + f_m} = \frac{\sum_{i=1}^{m} f_i m_i}{n} \tag{3.95}$$

where $f_1 + f_2 + \cdots + f_m = \sum_{i=1}^{m} f_i = n$ and $m =$ Number of classes in the frequency distribution.

In our example $m = 10$, $n = 50$, and from column 6 of the Table in Section 3.3 we have:

$$\sum_{i=1}^{10} f_i m_i = 4{,}144$$

Therefore, $\overline{X} = \dfrac{\sum_{i=1}^{10} f_i m_i}{n} = \dfrac{4{,}144}{50} = 82.88.$

3.3.2 Measures of Dispersion

In this section we will discuss the methods of calculation for the Range, Interquartile Range, Interpercentile Range, Variance, and Standard Deviation. From these discussions it will become apparent that other dispersion measures that one might wish to consider can be similarly calculated.

3.3.2.1 Range

From the basic definition of the Range as the difference between the highest and lowest values in a data set, since $H = m_m$ and $L = m_1$ in a grouped data set, we obtain:
$$R = H - L = m_m - m_1 = 126 - 27 = 99$$
in our example, where m_m and m_1 are the class marks of the last and first classes respectively.

3.3.2.2 Interquartile Range

Since the IQR has been defined as IQR $= Q_3 - Q_1$, it is obvious that we need to calculate Q_3 and Q_1 first. The methods used to calculate Q_3 and Q_1 are similar to the methods used to calculate the median, $X_{0.5}$, which is identical to Q_2.

Approximately, Q_1 and Q_3 can be calculated from the Ogive, using the "Graphic Method".

If more accuracy is desired, then Algebraic Interpolation formulas, similar to the one used for the median, can be employed.

In particular for Q_1 we have:

$$Q_1 = L_{Q1} + \left[\frac{\frac{(n+1)}{4} - F_{PQ1}}{f_{Q1}} \right] C \qquad (3.96)$$

Since $(n + 1)/4 = 51/4 = 12.75$, the Q_1 class is the 5th where $F_{Q1} = 19$ while $F_{PQ1} = 10$. Since $f_{Q1} = 9$. and $L_{Q1} = 66$, we obtain:

$$Q_1 = 66 + [(12.75 - 10)/9]11 = 66 + 3.36 = 69.36$$

Similarly we can write for Q_3:

$$Q_3 = L_{Q3} + \left[\frac{3 \times \frac{(n+1)}{4} - F_{PQ3}}{f_{Q3}} \right] C \qquad (3.97)$$

since $[3(n + 1)]/4 = 3(12.75) = 38.25$, the Q_3 class is the 8th since $F_{Q3} = 43$ while $F_{PQ3} = 38$. Also from the Q_3 class we obtain: $F_{Q3} = 5$ and $L_{Q3} = 99$. Therefore, $Q_3 = 99 + [(38.25 - 38)/5]11 = 99 + (0.25/5)11 = 99 + 0.55 = 99.55$.

Now we are in a position to calculate IQR, and we obtain:

$$IQR = Q_3 - Q_1 = 99.55 - 69.36 = 30.19 \qquad (3.98)$$

3.3.2.3 Interpercentile Range and Interdecile Range

Since the Interpercentile Range $IPR = P_{75} - P_{25}$ is identical to the Interquartile Range IQR, it would appear that there is no need to further discuss the percentiles, however, in our discussion of the coefficient of Peakedness, we will need to calculate P_{90} and P_{10} and other occasions may also arise in which the calculation of the i-th percentile is important.

As was the case with the quartiles, approximate values for the percentiles can be obtained from the Ogive, using the "Graphic Method". For more accuracy, we use the interpolation formula:

$$P_i = L_{Pi} + \left[\frac{i \times \frac{(n+1)}{100} - F_{P,Pi}}{f_{Pi}} \right] C \quad 1 \le i \le 99 \qquad (3.99)$$

We will use this general formula to calculate P_{10} and P_{90} which are needed in the definition of the coefficient of Peakedness, using the frequency distribution of our example.

Since $[10(50 + 1)]/100 = 5.1$, the P_{10} class is the 3rd class, with Cumulative Class Frequency $= 8$, $f_{P_{10}} = 5$, and $L_{P_{10}} = 44$.

Also $C = 11$, and $F_{P_{10}} = 3 =$ Cumulative frequency of the class which precedes the P_{10} class.

Then we have $P_{10} = 44 + [(5.1 - 3)/5]11 = 44 + 4.62 = 48.62$

Using a similar analysis we find that the P_{90} class is the 9th (since $[90(50 + 1)]/100 = 45.9$) with $F_{P90} = 46$, $f_{P90} = 3$ and $L_{P90} = 110$. Since $C = 11$ and $F_{p,p90} = 43$, we obtain:

$$P_{90} = L_{P90} + [(45.9 - 43)/3]11 = 110 + (2.9/3)11 = 110 + 10.63 = 120.63$$

Since $U_9 = 120$ and $P_{90} > U_9$, we let $P_{90} = \min(U_9 = 120, 120.63) = 120$.

Therefore, $IDR =$ InterDecile Range $\hspace{2cm}$ (3.100)

$$= P_{90} - P_{10}$$

$$= 120.00 - 48.62 = 71.38$$

3.3.2.4 Variance and Standard Deviation

When we discussed the biased (s^2) and unbiased ($\hat{s}^2$) Variances for the ungrouped data set, we concluded that the main ingredient of both definitions was the summation:

$$\sum_{i=1}^{n}(X_i - \overline{X})^2 = \frac{n\sum_{i=1}^{n}X_i^2 - \left(\sum_{i=1}^{n}X_i\right)^2}{n} \hspace{2cm} (3.101)$$

where we assumed that each observation occurred only once. If certain values occurred more than once, we did not group them together but treated each one individually.

In grouped data sets, the value of the observations in class i is m_i and the number of observations falling in class i is f_i. Therefore, the contribution of class i to the sum of the values is $f_i m_i$, while its contribution to the sum square of the values is $f_i m_i^2$. Using this type of analysis, we can write:

$$\sum_{i=1}^{n}X_i = \sum_{i=1}^{m}f_i m_i \hspace{2cm} (3.102)$$

and

$$\sum_{i=1}^{n}X_i^2 = \sum_{i=1}^{m}f_i m_i^2 \hspace{2cm} (3.103)$$

and $\quad \displaystyle\sum_{i=1}^{n}(X_i - \overline{X})^2 = \sum_{i=1}^{m}f_i(m_i - \overline{X})^2 = \frac{n\sum_{i=1}^{m}f_i m_i^2 - \left(\sum_{i=1}^{m}f_i m_i\right)^2}{n}$ $\quad$ (3.104)

To evaluate the right-hand side of this expression we use columns (6) and (7) of our Frequency Distribution table to obtain, since $n = 50$:

$$\frac{50(372,456) - (4,144)^2}{50} = \frac{18,622,800 - 17,172,736}{50} = \frac{1,450,064}{50} = 29,001.28$$

Then, since the unbiased variance ($\hat{s}^2$) is defined as:

$$\hat{s}^2 = \frac{1}{n-1}\sum_{i=1}^{m}f_i(m_i - \overline{X})^2 = (1/49)(29,001.28) = 591.86,$$

and $\quad \hat{s} = \sqrt{591.86} = 24.3$

The biased variance (s^2) is then defined by:

$$s^2 = \frac{1}{n} \sum_{i=1}^{m} f_i \left(m_i - \overline{X} \right)^2 = (1/50)(29{,}001.28) = 580.0256,$$

and $\quad s = \sqrt{580.0256} = 24.1$

3.3.2.5 Linear Coding

When columns (6) and (7) of the Frequency Distribution table of section 3.3 are examined we notice that because of the multiplication involved in generating these columns, the entries of the columns become very large, and larger numbers usually imply more errors. To avoid errors due to the large numbers involved we can use "Linear Coding" which is a technique for transforming a given data set and thus generating an "artificial" data set with much easier numbers to work with. After all the calculations are performed with these "easy" numbers we must go back and perform "a sort-of inverse transform" in order to get the desired descriptive measures of the given data set and not of an "artificial" one. We list below the five basic steps involved in the Linear Coding Procedure:

1. In the frequency distribution table locate the median class and obtain its class mark. Call it m_o.
2. Obtain the value of C from the frequency distribution table.
3. Use the formula

$$U_i = \frac{m_i - m_o}{C} = \frac{(\text{class mark of class } i) - (\text{median class mark})}{C} \tag{3.105}$$

and obtain small and easy to use numbers.

4. Using the U_i, generated above as the data set, calculate $\overline{U}$ and $\hat{s}_U$ from the equations

$$\overline{U} = \frac{\sum_{i=1}^{m} f_i U_i}{n} \tag{3.106}$$

$$\hat{s}_U^2 = \frac{n \sum_{i=1}^{m} f_i U_i^2 - \left(\sum_{i=1}^{m} f_i U_i \right)^2}{n(n-1)} \tag{3.107}$$

5. Using the formula: $\qquad U_i = (X_i - m_o)/C \tag{3.108}$

and the values of $\overline{U}$ and $\hat{s}_U$ calculate $\overline{X}$ and $\hat{s}_X$ from the formulas:

$$\overline{X} = m_o + C\overline{U} \tag{3.109}$$

$$\hat{s}_X = C\hat{s}_U \tag{3.110}$$

Applying this procedure to the frequency distribution table of section 3.3, we obtain: $\qquad m_o = 82$ and $C = 11$.

Then using column (5) and step (3) above we generate the numbers U_i: -5, -4, -3, -2, -1, 0, 1, 2, 3, 4 which appear in column (8) of the table (under the U_i heading).

From column (9) we obtain: $\sum_{i=1}^{10} f_i U_i = 4$, while Column (10) produces:

$$\sum_{i=1}^{10} f_i U_i^2 = 240$$

Then $\overline{U} = 4/50 = 0.08$ and $\hat{s}_U^2 = (50 \times 240 - 4^2)/(50 \times 49) = 4.89$ and

$$\hat{s}_U = \sqrt{4.89} = 2.21$$

Now using $\overline{U} = 0.08$, $\hat{s}_U = 2.21$, and the step 5 formulas we obtain:

$$\overline{X} = m_0 + C\overline{U} = 82 + 11(0.08) = 82 + 0.88 = 82.88$$
$$\hat{s}_X = C\hat{s}_U = 11(2.21) = 24.3$$

Obviously the values of $\overline{X}$ and $\hat{s}_X$, computed above using Linear coding, are identical to the values obtained without Linear Coding, as they should be.

3.3.3 Measures of Skewness

We use the same coefficient of skewness, $S_{kp} = \dfrac{3(\overline{X} - X_{0.5})}{\hat{s}}$ which we used in the analysis of ungrouped data, and with the same interpretation, namely:

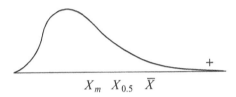

1. If $S_{kp} > 0$, the distribution is Positively Skewed.

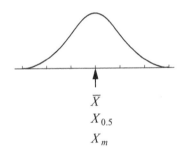

2. If $S_{kp} = 0$, the distribution is Symmetric.

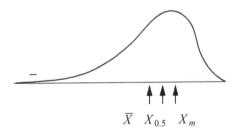

3. If $S_{kp} < 0$, the distribution is Negatively Skewed.

However, the values of $\overline{X}, X_{0.5},$ and $\hat{s}$ are now calculated using the Grouped Data methods discussed above.

3.3.4 Measures of Peakedness (Kurtosis)

The same coefficient of Peakedness, $K = \dfrac{1/2(Q_3 - Q_1)}{P_{90} - P_{10}}$, which was used in the analysis of ungrouped data, is also used here, and with the same interpretation, namely:

1. If $K \approx 0.5$, the distribution is Leptokurtic (narrow).

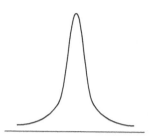

2. If $K \approx 0.25$, the distribution is Mesokurtic.

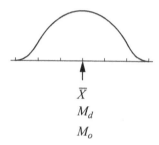

$\overline{X}$
M_d
M_o

3. If $K \approx 0$, the distribution is Platykurtic (wide).

However, the values of Q_3, Q_1, P_{90}, and P_{10} are now calculated using the Grouped Data Methods Discussed above.

3.4 Demonstrating the Need for Calculating the Coefficients of Skewness (S$_{kp}$) and Kurtosis (K)

It is possible for two distributions to have identical means and variances and still be different from each other. Obviously, in such cases, other considerations must be used to distinguish between the two distributions. We present below two examples in which it is necessary to calculate the S_{kp} and K coefficients in order to be able to tell the two distributions apart.

Example 11 shows the importance of the coefficient of skewness, while Example 12 makes it clear that the coefficient of kurtosis is also important.

Example 11

Suppose, after classifying two given data sets, we obtain the frequency distributions marked (a) and (b) respectively, and their respective histograms.

(a)

#	Class Marks	f_i	F_i	m_i
1	$0-10^*$	5	5	5
2	$10-20^-$	15	20	15
3	$20-30^-$	30	50	25
4	$30-40^-$	30	80	35
5	$40-50^-$	15	95	45
6	$50-60^-$	5	100	55

(b)

#	Class Marks	f_i	F_i	m_i
1	$0-10^*$	5	5	5
2	$10-20^-$	20	25	15
3	$20-30^-$	15	40	25
4	$30-40^-$	45	85	35
5	$40-50^-$	10	95	45
6	$50-60^-$	5	100	55

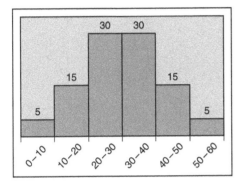

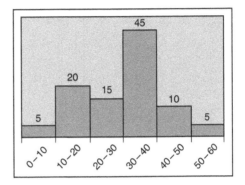

*where the "-" means: "Up to but not including"

By inspection of the histograms we see that distribution (a) is symmetrical (about the value 30) while distribution (b) is not. If, however, we had not plotted the histograms but depended only on the calculations of the mean and variance to perform the comparison, we might have concluded that distributions (a) and (b) are identical, because if we extended the above tables to calculate:

$\sum_{i=1}^{6} m_i f_i$ and $\sum_{i=1}^{6} m_i f_i^2$ we would have found that: $\sum_{i=1}^{6} m_i f_i = 3,000$ and $\sum_{i=1}^{6} m_i f_i^2 = 104,500$

for both distributions. Therefore, since $n = 100$ in both, we have:

$$\overline{X}_a = \overline{X}_b = \frac{3,000}{100} = 30 \text{ and } \hat{s}_a^2 = \hat{s}_b^2 = \frac{100(104,500)-(3,000)^2}{100(99)} = \frac{14,500}{99} \approx 146.44$$

and $\hat{s}_a = \hat{s}_b = 12.1$. If, however, we continued our calculations, we will find that $S_{kpa} = 0$, which implies that distribution (a) is symmetric as it can be verified from the histogram, while $S_{kpb} = -0.55$, which clearly indicates that distribution (b) is negatively skewed, and therefore, different than distribution (a).

■ ■ ■

Example 12

Now consider the frequency distributions (a) and (b) shown below, together with their respective histograms.

(a)

#	Class Marks	F_i	f_i	m_i
1	$-3.5 - -2.5^{-*}$	6	6	−3
2	$-2.5 - -1.5^-$	15	9	−2
3	$-1.5 - -0.5^-$	25	10	−1
4	$-0.5 - 0.5^-$	75	50	0
5	$0.5 - 1.5^-$	85	10	1
6	$1.5 - 2.5^-$	94	9	2
7	$2.5 - 3.5^-$	100	6	3

(b)

#	Class Marks	F_i	f_i	m_i
1	$-3.5 - -2.5^{-*}$	4	4	−3
2	$-2.5 - -1.5^-$	15	11	−2
3	$-1.5 - -0.5^-$	35	20	−1
4	$-0.5 - 0.5^-$	65	30	0
5	$0.5 - 1.5^-$	85	20	1
6	$1.5 - 2.5^-$	96	11	2
7	$2.5 - 3.5^-$	100	4	3

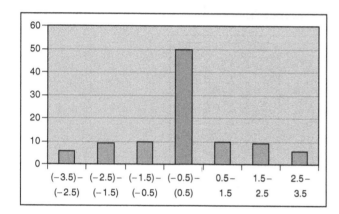

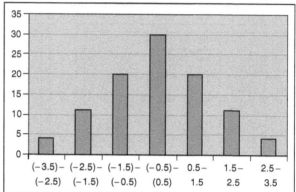

*where the "-" means "Up to but not including"

Obviously both distributions are symmetrical, which implies that the coefficient of skewness for both distributions is equal to zero (i.e., $S_{kpa} = S_{kpb} = 0$).

Also, the calculations of $\sum\limits_{i=1}^{7} m_i f_i$ and $\sum\limits_{i=1}^{7} m_i f_i^2$ are equal for both distributions, more specifically: $\sum\limits_{i=1}^{6} m_i f_i = 0$ for both distributions and $\sum\limits_{i=1}^{7} m_i f_i^2 = 200$ for both distributions.

Then, from the definitions of $\overline{X}$ and $\hat{s}^2$ we calculate that $\overline{X}_a = \overline{X}_b = 0$ and $\hat{s}_a = \hat{s}_b = 200/99$.

But obviously, the two distributions are not identical, even though their means, variances, and coefficients of skewness are identical.

From distribution (a) we obtain:

$P_{10} = -1.945$
$Q_1 = -0.495$
$Q_3 = 1.575$
$P_{90} = 2.155$

and, therefore, $K_a = 1/2[(Q_3 - Q_1)/(P_{90} - P_{10})] = 0.13$, which is close to zero and, therefore, implies that distribution (a) is almost a Platykurtic distribution.

The corresponding results for distribution (b) are:

$P_{10} = -1.946$

$Q_1 = -0.988$

$Q_3 = 1.038$

$P_{90} = 2.036$

Therefore $K_b = 0.254$, which implies that distribution (b) is Mesokurtic and different from distribution (a).

3.5 Comparison of Ungrouped and Grouped Results

Measure	Ungrouped Data Analysis	Grouped Data Analysis	Difference = Grouped − Ungrouped
MEDIAN = $X_{0.5}$	84	84.92	0.92
MODE = X_m	values: 71,84,94 each appear 3 times	89.93	N/A
MEAN = $\overline{X}$	83.70	82.88	−0.82
RANGE = R	101	99.00	−2
FIRST QUARTILE Q_1	71.00	69.36	−1.64
THIRD QUARTILE Q_3	98.50	99.55	1.05
INTERQUARTILE RANGE IQR	27.50	30.19	2.69
10th PERCENTILE P_{10}	47.20	48.62	1.42
90th PERCENTILE P_{90}	120.00	120.63	0.63
UNBIASED VARIANCE $\hat{s}^2$	591.60	591.86	0.26
BIASED VARIANCE s^2	579.77	580.03	0.26
UNBIASED STD.DEV. $\hat{s}$	24.32	24.30	−0.02
BIASED STD.DEV. s	24.078	24.10	0.022
COEFFICIENT OF SKEWNESS S_{kp}	−0.037	−0.252	−0.215
COEFFICIENT OF KURTOSIS K	0.1888	0.2096	0.0208

Examing the "Difference" column of the above table, we observe that there are differences in the values obtained for the descriptive measures when a given data set is analyzed both as an ungrouped and grouped data case, but these differences are not very large. These differences are to be expected because of the "mid-point" assumption, but let us not lose sight of the fact that we went into a grouped data analysis in order to obtain the "shape" of the population which generated the data set and which cannot be obtained from the ungrouped data. However, the ungrouped data analysis produces more accurate values for the different descriptive measures.

$^\text{l}$ The values under the "Grouped Data Analysis" column were extracted from the analysis performed in sections 3.3.1 and 3.3.2. To obtain the values under the "Ungrouped Data Analysis" column, one must use the ranked data set of chapter 2 and apply the methods and formulas presented in section 3.2. (Note that $\sum_{i=1}^{50} x_i = 4185$ and $\sum_{i=1}^{50} x_i^2 = 379,273$ for the Ungrouped data set. Therefore, $\overline{X} = 83.70$ and $\hat{s} = 24.32287$).

From the frequency distribution, the histogram, and the table above, we can draw certain conclusions pertaining to the type of population which produced the sample we analyzed.

1. The distribution is not exactly symmetrical because the Median, Mode, and Mean are not exactly equal. However, because they are close to each other, the distribution is approximately symmetrical.
2. Because the coefficient of skewness (S_{kp}) is a small negative number, the distribution is somewhat negatively skewed. Since the coefficient of kurtosis K is approximately equal to 0.25, this distribution is almost Mesokurtic.
3. Applying the Empirical rule (*i.e.*, finding the values: $\overline{X} - \hat{s}$, $\overline{X} - 2\hat{s}$, $\overline{X} - 3\hat{s}$, $\overline{X} + \hat{s}$, $\overline{X} + 2\hat{s}$, $\overline{X} + 3\hat{s}$ and counting the actual number of observations which fall between: $\overline{X} - \hat{s}$ to $\overline{X} + \hat{s}$, $\overline{X} - 2\hat{s}$ to $\overline{X} + 2\hat{s}$ and $\overline{X} - 3\hat{s}$ to $\overline{X} + 3\hat{s}$) we find that the proportions of the population falling in each of these intervals are approximately equal to those expected from a Normal Distribution.

In fact the number of observations between:

1. $\overline{X} - \hat{s} = 83.70 - 24.32 = 59.38$ and $\overline{X} + \hat{s} = 108.02$ is 34 out of 50 or $\dfrac{34}{50} \times 100 = 68\%$,

2. $\overline{X} - 2\hat{s} = 35.06$ and $\overline{X} + 2\hat{s} = 132.34$ is 49 out of 50 or $\dfrac{49}{50} \times 100 = 98\%$,

3. $\overline{X} - 3\hat{s} = 10.74$ and $\overline{X} + 3\hat{s} = 156.66$ is 50 out of 50 or $\dfrac{50}{50} \times 100 = 100\%$.

Then, combining these observations, we conclude that the data distribution is approximately Normally Distributed.

Summary of Descriptive Statistics Formulas

I) Ungrouped Data

Ungrouped Data: Few Distinct Values, but each occurs many times.	
Measure	**Ungrouped Data Formulas**
Median $- X_{0.5}$	Suppose $n = 12$; Then: Location $= \dfrac{n+1}{2} \rightarrow 6.5$, Value $= V_6 + 0.5(V_7 - V_6)$
Mean $- \overline{X}$	$\overline{X} = \dfrac{\sum X_i}{n} = \dfrac{X_1 + X_2 + \cdots + X_n}{n}$
Mode $- X_m$	Value which appears most frequently
Range $- R$	$R = X_{high} - X_{low}$
First Quartile Q_1	Suppose $n = 50$; Then: Location $= \dfrac{n+1}{4} \rightarrow 12.75$, Value $= V_{12} + 0.75(V_{13} - V_{12})$
Third Quartile Q_3	Suppose $n = 33$; Then: Location $= \dfrac{3(n+1)}{4} \rightarrow 25.5$, Value $= V_{25} + 0.5(V_{26} - V_{25})$
Inter Quartile Range $= IQR$	$IQR = Q_{3value} - Q_{1value}$
10th Percentile P_{10}	Suppose $n = 50$; Then: Location $= \dfrac{10(n+1)}{100} \rightarrow 5.1$, Value $= V_5 + 0.1(V_6 - V_5)$
90th Percentile P_{90}	Suppose $n = 44$; Then:

Measure	Ungrouped Data Formulas
90th Percentile P_{90}	$\text{Location} = \dfrac{90(n+1)}{100} \rightarrow 40.5 \ \text{Value} = V_{40} + 0.5(V_{41} - V_{40})$
Inter Decile Range $= IDR$	$IDR = P_{90value} - P_{10value}$
Average Deviation	$A.D. = \dfrac{1}{n} \displaystyle\sum_{i=1}^{n} (X_i - \overline{X}) = 0$
Absolute Ave. Deviation	$A.A.D. = \dfrac{1}{n} \displaystyle\sum_{i=1}^{n} |X_i - \overline{X}| \neq 0$
Unbiased Variance $= \hat{s}^2$	$\hat{s}^2 = \dfrac{1}{n-1} \displaystyle\sum (X_i - \overline{X})^2 = \dfrac{n\sum X_i^2 - (\sum X_i)^2}{n(n-1)}$
Biased Variance $= s^2$	$s^2 = \dfrac{1}{n} \displaystyle\sum (X_i - \overline{X})^2 = \dfrac{n\sum X_i^2 - (\sum X_i)^2}{n^2}$
Coefficient of Variation	$C.O.V. = \dfrac{\hat{s}}{\overline{X}}$
Empirical Rule Chebychev's Rule Standard Score	Applies only to Normal Data Applies to all data To convert a data set with $\overline{X} \neq 0$ and $\hat{s}_x \neq 1$ to one with Average $= 0$ & Standard Deviation $= 1$
Coefficient of Skewness	$S_{kp} = \dfrac{\overline{X} - X_m}{s} \approx \dfrac{3(\overline{X} - X_{0.5})}{\hat{s}} = \left[\begin{array}{l} > 0 \ \text{Positively Skewed} \\ = 0 \ \text{Symmetric} \\ < 0 \ \text{Negatively Skewed} \end{array} \right.$
Coefficient of Peakedness	$K = \dfrac{1/2(P_{75} - P_{25})}{P_{90} - P_{10}} = \dfrac{1/2(Q_3 - Q_1)}{P_{90} - P_{10}} = \left[\begin{array}{l} \approx 0.5 \ \text{Leptokurtic} \\ \approx 0.25 \ \text{Mesokurtic} \\ \approx 0 \ \text{Platykurtic} \end{array} \right.$

II)   Grouped Data

Grouped Data: Many distinct values, but each occurs few times.	
Measure	**Grouped Data Formulas**
Median $- X_{0.5}$	$X_{0.5} = L_{0.5} + \left[\dfrac{(n+1)/2 - F_p}{f_{0.5}} \right] C$
Mean $- \overline{X}$	$\overline{X} = \dfrac{\sum f_i m_i}{n}$
Mode $- X_m$	$X_m = L_m + \left[\dfrac{\Delta_1}{\Delta_1 + \Delta_2} \right] C$

Measure	Grouped Data Formulas
Range $- R$	$R = X_{\text{high}} - X_{\text{low}}$
First Quartile Q_1	$Q_1 = L_{Q1} + \left[\dfrac{(n+1)/4 - F_{PQ1}}{f_{Q_1}} \right] C$
Third Quartile Q_3	$Q_3 = L_{Q3} + \left[\dfrac{(3n+1)/4 - F_{PQ3}}{f_{Q_3}} \right] C$
Inter Quartile Range $= IQR$	$IQR = Q_{3\text{Value}} - Q_{1\text{Value}}$
10th Percentile P_{10}	$P_{10} = L_{P_{10}} + \left[\dfrac{10(n+1)/100 - F_{P_{10}}}{f_{p_{10}}} \right] C$
90th Percentile P_{90}	$P_{90} = L_{P_{90}} + \left[\dfrac{90(n+1)/100 - F_{P_{90}}}{f_{P_{90}}} \right] C$
Inter Decile Range $= IDR$	$IDR = P_{90\text{Value}} - P_{10\text{Value}}$
Average Deviation	$A.D. = \dfrac{1}{n} \sum_{i=1}^{n} \left(X_i - \overline{X} \right) = 0$
Absolute Average Deviation	$A.A.D. = \dfrac{1}{n} \sum_{i=1}^{n} |X_i - \overline{X}| \neq 0$
Unbiased Variance $= \hat{s}^2$	$\hat{s}^2 = \dfrac{1}{n-1} \sum f_i \left(m_i - \overline{X} \right)^2 = \dfrac{n \sum f_i m_i^2 - \left(\sum f_i m_i \right)^2}{n(n-1)}$
Biased Variance $= s^2$	$s^2 = \dfrac{n \sum f_i m_i^2 - \left(\sum f_i m_i \right)^2}{n^2}$
Coefficient of Variation	$C.O.V. = \dfrac{\hat{s}}{\overline{X}}$
Empirical Rule Chebychev's Rule Standard Score	Applies only to Normal Data Applies to all data To convert a data set with $\overline{X} \neq 0$ and $\hat{s}_x \neq 1$ to one with Average $= 0$ & Standard Deviation $= 1$
Coefficient of Skewness	$S_{KP} = \dfrac{\overline{X} - X_m}{s} \approx \dfrac{3\left(\overline{X} - X_{0.5}\right)}{\hat{s}} = \begin{bmatrix} > 0 \text{ Positively Skewed} \\ = 0 \quad \text{Symmetric} \\ < 0 \text{ Negatively Skewed.} \end{bmatrix}$
Coefficient of Peakedness	$K = \dfrac{1/2(P_{75} - P_{25})}{P_{90} - P_{10}} = \dfrac{1/2(Q_3 - Q_1)}{P_{90} - P_{10}} = \begin{bmatrix} \approx 0.5 \text{ Leptokurtic} \\ \approx 0.25 \text{ Mesokurtic} \\ \approx 0 \text{ Platykurtic} \end{bmatrix}$

3.6 References

Berenson, Marc, L., Levine, David, M., and Krehbiel, Timothy, C., 2004. *Basic Business Statistics*. 9th Edition. Pearson-Prentice Hall.

Black, Ken, 2004. *Business Statistics*. 4th Edition. Wiley.

Canavos, George, C., 1984. *Applied Probability and Statistical Methods*. Little, Brown.

Carlson, William, L., and Thorne, Betty, 1997. *Applied Statistical Methods*. Prentice Hall.

Chou, Ya-lun, 1992. *Statistical Analysis for Business and Economics*. Elsevier.

Freund, John, E., and Williams, Frank, J., 1969. *Modern Business Statistics*. Revised by Perles, Benjamin and Sullivan, Charles. Prentice Hall.

Freund, John, E., and Williams, Frank, J., 1982. *Elementary Business Statistics: The Modern Approach*. Prentice-Hall.

Johnson, Robert, 1973. *Elementary Statistics*. Duxbury Press.

McClave, James, T., Benson, George, P., and Sincich, Terry, 2001. *Statistics for Business and Economics*. 8th Edition. Prentice Hall.

Salvatore, Dominick, *Theory and Problems of Statistics and Econometrics*. SCHAUM'S OUTLINE SERIES, McGraw-Hill.

Steel, Robert, G.D., and Torrie, James, H., 1976. *Introduction to Statistics*. McGraw-Hill.

3.7 PROBLEMS

Use the table of data below for problems 1 and 2.

The following set of data represents final grades of 50 students in statistics, selected at random from among all students taking the course at a given university, in a given year:

66	58	47	40	93	74	70	56	34	66
61	72	81	42	95	78	65	74	86	44
67	79	42	82	34	67	65	60	75	85
53	36	62	56	98	68	67	44	76	88
87	51	92	49	67	89	62	78	55	76

1. Considering this data set as an UNGROUPED data.

   $(n = 50, \sum_{i=1}^{50} x_i = 3{,}312, \sum_{i=1}^{50} x_i^2 = 233{,}544)$

   a) Calculate $\bar{x}$, x_m, $x_{0.5}$.

   b) Calculate $\hat{s}^2$, $\hat{s}$.

   c) Calculate Q_1, Q_3.

   d) Calculate P_{90}, P_{10}.

   e) Calculate the coefficient of skewness, S_{kp}.

   f) Calculate the coefficient of Kurtosis, K.

2. Considering this data set as a GROUPED data.

   $\left(n = 50, \sum f_i m_i = 3{,}315, \sum f_i m_i^2 = 233{,}752.5\right)$

   a) Calculate $\bar{x}$, x_m, $x_{0.5}$.

   b) Calculate $\hat{s}^2$, $\hat{s}$.

   c) Calculate Q_1, Q_3.

d) Calculate P_{90}, P_{10}.

e) Calculate the coefficient of skewness, S_{kp}.

f) Calculate the coefficient of Kurtosis, K.

3. Use MINITAB to calculate descriptive statistics.

```
MTB > Set C1
DATA > 66   58   47   40   93   74   70   56   34   66
DATA > 61   72   81   42   95   78   65   74   86   44
DATA > 67   79   42   82   34   67   65   60   75   85
DATA > 53   36   62   56   98   68   67   44   76   88
DATA > 87   51   92   49   67   89   62   78   55   76
DATA > END
MTB > Describe C1
```

Descriptive Statistics: C1

Variable	N	N*	Mean	SE Mean	St.Dev.	Minimum	Q_1	Median	Q_3	Maximum
C_1	50	0	66.24	2.40	17.00	34.00	54.50	67.00	78.25	98.00

```
MTB > Histogram C1;
SUBC > MIDPOINT 35.5:95.5/10;
SUBC > Bar.
```

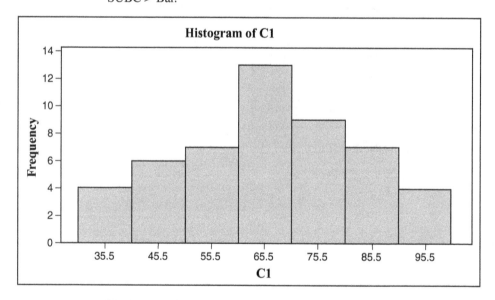

```
MTB > Dotplot C1
```

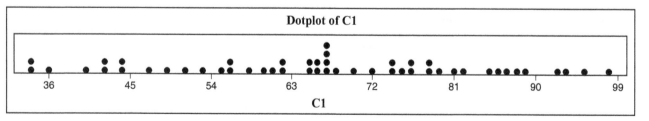

4. How do computer and hand calculations compare? Be specific!

5. What generalized and specific conclusions can you draw about this data set?

6. Compare the advantages and disadvantages of a) the mean, b) the median, and c) the mode as measures of central tendency.

7. For the same amount of capital invested in each of 3 years, an investor earned a rate of return of 1% during the first year, 4% during the second year, and 16% during the third. a) Find the geometric mean b) Find the arithmetic mean c) Which of the 2 means is more appropriate for this problem?

8. A plane traveled 200 miles at 600 miles/hour (or 100 at 600 miles/hour and another 100 miles also at 600 miles/hour) and 100 miles at 500 miles/hour. What was its average speed?

9. A driver purchases $10 worth of gasoline at $0.90 per gallon, and another $10 at $1.10 per gallon. What is the average price per gallon?

10. According to Chebychev's theorem, at least what proportion of the observations fall within a) 1.5 standard deviations from the mean? b) 2.5 standard deviation of the mean? c) How many standard deviations from the mean are needed to have 96% of the observations falling in this interval?

11. Treating the data set: 6, 3, 8, 5, 3 as an ungrouped data set. What effect does changing the 8 to a 9 have on the following statistical measures? Be specific!

    a) Mean   b) Median   c) Mode   d) Standard deviation   e) Midrange   f) Range

    g) Q_1 h) Q_3 i) Coefficient of variation   j) Coefficient of Skewness
       Use the table below for both problems 12 and 13.

    Given the following data array of ages of cars X (in years) found in a parking lot:

X(Age in Year)	1	2	3	4	5	6	7	8	9	10	11
F(Frequency)	4	9	11	8	7	5	4	2	2	0	1

12. a) Find the measures of central tendency ($\bar{x}$ = Mean, $x_{0.5}$ = Median, x_m = Mode)
    b) Find Q_1 and Q_3.
    c) Find P_{12} and P_{15}.
    d) Find the measures of dispersion (R = range, $\hat{s}^2$ = unbiased variance, $\hat{s}$ = standard deviation).

13. a) What proportion of the sample lies: 1) between $\bar{x} - \hat{s}$ and $\bar{x} + \hat{s}$? 2) between $\bar{x} - 2\hat{s}$ and $\bar{x} + 2\hat{s}$? 3) between $\bar{x} - 3\hat{s}$ and $\bar{x} + 3\hat{s}$?
    b) Compare the answers of part (a) to Chebychev's theorem.
    c) Compare the answers of part (a) to the Empirical rule.
    d) What conclusions can you draw from the results of parts (a) and (c) concerning the distribution form of this data set? Justify your conclusion.

14. Suppose the following relationships hold true for a data set:

    a) $\bar{x} = x_{0.5} + \dfrac{1}{3}\hat{s}$

    b) $IQR = 2\hat{s}$

    c) $P_{90} - P_{10} = 4\hat{s}$

    d) $\dfrac{\bar{x}}{\hat{s}} = \dfrac{1}{2}$

Using the information above, find:

i) The coefficients of Skewness and Peakedness and, using their calculated values, state the type of data distribution.

ii) The coefficient of variation.

iii) Find $\bar{x}$, $x_{0.5}$ and $\hat{s}$, if $Q_3 - Q_1 = 60$.

15. The ages of 25 women, at the birth of their first child, were obtained from the files of a hospital and given by the following data:

15	20	21	18	24	22	27	30	17	25	29
20	42	22	22	24	22	21	21	17	16	24
16	28	22								

a) Find the median age of these women.

b) Find the standard deviation of the ages of these women.

c) Find the range and midrange of the ages of these women.

d) Find Q_3 and P_{60} of the ages of these women.

16. Given the following partial frequency distribution:

Class#	1	2	3	4	5	6	7	8
Class Limits (L, U)	15 19	20 24	25 29	30 34	35 39	40 44	45 49	50 54
Frequency (f_i)	3	12	19	6	5	2	2	1

a) Complete the frequency distribution by computing the additional columns for: Cumulative frequency (F_i), class marks (m_i), $m_i f_i$, and $m_i^2 f_i$,

b) Find the mean of this data set.

c) Find the median of this data set.

d) Find the mode of this data set.

e) Find the standard deviation of this data set.

f) Find the coefficients of Skewness and Peakedness.

h) What kind of data distribution is this based on the results? Be specific.

17. The starting weekly salaries (in dollars) of ten recent college graduates are: 500, 750, 825, 680, 850, 780, 1000, 525, 760, and 750. Determine the arithmetic mean ($\bar{x}$), median ($x_{0.5}$), mode (x_m), and unbiased sample variance of this data set.

18. To produce a certain automobile in Detroit, the following quantities of labor are needed:

Unskilled labor = 200 hours

Semi-skilled labor = 150 hours

Skilled labor = 50 hours

If hourly wage rates for these workers are $10, $15, $20 per hour, what is the average labor cost per hour to produce this car?

19. Use the data of problem (17) to determine:

a) The Range of the data.

b) The Inter-Quartile Range $= Q_3 - Q_1$.

c) The Inter-Decile Range $= P_{90} - P_{10}$.

d) The coefficient of Skewness, S_{k_p}.

e) The coefficient of Kurtoris, K.

20. If the mean ($\bar{x}$) and standard deviation ($\hat{s}$) are computed from a large sample, which came from a known Normal distribution, and $\bar{x} = 12$ and $\hat{s} = 5$, use the Empirical rule to determine:

a) The proportion of the measurements that lie between 7 and 17.

b) The proportion of the measurements which are greater than 22.

c) The proportion of the measurements which are less than 7.

21. Sample data on the annual wages of professors and medical doctors in a certain city yielded the following results:

Professors	Medical Doctors
$\bar{x}_1 = \$75,000$	$\bar{x}_1 = \$140,000$
$\hat{s}_1 = 5,000$	$\hat{s}_2 = 10,000$

Are the professors' wages more or less variable than the wages of medical doctors?

22. a) What are the advantages and disadvantages of the Range?

b) What is the usefulness of the coefficient of variation?

23. The following are the ages of 20 people selected for jury duty by a court: 34, 48, 41, 58, 63, 33, 42, 52, 47, 57, 30, 31, 52, 53, 25, 38, 46, 49, 60, and 61. Find

a) The mean age and

b) Standard deviation of the ages of these jurors.

24. A passenger elevator has a rated maximum capacity of 4,200 pounds. Is the elevator overloaded if it carries:

a) 25 passengers whose average weight is 170 pounds?

b) 12 children whose mean weight is 70 pounds and 15 adults whose average weight is 160 pounds?

c) 10 women whose average weight is 125 pounds and 15 men whose average weight is 175 pounds?

25. The sales value of the 15 salespersons of a company, for a given month (in thousands of dollars) are given below: 75, 101, 90, 98, 80, 100, 110, 94, 88, 420, 95, 80, 100, 98, and 99. Find a) The mean; b) The median, and c) The mode. Which of those measures is more appropriate in expressing the typical performance of this sales force, and why?

26. Fifty persons were asked their favorite color, and their responses produced the following table of values

Favorite Color	Red	Blue	Green	Yellow	Brown	White	Purple	Orange	Black
Frequency	13	15	8	4	2	3	2	2	1

Question: What is their modal choice?

27. If a person invests $3,000 at 7 percent, $7,000 at 8 percent, and $20,000 at 9 percent, what is the average return on these investments?

28. A professor gives five tests during the semester of different duration and, when calculating the average grade, he weights these tests in proportion to their duration. If a student scores 65 on a 1-hour test, 75 on a second 1-hour test, 80 on a 30 minutes test, 90 on a second 30 minute test, and a 60 on the 2-hour final, what is the average grade of this student on these 5 tests?

29. In a study of insurance costs it was found that in one year 720 automobile property damage claims for $500 or less averaged $340, 160 claims for claims between $500 and $1,000 averaged $680, and 40 claims for over $1,000, averaged $1,700. What is the overall average of these claims?

30. If some objects whose average weight is 25 pounds weigh a total of 500 pounds, and some other objects whose average weight is 40 pounds, weigh a total 1,200 pounds, what is the average weight of all the objects combined?

31. The commissions earned by a sample of 5 salesmen in a given week were $490, $511, $480, $523, and $500.

    a) Calculate the mean $(\overline{x})$, Range (R) and the standard deviation $(\hat{s})$.

    b) Calculate $\overline{x}$, R, and $\hat{s}$ of this data set, after subtracting $500 from each value.

    c) What conclusion do you draw when you compare the results of (a) and (b)?

32. If the data of problem 31 are multiplied by 5, a) What are the mean, Range, and standard deviation of the new data set? b) What conclusion do you draw when you compare $\overline{x}$, R, and $\hat{s}$ of the original and new data sets?

33. For a large group of students the mean score on an aptitude test is 160 points and the standard deviation is 15 points. At least what percentage of the scores must lie between:

    a) 130 and 190 points; b) 100 and 220 points; c) 70 and 250 points.

34. If stock X_1 has an average price of $60 with a standard deviation of 10 and is currently selling for $72, and stock X_2 has an average price of $45, a standard deviation of 7 and sells currently for $52, and an investor who owns both of these stocks decides to sell one of them, which one would he sell and why?

35. A member of a large industrial sales force, whose average sales in a month are $15,000 with a standard deviation of $2000, has sales of $18,000 for the month. Similarly, a member of a large computer software sales force, whose average sales in the same month was $7,200 with a standard deviation of $500, had sales of $8,700 for the same month. Can we conclude from these data that the performance of the industrial salesman is better than the performance of the computer software salesman?

36. In a comparative study of bond yields, the following distribution was constructed of the yields to maturity of 50 bonds:

Yield (%)	f = number of Bonds
1.00–2.99	5
3.00–4.99	9
5.00–6.99	17
7.00–8.99	12
9.00–10.99	7

    a) Find the mean of this data distribution.

    b) Find the median of this data distribution.

    c) Find the mode of this data distribution.

    d) Find the standard deviation of this data distribution.

    e) Find the coefficient of Skewness S_{k_p}.

37. The following partial frequency distribution shows the ages of 100 members of a union.

Age(year)	20–24	25–29	30–34	35–39	40–44	45–49	50–54
Frequency	11	24	30	18	11	5	1

a) Find the mean of this frequency distribution.

b) Find the median of this frequency distribution.

c) Find Q_1 and Q_3 of this frequency distribution.

d) Find P_{10} and P_{90} of this frequency distribution.

e) Find the standard deviation of this frequency distribution.

f) Find the coefficient of Skewness, S_{K_p}.

g) Find the coefficient of Peakedness (or Kurtoris), K.

38. If, in a large population consisting of the times required to settle accident claims, the time required to settle a particular claim is 100 days, the standard score unit corresponding to this time is -3, and the ratio of the population mean to the standard deviation is 10, what are the population mean (μ) and standard deviation (σ)?

39. In a certain class, a student scored 90, 70, and 75 on the first quiz, midterm and final examination. If the professor considers the midterm to be 3 times as important as the first quiz, and the final to be 2 times as important as the midterm in determining the course grade, what is the students' average grade on these 3 tests?

40. In a clearance sale the library of a community raised a total of $4,270.00 on the sale of:

a) 1,000 books at an average price of $1.25 per book.

b) 600 books at an average price of $2.50 per book, and.

c) Some other books at an average price of $4.00 per book. What is the average price of all the books sold?

41. A room is 225/16 = 14 and 1/16 feet wide, 20 feet long, and has a height of 12 feet. What is the geometric mean of the dimensions of this room?

42. A general science test is given to a large group of students in a given school district. If the mean score is 40 points and the standard deviation is 5 points, what is the minimum fraction of the scores which must lie between 20 and 60 points?

43. If a person spends $40 on blank cassette tapes costing $8 per dozen and another $40 on tapes costing $10 per dozen, what is the average cost per tape?

44. If for a sample of size $n = 10, \displaystyle\sum_{i=1}^{10} x_i = x_1 + x_2 + \cdots + x_{10} = 30$ and

$$\sum_{i=1}^{10} x_i^2 = x_1^2 + x_2^2 + \cdots + x_{10}^2 = 126.$$

a) Find $\bar{x}$.

b) Find $\hat{s}^2$ and $\hat{s}$.

45. Given a sample x_1, x_2, x_3, x_4 for which $\displaystyle\sum_{i=1}^{4} x_i = 4$ and $\displaystyle\sum_{i=1}^{4} x_i^2 = 20$. Find the values of:

a) $\displaystyle\sum_{i=1}^{4}(x_i + 5)$ b) $\displaystyle\sum_{i=1}^{4}(2x_i - 3)$ c) $\displaystyle\sum_{i=1}^{4}(x_i + 2)^2$

SOLUTIONS

1. Ungrouped data calculations

   a) $\bar{x} = \sum x_i/n = 3312/50 = 66.24$

   $x_m = \text{Mode} = 67$ (occurs 4 times, more times than any other value)

   $x_{0.5}$ ↗ Location $= (n + 1)/2 = 25.5$

   ↘ Value $= V_{25} + 0.5(V_{26} - V_{25}) = 67 + 0.5(67 - 67) = 67$

   b) $\hat{s}^2 = \dfrac{50(233{,}544) - (3312)^2}{50(49)} = 288.9208$, and $\hat{s} = \sqrt{288.9208} = 16.9977$

   c) Q_1 ↗ Location $= \dfrac{n + 1}{4} = 12.75$

   ↘ Value $= V_{12} + 0.75(V_{13} - V_{12}) = 53 + 0.75(55 - 53) = 54.5$

   Q_3 ↗ Location $= 3\left(\dfrac{n + 1}{4}\right) = 38.25$

   ↘ Value $= V_{38} + 0.25(V_{39} - V_{38}) = 78 + 0.25(79 - 78) = 78.25$

   d) P_{90} ↗ Location $= \dfrac{90}{100}(n + 1) = 45.9$

   ↘ Value $= V_{45} + 0.9(V_{46} - V_{45}) = 88 + 0.9(89 - 88) = 88.9$

   P_{10} ↗ Location $= \dfrac{10}{100}(n + 1) = 5.1$

   ↘ Value $= V_5 + 0.1(V_6 - V_5) = 42 + 0.1(42 - 42) = 42.00$

   e) $S_{kp} = \dfrac{3(\bar{x} - x_{0.5})}{\hat{s}} = \dfrac{3(66.24 - 67)}{16.9977} = -0.134$

   f) $K = \dfrac{1/2(Q_3 - Q_1)}{P_{90} - P_{10}} = \dfrac{0.5(78.25 - 54.5)}{88.9 - 42.00} = 0.253$

2. Grouped data calculations

   a) $\bar{x} = \displaystyle\sum_{i=1}^{m} m_i f_i/n = 3{,}315/50 = 66.3$

   $x_m = 61 + \left[\dfrac{(13 - 7)}{(13 - 7) + (13 - 9)}\right](10) = 67$

   $x_{0.5} = 61 + \left[\dfrac{25.5 - 17}{13}\right](10) = 67.54$

b) $\hat{s}^2 = \dfrac{50\,(233{,}752.5) - (3315)^2}{50(49)} = 285.0612$ and $\hat{s} = 16.883756$

c) $Q_1 = 51 + \left[\dfrac{12.75 - 10}{7}\right](10) = 54.93$

$Q_3 = 71 + \left[\dfrac{38.25 - 30}{9}\right](10) = 80.17$

d) $P_{10} = 41 + \left[\dfrac{5.1 - 4}{6}\right](10) = 42.83$

$P_{90} = 81 + \left[\dfrac{45.9 - 39}{7}\right](10) = 90.86$

4. Compare hand and computer calculations

Item	Hand Calculations		MINITAB Results	Comments
	Ungrouped	**Grouped**		
n	50	50	50	1) The Ungrouped data calculations and MINITAB results are identical (where MINITAB results are available)
$\sum x_i$	3312	3315		
$\sum x_i^2$	233,544	233,752.50		
$\overline{x}$	66.24	66.30	66.24	2) The Grouped calculations are very close to the Ungrouped results but not identical to them (The difference is due to the Mid-point assumption)
x_m'	67	67		
$x_{0.5}$	67	67.54	67.00	
$\hat{s}^2$	288.9208	285.0612		
$\hat{s}$	16.9977	16.8838	17.00	
Q_1	54.5	54.93	54.5	
Q_3	78.25	80.17	78.25	
IQR	23.75	25.24		
P_{10}	42.00	42.83		
P_{90}	88.9	90.86		
IDR	46.9	48.03		
K	0.253	0.263		
S_{k_p}	−0.134	−0.2213		
m_r	66.00	65.50		
MIN	34.00	35.50	34.00	
MAX	98.00	95.50	98.00	

5. a) Since $\overline{x} \approx x_{0.5} \approx x_m$, the data set is almost symmetric (slightly negatively skewed).

b) Since $S_{k_p} = -0.134 \approx 0$, the data set is almost symmetric.

c) Since $K = 0.253$, the data set is almost mesokurtic.

d) Applying the empirical rule, we find:

α) The proportion between $\overline{x} - \hat{s}$ and $\overline{x} + \hat{s}$ is $\dfrac{31}{50} \times 100 = 62\%$

β) The proportion between $\overline{x} - 2\hat{s}$ and $\overline{x} + 2\hat{s}$ is $\dfrac{50}{50} \times 100 = 100\%$

γ) The proportion between $\overline{x} - 3\hat{s}$ and $\overline{x} + 3\hat{s}$ is $\dfrac{50}{50} \times 100 = 100\%$

Since these proportions are close to the expected proportions of 68%, 95%, and 99.7% of a normally distributed data set, we conclude that this data set, being almost symmetric, almost mesokurtic, and almost satisfying the empirical rule, is approximately normally distributed.

6. a) **Mean**

    i) **Advantages**

       A) It is familiar to almost everyone.

       B) All the observations in the data set are considered in the calculation of $\overline{x}$.

       C) It is used in the calculation of other measures ($\hat{s}^2$ for example) and in performing other statistical procedures and tests (H_0: $\mu = \mu_0$ for example).

    ii) **Disadvantages**

       A) It is affected by extreme values in the sample.

       B) It is time-consuming for a large ungrouped data set.

       C) It cannot be calculated when the last class of a grouped data is open-ended (*i.e.*, the mid-point of the last class can not be defined).

  b) **Median**

    i) **Advantages**

       A) It is not affected by extreme values.

       B) It is easily understood (*i.e.*, half of the data are smaller than the median and half are greater).

       C) It can always be calculated.

    ii) **Disadvantages**

       A) It uses at most 2 data values.

       B) It requires that the data is ranked (which can be time-consuming for a large ungrouped data set).

  c) **Mode**

    i) **Advantages**

       A) It is not affected by extreme values.

       B) It is easily understood (*i.e.*, it is the value which occurs most often).

    ii) **Disadvantages**

       A) It does not use all of the sample information.

       B) The mode is not always unique (*i.e.*, sometimes no value of the data is repeated more than once).

In general the mean is the most frequently used measure of central tendency and the mode is the least used.

7. a) Geometric mean

$$\bar{x}_g = \sqrt[3]{x_1 x_2 x_3} = \sqrt[3]{1 \times 4 \times 16} = (64)^{1/3} = (4^3)^{1/3} = 4$$

b) Arithmetic mean $= \bar{x} = \dfrac{x_1 + x_2 + x_3}{3} = \dfrac{1 + 4 + 16}{3} = \dfrac{21}{3} = 7$

c) The geometric mean is the more appropriate measure because the data being averaged is given in percentages.

8. A $\longleftarrow$ 200 miles $\longrightarrow$ B $\leftarrow$ 100 miles $\rightarrow$ C (physics solution)

Time to go from A to B $= t_{AB} = 200/600$; time to go from B to C $= t_{BC} = 100/500$.

Then, average speed $= \dfrac{\text{Total Distance Traveled}}{\text{Total time}} = \dfrac{200 + 100}{200/600 + 100/500}$

$$= \dfrac{300}{\dfrac{1}{3} + \dfrac{1}{5}} = \dfrac{300}{\dfrac{5 + 3}{15}} = \dfrac{300 \times 15}{8} = 562.5.$$

Harmonic mean $= \bar{x}_h = \dfrac{n}{\dfrac{1}{x_1} + \dfrac{1}{x_2} + \dfrac{1}{x_3} + \cdots + \dfrac{1}{x_n}} = \dfrac{3}{\dfrac{1}{600} + \dfrac{1}{600} + \dfrac{1}{500}}$

$$= \dfrac{3}{\dfrac{2}{600} + \dfrac{1}{500}} = \dfrac{3}{\dfrac{1,000 + 600}{300,000}} = \dfrac{3 \times 300,000}{1,600} = \dfrac{9,000}{16}$$

$$= 562.5 \text{ miles/hour}$$

9. Practical solution: The driver purchases x_1 gallons $= \dfrac{10}{0.9} = \dfrac{100}{9}$ gallons, and x_2 gallons $=$

$\dfrac{10}{1.1} = \dfrac{100}{11}$, for a total of $x_1 + x_2 = \dfrac{1,100 + 900}{99} = \dfrac{2,000}{99}$ gallons, and he spent $= 10 + 10 = \$20$.

Therfore, the average price per gallon is $= \dfrac{\text{Amount spent}}{\text{number of gallons}} = \dfrac{20}{\dfrac{2,000}{99}} = \dfrac{20 \times 99}{2,000} = \dfrac{99}{100}$

$\$0.99$ per gallon.

Harmonic mean solution: $\bar{x}_h = \dfrac{2}{\dfrac{1}{x_1} + \dfrac{1}{x_2}} = \dfrac{2}{\dfrac{1}{0.9} + \dfrac{1}{1.1}} = \dfrac{2}{\dfrac{1.1 + 0.9}{0.99}} = \dfrac{2}{2}(0.99)$

$$= \$0.99 \text{ per gallon.}$$

10. Chebychev's theorem can be stated as:

$$P\left[\bar{x} - k\hat{s} \le X \le \bar{x} + k\hat{s}\right] \ge 1 - \dfrac{1}{k^2}$$

a) When $k = 1.5 = 3/2$, $1 - \dfrac{1}{k^2} = 1 - \dfrac{1}{(3/2)^2} = 1 - \dfrac{1}{9/4} = 1 - \dfrac{4}{9} = \dfrac{5}{9} = 0.5555$

b) When $k = 2.5 = 5/2$, $1 - \dfrac{1}{k^2} = 1 - \dfrac{1}{(5/2)^2} = 1 - \dfrac{1}{25/4} = 1 - \dfrac{4}{25} = \dfrac{21}{25} = \dfrac{84}{100} = 0.84$

c) If $1 - \dfrac{1}{k^2} = 0.96$, then $\dfrac{1}{k^2} = 0.04$, or $k^2 = \dfrac{1}{0.04} = \dfrac{100}{4} = 25$, $k = 5$

PROBABILITY AND RANDOM VARIABLES

4 Elements of Probability Theory

Probability is the vehicle on which statistics is riding and without it Inferential Statistics, the decision-making part of statistics, is not possible. It is, therefore, important to understand and learn how to apply the basic rules of probability.

In this Chapter we define probability, briefly discuss the available theories of probability assignment, the basic laws that govern probability, as well as the concepts of conditional probability, joint probability, and statistical independence.

Also discussed are many probability applications.

4.1 Introduction

In the last three chapters we learned how to organize a data set and calculate as many useful measures as possible from the data set in order to characterize it as completely as possible.

Let us recall, at this point, that the ultimate objective of collecting a sample is to infer, from the sample characteristics, the properties of the population from which the sample came from. To accomplish this we need to go from Descriptive Statistics, which we have already discussed, to Inferential Statistics (*i.e.*, the decision-making part of statistics) which is the most interesting and challenging part of statistics. However, before we can discuss Inferential Statistics intelligently, we must first introduce Probability Theory and Random Variables. The reason for this is the fact that the Sample Statistics we calculated in Chapter 3 (*i.e.*, Mean, Median, Mode, Variance, Percentiles, Quartiles, etc.) are all random variables and can be easily analyzed in terms of their respective distributions. Therefore, in this chapter, we will discuss some elements of Probability theory which will allow us to go from descriptive to inferential statistics. It is not our intention to develop probability theory in its full axiomatic generality but to develop only those portions of it which are useful in the solution of business problems.

4.2 Elements of Probability

One way to understand the notion of probability is through the concept of "statistical regularity". There are many situations in nature in which we can predict in advance, based on previous experience, what would happen on the average but not what will happen exactly. In such cases we say that the occurrences are "random" as opposed to "deterministic" occurrences in which we know exactly what will happen. For example, if a "fair" coin is flipped many times, it will turn up heads on about half of the flips. This tendency of repeated similar experiments to result in the convergence of over-all averages, as more trials are performed, is "statistical regularity". To use statistical regularity to explain probability we will follow the procedure below:

1. First we will conduct a basic experiment (the rolling of a die is an example)
2. Second we will identify all the possible outcomes of our basic experiments (the possible outcomes of rolling a die are the numbers which can appear on the upper face), and
3. Repeat the basic experiment a large number of times, under similar conditions, and observe the results.

When this procedure is followed, we will define the probability of an outcome of a basic experiment as the ratio of "the number of times that the outcome of interest occurs" to the "Total number of repetitions" of the basic experiment. However, it is necessary to slow down a little and be somewhat more formal in our approach. We will do this by first introducing some new terminology, which will make our discussion easier.

4.2.1 Sample Points and Sample Spaces

We have previously defined an experiment as any activity, which generates data. A deterministic experiment is one in which the outcome is known precisely and, therefore, there is no need to perform the experiment. A stochastic experiment, on the other hand, is one in which the possible outcomes of the experiment are known (for example we know that when we roll a die the possible outcomes are the numbers 1, 2, 3, 4, 5, 6) but we do not know which of these outcomes will occur in any repetition of the experiment; *i.e.*, there is an element of uncertainty regarding the outcomes of the experiment. In what follows we are interested only in stochastic experiments with two or more possible outcomes in each.

Then, with each possible outcome of the experiment we may associate a geometric point which is called a "sample point". The totality of the sample points, corresponding to all possible outcomes of the experiment, is the "sample space" of the experiment. There are several ways of representing the sample space of an experiment, namely:

1. **Use a Venn Diagram** to represent the sample space as a large rectangle, with each sample point represented by a dot within the rectangle.

    This is justified because the sample space is equivalent to a Universal Set and the sample points are equivalent to the elements belonging to a Universal Set. As an example, if our basic experiment consists of rolling a single die once, then we can define the sample space and sample points of this experiment by:

$$S$$

●	●	●
1	2	3
●	●	●
4	5	6

Figure 4.1 Sample Space of Rolling a Single Die Once

where we have used S to represent the sample space and each dot is associated with a sample point of the experiment.

2. **Use the "Listing Method" of Set Theory** to represent a sample space.

    This method consists of using a pair of closed brackets within which the outcomes of the experiment are listed, separated by commas. There is no comma after the last outcome, or before the first outcome.

    Applying this method to the above example, we get

$$S = \{1, 2, 3, 4, 5, 6\} \tag{4.1}$$

    This method is good when the number of outcomes is relatively small and can be listed without too much difficulty. If the number of outcomes is large, this approach for representing a sample space can still be used but, usually, a property is used as a descriptor. We can write the above example as

$$S = \{x/x \text{ is an integer value between 1 and 6 including the end points}\} \tag{4.2}$$

which is read as: The set S consisting of the values x such that x is an integer value between 1 and 6 including the end points. This modified listing method is sometimes called the "Rule" method.

3. **Use the "Tree-Diagram" method**

    This method, which consists of drawing a line, starting from a single point, to represent each outcome of an experiment, is, perhaps, the best available method because, especially in more complex experiments, it allows the mapping of all the possible outcomes and, at the same time, facilitates the computation of the probability of each outcome. This will be demonstrated with several examples after probability has been formally defined and the several methods of probability assignment to events have been introduced. For now, let us give a "complex" example to demonstrate the use of the "tree diagram" approach to represent the sample space of the given experiment.

Example 1

Suppose a coin and a die are thrown together. Draw a tree diagram to show the possible outcomes of this experiment.

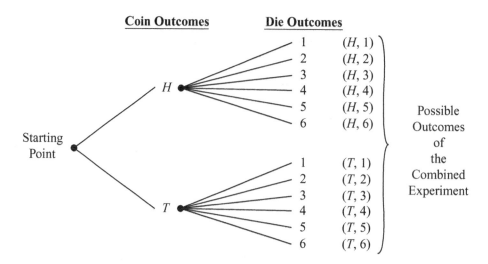

Figure 4.2 Tree Diagram of Example 1

If one starts at the "starting point" dot and traces all the possible paths, the possible outcomes of the experiment can be easily identified and listed.

Note: The first part of the tree diagram consists of the outcomes of the simple experiment "flip a coin once" which are clearly Heads (*H*) or Tails (*T*). The second part of the tree diagram consists of the outcomes of the simple experiment "roll a die once" which are clearly the numbers 1, 2, 3, 4, 5, and 6.

Since the two simple experiments do not influence each other (we will call this property "independence" later on) the outcomes of the combined experiment consist of the twelve outcomes shown. It can be easily verified that no other combinations of the two simple experiment outcomes are possible, and the tree diagram clearly shows all the possibilities. After probability assignments have been made for $P(H)$ and $P(T)$ for the simple coin experiment and for $P(1)$, $P(2)$, $P(3)$, $P(4)$, $P(5)$, and $P(6)$ of the simple die experiment, these probabilities will be combined to generate the probabilities for the outcomes of the combined experiment, namely: $P[(H, 1)]$, $P[(H, 2)]$, ..., $P[(T, 6)]$.

Sometimes basic experiments are repeated many times and the resulting number of outcomes increases accordingly.

For example, if we flip a coin twice or, equivalently, flip two coins once simultaneously, we obtain:

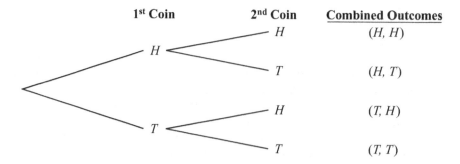

Figure 4.3 Tree Diagram for Repeated Experiment

In general, if the basic experiment has m possible outcomes ($m = 2$ for the coin experiment and $m = 6$ for the die experiment) and the basic experiment is repeated n times ($n = 1, 2, \ldots$), the number of the resulting outcomes (N) is given by

$$N = m^n \tag{4.3}$$

Clearly, if the coin was flipped 3 times, then

$$N = 2^3 = 8.$$

4.2.2 Events and their Characteristics

The outcomes in a Sample Space, S, must be "Mutually Exclusive" and "Collectively Exhaustive" which means that two outcomes cannot occur simultaneously and there are enough outcomes to cover all the possibilities of the experiment.

Given an experiment and the resulting Sample Space of the experiment we define "Events" on the Sample Space to be "Small Portions" or "Subsets" of the Sample Space, and represent them by capital letters of the English alphabet such as: $A, B, C, D, E, E_1, E_2, \ldots, E_k$.

If a set consists of n elements (*i.e.*, a Sample Space consists of n outcomes), then the number of subsets or Events that can be defined over this Sample Space is equal to 2^n. The value of 2 comes about because each outcome can be part of the event or not be part of the event.

As an illustration consider the following simple example.

Let $S = \{a, b, c\}$ and, according to the above discussion, the number of possible events are $2^3 = 8$; They are the following:

$$A_0 = \{\ \} = \varnothing \quad \text{(the Null Event)}$$
$$A_1 = \{a\}$$
$$A_2 = \{b\}$$
$$A_3 = \{c\}$$
$$A_4 = \{a, b\}$$
$$A_5 = \{a, c\}$$
$$A_6 = \{b, c\}$$
$$A_7 = \{a, b, c\}$$

With each event, E_k, we associate a number, $n(E_k)$, which is the number of sample points included in the definition of the event E_k.

An Event E is called "simple" if its definition consists of exactly one and only one sample point of the Sample Space, while a "composite"event contains more than one sample points.

Two (or more) Events, E_i and E_j, are called "Mutually Exclusive" or "Disjoint" if

$$E_i \cap E_j = \{\} = \varnothing \quad \text{for all } i \text{ and } j \text{ and } i \neq j \tag{4.4}$$

i.e., if the intersection of the events is the empty ($\varnothing$) set.

Two (or more) Events are called "Collectively Exhaustive" if their Union is equal to the Sample Space, or

$$E_1 \cup E_2 \cup \cdots \cup E_k = S \tag{4.5}$$

When a set of Events, E_1, E_2, ..., E_k, defined over a Sample Space, S, are both mutually Exclusive and Collectively Exhaustive, we say that they "form a partition of S", as is shown below, where events E_1, E_2, E_3, E_4, E_5 are both Mutually Exclusive and Collectively Exhaustive and,

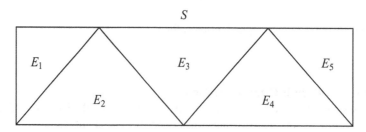

Figure 4.4 Partition of a Sample Space

therefore, they form a partition in S. The partition is a very important concept because the Axioms of Probability, which are discussed in the next section and apply to a set of Events defined in a Sample Space, assume that the Events form a partition of the Sample Space. Also, if the Events form a partition, exactly one of the events will occur whenever the experiment is performed. This is so because:

1. If two (or more) events are Mutually Exclusive, they cannot occur together. At most, one event will occur.
2. If two (or more) events are Collectively Exhaustive, at least one of them will occur.
3. Therefore, if a set of events forms a partition in S (*i.e.*, they are both Mutually Exclusive and Collectively Exhaustive) exactly one of the events will occur.

4.2.3 Axioms of Probability for Finite and Infinite Sample Spaces

The Sample Space (S) of an experiment, as defined above, can be either finite (if the sample points in S can be counted) of infinite (if the sample points in S can not be counted).

Finite Sample Spaces are analyzed in terms of Summations while infinite Sample Spaces are analyzed using Integration. The Probability theory of both finite and infinite Sample Spaces is based on three "axioms" which must be stated differently for finite and infinite Sample Spaces because the corresponding tools of analysis are different. However, these axioms, whether expressed in terms of summation or in terms of integration are completely equivalent, as will be shown.

Axioms are certain beliefs that are assumed to be true without needing proof as opposed to theorems, which require proof.

Every science has a set of axioms on which the entire structure of the science is based. If one or more of these axioms is proven wrong, the entire structure of the science collapses. An example of this is the science of Astronomy that had been developed based on the axiom that the Earth was the center of the Universe. When this axiom was proved wrong after the Middle Ages, the "old" astronomy collapsed and a new one was developed with a new set of axioms. Since probability theory is a science, it too is based on a set of axioms, which are the following:

1. **Axioms of Probability for Finite Sample Spaces**
   Suppose the events E_1, E_2, ..., En form a partition of a finite Sample Space S. Then, the following three axioms are stated:
   a) For any event E_i, the probability of the occurrence of the event is a positive number between 0 and 1, including the end points. This axiom can be stated mathematically as:

$$0 \leq P(E_i) \leq 1 \qquad (4.6)$$

b) The sum of the probabilities of occurrence of the events $E_1, E_2, ..., E_i, ..., E_n$ is equal to the probability of occurrence of the Sample Space S, which is equal to 1. Using mathematical notation, this axiom can be stated as:

$$P(S) = \sum_{i=1}^{n} P(E_I) = 1 \qquad (4.7)$$

c) If we form the Union of any two events E_i and E_j, $E_i \cup E_j$, and then find the probability of occurrence of the Union, this probability is equal to the sum of $P(E_i)$ and $P(E_j)$, if the intersection of E_i and E_j is the empty set. Since the events $E_1, E_2, ..., E_n$ form a partition in S, $E_i \cap E_j = \varnothing$ for any sets i and j.

Using mathematical notation, we can state this axiom as:

$$P(E_i \cup E_j) = P(E_i) + P(E_j) \qquad \text{if } E_i \cap E_j = \varnothing \qquad (4.8)$$

2. **Axioms of Probability for Infinite Sample Spaces**

When the Sample Space is infinite (*i.e.*, it has an infinite number of Sample points) the probability of occurrence of each sample point is zero, because the sample point of interest has only one chance of occurring out of an infinite number of possibilities. Because of this, events in an infinite Sample Space are defined as line intervals, areas, or volumes depending on whether the Sample Space is a line, a plane, or a volume.

Suppose the Sample Space of interest is the area under a curve, $f(x)$, in which the value of x can extend from $-\infty$ to $+\infty$, as shown below:

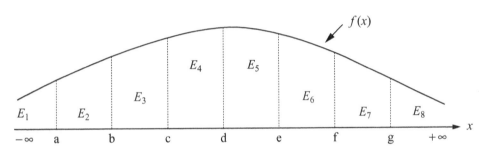

Figure 4.5 Sample Space of a Continuous Varible

If $f(x)$ has been properly normalized (*i.e.*, multiplied by an appropriate constant) the area under the curve $f(x)$ and for x varying from $-\infty$ to $+\infty$ is equal to 1. Then, depending on the value of x, we can define the following events and their corresponding probabilities which are now defined as areas under the curve $f(x)$ and between two x values:

a) Event E_1, when $-\infty < x \leq a$ with: $P(E_1) = \displaystyle\int_{-\infty}^{a} f(x)dx$

b) Event E_2, when $a < x \leq b$ with: $P(E_2) = \displaystyle\int_{a}^{b} f(x)dx$

c) Event E_3, when $b < x \leq c$ with: $P(E_3) = \displaystyle\int_{b}^{c} f(x)dx$

d) Event E_4, when $c < x \leq d$ with: $P(E_4) = \displaystyle\int_{c}^{d} f(x)dx$

e) Event E_5, when $d < x \leq e$ with: $P(E_5) = \int_d^e f(x)dx$ (4.9)

f) Event E_6, when $e < x \leq f$ with: $P(E_6) = \int_e^f f(x)dx$

g) Event E_7, when $f < x \leq g$ with: $P(E_7) = \int_f^g f(x)dx$

h) Event E_8, when $g < x \leq \infty$ with: $P(E_8) = \int_g^\infty f(x)dx$

Obviously we could have defined fewer or more such events on the given Sample Space.

Since the defined events $E_1, E_2, \ldots, E_8$ are such that:

$$P(E_i \cap E_j) = \varnothing \quad \text{for any } i \text{ and } j \tag{4.10}$$

and

$$P(E_1 \cup E_2 \cup E_3 \cup E_4 \cup E_5 \cup E_6 \cup E_7 \cup E_8) = P(S) \tag{4.11}$$

these events form a partition in S and the three axioms of probability can now be stated as:

a) $0 \leq P(E_i) \leq 1$ (4.12)

Since the area under the curve in each of the above integrals is at least zero (area cannot be negative) and at most equal to 1, since by definition the area under the entire curve f(x), from $x = -\infty$ to $x = +\infty$, is equal to 1.

b) $P(S) = \displaystyle\sum_{i=1}^{n} P(E_i) = P(E_1) + P(E_2) + \cdots + P(E_8)$

$$= \int_{-\infty}^a f(x)dx + \int_a^b f(x)dx + \cdots + \int_g^a f(x)dx$$

$$= \int_{-\infty}^\infty f(x)dx = 1 \qquad \text{(by definition)} \tag{4.13}$$

3. $P(E_i \cup E_j) = P(E_i) + P(E_j)$ since $E_i \cap E_j = \varnothing$

For example, if $E_i = E_2$, and $E_j = E_3$, we have:

$$P(E_2 \cup E_3) = P(E_2) + P(E_3)$$

$$= \int_a^b f(x)dx + \int_b^c f(x)dx$$

$$= \int_a^c f(x)dx \quad \text{since} \quad E_2 \cap E_3 = \varnothing \tag{4.14}$$

4.2.4 Probability Assignment to Events

Having stated the axioms on which probability theory is based we are now in a position to decide how to assign probabilities to events of interest in a given Sample Space.

From the axioms above we know that the probability of any event E, $P(E)$, is a positive number or zero and varies between zero and one.

We introduce the following definitions:

1. **Impossible Event** is an event, which can never occur in this Sample Space and has probability of occurrence equal to zero.

2. **Certain or Definite Event** is an event which always occurs in this Sample Space and has probability of occurrence equal to one.

The impossible and certain events are not of great interest because their probabilities are known in advance and there is no need to perform the experiment to obtain these probabilities. They are important, however, because they define the limits of variation of probability of the more interesting events, whose probability of occurrence falls between zero and one. The question then arises: How does one assign probabilities of occurrence to events other than the impossible and certain events?

The answer to this question depends on the theory one uses for such assignment and there are three such theories, the following:
1. Classical Theory of Probability
2. Relative-frequency Theory of Probability
3. Personalistic Theory of Probability

The Classical Theory approach to Probability assignment of events is based on the assumption of equally likely outcomes of a stochastic experiment.

If there are N possible and equally likely outcomes in a given stochastic experiment, then the probability of occurrence of each sample point is equal to $1/N$, or, in terms of mathematics:

$$P(\text{Each Sample Point}) = 1/N \qquad (4.15)$$

Then, if an Event E is defined on the Sample Space consisting of $n(E)$ sample points, the probability of event E is given by:

$$P(E) = \frac{n(E)}{N} \qquad (4.16)$$

For example, when rolling a single die once, the sample space of the experiment consists of six outcomes, namely the numbers 1, 2, 3, 4, 5, 6. Therefore, $N = 6$.

Suppose on this Sample Space we define the event E to consist of all the Sample points whose face value is less than 3. Since there are only two such sample points (namely the numbers 1 and 2), $n(E) = 2$, and the probability of E,

$$P(E) = n(E)/N = 2/6 = 1/3.$$

The classical theory of probability works well with "fair" instruments of experimentation, such as perfectly balanced coins and dice. If the instruments of experimentation are imperfect the classical theory will yield wrong probabilities. When the classical theory fails, we should attempt to use the **Relative Frequency theory of Probability** assignment, which assigns probabilities to events based on the results of repetitive experiments.

For example, if a die is "loaded" and we are not aware of it we will tend to assume that $P(5)$, for example, is equal to 1/6.

However, if we repeat this experiment, say 1,200,000 times, and we observe that the number 5 occurred, say 400,000 times, it would be wrong to say that $P(5) = 1/6$ when in reality $P(5) = 1/3$, according to the results of the experiment. Such probability assignment is made in accordance with the Relative Frequency theory, which assigns probabilities based on repetitive experimentation and is based on the formula:

$$P(E) = \lim_{n \to \infty} \left(\frac{X}{n} \right) \qquad (4.17)$$

where $P(E)$ is the probability of the event of interest E

n is the number of times the experiment is repeated

X is the number of times E occurs in the n repetitions

and $\lim_{n \to \infty}$ implies that the experiment should be repeated many times.

The **Classical and Relative Frequency Theories** are called objective theories because they assign probabilities to events based either on deduction from a set of assumptions (classical) or on repeated empirical observations (Relative Frequency). These are in contrast to the "Personalistic" theory which considers probability as a measure of personal assessment of a given situation and, therefore, differs from person to person.

The **Personalistic Theory** is employed when the other two can not be used for probability assignment either because the "equal likelihood" assumption does not apply or repetition of the experiment is impractical. Then an "expert" is consulted who assigns appropriate weights to the outcomes of a given situation. Since different individuals assign different weights it may be useful to consult several experts and then **average** the results. The sum of the weights must, of course, be equal to one, and each weight must be a number between zero and one so that the axioms of probability are satisfied.

The three methods of probability assignment that we discussed above are complementary of each other and not in competition. The method selected in a given situation will depend on the conditions of the experiment.

Consider, for example, the following situation. A large company is considering to compete for a large government contract with nine other companies. To enter the competition will involve substantial expenditures in funds and professional personnel assignments to the program. How should the company assess its probability of winning the contract? The classical theory would assign 1/10 as the probability of winning to each company which is obviously incorrect since the companies are different from each other with different sets of strengths and weaknesses. The relative frequency theory can not be used here because this is a "one-shot" experiment which does not "allow" repetition.

Obviously the only method available is the use of "experts" who will assess the overall position of the company (Technical, Financial, Political, Geographical, etc.) and determine the company's chances of winning. Then the "decision maker" (president or CEO) will have to decide whether the anticipated benefits warrant the expected expenditure.

But, regardless of which method is used in a given situation, once the probability assignments have been made in agreement with the axioms, the rules of analysis are the same for all.

4.2.5 Relationship between probability and Odds

We are all familiar with the weather reports or the prognostications regarding the outcome of an athletic event which are usually expressed in terms of "odds".

We say, for example, that the odds in favor of an event E are 3 to 1 (or in general x to y). How is such a statement related to probability?

If the odds in favor of the event E are x to y, then

$$P(E) = \frac{x}{x + y} \tag{4.18}$$

while $P(\overline{E}) = 1 - P(E) = 1 - \left(\frac{x}{x + y}\right) = \frac{y}{x + y},$ $\tag{4.19}$

where $P(\overline{E})$ is the probability against the event E occurring.

On the other hand, if the probability of an event E is given, and we wish to determine the odds in favor and against the event we can do so by starting with

$$P(E) = \frac{x}{x + y}$$

and find that:

1. The odds in favor of the Event E, when $P(E)$ is known, are: $P(E)$ to $[1 - P(E)]$. (4.20)
2. The odds against the Event E, when $P(E)$ is known, are: $[1 - P(E)]$ to $P(E)$. (4.21)

4.2.6 Basic Probability Theorems

It should be obvious from our discussion above that many theories of probability assignment to Events exist. But even though there are many such theories, there is no disagreement about the properties of "probability functions" which are rules that assign Probabilities to events defined in a Sample Space. Also no disagreement exists in the calculation of Event Probabilities, after the initial probability assignment has been made.

   Probability functions satisfy the three axioms of probability stated earlier and in fact they are renamed and restated below as theorems 1, 2, and 3. Four other theorems are also added to raise the total list of basic probability theorems to seven. They are:

1. **Theorem 1** is a restatement of the first axiom of Probability and states that if E is an event defined in a Sample Space S, then $0 \leq P(E) \leq 1$. It is called the **"Non-Negativity" Law**.
2. **Theorem 2** is a restatement of the second axiom and states that in a given stochastic experiment with Sample Space S, the probability that the Sample Space will occur is equal to 1 or $P(S) = 1$. It is called the **"Certainty" Law**.
3. **Theorem 3** is a restatement of the third axiom of probability and claims that if A and B are two events defined in a Sample Space S and such that $A \cap B = \emptyset$ (*i.e.*, A and B are disjoint) then the probability of the Union of the sets A and B (*i.e.*, $P(A \cup B)$) is equal to the sum of the probabilities of the events A and B, or:

$$P(A \cup B) = P(A) + P(B) \quad \text{if} \quad A \cap B = \emptyset \qquad (4.22)$$

   It is called "**The Special Additive**" Law and can be extended to any number of Mutually Exclusive (disjoint) events $E_1, E_2, \ldots, E_k$.

   We write: $P(E_1 \cup E_2 \cup \cdots \cup E_k) = \displaystyle\sum_{i=1}^{k} P(E_i)$ if $E_i \cap E_j = \emptyset$ for all i, j (4.23)

4. **Theorem 4** is a generalization of Theorem 3 in that the events A and B do not have to be Mutually Exclusive. It is called the "**General Additive**" Law and states that:

$$P(A \cup B) = P(A) + P(B) - P(A \cap B) \quad \text{where} \quad A \cap B \neq \emptyset \qquad (4.24)$$

Note: If $A \cap B = \emptyset$ the General Additive Law reduces to the Special Additive Law above. The justification for subtracting $P(A \cap B)$ is the fact that if the Events A and B do overlap, then the term $P(A) + P(B)$ counts region (2) in Figure 4.6 below twice, once in P(A) and the second time in P(B). We must, therefore, subtract $P(A \cap B)$ to keep the equation valid.

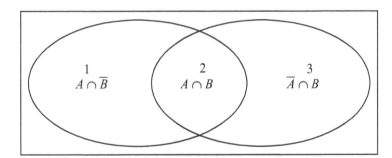

Figure 4.6 Illustration of General Additive Law

From the figure above $P(A) = P(A \cap \overline{B}) + P(A \cap B)$

$$P(B) = P(A \cap B) + P(\overline{A} \cap B)$$

and $\qquad P(A) + P(B) = P(A \cap \overline{B}) + 2P(A \cap B) + P(\overline{A} \cap B) \qquad (4.25)$

Applying the definition of the Union of two events to the figure above, we obtain

$$
\begin{aligned}
P(A \cup B) &= P(A \cap \overline{B}) + P(A \cap B) + P(\overline{A} \cap B) \\
&= [P(A \cap \overline{B}) + P(A \cap B)] - P(A \cap B) + [P(A \cap B) + P(\overline{A} \cap B)] \\
&= P(A) - P(A \cap B) + P(B) \\
&= P(A) + P(B) - P(A \cap B) \qquad (4.26)
\end{aligned}
$$

It can be easily extended to 3 events A, B, C

$$
\begin{aligned}
P(A \cup B \cup C) = {}&P(A) + P(B) + P(C) - P(A \cap B) \\
&- P(A \cap C) - P(B \cap C) + P(A \cap B \cap C) \quad (4.27)
\end{aligned}
$$

and then to four events A, B, C, D as

$$
\begin{aligned}
P(A \cup B \cup C \cup D) = {}&P(A) + P(B) + P(C) + P(D) - P(A \cap B \cap C) \\
&- P(A \cap B \cap D) - P(A \cap C \cap D) - P(B \cap C \cap D) \\
&+ P(A \cap B) + P(A \cap C) + P(A \cap D) \\
&+ P(B \cap C) + P(B \cap D) + P(C \cap D) \\
&- P(A \cap B \cap C \cap D) \qquad (4.28)
\end{aligned}
$$

Even though we will have no need to extend this rule to more than four events, the extension is straight forward as can be seen by going from 2 to 3 and to 4 events.

5. **Theorem 5** claims that the probability of the impossible event is equal to zero, or, in equation form:

$$P(\varnothing) = 0 \qquad (4.29)$$

Clearly, for the event to be impossible, it would have to be defined outside the given Sample Space S, and we know that only Sample points inside the Sample Space have probabilities other than zero.

6. **Theorem 6** Given a Sample Space S and an event E defined in S, with Probability of occurrence $P(E)$, then the event $\overline{E}$, which is the complement of the event E, has a probability of occurrence

$$P(\overline{E}) = 1 - P(E). \qquad (4.30)$$

This can be easily verified by remembering that events E and $\overline{E}$ are Mutually exclusive and Collectively Exhaustive (*i.e.*, they form a Partition in S).

Then if $n(E)$ is the number of Sample points defining event E, $n(\overline{E})$ is the number of sample points defining event $\overline{E}$, and $n(S)$ is the number of sample points in the Sample Space S, we must have

$$n(E) + n(\overline{E}) = n(S) \qquad (4.31)$$

Dividing through by $n(S)$ and recalling that $P(E) = \dfrac{n(E)}{n(S)}$ and $P(\overline{E}) = \dfrac{n(\overline{E})}{n(S)}$, according to the Classical Theory, we obtain

$$P(E) + P(\overline{E}) = 1 \qquad (4.32)$$

from which (4.30) above can be easily obtained.

7. **Theorem 7** states that the probability of the complement of the complement of an event E is equal to the probability of the original event, *i.e.*,

$$P(E) = P(\overline{\overline{E}}) \qquad (4.33)$$

Given the event E in a Sample Space S, its complement is $\overline{E}$ and according to theorem 6 above we have

$$P(\overline{E}) = 1 - P(E) \tag{4.34}$$

If we now regard $\overline{E}$ as the given event, its complement is $\overline{\overline{E}}$ and their probabilities are related by

$$P(\overline{\overline{E}}) = 1 - P(\overline{E}) \tag{4.35}$$

When equation (4.34) is substituted for $P(\overline{E})$ above we obtain

$$P(\overline{\overline{E}}) = 1 - [1 - P(E)] = 1 - 1 + P(E) = P(E) \tag{4.36}$$

We have briefly discussed and presented the above theorems so that we may use them in future analysis without the need for further proof and justification. Even though they appear to be straight forward and simple, having to digress and prove them every time we use them, could prove distracting and time consuming.

4.2.7 Conditional versus Unconditional Probability

The probabilities of events we have calculated up to now, based on the Sample Space of a given experiment, are called "**unconditional**" probabilities.

For example, when a single die is rolled once, the Sample Space $S = \{1, 2, 3, 4, 5, 6\}$ and if we define the two events:

A: The number 3 shows up

B: An odd number (*i.e.*, 1, 3, 5) shows up,

then, from the Sample Space we calculate:

$$P(A) = \frac{n(A)}{n(S)} = \frac{1}{6}$$

$$\text{and} \quad P(B) = \frac{n(B)}{n(S)} = \frac{3}{6}$$

and $P(A)$ and $P(B)$ are "**unconditional**" probabilities for the events A and B.

However, when some additional information regarding the outcome of an experiment, beyond that provided by the Sample Space of the experiment, becomes available the resulting probabilities of the events which depend on the additional information are called "**conditional**" probabilities and are usually, but not always, different than the "**unconditional**" probabilities of the events.

Below we first introduce some notation, which will discriminate between **conditional** and **unconditional** probabilities, and then we discuss two methods for computing **conditional** probabilities.

The notation $P(A/B)$ is used to represent the **conditional** probability of the event A given that the event B has already occurred. Also, $P(B/A)$ is the conditional probability that the event B has occurred given that the event A has occurred. Note that when additional information is given about the outcome of an experiment, the effect it has on the Sample Space of the experiment is to reduce it, thus resulting in a new and "**reduced**" Sample Space which we denote by S'. For example S' of the above example becomes $S' = \{1, 3, 5\}$ since, if we are told that the number which showed up is an odd number, the number 2, 4, and 6 cannot possibly occur, because they are even numbers.

The reduced Sample Space S' is the basis of one of the methods for calculating conditional probabilities, while the original Sample Space S is used, together with a formula which will be discussed later, in the second method.

The method using S' is direct and based on the formula

$$P(A/B) = \frac{n(A)}{n(S')} \tag{4.37}$$

Since $n(S') = 3$ and $n(A) = 1$ in the reduced Sample Space S', $P(A/B) = 1/3$ which is different than the unconditional probability $P(A) = 1/6$. In this case we say that event B had an influence on the outcome of event A. Such events, which affect the occurrence of each other will be defined shortly as "**dependent**" events. On the other hand events which do not affect the occurrence of each other will be defined as **independent** events. For **independent** events the **unconditional** and **conditional** probabilities are the same.

Similarly we can define $P(B/A) = \dfrac{n(B)}{n(S')}$ and, since $n(B) = 3$ and $n(S') = 3$ in S', $P(B/A) = 1$ which is different than $P(B) = 3/6$. The conclusion again is that the events A and B influence each other and, therefore, are dependent.

Before the second method can be used to calculate conditional probabilities, we must use the original Sample Space in which events A and B are defined to form the intersection of events A and B (*i.e.*, form $A \cap B$) and then calculate $P(A \cap B)$ from:

$$P(A \cap B) = \frac{n(A \cap B)}{n(S)} \tag{4.38}$$

In the example above $A = \{3\}$ and $B = \{1, 3, 5\}$. Clearly $A \cap B = \{3\}$ and $P(A \cap B) = 1/6$, because $n(A \cap B) = 1$ and $n(S) = 6$.

Then the conditional probability of A given B, $P(A/B)$, is calculated from:

$$P(A/B) = \frac{P(A \cap B)}{P(B)} \quad \text{provided } P(B) \neq 0 \tag{4.39}$$

Since in the example above, $P(A \cap B) = 1/6$ and $P(B) = 3/6$, $P(A/B) = \dfrac{1/6}{3/6} = \dfrac{1}{3}$, which is the same result we obtained for $P(A/B)$ when the reduced Sample Space S' used.

Similarly, we can write $P(B/A) = \dfrac{P(B \cap A)}{P(A)}$ with $P(A) \neq 0$

Since the events $A \cap B$ and $B \cap A$ are identical, $P(B \cap A) = P(A \cap B) = 1/6$ and $P(B/A) = \dfrac{1/6}{1/6} = 1$ as before.

In general $P(A/B) \neq P(B/A)$ even though $P(A \cap B) = P(B \cap A)$.
This is so because in general $P(A) \neq P(B)$.
However, it is true that

$$P(A \cap B) = P(B \cap A) = \begin{cases} P(B/A) \times P(A) \\ P(A/B) \times P(B) \end{cases} \tag{4.40}$$

and we may use either expression to find the probability of the intersection. The choice will depend on what information is available at a given time.

4.3   Joint Probabilities

Events such as $A \cap B$, which are defined as the intersection of two or more other events (A and B here) defined over a Sample Space S are also called "Joint" events and their corresponding probabilities are referred to as the "Joint" probabilities of the events, and the objective of this section is to discuss ways of calculating joined probabilities from the individual probabilities of the events and other considerations (such as conditional probabilities).

Formula (4.40),

$$P(A \cap B) = P(B \cap A) = \begin{cases} P(B/A) \times P(A) \\ P(A/B) \times P(B) \end{cases}$$

which was stated above clearly shows that the probability of the joint event $A \cap B$, $P(A \cap B)$, can be obtained as the product of a conditional and an unconditional probability. This formula, known as the "**General Multiplicative**" theorem, can be extended to three or more events. For example

$$P(A \cap B \cap C) = P(A)P(B/A)P(C/A \cap B) \qquad (4.41)$$

and similar expressions can be written for the intersection of four or more events. Even though these formulas are easy to write down, calculating the joint probability of many events is not easy because the General Multiplicative theorem requires the calculation of several conditional probabilities. However, considerable simplifications occur to this theorem if the events forming the intersection are independent of each other. Therefore, we will distinguish between **dependent** and **independent** events, before we can introduce simplifications to the calculation of joint probabilities.

In general, two (or more) events are called "**dependent**" if the probability of occurrence of one event is affected by the occurrence of another event. **Dependent** events are generated by random sampling "**without replacement**" (*i.e.*, if the item chosen for study is not returned to the population from which it was drawn).

On the other hand, two (or more) events are called "**independent**" if the probability of occurrence of one event is not affected by the occurrence of another event. **Independent** events are generated by random sampling "**with replacement**" (*i.e.*, the item chosen for study is returned to the population from which it was drawn, after the needed measurements were made).

Example 2

Suppose a deck of cards is well shuffled, and cards are drawn from it. Let

$\quad\quad A$ = Event that the first card is the Queen of diamonds

and $\quad\;\; B$ = Event that the second card drawn is the king of Hearts

$\quad\quad$ Clearly, since there is only one Queen of diamonds in the deck consisting of 52 cards,

$$P(A) = 1/52$$

Now, if the first card is indeed the Queen of diamonds we are faced with the choice of:

1. Drawing a second card from the deck, without returning the first card drawn (Sampling without replacement), or
2. Drawing a second card from the deck, after first returning the first card to the deck, before drawing the second card (Sampling with replacement).

If the sampling is done without replacement, $P(B/A) = 1/51$ since there is only one king of hearts in the deck which now has 51 cards (since the first card was not returned to the deck). Clearly the occurrence of the event A affected the occurrence of the event B because it changed its probability from 1/52 to 1/51.

Therefore the events A and B are **dependent**.

However, if the sampling is done with replacement, $P(B/A) = 1/52$. Since the unconditional probability of B, $P(B)$, is also 1/52, event A had no influence on the occurrence of event B and, clearly, events A and B are **independent**.

In general, if

$$P(B/A) = P(B) \qquad (4.$$

events A and B are called independent and we can see from the General Multiplica theorem (see equation (4.40)) that

$$P(A \cap B) = P(B) \cdot P(A) \qquad (4$$

which is a considerable simplification in the calculation of the joint probability $P(A \cap B)$.

■ ■ ■

Example 3

An urn contains one read, one white, and one blue ball. Draw a sample of two balls (one after the other) from the urn when sampling is done a) with replacement; b) when sampling is done without replacement.

Draw tree diagrams in each case, define the resulting events and assign event probabilities.

■ Sampling with Replacement

Since there are 3 balls in the urn and the first draw is random, each of the 3 balls has probability of 1/3 of being selected. To draw the second sample with replacement, we must return the drawn ball to the urn, mix well and draw again. Since again there are 3 balls in the urn and the drawing is random, each of the 3 balls can be drawn with probability of 1/3, regardless of which ball was chosen in the first draw.

Combing these facts together, we obtain the tree diagram below:

Note: There are 9 outcomes each with probability of 1/9.

As an illustration of showing how these probabilities are calculated, consider the event $R \cap W$.

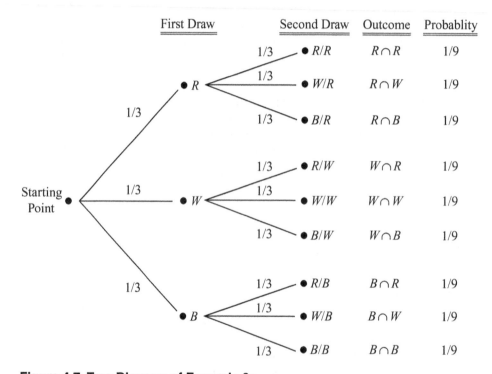

Figure 4.7 Tree Diagram of Example 3a

From the General Multiplicative theorem, we have:

$$P(R \cap W) = P(R) \cdot P(W/R) = (1/3)(1/3) = 1/9$$

and similarly for the other outcomes. Note that the events R and W are independent since $P(W/R) = P(W) = 1/3$. Similar analysis leads to the conclusion that events R, W, B are independent of each other.

Note: In order to find the probability of the outcomes, using the tree diagram, the probability of each event is found using the information generated from the experiment and then these probabilities are attached to the branches of the tree diagram. Then the probability of each outcome is found by the product of all the "branch" probabilities appearing in each path, which leads from the starting point to an end point.

If we now wish to define a new event on the Sample Space, which has these outcomes as its sample points, the probability of the new event is found by summing the appropriate outcome probabilities. For example, let E be the event in which both balls drawn are of the same color. For the event E to occur both balls must be either red, white, or blue. Therefore,

$$P(E) = P(R \cap R) + P(W \cap W) + P(B \cap B) = 1/9 + 1/9 + 1/9 = 1/3$$

■ Sampling Without Replacement

After the first draw, which can result in a red, white, or blue ball selected with probability of 1/3, the item is not returned to the urn. Therefore, the total number of items in the urn, as we get ready to make our second selection, is two and the conditional probabilities of choosing the second item is 1/2. In this experiment we cannot choose two balls of the same color because the color of the ball chosen in the first draw is not available in the second draw. These considerations lead to the following tree diagram, outcomes, and corresponding probabilities.

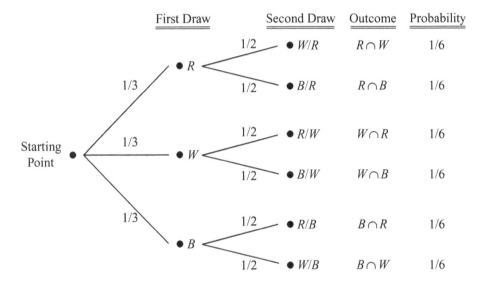

Figure 4.8 Tree Diagram of Example 3b

Since, for example, $P(W/R) = 1/2$ and $P(W) = 1/3$, the events R and W are dependent since $P(W/R) \neq P(W)$. Similar analysis leads to the conclusion that the events R, W and B are dependent in this example.

■ ■ ■

4.3.1 Bayes' Formula

There is a certain class of important problems, which arise when an event has occurred and one wishes to know which one of several possible related events caused the occurrence. In such problems the probabilities of the various causes and the conditional probabilities of occurrence of the event corresponding to the various possible causes are given. Such problems can be viewed as two-stage experiments. The first stage can be described by stating that exactly one of $K(K = 1, 2, \ldots,)$ possible outcomes must occur when the complete experiment is performed. Denote these outcomes by $A_1, A_2, \ldots, A_k$. They are the possible causes, which produce the outcome of the second stage of the experiment. In the second stage there are P possible outcomes, exactly one of which must occur. Denote these by $B_1, B_2, \ldots, B_p$. The probabilities $P(A_1), \ldots, P(A_k)$ are given. Also given are the conditional probabilities $P(B_i/A_j)$ which is the probability that the second-stage event B_i will occur when it is known that the first-stage event A_j has occurred.

The tree-diagram representation of this type of problem is similar to the tree diagram shown above as Figure 4.8 with the "first-stage" corresponding to "First Draw" and "second-stage" outcomes corresponding to "Second Draw".

We will demonstrate this approach by carrying out the calculations for $P(A_1/B_1)$. All other calculations are similar.

Since
$$P(A_1/B_1) = \frac{P(A_1 \cap B_1)}{P(B_1)} \tag{4.44}$$

the desired probability can be found if $P(A_1 \cap B_1)$ and $P(B_1)$ are known.

But $P(A_1 \cap B_1) = P(B_1/A_1)P(A_1)$, and since $P(A_1)$ and $P(B_1/A_1)$ are both given, the numerator in the above equation is known.

The value of $P(B_1)$, which appears in the denominator of the above equation, can be found by summing up the probabilities of all the mutually exclusive ways in which B_1 can occur in conjunction with the first stage of the experiment, namely:

$$
\begin{aligned}
P(B_1) &= P(A_1 \cap B_1) + P(A_2 \cap B_1) + \cdots + P(A_k \cap B_1) \\
&= P(B_1/A_1)P(A_1) + P(B_1/A_2)P(A_2) + \cdots + P(B_1/A_K)P(A_K) \\
&= \sum_{j=i}^{K} P(B_1/A_j)P(A_j)
\end{aligned}
\tag{4.45}
$$

Since all the $P(A_j)$ and $P(B_1/A_j)$ are known, $P(B_1)$ is also known.

Therefore
$$P(A_1/B_1) = \frac{P(B_1/A_1)P(A_1)}{\displaystyle\sum_{j=i}^{K} P(B_1/A_j)P(A_j)} \tag{4.46}$$

which is known as Bayes' Formula. To calculate $P(A_j/B_i)$ for any other pair make the appropriate subscript changes in the formula above.

Example 4

A box contains 2 red balls and 1 white ball, while a second box contains 3 red and 2 white balls. One of the boxes is selected at random and a ball is drawn from it. If the ball selected is white, what is the probability that it came:

a) From the first box?
b) From the second box?

Solution The first-stage experiment consists of choosing between the two boxes. Let A_1 be the event that box 1 is selected and A_2 be the event that box 2 is selected. Since the selection is done randomly $P(A_1) = P(A_2) = 1/2$.

The second-stage experiment consists of the possible types of balls which can be drawn. Let B_1 be the event that the ball drawn is red and B_2 be the event that the ball drawn is white. From the statement of the problem we have:

$$P(B_1/A_1) = P(\text{ball drawn is red/box 1 is selected}) = 2/3$$
$$P(B_2/A_1) = P(\text{ball drawn is white/box 1 is selected}) = 1/3$$
$$P(B_1/A_2) = P(\text{ball drawn is red/box 2 is selected}) = 3/5$$
$$P(B_2/A_2) = P(\text{ball drawn is white/box 2 is selected}) = 2/5$$

The problem is to find $P(A_1/B_2)$ and $P(A_2/B_2)$.
Applying Bayes' Formula, we obtain:

$$P(A_1/B_2) = \frac{P(A_1)P(B_2/A_1)}{P(A_1)P(B_2/A_1) + P(A_2)P(B_2/A_2)}$$

$$= \frac{1/2\,(1/3)}{1/2\,(1/3) + 1/2\,(2/5)} = \frac{1/6}{1/6 + 1/5} = \frac{1/6}{11/30} = \frac{5}{11}$$

$$P(A_2/B_2) = \frac{P(A_2)P(B_2/A_2)}{P(A_1)P(B_2/A_1) + P(A_2)P(B_2/A_2)}$$

$$= \frac{1/2\,(2/5)}{1/2\,(1/3) + 1/2\,(2/5)} = \frac{1/5}{1/6 + 1/5} = \frac{1/5}{11/30} = \frac{6}{11}$$

■ ■ ■

4.3.2 Statistical Independence

We have defined two (or more) events to be independent of each other if the occurrence of one has no effect on the occurrence of the other. For two events A and B this implies that

$$P(A/B) = P(A)$$

$$\text{or} \quad P(B/A) = P(B) \tag{4.47}$$

Another way of stating independence is to require that:

$$P(A \cap B) = P(A)P(B) \tag{4.48}$$

These two interpretations are identical because from the definition of conditional probability $P(A/B) = \dfrac{P(A \cap B)}{P(B)}$, if we substitute in it the above expression for $P(A \cap B)$, we obtain:

$$P(A/B) = \frac{P(A \cap B)}{P(B)} = \frac{P(A)P(B)}{P(B)} = P(A) \tag{4.49}$$

This expression then will be adopted as the formal definition for independence between two events and makes it clear of what needs to be done to establish independence between two events, namely: Calculate the probabilities of each event separately and the probability of their intersection (joint event); If the product of the individual probabilities is equal to the probability of their intersection the events are independent. Otherwise, they are not! We will illustrate these concepts by means of the following example.

Example 5

Roll two dice, one white and one black, simultaneously and over the resulting Sample Space define the events:

  A: The white die shows a number equal to or greater than 5
  B: The black die shows a number equal to or less than 4
  C: Double numbers occur
  D: Both numbers are 2

Investigate the independence or dependence of sets:

1. *A* and *B*
2. *C* and *D*

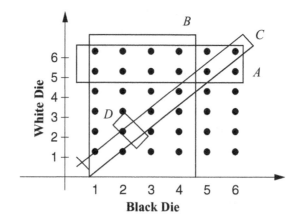

Figure 4.9

The Sample Space of the experiment consists of the 36 ordered pairs represented by dots in the diagram above. Over this Sample the four given events A, B, C and D are as shown.

Using the basic definition of the probability of an event E, $P(E) = \dfrac{n(E)}{n(S)}$, we obtain:

$$P(A) = \frac{n(A)}{n(S)} = \frac{12}{36} = {}^1/_3$$

$$P(B) = \frac{n(B)}{n(S)} = \frac{24}{36} = {}^2/_3$$

Since $A \cap B = \{(1,\ 5),\ (1,\ 6),\ (2,\ 5),\ (2,\ 6),\ (3,\ 5),\ (3,\ 6),\ (4,\ 5),\ (4,\ 6)\}$, $n(A \cap B) = 8$, and

$$P(A \cap B) = \frac{n(A \cap B)}{n(S)} = \frac{8}{36} = {}^2/_9$$

Therefore, since $P(A \cap B) = P(A)\,P(B)$ the events A and B are independent.

However, $P(C) = \dfrac{n(C)}{n(S)} = \dfrac{6}{36} = {}^1/_6, \quad P(D) = \dfrac{n(D)}{n(S)} = \dfrac{1}{36}, \quad$ and

$P(C \cap D) = \dfrac{n(C \cap D)}{n(S)} = \dfrac{1}{36}$, since $C \cap D = \{(2, 2)\}$ and, therefore, $n(C \cap D) = 1$

But $P(C \cap D) \neq P(C)P(D)$ and the events C and D are dependent.

The rule can be extended to n events $E_1, E_2, \ldots, E_n$. We say that n events are independent if and only if they are independent by pairs, by triples, quadruples, etc.

As an example, for 3 events A, B, C to be independent, we must have all of the following to be true, namely:

$$P(A \cap B) = P(A)P(B)$$
$$P(A \cap C) = P(A)P(C)$$
$$P(B \cap C) = P(B)P(C) \qquad\qquad (4.50)$$

and $$P(A \cap B \cap C) = P(A)P(B)P(C)$$

If one or more of the above relationships are not satisfied in a given situation, then the 3 events are not independent of each other.

We close this section by noting that 2 Mutually Exclusive events are dependent events because one influences the other (the occurrence of one precludes the occurrence of the other). This conclusion can also be arrived at mathematically by recalling that:

a) For 2 events A and B to be independent, $P(A \cap B) = P(A)P(B)$ when $P(A) \neq 0$ and $P(B) \neq 0$.

and b) For 2 events A and B to be Mutually Exclusive, $P(A \cap B) = 0$.

Then, since for 2 independent events $P(A \cap B) \neq 0$. (when $P(A) \neq 0$ and $P(B) \neq 0$), 2 Mutually Exclusive events can not be independent.

■ ■ ■

4.4 Counting Principles

The tree diagram method of depicting the Sample Space of a given experiment has been used as the main vehicle in our analysis of probabilities of desired events. The tree diagram not only generates the correct probabilities, when applied correctly, but it also adds a lot of visibility in the analysis of a given problem. To find the probability of a desired event all we have to do is count the number of favorable outcomes and divide this number by the total number of possible outcomes since $P(E) = \dfrac{n(E)}{n(S)}$ for any event E.

Unfortunately this method becomes cumbersome and difficult to keep track of as the number of repetitions of the basic experiment increases, giving rise to many more possible outcomes.

Fortunately, to find $P(E)$ we need only $n(E)$ and $n(S)$ and these numbers can be found without the use of a tree diagram by using efficient methods for counting these numbers, called "**Counting Principles**", which are based on a simple concept called the "**Principle of Multiplication**", which states the following:

"**If an operation can be performed in n_1 ways, and after that a second operation can be performed in n_2 ways, … then k operations can be performed in $n_1 \times n_2 \times \cdots \times n_k$ ways**".

We will use this principle to discuss two counting techniques, **Permutations** and **Combinations**, both of which are arrangements of objects. In **Permutations** the order in which the objects appear is important while in **Combinations** the order is not important. This distinction is important because it is also important in real life. Consider for example the statistics of a baseball player. His batting average at the end of the season depends on the number of hits he gets relative to the total number of his plate appearances without regard to the timing of his hits. However, his RBIs (or runs batted in) depend on the number of players being on base when he gets his hits.

Before we discuss Permutations and Combinations extensively, let us consider a simple example, which will allow us to understand the two counting principles clearly and allow us to discriminate between them without confusion.

Example 6

Suppose three people buy three theater ticket seats together. In how many ways may they occupy the 3 seats?

Let A, B, C represent the 3 people. Any one of the three may take the first seat. Next, any of the two remaining may sit in the second. Finally the last person must sit in the last seat.

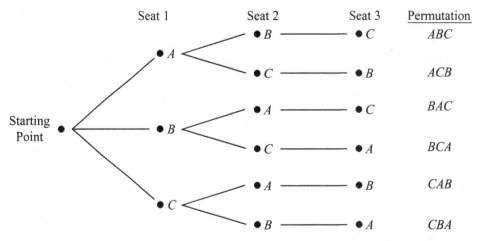

Figure 4.10

Altogether there are $3 \times 2 \times 1 = 6$ possible seating arrangements. The tree diagram above shows these 6 Permutations clearly.

Note: The six permutations listed are all distinct from each other even though they all include the letters A, B, C. Their "distinctness" is due to the fact that the order in which these letters appear is different. However, since order of appearance is not important in determining the number of Combinations, the above six Permutations correspond to only one Combination. In general, the number of Permutations in arranging a group of objects is larger than the number of Combinations.

■ ■ ■

4.4.1 Permutations

We have previously defined Permutations as arrangements of objects when order of appearance of the objects is important. To make the discussion absolutely clear, we will consider two separate cases.

Case 1 The N objects which we wish to arrange (or permute) are distinct from each other.

Then we are interested in the number of possible Permutations when:

a) All N objects are taken together
b) The N objects are taken r at a time, where $r \leq N$.

Case 2 The N objects are not distinct but fall into classes such that:

n_1 of them are alike and fall into class 1
n_2 of them are alike and fall into class 2

....

n_k of them are alike and fall into class k

with $n_1 + n_2 + \cdots + n_k = N$

Here again we are interested in the number of Permutations when:

a) there are k distinct classes with n_k elements in each
b) there are only 2 distinct classes with r and $N - r$ elements

Case 1 The derivation of the required formulas follows directly from the Multiplicative Principle.

a) Let $_NP_N$ represents the number of Permutations of N things taken all together. We need to find an expression for $_NP_N$ as a function of N. We arrive at this formula as follows: Suppose N bins are to be filled by N objects with one object in each bin. In how many ways can these bins be filled?

The first bin can be filled by any one of N objects. The second bin can be filled by any one of $N - 1$ objects, ..., the N-th bin by 1 object. Then using the "**Principle of Multiplication**" the N bins can be filled in $N \times (N - 1) \times (N - 2) \times \cdots \times (1)$ ways. But $N \times (N - 1) \times (N - 2) \times \cdots \times (1)$ is the factorial of the number N, written as $N!$

Therefore $\qquad\qquad {}_N P_N = N!$ $\qquad\qquad$ (4.51)

b) Let ${}_N P_r$ represent the number of Permutations of N things taken r at a time from $N (r \leq N)$.

Suppose r bins are to be filled, when N objects are available, where $r \leq N$. The first bin can be filled in N ways, the second bin in $N - 1$ ways, ..., the rth bin in $N - r + 1$ ways. Then, using the "**Principle of Multiplication**" we obtain:

$${}_N P_r = N \times (N - 1) \times (N - 2) \times \cdots \times (N - r + 1) \qquad (4.52)$$

If we multiply the right-hand side of the above equation by the fraction:

$\dfrac{(N - r)(N - r - 1)(N - r - 2) \cdots (1)}{(N - r)(N - r - 1)(N - r - 2) \cdots (1)}$ the right-hand side of $\qquad$ (4.52)

doesn't change, since the value of the fraction is equal to 1. This technique, however, allows us to obtain a much simpler formula because:

$$N \times (N - 1) \times (N - 2) \times \cdots \times (N - r + 1) \times$$

$$\times \left[\frac{(N - r)(N - r - 1)(N - r - 2) \cdots (1)}{(N - r)(N - r - 1)(N - r - 2) \cdots (1)} \right] = \frac{N!}{(N - r)!} \quad (4.53)$$

Note: If $r = N$, $(N - r)! = (N - N)! = 0! = 1$ by definition and this formula becomes identical to ${}_N P_N = N!$ as it should.

Example 7

Problem (a): Suppose a license plate number consists of 10 numbers. How many such license plate numbers, Q, are possible if:

1. The numbers are all distinct
2. Repetitions of numbers are allowed

Solution to (a1)

1. Since there are 10 numbers available (0, 1, 2, 3, 4, 5, 6, 7, 8, 9) to fill 10 positions, the number of Permutations is 10!
   Then:

$$Q = {}_{10} P_{10} = 10! = [10 \times 9 \times 8 \times 7 \times 6 \times 5] \times [4 \times 3 \times 2 \times 1]$$
$$= (151,200)(24) = 3,628,800$$

Solution to (a2)

2. If repetitions of numbers are allowed, then there are ten (10) ways to fill each position. Therefore:

$$Q = (10)(10) \cdots (10) = 10^{10}$$

Problem (b): Suppose a license plate number consists of 6 numbers. How many such license plate numbers, Q, are possible if:

1. The numbers are all distinct
2. Repetitions of numbers are allowed

Solution to (b1)

1. Since there are 10 numbers available to fill 6 positions, the number of Permutations Q is given by $_{10}P_6$, or

$$Q = {}_{10}P_6 = \frac{10!}{4!} = \frac{(10 \times 9 \times 8 \times 7 \times 6 \times 5) \times 4!}{4!}$$

$$= 10 \times 9 \times 8 \times 7 \times 6 \times 5 = 151{,}200$$

Solution to (b2)

2. If repetitions of numbers are allowed, then there are ten (10) ways to fill each of the six (6) positions. Therefore:

$$Q = (10)(10)(10)(10)(10)(10) = 10^6$$

■ ■ ■

Example 8

Lotto is a game of chance in which, in order ot win, you have to chose 6 numbers (the winning numbers), from a total of 54 numbers.

What is the Probability of Winning the Lotto, with a single ticket?

Solution We can write:

$$P(\text{Winning Lotto}) = \frac{\text{Number of Possible ways of choosing the 6 winning numbers}}{\text{Number of Total possibilities}}$$

$$= n(W\ L)/n(S)$$

We will use the "Principle of Multiplication" to find $n(W\ L)$ and $n(S)$.

1. To find $n(W\ L)$, consider the problem of filling 6 bins in a box with 6 objects (the 6 winning numbers). Since there are 6 possibilities of filling the first bin (*i.e.*, we could choose first any of the 6 numbers), then there are 5 possibilities for filling the 2nd bin, 4 for the 3rd, 3 for the fourth, 2 for the fifth, and 1 for the sixth.

    Then, using the **Principle of Multiplication**, the total number of ways of selecting the 6 winning numbers, $n(W\ L)$ is given by:

$$n\big(W\ L\big) = 6 \times 5 \times 4 \times 3 \times 2 \times 1 = 6! = 720$$

2. To find $n(S)$, consider the problem of filling 6 bins in a box with 54 objects (the total number of numbers from which the 6 winning numbers are to be drawn). Since there are 54 possibilities of filling the first bin (*i.e.*, we could choose any of the 54 numbers first), then there 53 possibilities for the 2nd, 52 for the 3rd, 51 for the 4th, 50 for the 5th, and 49 for the sixth (6th).

    Then, using the **Principle of Multiplication** again, the total number of possibilities, $n(S)$, is given by:

$$n(S) = 54 \times 53 \times 52 \times 51 \times 50 \times 49$$

$$= 54 \times 53 \times 52 \times 51 \times 50 \times 49 \times \left(\frac{48!}{48!}\right) = \frac{54!}{48!} = \frac{54!}{(54-6)!}$$

$$= 18{,}595{,}558{,}800$$

3. Therefore,

$$P(\text{Winning Lotto}) = \frac{n(W\ L)}{n(S)} = \frac{6!}{\dfrac{54!}{(54-6)!}} = \frac{720}{18{,}595{,}558{,}800} = \frac{1}{25837165}$$

Case 2 When the N objects are not all distinct, but fall into k classes with the number of objects in each class n_k and such that $n_1 + n_2 + \cdots + n_k = N$.

It is assumed that the elements in each class are identical. Then, if we let $_NP_{n1, n2, \ldots, nk}$ be the number of permutations under the stated conditions, the number of Permutations, Q, is given by:

$$Q = {_NP_{n1, n2, \ldots, nk}} = \frac{N!}{n_1!n_2! \cdots n_k!} \text{ (where: } n_1 + n_2 + \cdots + n_k = N.) \quad (4.54)$$

Note: If $n_1 = n_2 = \cdots = n_k = 1$, then there is only one element in each class and all of the objects are distinct.

Since $1! = 1$, Q in this case becomes equal to $N!$ which is as it should be.

■ ■ ■

Example 9

Assume that 10 objects fall into four categories such that $n_1 = 1$, $n_2 = 2$, $n_3 = 3$, $n_4 = 4$. Find the number of Permutations that can be formed with these objects.

Using formula (4.54) above, $Q = {_{10}P_{1, 2, 3, 4}} = \dfrac{10!}{1!2!3!4!}$, we find:

$$Q = \frac{10 \times 9 \times 8 \times 7 \times 6 \times 5 \times 4!}{(1)(1 \times 2)(1 \times 2 \times 3) \times 4!} = 12{,}600$$

If the objects had been all distinct (*i.e.*, if we had 10 classes each with one object) then $Q = 10! = 3{,}628{,}800$.

Clearly, the number of Permutations is reduced considerably if the objects we wish to arrange are not all distinct.

A special case of the above general rule occurs when the number of classes into which the N objects fall is two (2) such that class 1 has $n_1 = r$ objects in it while the second one has $n_2 = N - r$, since $n_1 + n_2 = N$.

Under these conditions, the number of Permutations, Q, is given by:

$$Q = {_NP_{r, N-r}} = \frac{N!}{r!(N - r)!} \quad (4.55)$$

This last formula will prove very useful in our calculation of probabilities. Objects which are chosen to participate in a given activity may be assumed to fall into class 1, while those which are not chosen fall into class 2. The above formula then gives us the possible number of Permutations. We will illustrate the use of Permutations in probability calculations with an example in Section 4.4.3 after we discuss briefly the other method of object arrangement, namely **Combinations**.

■ ■ ■

4.4.2 Combinations

We have previously defined Combinations as the arrangement of objects when order is not important. To illustrate this concept more clearly consider the 3 objects A, B, C which need to be arranged two at a time.

The number of Permutations in arranging 3 objects in groups of 2 (*i.e.*, taken two at a time) is given by:

$$Q = \frac{N!}{(N - r)!} = \frac{3!}{(3 - 2)!} = \frac{3!}{1!} = 3! = 6,$$

and they are:

$$AB \quad AC \quad BC$$
$$BA \quad CA \quad CB$$

When discussing Permutations, AB and BA are different arrangements, even though they involve the same objects, because the order of appearance of these objects is different.

However, if the order of appearance is not important, then arrangements AB and BA are identical. The same can be said about arrangements AC and CA and also about arrangements BC and CB. But when the order is disregarded, the arrangements are called "Combinations", and the number of Combinations of N objects taken r at a time is represented by $_NC_r$ and is given by:

$$_NC_r = \binom{N}{r} = \frac{N!}{r!(N-r)} \qquad \text{where } r \le N \qquad (4.56)$$

If $r = 1$, then $_NC_r = \binom{N}{1} = \frac{N!}{1!(N-1)!} = \frac{N \times (N-1)!}{(N-1)!} = N$

If $r = N$, then $_NC_r = \binom{N}{N} = \frac{N!}{N!(N-N)!} = \frac{N!}{N!0!} = 1$

If $r = N - r$, then $_NC_{N-r} = \binom{N}{N-r} = \frac{N!}{(N-r)!(N-N+r)!}$

$$= \frac{N!}{(N-r)!r!}$$

From which we can deduce that:

$$_NC_r = \,_NC_{N-r} \qquad (4.57)$$

Comparing the expression for the number of Combinations of N objects taken r at a time ($_NC_r$) and the number of Permutations of N objects taken r at a time ($_NP_r$), we see that:

$$_NP_r = \frac{N!}{(N-r)!} = (r!)_NC_r \qquad (4.58)$$

which shows that there are $r!$ more Permutations than Combinations. For example, there is only one way of selecting all objects, say $r = N$, when all are different (*i.e.*, there is only one combination), while there are $r! = N!$ Permutations.

When the expression for the number of Combinations $_NC_r$ is compared to the expression for the number of Permutations when the objects are not distinct but fall into two classes (one with r objects and the other with $N - r$ objects), namely $_NP_{r, N-r}$, we see that they are identical. Therefore, we may conclude that "Combinations are Permutations on which certain restrictions have been imposed".

4.4.3 An Example 10

A committee of three (3) is to be selected from a group of ten (10) people, of which six (6) are men and four (4) are women.

1. What is the probability that the committee consists of 2 men and 1 women?
2. What is the probability that the committee consists of 1 man and 2 women?
3. What is the probability that the committee consists of 3 men and no women?
4. What is the probability that the committee consists of 0 men and 3 women?

We will solve this problem using both the "tree-diagram" approach and the "Permutations" approach and then compare the two.

In any case we are looking for:

1. P (2 men and 1 woman) $= P(2M \cap 1W)$
2. P (1 men and 2 woman) $= P(1M \cap 2W)$
3. P (3 men and 0 woman) $= P(3M \cap 0W)$
4. P (0 men and 3 woman) $= P(0M \cap 3W)$

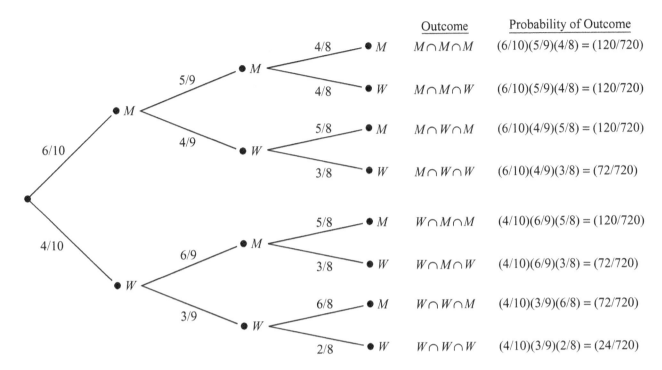

Figure 4.11 Tree Diagram for Example 10

■ Using the "tree-diagram" approach

But $P(2M \cap 1W) = P(M \cap M \cap W) + P(M \cap W \cap M) + P(W \cap M \cap M)$

   Therefore

$$P(2M \cap 1W) = (120/720) + (120/720) + (120/720) = (360/720) = 0.5 = 15/30$$

   Also

$$P(1M \cap 2W) = P(M \cap W \cap W) + P(W \cap M \cap W) + P(W \cap W \cap M)$$
$$= (72/720) + (72/720) + (72/720) = 3(72/720) = 0.3 = 9/30$$

   Similarly $P(3M \cap 0W) = P(M \cap M \cap M) = (120/720) = 1/6 = 5/30$,

and $P(0M \cap 3W) = P(W \cap W \cap W) = (24/720) = 1/30$

■ Using the "Permutations" approach

Since, for any event E, $P(E) = \dfrac{n(E)}{n(S)}$, we will use Permutations to first compute $n(E)$ and $n(S)$ for each of the above four (4) events. Then their ratio will give us the desired probability.

   Consider first the event $E_1 = (2M \cap 1W)$ whose probability can be written down immediately as $P(2M \cap 1W) = \dfrac{n(2M \cap 1W)}{n(S)}$.

The denominator, $n(S)$, is the number of 3-member committees that can be formed from a group of 10 people without gender distinction. It is given by the number of Permutations of 10 objects, 3 of which will belong to the committee and the other 7 will not belong to the committee. Therefore

$$n(S) = \frac{N!}{r!(N-r)!} = \frac{10!}{3!7!} = \frac{(10 \times 9 \times 8) \times (7!)}{(1 \times 2 \times 3) \times (7!)} = 120$$

The numerator, $n(2M \cap 1W)$, represents the number of 3-member committees that can be formed having 2 male and one female members. Obviously the 2 males in the committee must be chosen from the 6 males in the group. The number of ways of choosing 2 males to belong to the committee from a group of 6 is given by:

$$_6P_2 = \frac{6!}{2!(6-2)!} = \frac{6!}{2!4!} = 15$$

Similarly the female member of the committee must be chosen from the four women available in the group, and the number of ways this can be done is given by:

$$_4P_1 = \frac{4!}{1!(4-1)!} = \frac{4!}{1!3!} = 4$$

Then, according to the "Principle of Multiplication", the number of ways of selecting 2 out of 6 males and 1 out of 4 females to belong to the committee is given by the product of the number of ways the males can be chosen times the number of ways the females can be chosen.

Clearly then $n(2M \cap 1W) = (_6P_2)(_4P_1) = (15)(4) = 60$

and $P(2M \cap 1W) = \dfrac{n(2M \cap 1W)}{n(S)} = \dfrac{60}{120} = 0.5$

We have derived the above probability, which agrees with the value obtained using the "tree-diagram" approach, in great detail because we wanted to make the "Permutations" approach perfectly clear. However, once this has been accomplished, the solutions to the other parts of the problem can be written down by inspection, as follows:

$$P(1M \cap 2W) = \frac{n(1M \cap 2W)}{n(S)} = \frac{(_6P_1)(_4P_2)}{(_{10}P_3)} = \frac{(6)(6)}{120} = {}^{36}\!/_{120} = 0.3$$

$$P(3M \cap 0W) = \frac{n(3M \cap 0W)}{n(S)} = \frac{(_6P_3)(_4P_0)}{(_{10}P_3)} = \frac{(20)(1)}{120} = {}^1\!/_6$$

$$P(0M \cap 3W) = \frac{n(0M \cap 3W)}{n(S)} = \frac{(_6P_0)(_4P_3)}{(_{10}P_3)} = \frac{(1)(4)}{120} = {}^1\!/_{30}$$

and all of these results agree with the corresponding results obtained using the "tree-diagram" approach.

However, after the original discussion concerning the application of the method, the amount of work needed is considerably less when we use the "Permutations" approach as compared to the amount of work needed to use the "tree-diagram" approach.

This becomes much more obvious when the size of the committee (*i.e.*, the number of repetitions) increases from 3 to, say, 5. The tree diagram will become much bigger, the number of outcomes will increase to 32, and finding the probabilities of the "asked-for" events will require the scanning of the Sample Space and the combining of many more outcomes. In the "Permutations" approach, on the other hand, the method remains essentially the same and only the subscripts change which tell us to find the factorials of what numbers. Clearly the "**Permutations**" method is a more systematic and efficient approach.

4.5   References

Berenson, Marc, L., Levine, David, M., and Krehbiel, Timothy, C., 2004. *Basic Business Statistics*. 9th Edition. Pearson-Prentice Hall.

Black, Ken, 2004. *Business Statistics*. 4th Edition. Wiley.

Canavos, George, C., 1984. *Applied Probability and Statistical Methods*. Little, Brown.

Carlson, William, L., and Thorne, Betty, 1997. *Applied Statistical Methods*. Prentice Hall.

Chou, Ya-lun, 1992. *Statistical Analysis for Business and Economics*. Elsevier.

Freund, John, E., and Williams, Frank, J., 1969. *Modern Business Statistics*. Revised by: Perles, Benjamin and Sullivan, Charles. Prentice-Hall.

Freund, John, E., and Williams, Frank, J., 1982. *Elementary Business Statistics: The Modern approach*. Prentice-Hall.

Johnson, Robert, 1973. *Elementary Statistics*. Duxbury Press.

McClave, James, T., Benson, George, P., and Sincich, Terry, 2001. *Statistics for Business and Economics*. 8th Edition. Prentice Hall.

Salvatore, Dominick, *Theory and Problems of Statistics and Econometrics*. SCHAUM'S OUTLINE SERIES, McGraw-Hill.

Steel, Robert, G.D., and Torrie, James, H., 1976. *Introduction to Statistics*. McGraw-Hill.

4.6 PROBLEMS

1. When a voter is questioned about his preference for a particular candidate for office his choices are: F (Favorable) and U (Unfavorable). If three voters are similarly questioned, what are the elements of the sample space? Use a tree diagram to show the sample points:

2. An investor is planning to select two of five investment opportunities recommended to him. Describe the sample space representing the investors' possible choices.

3. A coin and a die are tossed, and over the resulting sample space the following two events are defined:

   A: The coin shows Tails and the die shows Even

   B: The coin shows Heads and the die shows Odd

   a) Are events A and B Mutually Exclusive?

   b) Are events A and B Collectively Exhaustive?

   c) Do events A and B form a Partition of the sample space?

   d) Are events A and B Independent or Dependent?

   Why or why not in each case?

4. Three contractors are bidding for a contract to construct a school building. It is believed that A is four times as likely to obtain the contact as B, who in turn is 3 times as likely to obtain the contract as C.

   What are the respective probabilities for each to obtain the contract?

5. Three drugs (A, B, C) are under consideration to treat a given ailment. In the past 10,000 applications, drug A was used 2,500 times, drug B was used 4,000 times and drug C was used 3,500 times.

   When an "expert" was asked to rank the effectiveness of the 3 drugs, he replied: "Drug B is twice as likely to be used as drug A and drug B is three times as likely to be used as drug C." What is the probability of using each drug in the next application according to the:

   a) Classical Theory

   b) Relative Frequency Theory

   c) Personalistic Theory

6. Two fair coins are tossed and on the resulting sample space we define the events:

   A: Head occurs on the first coin

   B: The two coins fall alike (*i.e.*, they show the same face)

   Are events A and B dependent or independent? Justify your answer.

7. A committee of five is to be chosen, without replacement, from a group of six men and four women. Find the probabilities that the committee will consist of:

   a) Five men and 0 women

   b) Four men and 1 woman

   c) Three men and 2 women

   d) Two men and 3 women

   e) One man and 4 women

   f) 0 men and 5 women

8. A box contains four Red and six Green balls. Two balls are drawn at random, without replacement.

   a) What are the possible outcomes of this experiment?

   b) Determine the probability of obtaining:

      i) Two Red balls

      ii) A Red ball and then a Green ball

      iii) A Green ball and then a Red ball

      iv) 2 Green balls

      v) A Red ball and a Green ball

9. Two slates of Candidates for the board of directors (A and B) are competing for control of a corporation. The probabilities that these 2 slates will win are 0.7 and 0.3 respectively. If Slate A wins, the probability of introducing a new product is 0.8. If Slate B wins, the corresponding probability is 0.4. What is the probability that the new product will be introduced after the election?

10. A certain output is known to be subject to 3 types of defects: A, B and C. Among 1,000 units produced one day, the assembly line inspector reported the following results:

Defect	A	B	C	$A \cap B$	$A \cap C$	$B \cap C$	$A \cap B \cap C$
No of Units	30	35	20	5	5	4	2

   a) What is the probability of selecting a unit with at least one defect?

   b) What is the probability of units having exactly one defect?

   c) What is the probability of units having exactly two defects?

   d) What is the probability of units which have no defects?

11. A factory has 200 employees classified according to skill and gender as shown in the table:

SKILL	GENDER		TOTAL
	M: MALE	F: FEMALE	
A: SKILLED	$n(A \cap M) = 50$	$N(A \cap F) = 10$	$n(A) = 60$
B: SEMI-SKILLED	$n(B \cap M) = 70$	$n(B \cap F) = 18$	$n(B) = 88$
C: UNSKILLED	$n(C \cap M) = 30$	$n(C \cap F) = 22$	$n(C) = 52$
TOTAL	$n(M) = 150$	$n(F) = 50$	$N = 200$

Assume that one worker is selected at random;

a) Find

$$P(A), P(B), P(C), \left[P(M) = \frac{n(M)}{N} = \frac{150}{200} = \frac{3}{4}; \; P(F) = \frac{n(F)}{N} = \frac{50}{200} = \frac{1}{4} \right]$$

b) Find $P(A \cap M), P(BM), P(C \cap M), P(A \cap F), \; P(B \cap F), P(C \cap F)$

c) Find $P(A/M), P(B/M), P(C/M), P(M/A), P(F/B), P(C/F)$

12. When a job candidate comes to interview for a job at K Industries, the probability that the candidate will want the job (Event A) after the interview is 0.88. Also, the probability that K Industries will want the candidate (Event B) is 0.45.

a) Find $P(A \cap B)$ if $P(A/B) = 0.92$

b) Find $P(B/A)$

13. A box contains four red and three blue poker chips. What is the probability that when three are selected randomly all three will be red, if each chip is selected:

a) With replacement

b) Without replacement

14. A man owns both his business and his home. In any one year the probability of a home being burglarized is 0.02 and the probability of burglarization of his business is 0.10. Assuming that these are independent occurrences, find:

a) The probability that both will be burglarized this year

b) The probability that exactly one will be burglarized this year

c) The probability that neither will be burglarized

15. The probability that a certain door is locked is 0.7. The key to the door is one of 10 unidentified keys hanging on a key rack. Two keys are selected at random before approaching the door. What is the probability that the door may be opened without returning for another key?

16. Records kept by a town show that the probability that it rains on a single day is 0.35. If rain on different days constitutes independent events, find the probability that it:

a) Rains on both of two given days

b) Does not rain on either of two given days

c) Rains on exactly one of the two given days

17. The distribution of grades in a statistics class, at a University, have been $P(\text{Grade} = A) = 0.08$, $P(\text{Grade} = B) = 0.26$, $P(\text{Grade} = C) = 0.50$, $P(\text{Grade} = D) = 0.10$ and $P(\text{Grade} = F) = 0.06$.

a) What is the probability that a randomly selected student from such classes will get a grade of C or better?

b) Are the events: $E_1 = $ Passing the Statistics Class with a grade of C or better and $E_2 = $ Passing the Statistics Class with a grade of A Mutually Exclusive?

18. A single die is rolled 3 times. What is the probability that:

a) No sixes will occur

b) One six will occur

c) Two sixes will occur

d) Three sixes will occur

e) At least one six will occur?

19. Of the patients examined at the clinic, 0.20 had high blood pressure, 0.40 had excessive weight, and 0.10 had both.

a) If one of three patients is selected at random, what is the probability that he has at least one of these conditions?

b) Are the events: E_1 = Patient has high blood pressure, and E_2 = Patient has excessive weight independent or dependent? Justify answer.

20. At a certain college, students are required to take one Math and one English course. From past experience: P(Students receive A in the math course) = 0.15, P(Students receive A in the English course) = 0.10, and P(Students receive A in both courses) = 0.05. If a student is selected at random:

a) What is the probability that the student received an A on either Math or English or both?

b) What is the probability that the student received an A in English, given that he got an A in Math?

c) What is the probability that the student received an A in Math, given that he got an A in English?

21. The probability that a married man drinks tea is 0.4 and the probability that a married woman drinks tea is 0.6.

Assuming that the two events (MMDT and MWDT) are independent:

a) Find the probability that both drink tea.

b) Find the probability that the wife drinks tea, given that her husband drinks tea.

c) Find the probability that exactly one of them drinks tea.

d) Find the probability that neither one drinks tea.

22. The probabilities that a typist will make at most 5 mistakes when typing a report is 0.64 (*i.e.*, $P(NM \leq 5) = 0.64$) while the probability of making from 6 to 10 mistakes is 0.21 (*i.e.*, $P(6 \leq NM \leq 10) = 0.21$)

Find the probabilities that the typist will make:

a) At least six (6) mistakes

b) At most ten(10) mistakes

c) More than ten (10) mistakes

23. Suppose events A and B are known to be mutually exclusive, and it is also known that: $P(A) = 0.35$, and $P(B) = 0.4$. Find:

a) $P(\overline{A}) = P(A')$

b) $P(\overline{B}) = P(B')$

c) $P(A \cap B)$

d) $P(A \cup B)$

e) $P(\overline{A} \cap \overline{B}) = P(A' \cap B')$

f) $P(\overline{A} \cup \overline{B}) = P(A' \cup B')$

24. A consumer testing service is testing an antipollution device for cars and the probabilities that the device will be rated: poor, fair, good, very good and excellent are, respectively: P(poor) = 0.10, P(fair) = 0.20, P(good) = 0.30, P(very good) = 0.25, and P(excellent) = 0.15.

Find the probabilities that the testing service will rate the device as:

a) Poor or fair

b) At least good or better

c) At best good

d) Neither poor nor excellent

25. A businessman has two (2) secretaries, *A* and *B*. The probability that secretary *A* will be absent on any given date is 0.07, the probability that secretary *B* will be absent on any given date is 0.05, and the probability that both secretaries will be absent on any given day is 0.025. What is the probability that:

a) Either or both secretaries will be absent on any given day?

b) At least one secretary comes to work on any given day?

c) Only one secretary comes to work on any given day?

26. There are 60 applicants for a job at a television station. Some applicants are college graduates and some are not, and some have three or more years experience while others have less than three years of experience.

The exact breakdown is given by the table below:

	CollegeGraduates (*G*)	Not College Graduates (*G'*)	
At least 3 years experience (*T*)	12	6	n(AL3YE) = 18
Less than 3 years experience (*T'*)	24	18	n(LT3YE) = 42
	n(CG) = 36	n(NCG) = 24	

If the order in which the applicants are interviewed by the station managers is random, *G* is the event that the first applicant interviewed is a college graduate, and *T* is the event that the first applicant has at least three years' experience, find:

a) $P(G)$, b) $P(T)$, c) $P(G \cap T)$, d) $P(G' \cap T')$, e) $P(T/G)$, f) $P(G'/T')$

27. A bank manager has six male tellers and nine female tellers. If she selects two of them at random for special training, what are the probabilities that:

a) Both will be male

b) Both will be female

c) One male and one female

28. A Labor Union wage negotiator feels that the odds are 3 to 1 that the Union members will get a raise of 75 cents in their hourly wage, the odds are 15 to 5 against getting a raise of 50 cents in their hourly wage, and the odds are 7 to 3 against getting no raise at all.

a) Find the corresponding probabilities that they get a 75-cent raise, a 50-cent raise, or no raise at all.

b) What is the expected raise in their hourly wage?

29. Assuming that the ratio of male children is 1/2, find the probability that in a family of 6 children:

a) All 6 children will be of the same sex

b) The oldest 4 children will be boys and the 2 youngest will be girls

c) Five of the children will be boys and one will be a girl

30. A real estate developer has 8 basic designs, and on a given street he has 5 lots on which to build one of his houses.

a) If the community code does not permit look-alike houses on a given street, in how many different ways can the developer utilize his basic designs and still meet this restriction?

b) If there are no restrictions, how many arrangements are possible?

31. In order to function properly, an electrical device must have the two linked components, shown in the schematic, function properly, which can be accomplished if A functions and at least one of the two independently wired B components (B_1, B_2), must function.

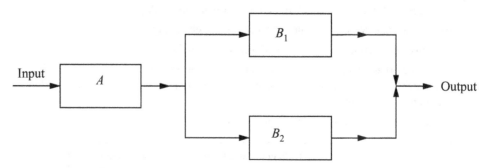

If the B_1, B_2 components function independently of each other and of A, and it is known that $P(A) = 0.9$, and $P(B_1) = P(B_2) = 0.8$, find the reliability (*i.e.*, probability of functioning) of the device.

32. A system consists of three main components A, B and C, which may be arranged in one of the four configurations shown below:

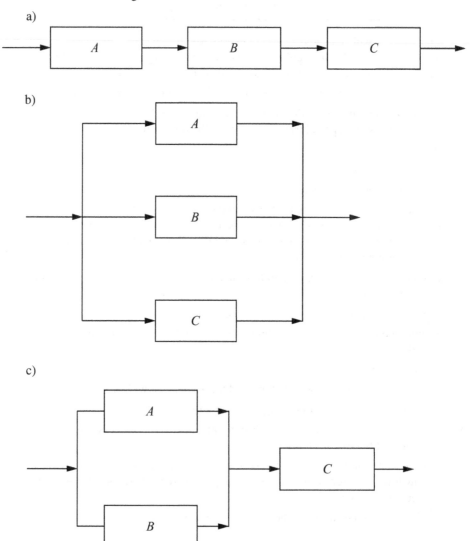

a)

b)

c)

d)

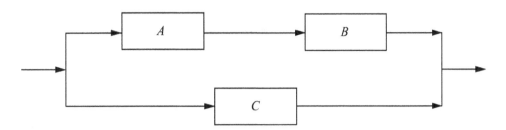

If the three components operate independently and the probability of each component operating is 0.95, determine the probability of system operation for each of the four configurations. Which one is the most reliable configuration?

33. A balanced coin is tossed ten times, and all the tosses produce heads. What is the probability of such an event? If the coin is indeed fair, what is the probability that the eleventh toss will be tails?

34. The employees of a company are divided into three distinct divisions: Administrative (*A*), Plant Operation (*PO*), and Sales (*S*), and the table shows the number of employees, in each division, according to their gender:

	Female (*F*)	Male (*M*)	Totals
Administrative (*A*)	20	30	50
Plant Operation (*PO*)	60	140	200
Sales (*S*)	100	50	150
Total	180	220	400

a) Are the events *PO* and *F* Mutually exclusive? Justify!

b) If an employee is chosen at random; find:
   i) P(Employee is Female)?
   ii) P(Employee works in Sales)?
   iii) P(Employee is male $\cap$ works in Administration)?
   iv) P(Employee works in *PO*/employee is Female)?
   v) P(Employee is Female/Employee works in *PO*)?

c) Are the events *S* and *M* statistically independent? Justify!

d) Are the events *A* and *F* statistically independent? Justify!

e) Determine the following Probabilities:

   i) $P(A \cup M)$; ii) $P(A \cup \overline{M})$; iii) $P(PO \cap F)$; iv) $P(M/A)$

35. A student has nine different textbooks, six of which are business books and the other three are humanities books.

a) If the student randomly picks one of the books to take home over the weekend, what is the probability that it will be:
   i) A Business book?
   ii) A Humanities book?

b) If the student randomly picks two of the books (without replacement) to take home, what is the probability that:
   i) Both will be Business books?
   ii) One will be a Business book and the other a Humanities book?
   iii) Both will be Humanities Books?

36. How many different permutations are there of the letters in the word "Statistics"?

37. Let C be the event that a certain missile will explode during lift-off and $P(C) = 0.03$, and let D be the event that the guidance system will fail in flight, and $P(D) = 0.03$, and the events C and D can be considered independent.

Find:

a) The probability that such a missile will not explode during lift-off.

b) The probability that such a missile will explode during lift-off or that its guidance system will fail in flight.

c) The probability that the missile neither will explode nor its guidance system fail in flight.

38. A real estate salesperson is negotiating the sale of two pieces of industrial property. If P(Selling the Smaller Property) $= 0.26$, P(Selling the Larger Property) $= 0.19$, and P(Selling both properties) $= 0.11$, find:

a) The probability that the salesperson will sell either one or both pieces of property.

b) The probability that the salesperson will sell neither of the two properties.

39. A box contains 12 shirts of which four have blemishes and eight do not.

If three shirts are randomly selected what is the probability that:

a) None of them will have blemishes

b) All will have blemishes

c) Two will have blemishes and the other will not

d) One will have blemishes and the other two will not

40. If Y is the event that a bond has a low yield (*i.e.*, effective interest rate) and R is the event that it has a high rating (*i.e.*, low risk), express in symbolic from the probabilities that:

a) A bond with a low yield will have a high rating

b) A bond with a high rating will have a low yield

c) A bond which does not have a high rating will have a low yield

d) A bond which does not have a low yield will not have a high rating

41. A box contains 50 slips of papers numbered from 1 to 50. If one of these slips of paper is drawn at random, what are the probabilities of getting a number which is:

a) Even

b) Greater than 35

c) Divisible by 12

42. A dental implant surgeon advised his patient that the tooth implant he is proposing has a probability of success p and only k attempts (where $k = 1, 2, 3, \ldots$) can be made to implant in the same tooth area, if the previous $k - 1$ attempts failed.

a) What is the probability of a successful implant after the first attempt?

b) What is the probability of a successful implant after the second attempt?

c) What is the probability of a failure after the second attempt?

d) What is the probability of a successful implant after k attempts?

e) What is the probability of a failed implant after a k attempts?

f) What are these probabilities if $p = 0.9$?

SOLUTIONS

1. The tree diagram is:

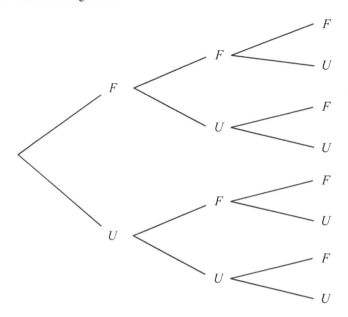

And the elements of the sample space are:

$F \cap F \cap F, F \cap F \cap U, F \cap U \cap F, F \cap U \cap U, U \cap F \cap F, U \cap F \cap U,$
$U \cap U \cap F, U \cap U \cap U$

2. Refer to the five investments as A, B, C, D, E and note that investment choices A, B and B, A are identical; then we have $(A, B), (A, C), (A, D), (A, E), (B, C), (B, D),$ $(B, E), (C, D), (C, E)$ and (D, E) which are the 10 unique choices. A tree-diagram can also be drawn to show these choices, but we must remember to eliminate choices which have already occurred when we do this.

3. The sample space $S = \{(H \cap E), (H \cap O), (T \cap E), (T \cap O)\}$ and events A and B are defined as $A = \{(T \cap E)\}$ and $B = \{(H \cap O)\}$

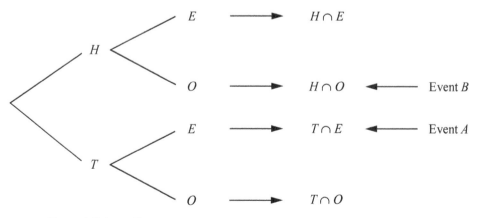

a) Since $A \cap B = \varnothing$, events A and B are Mutually Exclusive (*M.E.*)

b) Since $A \cup B \neq S$, events A and B are not Collectively Exhaustive (*C.E.*)

c) For two events A and B to form a Partition of the sample space, they must be both Mutually Exclusive and Collective Exhaustive. The events A and B are *M.E.* but they are not *C.E.*. Therefore, they do not form a Partition of the Sample Space

d) For the events A and B to be statistically independent, it is necessary that $P(A \cap B) = P(A)P(B)$. Here $P(A) = P(B) = 1/4$ but since $A \cap B = \emptyset$, $P(A \cap B) = 0/4 = 0$. Therefore, since $0 \neq (1/4)(1/4)$, events A and B are not independent (*i.e.*, they are dependent)

4. $P(A) + P(B) + P(C) = 1$; But $P(B) = 3P(C)$ and $P(A) = 4P(B)$, or $P(A) = 4[3P(C)] = 12P(C)$ Then: $12P(C) + 3P(C) + P(C) = 1$ or $P(C) = 1/16$; Then $P(B) = 3/16$ and $P(A) = 12/16$

5. a) Under the Classical Theory, $P(A) = P(B) = P(C) = 1/3$

   b) Under the Relative Frequency Theory,

   $P(A) = 2{,}500/10{,}000 = 0.25$

   $P(B) = 4{,}000/10{,}000 = 0.4$ and

   $P(C) = 3{,}500/10{,}000 = 0.35$

   c) Under the Personalistic Theory, $P(A) + P(B) + P(C) = 1$

   But $P(B) = 2P(A)$ or $P(A) = P(B)/2$ and $P(B) = 3P(C)$ or $P(C)=P(B)/3$

   Then $1/2P(B) + P(B) + 1/3\,P(B) = 1$ or $P(B)[1/2 + 1 + 1/3] = 1$ or

   $$P(B) = \frac{1}{(3+6+2)/6} = \frac{6}{11} \quad \text{Then} \quad P(A) = \frac{1}{2}P(B) = \frac{3}{11}$$

   and $\quad P(C) = \frac{1}{3}P(B) = \frac{2}{11}$

6.

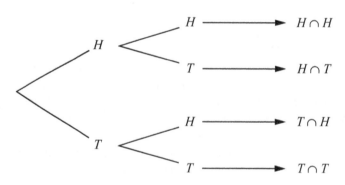

and the sample space, S, is $S=[(H \cap H), (H \cap T), (T \cap H), (T \cap T)]$

Also, $A = [(H \cap H), (H \cap T)]$ and $B = [(H \cap H), (T \cap T)]$,

and $P(A) = \frac{2}{4} = \frac{1}{2}$, and $P(B) = \frac{1}{2}$

Since $A \cap B = (H \cap H), P(A \cap B) = \frac{1}{4}$

Then, since $P(A \cap B) = \frac{1}{4} = P(A)P(B) = \left(\frac{1}{2}\right)\left(\frac{1}{2}\right)$

events A and B are independent.

7. $n(S) = \dfrac{10!}{5!5!} = 252$

   a) $P(5M \cap 0W) = \dfrac{n(5M \cap 0W)}{n(S)} = \dfrac{\left(\dfrac{6!}{5!1!}\right)x\left(\dfrac{4!}{0!4!}\right)}{252} = \dfrac{(6)(1)}{252} = \dfrac{6}{252}$

b) $P(4M \cap 1W) = \dfrac{n(4M \cap 1W)}{n(S)} = \dfrac{\left(\dfrac{6!}{4!2!}\right)x\left(\dfrac{4!}{1!3!}\right)}{252} = \dfrac{(15)(4)}{252} = \dfrac{60}{252}$

c) $P(3M \cap 2W) = \dfrac{n(3M \cap 2W)}{n(S)} = \dfrac{\left(\dfrac{6!}{3!3!}\right)x\left(\dfrac{6!}{2!2!}\right)}{252} = \dfrac{(20)(6)}{252} = \dfrac{120}{252}$

d) $P(2M \cap 3W) = \dfrac{n(2M \cap 3W)}{n(S)} = \dfrac{\left(\dfrac{6!}{2!4!}\right)x\left(\dfrac{4!}{3!1!}\right)}{252} = \dfrac{(15)(4)}{252} = \dfrac{60}{252}$

e) $P(1M \cap 4W) = \dfrac{\left(\dfrac{6!}{1!5!}\right)x\left(\dfrac{4!}{4!0!}\right)}{252} = \dfrac{(6)(1)}{252} = \dfrac{6}{252}$

f) $P(0M \cap 5W) = 0$ because, since there are only 4 women, you cannot choose 5.

8.

a) Sample space $S = \{(R \cap R), (R \cap G), (G \cap R), (G \cap G)\}$

b)

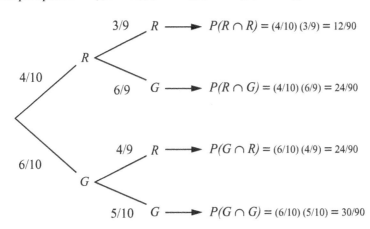

Then

i) $P(2$ Red balls$) = P(R \cap R) = 12/90$

ii) $P($Red, Green$) = P(R \cap G) = 24/90$

iii) $P($Green, Red$) = P(G \cap R) = 24/90$

iv) $P(2$ Green$) = P(G \cap G) = (6/10)(5/10) = 30/90$

v) Probability of Red and Green, regardless of which occurs first
   $= P(R \cap G) + P(G \cap R) = 24/90 + 24/90 = 48/90$

9. Probability of New Product is introduced

$= P($New Product is introduced/Slate A wins$) \times P($Slate A wins$)$

$+ P($New Product is introduced/Slate B wins$) \, P($Slate B wins$)$

$= P(N.P/A)P(A) + P(N.P/B)P(B)$

$= (0.8)(0.7) + (0.4)(0.3)$

$= 0.56 + 0.12$

$= 0.68$

10.

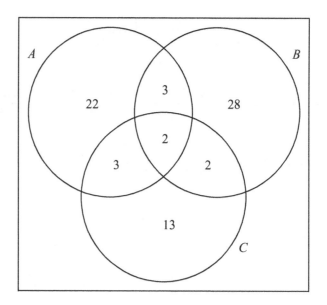

From the Venn Diagram we see that:

a) Number of Units with 3 defects $= 2$

b) Number of Units with 2 defects $= 3 + 3 + 2 = 8$

c) Number of Units with 1 defect $= 22 + 13 + 28 = 63$

d) Number of Units with no defects $= 1000 - (2 + 8 + 63) = 1000 - 73 = 927$

Then

   i) P (of units with one or more defects) $= 73/1000 = 0.073$

   ii) P (of units with exactly one defect) $= 63/1000 = 0.063$

   iii) P (of units with exactly two defects) $= 8/1000 = 0.008$

   iv) P (of units with no defects) $= 927/1000 = 0.927$

5 Random Variables and Probability Functions

The characteristics of the elements of a population are represented by random variables because these characteristics are not fixed but change from element to element.

The random variables can be either Discrete (if they can assume only a countable number of values in their interval of variation) or Continuous (if they can assume an infinite number of values in their interval of variation). Random variables are characterized by their distribution functions (which connect their possible values and their corresponding probabilities) which can be used to define and determine the important properties of random variables, such as their Expected Value, Median, Mode, Range, Variance, Standard Deviation, Coefficient of Skewness and Coefficient of Kurtosis.

In this chapter we show how random variables (both Discrete and Continuous) are analyzed, in general, while in chapter six and seven we show how specific Discrete and Continuous random variables are discussed and analyzed, respectively.

5.1 Introduction

As discussed earlier, a stochastic experiment terminates in an outcome which corresponds to a point in the Sample Space. For example, in a three-coin experiment the outcomes are: HHH, HHT, HTH, HTT, THH, THT, TTH, TTT, and the totality of these outcomes forms the Sample Space of the experiment. To proceed further with the development of probability we must decompose the Sample Space into mutually Exclusive subsets each of which can represent an event and with each of which we can associate a numerical value. If we assign a numerical value to the outcomes of an experiment, we find that we can do more analysis and gain better understanding of the processes under study. These observations lead us to consider:

1. Random Variables, and
2. Probability Distributions.

5.2 Random Variables and Probability Mass Function

Random Variables are functions or associations which assign a real value to the sample points of a stochastic experiment, with the assigned values being the values of the random variable.

Random Variables are symbolized by capital letters of the English Alphabet, most often by X, Y, Z, and their values by lower case letters, in their general representation.

If we let X represent the number of heads in a three-coin experiment, then X is a random Variable which transforms the sample points of the Sample Space S into the following numerical values:

Table 5.1 Numerical values of the Sample Space of the 3 coin Experiment							
	Sample Points						
S	HHH	HHT	HTH	HTT	THH	THT	TTH	TTT
X	3	2	3	1	2	1	1	0

The outcome of a random experiment determines a point in the Sample Space called the "domain" of the random variable (X), while the function or association $(Y = f(X))$ transforms each sample point to a set of real numbers which form the "range" of the random variable.

The Sample Space above with its eight points is the domain of the random variable X, while the values 0, 1, 2, and 3 are the range of X. They are also called the values of the random variable X. This random variable X is discrete because only few of the possible values in the range of X $(0 \leq X \leq 3)$ are possible. But random variables can also be continuous, if they assume all possible values in their stated ranges.

We shall first consider discrete variables and, after we have gained some familiarity with them, we will generalize the discussion and introduce and analyze continuous variables also.

Each value of a discrete random variable is an event and, as such, it must have a probability of occurrence associated with it. This association of probabilities with the various values of a discrete random variable is accomplished through a function called "probability function" or "probability mass function" or simply PMF(X).

Based on the above discussion we can state the following definition: "If X is a random variable which can assume the values $x_1, x_2, \ldots, x_n$ with associated probabilities $p_1, p_2, \ldots, p_n$, then the set of ordered pairs $(x_1, p_1), (x_2, p_2), \ldots, (x_n, p_n)$ is called a probability mass function (PMF) for the random variable X".

Obviously the probabilities $p_1, p_2, \ldots, p_n$ must satisfy the axioms of probability discussed in the previous chapter.

The PMF of a random variable can be represented either by a table or an equation. Usually it is relatively easy to go from an equation representation to a table representation. The converse may not be as simple.

Consider the following example

Example 1

"Roll two dice simultaneously, observe the two faces which show up, and let X be the random variable which represents the sum of the two numbers which show up". Find the PMF of X and represent it both as a table and as an equation.

Representing the Sample Space of this experiment as the two-dimensional space shown below, each dot is the geometric representation of the two numbers which form the intersection and their sum is our object of interest here. We note that the smallest value of X is the value of 2, which is found by adding 1 and 1. Since each sample point in the Sample Space has equal probability of occurrence and there are 36 such sample points, $P(X = 2) = 1/36$. Similarly the highest value of X is 12 (found by adding 6 and 6) with $P(X = 12) = 1/36$, since there is only one point in the Sample Space which can produce the sum of 12.

The value of $X = 3$ can be obtained in two distinct ways, namely:

Die 1 shows 1 and die 2 shows 2 or die 1 shows 2 and die 2 shows 1. Therefore, $P(X = 3) = P(1,2) + P(2,1) = 2/36$.

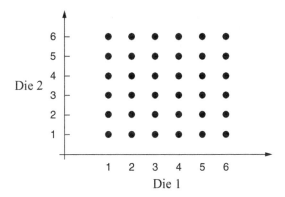

Figure 5.1 Sample Space of Example 1

Continuing in this way, we can find the probabilities which correspond to each value of X and which together with the values of X form the PMF of X shown in the table below:

Table 5.2 PMF of the Variable of Example 1											
X	2	3	4	5	6	7	8	9	10	11	12
$P(X)$	1/36	2/36	3/36	4/36	5/36	6/36	5/36	4/36	3/36	2/36	1/36

The same information is also included in the equation:

$$P(X = x) = \frac{6 - |x - 7|}{36} \tag{5.1}$$

with $\qquad\qquad x = 2, 3, 4, \ldots, 10, 11, 12$

and where $|\ \ |$ indicate the absolute value of the argument (*i.e.*, the expression within the two vertical lines).

Some additional information can be extracted by plotting $P(X)$ against X and noting the resulting symmetry (See Figure 5.2 below).

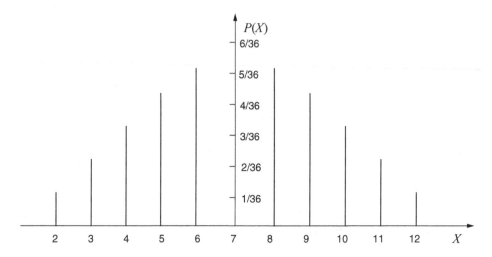

Figure 5.2 Plot of the PMF(X) of Example 1

The derivation of the equation for $P(X)$ (*i.e.*, Equation (5.1)) is somewhat complicated, and it is based on functional analysis and the symmetry of $P(X)$. The point we are trying to make here is that the PMF can be represented either as a table or as an equation. Whether the equation can be derived easily or not is another matter.

Requiring that the probabilities $p_1, p_2, \ldots, p_n$, associated with the values $x_1, x_2, \ldots, x_n$ of a random variable X, satisfy the axioms of probability gives rise to the following formal definition of a probability function:

A function of a discrete random variable X with **n** values $x_1, x_2, \ldots, x_n$ is a probability function if and only if:

1. $P(X = x_i) \geq 0$ for all values of X, and

2. $\displaystyle\sum_{i=1}^{n} P(X = x_i) = 1$ \qquad\qquad (5.2)

The PMFs of random variables can be, and are characterized in terms of Central Tendency, Dispersion, Skewness, and Peakedness, just like the sample data distributions we discussed in Descriptive Statistics. In what follows we will first discuss the "**Cumulative Distribution Function**" of a random variable X (or CDF(X)), a concept similar to the Cumulative Frequency of the sample data distributions and, then, we will discuss the measures of **Central Tendency, Dispersion, Skewness,** and **Peakedness** which are applicable to Random Variables. Since, at this point, we are mainly interested in introducing these concepts which are defined for any random variable X (discrete or continuous), we will do so by assuming that X is a discrete random variable. This approach will make it easier to discuss the various measures and their properties. After we gain familiarity with them, then a continuous random variable will be assumed, the necessary measures will be defined for it and our discussion will be complete.

5.3   Cumulative Distribution Function

The probability mass function (PMF) of a discrete random variable X gives rise to a function which provides probabilities that the random variable X will be less than or equal to a specified value x_0. We use the notation $P(X \leq x_0)$ to represent the probability that the random variable X takes a value which is less than or equal to the value x_0. This function is called the **Cumulative Distribution Function** of the random variable X (CDF(X)) and is found from the Probability Mass Function of X by appropriate summations. We will illustrate these calculations and the most important properties of CDF(X) through a specific example.

Let X be a discrete random variable with the probability mass function (PMF) given by Table 5.3 below and calculate and plot the CDF(X) as shown in Table 5.3 and Figure 5.3 respectively:

Table 5.3 PMF(X) and CDF(X) for a General Example		
X	$P(X)$	**CDF(X) = $P(X \leq x_k)$*** **(* Where k = 1, 2, 3, 4, 5)**
x_1	p_1	p_1
x_2	p_2	$p_1 + p_2$
x_3	p_3	$p_1 + p_2 + p_3$
x_4	p_4	$p_1 + p_2 + p_3 + p_4$
x_5	p_5	1

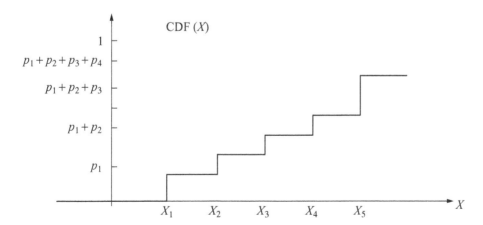

Figure 5.3   Plot of CDF(X) for a General Example

Clearly, $$\text{CDF}(X) = \text{Prob}(X \le x_k)^* = \sum_{i=1}^{k} p_i \qquad (5.3)$$

Note from the plot of CDF(X) that it is a step (stair-case) function and this is a characteristic of every CDF of a discrete random variable. In contrast to this, the CDF of a continuous random variable is a smooth function as we will see in our discussion of continuous random variables later. We list below some of the most important properties of CDF:

1. The CDF starts at zero and ends at 1 (*i.e.*, $0 \le \text{CDF}(X) \le 1$)
2. The CDF is a non-decreasing function. It may stay at the same level between two values of X but it never decreases. In general we say that:
   $\text{CDF}(X = a) \le \text{CDF}(X = b)$ if $a \le b$.
3. $\text{CDF}(-\infty) = 0$ and $\text{CDF}(+\infty) = 1$

5.4   Expected Value of a Random Variable

The Expected value of a random variable X, designated by $E(X)$, is the weighted average of the values that the random variable X can assume, with the probabilities with which these values occur being the weights.

According to this definition the expected value of the random variable X, whose PMF is given in table form in Section 5.3 above, is

$$E(X) = x_1 p_1 + x_2 p_2 + x_3 p_3 + x_4 p_4 + x_5 p_5 = \sum_{i=1}^{5} x_i p_i \qquad (5.4)$$

This definition is completely consistent with the sample average definition of:

$$\overline{X} = \frac{x_1 + x_2 + \cdots + x_n}{n} = \frac{\sum_{i=1}^{n} x_i}{n}$$

which we used in Chapter 3, because we can re-write $\overline{X}$ as $\overline{X} = \sum_{i=1}^{n} x_i \left(\frac{1}{n} \right)$; Then the

factor of $1/n$ corresponds to p_i. The factor $1/n$ shows that all of the sample values are weighted equally, while the possible values of a random variable are weighted according to their probability of occurrence.

$E(X)$ is a very basic property of the random variable and tells us where the "center of mass" for the random variable is. It is the average value of the variable when the experiment is repeated many times. The value of $E(X)$ need not be one of the values assumed by the random variable X, but it must be in the range of variation of X. Because all the possible values of the random variable are used in the calculation of the expected value of the random variable, $E(X)$ is equivalent to finding the average value of an entire population and, to be consistent with the notation we introduced earlier in this book, $E(X)$ can also be represented by μ. In fact the two notations will be used interchangeably (*i.e.*, $E(X) = \mu$).

The expected value of a random variable has many applications and is used in: Decision Theory, Game Theory, Systems Analysis, Management Science and any field that one may wish. As shown above it is found directly from the PMF by the construction of an additional column whose elements are the products of the X values times their corresponding probabilities and then by obtaining the summation of these products.

Using the general example of Section 5.3 above, we have.

Table 5.4 Calculation of $E(X)$

X	$P(X)$	$X \cdot P(X)$		X	$P(X)$	$X \cdot P(X)$
x_1	p_1	$x_1 p_1$		$x_1 = 1$	$p_1 = 0.1$	0.10
x_2	p_2	$x_2 p_2$	or, if we	$x_2 = 4$	$p_2 = 0.2$	0.80
x_3	p_3	$x_3 p_3$	substitute	$x_3 = 5$	$p_3 = 0.3$	1.50
x_4	p_4	$x_4 p_4$	numbers:	$x_4 = 8$	$p_4 = 0.3$	2.40
x_5	p_5	$x_5 p_5$		$x_5 = 10$	$p_5 = 0.1$	1.00
		$E(X) = \sum_{i=1}^{5} x_i p_i$				$E(X) = \sum_{i=1}^{5} x_i p(x_i) = 5.8$

Note: $E(X)$ **is also called the first moment of** X **about zero.** Other moments will be defined later.

The expected value and the variance which we will introduce below, are two members of a class of "Operators" which define certain operations to be performed on a random variable. Repeated use of these operators brought to light a number of useful properties which facilitate the calculations of the Expectation and the Variance of a Random Variable Y, from the corresponding Expectation and Variance of a random variable X, when X and Y are linearly related. These properties will be discussed in Section 5.6, after we first discuss the basic properties of the Variance Operator.

5.5   Variance of a Random Variable

The variance of a random variable X, represented by $V(X)$ or σ^2 (because it is a population variance, as explained above), tells us how closely the observations are about the mean, that is it provides a measure of spread or dispersion. It is defined by:

$$V(X) = \sigma^2 = E(X - \mu)^2 = \sum_{i=1}^{n} (x_i - \mu)^2 P(X = x_i) \qquad (5.5)$$

This formula represents the functional definition of variance but is not very convenient for computations. Another, more computationally convenient, formula can be obtained by replacing $(x_i - \mu)^2$ by its equivalent $x_i^2 - 2\mu x_i + \mu^2$, performing the Expectation Operations indicated, and recalling that $\mu = E(X)$ to obtain:

$$V(X) = \sigma^2 = E(X^2) - [E(X)]^2 = E(X^2) - \mu^2 \qquad (5.6)$$

This latest formulation makes the calculation of the variance of a random variable very easy. All one has to do is extend the PMF table one more column, beyond the one needed for the calculation of the Expected Value, to calculate $E(X^2)$ and then use the above formula.

Using the numerical example of the previous section we have:

X	P(X)	X · P(X)	X²P(X)
Table 5.5 Calculation of $E(X^2)$			
1	0.1	0.10	0.10
4	0.2	0.80	3.20
5	0.3	1.50	7.50
8	0.3	2.40	19.20
10	0.1	1.00	10.00
	1.0	$E(X) = 5.80$	$E(X^2) = 40.00$

Then $V(X) = E(X^2) - [E(X)]^2$

$$= 40.00 - (5.8)^2 = 40.00 - 33.64 = 6.36$$

Of course, once the variance is calculated, the standard deviation $\sigma(X)$ can be found as usual from

$$\sigma(X) = \sigma = \sqrt{V(X)} = \sqrt{6.36} \approx 2.52 \tag{5.7}$$

The definition formula for the variance, $V(X) = \sum_{i=1}^{n} (x_i - \mu)^2 P(X = x_i)$, is consistent with the variance formulation (biased) we gave in Chapter 3 for sampled data, namely

$$s^2 = \frac{1}{n} \sum_{i=1}^{n} \left(x_i - \overline{X}\right)^2 = \sum_{i=1}^{n} \left(x_i - \overline{X}\right)^2 \left(\frac{1}{n}\right)$$

In this formulation μ is replaced by $\overline{X}$ (which is the estimate of the mean available in a sampling study) and $P(X = x_i)$ has been replaced by $1/n$ (or $1/(n-1)$ if we use the Unbiased Variance definition) thus giving the same weight to all sample values.

Note: The variance $V(X)$, because of its definition, is also called the second moment of the random variable about its mean.

Together, the mean and the variance (or the standard deviation) contain a great deal of useful information concerning a population. The concept of the "Moments of a random variable either about zero or about its expected value" is very important because it will also be used to define the Skewness and Peakedness of a random variable. The variance operator, just like the Expectation Operator, has some useful properties which are used in the next section to find the Expected value and variance of another random variable Y, which is linearly related to the random variable X, from $E(X)$ and $V(X)$, which are assumed known (or can be calculated from the PMF of X).

5.6 Using the Expectation and Variance Operators

Suppose a random variable X has the PMF given in the example of the previous section, for which we calculated $E(X) = 5.8$ and $V(X) = 6.36$.

Further suppose that another random variable Y is defined as a linear function of the random variable X; i.e., $Y = a + bX$, where a and b are constants. The question that now arises is: How can we calculate $E(Y)$ and $V(Y)$ from the given information? There are two methods that we can use to answer this question.

Method 1

First derive the PMF of Y from the PMF of X and the linear relationship. Then use the definition of the Expectation and Variance to find $E(Y)$ and $V(Y)$. To simplify matters and to obtain a numerical answer for $E(Y)$ and $V(Y)$ let us suppose that $Y = a + bX = 5 + 2X$.

Clearly, as X takes the values 1, 4, 5, 8, 10, the random variable Y takes the values 7, 13, 15, 21, 25. These values are obtained from the equation $Y = 5 + 2X$ by successively substituting the X values 1, 4, 5, 8, 10 in it.

Also, since $Y = 7$ only when $X = 1$, it is obvious that $P(Y = 7) = P(X = 1) = 0.1$. Similarly we conclude that $P(Y = 13) = P(X = 4) = 0.2$, $P(Y = 15) = P(X = 5) = 0.3$, $P(Y = 21) = P(X = 8) = 0.3$, and $P(Y = 25) = P(X = 10) = 0.1$.

Since the PMF of a random variable consists of the ordered pairs formed by the values of the random variable and their corresponding probabilities, the PMF of Y is

Y	7	13	15	21	25
$P(Y)$	0.1	0.2	0.3	0.3	0.1

Now that the PMF of Y has been found, we can proceed to calculate $E(Y)$ and $V(Y)$ as follows:

Y	$P(Y)$	$Y \cdot P(Y)$	$Y^2 \cdot P(Y)$
7	0.1	0.7	4.9
13	0.2	2.6	33.8
15	0.3	4.5	67.5
21	0.3	6.3	132.3
25	0.1	2.5	62.5
	$\sum_{i=1}^{5} P(Y = y_i) = 1$	$E(Y) = \sum_{i=1}^{5} y_i\, P(Y = y_i) = 16.6$	$E(Y^2) = \sum_{i=1}^{5} y_i^2 P(Y = y_i) = 301$

Therefore $V(Y) = E(Y^2) - [E(Y)]^2 = 301.00 - 275.56 = 25.44$

Method 2

Apply the definitions of Expectation and Variance directly on the random variable Y, and then, within the summations, replace Y by its linear relationship involving the random variable X and perform the indicated summation operations.

$$E(Y) = \sum_{i=1}^{n} y_i\, P(Y = y_i) = \sum_{i=1}^{n} [a + bx_i]\, P(X = x_i)$$

$$= \sum_{i=1}^{n} aP(X = x_i) + \sum_{i=1}^{n} bx_i\, P(X = x_i)$$

$$= a\sum_{i=1}^{n} P(X = x_i) + b\sum_{i=1}^{n} x_i\, P(X = x_i)$$

But $\quad \sum_{i=1}^{n} P(X = x_i) = 1 \quad$ and $\quad \sum_{i=1}^{n} x_i P(X = x_i) = E(X)$

Therefore $\qquad\qquad\qquad E(Y) = a + bE(X)$ $\qquad\qquad$ (5.8)

Also
$$V(Y) = \sum_{i=1}^{n} [y_i - E(Y)]^2 \, P(Y = y_i)$$

$$= \sum_{i=1}^{n} \big[(a + bx_i) - (a + bE(X)) \big]^2 P(X = x_i), \text{ (using (5.8), and}$$

$$V(Y) = \sum_{i=1}^{n} [a + bx_i - a - bE(X)]^2 \, P(X = x_i)$$

$$= \sum_{i=1}^{n} [b(x_i - E(X))]^2 \, P(X = x_i)$$

$$= \sum_{i=1}^{n} b^2 [x_i - E(X)]^2 \, P(X = x_i)$$

$$= b^2 \sum_{i=1}^{n} [x_i - E(X)]^2 \, P(X = x_i)$$

Therefore $\hspace{4cm} V(Y) = b^2 V(X) \hspace{3cm}$ (5.9)

(since $V(X) = \sum_{i=1}^{n} \big[x_i - E(X) \big]^2 P(X = x_i)$)

In summary, we have shown that if $Y = a + bX$, where a and b are any constants, and X is a random variable with $E(X)$ and $V(X)$,

Then $\hspace{3cm} E(Y) = a + bE(X) \;\; \text{and} \;\; V(Y) = b^2 V(X)$

Therefore for the example above, where $Y = 5 + 2X$ and $E(X) = 5.8$ and $V(X) = 6.36$, we obtain:

$$E(Y) = 5 + 2E(X) = 5 + 2(5.8) = 5 + 11.6 = 16.6$$

$$V(Y) = b^2 V(X) = (2)^2 (6.36) = 4(6.36) = 25.44$$

Obviously the results are identical to those obtained earlier using the first method. But the second method, after the derivation of $E(Y)$ and $V(Y)$ which are always true for any two linearly related random variables, is much simpler because it only involves substitution and evaluation of two formulas.

We emphasize that the formulas $E(Y) = a + bE(X)$ and $V(Y) = b^2V(X)$ hold true only if $Y = a + bX$.

If the relationship between Y and X is non-linear the above formulas are not true, but corresponding formulas can be derived. However these formulas will be more complex and there may be no real advantage in using this approach over the direct method (*i.e.*, of finding the PMF of Y and then using it to find $E(Y)$ and $V(Y)$).

5.7 Standard Random Variables

The random variables which are usually encountered in real life have expected values which are different than zero and variances which are different than one. For example if P is a random variable which represents the yearly profit of a company for the last ten years, its expected value and variance will, in general, be different than zero and one, respectively.

As we will see in later chapters, it is much more convenient to work with a random variable whose expected value is equal to zero and its variance is equal to one. In some cases, for example when the random variable X is normally distributed with $E(X) \neq 0$ and $V(X) \neq 1$, it is not only a matter of convenience but a matter of necessity: *i.e.*, we must transform the variable X into another variable Z for which $E(Z) = 0$ and $V(Z) = 1$ or else we will not be able to calculate the required probabilities. Such random variables are called STANDARD RANDOM VARIABLES.

It is easy to standardize a random variable X with $E(X) = \mu \neq 0$ and $V(X) = \sigma^2 \neq 1$. We merely perform the linear transformation:

$$Z_i = \frac{X_i - \mu}{\sigma}, \tag{5.10}$$

that is from each value of X we subtract $\mu = E(X)$ and divide the difference by $\sigma(X) = \sigma = \sqrt{V(X)}$. The resulting Z_i numbers have an expected value of zero and variance of 1.

This can be shown to be true in general by noting that:

$$Z_i = \frac{X_i - \mu}{\sigma} = -\frac{\mu}{\sigma} + \frac{1}{\sigma}X_i$$
$$= a + bX_i$$

is a linear function of the random variable X_i for which $E(X_i) = \mu$ and $V(X_i) = \sigma^2$

Therefore, according to the formulas we derived in the previous section, we must have:

$$E(Z) = -\frac{\mu}{\sigma} + \frac{1}{\sigma}E(X_i) = -\frac{\mu}{\sigma} + \frac{1}{\sigma}(\mu) = 0$$

and

$$V(Z_i) = b^2 V(X_i) = \left(\frac{1}{\sigma}\right)^2 V(X_i) = \frac{1}{\sigma^2}(\sigma^2) = 1$$

Let us also standardize the random variable X, with the PMF shown below, to additionally illustrate the point.

X	$P(X)$	$XP(X)$	$X^2P(X)$	
3	1/3	1	3	Therefore:
6	1/3	2	12	$V(X) = E(X^2) - [E(X)]^2 = 42 - 36 = 6$
9	1/3	3	27	and $\sigma(X) = \sigma = \sqrt{6}$
		$E(X) = 6$	$E(X^2) = 42$	

Now let $Z_i = \dfrac{X_i - E(X)}{\sigma(X)} = \dfrac{X_i - 6}{\sqrt{6}}$

When the X_i values are substituted into $Z_i = \dfrac{X_i - 6}{\sqrt{6}}$, we obtain: $-3/\sqrt{6}$, 0,

$3/\sqrt{6}$ and therefore, we have the PMF for the random variable Z

Z	$P(Z)$	$ZP(X)$	$Z^2P(Z)$	
$-3/\sqrt{6}$	1/3	$-1/\sqrt{6}$	1/2	Therefore: $V(Z) = E(Z^2) - [E(Z)]^2 = 1 - 0 = 1$
0	1/3	0	0	
$3/\sqrt{6}$	1/3	$1/\sqrt{6}$	1/2	
		$E(Z) = 0$	$E(Z)^2 = 1$	

Clearly, the transformation $Z_i = \dfrac{X_i - 6}{\sqrt{6}}$ has "standardized" the random variable X because it changed it from one with $E(X) = 6 \neq 0$ and $V(X) = 6 \neq 1$ to another one with $E(Z) = 0$ and $V(Z) = 1$, which is precisely what a standardized variable is.

5.8 Chebychev's Inequality as Applied to Random Variables

To completely describe a random variable, we must know the PMF (or density function $f(X)$ in case of a continuous random variable) of the random variable under consideration. However, even if we only know $E(X)$ and $V(X)$ of a random variable X, some useful information about the probability distribution can be postulated. This information is provided by **Chebychev's Inequality** which had been stated as follows when applied to sample data: **"The proportion of the distribution, within K standard deviations from the mean (where $K > 1$), is at least $1 - 1/K^2$".**

When applied to a random variable X, with $E(X) = \mu$ and $V(X) = \sigma^2$, Chebychev's rule can be restated as: **"The probability that the random variable X is within K standard deviations from the mean, is at least $1 - 1/K^2$, where $K > 1$".** We can express this rule in the form of an equation and write:

$$P\left[\mu - K\sigma \leq X \leq \mu + K\sigma\right] \geq 1 - \frac{1}{K^2} \tag{5.11}$$

The assumptions required for the applicability of this rule are:

1. K is a positive number greater than 1 ($K > 1$)
2. μ and σ must both be finite.

The usefulness of the rule is based on the fact that this rule applies to any random variable with any type of PMF or density function $f(X)$. Therefore, because of this complete universality of the rule, the bounds provided by it are not very tight, as they are when the rule is constructed for a single distribution only, as for example the Empirical rule which we discussed in Chapter 3 and which applies only to the Normal distribution. But, even with these relatively "loose" bounds, the rule offers a substantial amount of information regarding the concentration and spread of a distribution.

We present an example below which illustrates the validity of the rule and also provides a method for computing the required bounds.

Suppose we use as an example the random variable X with the PMF that has been repeatedly used in previous sections, namely:

X	1	4	5	8	10
$P(X)$	0.1	0.2	0.3	0.3	0.1

for which $E(X) = \mu = 5.8$ and $\sigma(X) = \sigma = \sqrt{6.36} = 2.52$ as we showed in Section 5.5. Using these values form μ and σ, and allowing the multiplier K to assume the values 2 and 3, we get the following table:

K value	$\mu - K\sigma$	$\mu + K\sigma$	$P[\mu - K\sigma \leq X \leq \mu + K\sigma]$	$1 - \dfrac{1}{K^2}$
2	0.76	10.84	$P[0.76 \leq X \leq 10.84]$	0.75
3	−1.76	13.36	$P[-1.76 \leq X \leq 13.36]$	0.89

According to Chebychev's rule the probability that the random variable X is between 0.76 and 10.84 should be at least 0.75 and the probability that X is between −1.76 and 13.36 should be at least 0.89. Are these values satisfied by the given PMF? How do we check?

We merely sum up the probabilities between the given limits of X (for each K) in the PMF of X.

Clearly $P[0.76 \leq X \leq 10.84] = 1.00$, since this interval includes all of the X interval of variation as determined by its PMF where $1 \leq X \leq 10$.

Similarly $P[-1.76 \leq X \leq 13.36] = 1.00$ for the same reasons. Since both of these numbers are greater than the numbers specified by the rule (0.75 and 0.89 respectively) the rule is valid for this PMF. We can show, similarly, that it is valid for any type of PMF.

Note: The reason we make $K > 1$ is the fact that at $K = 1$, $1 - \dfrac{1}{K^2} = 0$ and stating that, $P[\mu - \sigma \leq X \leq \mu + \sigma] \geq 0$ conveys no information at all.

5.9   Additional Measures of Central Tendency and Dispersion

We have so far, in this chapter, learned how to calculate $E(X)$, $V(X)$, and $\sigma(X)$ for a discrete random variable X when its PMF is given. But, as we learned in Chapter 3 when analyzing sample data, there are many other measures of Central Tendency and Dispersion, such as: The Median, the Mode, the Range, the Average Absolute Deviation, the Interquartile Range, and the Interpercentile Range. All of these measures can be defined in terms of the PMF of the random variable X, some quite readily directly from the PMF table, while others use the PMF table and some additional calculations for their derivation. The mode and Range can be calculated directly from the PMF with very little additional work while the Average Absolute Deviation, Median, Interquartile and Interpercentile ranges require some additional work. We proceed by starting with the simpler ones first.

1. The Mode of a random variable X, X_m, is the value of the random variable, in its PMF table, with the highest probability of occurrence. It may or may not be unique. For example, the mode of the random variable X, with the following PMF.

X	1	4	5	8	10
$P(X)$	0.1	0.2	0.3	0.3	0.1

is not unique, because $X = 5$ and $X = 8$ both have probabilities of occurrence $= 0.3$. This is precisely the situation we encountered when analyzing sample data and, for the same reasons, the mode is not a very desirable measure.

2. The Range, R, is found from the usual formula $R = H - L$, where H and L are, respectively, the highest and smallest values of the random variable with probability of occurrence greater than zero. In the example above $H = 10$, because it is the highest X value with probability greater than zero, and $L = 1$ because it is the smallest X value with probability greater than zero.

Therefore $\qquad\qquad\qquad\qquad R = H - L = 10 - 1 = 9$

3. The Average Absolute Deviation, AAD, is defined by:

$$AAD = E(|X - \mu|) = \sum_{i=1}^{n} |x_i - \mu| P(X = x_i) \qquad (5.12)$$

It is obvious from this definition that to find AAD, we must first find $\mu = E(X)$, subtract it from each value of X, take absolute values, and then find $E(|X - \mu|)$.

Using the PMF above we obtain:

X	$P(X)$	$XP(X)$	$X - E(X)$	$|X - E(X)|$	$|X - E(X)|P(X)$
1	0.1	0.1	−4.8	4.8	0.48
4	0.2	0.8	−1.8	1.8	0.36
5	0.3	1.5	−0.8	0.8	0.24
8	0.3	2.4	2.2	2.2	0.66
10	0.1	1.0	4.2	4.2	0.42
		$E(X) = \mu = 5.8$			$E(|X - E(X)|) = 2.16$

4. For the calculation of the Median ($X_{0.5}$ or Q_2), the Quartiles (Q_1 and Q_3) and the percentiles (P_1, ..., P_{10}, ..., P_{25}, ..., P_{60}, ..., P_{99}, etc) we must first define the "Fractiles" of a random variable X:

Definition: A real number V is called an **f fractile** of the random variable X if the following two relationships are simultaneously true

$$P[X \leq V] \geq f \quad \text{and} \quad P[X \geq V] \geq 1 - f \qquad (5.13)$$

From this general definition, we proceed with the following specific definitions:
a) The Median of a random variable X is a value $V = X_{0.5}$, such that

$$P[X \leq X_{0.5}] \geq 0.5 \quad \text{and} \quad P[X \geq X_{0.5}] \geq 0.5 \qquad (5.14)$$

(where $f = 0.5$ and $1 - f = 0.5$ in the above general definition)
b) The Quartiles, $Q1$ and $Q3$, are defined by:

For Q_1: $P[X \leq Q_1] \geq 0.25 \quad \text{and} \quad P[X \geq Q_1] \geq 0.75 \qquad (5.15)$

For Q_3: $P[X \leq Q_3] \geq 0.75 \quad \text{and} \quad P[X \geq Q_3] \geq 0.25 \qquad (5.16)$

c) In a similar manner we can define any of the percentiles.
   For example:

$$P_{10}: \quad P[X \leq P_{10}] \geq 0.10 \quad \text{and} \quad P[X \geq P_{10}] \geq 0.90 \tag{5.17}$$

$$P_{90}: \quad P[X \leq P_{90}] \geq 0.90 \quad \text{and} \quad P[X \geq P_{90}] \geq 0.10 \tag{5.18}$$

Once the Quartiles and Percentiles have been defined, we can calculate the Interquartile and Interpercentile ranges from:

$$\text{IQR} = Q_3 - Q_1 \tag{5.19}$$

$$\text{IPR} = P_{75} - P_{25} \tag{5.20}$$

and it is obvious from these definitions that IQR = IPR

Example 2

Suppose we flip a coin 3 times, and let X be the random variable which counts the number of heads which can occur. Then the PMF of the random variable X is:

X	0	1	2	3
$P(X)$	1/8	3/8	3/8	1/8

Find $X_{0.5}$, Q_1, Q_3, and IQR.

To find each of these measures we need to select sequentially every value of the random variable X, and see whether the corresponding 2 equations of its definition are satisfied.

Calculating the median $X_{0.5} = Q_2$

Question: **Is $X = 0$ a median?** Since $P(X \leq 0) = \dfrac{1}{8} < 0.5$,

$X = 0$ is not a median value.

Is $X = 1$ a median? Since $P(X \leq 1) = \dfrac{4}{8} = 0.5$ and

$P(X \geq 1) = \dfrac{7}{8} > 0.5$,

$X = 1$ is a median value!

Is $X = 2$ a median value? Since $P(X \leq 2) = \dfrac{7}{8} > 0.5$ and

$P(X \geq 2) = \dfrac{4}{8} = 0.5$, $X = 2$ is also a median value.

Is $X = 3$ a median value? Since $P(X \leq 3) = 1 > 0.5$ but

$P(X \geq 3) = \dfrac{1}{8} < 0.5$, the value $X = 3$ is not a median value.

Conclusion: The median may or may not be unique. Whether it is or not depends on the experiment. For example, if the coin had been flipped 4 times instead of 3, in the resulting PMF the value of $X = 2$ would be a unique median value.

If the median is not unique, then there is an infinite number of median values because any value between the two median values (for example $X = 1.5$ in this case) is also a median.

Calculating Q_1

Question: **Is $X = 0$ a Q_1 value?** Since $P(X \leq 0) = \dfrac{1}{8} = 0.125 < 0.25$, $X = 0$ is not a Q_1 value.

Is $X = 1$ a Q_1 value? Since $P(X \leq 1) = \dfrac{4}{8} = 0.5 > 0.25$ and

$$P(X \geq 1) = \frac{7}{8} = 0.875 > 0.75, X = \textbf{1 is a } Q_1 \textbf{ value}$$

Is $X = 2$ a Q_1 value? Since $P(X \leq 2) = \frac{7}{8} = 0.875 > 0.25$ and

$$P(X \geq 2) = \frac{4}{8} = 0.5 < 0.75, X = 2 \text{ is not a } Q_1 \text{ value. Therefore}$$

$Q_1 = 1$ is a unique Q_1 value for this experiment, because $X = 3$ does not meet the criteria either.

Calculating Q_3

Question: Is $X = 0$ a Q_3 value? Since $P(X \leq 0) = 0.125 < 0.75$,

$X = 0$ is not a Q_3 value.

Is $X = 1$ a Q_3 value? Since $P(X \leq 1) = 0.5 < 0.75$, $X = 1$ is not a Q_3 value

Is $X = 2$ a Q_3 value? Since $P(X \leq 2) = 0.875 > 0.75$ and

$P(X \geq 2) = 0.5 > 0.25$, $X = 2$ is a Q_3 value, and it is unique since $X = 3$ does not meet the criteria.

Therefore, IQR $= Q_3 - Q_1 = 2 - 1 = 1$

In a similar manner we can calculate all the percentiles of interest.

All of the fractiles can also be calculated approximately from the graph of the CDF of X. The more care we take in plotting the CDF, the better the approximations will be.

5.10   Moments of a Random Variable

When we developed the formula for $E(X)$, we also referred to it as the "First moment of the random variable X about zero" and called the Variance $V(X)$ as the "Second moment of the random variable about its mean (or Expected Value)".

In general "Moments" are Expectations of different powers of the random variable X. Usually there are two types of moments:

1. Moments about zero, and
2. Moments about the mean (Expected Value),

even though moments can be defined about any fixed point in addition to zero and/or the expected value.

1. Moments about zero are defined as:

$$E(X^k) = \sum_{i=1}^{n} x_i^k \, P(X = x_i) \tag{5.21}$$

where k is any positive integer greater than or equal to 1 ($k \geq 1$)
In particular, when $K = 1$, we obtain:

$$E(X) = \sum_{i=1}^{n} x_i \, P(X = x_i) \tag{5.22}$$

which is the usual definition of the Expected value of the random variable X and this also explains why we referred to $E(X)$ as the first moment of the random variable X about zero.

2. Moments about the mean are defined as:

$$E\left[(X - \mu)^k\right] = \sum_{i=1}^{n}(x_i - \mu)^k \, P(X = x_i) \qquad (5.23)$$

where K is again a positive integer greater or equal to 1 ($K \geq 1$)
In particular, when $k = 2$, we obtain:

$$E\left[(X - \mu)^2\right] = \sum_{i=1}^{n}(x_i - \mu)^2 P(X = x_i) \qquad (5.24)$$

which is precisely the definition of the Variance of a random variable X and explains the reason for calling $V(X)$ the second moment of the random variable X about its mean.

We have defined the moments because we intend to use the second, third and fourth **"Central Moments"** (as the moments about the mean are usually called) to define the coefficients of Skewness (S_{KP}) and the coefficient of Kurtosis (K) of a random variable. We should recall here our discussion of sample data analysis of Chapter 3 where we emphasized that, in addition to the sample mean and sample variance, a measure of Skewness and Kurtosis were needed to completely define a data set. The same thing is true for Random Variables. Besides $E(X)$ and $V(X)$ the PMF of a random variable X is characterized by its degree of Skewness and Peakedness (Kurtosis), which we discuss below:

3. **The Coefficient of Skewness is defined as:** $S_{KP} = \dfrac{\mu_3}{\sigma_3}$ \qquad (5.25)

where

$$\mu_3 = E\left[(X - \mu)^3\right] = \sum_{i=l}^{n}(x_i - \mu)^3 \, P(X = x_i) \text{ is the third Central Moment} \quad (5.26)$$

and

$$\sigma^3 = [\sigma]^3 = \left[\sqrt{V(X)}\right]^3, \text{ where } V(X) = \mu_2 \text{ is the second Central Moment} \quad (5.27)$$

We have already shown how $V(X)$ can be calculated for a random variable X, when its PMF is given and, therefore, how the standard deviation of X can be obtained.

We show below, in Table 5.6, how the PMF of X can be used to find μ_3 (*i.e.*, the third Central Moment of X and, consequently, any Central Moment) before we interpret the meaning of the resulting values of S_{KP}. A similar procedure will be followed in our discussion of Peakedness (Kurtosis).

Table 5.6 The Calculation of μ, μ_3, and μ_4 for a Discrete Variable

1	2	3	4	5	6	7	8
X	$P(X)$	$XP(X)$	$X - \mu$	$(X - \mu)^3$	$(X - \mu)^3 P(X)$	$(X - \mu)^4$	$(X - \mu)^4 P(X)$
x_1	p_1	$x_1 p_1$	$x_1 - \mu$	$(x_1 - \mu)^3$	$(x_1 - \mu)^3 p_1$	$(x_1 - \mu)^4$	$(x_1 - \mu)^4 p_1$
x_2	p_2	$x_2 p_2$	$x_2 - \mu$	$(x_2 - \mu)^3$	$(x_2 - \mu)^3 p_1$	$(x_2 - \mu)^4$	$(x_2 - \mu)^4 p_2$
.	.	.	.	.	.	.	.
.	.	.	.	.	.	.	.
x_n	p_n	$x_n p_n$	$x_n - \mu$	$(x_n - \mu)^3$	$(x_n - \mu)^3 p_n$	$(x_n - \mu)^4$	$(x_n - \mu)^4 p_n$
$\sum_{i=1}^{n} P(X = x_i) = 1$	$E(X) = \sum_{i=1}^{n} x_i P(X = x_i)$ $= \mu$				$\mu_3 = \Sigma(x_i - \mu)^3 P(X = x_i)$		$\mu_4 = \sum_{i=1}^{n}(x_i - \mu)^4 P(X = x_i)$

Columns 1 and 2 of the table above represent the PMF of the random variable X. Column 3 shows the calculation of $E(X) = \mu$, which is used to form column 4 by subtracting μ from each value of X. Column 5 is formed by raising each element of column 4 to the 3rd power. Column 6 is then formed by multiplying the elements of column 2 by the corresponding elements of column 5. The sum of the elements of column 6 is the third Central Moment, μ_3.

Because the exponent 3 is odd, the elements of column 5 can be: positive (if $X_i - \mu > 0$), negative (if $X_i - \mu < 0$), or zero (if $X_i - \mu = 0$).

Therefore, since the elements of column 2 are always positive (because of the axioms of probability), the elements of column 6 can be positive, negative, or zero, and the same thing can be said about μ_3, the third Central Moment of the random variable X, which is the summation of the elements of column 6.

In other words, the range of variation of μ_3 is from $-\infty$ to $+\infty$, and we attach the following interpretation, regarding symmetry or lack of symmetry, to the distribution of the random variable X.

$$\text{if: } \mu = E\left[(X - \mu)^3\right] = \begin{cases} > 0, \text{ the distribution of the random variable is positively skewed (Long Right Tail, skewed to the right)} \\ \\ = 0, \text{ the distribution is symmetric about } \mu \\ \\ < 0, \text{ the distribution of the random variable is negatively skewed (Long Left Tail, skewed to the left)} \end{cases}$$

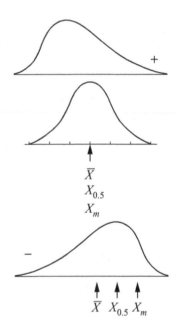

Unfortunately, μ_3 by itself is a poor measure for Skewness because it depends on the original units of measurement of X, which are now raised to the third power. What is needed is a measure which does not depend on the units, and such a measure is provided by S_{KP} which is merely the ratio of μ_3 to σ^3. Since both μ_3 and σ^3 have the same units, S_{KP} will be a pure (unitless) ratio, with the sign of S_{KP} being determined from the sign of μ_3 since σ^3 is always positive (the standard deviation $\sigma = +\sqrt{V(X)}$, and $V(X)$ is always positive).

The following interpretation is made to the calculated S_{KP} values:

1. If $S_{KP} = \pm 1$, the distribution of the random variable is highly skewed (positively if $S_{KP} = +1$, negatively if $S_{KP} = -1$).

2. If $0.5 \le S_{KP} < 1$ or $-1 < S_{KP} \le -0.5$, then the distribution is moderately skewed.

3. If $-0,5 \le S_{KP} \le 0.5$, the distribution is nearly symmetric.

4. **The Coefficient of Kurtosis (Peakedness) is defined as**

$$K = \frac{\mu_4}{\sigma^4},\tag{5.28}$$

where
$$\mu_4 = E\left[(X - \mu)^4\right] = \sum_{i=1}^{n}(x_i - \mu)^4\, P(X = x_i)\tag{5.29}$$

is the fourth Central Moment

and
$$\sigma^4 = \left(\sigma^2\right)^2 = (V(X))^2 = \mu_2^2\tag{5.30}$$

is the second Central Moment, μ_2, squared.

Since μ_4 and σ^4 are always positive, the value of K will always be positive. Note that the measure selected to represent the Peakedness of the distribution of a random variable is also a ratio (as was the case with the Skewness measure) and its selection was made for the same reason, namely to have a measure which does not depend on the units of measurement of the values of the random variable.

The calculation of the value of μ_4 was shown above and, since we already know how to calculate the variance, the value of K can be determined. The following interpretation is made to the calculated K values.

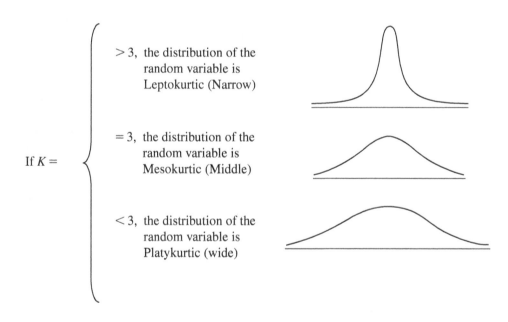

If $K =$

> 3, the distribution of the random variable is Leptokurtic (Narrow)

$= 3$, the distribution of the random variable is Mesokurtic (Middle)

< 3, the distribution of the random variable is Platykurtic (wide)

At this point we have finished with the introduction of the basic properties of discrete random variables. In the next section we will develop the corresponding properties of continuous random variables, in general. In Chapter 6 we will introduce and discuss random variables with specifically named discrete distributions (such as the Binomial, Poisson, Hypergeometric, etc.), while in Chapter 7 we will study Specific distributions of Continuous random variables (such as the Normal, Exponential, Uniform, etc.)

5.11   Continuous Random Variables

Not all of the random variables of interest are discrete. Indeed many real-life variables (such as: the height of male adults, the life of an electronic device, the arrival of a train in a station, etc.) are continuous random variables because the random variable of interest can assume all possible values in its interval of variation, in contrast to the discrete random variables which can assume only some of the possible values in their interval of variation.

Continuous variables are defined in terms of their density functions, represented by $f(X)$ for a random variable X, which are equations defined for all values of X in the internal of variation. As stated in previous chapters, events are now defined by intervals in continuous sample spaces (as opposed to a collection of sample points in discrete sample spaces) and their probabilities are found by integration of their density function between two appropriate limits. Other than these differences discrete and continuous random variables are very similar and are characterized by the same measures of Central Location, Dispersion, Skewness, and Peakedness.

Usually most students in a Business Curriculum find the discussion of continuous variables more difficult because of their fear of integral calculus. There is no need to be afraid. We have already discussed the basic elements of integral calculus in **Appendix B** and an example will be presented shortly which will highlight the required calculations. But it is important to understand that the discussion of continuous random variables is essential in the understanding of statistics and the use of statistical tables, usually found in any statistics book, because many real-life phenomena are described by continuous random variables obeying some of the more widely known density functions such as: Normal, Exponential, Uniform, Chi-square, Student-t, F, *etc.*, and the calculation of probabilities, using these density functions, require some form of Integration (*i.e.*, either *analytical integration* using the *indefinite integral*, or *numerical integration* using *statistical tables*).

Table 5.7 shows the formulas used in calculating the most important properties of a discrete random variable X with a given PMF and the corresponding formulas needed to calculate the same properties for a continuous random variable X obeying the density function $f(X)$.

The internal of variation for the continuous variable X will be assumed to be from $-\infty$ to $+\infty$ ($-\infty < X < +\infty$)unless otherwise specified.

We have already shown in previous sections of this chapter how the required calculations for a discrete random variable are performed. We now give an example to illustrate the appropriate calculations associated with a continuous random variable.

Table 5.7 Comparison of the Properties for Discrete and Continuous Variables

I) **Discrete Random Variables**	II) **Continuous Random Variables**
1. Defined in terms of their PMF	1. Defined in terms of their density function, $f(x)$. For example:

X	x_1	x_2	...	x_n
$P(X)$	p_1	p_2	...	p_n

$$f(X = x) = \left(\tfrac{3}{112}\right)x \quad 4 \le x \le 16$$

2. The PMF is proper if:

a) $0 \le P(X = x_i) \le 1$

b) $\displaystyle\sum_{i=1}^{n} P(X = x_i) = 1$

2. The density function is proper if:

a) $0 < P(a < X < b) = \displaystyle\int_a^b f(x)dx < 1$, for any

   a, b that such $a < b$

b) $P(-\infty < X < \infty) = \displaystyle\int_{-\infty}^{\infty} f(x)dx = 1$

3. $\text{CDF}(X) = \displaystyle\sum_{i=1}^{x_0} P_i = \text{Prob}\,(X \le x_0)$

3. $\text{CDF}(X) = \text{Prob}(X \le x_0) = \displaystyle\int_{-\infty}^{x_0} f(x)dx$

4. $E(X) = \displaystyle\sum_{i=1}^{n} x_i P(X = x_i) = \mu$

4. $E(X) = \displaystyle\int_{-\infty}^{\infty} x f(x)dx = \mu$

5. $E(X^2) = \displaystyle\sum_{i=1}^{n} x_i^2 P(X = x_i)$

5. $E(X^2) = \displaystyle\int_{-\infty}^{\infty} x^2 f(x)dx$

6. $V(X) = E(X^2) - \left[E(X)\right]^2 = \sigma^2$

6. $V(X) = E(X^2) - \left[E(X)\right]^2 = \sigma^2$

7. $\sigma(X) = \sqrt{V(X)} = \sigma$

7. $\sigma(X) = \sqrt{V(X)} = \sigma$

8. $\mu_3 = E\left[(X - \mu)^3\right] = \displaystyle\sum_{i=1}^{n} (x_i - \mu)^3 P(X = x_i)$

8. $\mu_3 = E\left[(X - \mu)^3\right] = \displaystyle\int_{-\infty}^{\infty} (x - \mu)^3 f(x)dx$

9. $\mu_4 = E\left[(X - \mu)^4\right] = \displaystyle\sum_{i=1}^{n} (x_i - \mu)^4 P(X = x_i)$

9. $\mu_4 = E\left[(X - \mu)^4\right] = \displaystyle\int_{-\infty}^{\infty} (x - \mu)^4 f(x)dx$

10. $\text{Prob}(x_a < X < x_b) = \displaystyle\sum_{i=x_{a+1}}^{x_{b-1}} P(X = x_i)$

10. $P(a < X < b) = \displaystyle\int_a^b f(x)dx$

11. $\text{Prob}(x_a \le X \le x_b) = \displaystyle\sum_{i=x_a}^{x_b} P(X = x_i)$

11. $P(a \le X \le b) = \displaystyle\int_a^b f(x)dx$

Example 3

Let $f(X = x) = Ax^{1/2}, 0 \le x \le 16$, be the density function and interval of variation of a continuous random variable X.

1. Determine the value of the multiplier A so that $f(x)$ is a proper probability density function.
2. Find and plot CDF (X)
3. Find $E(X)$ and $E(X^2)$
4. Find $V(X)$ and $\sigma(X)$
5. Find $P(4 \le X \le 9)$
6. Find μ_3 and μ_4
7. Find the Mode and the Range
8. Find the Quartiles and Percentiles.

Solutions

1. For $f(x)$ to be proper $\int_{-\infty}^{\infty} f(x)dx = \int_{0}^{16} f(x)dx = 1.$

   Substituting for $f(x)$ we have:

   $$\int_{0}^{16} Ax^{1/2}dx = A\int_{0}^{16} x^{1/2}dx = A\frac{x^{3/2}}{3/2}\bigg|_{0}^{16} = \frac{2}{3}Ax^{3/2}\bigg|_{0}^{16} = \frac{2}{3}A\big[16^{3/2} - 0^{3/2}\big]$$

   $$= \frac{2}{3}A\big[(4^2)^{3/2} - 0\big] = \frac{2}{3}A(4^3) = \frac{2}{3}(64)A = \frac{128}{3}A$$

   Since the value of this integral must be equal to 1 for the density function to be proper, we must have

   $$\frac{128}{3}A = 1, \text{ from which } A = \frac{3}{128}$$

   Therefore, the proper density function is

   $$f(x) = \frac{3}{128}x^{1/2} \quad 0 \le x \le 16$$

2. By definition:

   $$\text{CDF}(X) = \int_{-\infty}^{x_0} f(x)dx = \frac{3}{128}\int_{0}^{x_0} x^{1/2}dx = \frac{3}{128}\frac{x^{3/2}}{3/2}\bigg|_{0}^{x_0}$$

   $$= \frac{3}{128}\frac{2}{3}x^{3/2}\bigg|_{0}^{x_0} = \frac{1}{64}\big(x_0^{3/2} - 0^2\big)$$

   $$= \frac{1}{64}x_0^{3/2}$$

By letting $x_0 = 0,1,4,9,12,14,16$ and substituting in the formula above we find:

$$\text{CDF}(0) = 0$$
$$\text{CDF}(1) = \frac{1}{64} = 0.015625$$
$$\text{CDF}(4) = \frac{8}{64} = 0.125$$
$$\text{CDF}(9) = \frac{27}{64} = 0.421875$$
$$\text{CDF}(12) = 0.649519$$
$$\text{CDF}(14) = 0.818487$$
$$\text{CDF}(16) = 1$$

CDF (X)

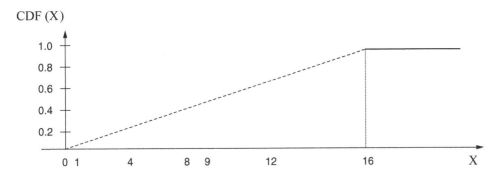

Figure 5.4 CDF(X) of $f(x) = \dfrac{3}{128}x^{1/2}$; $0 \le x \le 16$

Notice that the CDF of a continuous random variable is smooth in contrast to the CDF of a discrete random variable which has many discontinuity points and looks like a staircase.

The smooth CDF is usually taken as the identifying characteristic of a continuous random variable.

3. By definition: $E(X) = \displaystyle\int_{-\infty}^{\infty} xf(x)dx = \int_{0}^{16} x\left[\frac{3}{128}x^{1/2}\right]dx$

$$= \frac{3}{128}\int_{0}^{16} x^{3/2}dx = \frac{3}{128}\frac{x^{5/2}}{5/2}\bigg|_{0}^{16}$$

$$= \frac{3}{128}\frac{2}{5}x^{5/2}\bigg|_{0}^{16} = \frac{3}{320}\left[(16)^{5/2} - 0\right]$$

$$= \frac{3}{320}\left[(4^2)^{5/2}\right] = \frac{3}{320}(4)^5 = \frac{3 \times (16 \times 64)}{2 \times 10 \times 16}$$

$$= \frac{96}{10} = \frac{48}{5} = 9.6$$

4. By definition: $E(X^2) = \int_{-\infty}^{\infty} x^2 f(x)dx = \int_0^{16} x^2\left[\frac{3}{128}x^{1/2}\right]dx$

$$= \frac{3}{128}\int_0^{16} x^{5/2}dx = \frac{3}{128}\frac{x^{7/2}}{7/2}\Big|_0^{16}$$

$$= \frac{3}{64 \times 7}(16)^{7/2}$$

$$= \frac{3}{64 \times 7}\left[(4^2)^{7/2}\right] = \frac{3}{64 \times 7}(4)^7 = \frac{3 \times (4^3 \times 4^4)}{4^3 \times 7}$$

$$= \frac{3 \times 4^4}{7} = \frac{3}{7}(256) \approx 3(36.57) \approx 109.71$$

5. By definition: $V(X) = \sigma^2 = E(X^2) - [E(X)]^2$

$$= 109.71 - (9.6)^2$$

$$= 109.71 - 92.16 = 17.55$$

$$\sigma(X) = \sigma = \sqrt{V(X)} = \sqrt{17.55} \approx 4.185$$

6. $P(4 \le X \le 9) = P(4 < X < 9) = \int_4^9 f(x)dx = \int_4^9 \frac{3}{128}x^{1/2}dx$

$$= \frac{3}{128}\frac{2}{3}x^{3/2}\Big|_4^9 = \frac{1}{64}\left[9^{3/2} - 4^{3/2}\right]$$

$$= \frac{1}{64}\left[(3^2)^{3/2} - (2^2)^{3/2}\right] = \frac{1}{64}[3^3 - 2^3]$$

$$= \frac{1}{64}(27 - 8) = \frac{19}{64}$$

Note: $P(4 \le X \le 9) = P(4 < X < 9)$. This is true only if the random variable X is continuous and does not hold true for discrete variables. This is true for continuous random variables because the number of points in the interval is infinite and $P(X = 4) = 1/\infty = 0$, since there is only one point on the line where $X = 4$.

The other observation that we can make at this point is that:

$$P(4 \le X \le 9) = P(X \le 9) - P(X \le 4)$$

$$= \text{CDF}(9) - \text{CDF}(4)$$

$$= \frac{27}{64} - \frac{8}{64} = \frac{19}{64},$$

and this result agrees with the calculation above. We can generalize this conclusion by saying that we can find the probability between any two points in the interval of variation of the random variable by subtracting the CDF values at the corresponding points.

Therefore: $P(x_i < X < x_j) = \text{CDF}(x_j) - \text{CDF}(x_i)$ where $x_i < x_j$ (5.31)

7. To calculate μ_3 and μ_4, we first note that

$$(x - \mu)^3 = x^3 - 3\mu x^2 + 3\mu^2 x - \mu^3$$

and

$$(x - \mu)^4 = x^4 - 4\mu x^3 + 6\mu^2 x^2 - 4\mu^3 x + \mu^4$$

Therefore, we can write:

$$\mu_3 = \int_{-\infty}^{\infty} (x - \mu)^3 f(x) dx = \int_{-\infty}^{\infty} x^3 f(x) dx - 3\mu \int_{-\infty}^{\infty} x^2 f(x) dx$$

$$+ 3\mu^2 \int_{-\infty}^{\infty} x f(x) - \mu^3 \int_{-\infty}^{\infty} f(x) dx \tag{5.32}$$

$$\mu_4 = \int_{-\infty}^{\infty} (x - \mu)^4 f(x) dx = \int_{-\infty}^{\infty} x^4 f(x) dx - 4\mu \int_{-\infty}^{\infty} x^3 f(x) dx$$

$$+ 6\mu^2 \int_{-\infty}^{\infty} x^2 f(x) dx - 4\mu^3 \int_{-\infty}^{\infty} x f(x) dx + \mu^4 \int_{-\infty}^{\infty} f(x) dx \tag{5.33}$$

But since $\int_{-\infty}^{\infty} f(x) dx = 1$, as per the probability axiom, the last integrals in the μ_3 and μ_4 expressions can be replaced by 1.

The other integrals can be evaluated in accordance with the work we have already done. We merely substitute the given $f(x)$, multiply by the corresponding x power $\left(x^4, x^3, x^2, x\right)$ and then use the appropriate integration formula.

Note: Only four integrals need to be evaluated to calculate μ_3 and μ_4. This is so because three of the integrals are common to both μ_3 and μ_4 expressions.

8. **Calculating the Mode and Range**

   The Mode is defined as the value of the random variable X, in its interval of variation, for which $f(x)$ attains its highest value. Plotting $f(x)$ can aid considerably in this effort. By inspection of this $f(x)$ its highest value occurs when $x = 16$. Therefore, the Mode is $= 16$.

   The Range is defined as usual by: $R = H - L$, where H and L are respectively, the Highest and Lowest values defining the interval of variation of the random variable. In this example, $H = 16$ and $L = 0$. Therefore, $R = H - L = 16 - 0 = 16$.

9. **Calculating the Quartiles and Percentiles**

   To calculate the Median ($X_{0.5}$ or Q_2), the Quartiles (Q_1 and Q_3) and all of the Percentiles, we first define the FRACTILES of the continuous random variable by the upper limit, V, of the integral equation:

$$\text{FRACTILE } V = \int_a^V f(x) dx = f \tag{5.34}$$

   where **a** is the low limit of the interval of variation of the random variable X.
   Then, we use equation (5.34) to define the Median, Quartiles (Q_1, Q_3) and Percentiles (for example P_{10} and P_{90}) according to the following Table:

   a) Let $V = X_{0.5}$; Then $f = 0.5$
   b) Let $V = Q_1$; Then $f = 0.25$
   c) Let $V = Q_3$; Then $f = 0.75$
   d) Let $V = P_{10}$; Then $f = 0.10$
   e) Let $V = P_{90}$; Then $f = 0.90$

To actually find these measures, we need to substitute for V and f in equation (5.34) according to the Table above and solve the resulting equation for V in terms of f.

For the given example, $f(x) = Ax^{1/2}$ $0 \le x \le 16$

or $f(x) = \dfrac{3}{128}x^{1/2}$ $0 \le x \le 16$

and this density function is simple enough to be solved in general for V in terms of f, and then make the appropriate substitutions (instead of making the substitutions first and then solving for the appropriate measure).

Substituting $f(x) = \dfrac{3}{128}x^{1/2}$ into (5.34), with $a = 0$, we obtain:

Fractile $V = \displaystyle\int_0^V \dfrac{3}{128}x^{1/2}dx = f$, or: $\dfrac{3}{128}\displaystyle\int_0^V x^{1/2}dx = f$, or: $\dfrac{3}{128}\dfrac{x^{1/2+1}}{1/2 + 1}\Big|_0^V = f$,

or $\dfrac{3}{128}\dfrac{x^{3/2}}{3/2}\Big|_0^V = f$, or: $\dfrac{3}{128}\dfrac{2}{3}x^{3/2}\Big|_0^V = f$, or: $\dfrac{1}{64}x^{3/2}\Big|_0^V = f$,

or $\dfrac{1}{64}\left[V^{3/2} - 0^{3/2}\right] = f$, or: $\dfrac{1}{64}V^{3/2} = f$, or: $V^{3/2} = 64f$,

and finally $V = (64f)^{2/3} = (4^3f)^{2/3} = (4^3)^{2/3}f^{2/3} = 4^2f^{2/3} = 16f^{2/3}$

or $V = 16f^{2/3}$

Then: i) Median $= X_{0.5} = V(with\ f = 0.5) = 16\left(\dfrac{1}{2}\right)^{2/3} = 10.07937$

ii) First Quartile $= Q_1 = V(with\ f = 0.25) = 16\left(\dfrac{1}{4}\right)^{2/3} = 6.34960$

iii) Third Quartile $= Q_3 = V(with\ f = 0.75) = 16\left(\dfrac{3}{4}\right)^{2/3} = 13.20771$

iv) 10th Percentile $= P_{10} = V(with\ f = 0.10) = 16\left(\dfrac{1}{10}\right)^{2/3} = 3.44710$

v) 90th Percentile $= P_{90} = V(with\ f = 0.90) = 16\left(\dfrac{9}{10}\right)^{2/3} = 14.91472$

5.12   Joint Probability Distributions

When a stochastic experiment is performed and a Sample Space is constructed, consisting of all the possible outcomes of the experiment, one or more random variables can be defined over the resulting Sample Space.

We have seen previously how a single random variable can be defined in a Sample Space and then analyzed in terms of $E(X)$, $V(X)$, S_{kp}, K etc.

In this section we will show how two or more random variables are defined over the same Sample Space and how they are analyzed. It turns out that in this case we must be concerned not only with the individual random variable and its analysis but we must be also concerned how one random variable behaves in relation to the other. This gives rise to another probability function, called a joint probability distribution, which shows the probability with which certain joint events (*i.e.*, a combination of one value of random variable one and a value of random variable two) occur. Since it is a probability function, it must satisfy the axioms of probability. If the joint probability distribution is the probability function of two random variables, it can usually be represented by a table, having the values of random variable 1 on one axis, the values of the second random variable on the other perpendicular axis, and the probabilities of the joint events shown at the intersection of the corresponding random variable values. To represent the joint probability distribution of 3 random variables we will need a cube, which is three-dimensional and, therefore, more difficult to visualize. Therefore, since we only wish to introduce joint probability distributions and their basic properties, we will restrict our attention to the joint probability distributions of two variables. Our discussion will be based on a stochastic experiment in which 3 random variables will be defined. Two of these will be selected, analyzed individually, and then their joint distribution will be obtained and, from it, all of the important properties of joint variables will be extracted and discussed.

Example 4

Suppose 3 coins are flipped together (or one coin is flipped three times). Over the resulting Sample Space, defined by the tree diagram and the outcomes of the experiment, we define the 3 random variables:

    X: the random variable which counts the number of Heads in the outcomes

    Y: the random variable which counts the number of Tails in the outcomes

    R: the random variable which counts the number of Runs in the outcomes

        (*i.e.*, the number of different symbols which occur in each of the outcomes).

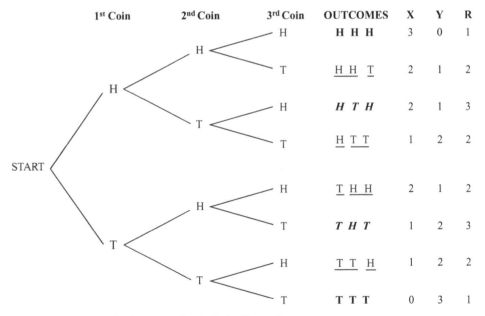

Figure 5.5 Sample Space of a 3 Coin Experiment

Since each of the outcomes has an equal chance of occurring,

$$P(\text{HHH}) = P((X = 3) \cap (Y = 0) \cap (R = 1)) = \frac{1}{8}$$

$$P(\text{HHT}) = P((X = 2) \cap (Y = 1) \cap (R = 2)) = \frac{1}{8}, \text{ etc.}$$

The simultaneous occurrence of the 3 random variables X, Y, R gives rise to the joint probability distribution $f(x_i, y_j, r_k)$. The joint event $(X = 3) \cap (Y = 0) \cap (R = 1)$, with probability of occurrence 1/8 , is one of the possible values of $f(x_i, y_j, r_k)$.

If we ignore the random variables Y and R and concentrate on the random variable X, we can obtain its PMF:

X	0	1	2	3
$P(X)$	1/8	3/8	3/8	1/8

from which, using the methods discussed previously, we find:

$$E(X) = 1.5, E(X^2) = 3, V(X) = \frac{3}{4}, \text{and } \sigma(X) = \frac{\sqrt{3}}{2} \approx 0.865$$

Similarly, if we concentrate on Y, ignoring X and R, we find the PMF of Y:

Y	0	1	2	3
$P(Y)$	1/8	3/8	3/8	1/8

from which we find:

$$E(Y) = 1.5, E(Y^2) = 3, V(Y) = \frac{3}{4}, \text{ and } \sigma(Y) = \frac{\sqrt{3}}{2} \approx 0.865$$

Note: The random variables X and Y are identically distributed because they have the same PMFs and, therefore, the same expected values and variances.

If we concentrate on R, ignoring X and Y, we find the PMF of R:

R	1	2	3
$P(R)$	2/8	4/8	2/8

from which we find:

$$E(R) = 2, E(R^2) = 4.5, V(R) = \frac{1}{2}, \text{and } \sigma(R) = \frac{\sqrt{2}}{2} \approx 0.707$$

But, in addition to the individual PMFs of the three random variables derived above and the joint probability distribution of the 3 variables $f(x_i, y_j, r_k)$, we can derive the joint probability distributions of two random variables:

1. $f(x_i, y_j)$ by ignoring the random variable R
2. $f(x_i, r_k)$ by ignoring the random variable Y
3. $f(y_j, r_k)$ by ignoring the random variable X.

These three, 2-variable joint probability distributions, are shown below:

■ The Joint Probability Distribution of (x_i, y_j)

		\multicolumn{4}{c} Y			
		0	1	2	3
	0				1/8
X	1			3/8	
	2		3/8		
	3	1/8			

In this table, which represents the joint probability function of the random variables X and Y, $f(x_i, y_j)$, the possible values of each of the two random variables are listed as shown and, at the intersection of two such values, we have the joint event whose probability of occurrence is the value shown in each cell. If a cell is blank, the probability of the corresponding joint event is zero and the event is impossible (it cannot occur).

The probabilities of the joint events are found from the outcomes of the sample space where the 3 events have been defined. We see that the joint event: $X = 3$ and $Y = 0$ (*i.e.*, $(X = 3) \cap (Y = 0)$) occurs only once in the 8 possible outcomes and as such has probability of occurrence of 1/8. This value is shown in the cell at the intersection of the values $X = 3$ and $Y = 0$. Similarly we see that the joint events $(X = 2) \cap (Y = 1)$ and $(X = 1) \cap (Y = 2)$ each occurs 3 times and, therefore, have probability of occurrence equal to 3/8, shown in the appropriate cells. Finally, the joint event $(X = 0) \cap (Y = 3)$ occurs only once and its probability of occurrence of 1/8 is shown in the corresponding cell.

A similar analysis produces the joint probability distributions $f(x_i, r_k)$ and $f(y_j, r_k)$ shown below:

■ The joint Probability Distribution $f(x_i, r_k)$

		\multicolumn{3}{c} R		
		1	2	3
	0	1/8		
X	1		2/8	1/8
	2		2/8	1/8
	3	1/8		

■ The joint Probability Distribution $f(y_j, r_k)$

		\multicolumn{3}{c} R		
		1	2	3
	0	1/8		
Y	1		2/8	1/8
	2		2/8	1/8
	3	1/8		

Note: Each of the 3 joint probability functions depicted above is proper because the probability of each cell is a number between 0 and 1, and the sum of all the cell probabilities is equal to 1.

To discuss the properties of joint distributions we will select $f(x_i, r_k)$ (*i.e.*, joint probability distribution (2) above) to illustrate these properties.
We will discuss the following:

1. Joint Probability Distributions
2. Marginal Distributions
3. Cumulative Distributions
4. Conditional Probability Distributions
5. Independence of random variables X and R
6. Expected value of a function of 2 variables
7. Variance of a sum of 2 (or more) random variables.

a) Joint Probability Distributions

A function of two variables, $f(x_i, r_k)$, is a probability distribution function if and only if:

1. $0 \leq f(x_i, r_k) \leq 1$ for each (x_i, r_k) combination and   (5.35)

2. $\displaystyle\sum_{i=1}^{I} \sum_{K=1}^{K} f(x_i r_k) = 1$ (5.36)

Since (See Table of "The Joint Probability Distributions of (x_i, y_j)") these two conditions are satisfied, $f(x_i, r_k)$ is a proper probability distribution.

b) Marginal Distributions

If the rows and columns of the $f(x_i, r_k)$ table are summed separately and the results written at the margins of the table we obtain, respectively, the PMF of X (when the rows are summed) and the PMF of R (when the columns are summed), which are called "Marginal Distributions" because they are found in the margins of the table.

Letting $f(x_i)$ be the PMF of X and $g(r_k)$ be the PMF of R and using (See Table of "The Joint Probability Distributions of (x_i, y_j)"), we obtain:

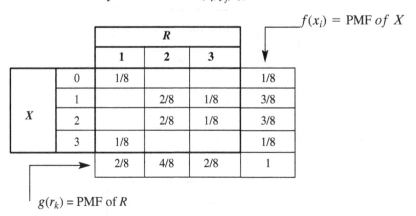

$f(x_i) =$ PMF *of* X

		R			$f(x_i)$
		1	**2**	**3**	
	0	1/8			1/8
	1		2/8	1/8	3/8
X	2		2/8	1/8	3/8
	3	1/8			1/8
		2/8	4/8	2/8	1

$g(r_k) =$ PMF of R

Note: $f(x_i)$ and $g(r_k)$ agree exactly with the individual random variable PMFs obtained directly from the Sample Space, and the sum of the probabilities of both random variables X and R is equal to 1, as expected.

The process of summing up the rows of the joint probability distribution to find $f(x_i)$ and the columns to find $g(r_k)$ can be expressed mathematically as:

$$f(x_i) = \sum_{k=1}^{k} f(x_i, r_k) \tag{5.37}$$

and

$$g(r_k) = \sum_{i=1}^{I} f(x_i, r_k) \tag{5.38}$$

Example 5

Find $P(x = 2)$ and $P(r = 1)$, using equations (5.37) and (5.38) and the table above

$$P(x = 2) = f(2) = \sum_{k=1}^{3} f(2, r_k) = f(2, 1) + f(2, 2) + f(2, 3)$$

$$= 0 + \frac{2}{8} + \frac{1}{8} = \frac{3}{8}$$

$$P(r = 1) = g(1) = \sum_{i=1}^{4} f(x_i, 1) = f(0, 1) + f(1, 1) + f(2, 1) + f(3, 1)$$

$$= \frac{1}{8} + 0 + 0 + \frac{1}{8} = \frac{2}{8}$$

■ ■ ■

c) Cumulative Distributions

Extending the definition of the Cumulative Distribution Function of one variable to functions of two variables, we write:

$$\text{CDF}(x, y) = P\big[(X \le x_i) \cap (Y \le y_j)\big] = \sum_{x_i \le x}\sum_{y_j \le y} f(x_i, y_j) \text{ for all } x, y$$

Example 6

Use the joint density $f(x_i, r_k)$ defined above to calculate:

$$\text{CDF}(x, y) = P\big[(X \le 2) \cap (R \le 2)\big] = \sum_{x_i \le 2}\sum_{r_k \le 2} f(x_i, r_k)$$

$$= [f(0, 1) + f(0, 2)] + [f(1, 1) + f(1, 2)] + [f(2, 1) + f(2, 2)]$$

$$= (1/8 + 0) + (0 + 2/8) + (0 + 2/8) = 5/8$$

■ ■ ■

d) Conditional Probability Distribution

Starting with the formula for finding the probability of the joint occurrence of two events A and B which we discussed in the previous chapter, namely:

$$P(A \cap B) = P(A)P(B/A) = P(B)P(A/B) \tag{5.39}$$

and extending it to the two random variables X and R which are jointly distributed, with their joint distribution being $f(x_i, r_k)$, we have:

$$f(x_i, r_k) = P[X = x_i \cap R = r_k]$$

$$= f(x_i)f\big(r_k/x_i\big) = g(r_k)f\big(x_i/r_k\big) \tag{5.40}$$

Therefore, the Conditional probability Distributions $f\left(x_i/r_k\right)$ and $f\left(r_k/x_i\right)$ are:

$$f\left(x_i/r_k\right) = \frac{f(x_i, r_k)}{g(r_k)} \tag{5.41}$$

and

$$f\left(r_k/x_i\right) = \frac{f(x_i, r_k)}{f(x_i)} \tag{5.42}$$

where $f(x_i)$ and $g(r_k)$ are the marginal distributions of X and R and $g(r_k) > 0\ \&\ f(x_i) > 0$

Example 7

Find the Conditional Probabilities $f(r_k = 3 / x_i = 2)$ and $f(x_i = 3 / r_k = 1)$

- $f\left(r_k = 3/x_i = 2\right) = \dfrac{f(x_i = 2 \cap r_k = 3)}{f(x_i = 2)} = \dfrac{f(2, 3)}{f(2)} = \dfrac{1/8}{3/8} = 1/3$

- $f\left(x_i = 3/r_k\right) = 1 = \dfrac{f(x_i = 3 \cap r_k = 1)}{g(r_k = 1)} = \dfrac{f(3, 1)}{g(1)} = \dfrac{1/8}{2/8} = 1/2$

■ ■ ■

e) Independence of X and R

Starting with the formula for calculating the probability of the joint occurrence of two independent events A and B, which we discussed in the previous chapter, namely:

$$P(A \cap B) = P(A)P(B) \tag{5.43}$$

and extending it to the two random variables X and R which have a joint probability distribution $f(x_i, r_k)$, we have:

$$f(x_i, r_k) = f(x_i)g(r_k) \text{ for all } X \text{ and } R \text{ pairs of values.}$$

An alternative way of expressing the independence of two random variables is to write:

$$f\left(x_i/r_k\right) = f(x_i) \text{ for all } i \text{ and } k \text{ for which } g(r_k) > 0 \tag{5.44}$$

and $f\left(r_k/x_i\right) = g(r_k)$ for all i and k for which $f(x_i) > 0$ \hfill (5.45)

Example 8

Are the random variables X and R, whose joint probability distribution is given by $f(x_i, r_k)$ (See Table of "The Joint Probability Distributions of (x_i, y_j)") independent?

According to the rule stated above, we have to test the validity of the rule $f(x_i, r_k) = f(x_i)g(r_k)$ for each and every combination of the i, k values. If we can find one for which the rule doesn't hold true, then the random variables are dependent.

Consider $x = 0$ and $r = 1$; from the table we have: $f(0,1) = 1/8$. Similarly from the marginal distributions we have: $f(0) = 1/8$ and $g(1) = 2/8$. Since, however, $f(0) \cdot g(1) \neq f(0, 1)$, the random variables X and R are dependent.

■ ■ ■

f) Expected value of a Function of 2 Random Variables

We showed earlier that, when X is a discrete random variable and its PMF function is known, the expected value of the random variable X, $E(X)$, was defined as:

$$E(X) = \sum_{i=1}^{n} x_i P(X = x_i) \tag{5.46}$$

If, instead of the random variable X, we are concerned with the expected value of a function of X, say $h(x)$, it can be defined as:

$$E[h(X)] = \sum_{i=1}^{n} h(x_i) P(X = x_i) \tag{5.47}$$

It is now a simple matter to extend the definition of Expectation to a function of two variables, say X and R, $h(x, r)$. We write:

$$E[h(X, R)] = \sum_{i=1}^{I} \sum_{k=1}^{K} h(x_i, r_k) f(x_i, r_k) \tag{5.48}$$

where I and K are the upper limits of the indices i and k. The function $h(X, R)$ can be any function of X and R whatsoever, however, our interest lies in some specific functions of X and R, namely:

i) $h(X, R) = X + R$
ii) $h(X, R) = X - R$
iii) $h(X, R) = XR$

Since cases i) and ii) differ only by a sign and lend themselves nicely to a joint treatment, we will combine cases i) and ii) and treat them together by considering $E(X \pm R)$. We will also investigate $E(XR)$ because both of these cases are of considerable interest.

g) The Expected Value of the Sum ($X + R$) and difference ($X - R$) of Two Random Variables

Using the generalized definition above we can write, when $h(X, R) = X \pm R$:

$$\begin{aligned}
E[X \pm R] &= \sum_{i=1}^{I} \sum_{k=1}^{K} (x_i \pm r_k) f(x_i, r_k) \\
&= \sum_{i=1}^{I} \sum_{k=1}^{K} x_i f(x_i, r_k) \pm \sum_{i=1}^{I} \sum_{k=1}^{K} r_k f(x_i, r_k) \\
&= \sum_{i=1}^{I} x_i \sum_{k=1}^{K} f(x_i, r_k) \pm \sum_{k=1}^{K} r_k \sum_{i=1}^{I} f(x_i, r_k) \\
&= \sum_{i=1}^{I} x_i f(x_i) \pm \sum_{k=1}^{K} r_k g(r_k) \\
&= E(X) \pm E(R)
\end{aligned}$$

Note: $\sum_{k=1}^{K} f(x_i, r_k) = f(x_i)$ and $\sum_{i=1}^{I} f(x_i, r_k) = g(r_k)$, and we have made use of the summation properties discussed in *Appendix D*.

In words this derivation shows that: The expected value of the sum or difference of two random variables is equal to the expected value of the sum or difference of the two variables. Instead of using the joint probability distribution to calculate the expected value of the sum (or difference) we can use the formula $E(X \pm R) = E(X) \pm E(R)$ which requires that we only know $E(X)$ and $E(R)$ and is much easier to evaluate.

This rule can be extended to find the expected value of the sum (difference) of any number of random variables.

We offer below an example which clearly demonstrates that the direct method (*i.e.*, using the joint probability distribution) is more complicated and time consuming than the indirect method (*i.e.*, finding $E(X)$ and $E(R)$ first from their individual PMFs and then using the formula $E(X \pm R) = E(X) \pm E(R)$).

Example 9

Consider again the joint probability distribution of the random variables X and R that we have used previously, namely:

$f(x_i)$ = PMF of X

$g(r_k)$ = PMF of R

We have shown previously that:

$E(X) = 1.5$ and $V(X) = 0.75$
and
$E(R) = 2$ and $V(R) = 0.5$

Using the direct method, we have:

$$
\begin{aligned}
E(X + R) = & [(0 + 1)(1/8) + (0 + 2)(0) + (0 + 3)(0)] \\
& + [(1 + 1)(0) + (1 + 2)(2/8) + (1 + 3)(1/8)] \\
& + [(2 + 1)(0) + (2 + 2)(2/8) + (2 + 3)(1/8)] \\
& + [(3 + 1)(1/8) + (3 + 2)(0) + (3 + 3)(0)] \\
= & \left[\frac{1}{8}\right] + \left[\frac{6}{8} + \frac{4}{8}\right] + \left[\frac{8}{8} + \frac{5}{8}\right] + \left[\frac{4}{8}\right] = \frac{28}{8} = \frac{7}{2} = 3.5
\end{aligned}
$$

■ ■ ■

Note: Each term consists of the sum of the X and R values of each cell, multiplied by the joint probability of occurrence of the combination in question, and each bracket includes all the possible terms corresponding to a fixed value of the random variable X as R is allowed to vary over its entire range. For example, the terms in the first bracket correspond to the value $X = 0$ as R takes the values 1, 2, and 3 successively.

If we wanted to calculate $E(X - R)$, we follow the same procedure as above except that instead of adding we subtract the corresponding terms. We obtain:

$$E(X - R) = [(0 - 1)(1/8) + (0 - 2)(0) + (0 - 3)(0)]$$
$$+ [(1 - 1)(0) + (1 - 2)(2/8) + (1 - 3)(1/8)]$$
$$+ [(2 - 1)(0) + (2 - 2)(2/8) + (2 - 3)(1/8)]$$
$$+ [(3 - 1)(1/8) + (3 - 2)(0) + (3 - 3)(0)]$$
$$= \left[(-1)\frac{1}{8}\right] + \left[(-1)\left(\frac{2}{8}\right) + (-2)\frac{1}{8}\right] + \left[(-1)\left(\frac{1}{8}\right)\right] + \left[(2)\left(\frac{1}{8}\right)\right]$$
$$= -\frac{1}{8} - \frac{2}{8} - \frac{2}{8} - \frac{1}{8} + \frac{2}{8} = -\frac{4}{8} = -0.5$$

Using the indirect method, we obtain:

$$E(X + R) = E(X) + E(R) = 1.5 + 2.0 = 3.5$$

and

$$E(X - R) = E(X) - E(R) = 1.5 - 2.0 = -0.5$$

Clearly the results of the indirect method are identical to the results of the direct method but the amount of work needed is much less.

h) The Expected Value of the product (XR) of two variables

When $h(X, R) = XR$, the expected value of the product is obtained by substituting XR for $h(X, R)$ in the general formula for the expectation of a function (see equation 5.48) and performing the indicated operations. We obtain:

$$E(XR) = \sum_{i=1}^{I}\sum_{k=1}^{K} x_i r_k f(x_i, r_k) \tag{5.51}$$

If the variables X and R are dependent the formula cannot be simplified anymore. However, if the variables X and R are independent, we can factor $f(x_i, r_k)$ into the factors $f(x_i)$ and $g(r_k)$ namely: $f(x_i, r_k) = f(x_i)g(r_k)$. (5.52)

Then, when we substitute (5.52) into (5.51), we obtain:

$$E(XR) = \sum_{i=1}^{I}\sum_{k=1}^{K} x_i r_k f(x_i)g(r_k) = \sum_{i=1}^{I} x_i f(x_i) \sum_{k=1}^{K} r_k g(r_k)$$
$$= E(X)E(R) \tag{5.53}$$

when X and R are independent.

Example 10

We will apply these two methods (*i.e.*, the direct method defined by (5.51) and the indirect method defined by (5.53)) to the random variables X and R with the joint probability distribution also used in the expectation of the summation of two random variables. Note that it is not necessary for the two formulas to produce the same result. This will happen only when the random variables X and R are independent or uncorrelated, a term to be discussed in the next section.

Using the direct method, we have:

$$E(XR) = [(0 \times 1)(1/8) + (0 \times 2)(0) + (0 \times 3)(0)]$$
$$+ [(1 \times 1)(0) + (1 \times 2)(2/8) + (1 \times 3)(1/8)]$$
$$+ [(2 \times 1)(0) + (2 \times 2)(2/8) + (2 \times 3)(1/8)]$$
$$+ [(3 \times 1)(1/8) + (3 \times 2)(0) + (3 \times 3)(0)]$$

$$= [0] + \left[\frac{4}{8} + \frac{3}{8}\right] + \left[\frac{8}{8} + \frac{6}{8}\right] + \left[\frac{3}{8}\right] = \frac{24}{8} = 3$$

Using the indirect method, we obtain:

$E(XR) = E(X) \times E(R) = (1.5) \times (2) = 3$, if we assume independence between X and R.

We have found the two answers to be identical. Do these results imply that X and R are in fact independent? This is not necessarily true!

As we will emphasize again in the next section, two random variables are independent if and only if $f(x_i, r_k) = f(x_i)g(r_k)$ for every pair of combinations of the indeces i and k. But we can, in this example, find pairs for which this is not the case. For example:

$$f(0, 1) \neq f(0) \times g(1) \text{ since } f(0, 1) = \frac{1}{8} \text{ and } f(0)g(1) = \left(\frac{2}{8}\right)\left(\frac{1}{8}\right) = \frac{3}{64} \neq \frac{1}{8}$$

Since we have found at least one combination of values of X and R for which $f(x_i, r_k) \neq f(x_i)g(r_k)$, the random variables X and R are not independent. However, since we have shown that $E(XR) = E(X) \times E(R) = 3$, we call the random variables X and R *uncorrelated*, a term which will become clear in the next section.

■ ■ ■

i) Variance of a Sum $(X + R)$ and Difference $(X - R)$ of 2 variables

Suppose that a random variable S is defined as the sum of two other variables X and R for which $E(X)$, $V(X)$, $E(R)$, and $V(R)$ are known. We wish to find $E(S)$ and $V(S)$ as a function of the parameters of the random variables X and R.

We let $S = X + R$ to start with, from which, using the properties of the Expectation Operator, which we discussed earlier, we find:

$$E(S) = E(X + R) \tag{5.54}$$
$$= E(X) + E(R)$$

always, regardless of whether X and R are dependent or independent random variables.

If X and R were independent random variables, we can apply the properties of the Variance Operator to the equation $S = X + R$ and obtain:

$$V(S) = V(X + R)$$
$$= V(X) + V(R) \tag{5.55}$$

only if X and R are independent random variables.

Since, however, we cannot always assume independence, we need to proceed in a somewhat different manner to cover the most general case which includes both dependent and independent random variables.

Starting with the definition of the Variance of a random variable (S is a random variable since X and R are random variables and any function of random variables is itself a random variable) we write: $V(S) = E\left[[S - E(S)]^2\right]$ $\qquad$ (5.56)

But $\qquad\qquad\qquad\qquad S = X + R \text{ and } E(S) = E(X) + E(R)$

Substituting these equations in the expression for V(S) we obtain:

$$V(S) = E\left[[X + R - E(X) - E(R)]^2\right]$$

$$= E[[(X - E(X)) + (R - E(R))]^2]$$

$$= E[[(X - E(X)]^2 + [R - E(R)]^2$$

$$+ 2[X - E(X)][R - E(R)]] \tag{5.57}$$

which is obtained by first regrouping terms appropriately and then squaring within the large brackets.

By applying the properties of the Expectation Operator we obtain:

$$V(S) = E[X - E(X)]^2 + E[R - E(R)]^2 + 2E[X - E(X)][R - E(R)]$$

$$= E[X - E(X)]^2 + E[R - E(R)]^2 +$$
$$2E[XR - XE(R) - RE(X) + E(X)E(R)]$$

$$= E[X - E(X)]^2 + E[R - E(R)]^2 + 2[E(XR) - E(X)E(R)$$
$$- E(R)E(X) + E(X)E(R)]$$

$$= E[X - E(X)]^2 + E[R - E(R)]^2 + 2[E(XR) - E(X)E(R)]$$

But $E[X - E(X)]^2$ is, by definition, equal to the Variance of the random variable X $(V(X))$, and $E\big[R - E(R)\big]^2 = V(R)$.

The quantity $E(XR) - E(X)E(R)$ is by definition referred to as the COVARIANCE between X and R, and we write:

$$COV(X,R) = E(XR) - E(X)E(R) \tag{5.58}$$

Therefore,

$$V(S) = V(X) + V(R) + 2COV(X, R) \tag{5.59}$$

From the above definition of the Covariance it is obvious that:

$COV(X, R) > 0$ when $E(XR) > E(X) E(R)$, $COV(X, R) = 0$ when $E(XR) = E(X)E(R)$, and $COV(X, R) < 0$ when $E(XR) < E(X)E(R)$.

When $COV(X, R) > 0$,the random variables X and R are said to be Positively Correlated while, when $COV(X, R) < 0$, they are said to be negatively Correlated. When $COV(X, R) = 0$, the random variables X and R are said to be Uncorrelated. Below we summarize the discussion above and offer some interpretation of the new terms we introduced,

$$COV(X, R) = E(XR) - E(X)E(R) = \begin{cases} > 0; \ X \text{ and } R \text{ are Positively Correlated} \\\\ = 0; \ X \text{ and } R \text{ are Uncorrelated} \\\\ < 0; \ X \text{ and } R \text{ are Negatively Correlated} \end{cases}$$

together with a geometric interpretation. In a later chapter, when we discuss BIVARIATE ANALYSIS, we will have an opportunity to discuss Covariance in greater detail.

Two random variables are said to be positively correlated if, when one increases, the other increases also. The weight and height of human beings is one such example. On the other hand, two random variables are said to be negatively correlated if, when one increases, the other decreases. The price and age of a car represent such an example. In both these cases a linear relationship between the variables can be derived, with a positive slope in the first and a negative one in the second.

When two variables are uncorrelated, it simply means that no linear relationship between the variables exists. But it doesn't mean that the variables are independent. In general, independence is a much stronger condition than uncorrelation. Independence can be stated as:

$$E(X^K R^K) = E(X^K)E(R^K) \text{ for all } K, \quad (\text{not just } K = 1) \tag{5.60}$$

while Uncorrelation, or linear independence, is defined as:

$$E(XR) = E(X)E(R), \quad \text{true only for } K = 1 \tag{5.61}$$

Obviously Uncorrelation (linear independence) is a subset of the conditions required for Independence, because it represents the case when $K = 1$. As a general rule, independence implies Uncorrelation, but the opposite is not true (*i.e.*, Uncorrelation does not imply independence). But there is an exception to this rule. If X and Y are uncorrelated and each is normally distributed, then they are also (statistically) independent, as we will show in the next section. However, before we undertake to discuss continuous joint variables, in which the example of the normal variables will be discussed, we will introduce the Correlation Coefficient, usually represented by the Greek letter ρ, which is a dimensionless way of expressing the Covariance between two random variables.

The Covariance has the same units as the Variance, which are the units of the original measurements but squared.

If we write

$$COV(X, R) = \rho \sigma_X \sigma_R, \tag{5.62}$$

where σ_X and σ_R are the standard deviations of the variables X and R respectively. Then:

$$\rho = \frac{COV(X, R)}{\sigma_X \sigma_R} \tag{5.63}$$

and ρ is a pure number which varies between -1 and $+1$ and measures the degree of the relationship that exists between the variables X and R. We have introduced the Correlation Coefficient because it will be used in the next section which discusses the joint probability distribution of two continuous random variables which are normally distributed.

If we define a random variable Y as the **sum of n independent random variables** $X_1, X_2, \ldots, X_n$, then:

$$Y = X_1 + X_2 + \cdots + X_n \tag{5.64}$$

$$E(Y) = E(X_1) + E(X_2) + \cdots + E(X_n) \tag{5.65}$$

and

$$V(Y) = V(X_1) + V(X_2) + \cdots + V(X_n) \tag{5.66}$$

Many computer programs exist for the analysis of Bivariate and Multivariate data and these include a Correlation Matrix which measures the degree of the relationship that exists between the variables. Such a Correlation Matrix is usually part of the computer output when such a problem is run on the computer. The interpretation we give to these Correlation Coefficients is as follows:

1) If ρ is approximately equal to -1, the variables are negatively correlated.
2) If ρ is approximately equal to 0, the variables are uncorrelated.
3) If ρ is approximately equal to $+1$, the variables are positively correlated.

For values of ρ between -1 and 0 $(-1 < \rho < 0)$ and between 0 and $+1$ $(0 < \rho < +1)$ there is a "decision" point, which depends on the sample size n and other considerations, which divides these segments of the real line either into correlation or non-correlation regions. But we will say more about this in our discussion of Bivariate Analysis.

J) Joint probability Distributions for Continuous Random Variables

Let us assume for simplicity that X and Y are two continuous random variables both of which are normally distributed with parameters:

$$E(X) = \mu_x, V(X) = \sigma_x^2, E(Y) = \mu_y, V(Y) = \sigma_y^2.$$

The normal distribution will be discussed at length in chapter 7 because it is one of the most important distributions in statistics.

But for now, all we have to do is specify the equation which describes a normal distribution. For the random variables X and Y this equation becomes:

$$f(X) = \frac{1}{\sqrt{2\pi}\sigma_X} e^{-\frac{1}{2\sigma_X^2}(x - \mu_Y)^2} \qquad -\infty < X < \infty \qquad (5.67)$$

and

$$g(Y) = \frac{1}{\sqrt{2\pi}\sigma_Y} e^{-\frac{1}{2\sigma_Y^2}(x - \mu_y)^2} \qquad -\infty < X < \infty \qquad (5.68)$$

When $f(X)$ is plotted against X or $g(Y)$ is plotted against Y the resulting shape is the well-known "bell-shaped" curve, which we will discuss in greater detail in Chapter 7.

The joint probability distribution of the random variables X and Y is given by $f(X, Y)$ where:

$$f(X, Y) = \frac{1}{2\pi\sigma_x\sigma_y(1 - \rho^2)^{1/2}} e^{-\frac{1}{2(1 - \rho^2)}\left[\frac{(x - \mu_x)^2}{\sigma_x^2} - \frac{2\rho(x - \mu_x)(y - \mu_y)}{\sigma_x\sigma_y} - \frac{(y - \mu_y)^2}{\sigma_y^2}\right]} \quad (5.69)$$

where ρ is the correlation coefficient.

Now, when $\rho = 0$, the variables X and Y are Uncorrelated, by definition. But when $\rho = 0$, the joint density $f(X, Y)$ becomes:

$$f\left(X, Y\right) = \frac{1}{2\pi\sigma_x\sigma_y} e^{-\frac{1}{2}\left[\frac{(x - \mu_x)^2}{\sigma_x^2} + \frac{(y - \mu_y)^2}{\sigma_y^2}\right]} \qquad (5.70)$$

$$= \left[\frac{1}{\sqrt{2\pi}\sigma_x} e^{-\frac{1}{2\sigma_x^2}(x - \mu_x)^2}\right]\left[\frac{1}{\sqrt{2\pi}\sigma_y} e^{-\frac{1}{2\sigma_y^2}(y - \mu_y)^2}\right] \qquad (5.71)$$

$$= f(X)g(Y)$$

But, since $f(X, Y) = f(X)g(Y)$, the variables X and Y are independent and we have shown that, in the case of normal variables, uncorrelation implies independence. The reverse is also true and can be proven by starting with $f(X, Y) = f(X)g(Y)$ and showing that the joint probability distribution is independent of ρ (i.e., $\rho = 0$). Therefore independence also implies uncorrelation.

The properties of the joint probability distributions for discrete variables which we discussed earlier can now be stated for continuous variables, and they are:

1. Proper Probability Function: $\displaystyle\int_{-\infty}^{\infty} \int_{-\infty}^{\infty} f(x, y)dxdy = 1$ (5.72)

2. Marginal Distributions:

a) $f(X) = \int_{-\infty}^{\infty} f(x, y)dy$ 　　　　　　　　　　　　　　(5.73)

b) $g(Y) = \int_{-\infty}^{\infty} f(x, y)dx$ 　　　　　　　　　　　　　　(5.74)

3. Cumulative Distribution: $\text{CDF}(X, Y) = \int_{-\infty}^{x} \int_{-\infty}^{y} f(x, y)dxdy$ 　　　(5.75)

4. Conditional probability Distributions:

a) $f(X/Y) = \dfrac{f(x, y)}{g(y)}$ 　　　　　　　　　　　　　　(5.76)

b) $f(Y/X) = \dfrac{f(x, y)}{f(x)}$ 　　　　　　　　　　　　　　(5.77)

5. $P(a < X < b \text{ and } c < Y < d) = \int_{a}^{b} \int_{c}^{d} f(x, y)dxdy$ 　　　(5.78)

Whether or not these integrals can be easily evaluated is another matter. As a matter of fact when $f(X)$ and $g(Y)$ are normally distributed these integrals cannot be evaluated in closed form using the rules of integration and numerical methods and/or tables of the normal distribution must be used for their evaluation.

The purpose of this section was to show that continuous variables can be handled almost as easily as discrete variables. As we have stated on many occasions previously, the only difference between analyzing discrete and continuous variables is the replacement of summations by integrations. We present a simple example below to illustrate the procedures summarized above.

Example 11

Let the joint probability distribution of the random variables X and Y be given by:

$$f(X, Y) = Axy \quad \text{with} \quad 2 \le x \le 6 \text{ and } 0 \le y \le 4$$

Find:

1. The value of the constant A so that $f(x, y)$ is a proper joint density function
2. The marginal Distributions $f(X)$ and $g(Y)$
3. $E(X)$, $E(Y)$, and $E(XY)$
4. $\text{CDF}(X, Y)$
5. If X and Y are dependent or independent and state the reasons.
6. If X and Y are correlated or uncorrelated and state the reasons.

Solutions

1. For $f(X, Y)$ to be proper we must have: $\int_{2}^{6} \int_{0}^{4} f(x, y)dxdy = 1$

or $\int_{2}^{6} \int_{0}^{4} Axydydx = 1$

To evaluate double integrals, we treat one of the variables as a constant while performing the integration with respect to the other variable. This procedure is similar to evaluating double summations or taking partial derivatives of functions of two or more variables.

Following this approach we have:

$$\int_2^6 \int_0^4 Axy\,dy\,dx = A\int_2^6 x\,dx \int_0^4 y\,dy$$

$$= A\left[\frac{x^2}{2}\Big|_2^6\right]\left[\frac{1}{2}y^2\Big|_0^4\right]$$

$$= \frac{A}{4}[36-4][16-0] = \frac{A}{4}(32)(16) = 128A,$$

and, since the value of this integral must equal 1, we obtain: $A = \dfrac{1}{128}$

2. By definition

$$f(X) = \int_0^4 f(x,y)\,dy = \frac{1}{128}\int_0^4 xy\,dy = \frac{x}{128}\int_0^4 y\,dy = \frac{x}{128}\left[\frac{y^2}{2}\right]\Big|_0^4$$

$$= \frac{x}{256}(16-0) = \frac{1}{16}x \qquad 2 \le X \le 6$$

$$g(Y) = \int_2^6 f(x,y)\,dx = \frac{1}{128}\int_2^6 xy\,dx = \frac{y}{128}\int_2^6 x\,dx = \frac{y}{128}\left[\frac{x^2}{2}\right]\Big|_2^6$$

$$= \frac{y}{256}(36-4) = \frac{1}{8}y \qquad 0 \le Y \le 4$$

3. $E(X) = \displaystyle\int_2^6 xf(x)\,dx = \frac{1}{16}\int_2^6 x^2\,dx = \frac{1}{16}\left[\frac{x^3}{3}\right]\Big|_2^6 = \frac{1}{48}[216-8]$

$$= \frac{208}{48} = \frac{4\times 52}{4\times 12} = \frac{4\times 13}{4\times 3} = \frac{13}{3}$$

$E(Y) = \displaystyle\int_0^4 yg(y)\,dy = \frac{1}{8}\int_0^4 y^2\,dy = \frac{1}{8}\left[\frac{y^3}{3}\right]\Big|_0^4 = \frac{1}{24}(64) = \frac{8}{3}$

$E(X,Y) = \displaystyle\int_2^6 \int_0^4 xyf(x,y)\,dy\,dx = \frac{1}{128}\int_2^6 \int_0^4 x^2 y^2\,dy\,dx$

$$= \frac{1}{128}\left[\int_2^6 x^2\,dx\right]\left[\int_0^4 y^2\,dy\right]$$

$$= \frac{1}{128}\left[\frac{1}{3}x^3\Big|_2^6\right]\left[\frac{1}{3}y^3\Big|_0^4\right] = \frac{1}{128}\left[\frac{1}{3}(216-8)\right]\left[\frac{1}{3}(64)\right]$$

$$= \frac{1}{9\times 128}(208)(64) = \frac{1}{9}\left(\frac{1}{2\times 64}\right)(16\times 13)(64) = \frac{8\times 13}{9} = \frac{104}{9}$$

Therefore: $COV(X,Y) = E(XY) - E(X)E(Y) = \dfrac{104}{9} - \left(\dfrac{13}{3}\right)\left(\dfrac{8}{3}\right) = 0$

4. $\mathrm{CDF}(X,Y) = \displaystyle\int_2^x \int_0^y f(x,y)dydx = \dfrac{1}{128}\left[\int_2^x xdx\right]\left[\int_0^y ydy\right]$

$$= \dfrac{1}{128}\left[\dfrac{1}{2}x^2\Big|_2^x\right]\left[\dfrac{1}{2}y^2\Big|_0^y\right] = \dfrac{1}{512}\left(x^2 - 4\right)y^2$$

when $X = 6$ and $Y = 4$, $\mathrm{CDF}(6,4) = 1$ as expected.

5. Since $f(X,Y) = f(X)g(Y) = \left(\dfrac{1}{16}x\right)\left(\dfrac{1}{8}y\right) = \dfrac{1}{128}xy$ the variables X and Y are independent.

6. Since X and Y are independent they are also uncorrelated because uncorrelation is a weaker condition than independence. But this can also be verified from the fact that $COV(X, Y) = 0$, as was shown in part c) above.

■ ■ ■

5.13   References

Berenson, Marc, L., Levine, David, M., and Krehbiel, Timothy, C., 2004. *Basic Business Statistics*. 9th Edition. Pearson-Prentice Hall.

Black, Ken, 2004. *Business Statistics*. 4th Edition. Wiley.

Canavos, George, C., 1984. *Applied Probability and Statistical Methods*. Little, Brown.

Carlson, William, L., and Thorne, Betty, 1997. *Applied Statistical Methods*. Prentice Hall.

Chou, Ya-lun, 1992. *Statistical Analysis for Business and Economics*. Elsevier.

Freund, John, E., and Williams, Frank, J., 1969. *Modern Business Statistics*. Revised by: Perles, Benjamin and Sullivan, Charles. Prentice-Hall.

Freund, John, E., and Williams, Frank, J., 1982. *Elementary Business Statistics: The Modern approach*. Prentice–Hall.

Johnson, Robert, 1973. *Elementary Statistics*. Duxbury Press.

McClave, James, T., Benson, George, P., and Sincich, Terry, 2001. *Statistics for Business and Economics*. 8th Edition. Prentice Hall.

Salvatore, Dominick, *Theory and Problems of Statistics and Econometrics*. SCHAUM'S OUTLINE SERIES, McGraw-Hill.

Steel, Robert, G.D., and Torrie, James, H., 1976. *Introduction to Statistics*. McGraw-Hill.

5.14 PROBLEMS

1. Three balls numbered 1, 2, 3 are placed in a box. A ball is drawn, the number is observed, and the ball is replaced. Then another ball is drawn.

   a) Describe the sample space of this experiment.
   b) Determine the PMF (Probability Mass Function) of the random variable X, where X is the product of the two numbers drawn.
   c) Find $P(X = 3)$;
   d) Find $P(X > 6)$;
   e) Find $(P \leq 2 \leq 6)$.

2. A contractor is constructing an addition to a home. He estimates that it will take between 8 and 12 working days. He feels that 10 days is the most likely time, and that 11 days is only half as likely. He estimates a time of 9 days as two-thirds as likely as that of 10 days. A time of 8 or 12 days is only half as likely as a time of 11 days.

   a) Determine the PMF (Probability Mass Function) of the random variable X, where X is the number of days it takes the contactor to complete the construction.
   b) Find the expected time to completion.
   c) Find the standard deviation of the time to completion.
   d) What is the probability that it will take more than 10 days to complete the job?
   e) Obtain the CDF of this distribution, and plot it, and use it to calculate the median value of this variable.

3. Suppose the density function of a continuous random variable X is given by:

   $$f(X = x) = Ax^2 \quad 2 \leq X \leq 5$$

   a) Find the value of A so that $f(x)$ is a proper probability function.
   b) Find $E(X)$, $E(X^2)$ and $V(X)$.
   c) Find $P(3 \leq X \leq 4)$.

4. A random variable X takes the value 1 with probability p and the value -1 with probability $1 - p$.

   a) Find $E(X)$ and $V(X)$.
   b) If Y is another random variable related to X by the linear function:

      $Y = 5 - 1/5\ X$, find: $E(Y)$ and $V(Y)$
   c) What are the values of $E(X)$, $V(X)$, $E(Y)$, $V(Y)$ when $p = 0.5$?

5. It is claimed that the PMF of a random variable X is given by the equation:

   $$P(X) = \frac{6 - |X - 7|}{36}, \text{ for } X = 1, 2, 3, ..., 12, \text{ and } |\quad| \text{ signifies absolute value.}$$

   a) Determine whether or not this function is a proper probability function
   b) Find $E(X)$
   c) Find $V(X)$

6. The average grade on a statistics test is 62.5 with a standard deviation of 10. The professor suspects that the test may have been too difficult. As a result, he wishes to adjust the grade so that the average is now 70 with a standard deviation of 8. What adjustment of the type: $Y = a + bX$, where X is the current grade, and Y is the adjusted grade, should he use?

7. Given a random variable X, with $E(X) = 1$, and $V(X) = 4$, find:

   a) $E(Y)$ and $V(Y)$ if $Y = X/3$.

   b) $E(S)$ and $V(S)$ if $S = kX$, where k is any constant.

   c) $E(T)$ and $V(T)$ if $T = (X/k) + k$, for $k \neq 0$.

8. Three balls numbered 1, 2, 6 are placed in a box. A ball is drawn, the number is observed, and the ball is replaced. Then another ball is drawn.

   a) Describe the sample space of this experiment.

   b) Determine the PMF (Probability Mass Function) of the random variable X, where X is the sum of the two numbers drawn.

   c) Find $P(X = X_1 + X_2 = 7)$.

   d) Find $P(X = X_1 + X_2 > 6)$.

   e) Find $P(3 < X = X_1 + X_2 < 8)$.

9. Inspection of a manufactured assembly consists of taking a sample of 4 items and classifying each item as good or defective. Define a random sample G which represents the number of good items in the sample. Suppose, on the basis of past experience, the probability distribution of the number of defectives is:

D	0	1	2	3	4
$P(D)$	0.80	0.09	0.05	0.03	0.03

   a) Find $E(G)$ and $V(G)$.

   b) If H is another random variable, related to random variable G, by the linear relationship: $H = 5 + 2G$, find: $E(H)$ and $V(H)$.

10. Determine whether the following functions are proper probability distributions and justify your answer in each case:

   a) $f(x) = x/14$ for $x = 2, 3, 4, 5$
   b) $f(x) = 1/4$ for $x = 0, 1, 2, 3$
   c) $f(x) = (2x-4)/5$ for $x = 2, 3, 4, 5, 6$
   d) $f(x) = 1/3$ for $x = 1, 2, 3, 4$

11. Find the mean and the standard deviation of the number of points rolled with a balanced die.

12. The probabilities of 0, 1, 2 or 3 armed robberies in a city in any given month are 0.4, 0.3, 0.2 and 0.1. Find the mean and the variance of this probability distribution.

13. The table below gives the probabilities that a computer will malfunction 0, 1, 2, 3, 4, 5, or 6 times on any given day:

Number of malfunctions	0	1	2	3	4	5	6
Probability	0.15	0.22	0.31	0.18	0.09	0.04	0.01

   Calculate the mean and the standard deviation of this probability distribution.

14. The probabilities that a building inspector will find 0, 1, 2, 3, 4, or 5 violations of the building code in a home built in a large development are 0.40, 0.25, 0.20, 0.10, 0.04 and 0.01. Find the mean and the variance of this probability distribution.

15. The number of marriage licenses issued in a certain city during the month of May average $\mu = 150$ with a standard deviation of $\sigma = 10$.

    a) What does Chebychev's theorem with $k = 5$, tells us about the number of marriage licenses issued in this city during the month of May?

    b) According to Chebychev's theorem, with what probability can we assert that between 70 and 230 marriage licenses will be issued in this city during the month of May?

16. If a balanced die is rolled 720 times, what is the least probability according to Chebychev's theorem that a 6 will turn up between 80 and 160 times?

17. Determine whether the following functions are proper probability density functions. Justify your answers.

    a) $f(x) = (x + 1)/14$ for $x = 1, 2, 3, 4$

    b) $f(x) = \dfrac{\dfrac{2!}{x!(2-x)!}}{4}$ for $x = 0, 1, 2$

    c) $f(x) = \dfrac{x^2+1}{18}$ for $x = 1, 2, 3$

18. Let X be a random variable representing the number of customers arriving per hour at a retail store, and its PMF(X) is given by:

X	0	1	2	3	4	5	6	7	8
$P(X)$	0.05	0.10	0.10	0.10	0.20	0.25	0.10	0.05	0.05

    Determine $E(X) = $ Expected value of X and $V(X) = $ Variance of X

19. Let X be a discrete random variable, with Probability Mass Function = PMF(X), given by: $P(X) = A/x$ for $x = 1, 2, 3, 4$.

    a) Determine the value of the multiplier A so that $P(X)$ is a proper probability function.

    b) Determine the probability $P(1 < X \leq 3)$

20. Let X be a continuous random variable with the density function:

    $$F(X) = \begin{cases} Ax^2 & -1 \leq x \leq 1 \\ 0 & elsewhere \end{cases}$$

    a) Determine the value of the multiplier A so that $f(x)$ is a proper probability (density) function.

    b) Determine the Cumulative Distribution Function of X[CDFC(X)]

    c) Determine $P(X \geq 1/2)$

    d) Determine $P\left(-\dfrac{1}{2} \leq X \leq \dfrac{1}{2}\right)$

21. Suppose the weekly income of professional consultants is represented by the random variable X with the probability density function:

    $$f(X) = \begin{cases} \dfrac{1}{800}e^{-x/800} & X > 0 \\ 0 & elsewhere \end{cases}$$

  a) Determine the Mean income (Expected value).

  b) Determine the Median income.

  c) Determine the Inter Quartile Range = IQR = $Q_3 - Q_1$

  d) Determine the Inter Decile Range = IDR = $P_{90} - P_{10}$

  e) Determine the probability of a consultant's weekly income exceeding the average income (*i.e.*, find $P(X \geq E(X))$).

22. A car owner whishes to sell his car and is thinking of spending $50 to advertise it. If the probability is 0.5 that he will sell the car at the "asked for" price of $750 without advertising, and the probability is 0.9 that he can sell the car at his price if he does advertise, *should he advertise*? Assume that if he does not sell the car for $750, he will let his friend buy it for $650.00.

23. An examination consists of 10 multiple-choice questions, and is administered to a group of students. Five of the questions have 2 choices, and the other five have 3 choices. The answers are either right or wrong, and 10 points are given for a right answer and 0 points for a wrong answer. If a student decides to answer the 10 questions using random selection (or using random numbers to select each of his choices), with all choices having an equal chance, what is his expected score?

24. The number of accidents that occur at a particular industrial plant during a working day is: 0, 1, 2 or 3, and the corresponding probabilities are: 0.94, 0.03, 0.02 and 0.01.

  a) What is the Expected number of accidents during one day?

  b) What is the Expected number of accidents in 100 days?

25. An individual who owns an ice cream concession at a festival area is expected to net $600 per day, if the day is sunny, $300 if the day is cloudy, and $100 if it rains. The respective probabilities are: 0.6, 0.3, 0.1.

  a) What is the expected profit?

  b) If he buys $400 worth of insurance against rain, and the insurance costs $90, what is the expected profit?

26. Would you pay 1 dollar to buy a ticket in a lottery that sells 1,000,000 tickets and gives: 1 prize of $100,000, 10 prizes of $10,000, and 100 prizes of $1,000?

27. Consider a man who buys a lottery ticket in a lottery that sells 100 tickets and gives: 4 prizes of $200, 10 prizes of $100, and 20 prizes of $10. How much should the man be willing to pay for this lottery?

28. A gambler receives $1 if a 6 appears when a fair die is tossed, and he wins nothing if another number shows up. Find the mean and variance of his winnings.

29. Suppose that the probability of death of a man aged 40, within a year, is 0.008. Find the mean and variance of the number of deaths, within a year, among 20,000 of this age.

30. A man invests a total of N dollars in a group of n securities, whose rates of return (interest rates) are independent random variables $X_1, X_2, \ldots, X_n$ with means $\mu_1, \mu_2, \ldots, \mu_n$ and variances $\sigma_1^2, \sigma_2^2, \ldots, \sigma_n^2$ respectively. If the man invests N_j dollars in the jth security, then his return in dollars on this particular portfolio is a random variable R given by: $R = N_1 X_1 + N_2 X_2 + \cdots + N_n X_n$. Let the standard deviation $\sigma(R)$ of R be used as a measure of the risk involved in selecting a given portfolio of securities.

In particular, let us consider the problem of distributing $N = 5500$ dollars between 2 securities, one of which has a rate of return X_1, with mean $= E(X_1) = 6\%$ and a standard deviation $= \sigma_1 = 1\%$, and the second has a rate of return X_2 with mean $= E(X_2) = 15\%$ and standard deviation $\sigma_2 = 10\%$

a) If it is desired to hold the risk to a minimum, what amounts N_1, and N_2 should be invested in the respective securities? What is the mean and variance of the return from this portfolio?

b) What is the amount of risk that must be taken in order to achieve a portfolio whose mean return is equal to 400 dollars?

c) Using Chebychev's inequality, find an interval symmetric about 400 dollars that, with probability greater than 75% will contain the return R from the portfolio with a mean return $E(R) = 400$ dollars.

d) Would you be justified in assuming that the return R is approximately normally distributed?

31. A random variable X can take the values: 1,2,3, …, n with probability of each value $= 1/n$. Find the Expected value, $E(X)$, and variance $= V(X)$ of the random variable X.

32. A random sample of 3 delegates is selected, without replacement from a group of 4 men and 3 women. What is the expected number of men in the sample?

33. Six tennis balls are in a bag and two are known to be from last year and soft. The balls are drawn one at a time from the bag and observed until both soft balls are removed.

a) Construct the sample space of this experiment. What probabilities are assigned to each sample point?

b) Let the random variable X be the number of trails required to get the two soft balls out of the bag. What is the PMF(X)?

c) Find $E(X)$ and $V(Y)$

34. The probability that a 30-year old man will survive one year is 0.99. An insurance company offers to sell such a man a $100,000 one year term life insurance policy at a premium of $1,200. What is the insurance company's expected gain?

35. In a given business venture a man can make a profit of $2000 or suffer a loss of $750. If the probability of making a profit is 0.6,

a) What is the expected profit in this venture?

b) What is the risk involved, if the standard deviation is taken as the risk?

36. Suppose that the number of deaths is 10 per 1000 of 30 year old people. An insurance company would like to offer a $20,000 one-year term insurance policy for this age group. What should the annual premium be if the company expects to gain $20 for each such policy issued?

37. Three balls are drawn at random, without replacement, from an urn containing 5 white and 2 black balls. Find:

a) The expected number of black balls in the sample

b) The expected number of white balls in the sample

38. A competitive game of skill is played by teams of two players, each of whom can score 0, 1, 2 or 3 points. The score of the team is the sum of the points gained by the two players. For each such team, the PMFs of the 2 players, respectively are: Assuming independence of X and Y, derive:

PMF of Player X

X_i	0	1	2	3
$f(x_i)$	0.1	0.3	0.4	0.2

PMF of Player Y

Y_i	0	1	2	3
$f(Y_i)$	0.3	0.1	0.4	0.2

a) The Joint Probability Distribution of X and Y

b) The Probability Distribution of the total Score
   (*i.e.*, $T = X + Y$) of the 2 players

c) Calculate $E(X)$, $E(Y)$, $E(T) = E(X + Y)$, and $E(XY)$

d) Is $E(T) = E(X) + E(Y)$?

e) Is $E(XY) = E(X)E(Y)$?

39. For the following joint contribution:

		Values of X				
		0	1	2	3	$g(y_i)$
Values of Y	1	1/8	0	0	1/8	2/8
	2	0	2/8	2/8	0	4/8
	3	0	1/8	1/8	0	2/8
	$f(xi)$	1/8	3/8	3/8	1/8	1

a) Compute $E(X)$ and $E(Y)$

b) Compute $E(XY)$. Is $E(XY) = E(X)E(Y)$?

c) Are X and Y independent? Explain.

40. Suppose the joint probability, distribution of X and Y is defined by

$f(x_i\, y_j) = 1/54\, (3x_i + 2y_j - 4)$, for $x_i = 1, 2, 3$ and $y_j = 1, 2, 3$.

a) Construct the joint Probability table

b) Find the marginal probability distribution of X and Y, respectively, and show that they are given by:

$f(x_i) = x_i /6$ for $x_i = 1, 2, 3$
and $g(y_j) = (y_j + 1)/9$ for $y_j = 1, 2, 3$

c) Find the conditional probabilities: $f(x_i /1), f(x_i /2)$ and $f(x_i /3)$ and show that they are given by:

$f(x_i /1) = (3x_i - 2)/12$ for $x_i = 1, 2, 3$
$f(x_i /2) = 3x_i /18$ for $x_i = 1, 2, 3$
$f(x_i /3) = (3x_i + 2)/24$ for $x_i = 1, 2, 3$

d) Find the conditional probabilities: $g(y_i /1) \cdot g(y_j /2)$ and $g(y_j /3)$ and show that they are given by:

$g(y_j/1) = (2y_j - 1)/9$ for $y_j = 1, 2, 3$
$g(y_j/2) = (y_j + 1)/9$ for $y_j = 1, 2, 3$
$g(y_j/3) = (2y_j + 5)/27$ for $y_j = 1, 2, 3$

e) Are X and Y independent? Justify!

SOLUTIONS

1. a) $S = \{(1,1), (1,2), (1,3), (2,1), (2,2), (2,3), (3,1), (3,2), (3,3)\}$, and the corresponding products are 1, 2, 3, 2, 4, 6, 3, 6, 9

b)

X	1	2	3	4	6	9
$P(X)$	1/9	2/9	2/9	1/9	2/9	1/9

c) $P(X = 3) = 2/9$;

d) $P(X > 6) = P(X = 9) = 1/9$

e) $P(2 \le X \le 6)$
$$= P(X = 2) + P(X = 2) + P(X = 3) + P(X = 4) + P(X = 6)$$
$$= 2/9 + 2/9 + 1/9 + 2/9$$
$$= 7/9$$

2. a) $P(X=8) + P(X=9) + P(X=10) + P(X=11) + P(X=12) = 1$ (Axiom 2)

If we let $P(X = 10) = x$, then: $P(X = 11) = x/2$, $P(X = 9) = 2/3x$,

$P(X = 8) = P(X = 12) = x/4$

Therefore

$$\frac{x}{4} + \frac{2}{3}x + x + \frac{x}{2} + \frac{x}{4} = 1, \text{ or}$$

$$x = \frac{1}{\left(\frac{1}{4} + \frac{2}{3} + 1 + \frac{1}{2} + \frac{1}{4}\right)} = \frac{1}{(32/12)} = \frac{12}{32} = \frac{3}{8} = 0.375,$$

and the PMF(X) is

X	8	9	10	11	12
$P(X)$	3/32	8/32	12/32	6/32	3/32

b)

$XP(X)$	24/32	72/32	120/12	66/32	36/32

and $E(X) = \Sigma (X_i) P(X_i) = 318/32 = 9.9375$

c)

$X^2P(X)$	192/32	684/32	1200/12	726/32	432/32

and $E(X^2) = \Sigma X_1^2 P(Xi) = 3198/32 = 99.9375$

Then $V(X) = E(X^2) - [E(X)]^2 = 99.9375 - (9.9375)^2 = 1.18$

d) $P(X > 10) = P(X = 11) + P(X = 12) = 6/32 + 3/32 = 9/32$

e)

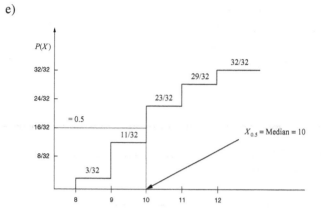

3. a)

$$\text{Area between 2 and 5} = \int_2^5 f(x)dx^2 dx = \int_2^5 Ax^2 dx = A\int_2^5 x^2 dx$$

$$= A\left[\frac{X^3}{3}\right]_2^5 = \frac{A}{3}[5^3 - 2^3] = \frac{A}{3}[125 - 8] = \frac{A}{3}(117)$$

$$= 39A$$

For the function to be a proper probability function, the area under the function, in the interval of variation, must be equal to 1. This can be accomplished, if we let $39A = 1$ or $A = 1/39$

Therefore $f(X = x) = \frac{1}{39}x^2$ $2 \leq X \leq 5$, and

b) $E(X) = \int_2^5 f(x)dx = \int_2^5 x\left[\frac{1}{39}x^2\right]dx = \frac{1}{39}\int_2^5 x^3 dx = \frac{1}{39}\left[\frac{x^4}{4}\right]_2^5$

$$= \frac{1}{156}[x^4]_2^5 = \frac{1}{156}[5^4 - 2^4] = \frac{1}{156}\left(625 - 16\right) = \frac{609}{156} = 3.903846$$

$E(X^2) = \int_2^5 f(x)dx = \int_2^5 x^2\left[\frac{1}{39}x^2\right]dx = \frac{1}{39}\int_2^5 x^4 dx = \frac{1}{39}\left[\frac{x^4}{4}\right]_2^5$

$$= \frac{1}{195}[x^5]_2^5 = \frac{1}{195}[5^5 - 2^5] = \frac{1}{195}(3,125 - 32) = \frac{3,093}{195} = 15.86$$

$V(X) = E(X^2) - [E(X)]^2 = 15.86 - (3.903846)^2 = 0.62$, and $\sigma(X) = 0.7874$

c) $P(3 \leq X \leq 4) = P(3 < X < 4) = \int_3^4 f(x)\, dx = \int_3^4 \frac{1}{39}x^2 dx = \frac{1}{39}\left[\frac{x^3}{3}\right]_3^4$

$$= \frac{1}{117}[x^3]_3^4 = \frac{1}{117}[4^3 - 3^3] = \frac{1}{117}(64 - 27) = \frac{37}{117} = 0.316$$

4. a)

X	1	−1
P(X)	p	1−p

Then

$$E(X) = \sum X_i P(X_i) = (1)(p) + (-1)(1-p) = p - 1 + p = 2p - 1$$

$$E(X^2) = \sum X_1^2 P(X_i) = (1^2)(p) + (-1)^2(1-p) = p + 1 - p = 1$$

Then

$$V(X) = E(X^2) - [E(X)]^2 = 1 - (2p-1)^2 = 1 - (4p^2 - 4p + 1)$$

$$= 4p(1-p) = 4p - 4p^2$$

b) Since $Y = 5 - \frac{1}{5}X$, $E(Y) = 5 - \frac{1}{5}E(X)$

$$= 5 - \frac{1}{5}(2p-1) = 5 + \frac{1}{5} - \frac{2}{5}p = 5.2 - 0.4p$$

$$V(Y) = \left(-\frac{1}{5}\right)^2 V(X) = \frac{1}{25}(4p - 4p^2) = \frac{4p}{25}(1-p)$$

c) When $p = 0.5$

$E(X) = 2p - 1 = 2(0.5) - 1 = 1 - 1 = 0$;
$V(X) = 4p(1-p) = 4(1/2)(1/2) = 1$
$E(Y) = 5.2 - 0.4p = 5.2 - 0.4(0.5) = 5.2 - 0.2 = 5$
and $V(Y) = 4/25 \, p(1-p) = 4/25 \, (1/2)(1/2) = 4/25 \, (1/4) = 1/25$

5. a) Substituting the values of $X = 2, 3, \ldots, 12$, we obtain

$P(X=2) = 1/36$, $P(X=3) = 2/36$, $P(X=4) = 3/36$, $P(X=5) = 4/36$, $P(X=6) = 5/36$, $P(X=7) = 6/36$, $P(X=8) = 5/36$, $P(X=9) = 4/36$, $P(X=10) = 3/36$, $P(X=11) = 2/36$ and $P(X=12) = 1/36$.

Since for each $P(X = i), 0 \le P(X = i) \le 1$, and $\sum_{i=2}^{12} P(X = i) = 1$, $P(X)$ is a proper probability function.

b) $E(X) = \sum_{i=2}^{12} X_i P(X_i)$

$= 2(1/36) + 3(2/36) + 4(3/36) + 5(4/36) + 6(5/36) + 7(6/36) + 8(5/36) + 9(4/36) +$
$\quad 10(3/36) + 11(2/36) + 12(1/36)$
$= 1/36(2 + 6 + 12 + 20 + 30 + 42 + 40 + 36 + 30 + 22 + 12)$
$= 252/36$
$= (7 \times 36) / 36$
$= 7$

c) $E(X^2) = \sum_{i=12}^{12} X_i^2 P(X_i)$

$$= 2^2\left(\frac{1}{36}\right) + 3^2\left(\frac{2}{36}\right) + 4^2\left(\frac{3}{36}\right) + 5^2\left(\frac{4}{36}\right) + 6^2\left(\frac{5}{36}\right) + 7^2\left(\frac{6}{36}\right)$$

$$+ 8^2\left(\frac{5}{36}\right) + 9^2\left(\frac{4}{36}\right) + 10^2\left(\frac{3}{36}\right) + 11^2\left(\frac{2}{36}\right) + 12^2\left(\frac{1}{36}\right)$$

$$= \frac{1974}{36}$$

$$= 54.8333$$

$$V(X) = E(X^2) - [E(X)]^2 = 54.8333 - 7^2 = 54.8333 - 49 = 5.8333 = 35/6$$

6. Given: $Y = a + bX$, and $E(Y) = a + b\,E(X)$ and $V(Y) = b^2 V(X)$

Then we have: $70 = a + b(62.5)$ (1)

and $8^2 = b^2(10)^2$ (2)

From (2) we obtain; $b^2 = 8^2/10^2 = (8/10)^2$ and $b = 8/10 = 0.8$,

and from (1) we obtain: $a = 70 - 62.5(0.8) = 70 - 50 = 20$

Therefore, $Y = a + bX = 20 + 0.8X$ (*i.e.*, if $X = 90$, $Y = 20 + 0.8(90) = 20 + 72 = 92$)

7. a) $E(Y) = E\left(\dfrac{X}{3}\right) = \dfrac{1}{3}E(X) = \dfrac{1}{3}(1) = \dfrac{1}{3}$;

$V(Y) = V\left(\dfrac{X}{3}\right) = \dfrac{1}{3^2}V(X) = \dfrac{1}{9}(4) = \dfrac{4}{9}$

b) $E(S) = E(kX) = kE(X) = k(1) = k$; $(V(S) = V(kX) = k^2 V(X) = 4k^2$

c) $E(T) = E\left[\dfrac{X}{k} + k\right] = \dfrac{1}{k}E(X) + k = \dfrac{1}{k}(1) + k = \dfrac{1}{k} + k$;

$V(T) = V\left(\dfrac{X}{k} + k\right) = V\left(\dfrac{X}{k}\right) + V(k) = \dfrac{1}{k^2}V(X) + 0 = \left(\dfrac{1}{k^2}\right)(4) = \dfrac{4}{k^2}$

8. a) The sample space of this experiment is given by S, where
$S = \{(1, 1), (1, 2), (1, 6), (2, 1), (2, 2), (2, 6), (6, 1), (6, 2), (6, 6)\}$, and the
corresponding sums are 2, 3, 7, 3, 4, 8, 7, 8, 12

b)

$X = X_1 + X_2$	2	3	4	7	8	12
$P(X)$	1/9	2/9	1/9	2/9	2/9	1/9

c) $P(X = 7) = 2/9$

d) $P(X > 6) = P(X = 7) + P(X = 8) + P(X = 12) = 2/9 + 2/9 + 1/9 = 5/9$

e) $P(3 < X < 8) = P(X = 4) + P(X = 7) = 1/9 + 2/9 = 3/9$

9. a) Since $G + D = 4$, $G = 4 - D$ and $E(G) = 4 - E(D) = 4 + (-1)D$, and
$V(G) = (-1)^2 V(D) = V(D)$ From the PMF above, we find

$$E(D) = \sum_{i=1}^{5} D_i P(D_i)$$
$$= 0(0.80) + 1(0.09) + 2(0.05) + 3(0.03) + 4(0.03)$$
$$= 0 + 0.09 + 0.10 + 0.09 + 0.12$$
$$= 0.4,$$

and $E(D^2) = 0^2(0.08) + 1^2(0.09) + 2^2(0.05) + 3^2(0.03) + 4^2(0.03)$
$$= 0 + 0.09 + 0.20 + 0.27 + 0.48$$
$$= 1.04,$$

and $V(D) = E(D^2) - [E(D)]^2 = 1.04 + (0.4)^2 = 1.04 - 0.16 = 0.88$

Therefore $E(G) = 4 - E(D) = 4 - 0.4 = 3.6$ and $V(G) = V(D) = 0.88$

b) $E(H) = E(5 + 2G) = 5 + 2E(G) = 5 + 2(3.6) = 5 + 7.2 = 12.2$
$V(H) = V(5 + 2G) = V(5) + V(2G) = 0 + 2^2 V(G) = 4(0.88) = 3.52$

10. a) Since $f(2) = 2/14$, $f(3) = 3/14$, $f(4) = 4/14$, and $f(5) = 5/14$, and
$f(2) + f(3) + f(4) + f(5) = 2/14 + 3/14 + 4/14 + 5/14 = 14/14 = 1$, this
is a proper probability function.

b) Since $f(0) = 1/4$, $f(1) = 1/14$, $f(2) = 1/14$, and $f(3) = 1/4$,
and $f(0) + f(1) + f(2) + f(3) = 1/4 + 1/4 + 1/4 + 1/4 = 1$, this is a proper
probability function.

c) Since $f(2) = 0$, $f(3) = 2/5$, $f(4) = 4/5$, $f(5) = 6/5$, $f(6) = 8/5$ and
$p(x = 5) = f(5) = 6/5 > 1$ (also $p(x=6)=f(6)=8/5>1$), this is not a proper
probability function because the axiom of probability which requires the
probability of every event, E, to be a random value between 0 and 1 is violated
(Axiom 1: $0 \leq P(E) \leq 1$)

d) Since $P(X = 1) = f(1) = 1/3$, $P(X = 2) = f(2) = 1/3$, $P(X = 3) = f(3)$
$= 1/3$, $P(X = 4) = f(4) = 1/3$, and
$P(X = 1) + P(X = 2) + P(X = 3) + P(X = 4) = 1/3 + 1/3 + 1/3 + 1/3$
$= 4/3 > 1$, this is not a proper probability function because the axiom of
probability which requires the sum of the probabilities of all the events to be equal
to 1 is violated
(Axiom 2: $\sum_{i=1}^{n} P(Ei) = 1$).

6 The Binomial and Other Discrete Variables

We have previously discussed random variables in general. In this chapter we concentrate our discussion on some discrete random variables such as the Binomial, Hypergeometric, and the Poisson.

We analyze each of these (and other) probability models separately, state the conditions under which each of these models holds true, derive their most important characteristics (such as Expected Value and Variance), and show how each is applied in the solution of real-life problems.

Finally, because Poisson distribution is a 1-parameter distribution, the Binomial a 2-parameter distribution, while the Hypergeometric distribution is a 3-parameter distribution, (and probability calculations are easier using distributions with fewer parameters), we show the conditions under which the Poisson can approximate the Binomial, the Binomial can approximate the Hypergeometric and, ultimately, the Poisson can approximate the Hypergeometric.

In general:

$$\text{Poisson} \approx \underset{n \to \infty}{\text{Lim}} (\text{Binomial}) \approx \underset{N \to \infty}{\text{Lim}} (\text{Hypergeometric,})$$

or

$$\frac{e^{-\lambda}\lambda^x}{x!} \approx \binom{n}{x} p^x (1 - p)^{n-x} \approx \frac{\binom{N_1}{x}\binom{N - N_1}{n - x}}{\binom{N}{n}},$$

when $n > 100$, $p < 0.01$, and $\frac{n}{N} < \frac{1}{20}$ and:

$$\lambda = np = n\left[\frac{N_1}{N}\right]$$

6.1   Introduction

In the previous chapter we discussed random variables in general. The properties we discussed apply to any random variable with a proper probability function (PMF for discrete variables and density functions for continuous variables). However, because some of these random variables are used more often than the others (because they are capable of representing many real-life processes) they have acquired specific names, their properties are well known, people refer to them as probability laws or probability models, and they can be either discrete or continuous.

In this chapter we will introduce and discuss the most important discrete probability models while in Chapter 7 we will do the same thing for the most important continuous probability models.

These probability models are very important because they help us to predict the behavior of future repetitions of an experiment, they add visibility on the existing relationships, and they make the calculation of the needed probabilities much easier.

The discrete probability laws (models) we will discuss in this chapter are the following:

1. The Bernoulli Probability Law (Model)
2. The Binomial Probability Law (Model)
3. The Hyper-Geometric Probability Law (Model)
4. The Poisson Probability Law (Model)
5. The Multinomial Probability Law (Model)
6. The Uniform Probability Law (Model)

As it will become apparent from discussing these probability laws, most of these discrete probability models are closely related to each other. In the last section of this chapter we will state the conditions that must hold true in order to substitute one probability law for another one. This is extremely important because some of these probability models have, in their mathematical equation which describes their behavior, one, two, three, or more parameters which control their overall behavior. It is a known fact that the calculation of probability of events of interest is more complicated for probability models with many parameters. Therefore, if certain conditions existed which would allow a probability model with m parameters (say $m = 3$) to be replaced by a model with $m - 1$ (that is $m - 1 = 2$) parameters, the probability calculations will be much easier to perform.

6.2 The Bernoulli Probability Model

For many experiments (and real life situations) there are only two possible outcomes. Thus a coin falls either a head or a tail, a machined part may be defective or non defective, the car starts or it does not start when we turn the ignition key, and so on. Such experiments provide the smallest sample space to which a random experiment can apply.

A sequence of experiments can be such that the outcome of one has no effect on the outcome of another. Such trials or experiments are said to be independent. In addition, the probabilities for two-outcome experiments are frequently constant from trial to trial. A coin has no memory, so that the probability of the outcomes of successive trials are constant.

Independent trials with only two possible outcomes and constant probabilities are called Bernoulli trials, after J. Bernoulli (1654−1705), who was a pioneer in the field of probability.

One of the outcomes of such a two-outcome experiment is designated as "success", with probability of occurrence p, and the other as "failure", with probability of occurrence q, where $q = 1 - p$ so that the probability axioms are satisfied.

Suppose then, that a random variable X can assume only two values, a and b, with probability of occurrence p and $1 - p$ respectively. Then, since the random variable X satisfies the two criteria of a Bernoulli trial, the random variable X is Bernoulli-distributed such that $X = a$ is "success" with probability of success equal to p and $X = b$ is "failure" with probability of failure equal to $1 - p$. Then, the PMF of the Bernoulli variable X is:

X	a	b
$P(X)$	p	$1 - p$

By using the properties of the Expectation Operator we discussed in the last chapter we obtain:

$$E(X) = \sum_{i=1}^{2} x_i \, p(x_i) = ap + b(1 - p) \tag{6.1}$$

$$E(X^2) = \sum_{i=1}^{2} x_i^2 \, p(x_i) = a^2 p + b^2(1 - p) \tag{6.2}$$

Knowledge of $E(X)$ and $E(X^2)$ allows us to calculate $V(X)$ and $\sigma(X)$ from the formulas:

$$V(X) = E(X^2) - \big[E(X)\big]^2 = \big[a^2 p + b^2(1-p)\big] - \big[ap + b(1-p)\big]^2 \quad (6.3)$$

and
$$\sigma(X) = \sqrt{V(X)} \quad (6.4)$$

Then, after some algebraic simplifications, we obtain:

$$V(X) = (a-b)^2 \; p(1-p) \quad (6.5)$$

and
$$\sigma(X) = (a-b)\sqrt{p(1-p)} \quad (6.6)$$

The formulas above have been derived for any values a and b whatsoever. It is customary to assign the values $a = 1$ and $b = 0$ to the Bernoulli variable. Substituting these values to the above formulas we obtain:

$$E(X) = p \quad (6.7)$$

$$E(X^2) = p \quad (6.8)$$

$$V(X) = p(1-p) \quad (6.9)$$

$$\sigma(X) = \sqrt{p(1-p)} \quad (6.10)$$

It is obvious from the PMF(X) and the above results that the Bernoulli probability model depends on only one parameter, namely the probability of "success" p.

While the Bernoulli model has interesting properties on its own right, the main reason we are studying the model is the fact that the Binomial variable (model) that we are studying next can be considered as the sum of n independent and identically distributed Bernoulli variables (sometimes referred to as "iid" variables) and this fact is very helpful in finding the expected value of the Binomial variable. Another important application of our ability to express the Binomial variable as the sum of n Bernoulli variables is the fact that we can use the "Central Limit Theorem" (which will be discussed in Chapter 8) to approximate the Binomial distribution by the Normal Distribution, as we will also see in Chapter 8.

6.3 The Binomial Probability Model

When we assigned the value of 1 to the Bernoulli variable X, with probability of success p, and the value of 0 with probability of failure $1 - p$, in effect we converted the PMF(X) from the table:

X	1	0
$P(X)$	p	$1-p$

to the equation:

$$P(X = x) = p^x(1-p)^{1-x} \qquad \text{for } x = 0, 1 \quad (6.11)$$

because when $x = 0$ we obtain $P(x = 0) = 1 - p$, and when $x = 1$ we obtain $P(x = 1) = p$, which agree with the above table values.

Usually, we have more than one observation, as when we toss a coin many times and observe the sequence of heads and tails. Since each toss and its corresponding outcome have no bearing on the outcome of any other toss, these are independent Bernoulli trials, and we may record the outcome of such an experiment as a sequence of n letters H and T (if the experiment was repeated n times). For example, if we toss a coin 5 times, we may observe the outcome *HTHTH*.

If each H is assigned the value of 1 and each T the value of 0, then we may also express this outcome as the 5-tuple (10101).

In general, if Y_i is the random variable associated with the ith trial, then $(Y_1, Y_2, \ldots, Y_n)$ represents the random outcome of the n repetitions of the basic Bernoulli experiment. Our observation will be a sequence of 1 and 0 since each Y_i can be assigned one of these two values, depending on whether a head (success) or tail (failure) occurred.

Then, if we add the numbers in the sequence, we get the number of times that the event success (head in this example) has occurred.

If we now let:

$$X = \sum_{i=1}^{n} Y_i \qquad (6.12)$$

the random variable X counts the number of successes in a Bernoulli experiment, which is repeated n times, and is called a Binomial variable. Clearly, the Binomial variable X is equal to the sum of n independent and identically distributed Bernoulli variables. We say that a random variable has the Binomial distribution if the following 4 conditions hold true:

1. A single trial is a Bernoulli variable and results in two possible outcomes, Success and Failure.
2. The probability of Success, p, remains constant from trial to trial.
3. The repeated trials are independent.
4. A fixed number, n, of trials will be conducted.

It is not difficult to force any experiment to have only two outcomes, regardless of the number of the sample points in its sample space.

It simply depends on how the event "Success" is defined. For example, rolling a single die once results in a sample space with six sample points. However, if we define success as the event that the number is, say, 5 or greater, we have divided the sample space in two mutually exclusive and collectively exhaustive events: Success = $\{5, 6\}$ and Failure = $\{1, 2, 3, 4\}$ with $P(\text{Success}) = p = 2/6$ and $P(\text{Failure}) = 1 - p = 4/6$.

To obtain the PMF of the Binomial variable, we will assume that a die, for which Success and Failure are as defined above, is rolled 5 times and we are interested in the probability that we will obtain 2 successes and 3 failures.

There are many ways of obtaining 2 successes and 3 failures in a Bernoulli experiment which is repeated 5 times. In fact, there are ten such ways, the following:

	1st	2nd	3rd	4th	5th	**Probability of Outcome**
1.	S	S	F	F	F	$pp(1-p)(1-p)(1-p)$
2.	S	F	S	F	F	$p(1-p)p(1-p)(1-p)$
3.	S	F	F	S	F	$p(1-p)(1-p)p(1-p)$
4.	S	F	F	F	S	$p(1-p)(1-p)(1-p)p$
5.	F	S	S	F	F	$(1-p)pp(1-p)(1-p)$
6.	F	S	F	S	F	$(1-p)p(1-p)p(1-p)$
7.	F	S	F	F	S	$(1-p)p(1-p)(1-p)p$
8.	F	F	S	S	F	$(1-p)(1-p)pp((1-p)$
9.	F	F	S	F	S	$(1-p)(1-p)p(1-p)p$
10.	F	F	F	S	S	$(1-p)(1-p)(1-p)pp$

Clearly, every one of these sequences containing 2 successes and 3 failures in five trials has probability $p^2(1 - p)^3$ as can be verified from the "probability of outcome" column above. But all these ten different sequences are mutually exclusive events. Then, according to the special additive law, we have:

$$P(\text{success}) = P(\text{sum of the individual probabilities of all favorable outcomes})$$
$$= 10p^2(1 - p)^3,$$

since there are 10 identical terms.

If we followed a procedure similar to the above, we will be able to show that:

$$p(\text{Success} = 0) = (1 - p)^5$$
$$p(\text{Success} = 1) = 5p(1 - p)^4$$
$$p(\text{Success} = 2) = 10p^2(1 - p)^3$$
$$p(\text{Success} = 3) = 10p^3(1 - p)^2$$
$$p(\text{Success} = 4) = 5p^4(1 - p)$$
$$p(\text{Success} = 5) = p^5$$

and, by letting $x =$ number of successes in 5 repetitions, we can combine the above results and write:

$$P(\text{Success} = X = x) = \frac{5!}{x!(5 - x)!} p^x(1 - p)^{5 - x} \quad \text{where } x = 0, 1, 2, 3, 4, 5 \quad (6.13)$$

from which we can obtain the above probabilities when the x values are substituted in.

Note: There are $n + 1$ possible values of x, to account for the fact that we may not have any success at all in the n trials.

This formula represents the PMF of the Binomial variable which, because of its prominence in probability theory and statistics, is designated by $b(x, n, p)$, which is read as: The PMF of the Binomial variable X with values x, in an experiment which is repeated n times, and with probability of success equal to p.

The "$n!$" is called the "factorial" of the number n and is defined as "the product of all integer numbers from 1 up to and including the number n. By definition, we have:

$$0! = 1$$
$$1! = 1$$
$$2! = 1 \times 2 = 2$$
$$3! = 1 \times 2 \times 3 = 6, \text{ etc.}$$

If the number of times that the basic experiment is repeated is changed from 5 to n, the Binomial law of a random variable X is given by:

$$b(X = x, n, p) = \frac{n!}{x!(n - x)!} p^x(1 - p)^{n - x} \quad x = 0, 1, 2, \ldots, n \quad (6.14)$$

Questions that can be answered with this probability law include the following:

1. What is the probability that the value of the random variable X is *at most* equal to k where $0 \le k \le n$?
2. What is the probability that X is *exactly* equal to k?
3. What is the probability that X is *at least* k?

The answers to the above questions are:

1. $P(X \leq k) = \sum_{x=0}^{k} b(x, n, p) = b(0, n, p) + b(1, n, p) + \cdots + b(k, n, p)$ (6.15)

2. $P(X = k) = b(k, n, p)$ (6.16)

3. $P(X \geq k) = \sum_{x=k}^{n} n(x, n, p) = b(k, n, p) + b(k + 1, n, p)$

$$+ \cdots + b(n, n, p)$$ (6.17)

The Binomial probability law is a two-parameter probability law, with the parameters being n and p. It derives its name from the fact that $b(x, n, p)$ is the general term of the binomial expansion:

$$[p + (1 - p)]^n = p^n + \binom{n}{n-1} p^{n-1}(1 - p) + \binom{n}{n-2} p^{n-2}(1 - p)^2 + \cdots$$

$$+ \binom{n}{r} p^r (1 - p)^{n-r} + \cdots + (1 - p)^n$$ (6.18)

where $$\binom{n}{r} = \frac{n!}{r!(n - r)!}$$ (6.19)

6.3.1 The Cumulative Binomial Distribution

Using the definition of the CDF of a random variable, as defined in Chapter 5, we write:

$$\text{CDF}(X) = \text{Prob}(X \leq k) = B(k, n, p) = \sum_{x=0}^{k} b(x, n, p)$$ (6.20)

$$= b(0, n, p) + b(1, n, p) + \cdots$$
$$+ b(k - 1, n, p) + b(k, n, p)$$

in which we have assigned the notation $B(k, n, p)$ to the CDF of the Binomial variable X because of its importance in probability and statistics.

The above expression can also be written as:

$$B(k, n, p) = B(k - 1, n, p) + b(k, n, p)$$

since $B(k - 1, n, p) = b(0, n, p) + b(1, n, p) + \cdots + b(k - 1, n, p)$ (6.21)

From the first expression of $B(k, n, p)$, as given by (6.20), we conclude that, given n and p, we can use the PMF of the Binomial variable $(b(k, n, p))$, to find $b(0, n, p)$, $b(1, n, p)$, ..., $b(k, n, p)$, and their sum produces the CDF of the Binomial variable. The second expression on the other hand, given by (6.21), tells us that if we have available the CDF for two successive x values, we can find the probability that $X = k$ by subtraction from:

$$P(X = k) = b(k, n, p) = B(k, n, p) - B(k - 1, n, p)$$ (6.22)

This fact is often used in the construction of Binomial tables for calculating probabilities associated with the Binomial variable. Extensive Binomial tables exist which allow the calculation of $b(k, n, p)$ for any n, p $(0 < p < 1)$, and $k(0 \leq k \leq n)$ with minimal computational effort. Unfortunately such tables are very bulky and usually only selected combinations of (n, p) values are shown in such tables, which are based on the above formula for selected values of n and p. For a sample cumulative

Binomial Distribution, $B(k, n, p)$ see Table 6.1 below. If the combination of n and p is not found in the table, one can always use the Binomial law for the calculation of the desired probabilities, or search the library for a more complete table. Basically the table works as follows: The n value is listed vertically in the left-hand margin of the table and next to it the value of k which ranges from 0 up to n. The probability of success is written horizontally on top of the table. For a given value of n and at the intersection of p and k, we find $B(k, n, p)$, while at the intersection of $k - 1$ and p, we find $B(k - 1, n, p)$. Then, subtracting $B(k - 1, n, p)$ from $B(k, n, p)$ produces $P(X = k) = b(k, n, p)$, as stated in equation (6.22).

6.3.2 The Expected Value and Variance of the Binomial Variable

Applying the definitions of the Expectation and Variance operators to the Binomial Variable, we can write:

$$E(X) = \sum_{x=0}^{n} x p(x) = \sum_{x=0}^{n} x b(x, n, p) \tag{6.23}$$

$$E\left(X^2\right) = \sum_{x=0}^{n} x^2 p(x) = \sum_{x=0}^{n} x^2 b(x, n, p) \tag{6.24}$$

and
$$V(X) = E\left(X^2\right) - \left[E(X)\right]^2 \tag{6.25}$$

where $b(x, n, p) = \dfrac{n!}{x!(n - x)!}\, p^x(1 - p)^{n-x}$ is the PMF of the Binomial Variable.

To simplify the above expressions and obtain useful results it is necessary to apply the summation theorems and other mathematical techniques.

However, we can arrive at the desired result much easier, by using the result we established above that the Binomial variable X can be considered as the sum of n independent and identically distributed Bernoulli Variables, $X_1, X_2, \ldots, X_n$, for which we have already established that:

$$E(X_i) = p \quad \text{and} \quad V(X_i) = p(1 - p)$$
(See equations (6.7) and (6.9) respectively)

Since
$$X = X_1 + X_2 + \cdots + X_n,$$
by applying the Expectation and Variance operators to this equation, we obtain:

$$
\begin{aligned}
E(X) &= E[X_1 + X_2 + \cdots + X_n] & &\leftarrow \text{since the Bernoulli Variables} \\
&= E(X_1) + E(X_2) + \cdots + E(X_n) & &\quad\text{ are identically distributed.} \\
&= p + p + \cdots + p & &\leftarrow \text{since the Bernoulli Variables} \\
&= np & &\quad\text{ are independent.}
\end{aligned}
$$

$$
\begin{aligned}
V(X) &= V[X_1 + X_2 + \cdots + X_n] \\
&= V(X_1) + V(X_2) + \cdots + V(X_n) & &\leftarrow \text{since the Bernoulli Variables} \\
&= p(1 - p) + p(1 - p) + \cdots + p(1 - p) & &\quad\text{ are identically distributed.} \\
&= np(1 - p)
\end{aligned}
$$

Therefore, for the Binomial Variable X, we have:

$$E(X) = np \tag{6.26}$$

$$V(X) = np(1 - p) \tag{6.27}$$

$$\sigma(X) = \sqrt{np(1 - p)} \tag{6.28}$$

Example 1

Four companies, representing a random sample, are classified depending on whether a given characteristic, which is expected to be present with probability 2/3, is or is not present.

1. What is the probability that this characteristic is present in exactly one of the companies?
2. What is the probability that this characteristic is present in at most one company?
3. What is the probability that this characteristic is present in at least three companies?

Solutions

1. $P(x = 1) = b(x = 1, n = 4, p = 2/3) = \left(\dfrac{4!}{1!3!}\right)(2/3)^1(1/3)^3$

    $= 4(2/3)(1/27) = 8/81$

2. $P(x \le 1) = P(x = 1) + P(x = 0)$

    $= 8/81 + \left(\dfrac{4!}{0!4!}\right)(2/3)^0(1/3)^4 = 8/81 + 1/81 = 9/81$

3. $P(x \ge 3) = P(x = 3) + P(x = 4)$

    $= b(x = 3, n = 4, p = 2/3) + b(x = 4, n = 4, p = 2/3)$

    $= \left(\dfrac{4!}{3!1!}\right)\left(\dfrac{2}{3}\right)^3\left(\dfrac{1}{3}\right)^1 + \left(\dfrac{4!}{4!0!}\right)\left(\dfrac{2}{3}\right)^4\left(\dfrac{1}{3}\right)^0$

    $= 4(8/27)\left(\dfrac{1}{3}\right) + 1(16/81) = 32/81 + 16/81 = 48/81$

To also demonstrate how this problem can be solved using the table, let us complete the calculations by also computing $P(x = 0)$ and $P(x = 2)$. Then we have:

$$P(x = 0) = b(0, 4, 2/3) = 1/81$$

$$P(x = 1) = b(1, 4, 2/3) = 8/81$$

$$P(x = 2) = b(2, 4, 2/3) = 24/81$$

$$P(x = 3) = b(3, 4, 2/3) = 32/81$$

$$P(x = 4) = b(4, 4, 2/3) = 16/81$$

Since the Binomial PMF is proper, we must have:

$$\underbrace{b(0, 4, 2/3) + b(1, 4, 2/3) + b(2, 4, 2/3)}_{P(x \le 2)} + \underbrace{b(3, 4, 2/3) + b(4, 4, 2/3)}_{P(x \ge 3)} = 1$$

Therefore, we may also write:

$$P(x \leq 2) + P(x \geq 3) = 1$$

from which we obtain: $\qquad P(x \geq 3) = 1 - P(x \leq 2)$

■ ■ ■

This method of computing probabilities of desired events may prove very useful because the number of terms involved in calculating $P(x \leq 2)$ may be much smaller than the number of terms needed to calculate $P(x \geq 3)$ directly. But, care should be exercised to identify the events properly and determine whether the equal sign should be included or not. This is very important for discrete variables because:

$$P(x \leq 2) = P(x = 0) + P(x = 1) + P(x = 2), \quad \text{for example, is different than}$$
$$P(x < 2) = P(x = 0) + P(x = 1), \quad \text{and in fact}$$
$$P(x \leq 2) - P(x < 2) = P(x = 2) \neq 0$$

On the other hand, for continuous variables, we do not have to be so careful because $P(x = k) = 0$ for any value of k, as we discussed in chapter 5 and, therefore,

$$P(x \leq 2) = P(x < 2)$$

A Binomial Table which shows the Cumulative Binomial Distribution, $B(k, n, p)$ would look as follows:

Table 6.1 Sample Cumulative Binomial Distribution, $B(k, n, p)$			
n	k	$p1 \ p2 \ p3 \ldots \ p = 2/3 \ldots$	$B(k, n, p)$
1	0		
	1		
2	1		
	0		
	2		
3	0		
	1		
	2		
	3		
4	0	1/81	$P(x \leq 0) = B(0, 4, 2/3)$
	1	9/81	$P(x \leq 1) = B(1, 4, 2/3)$
	2	33/81	$P(x \leq 2) = B(2, 4, 2/3)$
	3	65/81	$P(x \leq 3) = B(3, 4, 2/3)$
	4	81/81	$P(x \leq 4) = B(4, 4, 2/3)$

Therefore, to use such a table, or one with equivalent decimal entries to solve the above problem, we must first find the probabilities that $P(x = k)$ for $k = 0, 1, 2, 3, 4$.

We obtain:

$$P(x = 4) = b(4, 4, 2/3) = B(4, 4, 2/3) - B(3, 4, 2/3) = 81/81 - 65/81 = 16/81$$

$$P(x = 3) = b(3, 4, 2/3) = B(3, 4, 2/3) - B(2, 4, 2/3) = 65/81 - 33/81 = 32/81$$

$$P(x = 2) = b(2, 4, 2/3) = B(2, 4, 2/3) - B(1, 4, 2/3) = 33/81 - 9/81 \ = 24/81$$

$$P(x = 1) = b(1, 4, 2/3) = B(1, 4, 2/3) - B(0, 4, 2/3) = 9/81 \ - 1/81 \ = 8/81$$

$$P(x = 0) = b(0, 4, 2/3) = B(0, 4, 2/3) \qquad\qquad = 1/81 \qquad = 1/8$$

which are clearly identical to the values found when using the Binomial PMF directly, but with much less labor. All we need to do here is subtract two successive Cumulative Distribution values in the appropriate column found situated at the intersection of n/k and p values.

The Binomial probability model is symmetric when $p = 1/2$ and skewed when $p \neq 1/2$, being skewed to the right for $p < 1/2$ and skewed to the left for $p > 1/2$. This can be seen quite readily when one plots $b(x, n, p)$ against X, for a fixed value of p and with n as a parameter.

However, the skewness of the Binomial distribution, regardless of the size of p, becomes less and less apparent as n increases.

Many computer programs exist and are available in many computer systems, which calculate automatically $b(x, n, p)$ and $B(k, n, p)$ and make appropriate plots, when the user specifies n and p. MINITAB is such a program (or statistical tool).

For example, if X is a Binomial random variable with parameters n and p, MINITAB evaluates $b(x, n, p)$ using the command/subcommand:

> **MTB > pdf;**
> **SUBC > Binomial** $n\ p.$,

and $B(k, n, p)$ using the command/subcommand:

> **MTB > cdf;**
> **SUBC > Binomial** $n\ p.$

6.4 The Hypergeometric Probability Model

The Binomial probability model we discussed above applies to **sampling with replacement from a finite population or sampling without replacement from an infinite population.**

However, it is often necessary to sample without replacement, as in the case of many card games, from a finite population. Since the trials are not independent and the probabilities do not remain constant from trial to trial, the Binomial model does not apply here, and we need to come up with a different probability model.

Suppose that we have a finite population of N items, $N1$ of which are of one kind (perhaps good) and $N-N1$ are of a second kind. We wish to draw a sample of n items (where $n < N$) without replacement.

We are interested in the number of items x which are of the first kind. Of course $n - x$ will be of the second kind.

We are looking to derive the probability law which will give us exactly x items of the first kind in a random sample of size n. This probability law is called Hypergeometric, the random variable X which counts the number of occurrences x is called the Hypergeometric variable, and the probability law has three parameters: N, N_1, n.

We proceed as follows:

1. There are $\dfrac{N!}{n!(N-n)!}$ ways of drawing n distinct items from a population of size N (as we discussed in Chapter 4), without regard to their order of selection. Therefore, our sample space consists of

$$\binom{N}{n} = \frac{N!}{n!(N-n)!} \tag{6.29}$$

sample points, all of which are equally likely, and have probability of occurrence equal to $1/\dfrac{N!}{n!(N-n)!}$.

2. Let X be the random variable which counts the number of items of type 1 to be found in a sample of size n. Then the random variable X assigns a real value to each and every point in the sample space, which is its domain. When X takes the value x, then the sample will also include $n - x$ items of the second kind.

3. There are

$$\binom{N_1}{x} = \frac{N_1!}{x!(N_1 - x)!} \tag{6.30}$$

ways of drawing exactly x items of the first kind for the sample and

$$\binom{N - N_1}{n - x} = \frac{(N - N_1)!}{(n - x)![N - N_1 - (n - x)]!} \tag{6.31}$$

ways to draw the second kind. Then, according to the Multiplication principle, discussed in Chapter 4, a sample of size n, that includes x items of the first kind and $n - x$ of the second kind can be selected in

$$\binom{N_1}{x}\binom{N - N_1}{n - x} \text{ ways.} \tag{6.32}$$

4. Therefore, the probability associated with this sample is

$$P(X = x) = h(x, N, N_1, n) = \frac{\dbinom{N_1}{x}\dbinom{N - N_1}{n - x}}{\dbinom{N}{n}} \tag{6.33}$$

which is the Hypergeometric probability model or distribution, with

$\dbinom{N_1}{x}, \dbinom{N - N_1}{n - x}$ and $\dbinom{N}{n}$ defined by equations (6.30), (6.31), and (6.29) respectively.

Following the example of the Binomial law, we designate the Cumulative Hypergeometric Distribution by $H(x, N, n, N_1)$ and write:

$$H(k, N, n, N_1) = \sum_{x = \max[0,\, n - (N - N_1)]}^{k} h(x, N, n, N_1) \tag{6.34}$$

It is possible to construct table values for the Hypergeometric probability law, but such a table will be more complicated because this probability law has one more parameter than the Binomial and, therefore, it would need a 3rd axis to efficiently store the needed values. Since this is not possible, we can fix one of the parameters and then have a table similar to the Binomial. But, the Hypergeometric Law is relatively easy to compute (one only needs to calculate the factorial of three numbers) and, therefore, no table is warranted.

Applying the Expectation and Variance Operators to the Hypergeometric variable X, in the usual manner, we obtain:

$$E(X) = \sum_{x=\max[0,\, N-N_1]}^{k} x h(x, N, n, N_1) = n\left(\frac{N_1}{N}\right) \tag{6.35}$$

and

$$V(X) = n\left(\frac{N_1}{N}\right)\left(1 - \frac{N_1}{N}\right)\left(\frac{N-n}{N-1}\right) \tag{6.36}$$

The factor $\left(\dfrac{N-n}{N-1}\right)$ in the variance expression is called the "Finite Population Correction Factor" and it is important when N is finite. On the other hand, if N is very large (approximately infinite) and n is of "moderate" size, the factor $(N-n)/(N-1)$ approaches unity and can be dropped from the variance formula thus producing:

$$V_1(X) = n\left(\frac{N_1}{N}\right)\left(1 - \frac{N_1}{N}\right) \tag{6.37}$$

which is very close to $V(X)$. But for finite N, the variance formula must include the FPCF (Finite Population Correction Factor) and is given by:

$$V(X) = \left(\frac{N-n}{N-1}\right)V_1(X) = \left(\frac{N-n}{N-1}\right)n\left(\frac{N_1}{N}\right)\left(1 - \frac{N_1}{N}\right) \tag{6.38}$$

The example below will illustrate this and other computational aspects of the Hypergeometric probability law.

Example 2

Suppose a population consists of $N = 10$ items, of which $N_1 = 6$ are good, and $N - N_1 = 4$ are defective. A sample of size $n = 3$ is drawn from this population, without replacement.

1. What is the probability that the sample of 3 will contain 0, 1, 2, or 3 good items?
2. Use these results to calculate $E(X)$ and $V(X)$, by first calculating the PMF(X).
3. Compare the $E(X)$ and $V(X)$ results of step 2 to those obtained from the formulas for $E(X)$ and $V(X)$. Make appropriate adjustments to account for the fact that this is a finite population.
4. Also use the tree-diagram approach to find the desired probabilities and compare the results with those obtained using the Hypergeometric probability model.

Solutions

1. $h(0, 10, 6, 3) = \dfrac{\dbinom{6}{0}\dbinom{4}{3}}{\dbinom{10}{3}} = \dfrac{\dbinom{N_1}{0}\dbinom{N-N_1}{n}}{\dbinom{N}{n}} = \dfrac{(1)(4)}{120} = 1/30$

$$h(1, 10, 6, 3) = \frac{\binom{6}{1}\binom{4}{2}}{\binom{10}{3}} = \frac{(6)(6)}{120} = 9/30$$

$$h(2, 10, 6, 3) = \frac{\binom{6}{2}\binom{4}{12}}{\binom{10}{3}} = \frac{(15)(4)}{120} = 15/30$$

$$h(3, 10, 6, 3) = \frac{\binom{6}{3}\binom{4}{0}}{\binom{10}{3}} = \frac{(20)(1)}{120} = 5/30$$

2. From the above results we can construct the PMF of the Hypergeometric variable X and use it to find $E(X)$ and $V(X)$ in the usual manner.

X	$P(X)$	$XP(X)$	$X^2 P(X)$
0	1/30	0	0
1	9/30	9/30	9/30
2	15/30	30/30	60/30
3	5/30	15/30	45/30
		$E(X) = 54/30 = 1.8$	$E(X^2) = 114/30 = 3.8$

Then

$$V(X) = E(X^2) - \left[E(X)\right]^2$$

$$= 3.8 - (1.8)^2 = 3.80 - 3.24 = 0.56$$

3. From formulas (6.35), (6.37), and (6.38), we obtain:

$$E(X) = n\left(\frac{N_1}{N}\right) = 3\left(\frac{6}{10}\right) = 1.8$$

which agrees exactly with the result above

$$V_1(X) = n\left(\frac{N_1}{N}\right)\left(1 - \frac{N_1}{N}\right) = 3\left(\frac{6}{10}\right)\left(\frac{4}{10}\right) = 0.72$$

which overestimates the expected variance (0.72 to 0.56)

However, because this is a finite population we should use the finite correction factor and, using (6.38), we obtain:

$$V(X) = \left(\frac{N - n}{N - 1}\right)V_1(X)$$

or

$$V(X) = \left(\frac{10 - 3}{10 - 1}\right)(0.72) = \left(\frac{7}{9}\right)(0.72) = 7(0.8) = 0.56$$

which agrees exactly with the result we obtained above using the PMF(X).

4.   Tree-diagram Probability Calculations

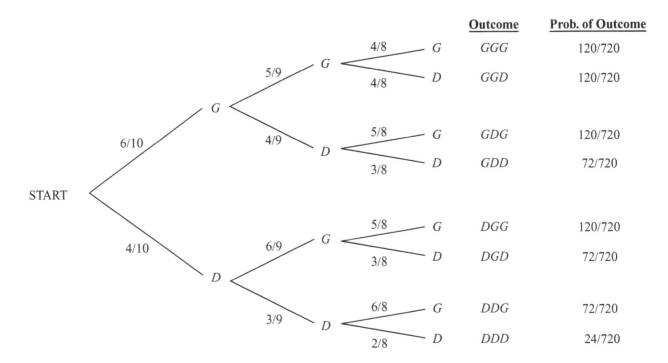

But $X = 3$ is equivalent to outcome GGG; $X = 2$ is equivalent to outcomes GDG, DGG, GGD; $X = 1$ is equivalent to outcomes GDD, DGD, DDG; and $X = 0$ is equivalent to outcome DDD. Therefore, we have:

$$P(X = 3) = P(GGG) = 120/720 = 5/30$$

$$P(X = 2) = P(GGD) + P(GDG) + P(DGG) = 3(120/720) = 15/30$$

$$P(X = 1) = P(GDD) + P(DGD) + P(DDG) = 3(72/720) = 9/30$$

$$P(X = 0) = P(DDD) = 24/720 = 1/30$$

and we see that we have obtained the same PMF for the Hypergeometric variable X. But, as we have discussed it before, the tree-diagram approach becomes very inefficient when the sample size n becomes greater than 5.

Recall that in Chapter 4, when we discussed combinational methods, we arrived at the same result as when using the Hypergeometric probability law.

■ ■ ■

6.5   The Poisson Probability Model

This probability law, which is named after the nineteenth century French probabilist Simeon Denis Poisson who first described it, is a very useful discrete distribution in which the random variable represents the number of occurrences of independent events that take place, at a constant rate, in a unit of time or space.

Typical examples are the number of arrivals to a service facility in a given time interval, the number of claims an insurance company processes in a given time, the number of accidents at an intersection, and so on. Also it offers an excellent approximation to the Binomial probability law when p is small and n is large.

The basic assumptions that lead to the Poisson probability model are the following:

1. The probability of an event occurring is proportional to the length of time or space.
2. The probability of more than one occurrence of the event in a very small unit of time (or space) is very small and can be neglected.
3. For non-overlapping units of time (or space), the number of occurrences of the event are independent.

These assumptions lead to the probability model:

$$P(x, \lambda) = \begin{cases} \dfrac{e^{-\lambda}\lambda^x}{x!} & x = 0, 1, 2, \ldots; \quad \lambda > 0 \\ 0 & \text{elsewhere} \end{cases} \tag{6.39}$$

in which the random variable X represents the number of independent random events that occur within a specified unit of time or space. This law is completely defined by the single parameter λ which represents the average number of occurrences of the random event per stated unit of time (or space).

There is a separate Poisson model for each value of λ greater than 0 and the sample space of the model is infinite. We can easily verify that $P(x, \lambda)$ is a proper probability model because:

$$\sum_{x=0}^{\infty} P(x, \lambda) = \sum_{x=0}^{\infty} \frac{e^{-\lambda}\lambda^x}{x!} = e^{-\lambda}\sum_{x=0}^{\infty}\frac{\lambda^x}{x!}$$

$$= e^{-\lambda}\left(1 + \lambda + \frac{\lambda^2}{2!} + \frac{\lambda^3}{3!} + \cdots\right) \tag{6.40}$$

$$= e^{-\lambda}\left(e^\lambda\right) = 1,$$

because the expansion inside the parentheses above is equal to e^λ.

The probability that a Poisson variable X is less than or equal to some specified value x_0 is given by the Cumulative Distribution Function:

$$P(X \le x_0) = \sum_{x=0}^{x_0} \frac{\lambda^x}{x!} = F(x, \lambda) \tag{6.41}$$

which can be used as the basis for constructing a probability table for selected values of x and λ. Such a table is really not necessary because the computational effort required to compute probabilities directly from the Poisson probability law is minimal with the help of a hand calculator. We note, however, that if such a table existed, it could be used to calculate individual probabilities using the relationship:

$$P(x, \lambda) = F(x, \lambda) - F(x-1, \lambda) \tag{6.42}$$

because the Poisson random variable is integer-valued.

The expected value and variance of the Poisson variable are obtained as follows:

$$E\left(X\right) = \sum_{x=0}^{\infty} x \frac{e^{-\lambda}\lambda^x}{x!} = e^{-\lambda}\sum_{x=0}^{\infty} x \frac{\lambda^x}{x!} = e^{-\lambda}\sum_{x=0}^{\infty} \frac{x\lambda^x}{x(x-1)!}$$

$$= e^{-\lambda}\sum_{x=1}^{\infty}\frac{\lambda^x}{(x-1)!} = \lambda e^{-\lambda}\sum_{x=1}^{\infty}\frac{\lambda^{x-1}}{(x-1)!}$$

$$= \lambda e^{-\lambda}\sum_{y=0}^{\infty}\frac{\lambda^y}{y!} \qquad \text{if we let } y = x-1 \qquad (6.43)$$

$$= \lambda$$

since

$$\sum_{y=0}^{\infty}\frac{\lambda^y}{y!} = 1 + \lambda + \frac{\lambda^2}{2!} + \frac{\lambda^3}{3!} + \cdots = e^{+\lambda}$$

In a similar manner we can show that

$$E\left(X^2\right) = \lambda^2 + \lambda \qquad (6.44)$$

Then

$$V\left(X\right) = E\left(X^2\right) - \left[E\left(X\right)\right]^2 = \lambda^2 + \lambda - \lambda^2 = \lambda, \qquad (6.45)$$

and we observe that the **Expected value** and **Variance of the Poisson random variable** are equal to the defining parameter λ $\left(\text{while } \sigma(X) = \sqrt{V(X)} = \sqrt{\lambda}\right)$.

Note: In a later chapter we will show how to obtain the "best" possible estimates for population parameters, using the sample data.

Example 3

Bank customers arrive at a teller's window at the rate of $\lambda = 8$ per 2 minutes, during a busy bank day.

1. What is the probability that no more than 4 customers will arrive in the next minute?
2. What is the probability that at least two customers will arrive in the next 4 minutes?

Solution Since for a Poisson variable the number of occurrences is proportional to the size of the time interval, in each of the two problems above, we must find the λ which is applicable for the stated time interval. Since it is given that $\lambda = 8$ for 2 minutes, it follows that $\lambda = 4$ for 1 minute, and $\lambda = 16$ for 4 minutes. Then using the Poisson probability law we have:

1. $P\left(X \le 4\right) = F\left(4, 4\right) = \sum_{x=0}^{4}\frac{e^{-4}4^x}{x!}$

$$= e^{-4} + 4e^{-4} + 8e^{-4} + \frac{32}{3}e^{-4} + \frac{32}{3}e^{-4}$$

$$= e^{-4}\left(1 + 4 + 8 + \frac{64}{3}\right) = \frac{103}{3}e^{-4}$$

$$2.\ P\big(X \geq 2\big) = 1 - P\big(X \leq 1\big) = 1 - F\big(1, 16\big)$$

$$= 1 - \sum_{x=0}^{1} \frac{e^{-16}16^{x}}{x!}$$

$$= 1 - \big(e^{-16} + 16e^{-16}\big)$$

$$= 1 - 17e^{-16}$$

■ ■ ■

6.6   The Multinomial Probability Model

The Binomial probability law that we discussed earlier is a special case of the Multinomial probability law in which independent trials result in more than two outcomes, in contrast to the Binomial law in which only two outcomes are possible.

Suppose a given experiment has k possible mutually exclusive outcomes $o_1, o_2, \ldots, o_k$, with respective probabilities: $p_1, p_2, \ldots, p_k$, such that:

$$p_1 + p_2 + \cdots + p_k = 1$$

If the experiment is repeated n times, with $p_1, p_2, \ldots, p_k$, remaining constant from trial to trial then, the probability of obtaining exactly x_1 occurrences of o_1, x_2 occurrences of $o_2, \ldots$, and x_k occurrences of o_k, (where: $x_1 + x_2 + \cdots + x_k = n$), is given by:

$$P\big(x_1, x_2, \ldots, x_k; p_1, p_2, \ldots, p_k; n\big) = \frac{n!}{x_1! x_2! \ldots x_k!} p_1^{x_1} p_2^{x_2} \ldots p_k^{x_k} \qquad (6.46)$$

In (6.46) each x_i can have the values 0, 1, 2, $\ldots, n$ subject to the condition:

$$x_1 + x_2 + \cdots + x_k = n$$

This law is arrived at when one considers the number of permutations of n things taken all at a time when all the x_1 are alike, all the x_2 are alike, $\ldots$, and all the x_k are alike.

The multinomial distribution can be illustrated in connection with a die problem where the outcome is any one of the numbers 1, 2, $\ldots$, 6. This particular case is also an example of the discrete uniform probability law, which we briefly discuss below.

6.7   The Discrete Uniform Probability Model

This law applies to an experiment that can terminate in N mutually exclusive and equally likely events each of which has $1/N$ probability of occurrence.

If we let $P\big(x, N\big)$ represent this probability law, then we can write:

$$P(x, N) = 1/N \quad \text{for } x = 1, 2, \ldots, N \qquad (6.47)$$

The Cumulative Distribution function of the discrete uniform probability law can be expressed as:

$$F\big(x\big) = P\big(X \leq x\big) = \sum_{t=0}^{x} P\big(t, N\big) = \frac{x}{N} \quad \text{for } x = 1, 2, \ldots, N \qquad (6.48)$$

where we have substituted t for x in the PMF because the upper limit in the summation is also x.

Applying the definitions of Expectation and Variance we find:

$$E(X) = \sum_{x=1}^{N} x P(x, N) = \sum_{x=1}^{N} x\left(\frac{1}{N}\right) = \frac{1}{N}\sum_{x=1}^{N} x = \frac{1}{N}\left(1 + 2 + \cdots + N\right)$$

$$= \frac{1}{N}\left[\frac{N(1 + N)}{2}\right] = \frac{N + 1}{2} \tag{6.49}$$

$$E(X^2) = \frac{1}{N}\sum_{x=1}^{N} x^2 = \frac{1}{N}\left(1^2 + 2^2 + \cdots + N^2\right)$$

$$= \frac{1}{N}\left[\frac{N(N + 1)(2N + 1)}{6}\right] = \frac{(N + 1)(2N + 1)}{6} \tag{6.50}$$

Therefore:

$$V(X) = E(X^2) - [E(X)]^2$$

$$= \frac{(N + 1)(2N + 1)}{6} - \left[\frac{(N + 1)}{2}\right]^2 = \left(\frac{N + 1}{2}\right)\left(\frac{2N + 1}{3} - \frac{N + 1}{2}\right)$$

$$= \left(\frac{N + 1}{2}\right)\left[\frac{4N + 2 - 3N - 3}{6}\right] = \left(\frac{N + 1}{2}\right)\left(\frac{N - 1}{6}\right) = \frac{N^2 - 1}{12} \tag{6.51}$$

If the experiment we described in general above is taken to be the rolling of a die in which $N = 6$, then from the above formulas for $E(X)$ and $V(X)$ we obtain:

$$E(X) = 7/2 = 3.5 \quad \text{and} \quad V(X) = 35/12$$

which are the well-known results of the die experiment.

6.8   Relationships Among the Discrete Probability Models

We have discussed several discrete probability models in this chapter, of which the most important ones are: 1. The Binomial, 2. The Hypergeometric, and 3. The Poisson.

From these discussions it became clear that each of these probability laws applies to different situations. It also became apparent that the degree of difficulty of probability calculations, using a given probability law, is directly proportional to the number of parameters used to define the given probability law.

That is, the more parameters used in the definition of a probability law, the more difficult the probability calculations.

Since only one parameter (λ) is needed to define the Poisson law, while two parameters (n, p) are needed to define the Binomial law while three parameters (N, $N1$, n) are needed to define the Hypergeometric, it would be beneficial if appropriate conditions could be found under which the Poisson law could be used in place of the Binomial and/or the Hypergeometric Laws.

In our discussion of the Poisson law we stated that it is an excellent approximation to the Binomial when p is small and n is large. We now amplify on this comment and state the following rule:

1. If n is large (*i.e.*, if $n > 100$) and p is small (*i.e.*, $p < 0.01$), then the Poisson law can accurately (to within three decimal places) approximate the Binomial law, and we can write:

$$\binom{n}{x} p^x(1 - p)^{n-x} \approx \frac{e^{-\lambda}\lambda^x}{x!} \quad \text{where} \quad \lambda = np \tag{6.52}$$

In general, it can be stated that the Poisson law is the limit of the Binomial law as $n \rightarrow \infty$

Next we will state some conditions under which the Binomial can be used to approximate the Hypergeometric.

When N is very large and n is very small such that the ratio $\dfrac{n}{N} \leq \dfrac{1}{20}$, the Binomial approximates the Hypergeometric very closely, and the approximation improves as N increases. When $N \rightarrow \infty$ the Binomial and Hypergeometric give identical results. Because of this fact we state that:

$$\textbf{Binomial Law} = \underset{N \rightarrow \infty}{\textit{Lim}} \textbf{ (Hypergeometric law)} \qquad (6.53)$$

These ideas are put together in the following rule:

2. If n (and therefore x) is very small compared to both N_1 and $N - N_1$, then the Binomial probability law approximates the Hypergeometric law very closely, and we can write:

$$h(x, N, N_1, n) = \frac{\dbinom{N_1}{x}\dbinom{N - N_1}{n - x}}{\dbinom{N}{n}} \approx \dbinom{n}{x} p^x (1 - p)^{n - x} = b(x, n, p) \quad (6.54)$$

where
$$p = \frac{N_1}{N}, \qquad (6.55)$$

and the approximation is acceptable if $\dfrac{n}{N} \leq \dfrac{1}{20}$

Since, in our discussion above, we have used the Poisson to approximate the Binomial, and then the Binomial to approximate the Hypergeometric, it stands to reason that the Poisson law can, under appropriate conditions, approximate the Hypergeometric.

Therefore, we can write:

$$h(x, N, N_1, n) = \frac{\dbinom{N_1}{x}\dbinom{N - N_1}{n - x}}{\dbinom{N}{n}} \approx \frac{e^{-\lambda}\lambda^x}{x!} = p(x, \lambda) \qquad (6.56)$$

where
$$\lambda = np = n\left[\frac{N_1}{N}\right] \qquad (6.57)$$

In the next two chapters we will show how the Binomial and, through the Binomial, the Poisson and Hypergeometric laws can be approximated by the Normal probability law, which is a continuous probability model.

6.9 References

Berenson, Marc, L., Levine, David, M., and Krehbiel, Timothy, C., 2004. *Basic Business Statistics*. 9th Edition. Pearson-Prentice Hall.

Black, Ken, 2004. *Business Statistics*. 4th Edition. Wiley.

Canavos, George, C., 1984. *Applied Probability and Statistical Methods.* Little, Brown.

Carlson, William, L., and Thorne, Betty, 1997. *Applied Statistical Methods*. Prentice Hall.

Chou, Ya-lun, 1992. *Statistical Analysis for Business and Economics.* Elsevier.

Freud, John, E., and Williams, Frank, J., 1969. *Modern Business Statistics*. Revised by: Perles, Benjamin and Sullivan, Charles. Prentice-Hall.

Freud, John, E., and Williams, Frank, J., 1982. *Elementary Business Statistics: The Modern approach*. Prentice-Hall.

Johnson, Robert, 1973. *Elementary Statistics*. Duxbury Press.

McClave, James, T., Benson, George, P., and Sincich, Terry, 2001. *Statistics for Business and Economics*. 8th Edition. Prentice Hall.

Salvatore, Dominick, *Theory and Problems of Statistics and Econometrics*. SCHAUM'S OUTLINE SERIRES, McGraw-Hill.

Steel, Robert, G.D., and Torrie, James, H., 1976. *Introduction to Statistics*. McGraw-Hill.

6.10 PROBLEMS

1. A major league pitcher has a history of throwing 60% strikes.

   a) Write the equation of this probability law, if the pitcher threw n pitches and got x strikes.

   b) What is the probability that the next batter "sees" "four balls" in the next 5 pitches thrown to him? (*i.e.*, what is the probability that the batter "walks" in 5 pitches?)

   c) What is the probability that he strikes out on 3 consecutive pitches?

   d) Find the mean and variance of the probability law in (a) if $n = 5$

2. The engines on an airliner operate independently. The probability that an individual engine will operate for a given trip is 0.9. A plane will be able to complete a trip successfully if *at least* half of its engines operate for the entire trip. Determine whether a two, three, or four-engine plane has the higher probability of a successful trip.

3. The Decision Sciences department of a University has three (3) graduate assistantships to offer. It was decided that four (4) offers will be made from the list of candidates. In the past 30% of the offers have been turned down.

   a) What is the probability that there will be at least 3 acceptances?

   b) What is the probability that there will be too many acceptances?

   c) If the University wishes to be at least 90% certain of getting a minimum of 3 acceptances, what is the minimum number of offers it should make? (Hint: This is a trial and error process, but set up the equation from which the answer can be obtained)

4. A coin is biased in a manner that causes tails to be three (3) times more likely to occur than heads. What is the probability of observing exactly 2 heads, if this coin is tossed 3 times?

5. Find the number of children a couple should have in order that the probability of them having at least 2 boys will be greater than 0.75.

6. A machine normally makes items of which 5% are defective. The practice of the manufacturer is to check the machine every hour by drawing a sample of size 10,

which he inspects. If the sample contains no defectives, he allows the machine to run for another hour.

    a) What is the probability that this practice will lead him to leave the machine alone when in fact it has shifted and is producing items of which 10% are defective?

    b) How large a sample should be inspected to ensure that if $p = 0.1$ the probability that the machine will not be stopped is less than or equal to 0.01?

7. An experiment consists of tossing 2 fair dice independently, and consider a sequence of n repeated independent trials of the experiment. What is the probability that the nth throw will be the first time that the Sum of the 2 dice is a 7?

8. Give the formulas and identify the probability law of each of the following random variables:

    a) The number of defectives in a sample size of 20, chosen without replacement from a batch of 200 articles, of which 5% are defective.

    b) The number of baby boys in a series of 30 independent births, assuming the probability at each birth that a boy will be born is $p = 0.51$.

    c) The minimum number of babies a woman must have in order to give birth to a boy (ignore multiple births, assume independence, and $p(\text{boy}) = 0.51$).

    d) The number of patients in a group of 35, having a certain ailment, who will recover if $p(\text{recovery}) = 0.75$. Assume independent chance of recovery for each patient.

9. In a certain published book of 520 pages 390 typographical errors occur. Assume that typographical errors occur according to the Poisson probability law at the rate of $390/520 = 3/4$ errors per page. What is the probability that four (4) pages, selected randomly will be free from errors?

10. A retailer discovered that the number of items of a certain part, demanded by customers in a given period, obeys a Poisson probability law with a known parameter λ. What stock K of this item should the retailer have on hand, at the beginning of the time period, in order to have a probability of 0.99 that he will be able to supply immediately all customers who demand the item during the time period under consideration?

11. Suppose that customers enter a certain shop at the rate of 30 persons per hour. What is the probability that during a 2-minute interval either no one will enter the shop or at least 2 persons will enter the shop?

12. In a large fleet of delivery trucks the average number of inoperative trucks on any day is 2, because of repairs. Two standby trucks are available. What is the probability that on any day

    a) No standby truck will be needed?

    b) The number of standby trucks is inadequate?

13. Workers in a certain factory incur accidents at the rate of 2 accidents per week. Calculate the probability that there will be 2 or fewer accidents during:

    a) 1 week

    b) 2 weeks

    c) each of 2 weeks

14. The incidence of polio during the years 1949–1954 was approximately 25 per 100,000 population.

    a) What is the probability of having 5 or fewer cases in a city of 40,000?

    b) What is the probability of having 5 or fewer cases in a city of 1,000,000?

15. A manufacturer of wool blankets inspects the blankets by counting the number of defects (a defect may be a tear, an oil spot, etc). From past records it is known that the mean number of defects per blanket is 5. What is the probability that the blanket will contain 2 or more defects?

16. Bank Tellers in a certain bank make errors by entering figures in their computers at the rate of 0.75 errors per page of entries. What is the probability that in 4 pages of entries there will be:

    a) No errors?

    b) At most 1 error?

    c) At least 2 errors?

17. It is reported that the suicide rate in a certain state is 1 suicide per 250,000 inhabitants per week.

    a) What is the probability that in a certain town, with population 500,000, there will be 6 or more suicides in a week?

    b) What is the expected number of weeks in a year in which 6 or more suicides will be reported in this town?

18. If four clerks prepare all the billings in a company office and it has been determined that 40 percent of all erroneous billings are prepared by clerk A, 20 percent by clerk B, 10 percent by clerk C, and the rest by clerk D, what is the probability that among seven randomly selected erroneous billings two were prepared by A, one by B, one by C, and three by D?

19. Among a department store's 16 delivery trucks, five have worn brakes. If 8 trucks are randomly selected for inspection what is the probability that the sample will include at least three trucks with worn brakes?

20. What is the probability that an IRS auditor will get 3 tax returns with unallowable deductions, if he randomly selects five returns from among 12 returns, six of which contain unallowable deductions?

21. If the number of complaints which a restaurant receives per day is a random variable having the Poisson distribution with $\lambda = 4.0$, find the probabilities that a given restaurant will receive:

    a) No complaints

    b) At least one complaint

    c) Two complaints

    d) 4 complaints

22. Among the 200 employees of a company, 160 are union members, and 40 are non union. If 4 of the employees are randomly selected to serve on the pension committee, what is the probability that two (2) of them will be union members and the other 2 non union?

23. Solve problem 22 again using the Binomial approximation to the Hypergeometric. What is the error of the approximation?

24. The probabilities that a state tax return will: a) Be filled out correctly is 0.5 b) That it will contain only errors favoring the tax payer is 0.20; c) That it will contain only errors favoring the government is 0.02, and d) That it will contain both types of errors is 0.10. What is the probability that among 12 such tax returns, randomly chosen for audit, five will be filled correctly, 3 will contain errors favoring the taxpayer, 3 will contain errors favoring the government, and one will contain both kinds of errors?

25. A multiple choice test consists of eight questions and 3 answers to each question, only one of which is correct. If a student answers each question by rolling a fair die and selecting answer (a) if the die shows 1 or 2, answer (b) if the die shows 3 or 4, and answer (c) if the die shows 5 or 6, find the probability of getting:

    a) Exactly 3 correct answers

    b) No correct answers

    c) At least six correct answers

26. A study has shown that 50 percent of the families in a certain large area have at least two cars. Find the probabilities that among 15 families randomly selected in this area for a market research study:

a) Eight (8) have at least two cars

b) More than eleven (11) have at least two cars

c) At most five (5) have at least two cars

d) From nine (9) to twelve (12) have at least two cars

27. Twenty five members, 10 women and 15 men, of a neighborhood association are attending a large zoning hearing. Three members are selected randomly and are allowed to address the meeting. What is the probability that:

a) No women are selected

b) One woman is selected

c) Two women are selected

d) Three women are selected

28. If a bank receives on the average 6 bad checks per day, what is the probability that it will receive:

a) At most 1 bad check on a given day

b) At least 3 bad checks in a day

c) Exactly 4 bad checks in a given day

29. It is know from past experience that 2.8 percent of the calls received at a company switchboard are wrong numbers. Use the Poisson approximation to the Binomial to determine the probability that among the 250 calls received at the switchboard, 6 are wrong numbers.

30. The manager of a television station (X) tells a prospective advertiser that on Saturday nights his station has 60 percent of the family viewing audience, while his two competitors, stations Y and Z, have 30 percent and 10 percent. If this is so, what is the probability that among eight (8) randomly selected families watching television on a Saturday night, four (4) will be watching station X, two (2) will be watching station Y, and two (2) will be watching station Z?

31. In a certain industry, the number of mergers per year is a random variable having the Poisson distribution with $\lambda = 0.6$. What are the probabilities that in a given year there will be:

a) 0 merger

b) 1 merger

c) 2 mergers

32. If a store's security force catches on the average 5 shoplifters per day, what is the probability that it will catch 4, 5, or 6 shoplifters on a given day?

33. The probabilities are 0.40, 0.40, and 0.2 that in expressway driving a compact car will average less than 25 mpg, from 25 to 30 mpg, or more than 30 mpg. What is the probability that among ten such cars, three will average less than 25 mpg, six will average from 25 to 30 mpg, and one will average more than 30 mpg?

34. Among 16 houses advertised for sale, four have swimming pools. If a real estate salesperson randomly selects five of the houses to show to a client, what is the probability that two of them will have swimming pools?

35. If the probability is 0.20 that a burglar will get caught on any given "job," what is the probability that the burglar will get caught for the first time on his sixth "job?"

36. It is known that 30 percent of all persons given a certain medication get drowsy within 2 minutes. What is the probability that among 10 persons given the medication:

a) At most 2 get drowsy within two minutes

b) At least 5 get drowsy within two minutes

c) 4, 5, or 6 get drowsy within two minutes

37. A quality control engineer wants to determine whether 95 percent of the components shipped by his company are in good working condition, in accordance with specifications. He randomly selects 12 from each large lot ready to be shipped, and passes the lot, if all 12 are in good working condition; otherwise each of the components in the lot is checked. Assuming the Binomial distribution can be used (because the lots are large), find the probabilities that he will commit the error of:

a) Holding a lot for further inspection, even though 95% of the components are in good working condition

b) Passing a lot even though only 90% of the components are in good working condition

c) Passing a lot even though only 80% of the components are in good working condition

38. A building inspector in a community decides to inspect two of sixteen new buildings for possible violations of the building code. If the selection is random and there are violations in six of the new buildings, find the probabilities that the building inspector will catch:

a) None of the buildings with violations

b) One of the buildings with violations

c) Two of the buildings with violations

39. If 4 percent of all cars fail to meet emission standards, what is the probability that among 50 cars selected at random there will be:

a) No car that fails to meet emission standards

b) One car that fails to meet emission standards

c) At most one car that fails to meet emission standards

40. It is known from experience that 2.4 percent of all items purchased at a store are returned. What are the probabilities that in a random sample of 200 items purchased at this store:

a) No items will be returned

b) At least one item will be returned

c) Three items will be returned

SOLUTIONS

1. a) $P(X = x) = \dfrac{n!}{x!(n-x)!}(0.6)^x(0.4)^{n-x}$

b) $n = 5$, $x = 1$, and $n - x = 5 - 1 = 4$; Then

$$P(X = 1) = \frac{5!}{1!4!}(0.6)^1(0.4)^4 = 5(0.6)(0.0256) = 0.0768$$

c) $n = 3$, $x = 3$, and $n - x = 3 - 3 = 0$; Then

$$P(X = 3) = \left(\frac{3!}{3!0!}\right)(0.6)^3(0.4)^0 = (1)(0.216)(1) = 0.216$$

d) $E(X) = np = 5(0.6) = 3$ and $V(X) = np(1 - p) = 5(0.6)(0.4) = 1.2$

2. If n = # of engines and X = # of operating engines, and: Probability of a successful trip = $P(X \geq n/2)$; Then:

a) $P(X \geq n/2) = P(X \geq 1) = P(X = 1) + P(X = 2)$, When $n = 2$

$$= \frac{2!}{1!1!}(0.9)^1(0.1)^1 + \frac{2!}{2!0!}(0.9)^2(0.1)^0$$

$$= 2(0.9)(0.1) + 1(0.9)^2(1) = 0.18 + 0.81 = 0.99$$

b) $P(X \geq n/2) = P(X \geq 3/2) = P(x = 2) + P(x = 3)$, When $n = 3$, (because a full engine must operate)

$$= \frac{3!}{2!1!}(0.9)^2(0.1)^1 + \frac{3!}{3!0!}(0.9)^3(0.1)^0$$

$$= 3(0.9)^2(0.1) + 1(0.9)^3(1) = 0.243 + 0.729 = 0.972$$

c) $P(X \geq n/2) = P(X \geq 2) = P(x = 2) + P(x = 3) + P(x = 4)$, when $n = 4$

$$= \frac{4!}{2!2!}(0.9)^2(0.1)^2 + \frac{4!}{3!1!}(0.9)^3(0.1)^1 + \frac{4!}{4!0!}(0.9)^3(0.1)^0$$

$$= 6(0.9)^2(0.1)^2 + 4(0.9)^3(0.1) + 1(0.9)^4(1)$$

$$= 0.0486 + 0.2916 + 0.6561 = 0.9963$$

Clearly the 4-engine plane has the highest probability for a successful trip.

3. $n = 4$, $P_{acceptance} = 1 - P_{rejection} = 0.7$, and $P(X) = \frac{4!}{x!(4-x)!}(0.7)^x(0.3)^{4-x}$

a) Prob(at least 3 acceptances) = $P(X \geq 3) = P(x = 3) + P(x = 4)$

$$= \frac{4!}{3!1!}(0.7)^3(0.3)^1 + \frac{4!}{4!0!}(0.7)^4(0.3)^0$$

$$= 4(0.7)^3(0.3)^1 + 1(0.7)^4(1) = 4(0.343)(0.3) + 0.2401$$

$$= 0.4116 + 0.2401 = 0.6517$$

b) Prob(of too many acceptances) = $P(x = 4) = 0.2401$

c) We must have: $P(X \geq 3) \geq 0.9$ and solve for n, or:

$$P(X \geq 3) = \sum_{x=3}^{n} \frac{n!}{x!(n-x)!}(0.7)^x(0.3)^{n-x} \geq 0.9$$

i) when $n = 4$, $P(X \geq 3) = 0.6517$ (see part a) but $P(X \geq 3) < 0.9$

ii) when $n = 5$, $P(X \geq 3) = P(x = 3) + P(x = 4)$

$$+ P(x = 5) = 0.83692 < 0.9$$

iii) when $n = 6$, $P(X \geq 3) = P(x = 3) + P(x = 4)$

$$+ P(x = 5) + P(x = 6) = 0.92953 > 0.9$$

Therefore, to have $P(X \geq 3) \geq 0.9$, $n = 6$

4. Since $P(H) + P(T) = 1$ and $P(T) = 3P(H)$, $P(H) = 1/4$ and $P(T) = 3/4$

Then $P(X = 2) = \frac{3!}{2!1!}\left(\frac{1}{4}\right)^2\left(\frac{3}{4}\right)^1 = 3\left(\frac{1}{4}\right)^2\left(\frac{3}{4}\right) = 3\left(\frac{1}{16}\right)\left(\frac{3}{4}\right) = \frac{9}{64}$

5. Assume that each child has a probability of 0.5 of being a boy, then:

$$P(X) = \frac{n!}{x!(n-x)!}(0.5)^x(0.5)^{n-x} = (0.5)^n\frac{n!}{x!(n-x)!} = \frac{1}{2^n}\frac{n!}{x!(n-x)!} \text{ and}$$

Prob. of at least 2 boys $= P(x \geq 2) = \dfrac{1}{2^n} \displaystyle\sum_{x=2}^{n} \dfrac{n!}{x!(n-x)!}$

$$= \dfrac{1}{2^n}\left[\dfrac{n!}{0!n!} + \dfrac{n!}{1!(n-1)!} + \dfrac{n!}{2!(n-2)!} + \cdots + \dfrac{n!}{n!0!}\right];$$

when $n = 2$, $P(X \geq 2) = \dfrac{1}{4} < 0.75$; when $n = 3$, $P(X \geq 2) = 0.5 < 0.75$;

when $n = 4$, $P(X \geq 2) = 0.6875 < 0.75$;
when $n = 5$, $P(X \geq 2) = 0.8125 > 0.75$

6. a) If $p = 0.1$, the probability of 0 defectives

$$= P(X = 0) = \dfrac{10!}{0!(10-0)!}(0.9)^{10}(0.1)^0 = 0.349$$

b) $P(X = 0) = \dfrac{n!}{0!(n-0)!}(0.9)^n(0.1)^0 = (0.9)^n \leq 0.01$, from which we obtain:

$$n\log(0.9) \leq \log(0.01), \text{ or: } n \leq \dfrac{\log 0.01}{\log 0.9} = \dfrac{-2}{-0.0457575} \text{ and } n \leq 43.7$$

or $n \leq 44$ (when $n = 43$, Prob $= 0.0107$ and when $n = 44$, Prob $= 0.009697$)

7.

Sum	2	3	4	5	6	7	8	9	10	11	12
P(Sum)	1/36	2/36	3/36	4/36	5/36	6/36	5/36	4/36	3/36	2/36	1/36

Then: $P(\text{Sum} = 7) = 6/36 = 1/6$ and $P(\text{Sum} \neq 7) = 5/6$

In order for the nth throw to be the first time that the Sum $= 7$, we must have gotten a Sum $\neq 7$ the first $(n-1)$ times, and the probability of getting a Sum $\neq 7$ the first $(n-1)$ times is $\left(\dfrac{5}{6}\right)^{n-1}$. Then the probability of getting a Sum $= 7$ in the nth throw, for the first time, is equal to $= \left(\dfrac{1}{6}\right)\left(\dfrac{5}{6}\right)^{n-1}$. This is an example of the Geometric Probability Model.

8. a) Hypergeometric; $P(X) = \dfrac{\dbinom{N_1}{x}\dbinom{N - N_1}{n - x}}{\dbinom{N}{n}}$, with parameters:

$N = 200, n = 20, p = 0.05$, and $N_1 = N_p = 200(0.05) = 10$ and $N - N_1 = 190$.

Then $P(X) = \dfrac{\dbinom{10}{x}\dbinom{190}{20 - x}}{\dbinom{200}{20}}$

b) Binomial with parameters: $n = 30$ and

$p = 0.51$; $P(X) = \dfrac{30!}{x!(30 - x)!}(0.51)^x(0.49)^{30-x}$

c) Geometric, with $p = 0.51$; $P(X) = p(1 - p)^{n-1} = (0.51)(0.49)^{n-1}$.

d) Binomial with parameters; $n = 35$ and
$$p = 0.75; P(X) = \frac{35!}{x!(35 - x)!}(0.75)^x(0.25)^{35-x}$$

9. The number of errors in 4 pages then obeys the Poisson probability error with parameter $\lambda = \frac{3}{4}(4) = 3$, and the probability law is $P(X) = e^{-\lambda}\frac{\lambda^x}{x!}$ or $P(X) = e^{-3}\frac{3^x}{x!}$ for $x = 0, 1, 2, 3, \ldots$

Then, $P(x = 0) = e^{-3}\frac{3^0}{0!} = e^{-3} = 0.049787$

10. We are looking for the value of K such that:
$$\sum_{k=0}^{K} e^{-\lambda}\frac{\lambda^k}{k!} \geq 0.99 \text{ or } \sum_{k=K+1}^{\infty} e^{-\lambda}\frac{\lambda^k}{k!} \leq 0.01$$

The exact solution can be found only by trial and error, for small values of λ. However, if λ is very large so that the Poisson law may be approximated by the Normal, the first summation term is approximately equal to

$$N\left(\frac{K - \lambda + 1/2}{\sqrt{\lambda}}\right) \text{ and } K \text{ should be chosen so that}$$

$$\frac{K - \lambda + 1/2}{\sqrt{\lambda}} = 2.33 \text{ or } K = 2.33\sqrt{\lambda} + \lambda - 1/2$$

Note: For large λ, $\sum_{k=a}^{b} e^{-\lambda}\frac{\lambda^k}{k!} \approx \frac{1}{\sqrt{2\pi}} \int_{\frac{a-\lambda-0.5e}{\sqrt{\lambda}}}^{\frac{b-\lambda+0.5}{\sqrt{\lambda}}} e^{\frac{y^2}{2}} dy$

7 The Normal and Other Continuous Variables

The normal density function is one of the most important models used in Probability and Statistics. Its density function, $f(x) = \dfrac{1}{\sqrt{2\pi}}\dfrac{1}{\sigma}e^{-\frac{1}{2\sigma^2}(x-\mu)^2}$ $-\infty < x < \infty$, when plotted, produces the well-known "bell-shape" curve. In this chapter, we discuss the properties and important characteristics of the normal variable (such as its Expected Value and Variance) and show how tables are used to calculate probabilities since the nature of its density function does not allow the use of closed-form integration.

Other important continuous distributions discussed in this chapter are: 1) The Uniform probability model which can be used to derive (from a set of uniform numbers which can be generated by any computer using the function RND), by suitable mathematical transformations a set of random variables having the density function of our choice, and 2) The Gamma probability model, which is a very versatile distribution, capable of exhibiting many shapes, depending on the values of its "shape" parameter α, and "scale" parameter θ. For example the exponential model results when the shape parameter $\alpha = 1$, while the chi-square model is obtained when $\alpha = \delta/2$ and $\theta = 2$.

Also discussed in this chapter are: 1) The F-distribution, where the F-variable is defined as the ratio of 2 chi-square variables, and 2) the t-distribution in which the t-variable is defined as the ratio of a z-variable (*i.e.*, standard normal) and the square root of a chi-square variable.

Taken together the four distributions: z, χ^2, F, and t represent the most important distributions used in applied statistics. Also discussed in this chapter is the relationship among the t, F, and χ^2 variables, and the special conditions under which the binomial distribution can be approximated by the normal.

7.1   Introduction

As we have discussed previously, the set of possible outcomes for a random variable is not always finite in number. As an example consider the problem of listing the possible outcomes of an experiment which measures the height and weight of students. Such variables do not proceed through their range of variation (0 < Height < 100 inches, 0 < weight < 1200 lbs) in discrete steps (*i.e.*, whole inches or pounds) but go throughout their ranges continuously, being limited only by the accuracy of the measuring devices used, thus, measuring and recording to the nearest second, millimeter, kilogram, etc.

We call such variables Continuous Variables and in this chapter we will discuss some of the better known and widely used continuous variables, just as we did with discrete variables in chapter 6.

The Continuous Variables discussed in this chapter are those obeying the following probability models:

1. The Uniform Probability Model
2. The Gamma Probability Model
    a) The Negative Exponential Probability Model
    b) The Chi-Square (χ^2) Probability Model
3. The Generalized and Standardized Normal Probability Models
4. The Student t Probability Model
5. The F Probability Model

From these models, the Uniform, Gamma and Normal can be considered as "postulated" models because they describe exactly or approximately several natural phenomena. Given their existence, the Negative Exponential and the Chi-square models can be considered as special cases of the Gamma Probability model by assigning appropriately chosen values to the two parameters of the Gamma model. The Exponential model results when $\alpha = 1$, while the chi-square model is obtained by letting $\alpha = \delta/2$ and $\theta = 2$. Thus the Chi-square model is completely defined by the single parameter δ which is called the "degrees of freedom", a concept which is also used in the definitions of the t and F models and which will be discussed at some length in the next chapter. Having derived the chi-square model as a special case of the gamma model and assuming the existence of the normal as a postulated model, the variables T and F are defined as:

$$T = \frac{Z}{\sqrt{Y/\delta}} \quad \text{and} \quad F = \frac{Y_1/\delta_1}{Y_2/\delta_2}$$

where Z is a standard normal variable and Y, Y_1, and Y_2 are Chi-square Variables with δ, δ_1, and δ_2 degrees of freedom respectively. Then their probability models are derived from their definitions and the known probability models of the variables in their defining equations in accordance with accepted probability methods.

In the next chapter we will discuss at some length "degrees of freedom", a concept associated with sums of squares of sample observations, and show how the Chi-square, t and F distributions can also be derived by sampling from Normal distributions and suitable treatment of the observed values. These last 3 probability models together with the Normal are extremely important in Statistics because, as we will show in the next chapter (Sampling Distributions), the distributions of the sample mean $(\bar{x})$ and Sample variance $(\hat{s}^2)$ or certain functions of them can be described in terms of these probability models (laws) and this fact gives us a method of analyzing the corresponding population parameters μ and σ^2.

7.2   The Continuous Uniform Density Function

If an event occurs in such a way that the probability of the random variable, representing the event, falling in each sub-interval of equal length is the same, such a random variable is said to be uniformly distributed in the interval.

More formally, a random variable X is said to be uniformly distributed in the interval (a, b) if the probability density function of X is given by:

$$f(x) = \begin{cases} A & a \le X \le b \\ 0 & \text{for all other values of } X \end{cases} \tag{7.1}$$

where A is a constant value.

For $f(x)$ to be a proper density function (or probability function) we must have:

$$\int_a^b f(x)\,dx = 1 \text{ or } \int_a^b A\,dx = 1, \qquad \text{from which we obtain:}$$

$$Ax\Big|_a^b = 1 \text{ or } (b-a)A = 1, \text{ and finally } A = \frac{1}{b-a}$$

Therefore $f(x) = \begin{cases} \dfrac{1}{b-a} & a \leq X \leq b \\ 0 & elsewhere \end{cases}$ (7.2)

The Cumulative Density Function can also be obtained by integration and is given by:

$$\text{CDF}(X) = \text{prob}(X \leq x) = \int_a^x f(x)dx = \left.\frac{x}{b-a}\right|_a^x \qquad (7.3)$$

$$= \frac{1}{b-a}(x-a) = \left(\frac{1}{b-a}\right)x - \left(\frac{a}{b-a}\right)$$

When written in this last form it is seen that the CDF(X) is a linear function of x, between the points $x = a$ and $x = b$, with slope $= 1/(b-a)$ and y-intercept $= -a/(b-a)$.

Therefore, we only need to establish two ordered pairs of values $(x, \text{CDF}(X))$, before the entire CDF(X) can be completely drawn.

At $x = a$, CDF($X = x = a$) $= 0$, while when $x = b$, CDF($X = x = b$) $= 1$, and stays at 1 for values of $x > b$. Figure 1 below shows the graphical representation for both $f(x)$ and CDF(X).

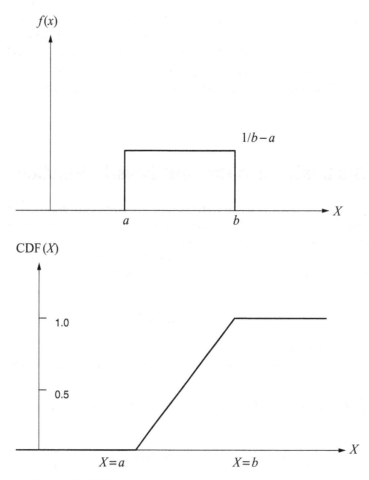

Figure 7.1 $f(X)$ **and CDF(X) versus** X

Applying the Expectation and Variance operators to this density function, we obtain:

$$E(X) = \int_a^b xf(x)dx = \frac{1}{b-a}\int_a^b xdx = \frac{1}{b-a}\left[\frac{1}{2}x^2\right]_a^b \tag{7.4}$$

$$= \frac{1}{2(b-a)}(b^2 - a^2) = \frac{(b+a)(b-a)}{2(b-a)} = \frac{b+a}{2}$$

$$E(X^2) = \int_a^b x^2f(x)dx = \frac{1}{b-a}\int_a^b x^2dx = \frac{1}{b-a}\left[\frac{1}{3}x^3\right]_a^b \tag{7.5}$$

$$= \frac{1}{3(b-a)}(b^3 - a^3) = \frac{(b^2 + ab + a^2)(b-a)}{3(b-a)} = \frac{b^2 + ab + a^2}{3}$$

$$V(X) = E(X^2) - [E(X)]^2 = \frac{b^2 + ab + a^2}{3} - \frac{(b+a)^2}{4} = \frac{(b-a)^2}{12} \tag{7.6}$$

If we wished to find $P(c \leq X \leq d)$, when the random variable X is uniformly distributed in the interval (a, b), and where $a \leq c \leq d \leq b$, then:

$$P(c \leq X \leq d) = P(c < X < d) = \int_c^d f(x)dx$$

$$= \int_c^d \left(\frac{1}{b-a}\right)dx = \frac{1}{b-a}\int_c^d dx$$

$$= \left(\frac{1}{b-a}\right)x \bigg|_c^d = \frac{d-c}{b-a}$$

This result shows that the probability of the random variable X falling in the subinterval (c, d) is equal to $\left(\dfrac{1}{b-a}\right)$ times the length of the subinterval (c, d) and therefore, this probability is equal to the probability of X falling in any other subinterval in (a, b) of equal length.

If the coefficients of Skewness and Kurtosis are computed, as described in Chapter 5,

$$(i.e., S_{kp} = E(X - \mu)^3/\sigma^3 \text{ and } K = E(X - \mu)^4/\sigma^4), \text{ we will find that:}$$

$$S_{kp} = 0 \quad \text{and} \quad K = 1.8$$

In a later section of this chapter, when we discuss the Normal density function, we will show that for the Normal random variable which we will use as the basis of comparison, $S_{kp} = 0$ and $K = 3$.

Therefore, a uniform density function (the probability law of a continuous random variable is referred to as a density function in contrast to the Probability Mass Function (PMF) of a discrete random variable) is symmetric about the mean (just like the Normal) but less peaked than the Normal density function.

When b and a are assigned the values: $b = 1$ and $a = 0$, we have a uniform density function in the interval $(0, 1)$ with the density function:

$$f(x) = 1 \quad 0 \leq X \leq 1 \tag{7.7}$$

for which $E(X) = 1/2$ and $V(X) = 1/12$.

This is a very important density function because of the key role it plays in the generation of uniform and, through mathematical transformations, any other type of random variables (Normal, Exponential, etc.) in the computer, which make computer simulation possible. Every computer system is equipped with a special function, usually called RND, which, when invoked, repeatedly, generates a sequence of uniform random variables, $U_1, U_2, \ldots, U_n$. Then, by suitable mathematical transformations these uniform random variables may be converted to the random variables of our choice.

For example, the two equations below:

$$Z_1 = (-2 \ln U_1)^{1/2} \sin(2\pi U_2) \tag{7.8}$$

and

$$Z_2 = (-2 \ln U_1)^{1/2} \cos(2\pi U_2)$$

convert two uniform random variables U_1 and U_2 (in the interval $(0, 1)$) into two Standard Normal Random Variables Z_1 and Z_2, where $E(Z_1) = E(Z_2) = 0$ and $V(Z_1) = V(Z_2) = 1$.

As another example, the equation:

$$X = -\theta \ln(1 - U) \tag{7.9}$$

converts a random variable U, uniformly distributed in the interval $(0, 1)$, to a random variable X which is exponentially distributed in the interval $(0, \infty)$, with parameter θ.

The density function of the exponential random variable X is given by:

$$f(x) = \frac{1}{\theta} e^{-x/\theta} \quad X \geq 0, \quad \theta > 0 \tag{7.10}$$

as we will discuss later in this chapter. It is characterized by the single parameter θ, and is a special case of the Gamma density function which we discuss below.

7.3   The Gamma Density Function and Related Probability Laws

The Gamma density function, represented by the equation:

$$f(x; \alpha, \theta) = \frac{1}{\Gamma(\alpha)\theta^\alpha} x^{\alpha-1} e^{-x/\theta} \quad X > 0, \alpha > 0, \theta > 0 \tag{7.11}$$

where,

$$\Gamma(\alpha) = \int_0^\infty u^{\alpha-1} e^{-u} du \tag{7.12}$$

is the gamma function of argument α, and is a tabulated function, and u is any random variable and not necessarily uniform, is a very versatile distribution that is capable of exhibiting many shapes depending on the value of the "shape" parameter α. For $\alpha \leq 1$ the density function looks like a reverse J, while for values of $\alpha > 1$ it has a single peak which occurs when $x = \theta(\alpha - 1)$. Since for a fixed α, the basic shape of the density function does not change as θ is allowed to vary, θ is called the "scale" parameter.

The gamma distribution has been used extensively in waiting line problems to represent the total length of time to complete service, if service is made up of exactly α distinct operations, each requiring its own completion of service, the distinct operations are independent of each other, and occur at a constant rate of $\lambda = \dfrac{1}{\theta}$.

The gamma function $\Gamma(\alpha)$ was incorporated as a multiplier in the density function to insure that $f(x; \alpha, \theta)$ is a proper density function, as is shown below:

We write:
$$\int_0^\infty f(x; \alpha, \theta)dx = \frac{1}{\Gamma(\alpha)\theta^\alpha} \int_0^\infty x^{\alpha-1}e^{-x/\theta}dx$$

Now by letting $u = \dfrac{x}{\theta}$ the limits of integration remain the same (because $u = 0$ when $x = 0$ and $u = \infty$ when $x = \infty$) but, since $x = \theta u$, we now have:

$$dx = \theta du \quad \text{and} \quad x^{\alpha-1} = (\theta u)^{\alpha-1} = \theta^{\alpha-1}u^{\alpha-1}$$

Substituting in the integral above we obtain:

$$\int_0^\infty f(x; \alpha, \theta)dx = \frac{1}{\Gamma(\alpha)\theta^\alpha} \int_0^\infty \theta^{\alpha-1}u^{\alpha-1}e^{-u}\theta dx = \frac{\theta^{\alpha-1}\theta}{\Gamma(\alpha)\theta^\alpha} \int_0^\infty u^{\alpha-1}e^{-u}du$$

$$= \frac{\theta^\alpha}{\Gamma(\alpha)\theta^\alpha}\Gamma(\alpha) \quad \text{by using the definition of } \Gamma(\alpha) \text{ above.}$$

$$= 1$$

Applying the Expectation and Variance operators and performing the indicated integrations (integration by parts), we obtain:

$$E(X) = \int_0^\infty xf(x; \alpha, \theta)dx = \alpha\theta \tag{7.13}$$

$$V(X) = \int_0^\infty [x - E(X)]^2 f(x; \alpha, \theta)dx = E(x^2) - [E(X)]^2 = \alpha\theta^2 \tag{7.14}$$

By performing additional integrations and using the proper definitions, we can show that the coefficients of Skewness (S_{kp}) and Kurtosis (K) are given respectively, by:

$$S_{kp} = \frac{E[x - E(X)]^3}{\sigma^3} = \frac{\int_0^\infty [x - E(X)]^3 f(x; \alpha, \theta)dx}{(\sqrt{\alpha\theta})^3} = \frac{2}{\sqrt{\alpha}} \tag{7.15}$$

$$K = \frac{E[x - E(X)]^4}{\sigma^4} = \frac{\int_0^\infty [x - E(X)]^4 f(x; \alpha, \theta)dx}{(\alpha\theta)^2} = 3\left(1 + \frac{2}{\alpha}\right) \tag{7.16}$$

Clearly the gamma distribution is positively skewed (since $S_{kp} > 0$) and more peaked than the normal distribution since $K > 3$ for $\alpha > 0$.

The Cumulative Distribution Function is given by the expression

$$P(X \le x) = F(x; \alpha, \theta) = \frac{1}{\Gamma(\alpha)\theta^\alpha} \int_0^x t^{\alpha-1}e^{-t/\theta}dt \quad x > 0 \tag{7.17}$$

where we replaced x by t, since the upper limit of the integration is also x.

If we change the variable of integration to u, by letting $u = \dfrac{t}{\theta}$, we can rewrite the above integral as:

$$P(X \le x) = F(x; \alpha, \theta) = \frac{1}{\Gamma(\alpha)} \int_0^{x/\theta} u^{\alpha-1} e^{-u} du \qquad (7.18)$$

This integral, which is known as the "incomplete gamma function" **cannot be integrated in a closed form**, but has been extensively tabulated.

One of the important reasons for studying the gamma distributions is, as stated above, its extensive use in waiting line problems.

A second important reason is the fact that the gamma density serves as a "parent" distribution from which other useful distributions can be derived by choosing appropriate values for the shape and scale parameters. Two such "derived" distributions are:

1. The Exponential density function, and
2. The Chi-square density function with δ degrees of freedom.

We briefly discuss these two density functions below:

▪ The Exponential Density Function

When the shape parameter $\alpha = 1$, the Gamma density function reduces to the equation:

$$f(x; 1, \theta) = f(x; \theta) = \frac{1}{\theta} e^{-x/\theta} \quad X > 0, \theta > 0 \qquad (7.19)$$

since $\Gamma(1) = 1$, as can be seen from equation (7.12).

This form of the gamma density function is known as the Exponential density function and has been extensively used to represent random time lengths.

The Exponential model has its origin in the Poisson model. If you recall our discussion of the Poisson model, a fixed interval of time (or space) is designated and then the number of occurrences of the event of interest, within this interval, are counted. In the exponential model, we fix the number of occurrences of the event and wish to know the length of the interval that is required to observe this number of occurrences. In particular, the random variable of an exponential model can be regarded as the length of time until the occurrence of the first Poisson event. The Poisson model is discrete but the exponential is continuous. It has been used to describe the life of an electronic device, the time intervals between accidents, the time interval between breakdowns of electrical mechanisms, and a great variety of other random situations.

The exponential model is characterized by the single parameter θ which represents the expected time between two independent Poisson events. In reliability analysis, θ is referred to as the "mean time between failures" (MTBF) while $\lambda = 1/\theta$ is known as the "failure rate" (number of occurrences per unit time).

The Exponential model is a proper probability law as can be easily verified by integration, since:

$$\int_0^\infty f(x)dx = \int_0^\infty \frac{1}{\theta} e^{-x/\theta} dx = -\int_0^\infty e^{-x/\theta} \left(-\frac{1}{\theta} dx \right) = -e^{-x/\theta} \Big|_0^\infty$$

$$= -(0 - 1) = 1$$

The Cumulative Distribution Function of the Exponential model, unlike the Gamma model, can be obtained in closed form and is given by:

$$P(X \leq x) = F(x; \theta) = \int_0^x \frac{1}{\theta} e^{-t/\theta} dt = -e^{-t/\theta} \Big|_0^x = 1 - e^{-x/\theta} \qquad (7.20)$$

We can obtain the expected value and variance of the exponential random variable by applying the Expectation and Variance operators directly to the Exponential density function and obtain:

$$E(X) = \int_0^\infty x f(x) dx = \int_0^\infty x \left[\frac{1}{\theta} e^{-x/\theta} \right] dx = \theta \qquad (7.21)$$

$$V(X) = \int_0^\infty [x - E(X)]^2 f(x) dx = E(X^2) - [E(X)]^2 = \theta^2 \qquad (7.22)$$

where integration by parts is needed to evaluate the two integrals above.

But, since we have already obtained the Expected value and Variance of the gamma random variable, from whose density function the exponential model was derived by letting $\alpha = 1$, we can obtain $E(X)$ and $V(X)$ from the $E(X)$ and $V(X)$ of the gamma variable by substituting $\alpha = 1$ in them.

We obtain:

$$E(X)_{exponential} = E(X)_{gamma} \Big|_{\alpha=1} = \alpha\theta \Big|_{\alpha=1} = \theta$$

$$V(X)_{exponential} = V(X)_{gamma} \Big|_{\alpha=1} = \alpha\theta^2 \Big|_{\alpha=1} = \theta^2$$

Using similar reasoning we can also obtain the coefficients of Skewness and Kurtosis for the exponential model from the corresponding gamma model coefficients by letting $\alpha = 1$.

The results are:

$$S_{kp} = \frac{2}{\sqrt{\alpha}} \Big|_{\alpha=1} = 2 \qquad (7.23)$$

$$K = 3\left(1 + \frac{2}{\alpha}\right) \Big|_{\alpha=1} = 9 \qquad (7.24)$$

and show that the exponential model is positively skewed and much more peaked than the normal model.

■ The Chi-square $\left(\chi^2\right)$ Density Function with δ Degrees of Freedom

Another special case of the Gamma density function is the Chi-square model which is obtained when $\alpha = \frac{\delta}{2}$ and $\theta = 2$ are substituted in the gamma model. The result is:

$$f\left(x; \alpha = \frac{\delta}{2}, \theta = 2\right) = f\left(x = \chi^2, \delta\right) = \frac{1}{\Gamma\left(\frac{\delta}{2}\right) 2^{\delta/2}} x^{(\delta/2)-1} e^{-x/2} \qquad X > 0 \qquad (7.25)$$

The Chi-square model is completely defined by the single parameter δ which is called the "degrees of freedom", a concept that we will discuss at some length in the next chapter (Sampling Distributions), and which is associated with "sums of squares of random observations". For different values of δ, we obtain an entire family of Chi-square density functions, each of which is proper. As we will see in the next few chapters this model plays a significant role in statistical inferences, especially those concerning variances. We started discussing the model here because it could be derived as a special case of the gamma model (later it would be re-derived as a sampling distribution when n independent samples $Z_1, Z_2, \ldots, Z_n$, are drawn from a Standard Normal population ($E(Z) = 0, V(Z) = 1$), and the random variable $Y = Z_1^2 + Z_2^2 + \cdots + Z_n^2$ will be shown to be Chi-square distributed with n degrees of freedom) and plan to use it and the normal variable, to be discussed in the next section of this chapter, to derive two other density functions (or models) which also play an important role in statistical inference. These two other models are:

1. The Student-t model in which the random variable T is defined as

$$T = \frac{Z}{\sqrt{\dfrac{Y}{\delta}}} \tag{7.26}$$

   where Z is a normally distributed variable with $E(Z) = 0$ and $V(Z) = 1$, and Y is a Chi–square distributed variable with δ degrees of freedom.
2. The F model in which the random variable F is defined as:

$$F = \frac{Y_1/\delta_1}{Y_2/\delta_2} \tag{7.27}$$

   where Y_1 and Y_2 are both Chi-square variables with δ_1 and δ_2 degrees of freedom respectively.

Since the density functions of Z, Y, Y_1, and Y_2 are known, the density functions of T and F can be derived using well established probability methods. Then, in the next chapter, where we discuss Sampling Distributions of the Sample Statistics we derived in chapter 3, we will be in a position to identify the sampling distribution of the sample mean $(\overline{x})$ as being either **normal** or **t-distributed** depending on certain additional conditions. Also the sampling distribution of $\hat{s}^2$ will be shown to be Chi-square with $\delta = n - 1$ degrees of freedom, while the ratio of two sample variances, $\hat{s}_1^2/\hat{s}_2^2$ will be shown to be F-distributed with $\delta_1 = n_1 - 1$ degrees of freedom in the numerator and $\delta_2 = n_2 - 1$ degrees of freedom in the denominator.

After the sampling distributions of the sample statistics have been identified, it will be a relatively simple matter to perform statistical inferences on the parameters of the corresponding populations.

To complete our discussion on the Chi-square density function we note that since we have already shown that the gamma density function is proper, it follows that the Chi-square density function, being a special case of the gamma density function, is also proper. Similarly we can obtain the Chi-square characteristics from the gamma density function characteristics by substituting $\alpha = \dfrac{\delta}{2}$ and $\theta = 2$. The results are:

$$E(X)_{\chi^2} = E(X)_{gamma} = \alpha\theta \left|\begin{array}{c} \alpha = \delta/2 \\[6pt] \\[6pt] \theta = 2 \end{array}\right. = \delta \tag{7.28}$$

$$V(X)_{\chi^2} = V(X)_{gamma} = \alpha\theta^2 \left|_{\substack{\alpha = \delta/2 \\ \theta = 2}} \right. = 2\delta \tag{7.29}$$

$$S_{kp\chi^2} = S_{kp\ gamma} = \frac{2}{\sqrt{\alpha}} \left|_{\substack{\alpha = \delta/2 \\ \theta = 2}} \right. = \frac{2\sqrt{2}}{\sqrt{\delta}} \tag{7.30}$$

$$K_{\chi^2} = K_{gamma} = 3\left(1 + \frac{2}{\alpha}\right) \left|_{\substack{\alpha = \delta/2 \\ \theta = 2}} \right. = 3\left(1 + \frac{4}{\delta}\right) \tag{7.31}$$

Note: The Variance of a Chi-square variable is twice the expected value of the variable, which is equal to the degrees of freedom. Also, the Chi-square density is positively skewed and more peaked than the normal (since $K > 3$), but, in the limit as $\delta \to \infty$, it approaches a symmetric distribution since $\underset{\delta \to \infty}{Lim} (S_{kp}) \to 0$, and its kurtosis approaches that of a normal distribution since

$$\underset{\delta \to \infty}{Lim} (K_{\chi^2}) = \underset{\delta \to \infty}{Lim} 3\left(1 + \frac{4}{\delta}\right) = 3\left[1 + \frac{4}{\infty}\right] = 3[1 + 0] = 3$$

The Cumulative Distribution Function of the Chi-square variable is given by:

$$P(X \le x) = F(x; \delta) = \int_0^x \frac{1}{\Gamma\left(\delta/2\right)2^{\delta/2}} t^{(\delta/2)-1} e^{-t/2} dt \tag{7.32}$$

$$= \frac{1}{\Gamma\left(\delta/2\right)2^{\delta/2}} \int_0^x t^{(\delta/2)-1} e^{-t/2} dt \quad X > 0$$

Because no closed form can be found for this integral, the CDF of the Chi-square variable is extensively tabulated.

The χ^2 table in Part IX Appendices & Tables, gives selected values of the Cumulative Distribution Function, for various values of δ and $1 - \alpha$ (or α).

The table is based on setting the CDF equal to a desired value and then finding the value of χ^2, designated by $\chi^2_{1-\alpha,\ \delta}$, which divides the area under the Chi-square density function into two parts; One in which the CDF $= 1 - \alpha$, and the other, to the right of $\chi^2_{1-\alpha,\ \delta}$ which is equal to α. The value of $\chi^2_{1-\alpha,\ \delta}$ depends on δ, as the subscript indicates, and also on α. Keeping α fixed and varying δ would change the value of $\chi^2_{1-\alpha,\ \delta}$. Similarly, keeping δ fixed but varying α, would again change the value of $\chi^2_{1-\alpha,\ \delta}$.

These ideas are made clear in Figure 7.2 below and in the example which follows, using a portion of such a table.

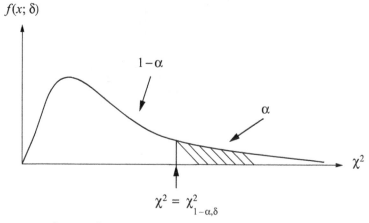

Figure 7.2 $\text{CDF}\left(X = \chi^2\right)$

$$\text{CDF}\left(X \le \chi^2\right) = P\left(X \le \chi^2_{1-\alpha,\,\delta}\right) = \frac{1}{\Gamma\left(\dfrac{\delta}{2}\right)2^{\delta/2}} \int_0^{\chi^2_{1-\alpha,\delta}} t^{\delta/2-1} e^{-t/2}\, dt = 1 - \alpha$$

δ	$\chi^2_{1-\alpha,\delta}$					
	$\chi^2_{0.010}$	$\chi^2_{0.025}$	$\chi^2_{0.050}$	$\chi^2_{0.950}$	$\chi^2_{0.975}$	$\chi^2_{0.990}$
5	0.55	0.83	1.15	11.07	12.84	15.09
10	2.55	3.24	3.94	18.31	20.50	23.19
15	5.23	6.26	7.26	25.00	27.50	30.61

For example, if $\delta = 15$ and we wanted the unshaded area to be equal to 0.95 (and, therefore, the shaded area to be equal to 0.05), the value of $\chi^2 = \chi^2_{0.95,\,15}$ that accomplishes that is equal to 25, and we write: $\chi^2_{0.95,\,15} = 25$.

Other tables may be constructed which give the value of α instead of the value of $1 - \alpha$, but they are equivalent. In one such table the right hand side of the χ^2 density function is represented by $\chi^2_{\delta,\,\alpha}$, while the left hand side is represented by $\chi^2_{\delta,\,1-\alpha}$, as shown in Figure 7.3 below:

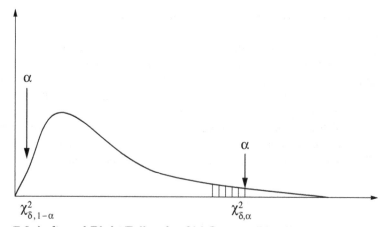

Figure 7.3 Left and Right Tails of a Chi-Square Distribution

In these representations $\chi^2_{\delta, \alpha}$ and $\chi^2_{\delta, 1-\alpha}$ are defined as the lower limits of the integrals

$$\int_{\chi^2_{\delta, \alpha}}^{\infty} f(\chi^2) d\chi^2 = \alpha \quad \text{and} \quad \int_{\chi^2_{\delta, 1-\alpha}}^{\infty} f(\chi^2) d\chi^2 = 1 - \alpha \text{ (i.e., they are the values of the } \chi^2$$

variable that make the area to the right of these values and up to ∞ equal to α and $1 - \alpha$ respectively.

This representation is used in future chapters not only for the Chi-square but also for the Normal, t, and F distributions, and is very useful, especially in the construction of confidence intervals for the population parameters, as will be done extensively in Chapter 11.

7.4 The Generalized and Standardized Normal Density Functions

The normal distribution (sometimes also referred to as the "Gaussian distribution" because Gauss considered it in a paper which was published in 1809) is without doubt the most important and most widely used continuous probability distribution. Its importance is based on the following observations:

1. Many continuous random variables (such as heights of adults, IQ tests, etc) are approximately normally distributed.
2. Any measurement (such as height, weight, length, etc) can be assumed to consist of the sum of two terms: The true magnitude and an error term which is normally distributed.
3. The Normal serves as a good approximation to many discrete distributions such as the Poisson and the Binomial.
4. Many problems can be solved easily by assuming normality, even when it does not exist, because of the relatively simple probability calculations required.
5. Many of the sample statistics we calculated in Chapter 3 (such as: $\bar{x}, \Delta \bar{x} = \bar{x}_1 - \bar{x}_2, p, \Delta p = p_1 - p_2$) approach the normal distribution in the limit, as the sample size n approaches infinity.

This is a very important and useful observation, and we will come back to it again in the next chapter when we discuss "Sampling Distributions". We will show then, and in the chapters which follow it, that the normal distribution is the cornerstone of statistical inference.

Historically, the normal distribution goes back to the seventeenth and eighteenth centuries and is associated with the names of DeMoivre, who discovered it in 1773 as a limiting form of the Binomial probability law, Laplace, who studied it in 1774, and Gauss who was first to use it in 1809.

A random variable X is said to be normally distributed if its probability density function is given by:

$$f(x; \mu, \sigma^2) = n(x; \mu, \sigma^2) = \frac{1}{\sqrt{2\pi}\sigma} e^{-\frac{1}{2\sigma^2}(x-\mu)^2}$$
$$-\infty < x < \infty, -\infty < \mu < \infty, \sigma^2 > 0 \tag{7.33}$$

Note: We have designated the normal density function by the notation $n(x; \mu, \sigma^2)$, 'instead of the usual $f(x; \mu, \sigma^2)$, to emphasize the importance of the normal distribution.

We will also use the notation $N\left(x; \mu, \sigma^2\right)$ to represent the Cumulative Density Function of the normal random variable X. Often, the short hand notation $n\left(\mu, \sigma^2\right)$ will be used to indicate a random variable X which is normally distributed with $E(X) = \mu$ and Variance $V(X) = \sigma^2$.

When written in the form of equation (7.33), this probability distribution function is referred to as the "generalized normal distribution" and it is completely defined when the parameters μ and σ^2, which turn out to be the Expected value and Variance of the distribution, respectively, as we will see shortly, are assigned specific values.

However, as can be seen from equation (7.33), since each of the parameters of the normal distribution μ and σ^2 $\left(\text{or } \sigma, \text{ since } \sigma = \sqrt{\sigma^2}\right)$, can assume an infinite number of (μ, σ^2) combinations of values, such combinations define an infinite number of generalized normal distributions. This is a very interesting observation because, as we will show shortly, the normal density function cannot be integrated in closed form, thus making the use of tables a necessity. However, since there is an infinite number of Normal distributions, which ones do you choose to tabulate? Fortunately one does not have to choose because, by using the "linear standardization formula":

$$Z = \frac{X_i - \mu_i}{\sigma_i} \tag{7.34}$$

the distribution of any random variable X_i, with $E(X_i) = \mu_i$ and $V(X_i) = \sigma_i^2$, is converted to the distribution of the random variable Z, with $E(Z) = 0$ and $V(Z) = 1$, which is known as the "standardized normal distribution" and is the only one that needs to be tabulated since from (7.34) we can write:

$$X_i = \mu_i + \sigma_i Z \tag{7.35}$$

and the value of the random variable X can be obtained from the value of the random variable Z (which can be obtained from a Table) if μ_i and σ_i are defined.

Figure 7.4 below shows the general shape of the normal density function, the relationship between the variables X and Z and some important geometric properties of this probability law.

Note: The correspondence between the X values: $\mu - 3\sigma, \mu - 2\sigma, \mu - \sigma, \mu, \mu + \sigma, \mu + 2\sigma, \mu + 3\sigma$ and the Z values: $-3, -2, -1, 0, 1, 2, 3$.

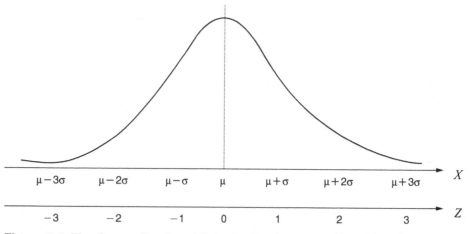

Figure 7.4 The Generalized and Standardized Normal Density Functions

This correspondence is established by using equation (7.34) to find the Z values when the X values are given or using equation (7.35) to find the values of X, when the Z values are specified.

If we designate the density function of the standardized normal variable Z by $n(Z) = f(Z; 0, 1)$, then $f(Z; 0, 1)$ is given by:

$$n(Z) = \frac{1}{\sqrt{2\pi}} e^{-z^2/2} \quad -\infty < Z < \infty \qquad (7.36)$$

The graphs of $n\left(x; \mu, \sigma^2\right)$ and $n(z; 0, 1)$ are symmetric bell-shaped curves, with a single peak value which occurs at $x = \mu$, with maximum value $= \dfrac{1}{\sqrt{2\pi}\sigma}$, or at $z = 0$ with maximum value $= \dfrac{1}{\sqrt{2\pi}}$.

The curves are concave downward in the center, but at a distance of 1 standard deviation on either side of the mean it changes to concave upward. These two points are called "points of inflection" and occur at: $x = \mu - \sigma$ and $x = \mu + \sigma$ on the generalized normal distribution and at $z = -1$ and $z = +1$ on the standardized normal distribution, as can be verified by the optimization methodology of differential calculus.

The functions $f(x; \mu, \sigma)$ and $f(z; 0, 1)$ are positive for all values of X and Z and

$$\int_{-\infty}^{\infty} f(x; \mu, \sigma)dx = 1 \quad \text{and} \quad \int_{-\infty}^{\infty} f(z; 0, 1)dZ = 1$$

Therefore both $f(x; \mu, \sigma)$ and $f(z; 0, 1)$ are proper probability density functions. The above integrations cannot be performed easily. In fact the normal density functions cannot be integrated in closed form. Numerical integration has to be performed but this is not a big problem, especially when one uses a computer and accuracies can be obtained to any desired degree.

Below we state 3 theorems which make it easy to derive the density function of linear combinations of normally distributed random variables. The proof of these theorems is based on the "Normal Generating Function" of a random variable which is a concept beyond the scope of this text.

Theorem 1   If X is a normally distributed random variable with $E(X) = \mu$ and $V(X) = \sigma^2$, then the random variable Y, where $Y = a + bX$ is a linear function of X, is also normally distributed with:

$$E(Y) = a + bE(X) \quad \text{and} \quad V(Y) = b^2 V(X) \qquad (7.37)$$

Theorem 2   If $X_1, X_2, \ldots, X_n$ are n normally distributed random variables which are independent of each other and identically distributed such that:

$E(X_i) = \mu$ and $V(X_i) = \sigma^2$ for all i, then the random variable S, where $S = X_1 + X_2 + \cdots + X_n$, is also normally distributed with:

$$E(S) = n\mu \quad \text{and} \quad V(S) = n\sigma^2 \qquad (7.38)$$

Theorem 3   If $X_1 \rightarrow N\left(\mu_1, \sigma_1^2\right)$, $X_2 \rightarrow N\left(\mu_2, \sigma_2^2\right)$, $X_3 \rightarrow N\left(\mu_3, \sigma_3^2\right)$ are 3 independent and normally distributed random variables, then the random variable R, where:

$$R = a_1 X_1 + a_2 X_2 + a_3 X_3$$

is also normally distributed with:

$$E(R) = a_1\mu_1 + a_2\mu_2 + a_3\mu_3$$

and

$$V(R) = a_1^2 \sigma_1^2 + a_2^2 \sigma_2^2 + a_3^2 \sigma_3^2 \quad \text{and} \quad \sigma(R) = \sqrt{a_1^2 \sigma_1^2 + a_2^2 \sigma_2^2 + a_3^2 \sigma_3^2} \quad (7.39)$$

Note: The above theorem can be generalized to include any number (n) of Random Variables.

Once a random variable is identified as normally distributed and its Expected value and Variance are determined, the calculation of the probability of a desired event, using the normal probability law becomes procedural. However, before we demonstrate the use of the Normal probability law, let us derive the properties of the Normal distribution. We will do so for the general model with density function:

$$f(x; \mu, \sigma) = n(x; \mu, \sigma) = \frac{1}{\sqrt{2\pi}\sigma} e^{-\frac{1}{2\sigma^2}(x-\mu)^2}$$

and then from these the properties of the standardized model can be obtained by substituting $E(X) = \mu = 0$ and $V(X) = \sigma^2 = 1$ in them.

Applying the Expectation and Variance operators ($E(X)$ and $V(X)$ respectively) we obtain:

$$E(X) = \int_{-\infty}^{\infty} x f(x; \mu, \sigma) dx = \frac{1}{\sqrt{2\pi}\sigma} \int_{-\infty}^{\infty} x e^{-\frac{1}{2\sigma^2}(x-\mu)^2} dx$$

To complete this integration let us introduce the variable $y = \dfrac{x - \mu}{\sigma}$ from which we obtain: $x = \mu + \sigma y$ and $dx = \sigma dy$, while the limits of integration remain the same.

Then we have:

$$E(X) = \frac{1}{\sqrt{2\pi}\sigma} \int_{-\infty}^{\infty} (\mu + \sigma y) e^{-y^2/2} \sigma dy$$

$$= \frac{1}{\sqrt{2\pi}\sigma} \int_{-\infty}^{\infty} \mu\sigma e^{-y^2/2} dy + \frac{1}{\sqrt{2\pi}\sigma} \int_{-\infty}^{\infty} \sigma^2 y e^{-y^2/2} dy$$

$$= \mu \int_{-\infty}^{\infty} \frac{1}{\sqrt{2\pi}} e^{-y^2/2} dy + \frac{\sigma}{\sqrt{2\pi}} \int_{-\infty}^{\infty} y e^{-y^2/2} dy$$

The value of the first integral from $-\infty$ to $+\infty$ is equal to 1, because it is the total area under the density function $f(y; 0, 1) = f(z; 0, 1)$.

The value of the second integral is equal to zero because the integrand (*i.e.*, the expression $y e^{-y^2/2}$ under the integral sign) is an odd function and we know from calculus that the integral of an odd function of the form $\int_{-a}^{a} f(y) dy = 0$, while the corresponding integral of an even function $\int_{-a}^{a} f(y) dy = 2 \int_{0}^{a} f(y) dy$.

Note: A function $f(y)$ is said to be an odd function if $f(-y) = -f(y)$ and an even function if $f(-y) = +f(y)$.

Since $f(y) = ye^{-y^2/2}$ here, replacing y by $-y$ we obtain: $f(-y) = -ye^{-(-y)^2/2}$ $= -ye^{-y^2/2} = -f(y)$. Therefore $f(y)$ is an odd function and the value of the integral is equal to zero.

Therefore:

$$E(X) = \mu(1) + \frac{\sigma}{\sqrt{2\pi}}(0) = \mu \tag{7.40}$$

In a similar manner we can show that:

$$E(X^2) = \mu^2 + \sigma^2 \tag{7.41}$$

Finally, since $V(X) = E(X^2) - [E(X)]^2$ for any random variable X,

$$V(X) = \mu^2 + \sigma^2 - \mu^2 = \sigma^2 \tag{7.42}$$

Therefore, the parameters μ and σ^2 which appear in the density function of the normal variable, are its expected value and Variance, respectively. And, since the normal distribution is symmetric about the mean μ, and attains its maximum value when $x = \mu$, the value of $x = \mu$ is not only the mean but also the median and the mode of any normally distributed variable X.

The corresponding mean and variance of the standardized normal variable are, therefore, $E(Z) = 0$ and $V(Z) = 1$, as expected.

In a similar manner we can show that:

$$E(X-\mu)^3 = \int_{-\infty}^{\infty} (x - \mu)^3 f(x; \mu, \sigma) dx = 0$$

and

$$E(X-\mu)^4 = \int_{-\infty}^{\infty} (x - \mu)^4 f(x; \mu, \sigma) dx = 3\sigma^4$$

Therefore, for any normal distribution the coefficients of Skewness and Kurtosis are given by:

$$S_{kp} = \frac{E(X - \mu)^3}{\sigma^3} = 0 \tag{7.43}$$

$$K = \frac{E(X - \mu)^4}{\sigma^4} = \frac{3\sigma^4}{\sigma^4} = 3 \tag{7.44}$$

In statistics we usually use the normal distribution as the "standard" and compare other distributions to it. Therefore distributions are positively or negatively skewed, depending on whether $S_{kp} > 0$ or $S_{kp} < 0$ respectively. Similarly distributions are more peaked or less peaked than the normal, depending on whether $K > 3$ or $K < 3$ respectively.

The probability that a normally distributed random variable X is equal to or less than some specified value x is given by the Cumulative Distribution Function given by:

$$P(X \le x) = F(x; \mu, \sigma) = N(\mu, \sigma) = \frac{1}{\sqrt{2\pi}\sigma} \int_{-\infty}^{x} e^{\frac{1}{2\sigma^2}(x-\mu)^2} dx \tag{7.45}$$

Note: The CDF of a Normally distributed random variable X, with parameters μ and σ can be evaluated using the following MINITAB command/subcommand:

$$\text{MTB} > \text{cdf at } x_0 \ (\rightarrow \text{ Specify value of } x_0);$$

$$\text{SUBC} > \text{Normal } \mu \ \ \sigma.$$

This integral cannot be found analytically in closed form. It could be tabulated as a function of μ and σ, but that would require a separate table for each (μ, σ) combination. Since there is an infinite number of such combinations, as noted earlier, this would be impossible to accomplish for all (μ, σ) combinations of values. But, as we have already stated, it is simplified by using the linear transformation for standardizing a variable, namely: $Z = \dfrac{X - \mu}{\sigma}$ which reduces every normal variable, with any μ and σ to the single standardized density $f(z; 0, 1)$.

The transformation $Z = \dfrac{X - \mu}{\sigma}$ (or $X = \mu + \sigma Z$) implies that:

$$P(X \le x) = P(\mu + \sigma Z \le x) = P\left(Z \le \frac{x - \mu}{\sigma} \right)$$

$$= \frac{1}{\sqrt{2\pi}} \int_{-\infty}^{\frac{x-\mu}{\sigma}} e^{-z^2/2} \, dz = F(Z; 0, 1) = N(Z; 0, 1) \ (7.46)$$

after making the appropriate changes dictated by the linear transformation above.

The function $F(Z; 0, 1) = N(Z; 0, 1)$ is extensively tabulated and appears as the z table in Part IX (Appendices & Tables), but a truncated version of this Table is shown below for illustrative purposes.

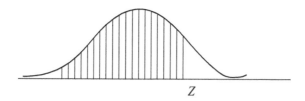

Z

Z	0.00	0.01	0.02	0.03	0.04	0.05	0.06	0.07	0.08	0.09
−3.0	0.0013	0.0013	0.0013	0.0012	0.0012	0.0011	0.0011	0.0011	0.0010	0.0010
...	...	...	...	...	...	...	...	...	...	...
−2.0	0.0228	0.0222	0.0217	0.0212	0.0207	0.0202	0.0197	0.0192	0.0188	0.0183
...	...	...	...	...	...	...	...	...	...	...
−1.0	0.1587	0.1562	0.1539	0.1515	0.1492	0.1469	0.1446	0.1423	0.1401	0.1379
...	...	...	...	...	...	...	...	...	...	...
0.0	0.500	0.5040	0.5080	0.5120	0.5160	0.5199	0.5239	0.5279	0.5319	0.5359
...	...	...	...	...	...	...	...	...	...	...
1.0	0.8413	0.8438	0.8461	0.8485	0.8508	0.8531	0.8554	0.8577	0.8599	0.8621
...	...	...	...	...	...	...	...	...	...	...
2.0	0.9772	0.9778	0.9783	0.9788	0.9793	0.9798	0.9803	0.9808	0.9812	0.9817
...	...	...	...	...	...	...	...	...	...	...
3.0	0.9983	0.9987	0.9987	0.9988	0.9988	0.9989	0.9989	0.9989	0.9990	0.9990

The CDF table for the standard normal distribution has the following structure:

$$P\left(Z \le z\right) = F\left(z; 0, 1\right) = \frac{1}{\sqrt{2\pi}} \int_{-\infty}^{z} e^{-z^2/2}\, dz$$

Note: $f(-z) = f(z)$

The left-hand column in this table gives the value of Z to one decimal place. For a second decimal place in the Z value, one has to locate the appropriate column to the right of Z. The values in the body of the table give the probability that the random variable Z is less than or equal to the specified value of Z. For example, the probability that Z is less than or equal to $Z \le 2.02$ is equal to 0.9783, which is the value found at the intersection of the row $Z = 2.0$ and column $Z = 0.02$. Such probabilities are represented by the shaded area in the above diagram which is the value of the integral of the standardized normal density function from $-\infty$ to Z.

This is one of two ways that this table can be used. That is: given the value of $Z = z_0$, find $P(Z \le z_0)$. The second way is to find the value of z_0, given the probability. As an example, suppose we are given: $P(Z \le z_0) = 0.8508$. What is the value of z_0? We search the body of the table and try to locate the probability which is exactly equal to the given value or comes closest to the given value. Sometimes the given value is in the table, and we simply read off the corresponding z_0-value in the margins of the table. This is the case here and we find that $P(Z \le z_0) = 0.8508$ when $z_0 = 1.04$. On other occasions the given probability value is not in the table, but can be located between two existing values. We can choose the closest and find the corresponding z_0-value or, if we want better accuracy, we can interpolate between two existing values.

For example, suppose the given value is 0.8585. Searching the body of the table we find that this value is between 0.8577 (which corresponds to $z_0 = 1.07$) and 0.8599 (which corresponds to $z_0 = 1.08$). We can choose $z_0 = 1.07$ since the given value (0.8585) is closer to 0.8577 (they differ by (0.00081) than to 0.8599 (they differ by (0.0014)). Or we can linearly interpolate between the two values and find:

$$Z_{0.8585} = Z_{0.8577} + \left(Z_{0.8599} - Z_{0.8577}\right) \times \left[\frac{\text{Given Probability} - P(Z < 1.07)}{P(Z < 1.08) - P(Z < 1.07)}\right]$$

$$= 1.07 + (1.08 - 1.07)\left[\frac{0.8585 - 0.8577}{0.8599 - 0.8577}\right] = 1.07 + 0.01\left(\frac{9}{22}\right)$$

$$= 1.07 + 0.01(0.41) = 1.0700 + 0.0041 = 1.0741$$

When the CDF is plotted, we get a smooth curve with a distinctive S-like shape, as shown in Figure 7.5 below:

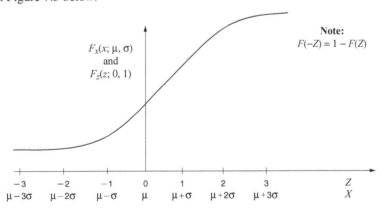

Figure 7.5 Cumulative Distribution Function for both the Generalized and Standard Normal Density Function

Other CDF Tables exist which do not add the value of 0.5 (which is the value of the definite integral: $\int_{-\infty}^{0} f(z)\,dz$ but give instead the value of the integral: $\int_{0}^{z} f(z)\,dz$, for a specified z value. For the solution of the Hypothesis testing problem and the construction of confidence intervals on population parameters whose estimators are Normally distributed (we will discuss Sampling distributions in Chapter 8 and Estimators in Chapter 9; for example the estimator of the population parameter μ is $\overline{X}$ which, under certain conditions is Normally distributed), we use the notation specified by the diagram below:

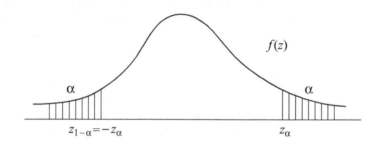

where z_α and $z_{1-\alpha}$ are respectively the lower limits of the definite integrals:

$$\int_{z_\alpha}^{\infty} f(z)\,dz = \alpha \quad \text{and} \quad \int_{z_{1-\alpha}}^{\infty} f(z)\,dz = 1 - \alpha.$$

This notation is similar to the one we used earlier for the χ^2 distribution and will also be used for t and F.

We now present two examples which will illustrate further the use of the normal distribution. The first example shows how the **Empirical rule** which we discussed back in Chapter 3 is derived, while the second one shows how the normal probability model is used to "**Grade on the curve**".

Example 1

Let X be $N(\mu, \sigma^2)$. Find the probability that X is:

1. Within one standard deviation of the mean.
2. Within two standard deviations of the mean.
3. Within three standard deviations of the mean.

Solutions

1. P (X is within one standard deviation of the mean)

$$= P(\mu - \sigma \le X \le \mu + \sigma)$$

$$= P\left[\frac{(\mu - \sigma) - \mu}{\sigma} \le Z \le \frac{(\mu + \sigma) - \mu}{\sigma}\right] = P\left[-1 \le Z \le 1\right]$$

$$= P(Z \le 1) - P(Z \le -1)$$

$$= 0.8413 - 0.1587 = 0.6826$$

where $Z = \dfrac{X - \mu}{\sigma}$,

and $P(Z \leq 1) = P\left[-\infty \leq Z \leq 0\right] + P\left[0 \leq Z \leq 1\right]$

$$= 0.5 + 0.3413 = 0.8413$$

$$P(Z \leq -1) = 1 - P(Z \leq 1) = 1 - 0.8413 = 0.1587$$

2. $P[\mu - 2\sigma \leq X \leq \mu + 2\sigma] = P\left[\dfrac{(\mu - 2\sigma) - \mu}{\sigma} \leq Z \leq \dfrac{(\mu + 2\sigma) - \mu}{\sigma}\right]$

$$= P[-2 \leq Z \leq 2] = P(Z \leq 2) - P(Z \leq -2)$$

$$= 0.9772 - 0.0228 = 0.9544$$

where $P(Z \leq 2) = P[-\infty \leq Z \leq 0] + P[0 \leq Z \leq 2]$

$$= 0.5 + 0.4772 = 0.9772,$$

and $P(Z \leq -2) = 1 - P(Z \leq 2) = 1 - 0.9772 = 0.0228$

3. $P[\mu - 3\sigma \leq X \leq \mu + 3\sigma] = P\left[\dfrac{(\mu - 3\sigma) - \mu}{\sigma} \leq Z \leq \dfrac{(\mu + 3\sigma) - \mu}{\sigma}\right]$

$$= P[-3 \leq Z \leq 3] = P(Z \leq 3) - P(Z \leq -3)$$

$$= 0.9987 - 0.0013 = 0.9974$$

where $P(Z \leq 3) = P[-\infty \leq Z \leq 0] + P[0 \leq Z \leq 3]$

$$= 0.5 + 0.4987 = 0.9987$$

and $P[Z \leq -3] = 1 - P(Z \leq 3) = 1 - 0.9987 = 0.0013$

Recall that these are exactly the probability values claimed by the **Empirical rule** we discussed in Chapter 3, and this is where these values came from!

■■■

Example 2 "Grading on the curve"

Assuming that the grade X that students obtain in a course, is a random variable obeying a normal probability law with parameters μ and σ (which the professor can estimate from the scores of many students), the properties of the normal distribution function provide the basis for the method of "grading on the curve" used in assigning final grades in large courses in American Universities. Under this system the letters *A, B, C, D* are used as passing grades, and of the students with passing grades, approximately 15% receive *A*, 35% receive *B*, 35% receive *C*, and 15% receive *D*. These percentages are obtained from the normal distribution as follows:

1. $P(\text{of getting a } A) = P(X > \mu + \sigma) = 1 - P(X < \mu + \sigma)$

$$= 1 - P\left(Z < \dfrac{(\mu + \sigma) - \mu}{\sigma}\right) = 1 - P(Z < 1)$$

$$= 1 - 0.8413 = 0.1587$$

2. $P(\text{of getting a } B) = P(\mu < X < \mu + \sigma) = P\left(\dfrac{\mu - \mu}{\sigma} < Z < \dfrac{(\mu + \sigma) - \mu}{\sigma}\right)$

$$= P(0 < Z < 1) = P(Z < 1) - P(Z < 0)$$

$$= 0.8413 - 0.5000 = 0.3413$$

3. $P(\text{of getting a } C) = P(\mu - \sigma < X < \mu) = P\left(\dfrac{(\mu - \sigma) - \mu}{\sigma} < Z < \dfrac{\mu - \mu}{\sigma}\right)$

$= P(-1 < Z < 0) = P(Z < 0) - P(Z < -1)$

$= 0.5000 - 0.1587 = 0.3413$

4. $P(\text{of getting a } D) = P(X < \mu - \sigma) = P\left(Z < \dfrac{(\mu - \sigma) - \mu}{\sigma}\right) = P(Z < -1)$

$= 0.1587$

Therefore, if one assigns the letter A to students whose score X is greater than $\mu + \sigma$, approximately 15% (actually 15.87%) of the students would receive the grade A. Similarly, if the grade B is assigned to students with scores between μ and $\mu + \sigma$, approximately 35% of the students would get a grade B. Also about 35% of the students would get a grade C, if C is assigned to students with scores between $\mu - \sigma$ and μ. Finally, if the grade D is assigned to students with scores less than $\mu - \sigma$, about 15% of the students, with passing grade, will get the grade D.

■ ■ ■

7.5   The Approximation of the Binomial Probability Law by the Normal

At the end of Chapter 6 we showed how the discrete probability laws were connected with each other and outlined certain conditions under which they could approximate each other.

More specifically we showed that the Hypergeometric can be approximated by the Binomial (if $n \leq N/20$), which in turn can be approximated by the Poisson (if $n > 100$ and $p < 0.01$). This, of course, implies that the Hypergeometric model is related to the Poisson through the Binomial, and we can write:

$$\frac{\dbinom{N_1}{x}\dbinom{N - N_1}{n - x}}{\dbinom{N}{n}} \approx \dbinom{n}{x} p^x (1 - p)^{n - x} \approx \frac{e^{-\lambda}\lambda^x}{x!} \quad \text{where } p = \frac{N_1}{N} \text{ and } \lambda = np$$

In this section we introduce a Normal approximation to the Binomial and, in view of the above, to the Hypergeometric and Poisson.

The reason for introducing this approximation is similar to the reasons for establishing the approximations among the discrete distributions, namely: greater ease of probability calculations; *i.e.*, we found that it is easier to calculate probabilities using the Binomial than the Hypergeometric, but much easier to use the Poisson than either of the other two because the Poisson model has only one parameter, the Binomial two and the Hypergeometric three.

Here we claim that if an appropriate approximation can be found, the normal will be much easier to use than any of the discrete models. The Normal approximation to the Binomial that we introduce is based on the following theorem known as the "**DeMoivre-Laplace Limit theorem**" (it was stated by DeMoivre in 1733 for the case $p = 1/2$ and proved for arbitrary values of p by Laplace in 1812) which states:

"The probability that a random phenomenon obeying the Binomial probability law with parameters n and p will have an observed value lying between a and b inclusive (for any two integers a and b), is given approximately by:

$$P(a \leq x \leq b) = \sum_{x=a}^{b} \binom{n}{x} p^x (1 - p)^{n - x}$$

$$\approx \frac{1}{\sqrt{2\pi}} \int_{\frac{a - np - 1/2}{\sqrt{np(1 - p)}}}^{\frac{b - np + 1/2}{\sqrt{np(1 - p)}}} e^{-z^2/2} \, dz \qquad (7.47)$$

$$= N\left(\frac{b - np + 1/2}{\sqrt{np(1 - p)}}\right) - N\left(\frac{a - np - 1/2}{\sqrt{np(1 - p)}}\right)$$

where $N(\ )$ is the tabulated CDF function of the standardized normal variable", evaluated at the z values shown in the parentheses.

In the above formula np and $\sqrt{np(1 - p)}$ are the expected value and standard deviation of the Binomial variable with parameters n and p, and the value of $1/2$ is known as the CCF (Continuity Correction Factor) and is introduced to take account of the fact that we are approximating probabilities for a discrete random variable from interval probabilities of a continuous random variable. The effect of the CCF is to make the approximation better as we shall see in the examples below. The approximation above is adequate as long as $np > 5$ when $p \le 1/2$ or when $n(1 - p) > 5$ for $p > 1/2$.

If we wanted to calculate $P(X = x = k)$ for the Binomial variable (with parameters n and p) using the above approximation, we set $b = a = k$, and obtain:

$$P(X = x = k) = N\left(\frac{k - np + 1/2}{\sqrt{np(1 - p)}}\right) - N\left(\frac{k - np - 1/2}{\sqrt{np(1 - p)}}\right) \qquad (7.48)$$

In the next chapter, when we discuss Sampling Distributions, we will show, using the Central Limit Theorem, that a random variable which can be expressed as the sum of n independent and identically distributed random variables $X_1, X_2, \ldots, X_n$ is approximately normally distributed, with the approximation getting better as $x \to \infty$.

Since we have shown in Chapter 6 that the Binomial variable X may be regarded as the sum of n independent and identically distributed Bernoulli variables, we are again led to the conclusion that the Binomial can be approximated by the Normal.

Example 3

Suppose a fair die ($p = 1/2$) is thrown 8 times. Find the probability that X is less than or equal to 5, using:

1. The Binomial distribution
2. The Normal approximation to the Binomial without the CCF.
3. The Normal approximation to the Binomial with the CCF.

Solution

1. $P(X \le 5) = \sum_{x=0}^{5} \binom{8}{x}\left(\frac{1}{2}\right)^x\left(\frac{1}{2}\right)^{8-x} = B(5, 8, 0.5) = 0.8555$

For parts 2 and 3 we need to calculate $E(X)$ and $\sigma(X)$. They are:

$$E(X) = np = 8\left(\frac{1}{2}\right) = 4$$

$$\sigma(X) = \sqrt{np(1-p)} = \sqrt{8\left(\frac{1}{2}\right)\left(\frac{1}{2}\right)} = \sqrt{2} \approx 1.414$$

Therefore:

2. $P(X \leq 5) = P(0 \leq x \leq 5) = N\left(\dfrac{5-4}{\sqrt{2}}\right) - N\left(\dfrac{0-4}{\sqrt{2}}\right)$

$$= N\left(\frac{1}{\sqrt{2}}\right) - N\left(-\frac{4}{\sqrt{2}}\right) = N\left(\frac{\sqrt{2}}{2}\right) - N(-2\sqrt{2})$$

$$= N(0.707) - N(-2.824) = 0.7630 - 0.0024 = 0.7606$$

3. $P(X \leq 5) = P(0 \leq x \leq 5) \approx N\left(\dfrac{5-4+1/2}{\sqrt{2}}\right) - N\left(\dfrac{0-4-1/2}{\sqrt{2}}\right)$

$$= N\left(\frac{3/2}{\sqrt{2}}\right) - N\left(\frac{-9\sqrt{2}}{\sqrt{2}}\right) = N(1.06) - N(-3.18)$$

$$= 0.8554 - 0.0007 = 0.8547$$

As can be seen from these results, the addition of the CCF produced results which are very close to the exact results, generated from the Binomial.

■ ■ ■

Example 4

Suppose that $n = 6000$ tosses of a fair die are made.

Find: 1. Find the probability that exactly 1000 of the tosses will result in a "three".
2. Find the probability that the number of tosses in which a "three" occurs is between 980 and 1030 inclusive.

Solutions

Let us first find $E(X)$ and $\sigma(X)$ of the Binomial variable for this example since we will use the Normal approximation to perform these probability calculations and $E(X)$ and $\sigma(X)$ are needed.

Therefore, we have:

$$E(X) = np = 6000\left(\frac{1}{6}\right) = 1000$$

$$\sigma(X) = \sqrt{np(1-p)} = \sqrt{6000\left(\frac{1}{6}\right)\left(\frac{5}{6}\right)} = \sqrt{5000/6} \approx 28.87$$

Then

1. $P(x = 1000) = \dbinom{6000}{1000}\left(\dfrac{1}{6}\right)^{1000}\left(\dfrac{5}{6}\right)^{5000}$

$$\approx N\left(\frac{1000 - 1000 + 1/2}{28.87}\right) - N\left(\frac{1000 - 1000 - 1/2}{28.87}\right)$$

$$= N\left(\frac{1}{57.74}\right) - N\left(-\frac{1}{57.75}\right) = N(0.017) - N(-0.017)$$

$$= 0.5068 - 0.4948 = 0.0120$$

It would have been quite laborious to evaluate this probability directly from the Binomial law.

2. $P(980 \le x \le 1030) = \sum_{x=980}^{1030} \binom{6000}{x} \left(\frac{1}{6}\right)^x \left(\frac{5}{6}\right)^{6000-x}$

$$\approx N\left(\frac{1030 - 1000 + 1/2}{28.87}\right) - N\left(\frac{980 - 1000 - 1/2}{28.87}\right)$$

$$= N(1.06) - N(-0.71) = 0.8554 - 0.2389 = 0.6165$$

Again, the labor involved in calculating the sum directly from the Binomial would have been tremendous, while the Normal approximation produced the answer quite easily.

■ ■ ■

7.6   The Student's *t* Distribution

The *t* distribution was developed in 1908 by W.S. Gosset, who published his work under the pen name "student" because the company he worked for would not allow him to publish under his own name. It is a very useful distribution and, as we will see in the next section of this book "Inferential Statistics", it allows us to estimate and test the mean of a population when the sample size is relatively small, usually under 30. For values of $n \ge 30$, the normal distribution can be used without too much error.

In the next chapter of "Sampling Distributions" we will see how the *t* distribution can be derived when sampling from a Normal distribution. In this chapter, however, we wish to establish the theoretical foundation of the *t* distribution. Since we have already discussed the chi-square (χ^2) distribution, as a special case of the Gamma distribution, and the standard Normal distribution, we proceed as follows.

We let Z be a standard Normal variable (N(0, 1)), and Y be a chi-square random variable with δ degrees of freedom. If Z and Y are independent random variables, and we define the random variable T as a function of the random variables Z and Y by the equation:

$$T = \frac{Z}{\sqrt{Y/\delta}} \tag{7.49}$$

then, the random variable T has a Student's *t* distribution with δ degrees of freedom and its probability density function is given by:

$$f(t, \delta) = \frac{\Gamma\left[\dfrac{\delta + 1}{2}\right]}{\sqrt{\pi \delta \Gamma(\delta/2)}} \left(1 + \frac{t^2}{\delta}\right)^{-\left(\frac{\delta+1}{2}\right)} \qquad \delta > 0, \ -\infty < T < \infty \tag{7.50}$$

For $\delta > 0$, the *t* distribution is symmetric about zero and achieves its maximum value when $t = 0$. The shape of the *t* density function is very similar to that of the standard normal, but the *t* distribution has wider tails. This can also be seen from the variance of the T variable which is greater than the variance of the standard Normal variable, as shown below.

Application of the Expectation and Variance operators to the $f(t, \delta)$ density function of the T variable produces:

$$E(T) = 0 \qquad\qquad \delta > 1 \tag{7.51}$$

$$V(T) = \frac{\delta}{\delta - 2} = 1 + \frac{2}{\delta - 2} \qquad \delta > 2 \tag{7.52}$$

Clearly, for $\delta > 2$, $V(T) > 1$ and, therefore, $V(T) > V(Z)$, where $V(Z) = 1$ is the vari-ance of the standard normal variable. The set of all possible values of the T variable is in the interval: $-\infty < T < \infty$, since the values of the Z variable are in this infinite interval and the values of the chi-square variable are positive, and $\Gamma\left(\dfrac{\delta + 1}{2}\right)$ and $\Gamma\left(\dfrac{\delta}{2}\right)$ is the gamma function mentioned in our discussion of the Gamma distribution (See equation (7.12)).

Probability calculations with the Student's t density function are not easy because $f(t, \delta)$ cannot be integrated in closed form. However, just as was the case with the Normal, this probability function has been integrated numerically and is widely tabulated.

It should be remembered that there is a separate t distribution for each value of δ (degrees of freedom) and for this reason selected values of the Cumulative Density Function (CDF) of $f(t, \delta)$ are given in the t table in Part IX Appendices & Tables.

By definition, the CDF of the T random variable is given by:

$$P(T < t_{\delta,\,1-\alpha}) = CDF(T) = \int_{-\infty}^{t_{\delta,\,1-\alpha}} f(t, \delta)\,dt = 1 - \alpha \qquad (7.53)$$

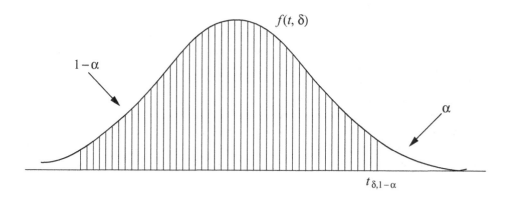

By specifying the value of α for a given δ (we will see in the next chapter how δ is related to the sample size n), the table gives the value of $T = t_{\delta,\,1-\alpha}$ which divides the $f(t, \delta)$ density function into two segments: one with area $1 - \alpha$ and the other with area α.

The most commonly used values of $1 - \alpha$ are:

$$0.010,\ 0.025,\ 0.050,\ 0.950,\ 0.975,\ 0.990,\ 0.900.$$

and those are the ones usually found in a table of the student t distribution which, for selected values of δ, may look as follows:

			$1 - \alpha$ values				
δ	$t_{0.010}$	$t_{\cdot 0.025}$	$t_{0.050}$	$t_{0.950}$	$t_{0.975}$	$t_{0.990}$	$t_{0.900}$
3	−4.541	−3.182	−2.353	2.353	3.182	4.541	1.638
5	−3.365	−2.571	−2.015	2.015	2.571	3.365	1.476
10	−2.764	−2.228	−1.812	1.812	2.228	2.764	1.372
15	−2.602	−2.131	−1.753	1.753	2.131	2.602	1.341
20	−2.528	−2.086	−1.725	1.725	2.086	2.528	1.325
25	−2.485	−2.060	−1.708	1.708	2.060	2.485	1.316
30	−2.457	−2.042	−1.697	1.697	2.042	2.457	1.310
100	−2.364	−1.984	−1.660	1.660	1.984	2.364	1.290

Notice the symmetry of the table. For example $t_{0.050} = -t_{0.950}$, and $t_{0.025} = -t_{0.975}$. This also implies that $t_{0.10} = -t_{0.90}$ (but $t_{0.10}$ is not shown in the Table above).

To use the table: Given the degrees of freedom δ and the desired α value, locate the value at the intersection of the δ row and $1 - \alpha$ column.

We will use such a table extensively when estimating the population mean or difference of two population means by a confidence interval when the sample size(s) is(are) less than 30 and the population standard deviation(s) is(are) unknown. It will also be used to perform Hypothesis Testing on the mean value of a single population or the difference of the means of two populations, as we will see in future chapters.

In Chapter 8, the Student's t, as well as the Chi-square and the F-distributions, will be re-derived as sampling distributions which is the usual way of treating them. However, we felt, that such future discussion would be greatly enhanced if these distributions could be discussed on a purely theoretical basis earlier and their basic properties established before they need to be applied. In fact, the purpose of this entire chapter is to facilitate the identification of the sampling distributions of some of the Sample Statistics we calculated back in chapter 3.

Note: As we did previously with the χ^2 and z distributions, to facilitate the solution of the Hypothesis Testing problem and the construction of Confidence Intervals, we will use the notation suggested by the diagram below:

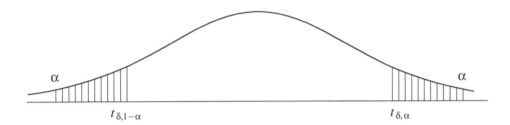

where $t_{\delta, \alpha}$ and $t_{\delta, 1-\alpha}$ are respectively the Low Integration Limits of the definite integrals:

$$\int_{t_{\delta, \alpha}}^{\infty} f(t)\, dt = \alpha \text{ and } \int_{t_{\delta, 1-\alpha}}^{\infty} f(t)\, dt = 1 - \alpha.$$

7.7 The F Distribution

The F distribution is so named after Sir Ronald A. Fisher, an English statistician, who made numerous important contributions to statistics in the last century, the most famous of which are: the discovery of the F distribution, the full development of small-sample theory, the theory of multivariate association analysis, the design of experiments, and the analysis of Variance.

Although the F distribution, just like the Chi-square and t distributions discussed previously, is considered a sampling distribution as we will show in the next chapter, it can also be established on a theoretical basis as the ratio of two Chi-square variables.

If Y_1 is a Chi-square variable with δ_1 degrees of freedom and Y_2 is also a Chi-square variable with δ_2 degrees of freedom, and Y_1 and Y_2 are independent, then the random variable:

$$F = \frac{Y_1/\delta_2}{Y_2/\delta_2} \tag{7.54}$$

is said to have an F distribution with probability density function

$$f(F, \delta_1, \delta_2) = \left[\frac{\Gamma\left(\dfrac{\delta_1 + \delta_2}{2}\right)}{\Gamma\left(\dfrac{\delta_1}{2}\right)\Gamma\left(\dfrac{\delta_2}{2}\right)} \right] \left(\frac{\delta_1}{\delta_2}\right)^{\frac{\delta_1}{2}} F^{\frac{(\delta_1 - 2)}{2}} \left(1 + \frac{\delta_1}{\delta_2} F\right)^{-\frac{(\delta_1 + \delta_2)}{2}} \tag{7.55}$$

where the interval of variation for F is: $0 \le F < \infty$.

The F distribution is completely determined by the degrees of freedom δ_1 and δ_2, and there is a different F distribution for each (δ_1, δ_2) combination. The F distribution is positively skewed for any values of δ_1 and δ_2, but becomes less skewed as δ_1 and δ_2 are assigned larger values.

Applying the Expectation and Variance operators to the density function $f(F, \delta_1, \delta_2)$ we obtain:

$$E(F) = \frac{\delta_2}{\delta_2 - 2} \qquad\qquad \text{for} \quad \delta_2 > 2 \tag{7.56}$$

$$V(F) = \frac{\delta_2^2(2\delta_2 + 2\delta_1 - 4)}{\delta_1(\delta_2 - 2)^2(\delta_2 - 4)} \qquad\qquad \text{for} \quad \delta_2 > 4 \tag{7.57}$$

Probability calculations with the F distribution are not easy because the density function $f(F, \delta_1, \delta_2)$ cannot be integrated in closed form. Therefore, the density function has been integrated numerically and the results are tabulated. However, because this distribution has two parameters (δ_1 and δ_2) we would need a three-dimensional table to store the results: one dimension for δ_1, the other for δ_2, and the third for the desired probability $1 - \alpha$. Since this is impractical, a separate table is constructed for each value of $1 - \alpha$ desired and, to keep the tables to a minimum, only few selected values of $1 - \alpha$ are used, namely: 0.900, 0.950, 0.975 and 0.990.

Usually no tables are constructed for $1 - \alpha$ equal to: 0.100, 0.050, 0.025 and 0.010, because these can be obtained from the previous ones using the reciprocal property of the F distributions as will be explained below. But let us first explain the structure and use of the F tables for the selected $1 - \alpha$ CDF values (with corresponding right-hand tails of areas equal to α) and then we will show how they can be used to generate left-hand tail areas also equal to α, without the need for extra tables.

Because of the definition of the F variable as a ratio of two Chi-square variables (Y_1 in the numerator with δ_1 degrees of freedom and Y_2 in the denominator with δ_2 degrees of freedom), the F variable is said to have δ_1 and δ_2 degrees of freedom in the numerator and denominator, respectively. Therefore, for a selected value of $1 - \alpha$, say $1 - \alpha = 0.95$ which makes the right-hand tail of the F distribution equal to $\alpha = 0.05$ (so that the sum of the two areas is equal to 1), the F table consists of a "matrix" of F values in which the degrees of freedom of the numerator (for different values of δ_1) form the headings of the columns of the matrix while the degrees of freedom of the denominator (for different values of δ_2) form the rows of the matrix. At the intersection of the given δ_1 (column) and δ_2 (row) we find a number, which we represent by $F_{\delta_2}^{\delta_1}(1 - \alpha)$ to indicate the degrees of freedom in the numerator and denominator and the value of the CDF at this particular value of the variable F. Note that the area under the density function $f(F, \delta_1, \delta_2)$ from 0 to $F_{\delta_2}^{\delta_1}(1 - \alpha)$, is equal to $1 - \alpha$. For different (δ_1, δ_2) combinations the value $F_{\delta_2}^{\delta_1}(1 - \alpha)$ changes since it correspondents to a different F distribution.

The CDF mentioned above is defined as:

$$CDF(F) = P(F < F_{\delta_2}^{\delta_1}(1 - \alpha) = \int_{0}^{F_{\delta_2}^{\delta_1}(1 - \alpha)} f(F, \delta_1, \delta_2)\, dF = 1 - \alpha$$

The table below shows a small section of such an F table for $1 - \alpha = 0.95$. More extensive F tables are to be found in Part IX Appendices & Tables.

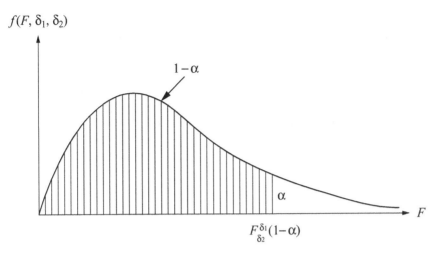

δ_2	1	2	5	10	15	20	30	40	50	100	1000
1	161.45	199.5	230.16	241.88	245.96	248.01	250.08	251.15	251.77	253.01	254.17
2	18.51	19.0	19.30	19.40	19.43	19.45	19.46	19.47	19.48	19.19	19.50
5	6.61	5.79	5.05	4.73	4.62	4.56	4.5	4.46	4.44	4.41	4.37
10	4.96	4.10	3.33	2.98	2.85	2.77	2.7	2.66	2.64	2.59	2.54
15	4.54	3.68	2.90	2.54	2.40	2.33	2.25	2.20	2.18	2.12	2.07
20	4.35	3.49	2.71	2.35	2.20	2.12	2.04	1.99	1.97	1.91	1.85
30	4.17	3.32	2.53	2.16	2.01	1.93	1.84	1.79	1.76	1.70	1.63
40	4.08	3.23	2.45	2.08	1.92	1.84	1.74	1.69	1.66	1.59	1.52
50	4.03	3.18	2.40	2.03	1.87	1.78	1.69	1.63	1.60	1.52	1.45
100	3.94	3.09	2.31	1.93	1.77	1.68	1.57	1.52	1.48	1.39	1.30
1000	3.85	3.01	2.22	1.84	1.68	1.58	1.47	1.41	1.36	1.26	1.11

Table header: $1 - \alpha = 0.951$ — $\delta_1 = $ Degrees of freedom for Numerator

As an example if $\delta_1 = 20$ and $\delta_2 = 10$, then the F value: $F_{10}^{20}(0.95) = 2.77$ makes the area under the $f(F, 20, 10)$ density function, from 0 to 2.77, equal to 0.95, while the area from 2.77 to $+\infty$ is 0.05.

Clearly, the fact that the

$$CDF(F) = P\left[F < F_{10}^{20}(0.95)\right] = \int_0^{F_{10}^{20}(0.95)} f(F, 20, 10)\, df = 0.95,$$

also implies that: $\int_{F_{10}^{20}(0.95)}^{\infty} f(F, 20, 10) dF = 0.05$, since we can write

$$\int_0^{\infty} f(F, 20, 10) dF = \int_0^{F_{10}^{20}(0.95)} f(F, 20, 10) dF + \int_{F_{10}^{20}(0.95)}^{\infty} f(f, 20, 10)\, dF = 1$$

Therefore, the F value $F_{10}^{20}(0.95) = 2.77$ divides the total area under the $f(F)$ density function into two areas: one from 0 to 2.77 whose area is equal to 0.95 and the second one, which is in the right-hand tail of the distribution, whose area is equal to $\alpha = 0.05$.

There are, however, many occasions (such as Interval Estimation and Hypothesis Testing) as we will see in future chapters, which also require the calculation of an area equal to α ($\alpha = 0.05$ in this example) on the left-hand tail of the distribution. That is we are looking

for the F value $F_{\delta_2}^{\delta_1}(\alpha) = F_{10}^{20}(0.05)$ such that: $\displaystyle\int_0^{F_{10}^{20}(0.05)} f(F, 20, 10)dF = 0.05$.

Note: Such calculations are based on other F tables which calculate only the right hand tails for values of $\alpha = 0.1, 0.05, 0.025, 0.01, 0.005$ and then use the Reciprocal property of the F distribution to calculate left-hand tailed values. Such tables are based on the notation specified by the diagram below.

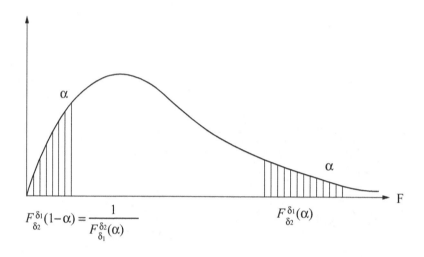

$$F_{\delta_2}^{\delta_1}(1-\alpha) = \frac{1}{F_{\delta_1}^{\delta_2}(\alpha)} \qquad\qquad F_{\delta_2}^{\delta_1}(\alpha)$$

where $F_{\delta_2}^{\delta_1}(\alpha)$ and $F_{\delta_2}^{\delta_1}(1 - \alpha)$ are the low limits of integration of the definite integrals:

$$\int_{F_{\delta_2}^{\delta_1}(\alpha)}^{\infty} f(F)dF = a \quad \text{and} \quad \int_{F_{\delta_2}^{\delta_1}(1-\alpha)}^{\infty} f(F)dF = 1 - \alpha, \text{respectively.}$$

As we stated earlier, in our discussion of the χ^2, Z and t distributions, such tables are very convenient for the solution of the Hypothesis Testing Problem and the construction of Confidence Intervals, and this notation is used extensively in Chapter 11, where these problems are discussed at length.

Note that the left-hand tailed value is calculated from a right-hand tailed F value but one in which the degrees of freedom have been interchanged (this is the **Reciprocal property** represented by equation (7.58) below).

Now, to get back to our example, the figure below shows the two areas in the two tails of the distribution. The right-hand tail is defined by the value 2.77 obtained from such a revised F table. Now we like to define the value of $F_{10}^{20}(0.05)$, on the left-hand tail.

We could, of course, construct a separate table for this value of $CDF(F)$ but this is really not necessary since we can relate the value $F_{\delta_2}^{\delta_1}(\alpha) = F_{10}^{20}(0.05)$ to the value $F_{\delta_2}^{\delta_1}(1 - \alpha) = F_{10}^{20}(0.95)$ according to the "reciprocal property" of the F distributions which can be stated as:

$$F_{\delta_2}^{\delta_1}(1 - \alpha) = \frac{1}{F_{\delta_1}^{\delta_2}(\alpha)} \qquad\qquad (7.58)$$

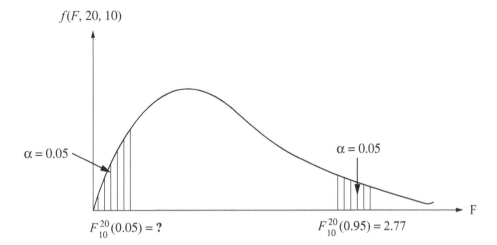

$$F_{10}^{20}(0.05) = ? \qquad F_{10}^{20}(0.95) = 2.77$$

In our example this implies that: $F_{10}^{20}(0.05) = \dfrac{1}{F_{20}^{10}(0.95)} = \dfrac{1}{2.35} = 0.4255$.

Note that in (7.58) the degrees of freedom in the quantity in the denominator have been interchanged: δ_2 is now the degrees of freedom in the numerator and δ_1 is the degrees of freedom of the denominator. Equation (7.58) is based on the fact that if the variable F has the F distribution with δ_1 and δ_2 degrees of freedom, then the variable

$$G = \frac{1}{F} = \frac{1}{\dfrac{Y_1/\delta_1}{Y_2/\delta_2}} = \frac{Y_2/\delta_2}{Y_1/\delta_1} \text{ is also } F \text{ distributed but with degrees of freedom } \delta_2 \text{ and } \delta_1.$$

Therefore $\qquad P\left[F \le F_{\delta_2}^{\delta_1}(1 - \alpha) \right] = P\left[\frac{1}{F} > \frac{1}{F_{\delta_2}^{\delta_1}(1 - \alpha)} \right] = 1 - \alpha \qquad (7.59)$

or $\qquad P\left[\frac{1}{F} \le \frac{1}{F_{\delta_2}^{\delta_1}(1 - \alpha)} \right] = \alpha \qquad (7.60)$

But $\dfrac{1}{F} = G$ which is F distributed with δ_2 and δ_1 degrees of freedom.

Therefore, we can write for the variable G:

$$P\left[G \le F_{\delta_1}^{\delta_2}(\alpha) \right] = \alpha \qquad (7.61)$$

But, since equations (7.60) and (7.61) are identical, we can write:

$$F_{\delta_2}^{\delta_1}(1 - \alpha) = \frac{1}{F_{\delta_1}^{\delta_2}(\alpha)}$$

which illustrates the validity of the reciprocal property of the F distribution.

7.8   Relationship Among Student's t, Chi-square, and F distributions

From the definition of the T variable, namely: $T = \dfrac{Z}{\sqrt{Y/\delta}}$

where: $Z \to N(0, 1)$ and $Y \to \chi_\delta^2$, it is obvious that the T and χ^2 variables are related.

Similarly from the definition of the F variable, namely:

$F = \dfrac{Y_1/\delta_1}{Y_2/\delta_2}$ where: $Y_1 \to \chi^2_{\delta_1}$ and $Y_2 \to \chi^2_{\delta_2}$, it is clear that the F and χ^2 variables are also related. What remains to be shown is that the T and F variables are also related.

This can be accomplished by squaring both sides of the equation $T = \dfrac{Z}{\sqrt{Y/\delta}}$ to obtain:

$$T^2 = \frac{Z^2}{Y/\delta}. \tag{7.62}$$

We will show in the next chapter, when we demonstrate that the t, χ^2 and F distributions can be obtained by repeated sampling from a standardized Normal distribution, that Z^2 is a Chi-square variable with 1 degree of freedom, when $Z \to N(0,1)$, while Y is still a Chi-square variable with δ degrees of freedom.

Rewriting $T^2 = \dfrac{Z^2}{Y/\delta}.$ as $T^2 = \dfrac{\chi^2_{1/1}}{\sqrt{\chi^2_{\delta/\delta}}}$, we see that T^2 is the ratio of two χ^2 variables, and as such, must be F distributed with 1 and δ degrees of freedom in the numerator and denominator, respectively.

Therefore, we can write:

$$T^2 = F^1_\delta \tag{7.63}$$

and we have demonstrated that the three distributions: Student's t, χ^2 and F are related to each other.

As mentioned previously, in the next chapter where we discuss Sampling Distributions, we will show how each of these 3 distributions can also be derived by Sampling from a Standardized Normal Distribution.

7.9   References

Berenson, Marc, L., Levine, David, M., and Krehbiel, Timothy, C., 2004. *Basic Business Statistics.* 9th Edition. Pearson-Prentice Hall.

Black, Ken, 2004. *Business Statistics.* 4th Edition. Wiley.

Canavos, George, C., 1984. *Applied Probability and Statistical Methods.* Little, Brown.

Carlson, William, L., and Thorne, Betty, 1997. *Applied Statistical Methods.* Prentice Hall.

Chou, Ya-lun, 1992. *Statistical Analysis for Business and Economics.* Elsevier.

Freund, John, E., and Williams, Frank, J., 1969. *Modern Business Statistics.* Revised by: Perles, Benjamin and Sullivan, Charles. Prentice-Hall.

Freund, John, E., and Williams, Frank, J., 1982. *Elementary Business Statistics: The Modern approach.* Prentice-Hall.

Johnson, Robert, 1973. *Elementary Statistics.* Duxbury Press.

McClave, James, T., Benson, George, P., and Sincich, Terry, 2001. *Statistics for Business and Economics.* 8th Edition. Prentice Hall.

Salvatore, Dominick, *Theory and Problems of Statistics and Econometrics.* SCHAUM'S OUTLINE SERIES, McGraw-Hill.

Steel, Robert, G.D., and Torrie, James, H., 1976. *Introduction to Statistics.* McGraw-Hill.

7.10 PROBLEMS

1. The average age of congressman in 1985 was 49.65 years with a standard deviation of 5 years. Assuming that the ages of congressman follow a normal distribution, what is the probability that a congressman, selected at random, will be:

   a) Younger than 38 years old?

   b) Older than 60 years old?

   c) Between 45 and 55 years old?

2. By route A the travel time, in minutes, from a hotel to the airport is normally distributed with $\mu_A = 27$ and $\sigma_A = 5$ minutes. By route B the travel time is normally distributed with $\mu_B = 30$ and $\sigma_B = 2$ minutes.

   a) Which route is of better choice if:

      i) One has 30 minutes available?

      ii) One has 32 minutes available?

      iii) One has 34 minutes available?

   b) What conclusion can you draw from the above results? Be specific!

3. The annual rainfall (in inches) in a certain region is normally distributed with $\mu = 39.5$ inches and $\sigma = 3.5$ inches. Considering the annual amounts of rainfall as independent, find the probability that in 4 consecutive years:

   a) The first 2 amounts of rainfall will be less than 36.7 inches and the next 2 greater than 42.3 inches.

   b) Some pair or other will be less than 36.7 inches and the remaining pair will be greater than 42.3 inches

4. Suppose that you drive from New York to San Francisco, 3040 miles by a certain route, starting with new spark plugs in your eight cylinder engine. Suppose that the satisfactory life of a spark plug is normally distributed with mean of 5000 miles and a standard deviation of 1000 miles. What is the probability that you will cross over the Bay Bridge with the original spark plugs working on all 8 cylinders?

5. For a certain income level, the IRS knows that the amounts claimed for medical deductions (X_1), charitable contributions (X_2), and miscellaneous deductions (X_3), are independent normally distributed random variables with means $400, $800, and $100, and standard deviations $100, $250, and $40, respectively.

   a) What is the probability that the total amount claimed for these three deductions is no more than $1,600?

   b) If someone from this income level reports on his return a total of $2,100 for these deductions, how likely is this or a larger amount?

6. The revenue of a company can be expressed by a random variable X obeying a normal probability law with mean 1000 and variance 14,400, while the cost of doing business for the same company can be represented by a random variable Y obeying a normal probability law with mean 1260 and variance 2500.

   Assuming that X and Y are independent, find:

   a) The probability that this company makes a profit

   b) The probability that this company breaks even

   c) The probability that this company incurs a loss

7. Tobacco pipes are being packed in fancy plastic boxes. The length of the pipes is normally distributed with a mean of 5 inches and a standard deviation of 0.04 inches. The internal length of the boxes is normally distributed with a mean of 5.1 inches and a standard deviation of 0.03 inches. What is the probability that the box will be too small for the pipe?

8. A traffic light at an intersection is green for 40 seconds, yellow for 5 seconds, and red for 15 seconds. Assuming a rectangular distribution, what is the probability that a motorist arriving at the intersection at random time:

   a) will go through without stopping?

   b) will have to wait?

9. Let X_1, X_2, and X_3 be independent random variables, each uniformly distributed on the interval 0 to 1. Determine the number **a** such that the probability that at least one of the variables is greater than **a** is 0.9.

10. A young man and a young lady plan to meet between 5 and 6 P.M., each agreeing not to wait more than 10 minutes for the other. Find the probability that they will meet if they arrive independently at random times between 5 and 6 P.M.

11. A continuous random variable X is uniformly distributed in the interval 2 to 10. Find the probability that:

   a) The random variable X is between 4 and 6.

   b) The random variable X will be less that 7.

   c) The random variable X will be greater than 8.

12. A continuous random variable X has the triangular density given by:
   $f(x) = \dfrac{x}{8}$ in the interval of $0 \le x \le 4$. Find the probabilities that the random variable X will be:

   a) less than 1.

   b) greater than 2.

   c) between 1.5 and 2.5.

13. A continuous random variable X takes on values on the interval from 0 to 2 and its density function is:

   $$f(x) = 1 - \frac{1}{2}x, \ 0 \le x \le 2.$$

   a) Verify that the total area, under $f(x)$, in the interval $0 \le x \le 2$ is equal to 1.

   b) Find $P(X < 1)$.

   c) Find $P(1 < X < 1.5)$.

14. A random variable X has an exponential distribution with $\theta = 10$. Find the probability that:

   a) X is between 0 and 4.

   b) X is greater than 6.

   c) X is between 8 and 12.

15. The lifetime of a certain kind of battery is a random variable which has an exponential distribution with a mean of $\theta = 200$ hours. What is the probability that such a battery will:

   a) last at most 100 hours?

   b) last between 400 and 600 hours?

16. In a certain brokerage house, the time a customer has to wait for confirmation of a transaction has an exponential distribution with $\theta = 30$ minutes. What is the probability that a customer will have to wait between 12 and 36 minutes for such a transaction?

17. The time, measured in minutes, required by a certain person to travel from their home to a train station is a random phenomenon obeying a uniform probability law over the interval 20 to 25 minutes. If the person leaves the home promptly at 7:05 AM, what is the probability that the person will catch the train that leaves the station promptly at 7:28 AM?

18. Consider a baby who cries at random times at a mean rate of 6 distinct times per hour. If a baby's parents respond only to every second time, what is the probability that 10 or more minutes

$$\left(\text{or } \frac{10}{60} = \frac{1}{6} \text{ hours} \right) \text{ will elapse between 2 responses of the parents of the baby?}$$

19. A normal distribution has the mean $\mu = 56.6$. Find its standard deviation if 80 percent of the area under the curve lies to the left of 65.0.

20. A random variable X has a normal distribution with a standard deviation of $\sigma = 1.2$. Find its mean if the probability is 0.0062 that it will take on a value greater than 116.0.

21. If X is a normal variable and $P(X < 10) = 0.8413$ and $P(X < -10) = 0.0668$, find: $E(X)$ and $V(X)$.

22. If X is uniform in the interval (a, b), the density function $f(x)$ is:

$$f(x) = \begin{cases} \dfrac{1}{b-a} & \text{if} \quad a < x < b \\ 0 & \text{elsewhere} \end{cases}, \text{ and } E(X) = \frac{b+a}{2}, V(X) = \frac{(b-a)^2}{12},$$

$$\sigma(X) = \frac{b-a}{2\sqrt{3}}$$

a) What is the probability that a value of X will be within one standard deviation of the mean?

b) Can a value of X be as many as 2 standard deviations from the mean?

23. Let X be uniformly distributed on the interval (a, b). If $E(X) = 10$ and $V(X) = 12$, determine a and b.

24. Suppose the concentration of a certain pollutant is uniformly distributed in the range 4 to 20 parts per million. If a concentration in excess of 15 parts per million is considered dangerous, what is the probability that a sample will yield a dangerous concentration level?

25. A random variable X is gamma distributed with parameters $\alpha = 2$ and $\theta = 50$.

a) What is the probability that X is less than the mean?

b) What is the probability that X is more than 2 standard deviations from the mean?

c) What is the probability that X will be less than its mode?

26. Suppose Y is an exponentially distributed variable with parameter θ.

a) What is the probability that X exceeds then mean?

b) What is the probability that X is within one standard deviation of the mean?

c) What is the probability that X is within two standard deviations of the mean?

27. A manufacturer of automobile mufflers wants to guarantee his mufflers for the life of the automobile. The manufacturer assumes that the life of his muffler is a normally distributed random variable with average life of 3 years and a standard deviation of 6 months (0.5 years). If the unit replacement cost is $10, what should be the total replacement cost for the first 2 years if 1,000,000 such mufflers are installed?

28. A large University expects to receive 16,000 freshman student application for the coming year. Assume that the SAT scores are normally distributed with mean 950 and standard deviation 100. If the University decides to admit the top 25 percent by SAT scores, what is the minimum SAT score required for admission?

29. The monthly demand for product A is normally distributed with mean 200 units and standard deviation 40 units. The demand for another product B is also normally distributed with mean 500 units and standard deviation 80 units. If a seller of these products stocks 280 units of A and 650 units of B at the beginning of a month, what is the probability that the seller will experience a stockout for both products during the month? Assume products A and B sell independently.

30. A polling organization is planning a survey to gauge voter sentiment concerning two candidates, A and B, who are running against each other for public office. Suppose a random sample of 1,000 potential voters is taken. What is the probability that 550 or more of these voters will indicate a preference for candidate A if the population of voters is evenly divided between these candidates?

31. The annual cost for snow removal in a large northern city is a normal variable with a mean of $4,000,000 and a standard deviation of 200,000. The city budget line item for a snow removal is set at the mean cost (*i.e.*,$\mu = 4,000,000$). Determine the probability that:

    a) The cost is less than 3.5 million.

    b) The cost is between 3.65 millipon and 4.25 million.

    c) The city will need to borrow money beyond its reserve for snow removal (the city maintains a reserve of $400,000 for emergency expenditures beyond its budget).

32. The end-of-month cash flow for a company can be represented by a random variable X, which is normal with $E(X) = 10,000$ and $\sigma(X) = 7,000$. The treasurer of the company is concerned about the possibility of a cash shortage and wants to develop a methodology to manage cash flow.

    a) What is the probability that monthly cash flow becomes negative?

    b) The treasurer wants to establish a reserve fund that can be used in case of negative cash flow. If the treasurer wants to be able to cover all but 1% of the monthly cash flow, how much money should be in the reserve fund?

    c) Determine the upper limit on the cash flow that will be exceeded only 5% of the time?

33. The time between arrivals at the bank is an exponential distribution with mean $\lambda = 20$ arrivals per hour.

    a) Find the probability that the time between arrivals is less than or equal to 3 minutes (or $3/60 = 0.05$ hours).

    b) Find the probability that the time between arrivals is greater than 3 minutes.

    c) Find the probability that the time is between 2 and 5 minutes.

    d) Find the probability of two consecutive arrivals between 2 and 5 minutes.

34. If 40 percent of the customers of a service station pay for their purchases with cash and the rest pay with credit cards, what is the probability that among 400 customers more than 150 pay with cash?

35. The probability that an MBA student will drop out of the program without completing it is 0.25. What it the probability that among 200 students fewer than 45 will drop out without completing the program?

36. It is known from experience that 2/3 of all answers given to a particular problem on the GMAT are wrong. What is the probability that in 120 GMAT papers, selected at random, this problem is wrong on:

a) At most 70 of them?

b) At least 70 of them?

c) Exactly 70 of them?

37. In a large suburban area, the monthly food expenditures of families are normally distributed with a mean of $326.55 and $\sigma = \$27.30$.

a) What proportion of these families have monthly food expenditures less than $275.00?

b) What proportion of these families have monthly food expenditures greater than $330.00?

c) Above what value does the highest 10 percent of these monthly food expenditures lie?

38. What is the probability of getting at least 12 replies to questionnaires mailed to 100 persons, when the probability is 0.18 that any one of them will reply?

39. The number of days which guests stay at a resort is a normally distributed random variable with $\mu = 8.5$ and $\sigma = 2.2$. Among 1000 geusts, how many are expected to stay at the resort from 5 to 10 days?

40. An airline knows from experience that the number of suitcases it loses each week on a certain route is a normally distributed random variable with $\mu = 31.4$ and $\sigma = 4.5$ What are the probabilities that in any given week it will lose:

a) Exactly 20 suitcases?

b) At most 20 suitcases?

41. If 70 percent of all persons flying across the Atlantic Ocean feel the effect of the time difference for at least 24 hours, what is the probability that among 140 randomly selected passengers, flying across the Atlantic, at least 100 will experience this feeling?

42. The head of the complaint department of a department store knows from experience that the number of complaints he receives each day is a normally distributed random variable with mean $\mu = 33.4$ and $\sigma = 5.5$.
Find the probabilities that in one day he will receive:

a) more than 40 complaints.

b) at least 40 complaints.

c) between 30 and 40 complaints, not inclusive.

43. The average time required to perform job A is 85 minu.tes with a standard deviation of 16 minutes, and the average time required to perform job B is 110 minutes with a standard deviation of 11 minutes. Assuming normal distributions,

a) what proportion of the time will job A take longer than the average of job B and

b) what proportion of the time will job B take less time than the average of job A?

SOLUTIONS

1. Let X be the age of congressman which is normal with $\mu = E(X) = 49.65$ and $\sigma = \sigma(x) = 5$. To answer the questions we need to change the random variable X, to random variable Z using the standard score formula $Z = \dfrac{X - \mu}{\sigma}$, and then use the standard normal table.

Then, we have:

a) $P(X < 38) = P\left(\dfrac{X - \mu}{\sigma} < \dfrac{38 - \mu}{\sigma}\right) = P\left(Z < \dfrac{38 - 49.65}{5}\right)$

$$= P\left(Z < \dfrac{-11.65}{5}\right)$$

$$= P(Z < -2.33) = P(Z > 2.33)$$
$$= 0.5 - P(0 < Z < 2.33)$$
$$= 0.5 - 0.49 = 0.01$$

b) $P(X > 60) = \left(Z > \dfrac{60 - 49.65}{5}\right) = P\left(Z > \dfrac{10.35}{5}\right) = P(Z > 2.07)$

$$= 0.5 - 0.4808 = 0.0192$$

c) $P(45 < X < 55) = \left(\dfrac{45 - 49.65}{5} < \dfrac{X - 49.65}{5} < \dfrac{55 - 49.65}{5}\right)$

$$= P\left(\dfrac{-4.65}{5} < Z < \dfrac{5.35}{5}\right)$$
$$= P[-0.93 < Z < 1.07]$$
$$= P[-0.93 < Z < 0] + P[0 < Z < 1.07]$$
$$= P[0 < Z < 0.93] + P[0 < Z < 1.07]$$
$$= 0.3238 + 0.3577 = 0.6815$$

2. a) $P(t \le t_0) = P\left(\dfrac{t - \mu}{\sigma} < \dfrac{t_0 - \mu}{\sigma}\right) = P\left(Z < \dfrac{t_0 - \mu}{\sigma}\right)$

For route A

i) $P\left(Z < \dfrac{30 - 27}{5}\right) = P(Z < 0.6) = P(-\infty < Z < 0) + P(0 < Z < 0.6)$

$$= 0.5 + 0.2257 = 0.7257$$

ii) $P\left(Z < \dfrac{32 - 27}{5}\right) = P(Z < 1) = P(-\infty < Z < 0) + P(0 < Z < 1)$

$$= 0.5 + 0.3413 = 0.8413$$

iii) $P\left(Z < \dfrac{34 - 27}{5}\right) = P(Z < 1.4) = P(-\infty < Z < 0) + P(0 < Z < 1.4)$

$$= 0.5 + 0.4192 = 0.9192$$

For route B

i) $P\left(Z < \dfrac{30 - 30}{2}\right) = P(Z < 0) = P(-\infty < Z < 0) = 0.5$

ii) $P\left(Z < \dfrac{32 - 30}{2}\right) = P(Z < 1) = P(-\infty < Z < 1) + P(< Z < 1)$

$$= 0.5 + 0.3413 = 0.8413$$

iii) $P\left(Z < \dfrac{34 - 30}{2}\right) = P(Z < 2) = P(-\infty < Z < 0) + P(0 < Z < 2)$

$$= 0.5 + 0.4772 = 0.9772$$

b) Cleary if the available time, $t_0 < 32$ minutes, route A is the better choice. If $t_0 = 32$ minutes the two routes are equally good while, if $t_0 > 32$ minutes route B is preferable (because it gives a higher probability of making the flight).

3. Let X_i = Amount of rain in year i and X_i is normally distributed with $\mu_i = \mu = 39.5$ and $\sigma_i = \sigma = 3.5$; Then:

a) P[In 4 consecutive years the first two will be less than 36.7 and the other $2 > 42.3$]

$= P(X_1 < 36.7)\, P(X_2 < 36.7)\, P(X_3 > 42.3)\, P(X_4 > 42.3) \leftarrow$ because of independence

$$= P\left[Z < \frac{36.7 - 39.5}{3.5}\right] P\left[Z < \frac{36.7 - 39.5}{3.5}\right] P\left[Z > \frac{42.3 - 39.5}{3.5}\right].$$
$$P\left[Z > \frac{42.3 - 39.5}{3.5}\right]$$

$= P[Z < -0.8]P[Z < -0.8]P[Z > 0.8]P[Z > 0.8]$

$= P[Z > 0.8]^4$ because $P[Z < -0.8] = P[Z > 0.8]$

$= P[0.5 - 0.2881]^4$

$= (0.2119)^4 = 0.002016 \approx 0.002$

b) P[Any two amounts are less than 36.7 and the other 2 are greater than 42.3]

$$= \frac{4!}{2!2!}[P(Z < -0.8)]^2\left[P(Z > 0.8)\right]^2 = 6(0.2119)^4 = 6(0.002) = 0.012$$

4. P[Arriving in S.F. without changing spark plugs]

$= P(X_1 \cap X_2 \cap X_3 \cap X_4 \cap X_5 \cap X_6 \cap X_7 \cap X_8)$

$= P(X_1)P(X_2)P(X_3)P(X_4)P(X_5)P(X_6)P(X_7)P(X_8) \leftarrow$ because of independence

$= [P(X_i)]^8$, where: $X_i, i = 1, 2, \ldots, 8$, stands for each spark plug, and $P(X_i) = P(X_i > 3,040)$ = Prob. each plug lasts at least 3040 miles

$$= P\left(\frac{X_i - 5,000}{1,000} > \frac{3,040 - 5,000}{1,000}\right) = P(Z > -1.96) = P(Z < 1.96)$$

$= P(-\infty < Z < 0) + P(0 < Z < 1.96) = 0.5 + 0.475 = 0.975$

and $\left[P(X_i)\right]^8 = (0.975)^8 = 0.816652$

5. Let $S = X_1 + X_2 + X_3$ and S is a normally distributed variable because it is a linear combination of a normally distributed variables, with:

$E(S) = E(X_1 + X_2 + X_3) = E(X_1) + E(X_2) + E(X_3)$

$$= 400 + 800 + 100 = 1,300 \text{ and}$$

$$\sigma(S) = \sqrt{V(X_1) + V(X_2) + V(X_3)} = \sqrt{(100)^2 + (250)^2 + (40)^2} = \sqrt{10,000 + 62,500 + 1,600}$$
$$= \sqrt{74,100} = 272.2132$$

Then

a) $P(S < 1600) = P\left(\dfrac{S - 1300}{272.2132} < \dfrac{1600 - 1300}{272.2132}\right) = P(Z < 1.1)$

$= P(-\infty < Z < 0) + P(0 < Z < 1.1)$
$= 0.5 + 0.3643 = 0.8643$

b) $P(S > 2100) = P\left(Z > \dfrac{2100 - 1300}{272.2132}\right) = P(Z > 2.94)$

$= 0.5 - P(0 < Z < 2.94) = 0.5 - 0.4984 = 0.0016$

6. Let $D = X - Y = (+1)X + (-1)Y$; Then D is normally distributed (with:
$E(D) = E(X) - E(Y) = 1000 - 1260 = -260$ and
$V(D) = (1)^2 V(X) + (-1)^2 V(Y) = 14,400 + 2,500 = 16,900$ and $\sigma(D) = 130$)
because it is a linear combination of normally distributed variables
Then:

a) $P(\text{of making a profit}) = P(X > Y) = P(X - Y > 0) = P(D > 0)$

$= P\left(\dfrac{D - E(D)}{\sigma(D)} > \dfrac{0 - (-260)}{130}\right) = P(Z > 2)$

$= 0.5 - 0.4772 = 0.0228$

b) $P(\text{of breaking even}) = P(X = Y) = P(D = 0) = \dfrac{n(D = 0)}{n(S)} = \dfrac{1}{\infty} = 0$

c) $P(\text{of incurring a loss}) = P(X < Y) = P(X - Y < 0) = P(D < 0)$

$= P\left[Z < \dfrac{0 - (-260)}{130}\right] = P[Z < 2]$

$= P[-\infty < Z < 0] + P[0 < Z < 2]$

$= 0.5 + 0.4772 = 0.9772$

7. Let $X = $ internal length of the box and $Y = $ length of the pipes, and
$D = X - Y = (+1)X + (-1)Y$. The random variable D is normally distributed because it is a linear combination of normally distributed variable, with:
$E(D) = E(X) - E(Y) = 5.1 - 5 = 0.1$ and
$V(D) = (1)^2 V(X) + (-1)^2 V(Y) = (0.03)^2 + (0.04)^2$
$= 0.0009 + 0.0016 = 0.0025$ and
$\sigma(D) = \sqrt{0.0025} = 0.05$
Then
$P(\text{Box will be too small}) = P(\text{Length of the box is smaller than the length of the pipes})$

$= P(X < Y) = P(X - Y < 0) = P(D < 0)$

$= P\left(\dfrac{D - E(D)}{\sigma(D)} < \dfrac{0 - 0.1}{0.05}\right) = P(Z < -2) = P(Z > 2)$, because of

symmetry

$= 0.5 - P(0 < Z < 2)$

$= 0.5 - 0.4772 = 0.0228$

8. The assumption of a rectangular distribution implies that the probabilities are proportional to the length of the time interval. Therefore,

   a) P(that the motorist will go through without stopping) $= \dfrac{40}{60} = \dfrac{2}{3}$ and

   b) P(that the motorist will have to stop) $= P$(Yellow light) $+ P$(Red light)

   $= \dfrac{5}{60} + \dfrac{15}{60} = \dfrac{20}{60} = \dfrac{1}{3}$

9. Looking for: P[at least one of the variables X_1, X_2, X_3 is greater than a] $= 0.9$

   We have: $P(X_1 \geq a) = 1 - a$, $P(X_2 \geq a) = 1 - a$, $P(X_3 \geq a) = 1 - a$ and $P(X_1 \leq a) = a$, $P(X_2 \leq a) = a$, $P(X_3 \leq a) = a$,

   Then

   $$P(\text{At least one of the variables } X_1, X_2, X_3 > a) = \sum_{i=1}^{3} \frac{3!}{x!(3-x)!}(1-a)^x a^{3-x}$$

   $$= \frac{3!}{1!\,2!}(1-a)a^2 + \frac{3!}{2!1!}(1-a)^2 a + \frac{3!}{3!0!}(1-a)^3 a^0$$
   $$= 3(1-a)a^2 + 3(1-a)^2 a + (1-a)^3$$
   $$= (1-a)\left[3a^2 + 3a(1-a) + (1-a)^2\right]$$
   $$= (1-a)\left[3a^2 + 3a - 3a^2 + 1 - 2a + a^2\right]$$

   If this probability is to be equal to 0.9, we must have:

   $$1 - a^3 = 0.9 \text{ or } a^3 = 1 - 0.9 = 0.1 \text{ or } a^3 = 1$$

10. Let X represent the young man's arrival time between 5 and 6 P.M.

    Let Y represent the young lady's arrival time between 5 and 6 P.M.,

    both of which are assumed to be uniformly distributed in the interval between 5 and 6 P.M.

    If we let $D = X - Y$, we can show that

    $$f(D) = \begin{cases} D + 1 & if \; -1 < D < 0 \\ 1 - D & if \quad 0 < D < 1 \end{cases}$$

    Then $P: \left(|X - Y| < 10 \text{ minutes or } \dfrac{1}{6} \text{ hours} \right)$

    $$= P\left(|D| < \frac{1}{6} \right) = P\left(-\frac{1}{6} < D < \frac{1}{6} \right)$$

    $$= P\left(-\frac{1}{6} < D < 0 \right) + P\left(0 < D < \frac{1}{6} \right)$$

    $$= \int_{-1/6}^{0} (D + 1)dD + \int_{0}^{1/6} (1 - D)dD$$

    $$= \left[\frac{1}{2}D^2 + D \right]_{-1/6}^{0} + \left[D - \frac{1}{2}D^2 \right]_{0}^{1/6} = \frac{11}{72} + \frac{11}{72} = \frac{11}{36}$$

## PART III

INFERENTIAL STATISTICS

Large Sample Statistics

Small Sample Statistics

8 Sampling Distributions

Statistical decision making depends, to a large extent, on our ability to identify the distribution of values (*i.e.*, the sampling distributions) of the sample statistics (such as $\bar{x}$, $\Delta\bar{x} = \bar{x}_1 - \bar{x}_2$, $x_{0.5} = $ Median, $x_m = $ Mode, R, $\hat{s}^2$, $\hat{s}$, $Q_1, Q_3, P_{10}, P_{90}, S_{kp}, K$, etc) that we learned how to calculate, from a given data set, in section 1 (Descriptive Statistics) of this book.

In this chapter we derive and identify the sampling distributions of the sample statistics whose definition involves:

1. The sum of the sample observations, $x_1 + x_2 + \cdots + x_n = \sum_{i=1}^{n} x_i$,

2. The sum of the squared sample observations, $x_1^2 + x_2^2 + \cdots + x_n^2 = \sum_{i=1}^{n} x_i^2$, and;

3. Combinations of $\sum_{i=1}^{n} x_i$ and $\sum_{i=1}^{n} x_i^2$

We show that when $n \geq 30$ (or when $n_1 \geq 30$ and $n_2 \geq 30$) the sample statistics $\bar{x}$ and $\Delta\bar{x}$, respectively, are normally distributed while, when $n < 30$ and σ is not known (or when n_1 and n_2 are not both large and σ_1 and σ_2 are not known) they are *t*-distributed. Actually, for large n (*i.e.*, $n > 30$), all of the sample statistics can be shown to be approximately normally distributed.

The sampling distribution of $\hat{s}^2$ (and $\hat{s}$) is approximately normal for large n but Chi-squared (χ^2_{n-1}) with Degrees of Freedom = DOF = $\delta = n - 1$, for $n < 30$.

Similarly the difference $D = \hat{s}_1^2 - \hat{s}_2^2$ is approximately normally distributed for n_1 and n_2 both large but the ratio, $R = \hat{s}_1^2 / \hat{s}_2^2$, for $n_1 < 30$ and $n_2 < 30$, is *F*-distributed with $\delta_1 = n_1 - 1$ DOF in the numerator and $\delta_2 = n_2 - 1$ DOF in the denominator (*i.e.*, $F_{n_2-1}^{n_1-1}$).

Also derived are the sampling distributions of a and b (of the linear equation $\hat{y} = a + bx$) and $r = $ sample correlation coefficient of a Bivariate data set, whose numerical value calculations (or definitions) are functions of both $\sum_{i=1}^{n} x_i$ and $\sum_{i=1}^{n} x_i^2$.

8.1 Introduction

In the first section of this book (Chapters 1, 2, 3) under the general heading of "Descriptive Statistics" we discussed methods of organizing, presenting, and calculating several measures of sample data. In the second section of the book (Chapters 4, 5, 6, 7) we discussed the elements of probability theory and random variables in general and then some important specific discrete and continuous probability models.

At first, it may seem that these two sections of the book are disjoint (*i.e.*, have nothing in common). But this is not the case. And the reason for this is the fact that the measures we calculated in Descriptive Statistics ($\bar{X}$, $X_{0.5}$, X_m, R, $\hat{s}^2$, $\hat{s}$, $Q_1, Q_3, \ldots$) are not single-valued quantities but, rather, they are themselves random variables. This becomes obvious if we repeat an experiment several times and calculate new measures in each sample. For example, if we consider the grades in a test of a statistics class as a random sample, we can calculate the measures $\bar{X}_1$, R_1, $\hat{s}_1^2$, etc. If a second test is given to the same class, and new measures are calculated from the resulting random sample, we will obtain $\bar{X}_2$, R_2, $\hat{s}_2^2$, etc., and the chances that these measures are identical to the first ones is practically zero. Continuous repetition of the experiment, will give rise to a set of values for each measure (for example for the sample mean $\bar{X}$ we will obtain: $\bar{X}_1, \bar{X}_2, \ldots, \bar{X}_n$)

which, when viewed as random samples from the distribution of $\overline{X}$ (which has not been defined yet) justify the identification of $\overline{X}$ as a random variable.

This is a very important observation because if we can identify the distributions of these descriptive measures and calculate numerical values for the parameters of these distributions, we will be able to use the probability methods we discussed in previous chapters to calculate the probability of occurrence of desired events and then use these probabilities in decision making which, after all, is the major task of INFERENTIAL STATISTICS whose discussion we begin in this chapter.

We will use the following procedure in our attempt to identify the distributions of the Descriptive Statistics (called SAMPLING Distributions). We will begin with an example of a simple population from which repeated samples of a fixed sample size are drawn. Then, using the definitions of the descriptive measures, we will calculate these measures for each sample drawn. Then, from the resulting values of each measure we will be able to calculate the PMF of each descriptive measure and from it, using the methods we discussed in Section II of this book, we can calculate its characteristics such as the Expected Value and Variance.

This example will make it absolutely clear that the descriptive statistics are indeed random variables, each possessing its own distribution function. Our next major task will be to identify the nature of these distributions (*i.e.*, are they: Binomial, Normal, Chi-square, etc.) by comparing the resulting sampling distributions to the specific probability models we have already discussed in Chapters 6 and 7. If this can be accomplished, then we can use the resulting probability models for probability calculations using the methods which we have already discussed.

Even though each descriptive statistic has its own distribution, we will restrict our discussion and analysis to the sampling distribution of only a few of these descriptive statistics, namely:

$$\overline{X},\ P,\ \Delta\overline{X} = \overline{X}_1 - \overline{X}_2,\ \Delta P = P_1 - P_2,\ \hat{s}^2,\ \Delta\hat{s}^2 = \hat{s}_1^2 - \hat{s}_2^2,\ \text{and}\ \hat{s}_R^2 = \hat{s}_1^2/\hat{s}_2^2.$$

The reason for selecting, at this time, these sample statistics is the fact that they are the most important ones needed in our inferential analysis in this section of the book. Later, when we discuss Bivariate and Multivariate analysis, additional sample statistics will be introduced and their sampling distributions will have to be identified before these sample statistics can also be used in decision making.

In our attempt to identify the sampling distributions of the descriptive statistics, it will be advantageous to separate them into 2 broad categories:

1. Sampling distributions when the sample size is large ($n \geq 30$) and
2. Sampling distributions when the sample size is small ($n < 30$)

This separation is based on the fact that, when the sample size n is large, the sampling distributions of the descriptive statistics tend to become approximately Normal while, for n small, they retain their own individual character. But, before the nature of these sampling distributions can be established, it will be necessary to introduce a number of important new concepts which will help us in our identification effort. These new concepts are:

1. The generation of independent and identically distributed (iid) random variables by drawing repeated samples from a population.
2. The sum of n independent and identically distributed random variables, the Expected value and Variance of such a sum and their applications to $\overline{X}$.
3. The Law of Large Numbers in Statistics.

4. The Central Limit Theorem.
5. The degrees of freedom associated with a sum of squares of n independent and identically distributed random variables.

These new concepts will be introduced as the need for each arises.

8.2 Generating Sampling Distributions for Selected Descriptive Statistics

Suppose a population consists of the 3 numbers: 2, 4, and 6. The population is mixed well, a number is selected randomly, recorded and returned to the population, and then a second number is drawn. From the resulting possible samples of this experiment, and using the definitions of the descriptive statistics, find the PMFs of: $\overline{X}$, $X_{0.5}$, R, $\hat{s}$, $\hat{s}^2$, and s^2 and then using the PMFs of these statistics find their Expected Values, Variances and Standard Deviations and compare, where applicable, to the parameters of the population.

Solution

1. Let us first calculate the parameters of the population. If we let X be the random variable which describes this population, then it is clear that the PMF of X is given by:

X	2	4	6
$P(X)$	1/3	1/3	1/3

since each element has an equal chance of being selected.
Then the $E(X)$ and $E(X^2)$ of this population can be computed from:

$$E(X) = \sum_{i=1}^{3} x_i p(x_i) = 2\left(\tfrac{1}{3}\right) + 4\left(\tfrac{1}{3}\right) + 6\left(\tfrac{1}{3}\right)$$

$$= \tfrac{1}{3}(2 + 4 + 6) = \tfrac{12}{3} = 4$$

$$E(X^2) = \sum_{i=1}^{3} x_i^2 p(x_i) = 4\left(\tfrac{1}{3}\right) + 16\left(\tfrac{1}{3}\right) + 36\left(\tfrac{1}{3}\right)$$

$$= \tfrac{1}{3}(4 + 16 + 36) = \tfrac{56}{3}$$

and the Variance and Standard deviation of X are respectively:

$$V(X) = E(X^2) - [E(X)]^2 = 56/3 - 16 = \frac{56 - 48}{3} = 8/3$$

$$\sigma(X) = \sqrt{V(X)} = \sqrt{8/3}$$

2. Now let us reach into this population and draw all the possible samples of size 2 as described in the statement of the problem. Since sampling is done with replacement, it is possible for the same value (2, 4, 6) to occur twice. Also, since there are three possibilities for selection one, and for each first selection there are three possibilities for

selection two, the total number of possible samples of size two drawn from this population, when sampling with replacement, is: $3 \times 3 = 9$.

Note: Later in this section we revise this problem and draw 3 and 4 samples from the same population. Therefore, to make the distinction between them clear, we designate the case for $n = 2$ as I, the case for $n = 3$ as II, and the case for $n = 4$ as III.

a) $n = 2$

In the table below, we list the nine possible samples in column 2, while columns 3, 4, 5, 6, 7 and 8 show the Sample Mean ($\overline{X}$), Sample Median ($X_{0.5}$), Sample Range (R), (Unbiased) Sample Variance ($\hat{s}^2$), (Biased) Sample Variance (s^2), and Unbiased Sample Standard Deviation ($\hat{s}$), respectively, for each sample.

The values of these descriptive statistics, for each sample, are obtained by using the definitions and methods discussed in Chapter three.

Table 8.1 Generating Sampling Distributions

Sample number (1)	Sample values X_1 X_2 (2)	Sample mean $\overline{X}$ (3)	Sample median $X_{0.5}$ (4)	Sample range R (5)	Unbaised sample variance $\hat{s}^2$ (6)	Biased sample variance s^2 (7)	Unbaised sample stand. dev. $\hat{s}$ (8)
1	2 2	2	2	0	0	0	0
2	2 4	3	3	2	2	1	$\sqrt{2}$
3	2 6	4	4	4	8	4	$2\sqrt{2}$
4	4 2	3	3	2	2	1	$\sqrt{2}$
5	4 4	4	4	0	0	0	0
6	4 6	5	5	2	2	1	$\sqrt{2}$
7	6 2	4	4	4	8	4	$2\sqrt{2}$
8	6 4	5	5	2	2	1	$\sqrt{2}$
9	6 6	6	6	0	0	0	0

Since there are nine possible values here for each of the six selected descriptive statistics, each sample value of each of these statistics has a probability of occurrence of 1/9. Concentrating on the sample mean $\overline{X}$, we observe that the possible values of $\overline{X}$ are: 2, 3, 4, 5, 6 and they occur with corresponding probabilities: 1/9, 2/9, 3/9, 2/9, 1/9.

Therefore, the PMF of the Sample Mean ($\overline{X}$) is given by:

Table 8.2 The Sampling Distribution of $\overline{X}$

$\overline{X}$	2	3	4	5	6	
$P(\overline{X})$	1/9	2/9	3/9	2/9	1/9	
$\overline{X} P(\overline{X})$	2/9	6/9	12/9	10/9	6/9	$E(\overline{X})=\sum_{i=1}^{5}\overline{X}_i P(\overline{X}_i) = 36/9 = 40$
$\overline{X}^2 P(\overline{X})$	4/9	18/9	48/9	50/9	36/9	$E(\overline{X}^2)=\sum_{i=1}^{5}\overline{X}_i^2 P(\overline{X}_i) = 156/9$

from which, by extending the table two more rows as shown, we obtain the Expected Values of $\overline{X}$ (*i.e.*, $E(\overline{X}) = 4$) and the Expected Value of $\overline{X}^2$ (*i.e.*, $E(\overline{X}^2) = 156/9$), and from them we find:

$$V(\overline{X}) = E(\overline{X}^2) - \left[E(\overline{X})\right]^2 = \frac{156}{9} - 16$$

$$= \frac{156 - 144}{9} = \frac{12}{9} = \frac{4}{3}$$

and
$$\sigma(\overline{X}) = \sqrt{V(\overline{X})} = \sqrt{4/3} = \frac{\sqrt{4}}{\sqrt{3}} = \frac{2}{\sqrt{3}} = \frac{2\sqrt{3}}{3}$$

It is interesting to plot the PMF of X (which represents the population) and the PMF of $\overline{X}$ (which represents the mean of the population) and compare them. This is done in Figures 8.1a and 8.1b below.

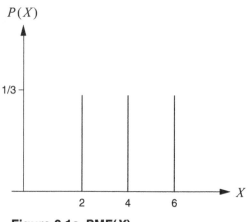

Figure 8.1a PMF(X)

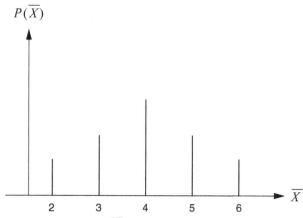

Figure 8.1b PMF($\overline{X}$)

Notice that even though the population has a (discrete) uniform distribution, the PMF($\overline{X}$) is symmetric with the most probable values occurring in the center (around 4 which is the expected value of the population and also of $\overline{X}$), while as we go away from the center, the probability of these values of $\overline{X}$ decreases. The PMF ($\overline{X}$) is the sampling distribution of the sample mean, and our ultimate objective is to identify the nature of this distribution so that we may be able to use what we have learned about distributions (probability models) in further analysis of the sampling distribution of $\overline{X}$. But, before we proceed to do this, let us also obtain the sampling distributions of the other five descriptive statistics mentioned above. By examining the table above we notice that the values of the sample median ($X_{0.5}$) are identical to the values of the sample mean ($\overline{X}$). This doesn't happen all the time. But it did happen here, and it implies that, for this example, the sampling distributions of $\overline{X}$ and $X_{0.5}$ are identical. Therefore no more analysis will be done on the sampling distribution of $X_{0.5}$. Whatever comments we made on $\overline{X}$ are equally applicable to $X_{0.5}$.

Let us now discuss the sampling distributions of R, $\hat{s}^2$, s^2 and $\hat{s}$ which are all measures of spread or dispersion. Based on their definitions these sample statistics cannot have negative values assigned to them. As a result, their sampling distributions, as we will see shortly, are not symmetric as the sampling distributions of $\overline{X}$ and $X_{0.5}$ but are positively skewed.

Table 8.3 The Sampling Distributions of R, $\hat{s}^2$, s^2 and $\hat{s}$							
R	$P(R)$	$\hat{s}^2$	$P(\hat{s}^2)$	s^2	$P(s^2)$	$\hat{s}$	$P(\hat{s})$
0	3/9	0	3/9	0	3/9	0	3/9
2	4/9	2	4/9	1	4/9	$\sqrt{2}$	4/9
4	2/9	8	2/9	4	2/9	$2\sqrt{2}$	2/9

Therefore, when we begin the identification process of the sampling distributions we will have to discuss at least 2 general types of sampling distributions.

The PMF of R, $\hat{s}^2$, s^2, and $\hat{s}$ can be derived directly from Table 8.1, and they are, while the graphical representation of these PMFs are shown in Figures 8.2a–8.2d.

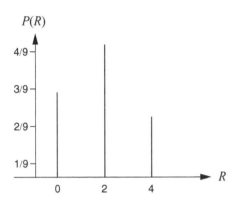

Figure 8.2a PMF(R)

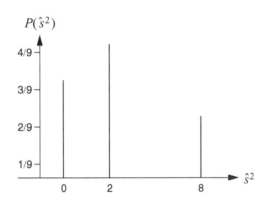

Figure 8.2b PMF($\hat{s}^2$)

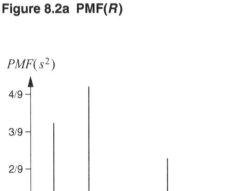

Figure 8.2c PMF(s^2)

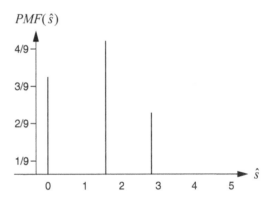

Figure 8.2d PMF($\hat{s}$)

■ **For the Range**

$$E(R) = \sum_{i=1}^{3} r_i P(R = r_i) = 16/9$$

$$E(R^2) = \sum_{i=1}^{3} r_i^2 P(R = r_i) = 48/9$$

$$V(R) = E(R^2) - [E(R)]^2 = 176/81$$

$$\sigma(R) = \frac{4}{9}\sqrt{11}$$

■ **For the Unbiased Sample Variance**

$$E(\hat{s}^2) = \sum_{i=1}^{3} \hat{s}_i^2 P(\hat{s}^2 = \hat{s}_i^2) = 8/3 = \sigma^2 \text{ of the Population } X$$

$$E\left[(\hat{s}^2)^2\right] = \sum_{i=1}^{3} (\hat{s}_i^2)^2 \; P(\hat{s}^2 = \hat{s}_i^2) = 16$$

$$V(\hat{s}^2) = E\left[(\hat{s}^2)^2\right] - \left[E(\hat{s}^2)\right]^2 = 16 - 64/9$$

$$= \frac{144 - 64}{9} = \frac{80}{9} = \frac{5 \times 16}{9}$$

$$\sigma(\hat{s}^2) = \sqrt{V(\hat{s}^2)} = \frac{4}{3}\sqrt{5}$$

■ **For the Biased Sample Variance**

$$E(s^2) = \sum_{i=1}^{3} s_i^2 P(s^2 = s_i^2) = 4/3 \neq \sigma^2 \text{ of the Population } X$$

$$E\left[(s^2)^2\right] = \sum_{i=1}^{3} (s_i^2)^2 P(s^2 = s_i^2) = 4$$

$$V(s^2) = E\left[(s^2)^2\right] - \left[E(s^2)\right]^2 = 4 - (4/3)^2$$

$$= 4 - \frac{16}{9} = \frac{36 - 16}{9} = \frac{20}{9} = \frac{4 \times 5}{9}$$

$$\sigma(s^2) = \sqrt{V(s^2)} = \sqrt{\frac{4 \times 5}{9}} = \frac{2}{3}\sqrt{5}$$

Note: Because $E(\hat{s}^2) = \sigma^2$ but $E(s^2) \neq \sigma^2$, $\hat{s}^2$ is called the Unbiased Sample Variance while s^2 is called the Biased Sample Variance.

This is so because, as we will show in the next chapter on Estimation theory, we will define Bias as:

BIAS = Expected value of Estimator − Population Parameter

or   BIAS = $E(\hat{\theta}) - \theta$, if θ = population parameter of interest and $\hat{\theta}$ = is the Estimator of the parameter.

Clearly, if $\theta = \sigma^2$ and $\hat{\theta} = \hat{s}^2$, the BIAS = 0, while if $\theta = \sigma^2$ but $\hat{\theta} = s^2$, the BIAS ≠ 0. Therefore, Unbiased Estimators produce BIAS = 0, while Biased Estimators produce BIAS ≠ 0.

■ For the "Unbiased" Standard Deviation ($\hat{s}$)

$$E(\hat{s}) = \sum_{i=1}^{3} \hat{s}_i P(\hat{s} = \hat{s}_i) = {}^{8}\!/_{9} \sqrt{2}$$

$$E\left[(\hat{s})^2\right] = \sum_{i=1}^{3} (\hat{s}_i)^2 P(\hat{s} = \hat{s}_i) = {}^{8}\!/_{3}$$

$$V(\hat{s}) = E\left[(\hat{s})^2\right] - \left[E(\hat{s})\right]^2 = \frac{8}{3} - \left(\frac{8}{9}\sqrt{2}\right)^2 = \frac{88}{81}$$

$$\sigma(\hat{s}) = \sqrt{V(\hat{s})} = \sqrt{\frac{88}{81}} = \frac{2}{9}\sqrt{22}$$

b) $n = 3$

If, instead of drawing a sample of 2 from the population of this example, we decided to draw a sample of 3, the experiment will consist of the following 27, 3-element samples:

(2, 2, 2)	(4, 2, 2)	(6, 2, 2)
(2, 2, 4)	(4, 2, 4)	(6, 2, 4)
(2, 2, 6)	(4, 2, 6)	(6, 2, 6)
(2, 4, 2)	(4, 4, 2)	(6, 4, 2)
(2, 4, 4)	(4, 4, 4)	(6, 4, 4)
(2, 4, 6)	(4, 4, 6)	(6, 4, 6)
(2, 6, 2)	(4, 6, 2)	(6, 6, 2)
(2, 6, 4)	(4, 6, 4)	(6, 6, 4)
(2, 6, 6)	(4, 6, 6)	(6, 6, 6)

Then, treating each 3-element sample as a separate data set and applying the definitions for the descriptive statistics we can generate their sampling distributions again. Even though we can generate each and everyone of them, we will restrict our attention to only 2, namely: 1. The sampling distribution, of $\overline{X}$, and 2. The sampling distribution of $X_{0.5}$.

The reason for these selections is the fact that in the next chapter on Estimation Theory we will discuss the problem of "Selecting the Best Estimator" for each Population Parameter of interest, when there are more than one available. For the Population Parameter μ there are 3 candidates: The Sample Mean $(\overline{X})$, the Sample Median $(X_{0.5})$, and the Sample Mode X_m. Which one of them is the "Best" Estimator for the Mean?

Our selection will be based on 4 criteria, namely: Unbiasedness, Consistency, Efficiency, and Sufficiency, and all of them will be explained in the next chapter. However, at this point, it is useful to point out that the Criterion of Efficiency consists of selecting the estimator with the smallest variance, and to calculate the variance of these estimators (actually only the variance of $\overline{X}$ and $X_{0.5}$ because the mode is not unique) we need the PMF $(\overline{X})$ and PMF $(X_{0.5})$. Recall that when $n = 2$, the PMF $(\overline{X})$ is identical to the PMF $(X_{0.5})$ and , therefore, for $n = 2$ they have the same variance. It is, therefore, important to calculate the variance of $\overline{X}$ and $X_{0.5}$ for $n = 3$ and $n = 4$ to see which of these 2 estimators is the more efficient (*i.e.*, which has the smallest variance).

These 2 PMFs are given below:

i) PMF $\left(\overline{X}\right)$

$\overline{X} \rightarrow$	2	8/3	10/3	4	14/3	10/3	6
$P(\overline{X}) \rightarrow$	1/27	3/27	6/27	7/27	6/27	3/27	1/27
$\overline{X}P(\overline{X})$	2/27	8/27	20/27	28/27	28/27	16/27	6/27
$\overline{X}^2 P(\overline{X})$	4/27	64/81	200/81	112/27	392/81	256/81	36/27

From the Table above we obtain: $E\left(\overline{X}\right) = \sum_{i=1}^{7} \overline{x}_i \left(P\overline{X} = \overline{x}_i\right) = 108/27 = 4$

$$E\left(\overline{X}^2\right) = \sum \overline{x}_i^2 P\left(\overline{X} = \overline{x}_i\right) = \frac{1368}{81} = \frac{152}{9}$$

Therefore: $V\left(\overline{X}\right) = E\left(\overline{X}^2\right) - \left[E\left(\overline{X}\right)\right]^2 = 152/9 - 4^2 = (152 - 144)/9 = 8/9$

ii) PMF $\left(X_{0.5}\right)$

$X_{0.5} \rightarrow$	2	4	6	
$P(X_{0.5}) \rightarrow$	7/27	13/27	7/27	
$X_{0.5} P(X_{0.5})$	14/27	52/27	42/27	$E(X_{0.5}) = \sum x_{i0.5} P(X_{0.5} = x_{i0.5}) = 108/27 = 4$
$X_{0.5}^2 P(X_{0.5})$	28/27	208/27	252/27	$E(X_{0.5}^2) = \sum x_{i0.5}^2 P(X_{0.5} = x_{i0.5}) = 488/27$

Therefore:

$$V\left(X_{0.5}\right) = E\left(X_{0.5}^2\right) - \left[E\left(X_{0.5}\right)\right]^2 = 488/27 - 4^2 = 56/27 \approx 2.074$$

Clearly, when $n = 3$, $V\left(\overline{X}\right) = 8/9 < V\left(X_{0.5}\right) = 56/27$

c) $n = 4$

Let us also draw 4 samples from this population, and once again construct the PMF $\left(\overline{X}\right)$ and PMF $\left(X_{0.5}\right)$. This time the experiment will consist of 81, 4-element samples (a small portion of which are the following: (2, 2, 2, 2), (2, 2, 2, 4), (2, 2, 2, 6), (2, 2, 4, 2), (2, 2, 4, 4), etc) and from which we obtain the following PMF $\left(\overline{X}\right)$ and PMF $\left(X_{0.5}\right)$.

i) PMF $\left(\overline{X}\right)$

$\overline{X} \rightarrow$	2	2.5	3	3.5	4	4.5	5	5.5	6
$P(\overline{X}) \rightarrow$	1/81	4/81	10/81	16/81	19/81	16/81	10/81	4/81	1/81
$\overline{X}P(\overline{X})$	2/81	10/81	30/81	56/81	76/81	72/81	50/81	22/81	6/81
$\overline{X}^2 P(\overline{X})$	4/81	25/81	90/81	196/81	304/81	324/81	250/81	121/81	36/81

From the Table above we obtain: $E\left(\overline{X}\right) = \sum \overline{x}_i P\left(\overline{X} = \overline{x}_i\right) = 324/81 = 4$

$$E\left(\overline{X}^2\right) = \sum \overline{x}_i^2 P\left(\overline{X} = \overline{x}_i\right) = \frac{1350}{81} = \frac{50}{3}$$

Therefore: $V\left(\overline{X}\right) = E\left(\overline{X}^2\right) - \left[E\left(\overline{X}\right)\right]^2 = 50/3 - 4^2$

$$= 50 - 48/3 = 2/3$$

ii) PMF $\left(X_{0.5}\right)$

$X_{0.5} \rightarrow$	2	3	4	5	6
$P(X_{0.5}) \rightarrow$	9/81	18/81	27/81	18/81	9/81
$X_{0.5} P(X_{0.5})$	18/81	54/81	108/81	90/81	54/81
$X_{0.5}^2 P(X_{0.5})$	36/81	162/81	432/81	450/81	324/81

Then, from the Table above we obtain:

$$E\left(X_{0.5}\right) = \sum x_{i\,0.5} P\left(X_{0.5} = x_{i\,0.5}\right) = 324/27\ 81 = 4$$

$$E\left(X_{0.5}^2\right) = \sum x_{i\,0.5}^2 P\left(X_{0.5} = x_{i\,0.5}\right) = 1404/81 = 52/3$$

Therefore:

$$V\left(X_{0.5}\right) = E\left(X_{0.5}^2\right) - \left[E\left(X_{0.5}\right)\right]^2 = \frac{1404}{81} - 4^2 = \frac{52}{3} - 16 = \frac{52 - 48}{3}$$

$$= \frac{4}{3}$$

Clearly, when $n = 4$, $V\left(\overline{X}\right) = {}^2\!/_3 < V\left(X_{0.5}\right) = {}^4\!/_3$

Let us now summarize our results, when samples of $n = 2$, $n = 3$, and $n = 4$ are drawn from the given population, so that we can compare the variances of $\overline{X}$ and $X_{0.5}$ easier.

Table 8.4 Comparing Expected Values and Variances for $\overline{X}$ and $X_{0.5}$

	i) $n = 2$	**ii) $n = 3$**	**iii) $n = 4$**
$\overline{X}$	$E(\overline{X}) = 4$ $V(\overline{X}) = 4/3$	$E(\overline{X}) = 4$ $V(\overline{X}) = 8/9 = 24/27$	$E(\overline{X}) = 4$ $V(\overline{X}) = 2/3$
$X_{0.5}$	$E(X_{0.5}) = 4$ $V(X_{0.5}) = 4/3$	$E(X_{0.5}) = 4$ $V(X_{0.5}) = 56/27$	$E(X_{0.5}) = 4$ $V(X_{0.5}) = 4/3$

Clearly, from Table 8.4, $E(\overline{X}) = E(X_{0.5}) = 4$ for all values of n (*i.e.*, $n = 2, 3, 4$) while $V(\overline{X}) < V(X_{0.5})$ for $n = 3$ and $n = 4$. When $n = 2$, $V(\overline{X}) = V(X_{0.5})$.

Therefore, since $V(\overline{X}) \leq V(X_{0.5})$, the sample mean $\overline{X}$ is a more efficient estimator than $X_{0.5}$.

8.3 Identifying the Sampling Distributions

Now that we have seen how Sampling distributions are generated, we must turn our attention to the task of identifying the nature of these distributions. We have already seen above that at least 2 types of sampling distributions occur: Namely one that is Symmetric and the other which is Positively skewed. Since these are associated with different sample statistics we will discuss them separately below. But we can, at this point, state that the symmetric distribution will be identified as an approximate Normal distribution under certain conditions, while the Positively skewed distribution will be identified as either Chi-square or F, depending on the population parameter(s) being investigated. However, even these positively skewed distributions can be approximated by a Normal distribution with appropriate parameters when the sample size n is large enough. For example, when $n \geq 30$, we can approximate the sampling distribution of $\hat{s}^2$, which will be identified as Chi-square, by a Normal distribution with $\mu = \delta$ and $\sigma = \sqrt{2\delta}$, where δ is the degrees of freedom of the Chi-square-distribution. Similarly, the sampling distribution of the sample statistic $\Delta \hat{s}^2 = \hat{s}_1^2 - \hat{s}_2^2$ which is the difference of the sample variances of two different populations, with each sample variance Chi-square distributed with δ_1 and δ_2 degrees of freedom respectively, can be approximated by a Normal distribution with parameters:

$$\mu = E(\Delta \hat{s}^2) = E(\hat{s}_1^2) - E(\hat{s}_2^2) = \delta_1 - \delta_2 \qquad (8.1)$$

and

$$\sigma^2 = V(\Delta \hat{s}^2) = (+1)^2 V(\hat{s}_1^2) + (-1)^2 V(\hat{s}_2^2) = V(\hat{s}_1^2) + V(\hat{s}_2^2)$$

$$= \frac{2}{\delta_1}\sigma_1^4 + \frac{2}{\delta_2}\sigma_2^4 \qquad (8.2)$$

provided that $n_1 \geq 30$ and $n_2 \geq 30$ simultaneously (preferably n_1 and n_2 should be ≥ 100). As we will show later in this chapter the degrees of freedom are a linear function of the sample size and, more specifically, $\delta_1 = n_1 - 1$ and $\delta_2 = n_2 - 1$. Of course, if either $n_1 < 30$ or $n_2 < 30$ or both are simultaneously less than 30 the exact, small-sample positively skewed distributions should be used. We will show that in such cases, instead of using the sample statistic $\Delta \hat{s}^2 = \hat{s}_1^2 - \hat{s}_2^2$, it is advantageous to use the alternate statistic $R\hat{s}^2 = \hat{s}_1^2 / \hat{s}_2^2$ which will be shown to have the F distribution with δ_1 and δ_2 degrees of freedom in the numerator and denominator, respectively.

8.3.1 Additional Concepts and Theorems Needed in the Identification process

Before we begin the identification process of the sampling distributions, which result when sampling from a population and the sample data is used to calculate desired sample statistics, let us briefly discuss the following concepts/theorems which have been previously listed and which will make the identification process much easier. They are:

1. The generation of independent and identically distributed (*iid*) random variables
2. The Sum of *n iid* random variables
3. The law of large Numbers in Statistics
4. The Central Limit Theorem
5. The Degrees of Freedom
6. The *t*, Chi-square, and *F* as sampling distributions derived when sampling from standardized Normal distribution(*s*).

8.3.1.1 Generating iid random variables

The generation of *iid* random variables is not as difficult as it may sound. Actually all one has to do, to generate a set of *iid* random variables, is to sample from a given population with replacement, if the population is finite, or without replacement, if the population is infinite. If we represent the resulting samples by $X_1, X_2, \ldots, X_n$, then each X_i is a random variable having the same PMF or density function as the population from which the samples were drawn from, and the set of X_i are identically distributed and independent of each other.

This fact can be demonstrated very easily by the following example:

Suppose a population consists of ten objects which are identical in all respects except for the number printed on them. Seven of these objects have the number 4 printed on them, while the other three have the number 5 printed on them. Clearly, if X is a random variable which represents the elements of this population, then the PMF of this population is given by:

X	4	5
$P(X)$	7/10	3/10

Further suppose that the elements of this population are mixed well and then an object is drawn, the number printed on it is noted and recorded, and the object is returned to the population. If we let X_1 represent the first object drawn, it is obvious that X_1 will be either a 4 or a 5, while the probabilities with which these two numbers can be drawn are 7/10 and 3/10 respectively. Therefore, the PMF of X_1 is given by:

X_1	4	5
$P(X_1)$	7/10	3/10

and we notice that the PMF of X_1 is identical to the PMF of the population from which the sample was drawn. Suppose now we repeat the experiment and draw a second object whose value will be represented by X_2. Obviously, since the population has remained unchanged (because the first item drawn was returned to the population), the possible values of X_2 are still 4 and 5 and their probabilities remain unchanged at 7/10 and 3/10 respectively. Clearly X_2 is identically distributed not only to the population X, but also to the first sample X_1 which, obviously, had no effect on X_2. Therefore X_1 and X_2 are independent of each other in addition to having identical distributions.

If this process is repeated n times, each time generating a random variable X_i which is identically distributed to the population from which the sample was drawn, then the set of random variables $X_1, X_2, \ldots, X_n$ thus generated are independent of each other and identically distributed and their common distribution is identical to the population from which these samples were drawn from.

If the population is infinite, it is not necessary to sample with replacement since the removal of a small number of elements from an infinite population will have little if any effect on the sampling distributions of future drawings (observations). For example, if the population consisted of 10,000,000 elements of which 7,000,000 had the number 4 printed on them and the other 3,000,000 had the number 5 printed on them, the PMF of the population is still the same as before, and so is the PMF of X_1. If now X_1 is not returned to the population, the probability with which the next sample X_2 will assume the values 4 and 5 will change very slightly, with the change being so small that it can be ignored. The same argument can be used for samples $X_3, X_4, \ldots, X_n$. Therefore, we have shown that, sampling with replacement from a finite population or sampling with or without replacement from an infinite population, generates a set of independent and identically distributed random variables whose distribution is identical to the distribution of the population from which the samples were drawn.

8.3.1.2 The Sum of *n iid* Random Variables

Having learned how to generate a set of independent and identically distributed random variables, let us now consider adding n such variables and designating their sum by S, where:

$$S = X_1 + X_2 + \cdots + X_n \qquad (8.3)$$

There are several reasons for wanting to find the sum S, which is clearly a random variable since any combination (which is linear in this case) of random variables is itself a random variable. One reason is the fact that the Central Limit Theorem (sometimes abbreviated as CLT), which we discuss below and which is one of the most important theorems of Statistics, is stated for a random variable defined as the sum of n *iid* random variables, and also requires the Expected value and Standard Deviation of the sum. Therefore, if we can find $E(S)$ and $\sigma(S)$, we would be able to apply the CLT to the Variable S and use it to identify the nature of the distribution of S.

Another important reason is the fact that the definition of the sample mean, $\overline{X}$, can be stated in terms of S, since the numerator in the $\overline{X}$ definition can be replaced by S, and we can write:

$$\overline{X} = \frac{X_1 + X_2 + \cdots + X_n}{n} = \frac{1}{n}S \qquad (8.4)$$

which makes $\overline{X}$ a linear function of the variable S. Recall that a random variable Y is said to be a linear function of another random variable X, if Y is related to X by the relationship:

$$Y = a + bX \qquad (8.5)$$

where a and b are constants. Then by comparison of (8.5) to (8.4), it can be seen that $a = 0$ and $b = 1/n$ in (8.4).

Recall also that if $E(X)$ and $V(X)$ are known and Y is a linear function of X, then:

$$E(Y) = a + bE(X) \tag{8.6}$$
$$V(Y) = b^2 V(X) \tag{8.7}$$

Therefore, if $E(S)$ and $V(S)$ can be found, equations (8.6) and (8.7) can be applied to the linear function $\overline{X} = \frac{1}{n}S$ to generate:

$$E\left(\overline{X}\right) = \frac{1}{n}E(S) \tag{8.8}$$

$$V\left(\overline{X}\right) = \frac{1}{n^2}V(S) \tag{8.9}$$

Note: *$E\left(\overline{X}\right)$ and $V\left(\overline{X}\right)$ are two of the three main ingredients (the other being the actual shape) needed to properly identify a symmetrical sampling distribution, and this will be accomplished with the help of the Central Limit Theorem.*

Applying the Expectation and Variance operators to equation (8.3) we obtain:

$$
\begin{aligned}
E(S) &= E(X_1 + X_2 + \cdots + X_n) \\
&= E(X_1) + E(X_2) + \cdots + E(X_n) \\
&= \mu + \mu + \cdots + \mu \\
&= n\mu
\end{aligned}
$$

Since the variables are identically distributed, they have the same mean (μ) and Variance (σ^2). (8.10)

$$
\begin{aligned}
V(S) &= V(X_1 + X_2 + \cdots + X_n) \\
&= V(X_1) + V(X_2) + \cdots + V(X_n) \\
&= \sigma^2 + \sigma^2 + \cdots + \sigma^2 \\
&= n\sigma^2
\end{aligned}
$$

Since the X_i in (8.3) are independent. (Note that independence was not needed in E(S)). (8.11)

and $\sigma(S) = \sqrt{V(S)} = \sqrt{n\sigma^2} = \sigma\sqrt{n}$ (8.12)

Note that the existence of independence among the random variables $X_1, X_2, \ldots, X_n$ does not affect the Expectation operator but it affects the Variance operator. If the variables were not independent, then: $V(X_1 + X_2 + \cdots + X_n) \neq V\left(X_1\right) + V\left(X_2\right) + \cdots + V\left(X_n\right)$, because for the equality to exist the right-hand side (RHS) must include all of the appropriate Covariance terms, as discussed in Chapter 5. However, because independence exists, all of the Covariance terms are equal to zero, thus producing the simplified Variance expression for $V(S)$, given by equation (8.11).

Therefore, since we have found $E(S)$ and $V(S)$ and $\overline{X} = \frac{1}{n}S$, we can easily calculate $E\left(\overline{X}\right), V\left(\overline{X}\right)$ and $\sigma\left(\overline{X}\right)$ from:

$$E\left(\overline{X}\right) = E\left[\frac{1}{n}S\right] = \frac{1}{n}E(S) = \frac{1}{n}\left[n\mu\right] = \mu \tag{8.13}$$

$$V\left(\overline{X}\right) = V\left[\frac{1}{n}S\right] = \frac{1}{n^2}V(S) = \frac{1}{n^2}\left[n\sigma^2\right] = \frac{\sigma^2}{n} \tag{8.14}$$

$$\sigma\left(\overline{X}\right) = \sqrt{V\left(\overline{X}\right)} = \frac{\sigma}{\sqrt{n}} \tag{8.15}$$

Equation (8.13) shows that the expected (average) value of $\overline{X}$ is equal to the population mean, while the Variance (and standard deviation) of $\overline{X}$, in addition to being dependent on σ^2 (or σ), it also depends on the sample size n, which appears in the denominator (equations (8.14) and (8.15)).

These results are truly remarkable because they indicate that the variance and standard deviation of $\overline{X}$ decrease as n increases and in the limit (*i.e.*, as $n \rightarrow \infty$) they approach zero, which implies that the sampling distribution of $\overline{X}$ approaches a rectangle whose base (width) goes to zero and height goes to infinity but in such a way that: (Base) $\times$ (Height) $= 1$, as required by the appropriate probability axiom. This observation then, gives rise to the **Law of Large Numbers in Statistics** which we discuss briefly below.

8.3.1.3 The Law of Large Number in Statistics

Equations (8.13) and (8.14) show two remarkable statistical results. They show that the Expected value of the sample mean $(\overline{X})$ is equal to the population mean (μ) while the Variance of $\overline{X}$ is equal to the population variance (σ^2) divided by the sample size n which tells us that the distribution of the random variable $\overline{X}$ is centered at μ for any sample size n (since $E(\overline{X})$ does not depend on n)while the spread of the distribution decreases as n increases and in the limit (*i.e.*, when $n \rightarrow \infty$) this distribution collapses to the single value $\overline{X} = \mu$ (Actually the distribution becomes a rectangle with base $= 0$ and height $= \infty$ but such that (Base) $\times$ (Height) $= 1$ so that the total area under the density function $f(\overline{X})$ continues to be equal to 1 even in the limiting case). What is the significance of these observations? Simply that as the sample size increases, the sample mean $(\overline{X})$ approaches the population mean (μ). We can generalize this result and apply it to any sample statistic. This generalized statement, known as the "Law of Large Numbers in Statistics" claims the flowing:

"The distribution of the sample statistic reduces to a single value, which is the corresponding population parameter, as the sample size n approaches infinity."

Thus, we now have a theoretical justification for the intuitive notion that the "accuracy of the sample statistic (*s*) gets better as the sample size increases".

In the next chapter, when we discuss Estimation theory and the properties of "Good" estimators, one such desirable property will be defined as "Consistency". We will show at that time that the "Law of Large Numbers in Statistics" is another way of stating the "consistency" property of estimators, where an estimator is a function of the observations (as for example $\overline{X}, \hat{s}^2$) whose aim is to provide the "best" possible value for the corresponding population parameter.

8.3.1.4 The Central Limit Theorem

Let, $X_1, X_2, \ldots, X_n$ be n independent and identically distributed random variables with an unspecified probability distribution, and having a finite mean μ and a finite variance σ^2. Then the sum:

$$S = X_1 + X_2 + \cdots + X_n$$

has a distribution with mean $E(S) = n\mu$ and variance $V(S) = n\sigma^2$ which tends to become approximately normal for n sufficiently large, and with the approximation improving as n increases. In the limit, as $n \rightarrow \infty$, this distribution becomes exactly normal.

The proof of this theorem is beyond the scope of this book but is based on showing that the "characteristic" function of S approaches the characteristic function of a Normally distributed variable as $n \rightarrow \infty$.

Note that the distribution of the parent population (*i.e.*, the population from which the samples were drawn) can be any type whatsoever.

Naturally, if the parent population is Normal, the distribution of S will be exactly Normal for any value of n, since S is a linear combination of Normally distributed variables.

The conclusion that we can draw from the Central Limit Theorem is that the standardized variable:

$$\frac{S - E(S)}{\sigma(S)} = \frac{S - n\mu}{\sqrt{n}\sigma} \rightarrow N(0, 1) \qquad \text{as } n \rightarrow \infty . \qquad (8.16)$$

Also, since we have shown that $\overline{X} = \dfrac{1}{n}S$ and $E(\overline{X}) = \mu$ and $\sigma(\overline{X}) = \dfrac{\sigma}{\sqrt{n}}$, we can state that the standardized distribution of $\overline{X}$ is approximately Normal, with the approximation improving as n increases, and we can write:

$$\frac{\overline{X} - E(\overline{X})}{\sigma(\overline{X})} = \frac{\overline{X} - \mu}{\sigma/\sqrt{n}} \rightarrow N(0, 1) \qquad \text{as } n \rightarrow \infty \qquad (8.17)$$

In most cases it is safe to conclude that the approximation is acceptable as long as $n \geq 30$.

But the real significance of the Central Limit Theorem, which is one of the most important theorems in statistics, is the fact that the sampling distribution of any sample statistic, whose definition involves the sum of n *iid* random variables, becomes approximately Normal for n sufficiently large.

Note: *The Central limit Theorem applies to any random variable (say Y), which can be expressed as the sum of n other variables $X_1, X_2, \ldots, X_n$.*

Then:

1. *If $X_1, X_2, \ldots, X_n$ are known to be Normally distributed, $Y = X_1 + X_2 + \cdots + X_n$ is also Normally Distributed, for any value of n.*

2. *If $X_1, X_2, \ldots, X_n$ are not Normally Distributed, then $Y = X_1 + X_2 + \cdots + X_n$ becomes approximately Normally Distributed if $n \geq 30$, and the approximation improves as $n \rightarrow \infty$.*

We will use this observation in a later section of this chapter when we attempt to identify the sampling distributions of many sample statistics of interest.

Example 1

A man plays a game in which the probability of winning or losing a dollar is $1/2$. Let S_n be the amount he has won or lost after n plays.

1. Find $E(S_n)$ and $V(S_n)$
2. Find the probability that after 10,000 plays of the game the change in the man's fortune (the amount he has won or lost) will be between -50 and 50 dollars.

Solution Let $X_i = $ the change in the man's fortune on the i-th play of the game.

Then: $S_n = X_1 + X_2 + X_3 + \cdots + X_n$

represents the man's fortune after n plays.

We know from the previous section that $E(S_n) = n\mu$ and $V(S_n) = n\sigma^2$, where $\mu = E(X_1) = E(X_2) = \cdots = E(X_n)$, and $\sigma^2 = V(X_1) = \cdots = V(X_n)$ and $n = 10,000$.

However, before we can find numerical values for $E(S_n)$ and $V(S_n)$ we must calculate μ and σ^2.

From the statement of the problem the possible values of X_i are -1 (lose a dollar) and $+1$ (win a dollar) and each occurs with probability $1/2$.

Therefore:

X_i	$P(X_i)$	$X_i P(X_i)$	$X_i^2 P(X_i)$
-1	$1/2$	$-1/2$	$1/2$
1	$1/2$	$+1/2$	$1/2$
		$E(X_i) = 0 = \mu_i$	$E(X_i^2) = 1$

$$V(X_i) = E(X_i^2) - \left[E(X_i)\right]^2 = 1 - 0 = 1 = \sigma_i^2$$

From this table we see that $\mu = 0$ and $\sigma^2 = 1$

1. Therefore: $E(S_n) = 10{,}000(0) = 0$ and $V(S_n) = 10{,}000(1) = 10{,}000$, and $\sigma(S_n) = 100$

2. $P(-50 < S_n < 50) = p\left(\dfrac{-50 - 0}{100} < \dfrac{S_n - E(S_n)}{\sigma(S_n)} < \dfrac{50 - 0}{100}\right)$

$$= P(-1/2 < Z < 1/2)$$

$$= N(1/2) - N(-1/2)$$

$$= 0.6915 - 0.3085 = 0.3830,$$

since S_n is Normally distributed, in accordance with the Central Limit Theorem.

■ ■ ■

8.3.1.5 The Degrees of Freedom

When we discussed the Chi-square, t and F distributions in the previous Chapter, we defined these distributions in terms of their "degrees of freedom" which we used there as parameters in order to distinguish the different distributions within each family of probability functions, as for example a Chi-square with 10 degrees of freedom and another one with 15 degrees of freedom.

The "degrees of freedom" is a mathematical concept which refers to the number of Linearly Independent observations occurring in a sum of squares.

If n is the sample size, then the degrees of freedom, δ, is defined as:

$$DOF = \delta = df = n - k \qquad (8.18)$$

where: k is equal to the number of estimators requiring calculation in the sum of squares.

If the sum of squares does not include any estimators requiring calculation, then the value of $k = 0$ and $\delta = n$.

If there is one estimator in the sum of squares requiring calculation, then $k = 1$ and $\delta = n - 1$. If there are two estimators requiring calculation, then $k = 2$ and $\delta = n - 2$. Therefore:

1. $\displaystyle\sum_{i=1}^{n} x_i^2 = x_1^2 + x_2^2 + \cdots + x_n^2$ has $\delta = n$ degrees of freedom.

2. $\sum_{i=1}^{n}\left(x_i - \mu\right)^2 = \left(x_1 - \mu\right)^2 + \left(x_2 - \mu\right)^2 + \cdots + \left(x_n - \mu\right)^2$ has $\delta = n$ degrees of freedom since μ is a parameter and not an estimator.

3. $\sum_{i=1}^{n}\left(x_i - \overline{X}\right)^2 = \left(x_i - \overline{X}\right)^2 + \cdots + \left(x_n - \overline{X}\right)^2$ has $\delta = n - 1$ degrees of freedom since $\overline{X}$ is an estimator that must be calculated from the observations.

4. $\sum_{i=1}^{n}\left(y_i - a - bx_i\right)^2 = \left(y_1 - a - bx_1\right)^2 + \cdots + \left(y_n - a - bx_n\right)^2$ has $\delta = n - 2$ degrees of freedom, since a and b are both estimators which must be evaluated from the observations.

The number of "Linearly Independent Observations in a Sum of Squares" refers to the freedom we have in assigning values to the observations $x_1, x_2, \ldots, x_n$.

Thus, in example 1 above there are no restrictions to the values that can be assigned to any of the observations and the degrees of freedom are equal to the number of data.

This, however, is not the case in example 3, where the estimator $\overline{X}$ is part of the sum of squares. Since $\overline{X}$ must be calculated using the observations (recall that $\overline{X} = \dfrac{X_1 + X_2 + \cdots + X_n}{n}$) some freedom in assigning the possible values to the observations is lost. Since one combination of the observations is used in the calculation of $\overline{X}$, we claim that we have the freedom to assign arbitrary values to $n - 1$ of the observations, but the last one is dictated to us by the definition of $\overline{X}$. Thus we say that in example 3 we have lost one degree of freedom and the degrees of freedom associated with this sum is $\delta = n - 1$.

Similarly, in the sum of squares of example 4 which occurs, as we will see later in Linear Regression, the degrees of freedom associated with this sum of squares is $\delta = n - 2$, since we must use two different combinations of the observations to calculate the estimators a and b.

8.3.1.6 The Chi-square, *t* and *F* as Sampling Distributions Derived When Sampling from Standardized Normal Distributions

1. **Generating the Chi-square as a Sampling Distribution**

   a) Suppose the parent population is standard normal (*i.e.*, $N(0,1)$) and, $Z_1, Z_2, \ldots, Z_n$ are n *iid* random variables drawn from the parent population. Clearly each Z_i is also standard Normal.

   If we now introduce a new random variable Y_n defined as:

   $$Y_n = Z_1^2 + Z_2^2 + \cdots + Z_n^2 = \sum_{i=1}^{n} Z_i^2 \tag{8.19}$$

   then the random variable Y_n is said to have the Chi-square distribution with $\delta = n$ degrees of freedom. We have discussed the Chi-square distribution in Chapter 7, where it was derived as a special case of the Gamma distribution. The density function of Y is given by equation (7.25), and $E(Y)$ and $V(Y)$ by equations (7.28) and (7.29) respectively.

   If: $Y_1 = Z_1^2$ with $Z_1 \rightarrow N(0,1)$, then Y_1 is Chi-square with $\delta = 1$

   If: $Y_2 = Z_1^2 + Z_2^2$ with $Z_1, Z_2 \rightarrow N(0,1)$ then Y_2 is Chi-square with $\delta = 2$

Finally, if: $Y_n = \sum_{i=1}^{n} Z_i^2$ where $Z_i \rightarrow N(0,1)$, then Y_n is Chi-square with $\delta = n$

b) If the parent population is Normal with mean μ and standard deviation σ, and $X_1, X_2, ..., X_n$ are n *iid* random variables drawn from this population, then each

$$X_i \rightarrow N(\mu, \sigma^2).$$

If we standardize the random variables X_i, square them, and sum them up and call the result a random variable Y_n, where:

$$
\begin{aligned}
Y_n &= \left(\frac{X_1 - \mu}{\sigma}\right)^2 + \left(\frac{X_2 - \mu}{\sigma}\right)^2 + \cdots + \left(\frac{X_n - \mu}{\sigma}\right)^2 \\
&= \sum_{i=1}^{n} \left(\frac{X_i - \mu}{\sigma}\right)^2
\end{aligned}
\tag{8.20}
$$

then the random variable Y_n again is said to be Chi-square distributed with $\delta = n$ degrees of freedom.

In either case probability calculations, using the Chi-square distribution, are done with the use of Tables and using the procedure discussed in Chapter 7, where we also discussed the features of the Chi-square table.

c) However, in practice, we are usually interested in finding the distribution not of $\sum_{i=1}^{n} \left(\frac{X_i - \mu}{\sigma}\right)^2$ but of $\sum_{i=1}^{n} \left(X_i - \overline{X}\right)^2$ which forms the basis of the definition of the sample variance $\hat{s}^2 = \frac{1}{n-1} \sum_{i=1}^{n} \left(X_i - \overline{X}\right)^2$.

To make inferences on the population variance (of one or two populations), we need to identify the distribution of $\sum_{i=1}^{n} \left(X_i - \overline{X}\right)^2$.

There are two ways of arriving at this distribution:

The first consists of transforming the definition of $\hat{s}^2$ into a form similar to equation (8.20) and then using the definition of degrees of freedom to arrive at the result, as shown below:

By multiplying both sides of $\hat{s}^2$ by $(n-1)$, in the definition of $\hat{s}^2$, we obtain

$$\sum_{i=1}^{n} \left(X_i - \overline{X}\right)^2 = (n-1)\hat{s}^2 \tag{8.21}$$

Then, by dividing both sides of (8.21) by σ^2, we obtain:

$$\frac{\sum_{i=1}^{n} \left(X_i - \overline{X}\right)^2}{\sigma^2} = \frac{(n-1)\hat{s}^2}{\sigma^2}; \text{ or: } \frac{(n-1)\hat{s}^2}{\sigma^2} = \frac{\sum_{i=1}^{n} \left(X_i - \overline{X}\right)^2}{\sigma^2} \tag{8.22}$$

The right hand side of (8.22) is similar to (8.20) with the exception that $\overline{X}$ has replaced μ. But since Y_n in (8.20) is Chi-square with $\delta = n$ degrees of freedom and $\overline{X}$ in (8.22) needs to be estimated from the data, thus losing one degrees of freedom, the random variable

$$Y = \frac{(n-1)\hat{s}^2}{\sigma^2} \text{ is Chi-square with } \delta = n - 1 \text{ d.f.} \tag{8.23}$$

The second method starts also with $\sum_{i=1}^{n} \left(X_i - \overline{X}\right)^2$ but arrives at the same conclusion by algebraic methods and logical inferences.

It accomplishes this by first adding and subtracting μ within the squared parenthesis, regrouping, and expanding. The resulting equation confirms that the summation $\sum_{i=1}^{n}\left(\dfrac{X_i - \overline{X}}{\sigma}\right)^2$ is Chi-square with $\delta = n - 1$ d.f.

Analytically we have:

$$\sum_{i=1}^{n}\left(X_i - \overline{X}\right)^2 = \sum_{i=1}^{n}\left[X_i - \mu + \mu - \overline{X}\right]^2 = \sum_{i=1}^{n}\left[\left(X_i - \mu\right) - \left(\overline{X} - \mu\right)\right]^2$$

$$= \sum_{i=1}^{n}\left[(X_i - \mu)^2 - 2(\overline{X} - \mu)(X_i - \mu) + (\overline{X} - \mu)^2\right]$$

$$= \sum_{i=1}^{n}(X_i - \mu)^2 - 2(\overline{X} - \mu)\sum_{i=1}^{n}(X_i - \mu) + n(\overline{X} - \mu)^2$$

$$\left(\text{Since } \sum_{i=1}^{n}(\overline{x} - \mu)^2 = n(\overline{x} - \mu)^2\right)$$

$$= \sum_{i=1}^{n}(X_i - \mu)^2 - 2(\overline{X} - \mu)\left[n(\overline{X} - \mu)\right] + n(\overline{X} - \mu)^2$$

$$= \sum_{i=1}^{n}(X_i - \mu)^2 - 2n(\overline{X} - \mu)^2 + n(\overline{X} - \mu)^2$$

$$= \sum(X_i - \mu)^2 - n(\overline{X} - \mu)^2 \tag{8.24}$$

By dividing both sides of (8.24) by σ^2 and re-arranging the terms of the equation, we obtain:

$$\frac{\sum_{i=1}^{n}(X_i - \mu)^2}{\sigma^2} = \frac{\sum_{i=1}^{n}(X_i - \overline{X})^2}{\sigma^2} + \frac{n(\overline{X} - \mu)^2}{\sigma^2} \tag{8.25}$$

which, by incorporating σ^2 within the summation of the first two terms and bringing n in the denominator of the third term, finally becomes:

$$\sum_{i=1}^{n}\left(\frac{X_i - \mu}{\sigma}\right)^2 = \sum_{i=1}^{n}\left(\frac{X_i - \overline{X}}{\sigma}\right)^2 + \frac{(\overline{X} - \mu)^2}{\sigma^2/n} \tag{8.26}$$

But, the term on the left-hand side of the equation has been previously identified as a Chi-square variable with $\delta = n$ d.f., while the second term on the right-hand side of the equation is a Chi-square variable with $\delta = 1$ d.f. since $\overline{X}$ is a normal Variable with $E(\overline{X}) = \mu$ and $V(\overline{X}) = \dfrac{\sigma^2}{n}$, and the expression $\dfrac{(\overline{X} - \mu)^2}{\sigma^2/n} = \left(\dfrac{\overline{X} - \mu}{\sigma/\sqrt{n}}\right)^2$ is clearly a standardized normal variable squared, which is precisely the definition of a Chi-square variable with $\delta = 1$ d.f.

The result shown in equation (8.26) is a special case of a more general theorem which states that the sum of k Chi-square variables with $\delta_1, \delta_2, \ldots, \delta_k$ degrees of freedom respectively is also a Chi-square variable with degrees of freedom δ equal to $\delta = \delta_1 + \delta_2 + \cdots + \delta_k$. In the special case of equation (8.26) $k = 2$, $\delta_1 = n - 1$, $\delta_2 = 1$ while $\delta = \delta_1 + \delta_2 = (n - 1) + (1) = n$, as expected.

2. **Generating the t as a Sampling Distribution**

Suppose a population is standard normal and $n + 1$ *iid* samples are drawn from this population and designated by $Z_0, Z_1, \ldots, Z_n$.

If the population is generalized Normal with expected value μ and variance σ^2 and $n + 1$ *iid* samples are drawn from it and designated by $X_0, X_1, \ldots, X_n$, it is obvious that each of these generalized variables with $E(X_i) = \mu$ and $V(X_i) = \sigma^2$ can be transformed into standardized Normal Variables by the linear transformation

$$Z_i = \frac{X_i - \mu}{\sigma} \text{ where } i = 0, 1, 2, \ldots, n$$

Therefore, in either case, we end up with a set of $n + 1$ $N(0, 1)$ *iid* variables $Z_0, Z_1, \ldots, Z_n$.

If we let $Y = Z_1^2 + Z_2^2 + \cdots + Z_n^2$, then Y is a Chi-square variable with $\delta = n$ degrees of freedom.

Now if we form the ratio $Z_0 / \sqrt{Y/\delta}$ and call this ratio T, we have:

$$\mathrm{T} = Z_0 / \sqrt{Y/\delta} \tag{8.27}$$

The distribution of the random variable T is said to be the Student-t distribution we discussed in Chapter 7 whose density function is given by equation (7.50) and $E(T)$ and $V(T)$ are given by equations (7.51) and (7.52) respectively.

Probability calculations using the t-distribution are performed with the help of a Table whose structure and usage were also explained in Chapter 7.

What makes the t-distribution important is the fact that the standardized distribution of $\overline{X}$, namely $\dfrac{\overline{X} - \mu}{\sigma/\sqrt{n}}$ is $N(0, 1)$ only if the population standard deviation is known in advance or if σ is not known but the sample size n is sufficiently large ($n \geq 30$). In the later case σ can be replaced by $\hat{s}$ (which is calculated from the data) and the distribution $\dfrac{\overline{X} - \mu}{\hat{s}/\sqrt{n}}$ is still $N(0, 1)$, even though only approximately.

However, if σ is not known and $n < 30$, the distribution of $\dfrac{\overline{X} - \mu}{\hat{s}/\sqrt{n}}$ is no longer Normal but t, and the t distribution must be used when we make inferences regarding a population mean, or the difference of two population means, as we will see in future Chapters.

3. **Generating the F as a Sampling Distribution**

Suppose we have two sets of data: $X_1, X_2, \ldots, X_{n_1}$ and $Z_1, Z_2, \ldots, Z_{n_2}$ all of which are $N(0, 1)$ *iid* random variables.

If we let

$$Y_1 = X_1^2 + X_2^2 + \cdots + X_{n_1}^2$$

and

$$Y_2 = Z_1^2 + Z_2^2 + \cdots + Z_{n_2}^2$$

then Y_1 is a Chi-square variable with $\delta_1 = n_1$ degrees of freedom and Y_2 is also a Chi-square variable with $\delta_2 = n_2$ degrees of freedom.

Then the ratio $F = \dfrac{Y_1/\delta_1}{Y_2/\delta_2}$ is said to have the F distribution with (δ_1, δ_2) degrees of freedom, which we also discussed in Chapter 7. The density function of F is given by equation (7.55) while $E(F)$ and $V(F)$ are given by equations (7.56) and (7.57) respectively.

Probability calculations using the F distribution are performed with the help of a Table whose usage and structure were also discussed in Chapter 7.

What makes the F distribution important is the fact that when we compare the variability of two different populations we can show that, under the assumption of equal variance between the populations, the ratio of their sample variances $\hat{s}_1^2/\hat{s}_2^2$ is F-distributed with (δ_1, δ_2) degrees of freedom and this finding allows this comparison to be made using sound statistical principles. We will discuss this further in the next several chapters and give several examples which will make the assumptions and the theory very clear. Another important application of the F distribution is the testing of the equality of the means of three or more populations.

As we will discuss at length in our chapter on "Analysis of Variance" the above problem can be reformulated and solved using the F distribution.

8.4   Sampling Distributions of Important Sample Statistics

In the next two chapters and beyond, while attempting to draw inferences concerning certain population parameters, we will need the Sampling distributions of $\overline{X}, \Delta \overline{X} = \overline{X}_1 - \overline{X}_2$, the Binomial variable X, the Sampling proportion $p = X/n, \Delta p = p_1 - p_2, \hat{s}^2, \Delta \hat{s} = \hat{s}_1^2 - \hat{s}_2^2, \hat{s}_1^2 / \hat{s}_2^2, X_{0.5},$ Range R, correlation coefficient r, the intercept a and slope b in a linear regression, and many others. Identifying the distribution of everyone of these variables exactly is a very difficult task. However, our task can be made somewhat easier if we group these sample statistics into three groups; namely:

1. Those whose definition includes the sum of the observations $X_1 + X_2 + \cdots + X_n$
2. Those whose definition includes the sum of the square of the observations $X_1^2 + X_2^2 + \cdots + X_n^2$
3. Those whose definition includes combinations of $\sum_{i=1}^{n} X_i$ and $\sum_{i=1}^{n} X_i^2$ or neither one of them. In this case it is more difficult to identify the sampling distributions but, fortunately, in these cases transformations of the variables produce sampling distributions which can be identified, as will be the case with the sampling distribution of the sample correlation coefficient, r, to be discussed under Bivariate Analysis in a later chapter.

8.4.1 Sampling Distributions of Sample Statistics with $\sum_{i=1}^{n} X_i$ in their definition

We mentioned earlier, under our discussion of CLT, that if the definition of a sample statistic includes the summation $X_1 + X_2 + \cdots + X_n$, then we can conclude that the sampling distribution of the statistic of interest is approximately Normal by invoking the Central Limit Theorem, provided the sample size n is sufficiently large.

The sample statistics which fall in this category are the following:

1. The Sample Mean, $\overline{X}$
2. The Difference of 2 Sample Means, $\Delta\overline{X} = \overline{X}_1 - \overline{X}_2$
3. The Number of Successes in n trials, X
4. The Sample Proportion, $P = X/n$
5. The Difference of 2 Sample Proportions, $\Delta p = p_1 - p_2$

The importance of claiming that the sampling distributions of these sample statistics is Normal, is the fact that the Normal distribution table can be used to solve probability calculation problems involving these sample statistics. But knowing the nature of their sampling distributions is not enough because a Normal distribution is completely defined only if its mean and standard deviation have also been computed. For example, if in a given problem we are interested in the probability that $\overline{X}$ is between 50 and 60, knowing that $\overline{X}$ is Normally distributed is not sufficient because:

$$P(50 \leq \overline{X} \leq 60) = P\left[\frac{50 - E(\overline{X})}{\sigma(\overline{X})} < \frac{\overline{X} - E(\overline{X})}{\sigma(\overline{X})} < \frac{60 - E(\overline{X})}{\sigma(\overline{X})}\right]$$

$$= P\left[\frac{50 - E(\overline{X})}{\sigma(\overline{X})} < Z < \frac{60 - E(\overline{X})}{\sigma(\overline{X})}\right]$$

and before the Z table can be used, we need to define $E(\overline{X})$ and $\sigma(\overline{X})$ so that $\dfrac{50 - E(\overline{X})}{\sigma(\overline{X})}$ and $\dfrac{60 - E(\overline{X})}{\sigma(\overline{X})}$ become pure numbers, say k_1 and k_2 respectively. Then the answer to the above problem becomes:

$$P(50 \leq \overline{X} \leq 60) = P[k_1 < Z < k_2] = N(K_2) - N(K_1),$$

where $N(k_1)$ and $N(k_2)$ are the values of the standard Normal Cumulative Distribution Function (CDF) evaluated at k_2 and k_1 and found directly from the Normal Table.

We have already showed that for $\overline{X}$, $E(\overline{X}) = \mu$ and $V(\overline{X}) = \dfrac{\sigma^2}{n}$, where μ and σ are the mean and variance of the population from which the sample (*i.e.*, the values $X_1, X_2, \ldots, X_n$) was drawn and n is the size of the sample. If μ and σ^2 are known in advance then $E(\overline{X})$ and $V(\overline{X})$ can be computed and then the problem above can be completely solved. If μ and σ^2 are not known but $n \geq 30$, we can replace μ and σ^2 by $\overline{X}$ and $\hat{s}^2$ and still use the Normal table to calculate the probability. However, if μ and σ^2 are not known and $n < 30$, we cannot use the Normal distribution anymore but must use the t distribution, as we will show later.

Before any of the other sample statistics listed previously can be used to solve a problem, we must calculate for each its expected value and standard deviation. The table below summarizes these characteristics for each of these sample statistics and also offers an explanation as to why the CLT is applicable. When a discrete random variable is approximated by the Normal distribution which is continuous, a Continuity Correction Factor (CCF) is also included in the Table.

In the table below we show how some of the characteristics of these sample statistics were derived, and then we present some examples, to illustrate their use.

If the sample Statistic is:	CLT Applies because:	Expected Value & Variance	The Sampling Distribution is:	Continuity Correction Factor
$\overline{X}$	$\overline{X} = \dfrac{X_1 + X_2 + \cdots + X_n}{n}$	$E(\overline{X}) = \mu$ $V(\overline{X}) = \sigma^2/n$ $\sigma(\overline{X}) = \sigma/\sqrt{n}$	$\dfrac{\overline{X} - \mu}{\sigma/\sqrt{n}} \rightarrow N(0,1)$	
$\Delta \overline{X} = \overline{X}_1 - \overline{X}_2$	$\Delta \overline{X}$ is a Linear Combination of Normally Distributed Variables $\overline{X}_1, \overline{X}_2$	$\begin{aligned} E(\Delta \overline{X}) &= E(\overline{X}_1 - \overline{X}_2) \\ &= E(\overline{X}_1) - E(\overline{X}_2) \\ &= \mu_1 - \mu_2 \\ &= \Delta \mu \end{aligned}$ $\begin{aligned} V(\Delta \overline{X}) &= V(\overline{X}_1 - \overline{X}_2) \\ &= V(\overline{X}_1) + E(\overline{X}_2) \\ &= \dfrac{\sigma_1^2}{n_1} + \dfrac{\sigma_2^2}{n_2} \end{aligned}$ $\sigma(\Delta \overline{X}) = \sqrt{\dfrac{\sigma_1^2}{n_1} + \dfrac{\sigma_2^2}{n_2}}$	$\dfrac{\Delta \overline{X} - \Delta \mu}{\sigma(\Delta \overline{X})} \rightarrow N(0,1)$	
$X =$ Number of Successes in n Trials	$X = X_1 + X_2 + \cdots + X_n$, where: $X_1, X_2, \ldots, X_n$ are Bernoulli Variables	$\begin{aligned} E(X) &= E(X_1 + \cdots + X_n) \\ &= E(X_1) + \cdots + E(X_n) \\ &= p + p + \cdots + p \\ &= np \end{aligned}$ $V(X) = np(1 - p)$ $\sigma(X) = \sqrt{np(1 - p)}$	$\dfrac{x - np}{\sqrt{np(1-p)}} \rightarrow N(0,1)$	CCF = 1/2 Note: See Chapter 7 on the proper use of CCF.
$p =$ Sample proportion $= X/n$	X is a sum of Bernoulli Variables	$E(p) = \pi$ $V(p) = \dfrac{\pi(1 - \pi)}{n}$ if Sampling with Replacement, and : $V(P) = (FPCF)\left[\dfrac{\pi(1 - \pi)}{n}\right]$ if Sampling without Replacement, where: $FPCF = \begin{pmatrix} Finite \\ Population \\ Correction \\ Factor \end{pmatrix} = \dfrac{N - n}{N - 1}$	$\dfrac{p - E(p)}{\sigma(\Delta p)} \rightarrow N(0,1)$	$CCF = \dfrac{1}{2n}$

If the sample Statistic is:	CLT Applies because:	$\sigma_p = \sqrt{V(P)}$ Expected Value & Variance	The Sampling Distribution is:	Continuity Correction Factor
$\Delta p = p_1 - p_2$ $= \dfrac{X_1}{n_1} - \dfrac{X_2}{n_2}$	Δp is a Linear Combination of Normally Distributed Variables p_1 and p_2	$E(\Delta p) = E(p_1 - p_2)$ $\quad = E(p_1) - E(p_2)$ $\quad = \pi_1 - \pi_2 = \Delta\pi$ $V(\Delta p) = V(p_1 - p_2)$ $\quad = V(p_1) + V(p_2)$ $\quad = \dfrac{\pi_1(1-\pi_1)}{n_1} + \dfrac{\pi_2(1-\pi_2)}{n_2}$ if sampling with replacement, and: $V(\Delta p) = \left(\dfrac{N_1 - n_1}{N_1 - 1}\right)\left[\dfrac{\pi_1(1-\pi_1)}{n_1}\right]$ $+ \left(\dfrac{N_2 - n_2}{N_2 - 1}\right)\left[\dfrac{\pi_2(1-\pi_2)}{n_2}\right]$ if sampling without replacement.	$\dfrac{\Delta p - E(\Delta p)}{\sigma(\Delta p)} \to N(0,1)$	

Example 2

The weight of first grade children is thought to be Normal with $\mu = 39$ and $\sigma = 2$. A sample of 25 first grade students are selected at random, the weights are recorded and $\overline{X}$ is calculated. What is the probability that $\overline{X}$ is between 38.5 and 40 lbs?

Solution Since the parent population is Normal, the Sampling Distribution of $\overline{X}$ is also Normal with $E(\overline{X}) = \mu = 39$, $V(\overline{X}) = \sigma^2/n$ and $\sigma(\overline{X}) = \dfrac{\sigma}{\sqrt{n}} = \dfrac{2}{\sqrt{25}} = \dfrac{2}{5} = 0.4$

Therefore

$$P\left[38.5 < \overline{X} < 40\right] = P\left[\frac{38.5 - 39}{0.4} < \frac{\overline{X} - E(\overline{X})}{\sigma(\overline{X})} < \frac{40 - 39}{0.4}\right]$$

$$= P\left[-1.25 < Z < 2.5\right]$$

$$= N(2.5) - N(-1.25) = 0.9938 - 0.1056 = 0.8882$$

■ ■ ■

Example 3

A sample of 16 items is drawn from a population of (unknown) nature whose mean value is known to be 50 but its variance is unknown and was estimated from the sample data to be 64. What is the probability that $\overline{X}$ will exceed 52.682?

Solution Since $n < 30$ and σ^2 is not known, $\overline{X}$ is t-distributed with $\delta = n - 1 = 15$ degrees of freedom.

Therefore

$$P(\overline{X} > 52.682) = 1 - P(\overline{X} < 52.682) = 1 - P\left(\frac{\overline{X} - E(\overline{X})}{\sigma(\overline{X})} < \frac{52.682 - E(\overline{X})}{\sigma(\overline{X})}\right)$$

But

$$E(\overline{X}) = \mu = 50$$

$$V(\overline{X}) = \frac{\hat{s}^2}{n} = \frac{64}{16} = 4 \text{ and } \sigma(\overline{X}) = \frac{\hat{s}}{\sqrt{n}} = \frac{8}{4} = 2$$

Therefore

$$P(\overline{X} > 52.682) = 1 - P\left(t_{15} < \frac{52.682 - 50}{2}\right) = 1 - P(t_{15} < 1.341)$$

$$= 1 - 0.9 = 0.10$$

■ ■ ■

Example 4

In competitive analysis it is accepted practice to test the equality of the "resources" of two companies. Suppose company A (population 1) is known to have a mean "resource" value of 10,000 with a variance of 36,000, while company B has a mean value of 9,000 with a variance of 21,000. The resources of company A were examined in 40 competitions and the resources of company B in 30 competitions. What is the probability that the difference in the sample means of the resources of the two companies will exceed 1080?

Solution The sample statistic of interest is $\Delta\overline{X} = \overline{X}_A - \overline{X}_B$, whose sampling distribution is Normal because the two population variances are known and the two sample sizes are large ($n_A = 40$ and $n_B = 30$). Therefore, to solve this problem we need to find $E(\Delta\overline{X})$ and $V(\Delta\overline{X})$.

$$E(\Delta\overline{X}) = E(\overline{X}_A - \overline{X}_B) = E(\overline{X}_A) - E(\overline{X}_B) = \mu_A - \mu_B = \Delta\mu$$
$$= 10{,}000 - 9{,}000 = 1{,}000$$

$$V(\Delta\overline{X}) = V(\overline{X}_A - \overline{X}_B) = V(\overline{X}_A) + V(\overline{X}_B)$$

$$= \frac{\sigma_A^2}{n_A} + \frac{\sigma_B^2}{n_B}$$

$$= \frac{36000}{40} + \frac{21000}{40} = 900 + 700 = 1600,$$

$$\sigma(\Delta\overline{X}) = \sqrt{1600} = 40$$

Therefore

$$P(\Delta\overline{X} > 1080) = 1 - P(\Delta\overline{X} < 1080)$$

$$= 1 - P\left(\frac{\Delta\overline{X} - E(\Delta\overline{X})}{\sigma(\Delta\overline{X})} < \frac{1080 - 1000}{40}\right)$$

$$= 1 - P(Z < 2)$$

$$= 1 - 0.9772 = 0.0228$$

■ ■ ■

Example 5

A buyer of large quantities of an electronic component, used in the manufacture of computers, has devised an acceptance plan that calls for the inspection of a sample of 100 components selected at random from a very large lot. The buyer accepts the entire lot if no more than 6 defective components are found in the sample. Otherwise, the lot is rejected. If it is known that the lot shipped to the buyer contains 10 percent defectives, what is the probability that the lot will be accepted?

Solution This problem can be solved using the Binomial distribution. If we let X be the number of defective components found in a sample of 100 items with $p_{defective} = 0.1$, then X is a Binomial variable with $E(X) = np = 100(0.1) = 10$, $V(X) = np(1 - p) = 10(0.9) = 9$ and $\sigma(X) = 3$.

We are looking for the probability of acceptance, $P(X \le 6)$

From the CDF of the Binomial distribution, we find:

$$P(\text{Acceptance}) = P(X \le 6) = B(6, P = 0.1, n = 100) = 0.11716$$

However, we have shown that the random variable X is also approximately Normally distributed.

Therefore

$$P(X \le 6) = P\left(\frac{X - E(X)}{\sigma(X)} \le \frac{6 - E(X)}{\sigma(X)}\right) = P\left(Z \le \frac{6 - 10}{3}\right)$$

$$= P(Z < -1.33) = 0.0918$$

The accuracy is not very good. However, as indicated in the table above, to get better accuracy we must use the Continuity Correction Factor (CCF) of $1/2$, since we are approximating a discrete distribution (Binomial) by a continuous one. In this case we obtain:

$$P(\text{Acceptance})$$
$$= P(X \le 6) = P\left(Z \le \frac{6 - E(X) + 1/2}{\sigma(X)}\right) = P\left(Z < \frac{6 - 10 + 0.5}{3}\right)$$

$$= P(Z < -1.17) = 0.1210$$

The accuracy has improved substantially, even though it is still not exact. As discussed in Chapter 6, the accuracy of the Normal approximation is best when $p = 1/2$ and decreases as p moves away from the value of $1/2$ which corresponds to a symmetrical Binomial distribution. When $p \ne 1/2$ we not only approximate a discrete distribution by a continuous one but also approximate a skewed distribution by a symmetric one.

■ ■ ■

Example 6

In a given election district, the proportion of registered voters who favor a given proposition is 40 percent. If a sample of 50 voters is selected at random, what is the probability that the sample proportion of voters who favor the proposition does not exceed 42%?

Solution If we let p represent the sample proportion of voters favoring the proposition, then p is a random variable with: $E(p) = \pi = 0.4$, $V(p) = \dfrac{\pi(1-\pi)}{n}$, and

$$\sigma(p) = \sqrt{\frac{\pi(1-\pi)}{n}} = \sqrt{\frac{0.4(0.6)}{50}} = \sqrt{\frac{0.48}{100}} \approx 0.07, \text{ and } p \text{ is approximately Normally}$$

distributed.

Therefore,

$$P(p \le 0.42) = P\left(\frac{P - E(p)}{\sigma(p)} \le \frac{0.42 - E(p) + 1/2n}{\sigma(p)} \right)$$

$$= P\left(Z \le \frac{0.42 - 0.4 + 1/100}{0.07} \right)$$

$$= P\left(Z \le \frac{0.42 - 0.40 + 0.01}{0.07} \right) = P\left(Z \le \frac{3}{7} \right)$$

$$= P(Z \le 0.43) = 0.6664$$

▪ ▪ ▪

Example 7

In a study of the smoking habits of men and women a random sample of 400 men revealed 190 smokers, and a random sample of 800 women produced 300 smokers. Assuming that the true proportion of men smokers is 0.5 and of women 0.4, what is the probability that the difference in the two sample proportions will exceed 0.16?

Solution If we let p_1 = Sample proportion of men smokers = 190 / 400 = 0.475
p_2 = Sample proportion of women smokers = 300 / 800 = 0.375

Then $\Delta p = p_1 - p_2$, is a random variable, approximately Normally distributed, with:

$$E(\Delta p) = E(p_1 - p_2) = E(p_1) - E(p_2) = \pi_1 - \pi_2 = 0.475 - 0.375 = 0.100$$

$$V(\Delta p) = \frac{\pi_1(1 - \pi_1)}{n_1} + \frac{\pi_2(1 - \pi_2)}{n_2} = \frac{0.475(0.525)}{400} + \frac{0.375(0.625)}{800}$$

$$= \frac{1}{400}\left[0.249375 + \frac{1}{2}(0.234375) \right] = \frac{1}{400}(0.366563), \text{ and}$$

$$\sigma(\Delta p) = \sqrt{V(\Delta p)} = \frac{1}{20}\sqrt{0.366563} = \frac{1}{20}(0.605) = 0.0302$$

Therefore

$$P(\Delta p > 0.16) = 1 - P(\Delta p < 0.16) = 1 - P\left(\frac{\Delta p - E(\Delta p)}{\sigma(\Delta p)} < \frac{0.16 - \Delta \pi}{0.03} \right)$$

$$= 1 - P\left(Z < \frac{0.16 - 0.10}{0.03} \right) = 1 - P\left(Z < \frac{0.06}{0.03} \right)$$

$$= 1 - P(Z < 2) = 1 - 0.9772 = 0.0228$$

▪ ▪ ▪

8.4.2 Sampling Distributions of Sample Statistics with $\sum\limits_{i=1}^{n} X_i^2$ in Their Definition

We have mentioned earlier, under our discussion of the Chi-square distribution, that if $X_1, X_2, \ldots, X_n$ are iid random variables drawn from a Normal distribution with parameters μ and σ^2, then the random variable

$$Y = \sum_{i=1}^{n}\left(\frac{X_i - \mu}{\sigma}\right)^2 \text{ is Chi-square with } \delta = n \text{ degrees of freedom.}$$

If the parent distribution were standardized Normal (i.e., $\mu = 0$ and $\sigma^2 = 1$) then

$$Y = \sum_{i=1}^{n} Z_i^2 \text{ is also Chi-square with } \delta = n \text{ d.f.}$$

The most important representative sample statistics of this category are :

1. The sample variance $\hat{s}^2 = \dfrac{1}{n-1}\sum_{i=1}^{n}(X_i - \overline{X})^2$ and b) the sample standard deviation

   $\hat{s}$, defined as: $\hat{s} = \sqrt{\hat{s}^2}$. We have already shown (see equation 8.23) that $\dfrac{(n-1)\,\hat{s}^2}{\sigma^2}$ is a Chi-square variable with $\delta = n - 1$ d.f.

2. The density function of a Chi-square variable with δ degrees of freedom is given by equation (7.25), while the Expected value and Variance of a Chi-square variable are given by equations (7.28) and (7.29) respectively, where $E(\chi_\delta^2) = \delta$ and $V(\chi_\delta^2) = 2\delta$.

$$\text{Since } \frac{(n-1)\,\hat{s}^2}{\sigma^2} \text{ is } \chi_{n-1}^2, \text{ then:}$$

$$E\left[\frac{(n-1)\hat{s}^2}{\sigma^2}\right] = \frac{n-1}{\sigma^2}E(\hat{s}^2) = (n-1) \text{from which: } E(\hat{s}^2) = \sigma^2 \quad (8.28)$$

and

$$V\left[\frac{(n-1)\hat{s}^2}{\sigma^2}\right] = \frac{(n-1)^2}{\sigma^4}V(\hat{s}^2) = 2(n-1)$$

from which

$$V(\hat{s}^2) = \frac{2\sigma^4}{n-1} \quad (8.29)$$

and

$$\sigma(\hat{s}^2) = \sqrt{\frac{2}{n-1}}\,\sigma^2 \quad (8.30)$$

Since $E(\hat{s}^2) = \sigma^2$, $\hat{s}^2$ is called an "Unbiased" estimator of σ^2, something we will discuss again in the next chapter of Estimation. Probability calculations on the sample variance are performed with the help of the Chi-square table.

Example 8

If a sample of size $n = 16$, $x_1, x_2, ..., x_{16}$, is drawn from a Normal distribution with population variance $\sigma^2 = 30$, what is the probability that the sample variance will be less than 50?

Solution We are looking for $P\left[\hat{s}^2 < 50\right]$. But:

$$P\left[\hat{s}^2 < 50\right] = P\left[\frac{(n-1)\hat{s}^2}{\sigma^2} < \frac{50(n-1)}{\sigma^2}\right] = P\left[\chi_{15}^2 < \frac{50(15)}{30}\right]$$

$$= P\left[\chi_{15}^2 < 25\right] = 0.95$$

1. The sampling distribution of the standard deviation, $\hat{s}$, is obtained from the sampling distribution of $\hat{s}^2$ and the fact that $\hat{s} = \sqrt{\hat{s}^2}$.

Since we have shown that $\dfrac{(n-1)\hat{s}^2}{\sigma^2} = \chi^2_{n-1}$, we can solve for $\hat{s}^2$ to obtain

$$\hat{s}^2 = \frac{\sigma^2}{n-1}\chi^2_{n-1} = \frac{\sigma^2}{\delta}\chi^2_\delta \quad (\delta = n-1 \text{ df}) \tag{8.31}$$

and finally $\hat{s} = \sqrt{\hat{s}^2} = \sqrt{\left(\dfrac{\sigma^2}{\delta}\right)\chi^2_\delta} = \sqrt{\left(\dfrac{\sigma^2}{n-1}\right)\chi^2_{n-1}} = \sigma\sqrt{\dfrac{\chi^2_\delta}{\delta}}$ (8.32)

When $\sigma = 1$ the resulting distribution is called "Chi distribution" (χ) with δ degrees of freedom and is given by:

$$f(\chi) = \frac{2(\delta/2)^{\delta/2}}{\sigma^\delta \Gamma(\delta/2)} \chi^{\delta-1} e^{-(\delta/2\sigma^2)\chi^2} \qquad \chi > 0 \tag{8.33}$$

and represents the sampling distribution of the sample standard deviation. When the Expected value, Variance, and Standard deviation are found, we obtain:

$$E(\chi) = E(\hat{s}) = C_2\sigma = C_2 \quad \text{when} \quad \sigma = 1 \tag{8.34}$$

$$V(\chi) = V(\hat{s}) = \left(1 - \frac{1}{\delta} - C_2^2\right)\sigma^2$$

$$= \left(1 - 1/\delta - C_2^2\right) \quad \text{when} \quad \sigma = 1 \tag{8.35}$$

$$\sigma(\chi) = \sigma(\hat{s}) = \left(\sqrt{1 - 1/\delta - C_2^2}\right)\sigma$$

$$= \sqrt{1 - 1/\delta - C_2^2} \quad \text{when} \quad \sigma = 1 \tag{8.36}$$

where

$$C_2 = \sqrt{\frac{2}{\delta}} \; \frac{\left(\dfrac{\delta-2}{2}\right)!}{\left(\dfrac{\delta-3}{2}\right)!} = \sqrt{\frac{2}{\delta}} \frac{\Gamma(\delta/2)}{\Gamma\left(\dfrac{\delta-1}{2}\right)} \quad (\text{since } \Gamma(\alpha) = (\alpha-1)!) \tag{8.37}$$

Tables, similar to the Chi-square (χ^2) could be constructed for the Chi (χ) distribution but this is not necessary, because probability calculations on the sample standard deviation can be made using the Chi-square distribution.

This is so because if we wanted to find, for example, $P[\hat{s} < s_0]$ we can write:

$$P[\hat{s} < s_0] = P[\hat{s}^2 < s_0^2] = P\left[\frac{(n-1)\hat{s}^2}{\sigma^2} < \frac{(n-1)}{\sigma^2}s_0^2\right]$$

$$= P\left[\chi^2_{n-1} < \frac{(n-1)}{\sigma^2}s_0^2\right] \tag{8.38}$$

The quantity $\dfrac{(n-1)}{\sigma^2} s_0^2$ is a numerical value, since $n-1, \sigma^2$ and s_0 are given. All that needs to be done now is to search the χ^2 table with $n-1$ degrees of freedom to find the probability which corresponds to χ_{n-1}^2 being less than the value $\dfrac{(n-1)}{\sigma^2} s_0^2$.

If we designate such probability by P_0, then $P\left[\hat{s} < s_0\right] = P_0$.

■ ■ ■

8.4.3 Sampling Distributions of Sample Statistics with "Complicated" Definitions

In this section we include the sampling distributions of the following sample statistics:

1. Sample Median, $X_{0.5}$.
2. Difference of two sample variances, $\Delta \hat{s}^2 = \hat{s}_1^2 - \hat{s}_2^2$
3. Sample statistics involved in Bivariate Analysis
   a) Sample correlation coefficient, r
   b) Sample y-intercept of a simple linear regression function, a
   c) Sample slope of a simple linear regression function, b
4. Sample Range, R.

We did not include the first 5 of these sample statistics among those with approximately Normal Sampling distributions, even though they are, because their definitions are more complicated and include terms other than $\sum\limits_{i=1}^{n} X_i$, and because additional conditions/assumptions may be needed before their Normality can be established. In the case of the sample correlation coefficient (r), a non-linear transformation of r is required before normality is established.

The Sampling distribution of the sample range is not Normal but is an example of a sample statistic with a simple definition (i.e., $R = X_{\text{HIGH}} - X_{\text{LOW}}$) but a complicated sampling distribution.

■ Sampling Distribution of the Median

If the parent population is Normal with parameters μ and σ^2, and a sample size of $n \geq 30$ is drawn from it, then the Sampling Distribution of the Median is approximately Normal with:

$$E(X_{0.5}) = \mu; \ \ V(X_{0.5}) = \frac{\pi}{2} \frac{\sigma}{n} \approx 1.57\sigma^2/n \text{ and } \sigma(X_{0.5}) \approx 1.253\,\sigma/\sqrt{n}$$

Therefore, under these conditions:

$$\frac{X_{0.5} - E(X_{0.5})}{\sigma(X_{0.5})} \to N(0,1) \tag{8.39}$$

The variance of $X_{0.5}$, $V(X_{0.5}) = \dfrac{\pi}{2}\dfrac{\sigma^2}{n} \approx 1.57\sigma^2/n$ is an important result and very useful when we select the "best" measure of "Central Location" as we will do in the next chapter. As we will see there, the "Efficiency" of an estimator is an important criterion in such a selection, and Efficiency is a function of the variance of the estimator.

■ Sampling Distribution of the Difference of two Sample Variances

When testing the equality of the variances of two populations, we will need a sampling distribution, with appropriate characteristics that will allow us to complete such a test. If the sample sizes from the two populations (n_1 and n_2) are relatively small, we can form the ratio σ_1^2/σ_2^2 (where σ_1^2 is the variance of population 1 and σ_2^2 is the variance of population 2) and show, as we will do later on, that the appropriate distribution to use is the F.

However, if n_1 and n_2 are both greater than or equal to 100 (where n_1 and n_2 are the sample sizes drawn from the two populations), then we can form the difference of the two sample variances ($\hat{s}_1^2$ computed from sample one with sample size n_1, and $\hat{s}_2^2$ computed from sample two with sample size n_2) and show that if $n_1 \geq 100$ and $n_2 \geq 100$, then $\Delta\hat{s}^2 = \hat{s}_1^2 - \hat{s}_2^2$ is approximately Normally distributed. We proceed as follows:

Let
$$\Delta\hat{s}^2 = \hat{s}_1^2 - \hat{s}_2^2 \tag{8.40}$$

Then
$$E[\Delta\hat{s}^2] = E[\hat{s}_1^2 - \hat{s}_2^2] = E(\hat{s}_1^2) - E(\hat{s}_2^2) = \sigma_1^2 - \sigma_2^2 = \Delta\sigma^2 \tag{8.41}$$

And
$$V[\Delta\hat{s}^2] = V[\hat{s}_1^2 - \hat{s}_2^2] = V(\hat{s}_1^2) + V(\hat{s}_2^2) = \frac{2\sigma_1^4}{n_1 - 1} + \frac{2\sigma_2^4}{n_2 - 1} \tag{8.42}$$

and
$$\sigma(\Delta\hat{s}^2) = \sqrt{\frac{2\sigma_1^4}{n_1 - 1} + \frac{2\sigma_2^4}{n_2 - 1}} \tag{8.43}$$

These derivations are based on the fact that $\dfrac{(n-1)\hat{s}^2}{\sigma^2}$ is a Chi-square variable with $\delta = n - 1$ degrees of freedom (see eq. 8.23) and the fact that, for a Chi-square variable with δ degrees of freedom, $E(\chi_\delta^2) = \delta$ and $V(\chi_\delta^2) = 2\delta$. Therefore, we have:

$$E\left[\frac{(n-1)\hat{s}^2}{\sigma^2}\right] = n - 1, \text{ since } \frac{(n-1)\hat{s}^2}{\sigma^2} \text{ has } n - 1 \text{ degrees of freedom}$$

and
$$V\left[\frac{(n-1)\hat{s}^2}{\sigma^2}\right] = 2(n - 1)$$

Then, using the properties of the Expectation and Variance operators we obtain:

$$E\left[\frac{(n-1)\hat{s}^2}{\sigma^2}\right] = \frac{(n-1)}{\sigma^2}\left[E(\hat{s}^2)\right] \text{ which must be equal to } n - 1$$

or
$$\frac{(n-1)}{\sigma^2}E(\hat{s}^2) = n - 1 \text{ and, solving for } E(\hat{s}^2), \text{ we obtain:}$$
$$E(\hat{s}^2) = \sigma^2 \tag{8.44}$$

Similarly, $V\left[\dfrac{(n-1)\hat{s}^2}{\sigma^2}\right] = \dfrac{(n-1)^2}{\sigma^4}\left[V(\hat{s}^2)\right] = 2(n-1)$ and solving for $V(\hat{s}^2)$, we obtain:

$$V(\hat{s}^2) = \frac{2\sigma^4}{n - 1} \tag{8.45}$$

Therefore, under the stated conditions:

$$\frac{\Delta\hat{s}^2 - E(\Delta\hat{s}^2)}{\sigma(\Delta\hat{s}^2)} \to N(0, 1) \tag{8.46}$$

▪ Sample Statistics Involved in Bivariate Analysis

In part IV of this book, and in particular in Chapter 13, we will discuss Bivariate Analysis, *i.e.*, the joint behavior of two random variables which occur simultaneously in the same experiment and which may or may not be independent of each other.

Bivariate Analysis usually consists of two distinct steps, namely:

1. Correlation Analysis, and
2. Linear regression Analysis

In Correlation Analysis we like to know whether two random variables X and Y are related to each other in the sense that the knowledge of the value of X (which is regarded as the independent variable) may be used to find the value of Y (which is regarded as the dependent variable). A measure of the strength of the relationship between the two variables is provide by the sample correlation coefficient, r, which is defined by:

$$r = \frac{\sum_{i=1}^{n}(X_i - \overline{X})(Y_i - \overline{Y})}{\left[\sum_{i=1}^{n}(X_i - \overline{X})^2\right]^{1/2}\left[\sum_{i=1}^{n}(Y_i - \overline{Y})^2\right]^{1/2}}$$

$$= \frac{n\sum_{i=1}^{n}X_iY_i - \left(\sum_{i=1}^{n}X_i\right)\left(\sum_{i=1}^{n}Y_i\right)}{\left[n\sum_{i=1}^{n}X_i^2 - \left(\sum_{i=1}^{n}X_i\right)^2\right]^{1/2}\left[n\sum_{i=1}^{n}Y_i^2 - \left(\sum_{i=1}^{n}Y_i\right)^2\right]^{1/2}} \qquad (8.47)$$

Obviously, r is a random variable (since X and Y are random variables and $r = f(X,Y)$) and we are interested in finding its sampling distribution to use in inferential analysis concerning the population correlation coefficient ρ.

If Correlation Analysis concluded that the two random variables X and Y are related, then we want to find the "best" linear function

$$Y = a + bX \qquad (8.48)$$

where a = the sample Y-intercept of a simple linear regression function
        b = the sample slope of a simple linear regression function

which connects the two variables. The problem consists of finding the values of a and b, based on the n ordered pairs of values (x_i, y_i) which are given, using the least squares methodology, to be discussed in greater detail in Chapter 13.

The expressions relating a and b to the (x, y) values are given by:

$$a = \frac{\left(\sum_{i=1}^{n}y_i\right)\left(\sum_{i=1}^{n}x_i^2\right) - \left(\sum_{i=1}^{n}x_i\right)\left(\sum_{i=1}^{n}x_iy_i\right)}{n\left(\sum_{i=1}^{n}x_i^2\right) - \left(\sum_{i=1}^{n}x_i\right)^2} \qquad (8.49)$$

$$b = \frac{n\left(\sum_{i=1}^{n}x_iy_i\right) - \left(\sum_{i=1}^{n}x_i\right)\left(\sum_{i=1}^{n}y_i\right)}{n\left(\sum_{i=1}^{n}x_i^2\right) - \left(\sum_{i=1}^{n}x_i\right)} \qquad (8.50)$$

These equations are obtained from the "Normal Equations for the Linear Model", which are derived by calculus optimization techniques as discussed in Appendix B. The Normal Equations are listed below, because they help identify the different combinations of the ordered pairs of data required.

$$na + b\sum_{i=1}^{n} x_i = \sum_{i=1}^{n} y_i \qquad (8.51)$$

$$a\sum_{i=1}^{n} x_i + b\sum_{i=1}^{n} x_i^2 = \sum_{i=1}^{n} x_i y_i \qquad (8.52)$$

Obviously equations (8.47), (8.49) and (8.50) depend not only on $\sum_{i=1}^{n} x_i$ and $\sum_{i=1}^{n} y_i$, which can be obtained very easily from the given ordered pairs of data (x_i, y_i) by summing the entries in the X and Y columns, but also on $\sum_{i=1}^{n} x_i^2$, $\sum_{i=1}^{n} y_i^2$, and $\sum_{i=1}^{n} x_i y_i$. To obtain these last three quantities we need to extend the original table, consisting of the X and Y columns, to generate the three additional columns X^2, Y^2, and XY. The entries under the X^2 column are obtained by squaring the corresponding x value, and similarly for the Y^2 column. The entries under the XY column are found by multiplying the corresponding x and y values. Then the extended table would look as follows:

X^2	X	Y	Y^2	XY
x_1^2	x_1	y_1	y_1^2	$x_1 y_1$
x_2^2	x_2	y_2	y_2^2	$x_2 y_2$
.	.	.	.	.
.	.	.	.	.
.	.	.	.	.
x_n^2	x_n	y_n	y_n^2	$x_n y_n$
$\sum_{i=1}^{n} x_i^2$	$\sum_{i=1}^{n} x_i$	$\sum_{i=1}^{n} y_i$	$\sum_{i=1}^{n} y_i^2$	$\sum_{i=1}^{n} x_i y_i$

Substituting the entries of the last row of this table into equations (8.47), (8.49), and (8.50) will provide a numerical value for the sample statistics r, a, and b. As is the case with r, the sample statistics a and b are also random variables and we need to find their sampling distributions to be used in appropriate Inferential Analysis.

■ The Sampling Distribution of r

The sample correlation coefficient r is a random variable and as such has a sampling distribution which is symmetric only when ρ (the population correlation coefficient) is zero (*i.e.*, when $\rho = 0$) and it is skewed when $\rho \neq 0$.

For a Normal Bivariate population (*i.e.*, if X and Y are Jointly Normally Distributed), the distribution of r approaches a Normal distribution as $n \to \infty$.

There are, however, two transformed values of r, given by Q and Z_r below, which have known distributions and can be used for Inferential Analysis.

1. When $\rho = 0$ the transformation, $Q = \dfrac{r\sqrt{n-2}}{\sqrt{1-r^2}}$ \qquad (8.53)

makes Q into a t variable with $n - 2$ degrees of freedom. We will use this fact when we discuss the sample correlation coefficient in greater detail in Chapter 13.

2. When $\rho \neq 0$ another transformation, called the "Z-transformation" makes r behave like a Normal variable.

The Z-transformation is given by:

$$Z_r = \frac{1}{2} \ln \frac{1+r}{1-r} \tag{8.54}$$

where Z_r is a Normally distributed variable with:

$$E(Z_r) = Z\rho \tag{8.55}$$

and

$$V(Z_r) = \frac{1}{n-3}, \tag{8.56}$$

where n = sample size

The same relationship which holds true for r and Z_r, given by equation (8.54), also holds true for ρ and Z_ρ, and we write:

$$Z\rho = \frac{1}{2}\left(\frac{1+\rho}{1-\rho}\right) \tag{8.57}$$

Note: ρ = Population Correlation Coefficient
r = Sample Correlation Coefficient

The interpretation to be attached to equation (8.54) is that if repeated Bivariate data of size n are obtained, the sample correlation coefficient r_i is calculated for each data set, then the Z_{r_i} obtained from equation (8.54) are approximately Normally distributed with $E(Z_r)$ and $V(Z_r)$ as stated above.

We will use equation (8.54) when making inferences on the population correlation coefficient ρ and demonstrate its application with examples in Chapter 13 (Bivariate Analysis).

■ The Sampling Distribution of *a*

It can be shown that, under the stated conditions in the derivation of the linear regression model, using the least squares methodology, the sampling distribution of a is Normally distributed with:

$$E(a) = \alpha \tag{8.58}$$

$$V(a) = \left[\frac{\displaystyle\sum_{i=1}^{n} x_i^2}{n \displaystyle\sum_{i=1}^{n}\left(x_i - \overline{X}\right)^2} \right] \hat{\sigma}^2 \tag{8.59}$$

where α is the population Y-intercept, and $\hat{\sigma}^2$ is the sample variance of regression, to be defined in Chapter 13.

If the origin of the coordinate system is chosen so that $\overline{X} = 0$, then $V(a)$ becomes:

$$V(a) = \frac{\hat{\sigma}^2}{n} \tag{8.60}$$

Equations (8.58), (8.59) and (8.60) will be used to make inferences on the regression population parameter α, as will be demonstrated through examples in Chapter 13. If the sample size n, is not sufficiently large (*i.e.*, if $n < 30$) then the distribution of a becomes t, instead of Z, with $n - 2$ degrees of freedom.

■ The Sampling Distribution of *b*

Similarly, it can be shown, that the sampling distribution of b (the slope of the regression line) is, under the stated assumptions, Normally distributed with:

$$E(b) = \beta \tag{8.61}$$

$$V(b) = \frac{\hat{\sigma}^2}{\sum_{i=1}^{n}(x_i - \overline{X})^2} \tag{8.62}$$

where β is the population slope.

Equations (8.61) and (8.62) will be used to make inferences on the population slope (β) and this will be illustrated through examples in Chapter 13. If the sample size n is less than 30, then the sampling distribution of b is t_{n-2} (*i.e.*, t with $n-2$ degrees of freedom) and it shall be used, when making inference on β, instead of the Z distribution (Normal).

■ Sampling Distribution of the Range

Since the range, R, is defined as the difference between the high and low values in a ranked data set (*i.e.*, $R = X_{HIGH} - X_{LOW}$), the sampling distributions of R is obtained in terms of "ordered" statistics. We proceed as follows:

Let $X_1, X_2, \ldots, X_n$ be a set of n independent random variables obtained from a population of interest. Now we can write the range, R, as:

$$R = V - U \tag{8.63}$$

where
$$V = \text{maximum } (X_1, X_2, \ldots, X_n) \tag{8.64}$$
$$U = \text{minimum } (X_1, X_2, \ldots, X_n) \tag{8.65}$$

It can be shown that the joint distribution function $F_{u,v}(U, V)$ is given by:

$$F_{U,V}(U,V) = \begin{cases} \big[F(V)\big]^n & \text{if } U \geq V \\ \big[F(V)\big]^n - \big[F(V) - F(U)\big]^n & \text{if } U < V \end{cases} \tag{8.66}$$

Then the joint probability density function of U and V is obtained by differentiation and is given by:

$$f_{U,V}(U,V) = \begin{cases} 0 & \text{if } U \geq V \\ n(n-1)\big[F(V) - F(U)\big]^{n-2} f(U)f(V) & \text{if } U < V \end{cases} \tag{8.67}$$

Then the probability density function of the range R of n independent continuous random variables, whose individual distribution functions are all equal to $F(X)$ and whose individual probability density functions are all equal to $f(X)$, is obtained by replacing U by $V - X$ (since $R = X = V - U$ from which it follows that $U = V - X$) in (8.67) and then integrating with respect to V, to obtain:

$$f_R(X) = \int_{-\infty}^{\infty} f_{U,V}(V - X, V) \, dV \tag{8.68}$$

$$= \begin{cases} 0 & \text{for } X < 0 \\ n(n-1)\int_{-\infty}^{\infty} \big[F(V) - F(V-X)\big]^{n-2} f(V-X)f(V)dV & \text{for } X > 0 \end{cases} \tag{8.69}$$

The CDF of R is then given by:

$$F_R(X) = \begin{cases} 0 & \text{if } X < 0 \\ n\displaystyle\int_{-\infty}^{\infty}\left[F(V) - F(V - X)\right]^{n-1}f(V)dV & \text{if } X > 0 \end{cases} \tag{8.70}$$

Equations (8.69) and (8.70) can be evaluated explicitly only in a few cases, such as that in which each random variable $X_1, X_2, \ldots, X_n$ is uniformly distributed in the interval 0 to 1. Then, from (8.69) we obtain, since $f(x) = 1$ and $F(x) = x$:

$$f_R(X) = \begin{cases} 0 & \text{for all other } X \text{ values} \\ n(n - 1)X^{n-2}(1-X) & \text{for } 0 \le X \le 1 \end{cases} \tag{8.71}$$

8.5 Concluding Remarks

We have tried to include in this chapter the sampling distributions of as many Sample statistics as possible but we are aware that many have not been included, such as the sampling distributions of the Mode, the Quartiles, the Percentiles, etc. Some of these are difficult to obtain but, even if this was not the case, we would have to exclude many to make this chapter of manageable size.

8.6 References

Berenson, Marc, L., Levine, David, M., and Krehbiel, Timothy, C., 2004. *Basic Business Statistics*. 9th Edition. Pearson-Prentice Hall.

Black, Ken, 2004. *Business Statistics*. 4th Edition. Wiley.

Canavos, George, C., 1984. *Applied Probability and Statistical Methods*. Little, Brown.

Carlson, William, L., and Thorne, Betty, 1997. *Applied Statistical Methods*. Prentice Hall.

Chou, Ya-lun, 1992. *Statistical Analysis for Business and Economics*. Elsevier.

Freund, John, E., and Williams, Frank, J., 1969. *Modern Business Statistics*. Revised by: Perles, Benjamin and Sullivan, Charles. Prentice-Hall.

Freund, John, E., and Williams, Frank, J., 1982. *Elementary Business Statistics: The Modern approach*. Prentice-Hall.

Johnson, Robert, 1973. *Elementary Statistics*. Duxbury Press.

McClave, James, T., Benson, George, P., and Sincich, Terry, 2001. *Statistics for Business and Economics*. 8th Edition. Prentice Hall.

Salvatore, Dominick, *Theory and Problems of Statistics and Econometrics*. SCHAUM'S OUTLINE SERIES, McGraw-Hill.

Steel, Robert, G.D., and Torrie, James, H., 1976. *Introduction to Statistics*. McGraw-Hill.

8.7 PROBLEMS

1. A small plane will take 4 passengers, in addition to the pilot. The safe payload for the 4 passengers is 720 pounds. Assuming that the 4 passengers are selected at random from a normal population, with mean weight (μ) of 150 pounds and a standard deviation (σ) of 30 pounds, what is the probability that the 4 passengers will overload the plane?

2. A die is tossed 72 times. What is the probability that

$$S = X_1 + X_2 + \cdots + X_{72} = \sum_{i=1}^{72} X_i \text{ will be equal to or less than 281?}$$

3. The weight of fourth grade students can be represented by the random variable X with $E(X) = 48 = \mu$ pounds. If a random sample of $n = 36$, $X_1, X_2, \ldots, X_{36}$, produced a sample standard deviation $\hat{s} = 3$, find the:

   a) Probability that $\bar{x}$ is more than 49 pounds.

   b) Probability that $\bar{x}$ is less than 47.5 pounds.

   c) Probability that $\bar{x}$ is between 47 and 49.

   d) Probability that $\bar{x}$ is exactly equal to 50 pounds.

4. A sample of 64 steel wires from factory A produced a mean breaking strength of 1200 pounds, with sample standard deviation equal to 50 pounds, and a sample of 81 steel wires from factor B produced a mean breaking strength of 1160 pounds and a sample standard deviation of 45 pounds. Find the following probabilities, if it is believed that the 2 factories produce steel wires with equal mean strength:

   a) Probability that $\Delta\bar{x} = \bar{x}_1 - \bar{x}_2$ is greater than 16 pounds.

   b) Probability that $\Delta\bar{x}$ is less than 8 pounds.

   c) Probability that $\Delta\bar{x}$ is between 10 and 12 pounds.

5. A random sample of 200 items is drawn from a large population for which it is known that the population proportion (π) of good items is 90%. What is the probability that the sample proportion, p, will be between 0.85 an 0.95? (Ignore the Continuity Correction Factor = CCF).

6. A college has 100 faculty members, 60 of whom have doctoral degrees. Two samples, with $n_1 = n_2 = 32$ are drawn from this faculty independently, with replacement, and the numbers having doctoral degrees are noted. Ignoring the CCF, what is the probability that the 2 samples will differ by 8 or more in the numbers with the doctoral degrees?

7. If μ is to be estimated by the median of a random sample of size n from a population (having the shape of a normal curve), how large must n be so that this estimate is equally as reliable as another estimate of μ based on the mean of a random sample of size 64?

8. When we sample from an infinite population, what happens to the standard error of the mean if the sample size is:

   a) increased from 25 to 225;

   b) Increased from 100 to 225;

   c) decreased from 625 to 100?

9. a) Show that if the mean of a random sample of size n is used to estimate the mean of an infinite population with the standard deviation σ, there is a fifty-fifty chance that the error, *i.e.*, $\varepsilon = \bar{x} - \mu$ is less than $0.6745 \dfrac{\sigma}{\sqrt{n}}$. This is called the probable error of the mean.

   b) What is the probable error of the mean if $n = 64$ and $\sigma = 16$?

10. It is stated that the weights of all air travelers has a mean of 160 pounds and a standard deviation of 20. What is the probability that the combined gross weight of 144 such passengers will exceed 23,300 pounds?

11. The mean of a random sample of size $n = 256$ is used to estimate the mean of an infinite population, which has a population standard deviation of $\sigma = 3.2$

   a) Using Chebychev's theorem, what is the probability that the error of estimation $(\varepsilon = \bar{x} - \mu)$ will be less than 0.4?

   b) Using the Central Limit Theorem, what is the probability that the error of estimation $(\varepsilon = \bar{x} - \mu)$ will be less than 0.4?

12. The mean of a random sample of size $n = 49$ is used to estimate the mean (μ) of a very large population of electronic components, which has a standard deviation of $\sigma = 42$ hours. Using the central limit theorem, what is the probability that our estimate will be "off" by: a) less than 12 hours? b) greater than 15 hours?

13. Random samples of size $n = 2$ are drawn from the finite population which consists of the numbers: 2, 4, 6, 8.

   a) Calculate the mean (μ) and variance (σ^2) of this population.

   b) Draw all the possible samples of size $n = 2$ that can be drawn from this population, without replacement, and find the sampling distribution of $\bar{x}$, $E(\bar{x})$, and $\sigma(\bar{x})$.

   c) Compare the results of $E(\bar{x})$ and $\sigma(\bar{x})$ with the expected theoretical results.

14. The weights of all packages shipped by air freight are normally distributed with a mean value of $\mu = 10$ pounds and a standard deviation of 2 pounds. What is the probability that the combined weights of 64 such packages exceed 688 pounds?

15. An appliance store carries three different brands of refrigerators. Let X_1, X_2 and X_3 be random variables representing monthly sales volumes for the three brands at this store. If X_1, X_2 and X_3 are independent normally distributed random variables with means $\mu_1 = \$8,000$, $\mu_2 = \$15,000$, $\mu_3 = \$12,000$ and standard deviations $\sigma_1 = \$2,000$, $\sigma_2 = \$5,000$, $\sigma_3 = \$3,000$, determine that, for a particular month, the total sales volume for all refrigerators:

   a) Will be less than $50,000

   b) Will exceed $50,000

   c) Will be between $38,000 and $45,000

16. For a certain aptitude test, it is known from past experience that that the average score is 1000 with standard deviation 250. If the test is administered to 400 students, randomly selected, find: a) $P(985 < \bar{x} < 1015)$; b) $P(\bar{x} < 975)$; c) $P(\bar{x} > 1025)$

17. A federal inspector for weights and measures visits a packaging plant to determine if the net weight of the packages is as indicated on the package. The plant manager assures the inspector that the average weight is 800 grams with a standard deviation of 10. The inspector selects 64 packages at random, and determines their average weight. What is the probability that $\bar{x}$ will be greater than 803 grams?

18. When producing a certain material, it is known that the standard deviation of the breaking strength of the material is $\sigma = 21$. What is the population average (μ) breaking strength, based on a random sample of 49 specimens, if it is known that the probability of the sample mean exceeding 230 pounds is 0.95?

19. In a survey of 500 TV viewers, there were 230 women, who watched an average of 24.2 hours per week and 270 men who watched an average of 23.6 hours per week. If the standard deviations of times were 6 and 7 hours, respectively;

   a) What is the standard deviation of the sample difference $(\Delta\bar{x} = \bar{x}_W - \bar{x}_M)$ in the mean times watched?

b) What is the probability that $\Delta\bar{x}$ is between 0.5 and 1.0 minute, if it is assumed that men and women watch an equal number of hours of TV per week?

20. A sample of 520 of the 5000 employees of a company is taken to determine the amount of time spent in commuting to and from work. If the standard deviation of such times is 15 for both male and female employees,

   a) Find $\sigma(\Delta\bar{x}) = \sigma(\bar{x}_M - \bar{x}_F)$ if the sample contains 320 male and 200 female employees.

   b) Find the probability that $\Delta\bar{x}$ is more than 8 minutes if it is known that $\Delta\mu = \mu_M - \mu_F = 5$.

21. If a random sample of $n = 16$ is drawn from a normal distribution with unknown mean, μ, and variance, σ^2, find:

   a) $P(\hat{s}^2/\sigma^2 \le 0.57)$;

   b) $P(\hat{s}^2/\sigma^2 \le 1.833)$; and

   c) $P(\hat{s}^2/\sigma^2 \le 2.0407)$

22. A cigarette manufacturer claims that one of its brands has an average nicotine content of 0.6 mg per cigarette. A random sample of 16 such cigarettes was selected and the nicotine content was measured. It was found that the sample average $(\bar{x})$ and sample standard deviation $(\hat{s})$ were 0.75 and 0.175 respectively. If we assume that the amount of nicotine is a normal variable, how likely is the sample result, given the manufacturers claim?

23. The variation in the number of units of a product that 2 operators A and B are turning out daily should be the same (i.e., $\sigma_A^2 = \sigma_B^2$). If a random sample of $n_A = 16$ days produced a standard deviation of $\hat{s}_A = 8.2$ units and a random sample of $n_B = 21$ days produced a standard deviation of $\hat{s}_B = 5.8$ units, do we have reason to believe that the variances are equal?

24. Random samples of size 2 are taken from the finite population which consists of the numbers: 6, 7, 8, 9, 10, 11

   a) Find the mean and standard deviation of this population.

   b) How many possible random samples of size 2 can be drawn from this population;

      i) Without repetition, ii) With repetition.

   c) List the possible random samples and use them to derive the sampling distribution of $\bar{x}$

   d) Calculate the mean of $\bar{x}$ and variance of $\bar{x}$, and compare results against those expected from theory.

25. For problem 8.24 find the sampling distribution of the median $x_{0.5}$, and calculate $E(x_{0.5})$ and $V(x_{0.5})$.

26. For problem 8.24 find the sampling distribution of R, and also calculate $E(R)$ and $V(R)$.

27. For problem 8.24, find the sampling distribution of the unbiased sample variance, $\hat{s}^2$, and also find $E(\hat{s}^2)$ and $V(\hat{s}^2)$. Is $E(\hat{s}^2) = \sigma^2$?

28. What is the probability that the difference between the sample mean $(\bar{x})$ and population mean will be less than 3 if we take a random sample of size $n = 16$ from an infinite population with a known standard deviation $\sigma = 4$?

29. The mean of a random sample of size $n = 64$ is used to estimate the mean life-time of a given brand of light bulbs. If it is known that the population standard deviation is $\sigma = 32$ hours, what is the probability that the error will be:

   a) Less than 8 hours?

   b) Greater than 12 hours?

30. What happens to the standard error of the mean, when sampling from an infinite population with standard deviation σ if the sample size is:

    a) Increased from $n = 49$ to $n = 196$?

    b) Decrease from $n = 324$ to $n = 36$?

31. The mean of a random sample of size $n = 64$ is used to estimate the mean of a population having a normal distribution with the standard deviation $\sigma = 12$. What is the probability that the standard error of the mean will be less than 3, if we use:

    a) Chebychev's Theorem; b) The Central Limit Theorem

32. An automobile inspection station employs 36 workers with varying job working experience. If we let X = number of weeks employed at the station and Y = number of cars inspected in a given day, the following data was collected:

    $$n = 36, \ \sum x_i = 72, \ \sum x_i^2 = 216, \ \sum y_i = 144, \ \sum y_i^2 = 784, \ \sum x_i y_i = 360$$

    a) Solve the normal equations to find the equation of the least squares line which will enable us to predict Y in terms of X.

    b) Calculate σ^2, $\sigma(a)$, and $\sigma(b)$.

    c) Determine the sampling distribution of a and b.

    d) What is the probability that a is between 1 and 3, if $E(a) = 2$?

    e) What is the probability that b is between 0.5 and 1.5, if $E(b) = 1$?

33. The following table shows the midterm (X) and final examination (Y) grades of eight students in a statistics course.

X	75	55	39	60	81	87	61	70
Y	80	58	57	66	72	90	52	76

    a) Find the lest–squares line which will enable us to predict the final examination grade (Y) from the midterm grade (X).

    b) Use the equation in part (A) to predict the final examination grade (Y) for a student who got a 68 on the midterm test.

    c) Calculate σ^2, $\sigma(a)$, and $\sigma(b)$.

    d) Determine the sampling distributions of a and b.

    e) What is the probability that a is between 22 and 25 if $a = a_0 = 20$.

    f) What is the probability that b is between 0.5 and 2 if $b = b_0 = 1$.

34. The men who reported for the U. S. Olympic Team volleyball trials had a mean weight of 195 lbs with a standard deviation of 18 lbs, a mean height of 6'2" with a standard deviation of 6", and a mean vertical jumping ability of 30" with a standard deviation of 9". The coach plans to have the men scrimmage on 6-man teams to observe the talent

    a) What is the probability that the average weight of a scrimmaging team is below 190 lbs?

    b) What is the probability that the average height of a scrimmaging team will be between 6' and 6' 4"?

    c) What is the probability that the average vertical jumping ability of a scrimmaging team will be above 32"?

35. The obstetrics ward of a hospital averages delivering 15 babies per day with a standard deviation of $\sigma = 4$ babies, and the number of babies delivered is a normally distributed variable.

a) What is the probability that in a sample of 1 day between 14 and 16 babies will be delivered?

b) What is the probability that in a sample of 2 days the average number of babies delivered will be between 14 and 16?

c) What is the probability that in a sample of 3 days the average number of babies delivered will be between 14 and 16?

d) Explain the difference in the answers.

36. A complex electronic process generates the following five responses: $-4, -2, 0, 2, 4$, with the same probability. Construct the sampling distribution for the sample mean, for samples of size $n = 2$. Assume sampling *with* replacement.

37. A complex electronic process generates the following five responses: $-4, -2, 0, +2, +4$, with equal probability. Construct the sampling distribution for the sample means, for samples of size $n = 2$. Assume sampling *without* replacement.

38. A random sample of size $n = 36$ is drawn from a population with a mean of 278. If 86% of the time the sample mean is less than 280, what is the population standard deviation?

39. A random sample of size $n = 81$ is drawn form a population with a standard deviation of 12. If only 17.88% of the time a sample mean greater than 300 is obtained, what is the population mean?

40. If a population proportion is known to be $\pi = 0.28$, and if a random sample of $n = 140$ is drawn from this population, what value of the sample proportion, p, will be less 30% of the time?

SOLUTIONS

1. We are looking for $P(S > 720)$, where $S = X_1 + X_2 + X_3 + X_4$ and each X_i is normal with $E(X_i) = 150$ and $\sigma(X_i) = 30$. The sampling distribution of S is normal because, even though $n = 4 < 30$, σ is known, (we also know that each X_i is normal and S being a linear combination of normally distributed variables is also normal) with $E(S) = 4\mu = 4(150) = 600$ and $V(S) = 4\sigma^2 = 4(30)^2 = 4(900) = 3600$,

and $\sigma(S) = \sqrt{V(S)} = \sqrt{3600} = 60$. Therefore,

$$P(S > 720) = P\left[\frac{S - E(S)}{\sigma(S)} > \frac{720 - 600}{60}\right]$$

$$= P\left[Z > \frac{120}{60}\right]$$

$$= P(Z > 2)$$

$$= 0.5 - P(0 < Z < 2) = 0.5 - 0.4772 = 0.0228$$

2. We are looking for $P(S \leq 281)$ where $S = X_1 + X_2 + \cdots + X_{72}$.

Since $n = 120 > 30$, the sampling distribution of S is normal with:
$E(S) = n\mu = 72(21/6) = 72(21) = 252$,

$$V(S) = n\sigma^2 = 72\left(\frac{105}{36}\right) = 2(105) = 210 \text{ and}$$

$\sigma(S) = \sqrt{V(S)} = \sqrt{210} = 14.49138$,

where μ and σ^2 come from the die experiments with:

$$\mu_1 = \mu_2 = \cdots = \mu_{72} = \mu = E(X) = \sum_{i=i}^{6} x_i \cdot p(x_i)$$

$$= 1(1/6) + 2(1/6) + 3(1/6) + 4(1/6) + 5(1/6) + 6(1/6) = \frac{21}{6}.$$

$$E(X^2) = \sum_{i=i}^{6} x_i^2 \cdot p(x_i) = 1^2(1/6) + 2^2(1/6) + 3^2(1/6) + 4^2(1/6)$$

$$+ 5^2(1/6) + 6^2(1/6) = \frac{91}{6},$$

and $V(X) = \sigma^2 = E(X^2) - [E(X)]^2 = 91/6 - (21/6)^2 = 105/36.$

Then: $P(S \le 281) = P\left[\dfrac{S - E(S)}{\sigma(S)} \le \dfrac{271 - 252}{14.49138} \approx \dfrac{281 - 252}{14.5} = \dfrac{29}{14.5}\right]$

$$= P(Z \le 2)$$

$$= P[-\infty < Z < 0] + P(0 < Z < 2)$$

$$= 0.5 + 0.4772 = 0.9772$$

3. Because $n = 36 > 30$, the sampling distribution of $\bar{x}$ is normal, with:
$E(\bar{x}) = \mu = 48$ and $\sigma(\bar{x}) = \hat{s}/\sqrt{n} = 3/\sqrt{36} = 1/2$. Then

a) $P(\bar{x} > 49) = P\left(\dfrac{\bar{x} - E(\bar{x})}{\sigma(\bar{x})} > \dfrac{49 - 48}{1/2}\right) = P\left(Z > \dfrac{1}{1/2}\right) = P[Z > 2]$

$$= P[0 < Z < \infty] - P[0 < Z < 2] = 0.5 - 0.4772 = 0.0228.$$

b) $P(\bar{x} < 47.5) = P\left(Z < \dfrac{47.5 - 48}{1/2}\right) = P\left(Z < \dfrac{-1/2}{1/2}\right)$

$$= P(Z < -1) = P(Z > 1) = P(0 < Z < \infty) - P(0 < Z < 1)$$

$$= 0.5 - 0.3413 = 0.1587$$

c) $P(47 < \bar{x} < 49) = P\left(\dfrac{47 - 48}{1/2} < \dfrac{\bar{x} - E(\bar{x})}{\sigma(\bar{x})} < \dfrac{49 - 48}{1/2}\right)$

$$= P[-2 < Z < 2] = 2P(Z < 2) = 2P(0 < Z < 2)$$
$$= 2(0.4772) = 0.9544$$

d) $P(\bar{x} = 50) = P\left(Z = \dfrac{50 - 48}{1/2}\right) = P(Z = 4) = 0$, because $\bar{x}$ is a continuous
variable and the probability that it is equal to any specific value is always equal to
zero because: $P(\bar{x} = Q) = \dfrac{n(\bar{x} = Q)}{n(S)} = \dfrac{1}{\infty} = 0$

4. The sampling distribution of $\Delta\bar{x}$ is normal because $n_1 = 64 > 30$ and $n_2 = 81 > 30$,
with: $E(\Delta\bar{x}) = E(\bar{x}_1) - E(\bar{x}_2) = \mu_1 - \mu_2 = \Delta\mu = 0$ and

$$\sigma(\Delta\bar{x}) = \sqrt{\dfrac{\hat{s}_1^2}{n_1} + \dfrac{\hat{s}_2^2}{n_2}} + \sqrt{\dfrac{50^2}{64} + \dfrac{45^2}{81}}$$

$$= \sqrt{39.0625 + 25} = \sqrt{64.0625} = 8.004 \approx 8$$

a) $P(\Delta\bar{x} > 16) = P\left(\dfrac{\Delta\bar{x} - E(\Delta\bar{x})}{\sigma(\Delta\bar{x})} > \dfrac{16 - 0}{8}\right) = P\left(Z > \dfrac{16}{8}\right) = P[Z > 2]$

$$= P[0 < Z < \infty] - P[0 < Z < 2] = 0.5 - 0.4772 = 0.0228$$

b) $P(\Delta \bar{x} < 8) = P\left(\dfrac{\Delta \bar{x} - E(\Delta \bar{x})}{\sigma(\Delta \bar{x})} < \dfrac{8-0}{8}\right) = P[Z < 1] = P[-\infty < Z < 0]$

$$+ \; P[0 < Z < 1] = 0.5 + 0.3413 = 0.8413$$

c) $P(10 < \bar{x} < 12) = P\left(\dfrac{10-0}{8} < \dfrac{\Delta \bar{x} - 0}{\sigma(\bar{x})} < \dfrac{12-0}{8}\right) = P\left[\dfrac{10}{8} < Z < \dfrac{12}{8}\right]$

$$= P[1.25 < Z < 1.5] = P[0 < Z < 1.5] - P[0 < Z < 1.25]$$

$$= 0.4332 - 0.3944 = 0.0388$$

5. The sampling distribution of p is normal because $n = 200 > 30$, with

$$E(p) = \pi = 0.9 \text{ and } \sigma(p) = \sqrt{\dfrac{\pi(1-\pi)}{n}} = \sqrt{\dfrac{0.9(0.1)}{200}} = \sqrt{\dfrac{0.09}{200}}$$

$$= \sqrt{0.00045} = 0.0212. \text{ Then}$$

$$P(0.85 < p \leq 0.95) = \left(\dfrac{0.85 - 0.90}{0.0212} \leq \dfrac{p - \pi}{\sigma(p)} < \dfrac{0.95 - 0.90}{0.0212}\right)$$

$$= P[-2.36 < Z < 2.36] = P[-2.36 < Z < 0] + P[0 < Z < 2.36]$$

$$= 2p[0 < Z < 2.36] = 2(0.4909) = 0.9818$$

6. The sampling distribution of $\Delta p = p_1 - p_2$ is normal because $n_1 = 32 > 30$ and

$n_2 = 32 > 30$, with $\sigma(\Delta p) = \sqrt{\dfrac{\pi_1(1-\pi_1)}{n_1} + \dfrac{\pi_2(1-\pi_2)}{n_2}}$

$$= \sqrt{\dfrac{0.6(0.4)}{32} + \dfrac{0.6(0.4)}{32}} \text{ or } \sigma(\Delta p) = \sqrt{2\left(\dfrac{0.6(0.4)}{32}\right)}$$

$$= \sqrt{\dfrac{1}{16}(0.24)} = \sqrt{0.015} = 0.12247, \text{ and}$$

$$E(\Delta p) = \Delta \pi = 0.$$

Then

$$P\left[-\dfrac{8}{32} < \Delta P < \dfrac{8}{32}\right] = P[-0.25 < \Delta P < 0.25]$$

$$= P\left[\dfrac{-0.25 - 0}{0.12247} \leq \dfrac{\Delta \pi - 0}{\sigma(\Delta p)} < \dfrac{0.25}{0.12247}\right]$$

$$= P[-2.04 < Z < 2.04] = 2P[0 < Z < 2.04]$$

$$= 2(0.4793) = 0.9586.$$

Therefore:

$$P\left(\Delta p > \dfrac{8}{12}\right) + P\left(\Delta p < -\dfrac{8}{32}\right) = 1 - P[-2.04 < Z < 2.04]$$

$$= 1 - 0.9586 = 0.0414.$$

7. The standard error of the mean is given by: $\sigma(\bar{x}) = \dfrac{\sigma}{\sqrt{n}}$, while the standard error of

the median is given by: $\sigma(x_{0.5}) = \sqrt{\dfrac{\pi}{2}} \cdot \dfrac{\sigma}{\sqrt{n}} \approx 1.25 \cdot \dfrac{\sigma}{\sqrt{n}}$. Since we must have:

$\sqrt{\dfrac{\pi}{2}} \cdot \dfrac{\sigma}{\sqrt{n}} = \dfrac{\sigma}{\sqrt{64}}$, we obtain: $\sqrt{\dfrac{\pi}{2}} \cdot \dfrac{1}{\sqrt{n}} = \dfrac{1}{8}$

$$\text{or: } \sqrt{n} = 8\sqrt{\frac{\pi}{2}} \text{ or } n = 64\,(\pi/2)$$

$$= 32\pi$$

$$\approx 32\,(3.14) = 100$$

8. The standard error of the mean $= \sigma(\bar{x}) = \dfrac{\sigma}{\sqrt{n}}$; Then:

a) $\sigma_1(\bar{x}) = \dfrac{\sigma}{\sqrt{n_1}} = \dfrac{\sigma}{\sqrt{25}} = \dfrac{\sigma}{5}$ and $\sigma_2(\bar{x}) = \dfrac{\sigma}{\sqrt{n_2}} = \dfrac{\sigma}{\sqrt{225}} = \dfrac{\sigma}{15}$

and $\sigma_2(\bar{x})/\sigma_1(\bar{x}) = \dfrac{\sigma/15}{\sigma/5} = \dfrac{5}{15} = \dfrac{1}{3}$; or it is divided by 3

b) $\sigma_1(\bar{x}) = \dfrac{\sigma}{\sqrt{100}} = \dfrac{\sigma}{10}$ and $\sigma_2(\bar{x}) = \dfrac{\sigma}{\sqrt{225}} = \dfrac{\sigma}{15}$;

Since: $\sigma_2(\bar{x})/\sigma_1(\bar{x}) = \dfrac{\sigma/15}{\sigma/10} = \dfrac{10}{15} = \dfrac{2}{3}$; or it is divided by 1.5

c) $\sigma_1(\bar{x}) = \dfrac{\sigma}{\sqrt{625}} = \dfrac{\sigma}{25}$ and $\sigma_2(\bar{x}) = \dfrac{\sigma}{\sqrt{100}} = \dfrac{\sigma}{10}$;

Since: $\sigma_2(\bar{x})/\sigma_1(\bar{x}) = \dfrac{\sigma/10}{\sigma/25} = \dfrac{25}{10} = 2.5$ or it is multiplied by 2.5

9. a) To include 50% of the area under the standard normal distribution we need to calculate the Z-values for which $P(0 < Z < ?) = 0.25$ and $P(-? < Z < 0) = 0.25$. The values closest to ? is 0.67 (which corresponds to 0.2486) and 0.68 (which corresponds to 0.2517). Therefore, when the Z-values differ by 0.01, the areas differ by: $0.2517 - 0.2486 = 0.0031$. Now if we want the areas to differ by: $0.0014 = 0.5 - 0.2486$, by how much (X) should the Z-values differ?

Interpolating, we obtain: $\dfrac{X}{0.01} = \dfrac{0.0014}{0.0031}$, or $X = 0.0045$. Therefore, the Z-value we are looking for is $= 0.67 + 0.0045 = 0.6745$

b) Probable error $= 0.6745\,\dfrac{\sigma}{\sqrt{n}} = 0.6745\,\dfrac{16}{8} = 0.6745\,(2) = 1.349$

10. The sampling distribution of $S = X_1 + X_2 + \cdots + X_{144}$ is normally distributed because $n = 144$ (and also $\sigma = 20$ is known), with: $E(S) = n\mu = 144\,(160) = 23{,}040$ and $\sigma(S) = \sqrt{n\sigma^2} = \sqrt{144(20)^2} = \sqrt{144 \times 400} = \sqrt{57{,}600} = 240$.

Then

$$P(S > 23{,}300) = P\!\left(\frac{S - E(S)}{\sigma(S)} > \frac{23{,}300 - 23{,}040}{240}\right) = P\!\left(Z > \frac{260}{240}\right)$$

$$P(Z > 1.083) = 0.5 - P(0 < Z < 1.083) = 0.5 - 0.4664 = 0.0336.$$

9 Estimation Theory

The Sampling Distributions of the Descriptive Statistics (such as $\bar{x}$, $\Delta\bar{x} = \bar{x}_1 - \bar{x}_2$, p, $\Delta p = p_1 - p_2$, and others) include unknown parameters which need to be assigned numerical values before such sampling distributions can be used for decision-making.

The assignment of numerical values to the unknown population parameters (such as: μ, $\Delta\mu = \mu_1 - \mu_2$, π, and $\Delta\pi = \pi_1 - \pi_2$) is accomplished by the use of estimators whose numerical values depend on the given sample data.

In this chapter we define two types of estimators: Point estimators and Interval estimators, and study their properties and characteristics, and their applications.

First we specify the desirable characteristics of Point estimators, learn how such estimators can be derived, and then identify the BEST Point estimators for the population parameters μ, σ^2, and σ.

Interval estimators (or Confidence Intervals) are then constructed for the population parameters μ, $\Delta\mu$, π and $\Delta\pi$, using their Point estimators $\bar{x}$, $\Delta\bar{x}$, p and Δp, and the fact that these Point estimators are normally distributed when the sample size n is large (*i.e.*, when $n \geq 30$) or $n_1 \geq 30$ and $n_2 \geq 30$ for tests involving the parameters $\Delta\mu$ and $\Delta\pi$.

Finally relationships are derived for each test which determine the required sample size(s) to satisfy a given tolerance.

9.1   Introduction

In the last chapter we discussed the (sampling) distributions of many of the sample (descriptive) statistics we learned how to calculate in Chapter 3. But, knowing the type of density function of a random variable is, usually, not enough to calculate probabilities and use these probabilities for decision-making.

This is so because probability density functions usually include unknown parameters and, before such density functions can be used in a specific application, numerical values must be assigned to these unknown parameters, using the given sample data (*i.e.*, the values: $x_1, x_2, \ldots, x_n$).

For example, if the random variable of interest X is known to be normally distributed, its density function $f(x)$ is given by:

$$f(x) = \frac{1}{\sqrt{2\pi}} \frac{1}{\sigma} e^{-\frac{1}{2\sigma^2}(x - \mu)^2}, \quad -\infty < x < \infty \tag{9.1}$$

and the unknown parameters of this density function are μ, σ, σ^2, and numerical values must be assigned to them.

As a second example suppose the random variable of interest X is known to be binomially distributed. In this case the Probability Mass Function of X, PMF(X) is given by:

$$P(X = x) = \frac{n!}{x!(n - x)!} p^x (1 - p)^{n - x}, \quad \text{where } x = 0, 1, 2, \ldots, n \tag{9.2}$$

and the unknown parameters of this PMF are n and p, and numerical values must be assigned to them.

9.2   Types of Estimators Available

In general, parameter estimation involves the use of sample data, and there are two ways of doing this: Point Estimation and Interval Estimation.

Any sample statistic that is used to estimate a population parameter is called an Estimator. For example, if we decide to use the sample mean, $\overline{x}$, to estimate the population parameter μ, the $\overline{x}$ is an estimator of μ.

A specific value of an estimator, based on a given sample, is called an estimate of the estimator. If a second sample is taken and a new value is calculated for the estimator, we will obtain a second estimate. Clearly, taking more and more samples and calculating new values for the estimator, will produce additional estimates for the estimator. Thus, if the estimator is $\overline{x}$, and its estimates from samples 1, 2, 3, ..., n are, respectively, $\overline{x}_1, \overline{x}_2, \overline{x}_3, \ldots, \overline{x}_n$, these estimates for the estimator $\overline{x}$ represent possible values for $\overline{x}$ and their distribution determines the sampling distribution of $\overline{x}$. In general, the estimator depends only on the sample data, and is free of any population parameter.

As an example $\overline{x}$ is defined, in terms of the sample data $x_1, x_2, \ldots, x_n$, as: $\overline{x} = (x_1 + x_2 + \cdots + x_n)/n$ and, clearly, does not depend on μ or any other population parameter.

An Estimator which assigns a single numerical value to an unknown population parameter is called a Point Estimator. A Point Estimator is often insufficient because it is either right or wrong. It becomes more useful if it is accompanied by an estimate of the error that may be involved.

On the other hand, an Estimator is called an Interval Estimator if it assigns an entire interval of values, with pre-assigned odds, as a value to an unknown population parameter.

For example the statement $P[45 < \mu < 53] = 0.95$ assigns to the population parameter μ the interval of values between 45 and 53 with 95% confidence, in contrast to a Point Estimator which may assign the single value $\mu = 50$ to the unknown parameter μ.

It is possible to use many descriptive statistics to estimate the same unknown population parameter. For example to estimate the unknown population parameter μ, we may use: a) $\overline{x}$ = sample mean, b) $x_{0.5}$ = sample median, or c) x_m = sample mode. Similarly, to estimate the unknown population variance σ^2, we may use: a) $\hat{s}^2$ = unbiased sample variance, and b) s^2 = biased sample variance.

Given this multiple estimator availability for the same population parameter, how does one select the "best" estimator for a population parameter, and what are the "criteria of goodness" on which such a selection is based?

To make it easier to answer these questions, and others that we will encounter in the remainder of this chapter, and all of the next chapter, we introduce the following notation. We let:

1. θ represent any population parameter (such as μ, σ, σ^2, etc.)

2. $\hat{\theta}$ represent an estimator for the population parameter θ (such as $\overline{x}$, $\hat{s}$, $\hat{s}^2$, etc.)

3. $\hat{\theta}_1, \hat{\theta}_2, \ldots, \hat{\theta}_k$ are k estimators (if more than one estimator exists) for the same population parameter θ.

4. $\sigma(\hat{\theta})$ represent the standard deviation of estimator $\hat{\theta}$.

5. $\sigma(\hat{\theta}_1), \sigma(\hat{\theta}_2), \ldots, \sigma(\hat{\theta}_k)$ represent the standard deviations of the k estimators $\hat{\theta}_1, \hat{\theta}_2, \ldots, \hat{\theta}_k$.

6. n represent the sample size.

Then, in general, we can make the statement that an estimator $\hat{\theta}$ of a parameter θ should possess a sampling distribution which is concentrated around, θ and the variance of the estimator should be as small as possible.

Since some estimators are better than others, we need to define a set of criteria which will allow us to select the "best" estimator from a set of estimators, each of which attempts to estimate the same unknown parameter.

9.3   Point Estimators

For a point estimator, $\hat{\theta}$, to be a good point estimator of the unknown population parameter, θ, it should possess a number of desirable properties, such as: Unbiasedness, Consistency, Efficiency, and Sufficiency.

But, to properly introduce these properties and discuss them in a meaningful manner, we first introduce the Mean Square Error of an Estimator.

Suppose $\hat{\theta}$ is an estimator of the population parameter θ. Then, the mean square error of $\hat{\theta}$, is defined as the expected value of the squared difference between $\hat{\theta}$ and θ.

In equation form this becomes:

$$\mathrm{MSE}(\hat{\theta}) = E(\hat{\theta} - \theta)^2, \tag{9.3}$$

and in expanded form:

$$= E(\hat{\theta}^2 - 2\theta\hat{\theta} + \theta^2)$$

$$= E(\hat{\theta}^2) - 2\theta E(\hat{\theta}) + \theta^2 \text{ (since } E(\theta^2) = \theta^2 \text{ because } \theta \text{ is a}$$
$$\text{parameter, } i.e., \text{ a constant)}$$

$$= \underbrace{E(\hat{\theta}^2) - [E(\hat{\theta})]^2}_{V(\hat{\theta})} \; + \; \underbrace{[E(\hat{\theta})]^2 - 2\theta E(\hat{\theta}) + \theta^2}_{[\theta - E(\hat{\theta})]^2}$$

$$\mathrm{MSE}(\hat{\theta}) = V(\hat{\theta}) + [\theta - E(\hat{\theta})]^2 \tag{9.4}$$

$$= V(\hat{\theta}) + (\mathrm{BIAS})^2, \text{ where } \mathrm{BIAS} = \theta - E(\hat{\theta}) \tag{9.5}$$

It is seen that in its expanded form the $\mathrm{MSE}(\hat{\theta})$ is the sum of 2 non-negative quantities, $i.e.$, the variance of the estimator and the square of its Bias. These two quantities are related directly to the desirable properties of an estimator ($i.e.$, its sampling distribution should be concentrated around the parameter and its variance should be as small as possible) as stated previously. This suggests as a possible solution to the problem of selecting as the best estimator of a population parameter the estimator with the smallest mean square error. Unfortunately, the problem is not that simple because, for most density functions $f(x, \theta)$ it is difficult, if not impossible, to find one estimator which minimizes the mean square error for all possible values of the parameter θ. This implies that one estimator may have a minimum mean square error for some values of θ, while another estimator has a minimum mean square error for other values of the parameter θ.

Example 1

Suppose $x_1, x_2, \ldots, x_n$ is a random sample from a distribution in which $E(x_i) = \mu$ and $Var(x_i) = \sigma^2$, for $i = 1, 2, \ldots, n$. Now let us consider the two estimators:

$$\hat{\theta}_1 = \frac{x_1 + x_2 + \cdots + x_n}{n} = \frac{\sum_{i=1}^{n} x_i}{n} \tag{9.6}$$

and

$$\hat{\theta}_2 = \frac{x_1 + x_2 + \cdots + x_n}{n + 2} = \frac{\sum_{i=1}^{n} x_i}{n + 2} \tag{9.7}$$

as possible estimators for the population parameter $\theta(= \mu)$. We will determine the $\mathrm{MSE}(\hat{\theta}_1)$ and $\mathrm{MSE}(\hat{\theta}_2)$ and show that $\mathrm{MSE}(\hat{\theta}_1) < \mathrm{MSE}(\hat{\theta}_2)$ for some values of θ, while for other θ values $\mathrm{MSE}(\hat{\theta}_1) > \mathrm{MSE}(\hat{\theta}_2)$.

For estimator $\hat{\theta}_1$ we have:

$$\text{MSE}(\hat{\theta}_1) = V(\hat{\theta}_1) + [\theta - E(\hat{\theta}_1)]^2 = \frac{\sigma^2}{n}, \tag{9.8}$$

because $V(\hat{\theta}_1) = V(\bar{x}) = \dfrac{\sigma^2}{n}$, while BIAS

$(\hat{\theta}_1) = [\mu - \mu]^2 = 0$, because $E(\hat{\theta}_1) = E(\bar{x}) = \mu$.

For estimator $\hat{\theta}_2$ we have:

$$\text{MSE}(\hat{\theta}_2) = V(\hat{\theta}_2) + [\theta - E(\hat{\theta}_2)]^2$$

Since $E(\hat{\theta}_2) = \dfrac{1}{n+2} E\left[\sum_{i=1}^{n} x_i\right] = \dfrac{1}{n+2}[\mu + \mu + \cdots + \mu] = \dfrac{n\mu}{n+2} \tag{9.9}$

and $V(\hat{\theta}_2) = \left(\dfrac{1}{n+2}\right)^2 V\left[\sum_{i=1}^{n} x_i\right] = \left(\dfrac{1}{n+2}\right)^2 \left[V(x_1) + V(x_2) + \cdots + V(x_n)\right]$

$$= \frac{1}{(n+2)^2}(n\sigma^2) = \frac{n}{(n+2)^2}\sigma^2 \tag{9.10}$$

$$\text{MSE}(\hat{\theta}_2) = \frac{n}{(n+2)^2}\sigma^2 + \left[\mu - \frac{n}{n+2}\mu\right]^2 = \frac{n}{(n+2)^2}\sigma^2 + \mu^2\left(1 - \frac{n}{n+2}\right)^2$$

$$= \frac{n\sigma^2 + 4\mu^2}{(n+2)^2} \tag{9.11}$$

For the $\text{MSE}(\hat{\theta}_1)$ to be greater than the $\text{MSE}(\hat{\theta}_2)$, we must have:

$$\text{MSE}(\hat{\theta}_1) > \text{MSE}(\hat{\theta}_2)$$

or $\qquad \dfrac{\sigma^2}{n} > \dfrac{n\sigma^2 + 4\mu^2}{(n+2)^2}$ or $\sigma^2\left(1 + \dfrac{1}{n}\right) > \mu^2 \tag{9.12}$

Also, for the $\text{MSE}(\hat{\theta}_1)$ to be less than the $\text{MSE}(\hat{\theta}_2)$, we must have:

$$\text{MSE}(\hat{\theta}_1) < \text{MSE}(\hat{\theta}_2)$$

or $\qquad \dfrac{\sigma^2}{n} < \dfrac{n\sigma^2 + 4\mu^2}{(n+2)^2}$ or $\mu^2 > \sigma^2(1 + \dfrac{1}{n}) \tag{9.13}$

Now, if $n = 10$ and $\sigma^2 = 100$, we obtain from (9.12) and (9.13) respectively:

I. If $\mu^2 < 100(1.1)$ or $\mu < \sqrt{110}$, $\text{MSE}(\hat{\theta}_1) > \text{MSE}(\hat{\theta}_2)$ and

II. If $\mu^2 > 100(1.1)$ or $\mu > \sqrt{110}$, $\text{MSE}(\hat{\theta}_1) < \text{MSE}(\hat{\theta}_2)$

Because of this fact, it is necessary to examine additional criteria for choosing the "best" estimator for a population parameter θ. The additional criteria we will examine are: Unbiasedness, consistency, efficiency, and sufficiency.

■ ■ ■

9.3.1 Desirable characteristics of Point Estimators
The four additional criteria mentioned above will be briefly discussed individually and then will be collectively applied in identifying the "best" estimators for several population parameters, such as μ, σ, and σ^2.

9.3.1.1 Unbiasedness

An estimator $\hat{\theta}$ is said to be an unbiased estimator of the population parameter θ if:

$$E(\hat{\theta}) = \theta \tag{9.14}$$

or if the bias of the estimator $\hat{\theta}$, $B(\hat{\theta}) = \theta - E(\hat{\theta})$, is equal to zero.

Since the square of the bias is a component of the mean square of the estimator (and a minimum mean square error is desirable) it is desirable to have an estimator whose mean (or expected value) is equal to the parameter (and this occurs when the Bias of the estimator is equal to zero).

Example 2

1. The sample mean $\bar{x} = \dfrac{\sum\limits_{i=1}^{n} x_i}{n}$ is an unbiased estimator of the population mean μ, because:

$$E(\bar{x}) = E\left[\frac{\sum\limits_{i=1}^{n} x_i}{n}\right] = \frac{1}{n}\sum_{i=1}^{n} E(x_i) = \frac{1}{n}[E(x_1) + E(x_2) + \cdots + E(x_n)]$$

$$= \frac{1}{n}[\mu + \mu + \cdots + \mu] = \frac{1}{n}[n\mu] = \mu, \text{ since } E(x_i) = \mu,$$

2. The unbiased sample variance, $\hat{s}^2 = \dfrac{1}{n-1}\sum\limits_{i=1}^{n}(x_i - \bar{x})^2$, is an unbiased estimator of the population variance, σ^2, because:

$$E(\hat{s}^2) = \frac{1}{n-1}E\left[\sum_{i=1}^{n}\left(x_i^2 - 2\bar{x}x_i + \bar{x}^2\right)\right]$$

$$= \frac{1}{n-1}E\left[\sum_{i=1}^{n}x_i^2 - 2\bar{x}\sum_{i=1}^{n}x_i + \sum_{i=1}^{n}\bar{x}^2\right]$$

$$= \frac{1}{n-1}E\left[\sum_{i=1}^{n}x_i^2 - 2n\bar{x}^2 + n\bar{x}^2\right], \text{ since } \sum_{i=1}^{n}x_i = n\bar{x} \text{ and } \sum_{i=1}^{n}\bar{x}^2 = n\bar{x}^2$$

$$= \frac{1}{n-1}E\left[\sum_{i=1}^{n}x_i^2 - n\bar{x}^2\right] = \frac{1}{n-1}E\left[\sum_{i=1}^{n}x_i^2 - n\left(\frac{\sum\limits_{i=1}^{n}x_i}{n}\right)^2\right]$$

$$= \frac{1}{n-1}\left[\sum_{i=1}^{n}E(x_i^2) - nE(\bar{x}^2)\right]$$

But, since $V(\bar{x}) = \dfrac{\sigma^2}{n} = E(\bar{x}^2) - [E(\bar{x})]^2,$ $\qquad\qquad$ (9.15)

it follows that $E(\bar{x}^2) = \dfrac{\sigma^2}{n} + \mu^2$, since $E(\bar{x}) = \mu$

Then, $E(\hat{s}^2) = \dfrac{1}{n-1}\left[E(x_1^2 + x_2^2 + \cdots + x_n^2) - n\left(\dfrac{\sigma^2}{n} + \mu^2\right)\right]$

$$= \frac{1}{n-1}\left[E(x_1^2) + E(x_2^2) + \cdots + E(x_n^2) - \sigma^2 - n\mu^2\right]$$

$$= \frac{1}{n-1}\left\{\left[(\mu^2 + \sigma^2) + (\mu^2 + \sigma^2) + \cdots + (\mu^2 + \sigma^2)\right] - \sigma^2 - n\mu^2\right\}$$

because $\qquad E(x_i^2) = V(x_i) + [E(x_i)]^2 = \sigma^2 + \mu^2$

Therefore, $\quad E(\hat{s}^2) = \dfrac{1}{n-1}\left[n\mu^2 + n\sigma^2 - \sigma^2 - n\mu^2\right] = \dfrac{1}{n-1}\left[(n-1)\sigma^2\right] = \sigma^2$

and $\hat{s}^2$ is an unbiased estimator of σ^2.

3. The biased sample variance, $s^2 = \dfrac{1}{n}\displaystyle\sum_{i=1}^{n}(x_i - \overline{x})^2$, is a biased estimator of the population variance, σ^2, because:

$$E(\hat{s}^2) = E\left[\dfrac{1}{n}\sum_{i=1}^{n}(x_i - \overline{x})^2\right] = \dfrac{1}{n}E\sum_{i=1}^{n}(x_i - \overline{x})^2 = \dfrac{1}{n}\sum_{i=1}^{n}E(x_i - \overline{x})^2$$

$$= \dfrac{1}{n}\left[(n-1)\sigma^2\right] = \dfrac{n-1}{n}\sigma^2 \neq \sigma^2$$

4. Even though $\hat{s}^2$ is an unbiased estimator of the population variance σ^2, $\hat{s} = \sqrt{\hat{s}^2}$ **is not** an unbiased estimator for the population standard deviation σ because, taking the square root of $\hat{s}^2$, somehow, introduces a bias. We can prove that $\hat{s}$ is not an unbiased estimator of σ as follows:

Assume that $E(\hat{s}) = \sigma$ and $E(\hat{s}^2) = \sigma^2$

Then $\quad V(\hat{s}) = E\left[\hat{s} - E(\hat{s})\right]^2 = E\left[\hat{s} - \sigma\right]^2 = E\left[\hat{s}^2 - 2\sigma\hat{s} + \sigma^2\right]$

$$= E(\hat{s}^2) - 2\sigma E(\hat{s}) + E(\sigma^2) = \sigma^2 - 2\sigma(\sigma) + \sigma^2$$

$$= \sigma^2 - 2\sigma^2 + \sigma^2 = 0$$

But this is impossible since $\hat{s}$ is a random variable, and random variables do not have variances equal to zero (only constants have zero variances).

Therefore, $E(\hat{s}) \neq \sigma$

In fact, $\qquad E(\hat{s}) = c_2\sigma = \left[\sqrt{\dfrac{2}{n}}\dfrac{\left(\dfrac{n-2}{n}\right)!}{\left(\dfrac{n-3}{2}\right)!}\right]\sigma.$ $\qquad$ (9.16)

■ ■ ■

9.3.1.2 Consistency

An estimator $\hat{\theta}$ is said to be a consistent estimator of the population parameter θ if, by letting the sample size n increase, we can make the probability as small as we wish that the estimator $\hat{\theta}$ differs from the parameter it estimates (θ) by more than a previously fixed amount, regardless of how small this amount is. This statement can be written in equation form as:

$$\underset{n\to\infty}{Lim}P\left[|\hat{\theta} - \theta| > \epsilon\right] = 0 \qquad (9.17)$$

This statement implies that the variance of a consistent estimator $\hat{\theta}$ decreases with increasing n and the mean of the sampling distribution of $\hat{\theta}$ approaches θ (the population parameter) as n increases.

Example 3

Since $V(\bar{x}) = \dfrac{\sigma^2}{n}$ and $V(\hat{s}^2) = \dfrac{2\sigma^4}{n-1}$ (shown in Chapter 11) and these variances decrease with n, and $E(\bar{x}) = \mu$ and $E(\hat{s}^2) = \sigma^2$, $\bar{x}$ and $\hat{s}^2$ are consistent estimators of the population parameters μ and σ^2 respectively.

The validity of equation (9.17) can be ascertained by applying Chebychev's inequality (see also Chapter 3) which can be stated as:

$$P\left[|\hat{\theta} - \theta| \le k\sigma\right] \ge 1 - \frac{1}{k^2} \qquad (9.18)$$

or

$$P\left[|\hat{\theta} - \theta| > k\sigma\right] \le \frac{1}{k^2} \qquad (9.19)$$

To prove that $\bar{x}$ is a consistent estimator for the population parameter μ, recall that $\bar{x}$ is a random variable with $E(\bar{x}) = \mu$, $V(\bar{x}) = \dfrac{\sigma^2}{n}$ and $\sigma(\bar{x}) = \dfrac{\sigma}{\sqrt{n}}$.

Then, if we replace $\hat{\theta}$ by $\bar{x}$, θ by μ, and σ by $\dfrac{\sigma}{\sqrt{n}}$ in (9.19) we obtain:

$$P\left[|\bar{x} - \mu| > \frac{k\sigma}{\sqrt{n}}\right] \le \frac{1}{k^2} \qquad (9.20)$$

If we now let $\epsilon = \dfrac{k\sigma}{\sqrt{n}}$, then $k^2 = \dfrac{n\epsilon^2}{\sigma^2}$, and we can write:

$$P\left[|\bar{x} - \mu| > \epsilon\right] \le \frac{\sigma^2}{n\epsilon^2}, \text{ and } P\left[|\bar{x} - \mu| > \epsilon\right] = 0 \text{ as } n \to \infty \qquad (9.21)$$

■■■

9.3.1.3 Efficiency

Efficiency is connected to the size of the variance of an estimator. If a given population parameter θ, can be estimated by two (or more) unbiased estimators $\hat{\theta}_1$ and $\hat{\theta}_2$, then we say that estimator $\hat{\theta}_1$ is a more efficient estimator for the parameter θ than estimator $\hat{\theta}_2$ if

$$\sigma^2(\hat{\theta}_1) \le \sigma^2(\hat{\theta}_2)\ (or\ Var\ (\hat{\theta}_1) \le Var\ \hat{\theta}^2) \qquad (9.22)$$

with strict inequality for some values of θ.

Usually we use the ratio: $\dfrac{Var(\hat{\theta}_1)}{Var(\hat{\theta}_2)}$, to determine the relative efficiency of estimator $\hat{\theta}_2$, with respect to estimator $\hat{\theta}_1$.

However, if the estimators are biased, then the mean square errors are used to determine relative efficiencies.

As an example, suppose the population parameter $\theta = \mu$ is to be estimated by the 2 parameters,

$$\hat{\theta}_1 = \bar{x} = \text{sample mean}$$

and

$$\hat{\theta}_2 = x_{0.5} = \text{sample median}$$

If the population is normally distributed, then both $\bar{x}$ and $x_{0.5}$ are unbiased and consistent estimators of μ. However, we still claim that $\bar{x}$ is a better estimator than $x_{0.5}$.

This is so because while $V(\bar{x}) = \dfrac{\sigma^2}{n}$, $V(x_{0.5}) \cong \dfrac{\pi}{2}\dfrac{\sigma^2}{n} \approx 1.57\sigma^2$ and, therefore,

$\dfrac{V(\overline{x})}{V(x_{0.5})} = \dfrac{\dfrac{\sigma^2}{n}}{\left(\dfrac{\pi}{2}\right)\dfrac{\sigma^2}{n}} = \dfrac{2}{\pi} \approx 0.64$, which implies that $\hat{\theta}_1 = \overline{x}$ is more efficient than

$\hat{\theta}_2 = x_{0.5}$.

If an estimator can be more efficient than another estimator, is there a "most efficient" estimator? Such an estimator would have the smallest possible variance. We can think of the most efficient estimator $\hat{\theta}$ as a minimum variance estimator such that:

$$E\left[(\hat{\theta} - E(\hat{\theta}))^2\right] < E\left[(\hat{\theta}^+) - E(\hat{\theta}^+))^2\right] \tag{9.23}$$

where $\hat{\theta}^+$ is any other estimator for the parameter θ, and $\hat{\theta}$ is the most efficient estimator. According to the Cramer-Rao Inequality, which establishes the lower bound for the variance of an estimator, the lower bound for the variance of an estimator $\hat{\theta}$ for the population mean, μ, cannot be less than $\dfrac{\sigma^2}{n}$. Since we already know that $V(\overline{x}) = \dfrac{\sigma^2}{n}$, the sample mean, $\overline{x}$, in addition to being an unbiased and consistent estimator for the population mean, μ, is also a minimum-variance estimator for μ.

If we are interested in finding a "Good" estimator for the population variance, σ^2, we have already shown that $\hat{\theta}_1 = \hat{s}^2 = \dfrac{1}{n-1}\sum_{i=1}^{n}(x_i - \overline{x})^2$ is an unbiased estimator for σ^2 (because $E(\hat{s}^2) = \sigma^2$), while $\hat{\theta}_2 = s^2 = \dfrac{1}{n}\sum_{i=1}^{n}(x_i - \overline{x})^2$ is a biased estimator for σ^2, because $E(s^2) = \left(\dfrac{n-1}{n}\right)\sigma^2 = \left(1 - \dfrac{1}{n}\right)\sigma^2 = \sigma^2 - \dfrac{\sigma^2}{n} \neq \sigma^2$. Also, since $\dfrac{(n-1)\hat{s}^2}{\sigma^2} = x_{n-1}^2$ or $\hat{s}^2 = \dfrac{\sigma^2}{n-1}x_{n-1}^2$, and $\dfrac{ns^2}{\sigma^2} = x_{n-1}^2$ or $s^2 = \dfrac{\sigma^2}{n}x_{n-1}^2$, and because $V(x_{n-1}^2) = 2(n-1)$, we can show that:

$$V(\hat{s}^2) = V\left[\dfrac{\sigma^2}{n-1} \cdot x_{n-1}^2\right] = \left(\dfrac{\sigma^2}{n-1}\right)^2 V(x_{n-1}^2)$$

$$= \dfrac{\sigma^4}{(n-1)^2}\left[2(n-1)\right] = \dfrac{2\sigma^4}{n-1} \tag{9.24}$$

and

$$V(s^2) = V\left[\dfrac{\sigma^2}{n} \cdot x_{n-1}^2\right] = \left(\dfrac{\sigma^2}{n}\right)^2 V(x_{n-1}^2)$$

$$= \dfrac{\sigma^4}{n^2}\left[2(n-1)\right] = \dfrac{2(n-1)}{n^2}\sigma^4 \tag{9.25}$$

However, because s^2 is a biased estimator of σ^2, we need to calculate its mean square error, or

$$\mathrm{MSE}(s^2) = V(s^2) + \mathrm{BIAS}(\hat{s}^2) = V(s^2) + \left[\sigma^2 - E(s^2)\right]$$

$$= \dfrac{2(n-1)}{n^2}\sigma^4 + \left[\sigma^2 - \left(\sigma^2 - \dfrac{\sigma^2}{n}\right)\right] = \dfrac{2(n-1)}{n^2}\sigma^4 + \dfrac{\sigma^2}{n}$$

$$= \dfrac{2}{n^2}\left[(n-1)\sigma^4 + \dfrac{n}{2}\sigma^2\right] = \dfrac{2\sigma^2}{n^2}\left[(n-1)\sigma^2 + \dfrac{n}{2}\right] \tag{9.25a}$$

Since $V(\hat{s}^2)$ and $V(s^2)$ (and also the MSE (s^2)) decrease as n increases, $\hat{s}^2$ and s^2 are both consistent estimators of the population parameter σ^2.

If we ignore the fact that s^2 is a biased estimator for σ^2, and calculate the relative efficiency of s^2 relative to $\hat{s}^2$, we obtain: $\dfrac{V(\hat{s}^2)}{V(s^2)} = \dfrac{2\sigma^4/n - 1}{2\sigma^4(n-1)/n^2} = \left(\dfrac{n}{n-1}\right)^2$, which indicates that s^2 is always more efficient than $\hat{s}^2$, but the 2 become almost equally efficient as n increases.

However, if we replace $V(s^2)$ by $MSE(s^2)$, because s^2 is a biased estimator of σ^2, then we obtain: $\dfrac{V(\hat{s}^2)}{MSE(s^2)} = \dfrac{2\sigma^4/n - 1}{2\sigma^2\left[(n-1)\sigma^2 + \dfrac{n}{2}\right]/n^2}$. For this ratio to be less than 1,

i.e., for $\hat{s}^2$ to be more efficient than s^2, $\sigma^2 < \dfrac{(n/2)(n-1)}{2n-1}$

For values of $\sigma^2 > \dfrac{(n/2)(n-1)}{2n-1}$, s^2 is still a more efficient estimator than $\hat{s}^2$.

9.3.1.4 Sufficiency

An estimator $\hat{\theta}$ is a sufficient estimator of the parameter θ if it conveys as much sample information as possible for the parameter, and no other estimator, calculated from the same sample, can supply additional information.

For example, $\overline{x} = \dfrac{\sum\limits_{i=1}^{n} x_i}{n}$, $m_R = \dfrac{H + L}{2}$, $m_Q = \dfrac{Q_1 + Q_3}{2}$, and $x_{0.5} =$ median are four reasonable estimators for the population parameter μ. However, we claim that $\overline{x}$ is better than the other three because of these 4 estimators only $\overline{x}$ used all the information in the sample in its calculation.

Note that the definition for the estimator $\hat{\theta}$, which is a sufficient estimator, does not include the parameter θ.

The criteria for determining a sufficient statistic (or estimator) is given by Neyman's factorization theorem, which states the following:

If $x_1, x_2, \ldots, x_n$ is a random sample from a distribution with density function $f(x)$, then the statistic (estimator) $\hat{\theta} = u(x_1, x_2, \ldots, x_n)$ is said to be a sufficient statistic (estimator) for θ if and only if the likelihood function,

$$L(x_1, x_2, \ldots, x_n; \theta) = f(x_1, \theta) \cdot (x_2, \theta) \ldots, (x_n, \theta) \qquad (9.26)$$

can be factored as:

$$L(x_1, x_2, \ldots, x_n; \theta) = h(t; \theta) \cdot g(x_1, x_2, \ldots, x_n) \qquad (9.27)$$

for every value t of $\hat{\theta} = u(x_1, x_2, \ldots, x_n)$, and $g(x_1, x_2, \ldots, x_n)$ does not include the parameter θ.

The usefulness of a sufficient statistic is that if an unbiased estimator $\hat{\theta}$ of a parameter θ is a function of a sufficient statistic (and the estimator $\hat{\theta}$ can be identical with the sufficient statistic), it will have a smaller variance than any other unbiased estimator of θ which does not depend on a sufficient statistic. We can state that if the efficient estimator for θ exists, it will be a sufficient statistic.

Example 4

Suppose $x_1, x_2, \ldots, x_n$ is a random sample from a Poisson distribution, given by

$$p(x, \lambda) = \frac{e^{-\lambda}\lambda^x}{x!} \tag{9.28}$$

Determine the efficient estimator for λ, and show that the efficient estimator for λ is a sufficient statistic. Taking natural logarithms of both sides of (9.28), we can write:

$$\ln p(x; \lambda) = -\lambda + x \ln \lambda - \ln(x!) \tag{9.29}$$

Then, the partial derivative of $\ln p(x; \lambda)$, with respect to λ, is:

$$\frac{\partial \ln p(x; \lambda)}{\partial \lambda} = -1 + \frac{x}{\lambda} = \frac{x - \lambda}{\lambda} \tag{9.30}$$

Then, taking expected values of both sides of (9.30) we obtain (after first squaring (9.30))

$$E\left[\left(\frac{\partial \ln p(x; \lambda)}{\partial \lambda}\right)^2\right] = E\left[\left(\frac{x - \lambda}{\lambda}\right)^2\right] = \frac{1}{\lambda^2}E(x - \lambda)^2 = \frac{Var(X)}{\lambda^2} \tag{9.31}$$

But, if X is a Poisson distributed random variable, then $Var(X) = \lambda = \sigma^2$.

Therefore,
$$E\left[\left(\frac{\partial \ln p(x; \lambda)}{\partial \lambda}\right)^2\right] = \frac{\lambda}{\lambda^2} = \frac{1}{\lambda} \tag{9.32}$$

At this point it is necessary to introduce the following definition concerning an efficient estimator:

If $\hat{\theta}$ is any unbiased estimator of a population parameter θ, with:

$$V(\hat{\theta}) = \frac{1}{n}\frac{1}{E\left[\left(\frac{\partial \ln f(x; \theta)}{\partial \theta}\right)^2\right]} \tag{9.33}$$

then $\hat{\theta}$ is said to be the efficient estimator of the parameter θ. Then, combining (9.32) and (9.33'), the variance of the efficient estimator of λ is

$$V(\hat{\theta}) = \frac{1}{n}\frac{1}{1/\lambda} = \frac{\lambda}{n} = \frac{\sigma^2}{n} \tag{9.34}$$

But, since $V(\bar{x}) = \dfrac{\sigma^2}{n}$, we conclude that the efficient estimator $(\hat{\theta})$ for the Poisson population parameter $\theta = \lambda$ is given by the sample mean $\hat{\theta} = \bar{x}$. Let us now show that $\bar{x}$ is a one-to-one function of a sufficient statistic for λ.

The likelihood function is:

$$L(x_1, x_2, \ldots, x_n; \lambda) = p(x_1; \lambda) \cdot p(x_2; \lambda) \cdot \cdots \cdot p(x_n; \lambda)$$

$$= \left[\frac{\lambda^{x_1} e^{-\lambda}}{x_1!}\right]\left[\frac{\lambda^{x_2} e^{-\lambda}}{x_2!}\right]\cdots\left[\frac{\lambda^{x_n} e^{-\lambda}}{x_n!}\right]$$

$$= \frac{\lambda^{x_1+x_2+\cdots+x_n} e^{-\lambda-\lambda\cdots-\lambda}}{(x_1!)(x_2!)\cdots(x_n!)} = \frac{\lambda^{\sum\limits_{i=1}^{n} x_i} e^{-n\lambda}}{\prod\limits_{i=1}^{n} x_i!} \tag{9.35}$$

$$= h\left(\sum_{i=1}^{n} x_i; \lambda\right) \cdot g(x_1, x_2, \ldots, x_n)$$

where $\qquad h(\sum_{i=1}^{n} x_i; \lambda) = \lambda^{\sum_{i=1}^{n} x_i} e^{-\lambda n} \qquad$ and $\qquad g(x_1, x_2, \ldots, x_n) = \dfrac{1}{\prod\limits_{i=1}^{n} x_i!}$

Then, according to (9.27), the statistic $\sum\limits_{i=1}^{n} x_i$ is sufficient for λ. Since the efficient estimator $\bar{x}$ is a one-to-one function of this statistic, $\bar{x}$ is also sufficient for λ.

■ ■ ■

9.3.2 Illustrating the Desirable Characteristics of Point Estimators

To illustrate the desirable properties of point estimators we will start with a small population, and then take from it samples of size 2, 3 and 4, and for each sample size obtain the PMF (Probability Mass Function) of $\bar{x}$, $x_{0.5}$, R, $\hat{s}^2$, and s^2, and then demonstrate the conditions under which, if any, the desirable properties of the estimators we discussed previously are satisfied.

Let us consider the population consisting of the elements 2, 4, 6. If we assign the elements of this population as values to the random variable X, then the PMF of X is given by:

X	2	4	6
$P(X)$	1/3	1/3	1/3

from which $E(X) = \sum\limits_{i=1}^{n} x_i P(x_i) = 2(1/3) + 4(1/3) + 6(1/3) = \dfrac{1}{3}(12) = 4,$

$E(X^2) = \sum\limits_{i=1}^{3} x_i^2 P(x_i)$ or

$E(X^2) = 2^2(1/3) + 4^2(1/3) + 6^2(1/3) = 4/3 + 16/3 + 36/3 = 56/3,$ and

$V(X) = \sigma^2 = E(X^2) - \left[E(X)\right]^2 = 56/3 - 4^2$

$\qquad = 56/3 - 16 = (56 - 48)/3 = 8/3.$

Therefore, this population has $\mu = E(X) = 4$, and $\sigma^2 = V(X) = 8/3$.

1. Let us now take a sample of $n = 2$, with replacement from this population. The tree diagram shows the possible outcomes of this experiment:

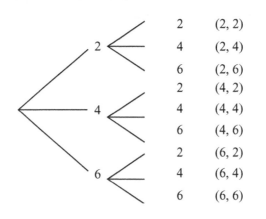

2	2	(2, 2)
	4	(2, 4)
	6	(2, 6)
4	2	(4, 2)
	4	(4, 4)
	6	(4, 6)
6	2	(6, 2)
	4	(6, 4)
	6	(6, 6)

The values for $\bar{x}$, $x_{0.5}$, R, $\hat{s}^2$ and s^2, for each of these samples, is as shown in the table below:

Sample →	2, 2	2, 4	2, 6	4, 2	4, 4	4, 6	6, 2	6, 4	6, 6
$\bar{x} = \sum\limits_{i=1}^{n} x_i / n$	2	3	4	3	4	5	4	5	6
$x_{0.5} = \dfrac{x_1 + x_2}{2}$	2	3	4	3	4	5	4	5	6
$R = H - L$	0	2	4	2	0	2	4	2	0
$\hat{s}^2 = \dfrac{1}{n-1}\sum\limits_{i=1}^{n}(x_i - \bar{x})^2 = \dfrac{(x_1 - x_2)^2}{2}$ *	0	2	8	2	0	2	8	2	0
$s^2 = \dfrac{1}{n}\sum\limits_{i=1}^{n}(x_i - \bar{x})^2 = \dfrac{(x_1 - x_2)^2}{4}$ *	0	1	4	1	0	1	4	1	0

*When $n = 2$, $\sum\limits_{i=1}^{n}(x_i - \bar{x})^2 = \sum\limits_{i=1}^{2}(x_i - \bar{x})^2 = \dfrac{2(x_1^2 + x_2^2) - (x_1 + x_2)^2}{2} = \dfrac{(x_1 - x_2)^2}{2}$.

Then, from this table we obtain the following 5 PMFs: PMF($\bar{x}$), PMF($x_{0.5}$), PMF(R), PMF($\hat{s}^2$), and PMF(s^2).

a)

$\bar{x}$	$P(\bar{x})$
2	1/9
3	2/9
4	3/9
5	2/9
6	1/9

b)

$x_{0.5}$	$P(x_{0.5})$
2	1/9
3	2/9
4	3/9
5	2/9
6	1/9

c)

R	$P(R)$
0	3/9
2	4/9
4	2/9

d)

$\hat{s}^2$	$P(\hat{s}^2)$
0	3/9
2	4/9
8	2/9

e)

s^2	$P(s^2)$
0	3/9
1	4/9
4	2/9

a) From the PMF of $\bar{x}$ we obtain:

$$E(\bar{x}) = \sum_{i=1}^{5}\bar{x}_i \cdot P(\bar{x}) = 2(1/9) + 3(2/9) + 4(3/9) + 5(2/9) + 6(1/9)$$

$$= 2/9 + 6/9 + 12/9 + 10/9 + 6/9 = 36/9 = 4 = \mu_{population}$$

$$E(\bar{x}^2) = \sum_{i=i}^{5}\bar{x}_i^2 \cdot p(\bar{x}_i) = 2^2(1/9) + 3^2(2/9) + 4^2(3/9) + 5^2(2/9) + 6^2(1/9)$$

$$= 4/9 + 18/9 + 48/9 + 50/9 + 36/9 = 156/9$$

and $V(\bar{x}) = E(\bar{x}^2) - \left[E(\bar{x})\right]^2 = 156/9 - (4)^2 = 156/9 - 16$

$$= (156 - 144)/9 = 12/9 = 4/3$$

b) From the PMF of $x_{0.5}$ which, for $n = 2$ is identical to the PMF of $\bar{x}$, we obtain:

$$E(x_{0.5}) = 4 = \mu_{pop}, \; E(x_{0.5}^2) = 156/9, \text{ and } V(x_{0.5}) = 4/3$$

c) From the PMF of R, we obtain:

$$E(R) = \sum_{i=1}^{3}R_i \cdot P(R_i) = 0(3/9) + 2(4/9) + 4(2/9) = 0 + 8/9 + 8/9 = 16/9$$

$$E(R^2) = \sum_{i=1}^{3}R_i^2 \cdot P(R_i) = 0^2(3/9) + 2^2(4/9) + 4^2(2/9) = 0 + 16/9 + 32/9 = 48/9$$

$$V(R) = E(R^2) - \left[E(R)\right]^2 = 48/9 - (16/9)^2 = 48/9 - 256/81 = 176/81$$

d) $E(\hat{s}^2) = \sum_{i=1}^{3} \hat{s}_i^2 \cdot P(\hat{s}_i^2) = 0(3/9) + 2(4/9) + 8(2/9)$

$$= 0 + 8/9 + 16/9 = 24/9 = 8/3 = \sigma^2_{population}$$

$E(\hat{s}^2)^2 = \sum_{i=1}^{3} (\hat{s}_i^2)^2 \cdot P(\hat{s}_i^2) = 0^2(3/9) + 2^2(4/9) + 8^2(2/9)$

$$= 0 + 16/9 + 128/9 = 144/9$$

$V(\hat{s}^2) = E(\hat{s}^2)^2 - \left[E(\hat{s}^2)\right]^2 = 144/9 - (8/3)^2 = 144/9 - 64/9 = 80/9$

e) $E(s^2) = \sum_{i=1}^{3} s_i^2 \cdot P(s_i^2) = 0(3/9) + 1(4/9) + 4(2/9) = 0 + 4/9 + 8/9$

$$= 12/9 = 4/3 \neq 8/3 (\neq \sigma^2) \text{ of population}$$

$E(s^2)^2 = \sum_{i=1}^{3} (s_i^2)^2 \cdot P(s_i^2) = 0^2(3/9) + 1^2(4/9) + 4^2(2/9)$

$$= 0 + 4/9 + 32/9 = 36/9 = 4$$

$V(s^2) = E(s^2)^2 - \left[E(s^2)\right]^2 = 4 - (4/3)^2 = 4 - 16/9$

$$= (36 - 16)/9 = 20/9$$

Then, since $E(\bar{x}) = \mu = 4$, and $E(x_{0.5}) = \mu = 4$, $\bar{x}$ and $x_{0.5}$ are both unbiased estimators of the population parameter μ. Similarly, since $E(\hat{s}^2) = \sigma^2 = 8/3$, $\hat{s}^2$ is an unbiased estimator of the population parameter σ^2, but s^2 is a biased estimator of σ^2 because $E(s^2) = 4/3 \neq \sigma^2$.

To demonstrate the other desirable properties of the estimators it is necessary to first obtain the PMFs for $\bar{x}$, $x_{0.5}$, $\hat{s}^2$ and s^2 for $n = 3$ and $n = 4$.

2. Let us now take a sample of $n = 3$, with replacement, from the given population. The possible outcomes (samples) are now the following 27:

(2, 2, 2), (2, 2, 4), (2, 2, 6), (2, 4, 2), (2, 4, 4), (2, 4, 6), (2, 6, 2), (2, 6, 4), (2, 6, 6), (4, 2, 2), (4, 2, 4), (4, 2, 6), (4, 4, 2), (4, 4, 4), (4, 4, 6), (4, 6, 2), (4, 6, 4), (4, 6, 6), (6, 2, 2), (6, 2, 4), (6, 2, 6), (6, 4, 2), (6, 4, 4), (6, 4, 6), (6, 6, 2), (6, 6, 4), (6, 6,6).

From these samples we now obtain the following PMFs for $\bar{x}$ and $x_{0.5}$. Also shown with each of them are the calculations for their expected values and variances.

a)

$\bar{x}$	$P(\bar{x})$	$\bar{x} \cdot P(\bar{x})$	$\bar{x}^2 \cdot P(\bar{x})$
2	1/27	2/27	4/27
8/3	3/27	8/27	64/81
10/3	6/27	20/27	200/81
4	7/27	28/27	112/27
14/3	6/27	28/27	392/81
16/3	3/27	16/27	256/81
6	1/27	6/27	36/27
	$\sum_{i=1}^{7} P(\bar{x}_i) = 1$	$E(\bar{x}) = \sum_{i=1}^{7} \bar{x}_i P(\bar{x})$ $= \dfrac{108}{27} = 4$	$E(\bar{x}^2) = \sum_{i=1}^{7} \bar{x}_i^2 P(\bar{x}_i)$ $= \dfrac{1368}{81} = \dfrac{152}{9}$

$$V(\overline{x}) = E(\overline{x}^2) - \left[E(\overline{x})\right]^2 = \frac{152}{9} - 4^2 = \frac{152}{9} - 16$$

$$= \frac{152 - 144}{9} = \frac{8}{9}$$

b)

$x_{0.5}$	$P(x_{0.5})$	$x_{0.5} \cdot P(x_{0.5})$	$x_{0.5}^2 \cdot P(x_{0.5})$
2	7/27	14/27	28/27
4	13/27	52/27	208/27
6	7/27	42/27	252/27
	$\sum_{i=1}^{3} P(x_{0.5_i}) = 1$	$E(x_{0.5}) = \sum_{i=1}^{7} x_{0.5}P(x_{0.5})$ $= \frac{108}{27} = 4$	$E(x_{0.5}^2) = \sum_{i=1}^{7} x_{0.5}^2 P(x_{0.5})$ $= \frac{488}{27}$

$$V(x_{0.5}) = E(x_{0.5}^2) - \left[E(x_{0.5})\right]^2 = \frac{488}{27} - 4^2 = \frac{488}{27} - 16$$

$$= \frac{488 - 432}{27} = \frac{56}{27} \approx 2.074$$

Once again, since $E(\overline{x}) = E(x_{0.5}) = \mu = 4$, $\overline{x}$ and $x_{0.5}$ are both unbiased estimators for the population parameter μ and, since $V(\overline{x}) < V(x_{0.5})$ for $n = 3$, we can say that $\overline{x}$ is a more efficient estimator for μ than $x_{0.5}$.

Similarly, the PMFs for $\hat{s}^2$ and s^2, are as shown below, together with the calculations for the Expected value and the Variance for each PMF.

c)

$\hat{s}^2$	$P(\hat{s}^2)$	$\hat{s}^2 \cdot P(\hat{s}^2)$	$(\hat{s}^2)^2 \cdot P(\hat{s}^2)$
0	3/27	0	0
4/3	12/27	(4/3)(12/27)	$(4/3)^2(12/27)$
4	6/27	4(6/27)	$4^2(6/27)$
16/3	6/27	16/3(6/27)	$(16/3)^2(6/27)$
	$\sum_{i=1}^{4} P(\hat{s}^2) = 1$	$E(\hat{s}^2) = \frac{8}{3} = \sigma^2$	$E(\hat{s}^2)^2 = \frac{864}{81}$

$$V(\hat{s}^2) = E(\hat{s}^2)^2 - \left[E(\hat{s}^2)\right]^2 = \frac{864}{81} - \left(\frac{8}{3}\right)^2 = \frac{864}{81} - \frac{64}{9}$$

$$= \frac{864 - 9(64)}{81} = \frac{864 - 576}{81} = \frac{288}{81} = 3.56$$

d)

s^2	$P(s^2)$	$s^2 \cdot P(s^2)$	$(s^2)^2 \cdot P(s^2)$
0	3/27	0	0
8/9	12/27	(8/9)(12/27)	$(8/9)^2(12/27)$
8/3	6/27	(8/3)(6/27)	$(8/3)^2(6/27)$
32/9	6/27	(32/9)(6/27)	$(32/9)^2(6/27)$
	$\sum_{i=1}^{4} P(s^2) = 1$	$E(s^2) = \frac{112}{81} \neq \sigma^2$	$E(s^2)^2 = \frac{10,368}{2,187}$

$$V(s^2) = E(s^2)^2 - \left[E(s^2)\right]^2 = \frac{10{,}368}{2{,}187} - \left(\frac{112}{81}\right)^2 = \frac{10{,}368}{2{,}187} - \frac{12{,}544}{6{,}561}$$

$$= \frac{18{,}560}{6{,}561} = 2.83$$

Obviously, $\hat{s}^2$ is an unbiased estimator for σ^2 because $E(\hat{s}^2) = \sigma^2$, but s^2 is a biased estimator for σ^2 because $E(s^2) \neq \sigma^2$.

However,   since $\sigma^2 = \dfrac{8}{3} > \left(\dfrac{n-1}{2n-1}\right)\left(\dfrac{n}{2}\right) = \dfrac{3}{5} \, for \, n = 3$,   as   expected

$V(s^2) < V(\hat{s}^2)$, and this implies that s^2 is more efficient than $\hat{s}^2$.

We can also state that $\overline{x}$, and $\hat{s}^2$ are consistent estimators for their respective population parameters because $V(\overline{x})_{n=3} < V(\overline{x})_{n=2}$, and $V(\hat{s}^2)_{n=3} < V(\hat{s}^2)_{n=2}$.

However, $x_{0.5}$ and s^2 do not appear to be consistent estimators because $V(x_{0.5})_{n=3} > V(x_{0.5})_{n=2}$, and $V(s^2)_{n=3} > V(\hat{s}^2)_{n=2}$; i.e., their variances increase, rather than decrease, as n increases.

3. Let us now take a sample of $n = 4$, with replacement, from the given population. The possible outcomes (samples) are now the following 81 ($N = m^n = 3^4 = 81$):

(2, 2, 2, 2), (2, 2, 2, 4), (2, 2, 2, 6), (2, 2, 4, 2), (2, 2, 4, 4), (2, 2, 4, 6), (2, 2, 6, 2),
(2, 2, 6, 4), (2, 2, 6, 6), (2, 4, 2, 2), (2, 4, 2, 4), (2, 4, 2, 6), (2, 4, 4, 2), (2, 4, 4, 4),
(2, 4, 4, 6), (2, 4, 6, 2), (2, 4, 6, 4), (2, 4, 6, 6), (2, 6, 2, 2), (2, 6, 2, 4), (2, 6, 2, 6),
(2, 6, 4, 2), (2, 6, 4, 4), (2, 6, 4, 6), (2, 6, 6, 2), (2, 6, 6, 4), (2, 6, 6, 6),

(4, 2, 2, 2), (4, 2, 2, 4), (4, 2, 2, 6), (4, 2, 4, 2), (4, 2, 4, 4), (4, 2, 4, 6), (4, 2, 6, 2),
(4, 2, 6, 4), (4, 2, 6, 6), (4, 4, 2, 2), (4, 4, 2, 4), (4, 4, 2, 6), (4, 4, 4, 2), (4, 4, 4, 4),
(4, 4, 4, 6), (4, 4, 6, 2), (4, 4, 6, 4), (4, 4, 6, 6), (4, 6, 2, 2), (4, 6, 2, 4), (4, 6, 2, 6),
(4, 6, 4, 2), (4, 6, 4, 4), (4, 6, 4, 6), (4, 6, 6, 2), (4, 6, 6, 4), (4, 6, 6, 6),

(6, 2, 2, 2), (6, 2, 2, 4), (6, 2, 2, 6), (6, 2, 4, 2), (6, 2, 4, 4), (6, 2, 4, 6), (6, 2, 6, 2),
(6, 2, 6, 4), (6, 2, 6, 6), (6, 4, 2, 2), (6, 4, 2, 4), (6, 4, 2, 6), (6, 4, 4, 2), (6, 4, 4, 4),
(6, 4, 4, 6), (6, 4, 6, 2), (6, 4, 6, 4), (6, 4, 6, 6), (6, 6, 2, 2), (6, 6, 2, 4), (6, 6, 2, 6),
(6, 6, 4, 2), (6, 6, 4, 4), (6, 6, 4, 6), (6, 6, 6, 2), (6, 6, 6, 4), (6, 6, 6, 6).

a)

$\overline{x}$	$P(\overline{x})$	$\overline{x} \cdot P(\overline{x})$	$\overline{x}^2 \cdot P(\overline{x})$
2	1/81	2/81	4/81
2.5	4/81	10/81	25/81
3	10/81	30/81	90/81
3.5	16/81	56/81	196/81
4	19/81	76/81	304/81
4.5	16/81	72/81	324/81
5	10/81	50/81	250/81
5.5	4/81	22/81	121/81
6	1/81	6/81	36/81
	$\displaystyle\sum_{i=1}^{9} P(\overline{x}_i) = 1$	$E(\overline{x}) = \displaystyle\sum_{i=1}^{9} \overline{x}_i P(\overline{x})$ $= \dfrac{324}{81} = 4 = \mu$	$E(\overline{x}^2) = \displaystyle\sum_{i=1}^{9} \overline{x}^2 P(\overline{x}_i)$ $= \dfrac{1350}{81} = \dfrac{50}{3}$

From these samples we obtain the PMFs for $\bar{x}$ and $x_{0.5}$, as shown. Also shown are the calculations required to compute Expected values and Variances for these estimators.

$$V(\bar{x}) = E(\bar{x}^2) - [E(\bar{x})]^2 = \frac{50}{3} - 4^2 = \frac{50}{3} - 16$$

$$= \frac{50 - 48}{3} = \frac{2}{3}$$

b)

$x_{0.5}$	$P(x_{0.5})$	$x_{0.5} \cdot P(x_{0.5})$	$x_{0.5}^2 \cdot P(x_{0.5})$
2	9/81	18/81	36/81
3	18/81	54/81	162/81
4	27/81	108/81	432/81
5	18/81	90/81	450/81
6	9/81	54/81	324/81
	$\sum_{i=1}^{5} P(x_{0.5_i}) = 1$	$E(x_{0.5}) = \sum_{i=1}^{5} x_{0.5}P(x_{0.5})$ $= \frac{324}{81} = 4 = \mu$	$E(x_{0.5}^2) = \sum_{i=1}^{5} x_{0.5}P(x_{0.5})$ $= \frac{1404}{81} = \frac{52}{3}$

$$V(x_{0.5}) = E(x_{0.5}^2) - [E(x_{0.5})]^2 = \frac{52}{3} - 4^2 = \frac{52}{3} - 16 = \frac{52 - 48}{3} = \frac{4}{3}$$

Clearly, since $E(\bar{x}) = \mu = 4$, and $E(x_{0.5}) = \mu = 4$, $\bar{x}$ and $x_{0.5}$ are both unbiased estimators of μ.

Also, since $V(\bar{x}) < V(x_{0.5})$, $\bar{x}$ is a more efficient estimator for μ than $x_{0.5}$. We can also state that $\bar{x}$ is a consistent estimator for μ, because

$V(\bar{x})_{n=4} < V(\bar{x})_{n=3} < V(\bar{x})_{n=2}$, i.e., the variance of $\bar{x}$ decreases $\left(\frac{2}{3} < \frac{8}{9} < \frac{4}{3} \right)$ as

n increases. The picture is not as clear for $x_{0.5}$, when it comes to consistency because even though $V(x_{0.5})_{n=4} < V(x_{0.5})_{n=3}, V(x_{0.5})_{n=4} = V(x_{0.5})_{n=2}$

$$\left(\frac{4}{3} \right) \qquad \left(\frac{56}{27} \right) \qquad \left(\frac{4}{3} \right) \qquad \left(\frac{4}{3} \right)$$

while $V(x_{0.5})_{n=3} > V(x_{0.5})_{n=2}$.

$$\left(\frac{56}{27} \right) \qquad \left(\frac{4}{3} \right)$$

Perhaps consistency sets in for $n \geq 4$, for $x_{0.5}$, because we know that for large n,

$V(x_{0.5}) \approx \frac{\pi}{2} \frac{\sigma^2}{n}$, and this suggests that $V(x_{0.5})$ should decrease as $n \to \infty$.

Similarly the PMFs for $\hat{s}^2$ and s^2 are shown below, together with the calculation for Expected value and Variance for each of these estimators.

c)

$\hat{s}^2$	$P(\hat{s}^2)$	$\hat{s}^2 \cdot P(\hat{s}^2)$	$(\hat{s}^2)^2 \cdot P(\hat{s}^2)$
0	3/81	0	0
1	16/81	16/81	48/243
4/3	12/81	16/81	64/243
8/3	12/81	32/81	256/243
11/3	24/81	88/81	468/243
4	8/81	32/81	384/243
16/3	6/81	32/81	512/243
	$\sum_{i=1}^{7} P(\hat{s}_i^2) = 1$	$E(\hat{s}^2) = \dfrac{216}{81} = \dfrac{8}{3} = \sigma^2$	$E(\hat{s}^2)^2 = \dfrac{2232}{243}$

$$V(\hat{s}^2) = E(\hat{s}^2)^2 - \left[E(\hat{s}^2)\right]^2 = \frac{2232}{243} - \left(\frac{8}{3}\right)^2 = \frac{2232}{243} - \frac{64}{9}$$

$$= \frac{2232 - 1728}{243} = \frac{504}{243} = 2.074$$

d)

s^2	$P(s^2)$	$s^2 \cdot P(s^2)$	$(s^2)^2 \cdot P(s^2)$
0	3/81	0	0
3/4	16/81	12/81	9/81
1	12/81	12/81	12/81
2	12/81	24/81	48/81
11/4	24/81	66/81	363/162
3	8/81	24/81	72/81
4	6/81	24/81	96/81
	$\sum_{i=1}^{7} P(s_i^2) = 1$	$E(s^2) = \dfrac{162}{81} = 2 \neq \sigma^2$	$E(s^2)^2 = \dfrac{837}{162}$

$$V(s^2) = E(s^2)^2 - \left[E(s^2)\right]^2$$

$$= \frac{837}{162} - 4 = \frac{279}{54} - 4$$

$$= \frac{279 - 216}{54} = \frac{63}{54} = \frac{7}{6}$$

Observe that when $n = 4$, $E(\hat{s}^2) = \dfrac{8}{3} = \sigma^2$, while $E(s^2) = 2 \neq \sigma^2$. Therefore, $\hat{s}^2$ is an unbiased estimator for σ^2, while s^2 is a biased estimator. Also $V(s^2) < V(\hat{s}^2)$; therefore s^2 is more efficient than $\hat{s}^2$.

The consistency and sufficiency, as well as the unbiasedness and efficiency properties can be seen best from the summary table below:

Summary			
Estimator	$n = 2$	$n = 3$	$n = 4$
$\bar{x}$ = Sample Mean	$E(\bar{x}) = 4 = \mu$ $V(\bar{x}) = 4/3$	$E(\bar{x}) = 4 = \mu$ $V(\bar{x}) = 8/9$	$E(\bar{x}) = 4 = \mu$ $V(\bar{x}) = 2/3$
$x_{0.5}$ = Sample Median	$E(x_{0.5}) = 4 = \mu$ $V(x_{0.5}) = 4/3$	$E(x_{0.5}) = 4 = \mu$ $V(x_{0.5}) = 56/27 \approx 2.074$	$E(x_{0.5}) = 4 = \mu$ $V(x_{0.5}) = 4/3$
$\hat{s}^2$ = Unbiased Sample Variance	$E(\hat{s}^2) = 8/3 = \sigma^2$ $V(\hat{s}^2) = 80/9 = 8.89$	$E(\hat{s}^2) = 8/3 = \sigma^2$ $V(\hat{s}^2) = 288/81 = 3.56$	$E(\hat{s}^2) = 8/3 = \sigma^2$ $V(\hat{s}^2) = 504/243 \approx 2.074$
s^2 = Biased Sample Variance	$E(s^2) = 4/3 \neq \sigma^2$ $V(s^2) = 20/9 = 2.22$	$E(s^2) = 112/81 \neq \sigma^2$ $V(s^2) = 18{,}560/6561 \approx 2.83$	$E(s^2) = 162/81 = 2 \neq \sigma^2$ $V(s^2) = 7/6 \approx 1.17$

From this table we see that both $\bar{x}$ and $x_{0.5}$ are unbiased estimators of μ, for all values of n considered in this example.

Also, since $V(\bar{x}) \leq V(x_{0.5})$, for all n values, $\bar{x}$ is a more efficient estimator for μ than $x_{0.5}$. Also, since $V(\bar{x})_{n=4} < V(\bar{x})_{n=3} < V(\bar{x})_{n=2}$, $\bar{x}$ is a consistent estimator for μ, because its variance decreases with increasing n, as is expected of a consistent estimator.

However, from this example, we cannot be certain about the consistency of $x_{0.5}$ because its variance does not seem to decrease uniformly with increasing n, as is the case with $\bar{x}$.

Finally, because $\bar{x}$ utilizes all the sample information in calculating the value of $\bar{x}$ (recall that $\bar{x} = (x_1 + x_2 + \cdots + x_n)/n$ while $x_{0.5}$ utilizes at most 2 values from the sample (one value when n is an odd number and 2 values if n is an even number, where n is the sample size) $\bar{x}$ is a sufficient estimator for μ, while $x_{0.5}$ is not.

Then, we may conclude from these observations, that $\bar{x}$ is a better estimator for μ than $x_{0.5}$.

Similarly we observe that $\hat{s}^2$ is an unbiased estimator for σ^2 because $E(\hat{s}^2) = \sigma^2$, while s^2 is a biased estimator because $E(s^2) \neq \sigma^2$, for all n values considered in this example.

However, s^2 appears to be a more efficient estimator than $\hat{s}^2$ because $V(\hat{s}^2) < V(s^2)$, for all n considered in this example.

Since $V(\hat{s}^2)_{n=4} < V(\hat{s}^2)_{n=3} < V(\hat{s}^2)_{n=2}$, $\hat{s}^2$ is a consistent estimator for σ^2. However, we cannot draw the same definitive conclusion about the consistency of s^2 because its variance does not decrease uniformly for all values of n considered in this example (perhaps consistency does set in for values of $n > 5$ for both $x_{0.5}$ and s^2, but this is not demonstrated in this example).

Finally, both $\hat{s}^2$ and s^2 are sufficient estimators for σ^2 because both use all of the sample information available, when calculating their respective values. In summary it appears that $\hat{s}^2$ is a better estimator than s^2 for σ^2, because it possesses more of the desirable estimator properties than s^2.

9.3.3 Methods of Finding Point Estimators

Having discussed the desirable properties for estimators above, we are now ready to discuss how to obtain estimators that generally have good properties. We will consider the following three methods:

1. Maximum Likelihood Method
2. Matching Moments Method, and
3. Least Squares Method

But we must state, at this point, that no known method of estimation can generate estimators which always possess all of the desirable properties.

9.3.3.1 Maximum Likelihood Method

This estimation method, first suggested by Fisher, consists of the generation of the Likelihood function (*i.e.*, the compound probability function for discrete random variables, or the compound density function for continuous random variables) of a specific observed sample, and then the maximization of this function with respect to the parameter of interest. This is accomplished using the Optimization methodology of Differential Calculus (see Appendix B) which consists of the following steps:

1. Given a function $y = f(x)$ to be optimized
2. Find $dy/dx = f'(x)$
3. Set $f'(x) = 0$, and solve for x, to obtain the critical point of the function, designated as $x*$
4. Find $d^2y/d^2x = f''(x)$
5. Evaluate $f''(x)$, at $x = x*$, to obtain $f''(x*)$. Then:
   a) If $f''(x*) > 0$, the function $y = f(x)$ has a local minimum at $x = x*$
   b) If $f''(x*) < 0$, the function $y = f(x)$ has a local maximum at $x = x*$
   c) If $f''(x*) = 0$, the function $y = f(x)$ has a Point of Inflection at $x = x*$

■ The Likelihood Function

If we sample from a population with an unknown parameter θ (the population may have 2 or more unknown parameters $\theta_1, \theta_2, \ldots, \theta_k$) represented by the random variable X with the density function $f(x, \theta)$, and obtain the observations $x_1, x_2, x_3, \ldots, x_n$, we note that each x_i is a random variable having the same density function $f(x_i, \theta)$, as the population from which the samples came from. (This is a conclusion we reached in Chapter 8, while trying to generate a set of independent and identically distributed (iid) random variables). Our objective here is to compute the Likelihood function, $L(x_1, x_2, \ldots, x_n, \theta)$, and then use it to obtain the maximum likelihood estimate for the unknown parameter θ. Assuming that the observations $x_1, x_2, x_3, \ldots, x_n$, are independent, the likelihood function is given by:

$$L(\theta) = L(x_1, x_2, x_3, \ldots, x_n) = f(x_1, \theta), f(x_2, \theta), \ldots, f(x_n, \theta) = \prod_{i=1}^{n} f(x_i, \theta) \quad (9.36)$$

But, because of the nature of the Likelihood function, the functions $L(\theta)$ and its natural logarithm, $\ln[L(\theta)]$, achieve their maximums for the same value of θ, we usually choose to maximize $\ln[L(\theta)]$, rather than $L(\theta)$, because it is easier to find the derivatives of $\ln[L(\theta)]$ than of $L(\theta)$.

Taking natural logarithms of both sides of (9.36), we obtain:

$$\ln\left[L(\theta)\right] = \ln f(x_1, \theta) + \ln f(x_2, \theta) + \cdots + \ln f(x_n, \theta) = \sum_{i=1}^{n} \ln f(x_i, \theta) \quad (9.37)$$

We will illustrate the application of the maximum likelihood method with the following examples.

Example 5

Suppose that observations $x_1, x_2, x_3, \ldots, x_n$, are drawn from the Poisson probability (mass) function $P(x) = \dfrac{e^{-\lambda}\lambda^x}{x!}$, with unknown λ. What is the maximum likelihood estimator for λ?

Solution The likelihood function $L(x, \theta) = L(x, \lambda)$ is given by:

$$L(x, \lambda) = \left(\frac{e^{-\lambda}\lambda^{x_1}}{x_1!}\right)\left(\frac{e^{-\lambda}\lambda^{x_2}}{x_2!}\right)\cdots\left(\frac{e^{-\lambda}\lambda^{x_n}}{x_n!}\right) = \frac{e^{-n\lambda}\lambda^{(x_1+x_2+\cdots+x_n)}}{x_1!x_2!\cdots x_n!} \tag{9.38}$$

and $\ln L(x, \lambda) = \ln e^{-n\lambda} + \ln \lambda^{(x_1+x_2+\cdots+x_n)} - \ln\left[x_1!x_2!\cdots x_n!\right]$

$$= -n\lambda + (x_1 + x_2 + \cdots + x_n)\ln\lambda - \ln\left[x_1!x_2!\cdots x_n!\right] \tag{9.39}$$

Then $\dfrac{d}{d\lambda}\left[\ln L(x, \lambda)\right] = -n + (x_1 + x_2 + \cdots + x_n)\dfrac{1}{\lambda} - 0$, and from

$$\frac{d}{d\lambda}\left[\ln L(x, \lambda)\right] = 0, \quad \text{we obtain} \quad \lambda = \frac{x_1 + x_2 + \cdots + x_n}{n} = \bar{x} = \lambda^*.$$

Since $\dfrac{d^2}{d\lambda^2}[\ln L(x, \lambda)] = -(x_1 + x_2 + \cdots + x_n)\dfrac{1}{\lambda^2}$, and

$$\frac{d^2}{d\lambda^2}\left[\ln L(x, \lambda = \lambda^*)\right] = -(x_1 + x_2 + \cdots + x_n)\frac{n^2}{(x_1 + x_2 + \cdots + x_n)^2}$$

$$= -\frac{n^2}{(x_1 + x_2 + \cdots + x_n)} < 0 \text{ (if } x_1 + x_2 + \cdots + x_n > 0)$$

the critical point $\lambda = \lambda^* = \bar{x}$ represents a local maximum and it is, therefore, the maximum likelihood estimate for the parameter λ.

■ ■ ■

Example 6

Suppose that observations $x_1, x_2, x_3, \ldots, x_n$, are drawn from the Binomial probability (mass) function $b(x, n, p) = \dfrac{n!}{x!(n-x)!}\, p^x(1-p)^{n-x}$ $(x = 0, 1, \ldots, n,$ and $0 < p < 1)$. Find the maximum likelihood estimator for the Binomial parameter p.

Solution Since in a Binomial experiment we observe exactly x successes in n trials, the likelihood function $L(x, n, p)$ is the same as $b(x, n, p)$, or

$$L(x, n, p) = b(x, n, p) = \frac{n!}{x!(n-x)!}p^x(1-p)^{n-x} \tag{9.40}$$

and $\ln L(x, n, p) = \ln(n!) - \ln\left[x!(n-x)!\right] + x \ln(p) + (n-x)\ln(1-p)$ (9.41)

Then $\dfrac{d}{dp}\left[\ln L(x, n, p)\right] = x\dfrac{1}{p}(1) + (n-x)\dfrac{1}{1-p}(-1) = \dfrac{x}{p} - \dfrac{(n-x)}{(1-p)}$,

and from $\dfrac{d}{dp}\left[\ln L(x, n, p)\right] = 0$, we obtain: $\dfrac{x}{p} - \dfrac{(n-x)}{(1-p)} = 0$, or $p = \dfrac{x}{n} = p^*$

Since $\dfrac{d^2}{dp^2}\big[\ln L(x, n, p)\big] = -\dfrac{x}{p^2} - \dfrac{(n-x)}{(1-p)^2}(-1) = -\dfrac{x}{p^2} + \dfrac{(n-x)}{(1-p)^2},$

and $\dfrac{d^2}{dp^2}\Big[\ln L\Big(x, n, p = p^* = \dfrac{x}{n}\Big)\Big] = -\dfrac{x}{(x/n)^2\big[1 - x/n\big]} < 0 \ \ (\text{for } \dfrac{x}{n} < 1),$

$p = p^* = \dfrac{x}{n}$ is a local maximum and represents the maximum likelihood estimate of the Binomial parameter p.

■ ■ ■

Example 7

Suppose that observations $x_1, x_2, x_3, \ldots, x_n$, are drawn at random from a population that has the functional form $f(x) = ke^{-kx}$, with the value of k unknown. What is the maximum likelihood estimator of k?

Solution The likelihood function is $L(x, k) = (ke^{-kx_1})(ke^{-kx_2})\cdots(ke^{-kx_n})$,

or $L(x, k) = k^n e^{-k(x_1 + x_2 + \cdots + x_n)} = k^n e^{-k\sum_{i=1}^{n} x_i}$ (9.42)

and $\ln[L(x, k)] = \ln[k^n e^{-k\sum_{i=1}^{n} x_i}] = \ln k^n + \ln(e^{-k\sum_{i=1}^{n} x_i}) = n \ln k - k\sum_{i=1}^{n} x_i$ (9.43)

Then $\dfrac{d}{dk}\big\{\ln\big[L(x, k)\big]\big\} = n\dfrac{1}{k} - \sum_{i=1}^{n} x_i$, and from $\dfrac{d}{dk}\big\{\ln\big[L(x, k)\big]\big\} = 0$,

we obtain

$$\dfrac{n}{k} - \sum_{i=1}^{n} x_i = 0, \quad \text{or} \quad \dfrac{1}{k} = \dfrac{\sum_{i=1}^{n} x_i}{n} = \overline{x}, \quad \text{or} \quad k = k^* = \dfrac{1}{\overline{x}} = \dfrac{n}{\sum_{i=1}^{n} x_i}$$

Since $\dfrac{d^2}{dk^2}\big\{\ln\big[L(x, k)\big]\big\} = -\dfrac{n}{k^2}$,

and

$$\dfrac{d^2}{dk^2}\bigg\{\ln\bigg[L\bigg(x, k = k^* = \dfrac{n}{\sum_{i=1}^{n} x_i}\bigg)\bigg]\bigg\} = -\dfrac{n}{\bigg(\dfrac{n}{\sum_{i=1}^{n} x_i}\bigg)} = -\dfrac{n}{n^2}\bigg(\sum_{i=1}^{n} x_i\bigg)^2 = -\dfrac{\bigg(\sum_{i=1}^{n} x_i\bigg)^2}{n} < 0,$$

$k = k^* = \dfrac{1}{\overline{x}}$ is a local maximum, and is the maximum likelihood estimator for the parameter k of the density function $f(x) = ke^{-kx}$.

Note: If we let $k = \dfrac{1}{\theta}$, the functional form becomes $f(x) = \dfrac{1}{\theta}e^{-\frac{x}{\theta}}$ which is the well-known exponential function. In this case the maximum likelihood of $\theta = \theta^* = \overline{x}$.

■ ■ ■

Example 8

Suppose that observations $x_1, x_2, x_3, \ldots, x_n$, are drawn at random from a population that has the normal density function

$$f(x, \mu, \sigma^2) = \frac{1}{\sqrt{2\pi}} e^{-\frac{1}{2\sigma^2}(x-\mu)^2}$$

What are the maximum likelihood estimators for μ and σ^2?

Solution The likelihood function $L(x_1, x_2, x_3, \ldots, x_n, \mu, \sigma^2)$ is a function of both μ and σ^2 and the MLE of μ and σ^2 are the combinations of μ and σ^2 values for which the likelihood function attains its maximum value.

The likelihood function is given by:

$$L(x_1, x_2, x_3, \ldots, x_n, \mu, \sigma^2) = \left[\frac{1}{\sqrt{2\pi}\sigma} e^{-\frac{1}{2\sigma^2}(x_i-\mu)^2} \right] \cdots \left[\frac{1}{\sqrt{2\pi}\sigma} e^{-\frac{1}{2\sigma^2}(x_n-\mu)^2} \right]$$

$$= \left(\frac{1}{\sqrt{2\pi}} \right)^n \left(\frac{1}{\sigma} \right)^n e^{-\frac{1}{2\sigma^2}\sum_{i=1}^{n}(x_i-\mu)^2}$$

$$= \left[\left(\frac{1}{2\pi} \right)^{\frac{1}{2}} \right]^n \left[\left(\frac{1}{\sigma^2} \right)^{\frac{1}{2}} \right]^n e^{-\frac{1}{2\sigma^2}\sum_{i=1}^{n}(x_i-\mu)^2}$$

$$= \left(\frac{1}{2\pi} \right)^{\frac{n}{2}} \left(\frac{1}{\sigma^2} \right)^{\frac{n}{2}} e^{-\frac{1}{2\sigma^2}\sum_{i=1}^{n}(x_i-\mu)^2} \qquad (9.44)$$

and

$$\ln L(x, \mu, \sigma^2) = -\frac{n}{2}\ln(2\pi) - \frac{n}{2}\ln(\sigma^2) - \frac{1}{2\sigma^2}\sum_{i=1}^{n}(x_i - \mu^2) \qquad (9.45)$$

Because $\ln L(x, \mu, \sigma^2)$ is a function of 2 unknowns (μ, σ^2), we need to take partial derivatives, (i.e., when differentiating $\ln L(x, \mu, \sigma^2)$ with respect to μ we treat σ^2 as a constant and when differentiating $\ln L(x, \mu, \sigma^2)$ with respect to σ^2 we treat μ as a constant) and obtain:

$$\frac{\partial \ln L(x, \mu, \sigma^2)}{\partial \mu} = -\frac{2}{2\sigma^2}\sum_{i=1}^{n}(x_i - \mu)(-1) = \frac{1}{\sigma^2}\sum_{i=1}^{n}(x_i - \mu) \qquad (9.46)$$

and

$$\frac{\partial \ln L(x, \mu, \sigma^2)}{\partial \sigma^2} = -\frac{n}{2}\frac{1}{\sigma^2} + \frac{1}{2\sigma^4}\sum_{i=1}^{n}(x_i - \mu)^2 \qquad (9.47)$$

Setting (9.46) and (9.47) equal to zero, and solving simultaneously, we obtain:

$$\frac{\partial \ln L(x, \mu, \sigma^2)}{\partial \mu} = 0, \quad \text{or} \quad \frac{1}{\sigma^2}\sum_{i=1}^{n}(x_i - \mu) = 0,$$

$$\text{or} \quad \sum_{i=1}^{n}(x_i - \mu) = 0, \quad \text{or} \quad \sum_{i=1}^{n}x_i - n\mu = 0, \quad \text{or} \quad \mu = \mu^* = \frac{\sum_{i=1}^{n}x_i}{n} = \overline{x} \qquad (9.48)$$

and $\dfrac{\partial \ln L(x, \mu, \sigma^2)}{\partial \mu} = 0$, or $\dfrac{n}{2\sigma^2} = \dfrac{\sum\limits_{i=1}^{n}(x_i - \mu)^2}{2\sigma^4}$, or $\dfrac{2\sigma^4}{2\sigma^2} = \dfrac{\sum\limits_{i=1}^{n}(x_i - \mu)^2}{n}$, or

$$\sigma^2 = \frac{\sum\limits_{i=1}^{n}(x_i - \mu)^2}{n} \tag{9.49}$$

$$= \frac{\sum\limits_{i=1}^{n}(x_i - \overline{x})^2}{n} = s^2, \text{ when } \mu = \overline{x} \text{ is substituted in (9.49)} \tag{9.50}$$

Clearly, in this example, the maximum likelihood estimator for μ, $\overline{x}$, is an unbiased estimator of μ but the MLE of σ^2, $s^2 = \dfrac{\sum\limits_{i=1}^{n}(x_i - \overline{x})^2}{n}$, is a biased estimator for σ^2 (Recall that an unbiased estimator for σ^2 is $\hat{s}^2$, where $\hat{s}^2 = \dfrac{1}{n-1}\sum\limits_{i=1}^{n}(x_i - \overline{x})^2$).

Note 1: The MLE method may not always generate unbiased estimators but they are usually consistent, efficient, and sufficient.

Note 2: The method of maximum likelihood possesses a desirable property, known as the INVARIANCE property, which claims that if $\hat{\theta}$ is the maximum likelihood estimator for a parameter θ, and $g(\theta)$ is a single-valued function of θ, then the maximum likelihood estimator for $g(\theta)$ is $g(\hat{\theta})$.

Therefore, since the MLE for $\sigma^2 = \dfrac{\sum\limits_{i=1}^{n}(x_i - \overline{x})^2}{n} = s^2$, and $\sigma = (\sigma^2)^{1/2}$ is a single-valued function of σ^2, the MLE for σ, is $\sigma = \left[\dfrac{\sum\limits_{i=1}^{n}(x_i - \overline{x})^2}{n} \right]^{1/2}$ in accordance with the INVARIANCE property of the maximum likelihood method.

■ ■ ■

Example 9 (A special example)

This example is different from the previous examples because the maximum likelihood estimator (MLE) cannot be obtained by differentiation.

Suppose that observations $x_1, x_2, x_3, \ldots, x_n$, are drawn from a population that has the functional form:

$$f(x, \theta) = \begin{cases} \dfrac{1}{\theta}, & \text{for } 0 < x < \theta \\ 0, & \text{elsewhere} \end{cases} \tag{9.51}$$

This is a proper density function because $\displaystyle\int_{-\infty}^{\infty} f(x, \theta)dx = \int_{0}^{\theta} \dfrac{dx}{\theta} = 1$.

Then the likelihood function is:

$$L(x, \theta) = L(x_1, x_2, \ldots, x_n, \theta) = \left(\frac{1}{\theta}\right)\left(\frac{1}{\theta}\right) \cdots \left(\frac{1}{\theta}\right) = \left(\frac{1}{\theta}\right)^n \tag{9.52}$$

and

$$\ln L(x, \theta) = \ln(\frac{1}{\theta})^n = -n \ln \theta \tag{9.53}$$

The derivative of $\ln L(x, \theta)$, $\dfrac{d \ln L(x, \theta)}{d\theta} = -\dfrac{n}{d\theta}$, but when we set $\dfrac{d \ln L(x, \theta)}{\theta} = 0$, (or $-\dfrac{n}{\theta} = 0$), no solution can be obtained for θ.

However, by inspection of (9.52), it is obvious, that $L(x, \theta)$ is maximized when θ assumes its smallest possible value. But, according to (9.51), θ cannot be smaller than the largest of the x_i observations for $i = 1, 2, \ldots, n$.

Thus the MLE for θ is: $\hat{\theta} = \max(x_1, x_2, x_3, \ldots, x_n)$ \hfill (9.54)

Note 3: It can be shown that the density function of $\hat{\theta}$, $f(y)$ is given by:

$$f(y) = \frac{n}{\theta^n} y^{n-1}, \tag{9.55}$$

with

$$E(\hat{\theta}) = \int_0^{\theta} y\, f(y) dy = \left(\frac{n}{n+1}\right)\theta, \text{ and} \tag{9.56}$$

$$V(\hat{\theta}) = E(\hat{\theta}^2) - \left[E(\hat{\theta})\right]^2 = \left(\frac{n}{n+2}\theta^2\right) - \left(\frac{n}{n+1}\right)^2 \theta^2 = \frac{\theta^2 n}{(n+1)^2(n+2)} \tag{9.57}$$

Obviously, from (9.56) the MLE estimator of θ is not an unbiased estimator for θ.

Note 4: The Variance of the MLE

The likelihood function (9.36) also provides a convenient method for obtaining an approximation to the variance of the MLE, $\hat{\theta}$, which is given by:

$$Var(\hat{\theta}) \approx -\left(\frac{\partial^2 \ln L(x, \theta)}{\partial \theta^2}\right)^{-1}, \tag{9.58}$$

and which is usually much easier to compute than the exact variance given by:

$$Var(\hat{\theta}) = E[\hat{\theta} - E(\hat{\theta})]^2 \tag{9.59}$$

To use (9.58), the sample values are replaced by their expected values after differentiation.

■ ■ ■

Example 10

Consider the exponential density function, given by: $f(x, \theta) = \dfrac{1}{\theta} e^{-\frac{x}{\theta}}$. Then for a random sample of: $x_1, x_2, x_3, \ldots, x_n$, the likelihood function is:

$$L(x, \theta) = L(x_1, x_2, \ldots, x_n, \theta) = \theta^{-n} e^{-\frac{1}{\theta}\sum\limits_{i=1}^{n} x_i} \tag{9.60}$$

and

$$\ln L(x, \theta) = -n \ln \theta - \frac{1}{\theta}\sum_{i=1}^{n} x_i, \tag{9.61}$$

Then

$$\frac{\partial \ln L(x, \theta)}{\partial \theta} = -\frac{n}{\theta} + \frac{1}{\theta^2} \sum_{i=1}^{n} x_i, \tag{9.62}$$

and

$$\frac{\partial^2 \ln L(x, \theta)}{\partial \theta^2} = \frac{n}{\theta^2} - \frac{2}{\theta^3} \sum_{i=1}^{n} x_i, \tag{9.63}$$

$$= \frac{n}{\theta^2} - \frac{2}{\theta^3} (n\theta),$$

when $\sum_{i=1}^{n} x_i$ is replaced by its expected value $= n\theta$

$$= \frac{n}{\theta^2} - \frac{2n}{\theta^2} = -\frac{n}{\theta^2} \tag{9.64}$$

When (9.64) is substituted into (9.58), we obtain: $Var(\hat{\theta}) \approx -\left(-\frac{n}{\theta^2}\right)^{-1} = \frac{\theta^2}{n}$, which also happens to be equal to the exact variance.

■ ■ ■

9.3.3.2 The Matching Moments Method

If we attempt to use the maximum likelihood method to obtain MLE for the parameters of the gamma density function given by:

$$f(x; \lambda, \alpha) = \frac{\lambda^\alpha x^{\alpha-1}}{\Gamma(\alpha)}, \text{ for } x > 0, \tag{9.65}$$

we find that

$$L(x; \lambda, \alpha) = \frac{\lambda^{n\alpha} e^{-\lambda \sum_{i=1}^{n} x_i} (x_1, x_2, \ldots, x_n)^{\alpha-1}}{[\Gamma(\alpha)]^n} \tag{9.66}$$

and

$$\ln L(x; \lambda, \alpha) = \alpha n \ln \lambda - n \ln \Gamma(\alpha) + (\alpha - 1) \sum_{i=1}^{n} \ln x_i - \lambda \sum_{i=1}^{n} x_i \tag{9.67}$$

from which we obtain

$$\frac{\partial \ln L(x; \lambda, \alpha)}{\partial \alpha} = n \ln \lambda - n \left[\frac{d}{d\alpha} \ln \Gamma(\alpha) \right] + \sum_{i=1}^{n} \ln x_i \tag{9.68}$$

and

$$\frac{\partial \ln L(x; \lambda, \alpha)}{\partial \lambda} = \frac{\alpha n}{\lambda} - \sum_{i=1}^{n} x_i \tag{9.69}$$

When (9.68) and (9.69) is each set equal to zero and attempt to solve them simultaneously for α and λ, we see that there is no close form solution. The only possible method of solution is by TRIAL-and-ERROR, which is not always easy to obtain.

A good approximation to the term: $\frac{d}{d\alpha} \ln \Gamma(\alpha)$, for $\alpha \geq 2$, is:

$$\frac{d}{d\alpha} \ln \Gamma(\alpha) \approx \ln\left(\alpha - \frac{1}{2}\right) + \frac{1}{24\left(\alpha - \frac{1}{2}\right)^2} \tag{9.70}$$

and this may help eliminate some of the difficulty encountered when (9.68) and (9.69) are solved simultaneously.

It may, however, be better in this and other similar situations to use a different estimation method, such as the Matching Moments method in which we equate moments of the sample with population moments, which in many cases is computationally easier.

But regardless of which method is used, the estimators obtained are generally "asymptotically normal", *i.e.*, as $n \to \infty$ the distribution of the estimator will approach the normal distribution.

Let us now get back to the problem of estimating the parameters of the gamma distribution, and suppose we have a random sample $x_1, x_2, x_3, \ldots, x_n$, from this distribution, from which we can calculate $\overline{x} = (x_1 + x_2 + x_3 + \cdots + x_n)/n$ and $\hat{s}^2 = \sum_{i=1}^{n} (x_i - \overline{x})^2/n - 1 = \left[n \sum_{i=1}^{n} x_i^2 - \left(\sum_{i=1}^{n} x_i \right)^2 \right] \Big/ n(n-1)$. If a random variable X follows the gamma density function given by (9.65), we can calculate its Expected Value, $E(X)$, and Variance, $V(X)$, from:

$$E(X) = \int_0^\infty x \, f(x; \lambda, \alpha) \, dx = \mu = \frac{\alpha}{\lambda} \tag{9.71}$$

and

$$V(X) = E[X - E(X)]^2 = \int_0^\infty \left(x - \frac{\alpha}{\lambda} \right)^2 f(x; \lambda, \alpha) = \sigma^2 = \frac{\alpha}{\lambda^2} \tag{9.72}$$

Then, setting

$$\mu = \frac{\alpha}{\lambda} = \overline{x} \tag{9.73}$$

and

$$\sigma^2 = \frac{\alpha}{\lambda^2} = \hat{s}^2 \tag{9.74}$$

and solving simultaneously (first replace $\dfrac{\alpha}{\lambda}$ in (9.74) by $\overline{x}$ to solve for λ), we obtain:

$$\lambda = \hat{\lambda} = \frac{\overline{x}}{\hat{s}^2} \quad \text{and} \quad \alpha = \hat{\alpha} = \hat{\lambda}\,\overline{x} = \frac{\overline{x}^2}{\hat{s}^2} = \left(\frac{\overline{x}}{\hat{s}} \right)^2 \tag{9.75}$$

obviously very little computational effort is needed to obtain the values of the estimators for the gamma parameters, using the Matching Moments method, as given by equation (9.75), while a considerable effort is required to obtain the MLE estimators. The numerical values obtained by the 2 methods may differ somewhat but we really are not sure which set of estimators is better. But, in general, we can say that for large samples the MLE estimators are better because their variances get smaller as n increases but for small samples there is no easy way to choose between the two methods of estimator.

9.3.3.3 The Least Squares Method

As we will show in greater detail in Chapter 13, where Linear Regression is discussed, the Best estimators for the ideal linear equation parameters (α, β, y) of:

$$y = \alpha + \beta x, \tag{9.76}$$

are given by the estimated equation: $\hat{y} = a + bx,$ (9.77)

in which the values of a and b are obtained from the Quadratic function:

$$Q(a, b) = \sum_{i=1}^{n} (y_i - a - bx_i)^2 \tag{9.78}$$

In (9.78), (x_i, y_i) are given bivariate data, and a and b are selected such that $Q(a, b)$ attains its smallest possible value. (This is where the name of the method is derived from). The Least Squares method is implemented as follows:

1. Obtain:
$$\frac{\partial Q(a, b)}{\partial a}, \frac{\partial Q(a, b)}{\partial b}, \frac{\partial^2 Q(a, b)}{\partial^2 a}, \frac{\partial^2 Q(a, b)}{\partial^2 b}, \frac{\partial^2 Q(a, b)}{\partial a \, \partial b} \tag{9.79}$$

2. Set $\dfrac{\partial Q(a, b)}{\partial a} = 0$, and $\dfrac{\partial Q(a, b)}{\partial b} = 0$ and solve simultaneously to obtain the Normal equations of the linear model:

$$na + b\sum_{i=1}^{n} x_i = \sum_{i=1}^{n} y_i \tag{9.80}$$

$$a\sum_{i=1}^{n} x_i + b\sum_{i=1}^{n} x_i^2 = \sum_{i=1}^{n} x_i\, y_i \tag{9.81}$$

Equations (9.80) and (9.81) when solved for a and b (because all the other quantities in equations (9.80) and (9.81) are known values derived from the given Bivariate data set (x_i, y_i), we obtain:

$$b = \dfrac{\displaystyle\sum_{i=1}^{n} x_i\, y_i - \dfrac{\left(\displaystyle\sum_{i=1}^{n} x_i\right)\left(\displaystyle\sum_{i=1}^{n} y_i\right)}{n}}{\displaystyle\sum_{i=1}^{n} x_i{}^2 - \dfrac{\left(\displaystyle\sum_{i=1}^{n} x_i\right)^2}{n}} = b^* \tag{9.82}$$

and

$$a = \dfrac{\displaystyle\sum_{i=1}^{n} y_i}{n} - \left(\dfrac{\displaystyle\sum_{i=1}^{n} x_i}{n}\right) b = \bar{y} - \bar{x}b = a^* \tag{9.83}$$

When (9.78) is evaluated using the b and a values of (9.82) and (9.83), it attains its smallest possible value $Q(a^*, b^*)$, which is then used, in accordance with the Markov theorem, to obtain the Variance of regression, namely:

$$\hat{\sigma}^2 = \dfrac{Q(a^*, b^*)}{n - 2} = \dfrac{\displaystyle\sum_{i=1}^{n} y_i{}^2 - a\sum_{i=1}^{n} y_i - b\sum_{i=1}^{n} x_i\, y_i}{n - 2} \tag{9.84}$$

Equations (9.82), (9.83) and (9.84) are the Least Squares Estimators of the parameters α, β, and σ^2. The estimators for α, β, and σ^2, (i.e., a, b, and $\hat{\sigma}^2$) are unbiased estimators because

$$E(a) = \alpha, \text{ and } E(b) = \beta, \text{ and } E(\hat{\sigma}^2) = \sigma^2.$$

This, however, is not the case with the Maximum Likelihood Estimators for α, β, and σ^2, as is shown below.

When we derived the Least Square Estimators for the unknown parameters, we did not specify the random errors, e_i. However, if we make the assumption that the e_i are independent normally distributed random variables with mean zero and variance σ^2, for all $i = 1, 2, \dots, n$, we can obtain maximum likelihood estimators for α, β, and σ^2.

Under this additional assumption concerning the nature of e_i, each y_i is also normally distributed with mean $= \alpha + \beta\, x_i$, and Variance $= \sigma^2$, because it is a linear function of a normally distributed random variable.

The maximum likelihood estimators are derived from the maximization of the likelihood function, which is given by:

$$L(x_1, x_2, x_3, \dots, x_n, \alpha, \beta, \sigma^2) = \dfrac{1}{\sqrt{2\pi}\,\sigma}\, e^{-\frac{1}{2\sigma^2}(y_1 - \alpha - \beta\, x_1)^2} \dots \dfrac{1}{\sqrt{2\pi}\,\sigma}\, e^{-\frac{1}{2\sigma^2}(y_n - \alpha - \beta\, x_n)^2}$$

$$= \left(\dfrac{1}{\sqrt{2\pi}\,\sigma}\right)^n e^{-\frac{1}{2\sigma^2}\sum_{i=1}^{n}(y_i - \alpha - \beta\, x_i)^2} \tag{9.85}$$

Taking the natural logarithm of both sides of (9.85) we obtain:

$$\ln L(x, \alpha, \beta, \sigma^2) = -\frac{n}{2}\ln(2\pi) - \frac{n}{2}\ln(\sigma^2) - \frac{1}{2\sigma^2}\sum_{i=1}^{n}(y_i - \alpha - \beta x_i)^2 \qquad (9.86)$$

Then the partial derivatives of $\ln L(x, \alpha, \beta, \sigma^2)$ with respect to α, β, σ^2 are respectively:

$$\frac{\partial \ln L(x, \alpha, \beta, \sigma^2)}{\partial \alpha} = \frac{1}{\sigma^2}\left[\sum_{i=1}^{n}y_i - n\alpha - \beta\sum_{i=1}^{n}x_i\right] \qquad (9.87)$$

$$\frac{\partial \ln L(x, \alpha, \beta, \sigma^2)}{\partial \beta} = \frac{1}{\sigma^2}\left[\sum_{i=1}^{n}x_i\, y_i - \alpha\sum_{i=1}^{n}x_i - \beta\sum_{i=1}^{n}x_i^{\,2}\right] \qquad (9.88)$$

$$\frac{\partial \ln L(x, \alpha, \beta, \sigma^2)}{\partial \sigma^2} = -\frac{n}{2\sigma^2} + \frac{1}{2\sigma^4}\sum_{i=1}^{n}(y_i - \alpha - \beta x_i)^2 \qquad (9.89)$$

Setting $\dfrac{\partial \ln L(x, \alpha, \beta, \sigma^2)}{\partial \alpha} = 0,\ \dfrac{\partial \ln L(x, \alpha, \beta, \sigma^2)}{\partial \beta} = 0$ and solving simultaneously, we obtain the same normal equations, namely:

$$n\alpha + \beta\sum_{i=1}^{n}x_i = \sum_{i=1}^{n}y_i \qquad (9.90)$$

$$\alpha\sum_{i=1}^{n}x_i + \beta\sum_{i=1}^{n}x_i^{\,2} = \sum_{i=1}^{n}x_i\, y_i \qquad (9.91)$$

which were obtained when we were deriving the Least Squares Estimators for α and β. Obviously solving equations (9.90) and (9.91) for α and β we obtain the same values for b and a given by equations (9.82) and (9.83) which are the Least Squares Estimators for β and α. However, when we set (9.89) equal to zero and solve for σ^2 we obtain:

$$\hat{\sigma}^2 = \sum_{i=1}^{n}(y_i - a - bx_i)^2/n \qquad (9.92)$$

The maximum likelihood estimators for α and β are unbiased but the MLE estimator for σ^2 is biased. However, for large n, the difference between the MLE and the Least Squares Estimators is negligible.

We obtained the MLE estimators for the unknown parameters in the simple linear model, even though they are the same as the Least Squares Estimators, because MLE estimators possess the desirable properties of Efficiency, Consistency, and Sufficiency.

The assumption of normality for the errors is justifiable for large values of n.

9.3.4 The Best Point Estimators for μ, σ^2, and σ

If we summarize the results of our discussion on the desirable properties of good point estimators, we conclude that:

1. The Best Point Estimator for the population mean (parameter) μ is $\bar{x}$ because $\bar{x}$ is an unbiased, consistent, efficient, and sufficient estimator for μ. Obviously $\bar{x} = (x_1 + x_2 + \cdots + x_n)/n$, where $x_1, x_2, x_3, \ldots, x_n$ is a set of random observations obtained from the population for which we wish to estimate its mean.

2. The Best Point Estimator for the population variance σ^2 is the unbiased sample variance, $\hat{s}^2$, because $\hat{s}^2$ is an unbiased, consistent, and sufficient estimator for σ^2, and

a nearly efficient estimator for σ^2, for large n. For a set of n random observations $x_1, x_2, x_3, \ldots, x_n$, $\hat{s}^2$ is given by:

$$\hat{s}^2 = \frac{1}{n-1} \sum_{i=1}^{n} (x_i - \overline{x})^2 = \frac{n \sum_{i=1}^{n} x_i^2 - \left(\sum_{i=1}^{n} x_i \right)^2}{n(n-1)}$$

3. The Best Point Estimator for the population standard deviation, σ, is

$$\hat{s} = \sqrt{\hat{s}^2} = \sqrt{\frac{1}{n-1} \sum_{i=1}^{n} (x_i - \overline{x})^2} = \sqrt{\frac{n \sum_{i=1}^{n} x_i^2 - \left(\sum_{i=1}^{n} x_i \right)^2}{n(n-1)}},$$

for a given set of n random observations $x_1, x_2, x_3, \ldots, x_n$, even though it is a biased estimator ($\hat{s}^2$ is unbiased but $\hat{s}$ is a biased estimator for σ, because $E(\hat{s}) \neq \sigma$, as we showed earlier in this chapter). However, $\hat{s}$ is a consistent and sufficient estimator and, for large n, a nearly efficient estimator.

9.4   Interval Estimators

As stated earlier, a Point Estimator assigns a single numerical value to an unknown population parameter, while an Interval Estimator assigns an entire interval of values as the value of an unknown population parameter, with pre-assigned odds, which are expressed by the confidence coefficient $1 - \alpha$, where α is the probability that the interval does not include the true population parameter. As an example we may, for a given situation state that:

"We are 95% confident that the mean of the population lies between 40 and 60", or in equation form: $P\left[40 \leq \mu \leq 60\right] = 0.95$.

But what does such a statement mean? It does not mean that the chance is 0.95 that the mean of the population falls within this interval. Instead, it means that if we select many random samples of the same sample size, and calculate a confidence interval for each of these samples, then in 95% of these intervals the population mean will lie within the interval.

Before proceeding with the construction of an interval estimator or confidence interval (as interval estimators are usually referred to), we note the following:

1. Given a Point Estimator and the method of generating it, we can determine whether the estimator possesses the desirable properties.
2. However, this knowledge is not enough to replace the parameter θ by its estimator $\hat{\theta}$, because it is desirable to associate a measure of precision with the estimator.
3. The precision of an unbiased estimator is measured by the standard deviation of the estimator, $\sigma(\hat{\theta})$. The smaller the $\sigma(\hat{\theta})$ is, the more precise the estimator $\hat{\theta}$ is, or the smaller the error in replacing θ by $\hat{\theta}$.
4. If the estimator $\hat{\theta}$ is biased its precision is measured by $E[(\hat{\theta} - \theta)^2]$, instead of $E\{[\hat{\theta} - E(\hat{\theta})]^2\}$.

9.4.1 Derivation of the $1 - \alpha$ Confidence Interval for any Population parameter θ, whose estimator $(\hat{\theta})$ is normally distributed, with standard deviation, $\sigma(\hat{\theta})$

To construct a confidence interval for a population parameter θ, whose estimator $\hat{\theta}$ is normally distributed with $E(\hat{\theta}) = \theta$ and standard deviation $= \sigma(\hat{\theta})$, we use the following functional equation:

$$P\left[\left(\begin{array}{c}Estimator\ of\\Parameter\end{array}\right) - Z_{\alpha/2}\left(\begin{array}{c}Standard\\deviation\ of\\Estimator\end{array}\right) \le Parameter \le \left(\begin{array}{c}Estimator\ of\\Parameter\end{array}\right)\right.$$

$$\left. + Z_{\alpha/2}\left(\begin{array}{c}Standard\\deviation\ of\\Estimator\end{array}\right)\right] = 1 - \alpha \tag{9.93}$$

or, in equation form:

$$P\left[\hat{\theta} - Z_{\alpha/2} \cdot \sigma(\hat{\theta}) \le \theta \le \hat{\theta} + Z_{\alpha/2} \cdot \sigma(\hat{\theta})\right] = 1 - \alpha \tag{9.94}$$

As an example, suppose $\theta = \mu, \hat{\theta} = \overline{x}$, and $\sigma(\overline{x}) = \dfrac{\sigma}{\sqrt{n}}$. Then if we make the assumption that either σ is known or $n \ge 30$ (or both σ is known and $n \ge 30$), then $\overline{x}$ is normally distributed (and $(\overline{x} - \mu)/\dfrac{\sigma}{\sqrt{n}}$ is standard normal) and (9.94) becomes (by direct substitution):

$$P\left[\overline{x} - Z_{\alpha/2} \cdot \sigma(\overline{x}) \le \mu \le \overline{x} + Z_{\alpha/2} \cdot \sigma(\overline{x})\right] = 1 - \alpha \tag{9.95}$$

If the estimator $\hat{\theta}$ is known to have a symmetrical distribution, but not necessarily normal, the multiplier in (9.94) is changed to K, so that (9.94) becomes:

$$P\left[\hat{\theta} - K\sigma(\hat{\theta}) \le \theta \le \hat{\theta} + K\sigma(\hat{\theta})\right] = 1 - \alpha \tag{9.96}$$

For example if $\theta = \mu$ and $\hat{\theta} = \overline{x}$, with $\sigma(\hat{\theta}) = \sigma(\overline{x})$, but $\dfrac{\overline{x} - \mu}{\dfrac{\hat{s}}{\sqrt{n}}}$ is t_{n-1} distributed, then:

$$K = t_{n-1}(\alpha/2) \tag{9.97}$$

Examining equations (9.93), (9.94), and (9.95), we observe that a confidence interval for a population parameter is constructed with the following four quantities:

1. The point estimator of the population parameter.
2. The standard deviation of the estimator, $\sigma(\hat{\theta})$.
3. A confidence coefficient (or a confidence multiplier) K, which depends on the distribution of the estimator $\hat{\theta}$.
      For example if $\hat{\theta}$ is normally distributed, $K = Z_{\alpha/2}$, while, if $\hat{\theta}$ is t_{n-1} distributed, $K = t_{n-1}(\alpha/2)$.
4. A confidence probability, called the level of confidence, and represented by $1 - \alpha$ (where α = probability of being outside of the C.I.)

But, how are equations (9.94) and (9.95) actually derived? Since we do not know the true value of θ in a particular instance, we must allow for the possibility that it may assume any value which is admissible, even though its actual value is unique.

To accomplish this we start with a standard normal distribution (*i.e.*, one with Expected value = 0 and Variance = 1) and, by design, we enclose in the confidence interval $1 - \alpha$ of the area under the standard normal distribution, $f(z)$.

We need to introduce the following notation to help us with the construction of the confidence interval (Note: A similar notation is used in Chapter 11, when the sampling distribution of the estimator is: Chi-square, t, or F).

We let

$Z_{\alpha/2}$ = The value of the variable Z, for which the area to the right of this value $= \alpha/2$ (9.98)

$Z_{1-\alpha/2}$ = The value of the variable Z, for which the area to the right of this value $= 1 - \alpha/2$ (9.99)

Note: Because the sampling distribution of $\hat{\theta}$ is symmetric (and normal) the probability of being outside of the confidence interval (C.I.) $= \alpha$ is split into 2 equal parts, each equal to $\alpha/2$, with one part on the left side of the distribution and the other on the right side.

These values and their relationship to the standard normal distribution can be better visualized in the diagram below:

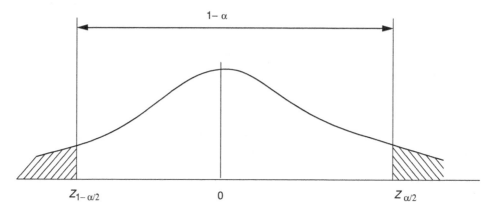

Clearly the area between these 2 values is equal to $1 - \alpha$. We can then write the general equation below which is valid for any random variable whose density function is the standard normal, namely:

$$P\left[Z_{1-\alpha/2} \leq Z \leq Z_{\alpha/2}\right] = 1 - \alpha \qquad (9.100)$$

But, since equation (9.100) is valid for any variable Z having the standard normal density $f(z)$, it must also be valid for the random variable:

$$Z = \frac{\hat{\theta} - \theta}{\sigma(\hat{\theta})}, \qquad (9.101)$$

because it is also $f(z)$-distributed.

When (9.101) is substituted for Z in (9.100) we obtain:

$$P\left[Z_{1-\alpha/2} \leq \frac{\hat{\theta} - \theta}{\sigma(\hat{\theta})} \leq Z_{\alpha/2}\right] \qquad (9.102)$$

To solve (9.102) for θ, we may follow the following procedure:

1. Multiply inside the brackets by $\sigma(\hat{\theta})$ to obtain:

$$P[Z_{1-\alpha} \cdot \sigma(\hat{\theta}) \leq \hat{\theta} - \theta \leq Z_{\alpha/2} \cdot \sigma(\hat{\theta})] = 1 - \alpha \qquad (9.103)$$

2. Identify the 2-inequalities:

$$Z_{1-\alpha/2} \cdot \sigma(\hat{\theta}) \leq \hat{\theta} - \theta \qquad (9.104)$$

and

$$\hat{\theta} - \theta \leq Z_{\alpha/2} \cdot \sigma(\hat{\theta}) \qquad (9.105)$$

3. Solve the inequality in (9.104) for θ to obtain:

$$\theta \leq \hat{\theta} - Z_{1-\alpha/2} \cdot \sigma(\hat{\theta}) \qquad (9.106)$$

and the inequality in (9.105) to obtain:

$$\hat{\theta} - Z_{\alpha/2} \cdot \sigma(\hat{\theta}) \leq \theta \tag{9.107}$$

4. Now combine (9.106) and (9.107) to obtain:

$$P\left[\hat{\theta} - Z_{\alpha/2} \cdot \sigma(\hat{\theta}) \leq \theta \leq \hat{\theta} - Z_{1-\alpha/2} \cdot \sigma(\hat{\theta})\right] = 1 - \alpha \tag{9.108}$$

But, because of the symmetry of the normal distribution,

$$Z_{1-\alpha/2} = -Z_{\alpha/2} \tag{9.109}$$

When (9.109) is substituted in (9.108), we finally obtain:

$$P\left\lfloor \hat{\theta} - Z_{\alpha/2} \cdot \sigma(\hat{\theta}) \leq \theta \leq \hat{\theta} + Z_{\alpha/2} \cdot \sigma(\hat{\theta}) \right\rfloor = 1 - \alpha \tag{9.110}$$

which is identical to equation (9.94).

9.4.2 Specific Combinations of: $1 - \alpha$, α, $\alpha/2$, and $Z_{\alpha/2}$

The quantities $Z_{\alpha/2}$ and $1 - \alpha$ that appear in equation (9.110) are not independent but are related through the normal distribution. In general, the larger the $1 - \alpha$ quantity, the larger the multiplier $Z_{\alpha/2}$.

The short table below, extracted directly from the standard normal table, shows the relationship between $1 - \alpha$ and $Z_{\alpha/2}$ for the most frequently constructed $1 - \alpha$ Confidence intervals, under the assumption that the estimator $(\hat{\theta})$ of the population parameter θ is normally distributed.

$1 - \alpha$	α	$\alpha/2$	$Z_{\alpha/2}$
0.90	0.10	0.05	1.65
0.95	0.05	0.025	1.96
0.98	0.02	0.01	2.33
0.99	0.01	0.005	2.58

Additional combinations of $1 - \alpha$ and $Z_{\alpha/2}$ can be extracted directly form the standard normal table. This can be accomplished by using the symmetry of the standard normal density function, and the value of the $\alpha/2$ column. Since 0.5 of the standard normal density is between 0 and $+\infty$ and, for a given value of Z_0, the area from Z_0 to $+\infty$ is $\alpha/2$ (by design), it follows that the area (or probability) between 0 and Z_0 is $0.5 - \alpha/2$, or:

$$P[0 \leq Z < Z_0] = 0.5 - \alpha/2 \tag{9.111}$$

Then, we search the standard normal table to locate the value $0.5 - \alpha/2$ (which is a pure number when $\alpha/2$ is defined), and at the margins of the table we read off the value of Z_0 which divides the 0.5 value of the standard normal table from 0 to $+\infty$ into the two portions: $0.5 - \alpha/2$ and $\alpha/2$.

As an additional example of this process suppose we wish to construct an 80% C.I. on the parameter θ, whose estimator $\hat{\theta}$ is normally distributed, with standard deviation $\sigma(\hat{\theta})$.

Then $1 - \alpha = 0.8$, $\alpha = 0.2$, and $\alpha/2 = 0.1$. Therefore, $0.5 - \alpha/2 = 0.5 - 0.1 = 0.4$. Attempting to locate the 0.4 value in the body of the standard normal table, we find that the closest value to 0.4 is 0.3997 (very close to 0.4) which corresponds to $Z_0 = Z_{\alpha/2} = 1.28$. A better accuracy can be obtained by interpolation if the desired probability value is not in the table. But usually the closest value will be sufficient. In a similar manner we can find additional combinations of $1 - \alpha$ and $Z_{\alpha/2}$.

9.4.3 Confidence Interval when $\theta = \mu$

When the population parameter θ, for which we want to construct a $1 - \alpha$ Confidence Interval is the population mean, μ, we recall that the point estimator for μ is $\bar{x}$ and, if σ of the population is known or if σ is not known but the sample size $n \geq 30$, the sampling distribution is $\bar{x}$ is the normal distribution with: $E(\bar{x}) = \mu$ and $\sigma(\bar{x}) = \sigma/\sqrt{n}$ (Note: If a random sample is drawn from a finite population with N elements, without replacement,

$$\sigma(\bar{x}) = \sigma/\sqrt{n} \cdot \sqrt{\frac{N - n}{N - 1}}, \text{ if } n \geq 0.05N)$$

Then, from equation (9.110), by replacing θ, $\hat{\theta}$ and $\sigma(\hat{\theta})$ by μ, $\bar{x}$, and $\sigma(\bar{x}) = \sigma/\sqrt{n}$, the $1 - \alpha$ Confidence interval for μ is given by:

$$P\left[\bar{x} - Z_{\alpha/2} \cdot \frac{\sigma}{\sqrt{n}} \leq \mu \leq \bar{x} + Z_{\alpha/2} \cdot \frac{\sigma}{\sqrt{n}}\right] = 1 - \alpha \qquad (9.112)$$

Pictorially, we can represent the problem by the diagram below:

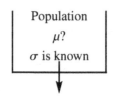

Population
μ?
σ is known

Draw a sample of size n,
with sample observations: $x_1, x_2, x_3, \ldots, x_n$
calculate: $\bar{x}$, $\hat{s}$

i.e., from a single population with an unknown μ but known σ, draw a sample of size n, calculate $\bar{x}$ and $\hat{s}$, and then construct a $1 - \alpha$ C.I. on μ. If σ is known, or if σ is not known but $n \geq 30$, $\dfrac{\bar{x} - \mu}{\sigma/\sqrt{n}}$ or $\dfrac{\bar{x} - \mu}{\hat{s}/\sqrt{n}}$ (if $n \geq 30$) is standard normal, and the $1 - \alpha$ C.I. on μ is given by (9.112) if σ is known, or if σ is known but $n \geq 30$, we replace σ by $\hat{s}$ and still use (9.112) to construct a $1 - \alpha$ Confidence Interval (C.I.) on μ.

Example 11

A population with an unknown population mean μ has a known standard deviation $\sigma = 120$. A random sample of $n = 100$ observations $(x_1, x_2, \ldots, x_{100})$ is drawn from this population and the sample mean $\bar{x}$ is calculated to be equal to $\bar{x} = 800$.

1. Find the best Point Estimator for the population parameter μ.
2. Construct 95%, 98%, and 99% C.I. on the population parameter μ.

Solution

1. The Best Point Estimator for μ is $\bar{x}$, or $\mu = \bar{x} = 800$
2. To construct the 3 asked for Confidence intervals for μ, we will use equation (9.112),
   with common information: $\bar{x} = 800$ and $\sigma(\bar{x}) = \dfrac{\sigma}{\sqrt{n}} = \dfrac{120}{\sqrt{100}} = 12$

   Then (9.112) becomes:

   $$p[800 - 12Z_{\alpha/2} \leq \mu \leq 800 + 12Z_{\alpha/2}] = 1 - \alpha$$

   Now, because when $1 - \alpha = 0.95$, $Z_{\alpha/2} = 1.96$,

   when $1 - \alpha = 0.98$, $Z_{\alpha/2} = 2.33$,

and when $1 - \alpha = 0.99$, $Z_{\alpha/2} = 2.58$, the Confidence Intervals are:

$$p[800 - 12(1.96) \le \mu \le 800 + 12(1.96)] = 0.95,$$

or
$$p[776.48 \le \mu \le 823.52] = 0.95,$$

$$p[800 - 12(2.33) \le \mu \le 800 + 12(2.33)] = 0.98,$$

or
$$p[772.04 \le \mu \le 827.96] = 0.98,$$

and
$$p[800 - 12(2.58) \le \mu \le 800 + 12(2.58)] = 0.99,$$

or
$$p[769.04 \le \mu \le 830.96] = 0.99.$$

■ ■ ■

9.4.3.1 Sample Size required for Given Tolerance

The difference between the estimator $(\hat{\theta})$ and the corresponding population parameter (θ) is defined as the sampling error. Expressing the sampling error in equation form, we can write:

$$\varepsilon = \hat{\theta} - \theta \tag{9.113}$$
$$= \overline{x} - \mu \ (\text{when } \theta = \mu \text{ and } \hat{\theta} = \overline{x})$$

From the left-hand side of (9.112) we find that: $\overline{x} - \mu \le Z_{\alpha/2} \dfrac{\sigma}{\sqrt{n}}$, by considering the inequality $\overline{x} - Z_{\alpha/2} \dfrac{\sigma}{\sqrt{n}} \le \mu$ and then interchanging μ and $Z_{\alpha/2} \dfrac{\sigma}{\sqrt{n}}$. Since the maximum sampling error, $\varepsilon_{\max}$ occurs when $\overline{x} - \mu$ is equal to $Z_{\alpha/2} \dfrac{\sigma}{\sqrt{n}}$, i.e., when the equal sign is considered, we can write:

$$\varepsilon_{\max} = \overline{x} - \mu = Z_{\alpha/2} \frac{\sigma}{\sqrt{n}} \tag{9.114}$$

Then, if we are willing to fix the maximum error we wish to accept, we can use equation (9.114) to find the sample size needed so that the maximum error will not be exceeded, with a confidence coefficient $1 - \alpha$. By squaring both sides of (9.114), and solving for n, we obtain:

$$n = \frac{Z_{\alpha/2}^2 \sigma^2}{\varepsilon^2_{\max}} = \left(\frac{Z_{\alpha/2} \cdot \sigma}{\varepsilon_{\max}} \right)^2 \tag{9.115}$$

Example 12

A department store wishes to estimate, with a confidence coefficient of 0.98 and a maximum error of \$5, the true mean dollar value of purchases, per month, by its customers with charge accounts. If the population standard deviating is $\sigma = 15$, what should the sample size be, to meet these specifications?

Solution Given that: $1 - \alpha = 0.98$ ($\rightarrow \alpha = 0.02$, and $Z_{\alpha/2} = Z_{0.01} = 2.33$), $\sigma = 15$ and $\varepsilon_{\max} = 5$, then:

$$n = \left(\frac{Z_{\alpha/2} \cdot \sigma}{\varepsilon_{\max}} \right)^2 = \left(\frac{2.33 \times 15}{5} \right)^2 = (2.33 \times 3)^2 = (6.99)^2 \approx 49$$

■ ■ ■

Example 13

If the maximum sampling error, ε_{max_1}, is changed to ε_{max_2}, and $\varepsilon_{max_2} = 2\,\varepsilon_{max_1}$, what happens to the corresponding sample size n_2? How is it related to n_1?

Solution When $\varepsilon_{max} = \varepsilon_{max_1}$, (9.115) generates $n_1 = \dfrac{(Z_{\alpha/2} \cdot \sigma)^2}{\varepsilon^2_{max_1}}$, and when $\varepsilon_{max} = \varepsilon_{max_2}$,

$$n_2 = \frac{(Z_{\alpha/2} \cdot \sigma)^2}{\varepsilon^2_{max_2}}, \quad \text{or} \quad (Z_{\alpha/2} \cdot \sigma)^2 = n_1 \cdot \varepsilon^2_{max_1} = n_2 \cdot \varepsilon^2_{max_2}$$

Since $\varepsilon_{max_2} = 2\varepsilon_{max_1}$, it follows that $\varepsilon^2_{max_2} = 4\varepsilon^2_{max_1}$ and $\dfrac{n_1}{n_2} = \dfrac{\varepsilon^2_{max_2}}{\varepsilon^2_{max_1}} = \dfrac{4\varepsilon^2_{max_1}}{\varepsilon^2_{max_1}} = 4$,

or $n_1 = 4n_2$, or $n_2 = \dfrac{1}{4} n_1$

Therefore, if the maximum error we are willing to accept doubles, the sample size needed to meet this specification is reduced by a factor of 4.

■ ■ ■

9.4.4 Confidence Interval when $\theta = \Delta\mu = \mu_1 - \mu_2$

Many times we need to compare the equality of the means for two populations; P_1 with unknown μ_1 and σ_1, and P_2 with unknown μ_2 and σ_2. To accomplish this, we introduce the new population parameter, $\Delta\mu$, where:

$$\Delta\mu = \mu_1 - \mu_2 \tag{9.116}$$

Suppose the two populations are as depicted below and random samples of size n_1 and n_2 are obtained respectively from populations 1 and 2 and the sample calculations $\overline{x}_1$, $\hat{s}_1^2$, and $\overline{x}_2$, $\hat{s}_2^2$ are obtained from the respective samples;

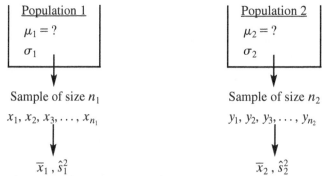

The question we wish to answer is whether $\mu_1 = \mu_2$, based on the sample information, or if $\Delta\mu = \mu_1 - \mu_2 = 0$, or to construct a confidence interval on $\Delta\mu$, from which to obtain the answer to our question.

The estimator for $\Delta\mu$ is $\Delta\overline{x}$, where $\Delta\overline{x} = \overline{x}_1 - \overline{x}_2 = 1 \cdot \overline{x}_1 + (-1) \cdot \overline{x}_2$, (9.117) which is a random variable, with:

$$E(\Delta\overline{x}) = E(\overline{x}_1 - \overline{x}_2) = E(\overline{x}_1) - E(\overline{x}_2) = \mu_1 - \mu_2 = \Delta\mu, \tag{9.118}$$

and
$$
\begin{aligned}
V(\Delta\overline{x}) &= V(\overline{x}_1 - \overline{x}_2) = V[1 \cdot \overline{x}_1 + -1 \cdot \overline{x}_2] \\
&= V(1 \cdot \overline{x}_1) + V[(-1) \cdot \overline{x}_2] \text{ (because the samples are independent)} \\
&= 1^2 V(\overline{x}_1) + (-1)^2 V(\overline{x}_2) = V(\overline{x}_1) + V(\overline{x}_2) \\
&= \frac{\sigma_1^2}{n_1} + \frac{\sigma_2^2}{n_2}, \tag{9.119}
\end{aligned}
$$

and
$$\sigma(\Delta\overline{x}) = \sqrt{V(\Delta\overline{x})} = \sqrt{\frac{\sigma_1^2}{n_1} + \frac{\sigma_2^2}{n_2}} \tag{9.120}$$

If σ_1 and σ_2 are known, the distribution of $\Delta\overline{x}$ is normal, regardless of the sample sizes n_1 and n_2. However, if σ_1 and σ_2 are not known but $n_1 \geq 30$ and $n_2 \geq 30$, $\overline{x}_1$ and $\overline{x}_2$ are still normally distributed (in accordance with the Central Limit Theorem), and $\Delta\overline{x}$, being a linear combination of normally distributed variables $\overline{x}_1$ and $\overline{x}_2$, is itself a normally distributed variable.

Then, from equation (9.110), by letting: $\theta = \Delta\mu$, $\hat{\theta} = \Delta\overline{x}$, and $\sigma(\hat{\theta}) = \sigma(\Delta\overline{x})$,

we obtain: $P[\Delta\overline{x} - Z_{\alpha/2} \cdot \sigma(\Delta\overline{x}) \leq \Delta\mu \leq \Delta\overline{x} + Z_{\alpha/2} \cdot \sigma(\Delta\overline{x})] = 1 - \alpha$ \qquad (9.121)

Example 14

The same vocational interest test was given to 36 salesmen of company A and to 49 salesmen of company B, and the following results were obtained:

Company A: $n_1 = 36, \overline{x}_1 = 76, \hat{s}_1^2 = 72$

Company B: $n_2 = 49, \overline{x}_2 = 70, \hat{s}_2^2 = 98$

Assuming independent samples, find 90%, 95% and 99% C.Is for the true difference in average points scored between the salesmen in companies A and B.

Solution Because $n_1 = 36 > 30$ and $n_2 = 49 > 30$, $\Delta\overline{x} = \overline{x}_1 - \overline{x}_2 (76 - 70 = 6)$ is a normally distributed random variable with:

$$E(\Delta\overline{x}) = \Delta\mu, \text{ and } \sigma(\Delta\overline{x}) = \sqrt{\frac{\sigma_1^2}{n_1} + \frac{\sigma_2^2}{n_2}} \approx \sqrt{\frac{\hat{s}_1^2}{n_1} + \frac{\hat{s}_2^2}{n_2}}$$

$$= \sqrt{\frac{72}{36} + \frac{98}{49}} = \sqrt{2 + 2} = 2$$

Then, substituting $\Delta\overline{x} = \overline{x}_1 - \overline{x}_2 = 76 - 70 = 6$ and $\sigma(\Delta\overline{x}) = 2$ in equation (9.121) we obtain: $P[6 - 2 Z_{\alpha/2} \leq \Delta\mu \leq 6 + 2Z_{\alpha/2}] = 1 - \alpha$

when $1 - \alpha = 0.90$, $Z_{\alpha/2} = 1.65$, and $P[2.70 \leq \Delta\mu \leq 9.30] = 0.90$

when $1 - \alpha = 0.95$, $Z_{\alpha/2} = 1.96$, and $P[2.08 \leq \Delta\mu \leq 9.92] = 0.95$

when $1 - \alpha = 0.99$, $Z_{\alpha/2} = 2.58$, and $P[0.84 \leq \Delta\mu \leq 11.16] = 0.99$

Since in each of these 3 Confidence Intervals the value of $\Delta\mu = \mu_1 - \mu_2 = 0$ falls outside of the interval, we conclude that $\Delta\mu \neq 0$ or that $\mu_1 \neq \mu_2$.

▪ ▪ ▪

9.4.4.1 Sample size required for given Tolerance

In this case the sampling error is defined as:

$\varepsilon = \hat{\theta} - \theta = \Delta\overline{x} - \Delta\mu$ and since from (9.121) $\Delta\overline{x} - \Delta\mu \leq Z_{\alpha/2} \cdot \sigma(\Delta\overline{x})$, and the maximum error occurs when we let $\varepsilon = \varepsilon_{max}$, we obtain:

$$\varepsilon = \varepsilon_{max} = \Delta\overline{x} - \Delta\mu = Z_{\alpha/2} \cdot \sigma(\Delta\overline{x}) = \left(\sqrt{\frac{\sigma_1^2}{n_1} + \frac{\sigma_2^2}{n_2}}\right) Z_{\alpha/2} \qquad (9.122)$$

If we square both sides of (9.122) we obtain:

$$\varepsilon^2 max = \left(\frac{\sigma_1^2}{n_1} + \frac{\sigma_2^2}{n_2}\right) Z_{\alpha/2}^2 \qquad (9.123)$$

Obviously (9.123) cannot be solved for n in terms of ε^2 max because n_1 and n_2 are usually different from each other.

However, if we make certain that $n_1 = n_2 = n$, then from equation (9.123) we obtain:

$$n = \frac{Z_{\alpha/2}^2}{\varepsilon^2_{max}}(\sigma_1^2 + \sigma_2^2) = \left(\frac{Z_{\alpha/2}}{\varepsilon_{max}}\right)^2(\sigma_1^2 + \sigma_2^2) \qquad (9.124)$$

9.4.5 Confidence Interval when $\theta = \pi$

The proportion of units that have a particular characteristic in a given population is symbolized by π. Then, if we know the proportion of units in a sample that has the same characteristic (which we represent by p), we can use this p as an estimator of π. It can be shown that p has all the desirable properties of point estimators, *i.e.*, p is an unbiased, consistent, efficient, and sufficient estimator of π. For example the product percent defective of a manufacturing process is the most important measure of the quality of the process for producing a given product.

Since a manufactured unit is either defective or non-defective, the number of detective units produced by the process is a Binomial random variable (assuming independence and constant probability), and this fact will make it possible to construct an exact Confidence Interval for π. Here, however, we are interested on constructing an approximate Confidence Interval of π, using the Normal distribution under the assumption that the sample size n is large (*i.e.*, $n \geq 30$). Normality can be assumed for X in accordance with the Central Limit Theorem, for large n, because X can be considered as the sum of n Bernoulli Variables, *i.e.*,

$$X = X_1 + X_2 + X_3 + \cdots + X_n \qquad (9.125)$$

with each X_i having the characteristics:

$$E(X_i) = \pi \qquad (9.126)$$

and $$V(X_i) = \pi(1 - \pi) \qquad (9.127)$$

Then, X is approximately normally distributed with:

$$E(X) = n\pi \qquad (9.128)$$

and $$V(X) = n\pi(1 - \pi), \qquad (9.129)$$

and $$p = \frac{X}{n} \qquad (9.130)$$

is approximately Normally distributed with:

$$E(p) = \frac{1}{n}E(X) = \frac{1}{n}\left[n\pi\right] = \pi \qquad (9.131)$$

and $$V(p) = \frac{1}{n^2}V(X) = \frac{1}{n^2}\left[n\pi(1 - \pi)\right] = \frac{\pi(1 - \pi)}{n} \qquad (9.132)$$

and $$\sigma(p) = \sqrt{\frac{\pi(1 - \pi)}{n}}$$

Note: If sampling is done without replacement from a finite population of size N,

$$\sigma(p) = \sqrt{\frac{\pi(1 - \pi)}{n}}\sqrt{\frac{N - n}{N - 1}} \qquad (9.133)$$

However, the value of π is usually not known and, to estimate $\sigma(p)$, we need to replace π by its estimator p.

Then, an approximate $1 - \alpha$ C.I. for π is given by:

$$P\left[p - Z_{\alpha/2}\sigma(p) \leq \pi \leq p + Z_{\alpha/2}\sigma(p)\right] = 1 - \alpha \qquad (9.134)$$

An improved Confidence Interval for π can be obtained by using the Continuity Correction Factor (CCF) which, for this case is:

$$\text{CCF for } p = 1/2n \qquad (9.135)$$

Then, the improved Confidence Interval for π can be expressed as:

$$P\left[\left(p - \frac{1}{2n}\right) - Z_{\alpha/2}\sigma(p) \le \pi \le \left(p + \frac{1}{2n}\right) + Z_{\alpha/2}\sigma(p)\right] = 1 - \alpha \quad (9.136)$$

Example 15

A manufacturer of a certain product claims that the product percent defective is no more than 4 percent. To substantiate his claim, the manufacturer will randomly select 100 units of his product, and count the number of defective units in the sample. Can the claim be substantiated, at $\alpha = 0.05$, if the number of defectives is 6?

Solution To substantiate the claim we will construct a 95% C.I. on π and if the claimed value of $\pi = 0.04$ is inside the Confidence Interval the claim will be substantiated while, if $\pi = 0.04$ is outside the Confidence Interval the claim will be rejected.

$$\text{Since } p = \frac{X}{n} = \frac{6}{100} = 0.06 \text{ and } \sigma(p) = \sqrt{\frac{(0.06)(0.94)}{100}} = \sqrt{\frac{0.0564}{100}} = 0.02375,$$

then from (9.134) we obtain:

$$P\left[0.06 - 1.96\,(0.02375) \le \pi \le 0.06 + 1.96(0.02375)\right] = 0.95$$

or

$$P\left[0.0135 \le \pi \le 0.1065\right] = 0.95$$

Since the claimed value of $\pi = 0.04$ is inside this Confidence Interval, the manufacturer's claim is substantiated.

▪ ▪ ▪

9.4.5.1 Sample size required for given Tolerance

In this case the maximum sampling error is defined as:

$$\varepsilon_{max} = \hat{\theta} - \theta$$

$$= Z_{\alpha/2}\sigma(p) = Z_{\alpha/2}\sqrt{\frac{\pi(1 - \pi)}{n}}, \text{ using (9.134) and (9.132)} \qquad (9.137)$$

However, since the value of π is not known, we assign to π the value $\pi = {}^1/_2$ because the value of the function $y = \pi(1 - \pi)$ is maximized when $\pi = {}^1/_2$.

When (9.137) is solved for n, we obtain:

$$n = \pi(1 - \pi)\left(\frac{Z_{\alpha/2}}{\varepsilon_{max}}\right)^2 \qquad (9.138)$$

$$= \frac{1}{4}\left(\frac{Z_{\alpha/2}}{\varepsilon_{max}}\right)^2, \text{ because of the statement above.}$$

9.4.6 Confidence Interval when $\theta = \Delta\pi = \pi_1 - \pi_2$

In section 9.4.5, we could have assumed that π was the population proportion of voters favoring a given issue, regardless of the gender of the voters. If we now assume that men and women come from 2 different populations (Population P_1 for men, with π_1 representing the population proportion favoring the given issue, and Population P_2 for women, with

π_2 representing the population proportion favoring the given issue), we can form the new population parameter:

$$\Delta\pi = \pi_1 - \pi_2 \qquad\qquad (9.139)$$

whose estimator is: $\Delta p = p_1 - p_2 = 1 \cdot p_1 + (-1)p_2$ $\qquad\qquad (9.140)$

with $\qquad\qquad E(\Delta p) = E(p_1) - E(p_2) = \pi_1 - \pi_2 = \Delta\pi \qquad\qquad (9.141)$

and $\qquad\qquad V(\Delta p) = V\big[1 \cdot p_1\big] + V\big[(-1)p_2\big] = 1^2 \cdot V(p_1) + (-1)^2 V(p_2)$

$$= V(p_1) + V(p_2)$$

$$= \frac{\pi_1(1 - \pi_1)}{n_1} + \frac{\pi_2(1 - \pi_2)}{n_2} \qquad\qquad (9.142)$$

and $\qquad\qquad \sigma(\Delta p) = \sqrt{\dfrac{\pi_1(1 - \pi_1)}{n_1} + \dfrac{\pi_2(1 - \pi_2)}{n_2}} \qquad\qquad (9.143)$

Since p_1 and p_2 are approximately normally distributed if n_1 and n_2 are both large (*i.e.*, if $n_1 \geq 30$ and $n_2 \geq 30$), Δp is also approximately normally distributed because it is a linear combination of normally distributed variables. Then, a $1 - \alpha$ Confidence Interval for the population parameter $\Delta\pi$ is:

$$P\big[\Delta p - Z_{\alpha/2}\sigma(\Delta p) \leq \Delta\pi \leq \Delta p + Z_{\alpha/2}\sigma(\Delta p)\big] = 1 - \alpha \qquad (9.144)$$

Example 16

Suppose in a random sample of 400 women 200 are in favor of abortion laws while in a random sample of 200 men 50 are in favor of abortion laws. Construct 90% and 98% Confidence Intervals for $\Delta\pi$.

Solution

$$p_1 = \frac{200}{400} = 0.5; \ p_2 = \frac{50}{200} = 0.25; \text{ and } \Delta p = p_1 - p_2 = 0.5 - 0.25 = 0.25$$

$$\text{Then } \sigma(\Delta p) = \sqrt{\frac{(0.5)(0.5)}{400} + \frac{(0.25)(0.75)}{200}} = \sqrt{\frac{0.25}{400} + \frac{0.1875}{200}}$$

$$= \sqrt{0.000625 + 0.0009375}$$

$$= \sqrt{0.0015625} = 0.03952847 \approx 0.03953, \text{ and}$$

$$P\big[0.25 - Z_{\alpha/2}(0.03953) \leq \Delta\pi \leq 0.25 + Z_{\alpha/2}(0.03953)\big] = 1 - \alpha$$

When $1 - \alpha = 0.90$, $Z_{\alpha/2} = 1.64$, and $P\big[0.18361 \leq \Delta\pi \leq 0.31639\big] = 0.90$

When $1 - \alpha = 0.98$, $Z_{\alpha/2} = 2.33$, and $P\big[0.1573 \leq \Delta\pi \leq 0.3427\big] = 0.98$

∎ ∎ ∎

9.4.6.1 Sample size required for given Tolerance

In this case the maximum sampling error is defined as:

$$\varepsilon_{max} = \hat{\theta} - \theta$$

$$= \Delta p - \Delta \pi$$

$$= Z_{\alpha/2}\, \sigma(\Delta p) = Z_{\alpha/2} \sqrt{\frac{\pi_1(1 - \pi_1)}{n_1} + \frac{\pi_2(1 - \pi_2)}{n_2}} \qquad (9.145)$$

For this problem to have a solution, it is necessary that

$$n = n_1 = n_2 \qquad (9.146)$$

Then, (9.145) can be written as: $\varepsilon_{max} = Z_{\alpha/2} \sqrt{\dfrac{\pi_1(1 - \pi_1) + \pi_2(1 - \pi_2)}{n}} \qquad (9.147)$

When (9.147) is solved for n, we obtain:

$$n = \left[\frac{Z_{\alpha/2}}{\varepsilon_{max}}\right]^2 \left[\pi_1(1 - \pi_1) + \pi_2(1 - \pi_2)\right] \qquad (9.148)$$

9.5   Minitab Solutions

In section 9.3.4 we summarized the properties of good point estimators and concluded that:

1. $\bar{x}$ is the best point estimator for the population parameter μ.
2. $\hat{s}^2$ is the best point estimator for the population parameter σ^2.
3. $\hat{s}$ is the best point estimator for the population parameter σ.

We now ask the question: How does MINITAB calculate Point Estimators?

Similarly, in section 9.4, we showed how to calculate interval estimators (*i.e.*, Confidence Intervals) for the population parameters μ, $\Delta\mu = \mu_1 - \mu_2$, π, $\Delta\pi = \pi_1 - \pi_2$, using either the generalized equation (9.110), applicable to any population parameter (θ) whose estimator ($\hat{\theta}$) is normally distributed and has the standard deviation $\sigma(\hat{\theta})$, or the specific equations: (9.112), which is applicable for the population parameter μ, equation (9.121) which is applicable for the population parameter $\Delta\mu = \mu_1 - \mu_2$, equation (9.134) which is applicable for the population parameter π, and equation (9.144) which is applicable for the population parameter $\Delta\pi = \pi_1 - \pi_2$.

Again, we ask the question: How does MINITAB calculate Interval Estimators or Confidence Intervals?

The answer to these questions depends on whether we are dealing with 1 or 2 populations and, for one population consists of the following steps, if one uses the "Session Window":

1. Identify the column in which you enter your data (MTB > SET C1).
2. Enter your numerical data (DATA > 50, 60, ...).
3. Issue appropriate MTB Commands to solve the problem, such as:
   a) NAME the Column in which you entered the data.
   b) SAVE the named Column (Once saved, the data can be retrieved).
   c) RETRIEVE the named Column of data.
   d) SORT the named column of data (data is arranged in order of magnitude).
   e) PRINT the Column of data. *Note*: Press "PRINT SCREEN" to copy the screen.

f) DOTPLOT the Column, to get the Line diagram of the Ungrouped Data.

g) HISTOGRAM the Column, to get the Histogram of the Grouped Data.

h) DESCRIBE the Column, to get numerical values for selected statistics.

i) ZINTERVAL ($K\%$), SIGMA $= K, C \ldots C$ Default is $K = 95\%$ Interval.

j) TINTERVAL ($K\%$) for $C \ldots C$ Default is $K = 95\%$ Interval.

Note: GHISTOGRAM, GDOTPLOT, GBOXPLOT are subcommands to the ZINTERVAL and TINTERVAL Commands.

Example

Suppose our data consists of the following 50 data values:
To apply the above procedure to this data set, we do the following:

75	97	71	65	84	27	108	91	122	84
97	58	94	43	116	123	91	120	94	43
74	73	68	54	50	49	81	128	103	76
120	94	79	80	83	71	88	88	47	73
71	106	86	108	84	93	77	107	44	127

```
MTB> SET C1
DATA>   75    97    71    65    64    27   108    91   122    84
DATA>   97    58    94    43   116   123    91   120    94    43
DATA>   74    73    68    54    50    49    81   128   103    76
DATA>  120    94    79    80    83    71    88    88    47    73
DATA>   71   106    86   108    84    93    77   107    44   127
DATA> END
MTB> NAME C1 'DSTAT'
MTB> SAVE 'DSTAT'
MTB> RETRIEVE 'DSTAT'
MTB> PRINT C1
MTB> DOTPLOT C1
MTB> HISTOGRAM 'DSTAT';
SUBC> MIDPOINT 27:126/11;
SUBC> BAR.
MTB> DESCRIBE C1
```

One command, with 2 subcommands, to generate a specific Histogram

The outputs for the MINITAB Commands: DOTPLOT, HISTOGRAM, and DESCRIBE are shown below:

Sample output for: MTB> DOTPLOT C1

Dotplot: DSTAT

Sample output for: MTB> HISTOGRAM 'DSTAT';
SUBC> MIDPOINT 27:126/11;
SUBC> BAR.

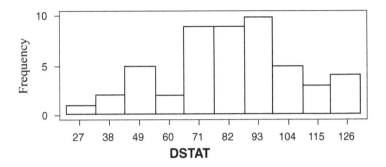

Sample output for: MTB> DESCRIBE C1

Descriptive Statistics: DSTAT

Variable	N	Mean	Median	TrMean	StDev	SE Mean
DSTAT	50	83.70	84.00	83.95	24.32	3.44

Variable	Minimum	Maximum	Q1	Q3
DSTAT	27.00	128.00	71.00	98.50

Note: From the output of the DESCRIBE Command we obtain the Point Estimators: $\bar{x}$ = Mean = 83.70, $x_{0.5}$ = Median = 84.00, and $\hat{s}$ = Standard Deviation = 24.32. Then since $\hat{s}^2 = (\hat{s})^2$, we obtain: $\hat{s}^2 = 591.4624$.

To construct a Confidence Interval for the population parameter μ, we use the ZIN-TERVAL if σ of the population is known and this must be supplied in the command.

If σ is not known, then the command to use is TINTERVAL. Both of these commands allow us to specify the $1 - \alpha$ Confidence Interval of our choice, by specifying the $K\%$, with the default value being: $K = 95\%$.

For this data set, these commands can be executed as follows:

MTB> ZINTERVAL 90, SIGMA = 25, 'DSTAT'

MTB> TINTERVAL 90, 'DSTAT'

To use the "WORKSHEET 1" window, type the data for each characteristic on a separate column of the worksheet, and then use the following steps to execute the above 2 commands:

STAT $\rightarrow$ BASIC STATISTICS $\rightarrow$ 1 – Sample Z

or STAT $\rightarrow$ BASIC STATISTICS $\rightarrow$ 1 – Sample t

The outputs for these MINITAB Commands are shown below:

One-Sample Z: DSTAT

The assumed sigma = 25

Variable	N	Mean	StDev	SE Mean	90.0% CI
DSTAT	50	83.70	24.32	3.54	(77.88, 89.52)

One-Sample T: DSTAT

Variable	N	Mean	StDev	SE Mean	90.0% CI
DSTAT	50	83.70	24.32	3.44	(77.93, 89.47)

To construct a Confidence Interval for the population parameter $\Delta\mu = \mu_1 - \mu_2$, when using the "SESSION WINDOW", we can start by SETting and NAMing the data from each population separately, as follows:

MTB> SET C1

DATA> ···

DATA> END

MTB> NAME C1 ' DSTAT 1 '   ← (DSTAT 1 = DSTAT)

MTB> DESCRIBE C1

MTB> SET C2

DATA> ⋯

DATA> END

MTB> NAME C2 ' DSTAT 2 '

MTB> DESCRIBE C2

Then, to construct a MINITAB-generated $K\%$ Confidence Interval for the parameter $\Delta\mu = \mu_1 - \mu_2$, we issue the Command:

MTB> TWO SAMPLE − T 90.0 ' DSTAT 1 ' ' DSTAT 2 ';

SUBC> ALTERNATIVE 0;   (For H_0: $\Delta\mu = 0$ vs H_1: $\Delta\mu \neq 0$)

$$(+1 \text{ if } H_1\text{: } \Delta\mu > 0\,;\ -1 \text{ if } H_1\text{: } \Delta\mu < 0)$$

SUBC> POOLED; (uses Pooled Variance $\hat{s}^2 = \dfrac{(n_1 - 1)\hat{s}_1^2 + (n_2 - 1)\hat{s}_2^2}{n_1 + n_2 - 2}$)

SUBC> GDOTPLOT.   (Displays Dot Plots)

Suppose the data from population 2 consists of the following 50 data values (Note: n_1 does not have to be equal to n_2):

66	58	47	40	93	74	70	56	34	66
61	72	81	42	95	78	65	74	86	44
67	79	42	82	34	67	65	60	75	85
53	36	62	56	98	68	67	44	76	88
87	51	92	49	67	89	62	78	55	76

(For this data set: $\overline{x}$ = Mean = 66.24, x_m = Median = 67.00, and $\hat{s}$ = Standard Deviation = 17.00).

Assume that the data from population 1 is the same used above to form 'DSTAT' which was used to construct a confidence interval for the parameter μ. Then the output from the TWOSAMPLE − T 90.0 command is as shown below:

Two-Sample T-Test and CI: C1, C2

```
Two-sample T for C1 vs C2
```

	N	Mean	StDev	SE Mean
C1	50	83.7	24.3	3.4
C2	50	66.2	17.0	2.4

```
Difference = mu C1 − mu C2
Estimate for difference:  17.46
90% CI for difference:  (10.48, 24.44)
T-Test of difference = 0 (vs not =): T-Value = 4.16
P-Value = 0.000   DF = 87
```

To use the "WORKSHEET 1" WINDOW, type the data from population 1 in column 1 and the data from population 2 in column 2, and then use the following steps to execute the TWOSAMPLE-T Command

$$STAT \rightarrow BASIC \ STATISTCIS \rightarrow 2\text{-SAMPLE } t$$

At this point we state that there are NO MINITAB Commands to construct Confidence Intervals for the population parameters π and $\Delta \pi = \pi_1 - \pi_2$, even though some calculation procedures are available.

But there exists a nonparametric sign confidence interval for the median which, when using the "SESSION WINDOW" can be stated as:

$$MTB > SINTERVAL \ 90.0 \ 'DSTAT'$$

and the output is as shown below:

Sign confidence interval for median

	N	Median	Achieved Confidence	Confidence interval		Position
DSTAT	50	84.00	0.8811	(77.00,	91.00)	20
			0.9000	(76.75,	91.00)	NLI
			0.9351	(76.00,	91.00)	19

To use the "WORKSHEET 1" WINDOW, type the data from population 1 in column $C1$, and then use the following steps to execute the Command:

$$STAT \rightarrow NONPARAMETRICS \rightarrow 1 - Sample \ sign$$

To compare 2 population medians, we use the Mann-Whitney Two-Sample Rank Sum Test which, after entering the 2 data sets as shown above, is implemented by:

$$STAT \rightarrow NONPARAMTERICS \rightarrow Mann\text{-}Whitney.$$

9.6 References

Berenson, Marc, L., Levine, David, M., and Krehbiel, Timothy, C., 2004. *Basic Business Statistics*. 9th Edition. Pearson-Prentice Hall.

Black, Ken, *Business Statistics*. 4th Edition. Wiley.

Canavos, George, C., 1984. *Applied Probability and Statistical Methods*. Little, Brown.

Carlson, William, L., and Thorne, Betty, 1997. *Applied Statistical Methods*. Prentice Hall.

Chou, Ya-lun, 1992. *Statistical Analysis for Business and Economics*. Elsevier.

Freund, John, E., and Williams, Frank, J., 1969. *Modern Business Statistics*. Revised by: Perles, Benjamin and Sullivan, Charles. Prentice Hall.

Johnson, Robert, 1973. *Elementary Statistics*. Duxbury Press.

McClave, James, T., Benson, George, P., and Sincinch, Terry, 2001. *Statistics for Business and Economics*. 8th Edition. Prentice Hall.

Steel, Robert, G.D., and Torrie, James, H., 1976. *Introduction to Statistics*. McGraw-Hill.

9.7 PROBLEMS

1. A certain population of unskilled laborers annual income has a standard deviation of $800. A random sample of $n = 36$, resulted in an $\bar{x} = \$5650$.

    a) Give a Point Estimate for the Population Mean Annual Income.

    b) Construct a 95% Confidence Interval for the Population Mean, μ.

    c) How large a sample is needed if the population mean (μ) is to be estimated, with 99% Confidence, to within $100?

2. A study is conducted to determine the Mean Age of College Students. A sample of $n = 49$ students gave a sample mean of $\bar{x} = 22$ years and a sample standard deviation $\hat{s} = 3$ years.

    a) Give point estimates for the population parameters μ, σ, and σ^2.

    b) State the 4 criteria used in selecting the Best point Estimators for the population parameters.

    c) Construct a 98% Confidence Interval for the population mean, μ.

3. An Industrial engineer has devised two methods for assembling a water pump. The first method assembled a sample of 40 units in an average of 20.2 minutes each and with a sample standard deviation of 2.5 minutes. The second method assembled 56 units in an average of 21 minutes each and with a sample standard deviation of 3.1 minutes. Construct a 98% Confidence Interval for the True Mean Difference of required time for the two methods.

4. The weights of full boxes of a certain kind of cereal are known to be normally distributed with a standard deviation $\sigma = 0.27$ ounce. If a random sample of 15 randomly selected boxes produced a sample mean weight ($\bar{x}$) of 9.87 ounces, find:

    a) A point Estimate for μ.

    b) 95% and 99% Confidence Intervals for the True Mean weight of a box of this cereal (μ).

5. The President of the United States of America claims that he has "the support of the majority of all voters". A poll of 1200 randomly selected voters was taken to test this claim and it was found that 645 voters supported the president. Construct a 98% Confidence Interval for the True proportion of voters who support the president.

6. A random sample of 100 men was selected in a given state and 60 were found to be in favor of a "more modern" divorce law. Also a random sample of 100 women were selected from the same state and at the same time, and revealed that 40 were in favor of such a new law. Construct a 95% Confidence Interval and using it state whether the proportion of men favoring a new divorce law is the same as the proportion of women in this state.

7. Using the Sample Information:

    a) $n = 30; x_1 + x_2 + \cdots + x_{30} = 492.50$ and
       $x_1^2 + x_2^2 + \cdots + x_{30}^2 = 24{,}402.75$

       Estimate the cost of dinner, in a major city, with a 90% Confidence Interval on μ (the mean cost).

    b) $n = 40; x_1 + x_2 + \cdots + x_{40} = 492.50$
       and $x_1^2 + x_2^2 + \cdots + x_{40}^2 = 24{,}402.75$

       Estimate the cost of dinner with a 90% C.I. on μ. How did the CI change?

    c) Using the information in (a) above, construct a 95% Confidence Interval on μ.

8. A certain population of unskilled workers annual incomes has a standard deviation of $800. A random sample of 36 results in $\bar{x} = 5650$.

   a) Give a Point estimate for the population mean (μ) annual income.

   b) Estimate μ with a 95% Confidence Interval.

   c) Estimate μ with a 99% Confidence Interval.

9. A sample of what size would be needed to estimate a population mean to within 4 units, with 95% confidence, if the population has a standard deviation of 12?

10. The lengths of 225 fish caught at Lake Ranconcoma had a mean length of 14.0. If the population standard deviation is 1.5 inches, find:

    a) The 90% confidence interval for the population mean length.

    b) The 98% confidence interval for the population mean length.

11. Checkout times at a supermarket are known to be normally distributed with a variance of 3.6.

    a) A sample of 36 customers revealed a mean checkout time of 15.5 minutes. Construct the 95% confidence interval for the population mean μ.

    b) If the mean of 15.5 minutes had resulted from 49 customers, find the 95% confidence interval for μ.

    c) What effect does the larger sample have on the confidence interval?

12. An office manager wishes to estimate the mean time required to handle customer complaints. If the times are normally distributed with a standard deviation of 18 minutes and a sample of 36 complaints resulted in a sample mean of 42.0 minutes, construct the 99% C.I. for the true mean time required to handle customer complaints.

13. A manufacturer of automobiles wishes to estimate the mean gasoline mileage that his customers will obtain with his new model. How many sample drive runs must be performed in order to estimate the mean to within 0.5 mile per gallon with a 98% confidence, if $\sigma = 2.5$?

14. A new vending machine was installed in the student centre of a university. It failed to operate successfully 16 times in the last 400 times it was used. Construct a 98% confidence interval for the true proportion of the times that the vending machine will fail.

15. The following sample statistics were obtained for the purpose of estimating the difference in the mean weights of college male and female students:

	n	$\bar{x}$	$\hat{s}$
Female	40	119.5	11.9
Male	50	173.8	18.9

    Construct the 95% and 98% confidence intervals for the difference between the mean weights of college male and female students.

16. The personnel manager of an automobile manufacturing company has examined the records of 35 randomly selected days to determine what percentage of the company's work force calls in sick on any given day. For this sample, the average proportion absent each day is 0.045 and the associated sample standard deviation is 0.0120.

    a) Give a point estimate for the proportion of the total work force that will call in sick on any given day.

    b) Estimate the population standard deviation associated with this call-in sick rate.

17. The mean grade point average for a sample of 49 students at a university business school is 2.45. Previous studies have determined that the population standard deviation is 0.7. If we wanted to construct intervals around sample means that would include the true mean grade point average 99.7 percent of the time, what interval would we construct?

18. From a random sample of 36 New York City civil service personnel, the average age and the sample standard deviation were found to be 38 years and 4.5 years respectively. Construct a 95% confidence interval for the mean age of Civil servants in New York City.

19. In a random selection of 81 of the 2,200 intersections in a small city, the mean number of automobile accidents per year was determined to be 3.2 and the sample standard deviation 0.9.

   a) Estimate the standard deviation of the population from the sample standard deviation.

   b) Estimate the standard error of the mean for this finite population.

   c) Construct a 95% confidence interval for the mean number of accidents per intersection per year.

20. A market research survey in which 64 purchasers were contacted found that 72 percent of all purchases of a nationally distributed food product were motivated by the product's advertising.

   a) Estimate the standard error of the proportion of purchases motivated by advertising.

   b) Construct a 90% confidence interval for this population proportion.

21. A U.S Coast Guard survey of 300 small boats in the Cape Cod area found 120 in violation of one or more major safety regulations. Given a confidence level of 0.98, construct a confidence for the proportion of unsafe small boats.

22. The maintenance department of a large denim manufacturing plan is responsible for 1,200 looms. The department manager has determined that 45 percent of the breakdowns, in a sample of 64, resulted from improper maintenance. Construct a 95% confidence interval for the population proportion of breakdowns due to improper maintenance.

23. A medical research team feels confident that a serum they have developed will cure 75 percent of the patients suffering from a certain disease. How large should the sample size be for the team to be 98% certain that the sample proportion of cures is within 0.04 of the proportion of all cases that the serum will cure?

24. A real estate developer wants to determine the average time required to sell a house in one of his developments. From previous experience the population standard deviation is known to be 9 days. How large should the sample be for the developer to be 95% confident that the sample average is within 2 days of the true average?

25. A manufacturer of a synthetic fiber wished to estimate the mean breaking strength of the fiber. An experiment is devised in which the breaking strengths (in pounds) are observed for 16 strands randomly selected from the process. The strengths are: 20.8, 20.6, 21.0, 20.9, 19.9, 20.2, 19.8, 19.6, 20.9, 21.1, 20.4, 20.6, 19.7, 19.6, 20.3, and 20.7. Assuming that the breaking strength of each fiber is normally distributed with a known standard deviation of $\sigma = 0.45$ pounds, construct a 98% confidence interval estimate for the true average breaking strength of the fiber.

26. The chamber of Commerce in a large city is interested in estimating the average amount of money that people attending conventions spend for meals, lodging, and entertainment per day. Sixteen persons were randomly selected from various conventions taking place in this city and were asked to record their expenditures for a given

day. The following information was obtained in dollars: 150, 175, 163, 148, 142, 189, 135, 174, 168, 152, 158, 184, 134, 146, 155, 163. If we assume the amount spent per day is a normally distributed variable, determine 90%, 95% and 98% confidence intervals for the true average amount.

27. Two state supported universities have distinct methods of registering students at the beginning of each semester. The two universities wish to compare the average time it takes students to go through registration. The registration times of 100 randomly selected students were observed at each university. The sample means and sample standard deviations obtained are:

$$n_1 = 100 \quad \bar{x}_1 = 50.2 \quad \hat{s}_1 = 4.8$$

$$n_2 = 100 \quad \bar{x}_2 = 52.9 \quad \hat{s}_2 = 5.4$$

If we assume sampling is from independent normal populations with equal variances,

a) Determine 90%, 95%, and 99% confidence interval estimates for the difference of mean registration times at the two universities. Based on this evidence, can we conclude that a real difference in mean registration time exists?

b) If we make certain that $n_1 = n_2 = n$, what sample size n is needed to make sure that the maximum error $(e_{max} = \Delta\bar{x} - \Delta\mu)$ does not exceed 1 unit, with 99% confidence?

28. Auditing firms usually select a random sample of a bank's customers to confirm checking account balances as reported by the bank. If an auditing firm is interested in estimating the proportion of accounts for which there is a discrepancy between customer and bank, how many accounts should be selected so that with 99% confidence the sample proportion will be within 0.05 units of the true proportion?

29. A manufacturer claims that the production percent defective of his product is 1% (or 0.01). Suppose that out of 200 items randomly selected and inspected, we find 8 defectives. Determine 90%, 95%, and 99% confidence intervals for the true proportion defective in this production process. Based on these results can we accept the manufacturer's claim?

30. A sample of 50 workers was selected from each of two factories to study the amount of time required to complete a complicated assembly. The data produced $\bar{x}_A = 59$ minutes and $\hat{s}_A = 10$ minutes for factory A and $\bar{x}_B = 55$ minutes and $\hat{s}_B = 8$ minutes for factory B. Construct 95%, 98% and 99% confidence intervals for the difference of the mean times. Statistically speaking, are these means equal?

31. A sample of 400 second-grade students was given an achievement test in arithmetic. The 180 girls in the sample had an average score of 80 and a standard deviation of 20, while the 220 boys had an average of 82 and a standard deviation of 22. Construct a 95% confidence interval for the true mean difference $\Delta\mu = \mu_B - \mu_G$. Did boys and girls score equally, on the average, on this test?

32. A manufacturing company wishes to estimate the proportion of defective units that it produces. To do so it decides to take a sample of size n and find the proportion of defectives in the sample. It decides that its estimate must have a probability of 0.95 of being in the interval $(p - 0.04, p + 0.04)$.

a) If it is known from earlier experience that each lot contains 60 percent good units, determine the sample size needed.

b) The company has a rule that if the sample proportion of defectives is larger than (or equal to) 0.3, it will stop production. If the true proportion is 0.2 (*i.e.*, if $\pi = 0.20$) what is the probability of stopping production, for the sample size found in part (a)?

33. Detectives followed 1,647 shoppers through department stores, and they discovered that 7.4 percent of the women and 5.0 percent of men were involved in "minor" shoplifting. Assuming that 70 percent of the shoppers were women, construct a 90% confidence interval and use it to determine whether there is sufficient evidence to conclude that a gender difference in shoplifting exists.

34. You have been asked to construct a 95% confidence interval for μ such that: $P[\bar{x} - 1 \le \mu \le \bar{x} + 1] = 0.95$. If the population standard deviation $= 5$ and n is large enough so that $\bar{x}$ is normally distributed, what is the sample size needed to obtain this confidence interval?

35. A random sample poll taken for a political candidate results in 40% of the sample favoring the candidate, with a maximum error of 3%.

    a) If we want to be 95% confident, what is the sample size needed?

    b) A second random sample poll, conducted a week later, with 900 observations indicated support from 46% of the sample. Construct a 95% confidence interval and determine if there has been a change in the percent of the population who support the candidate.

36. Determine the sample size necessary under the following conditions:

    a) To estimate μ with $\sigma = 44$, $e_{max} = 3$, and 95% confidence.

    b) To estimate μ with the confidence interval $P[20 \le \mu \le 88] = 0.9$ and $e_{max} = 2$.

    c) To estimate π, with unknown π, with $e_{max} = 0.04$ and 98% confidence.

    d) To estimate π, with $e_{max} = 0.03$ and 95% confidence interval. Use $\pi = 0.7$.

37. A company is interested in estimating μ, the mean number of days of sick leave taken by all its employees. The firm's statistician selects at random 100 personnel files and notes the number of sick days taken by each employee. The following sample statistics are computed: $\bar{x} = 12.2$ days and $\hat{s} = 10$ days.

    a) Estimate μ using a 99% confidence interval.

    b) How many personnel files would the statistician have to select in order to estimate μ to within 2 days with a 99% confidence interval?

38. The quality control manager at a light bulb factory needs to estimate the mean life of a large shipment of light bulbs. The process standard deviation is known to be 100 hours. A random sample of 64 light bulbs indicated a sample mean life of 350 hours.

    a) Set up a 95% confidence interval estimate of the true population mean life of light bulbs in this shipment.

    b) Do you think that the manufacturer has the right to state that the light bulbs last an average of 400 hours? Explain.

    c) Does the population of light bulb life have to be normally distributed here? Explain.

    d) Suppose the process standard deviation changed to 80 hours. What would be now the answers of parts (a) and (b)?

39. The telephone company wants to estimate the proportion of households that would purchase an additional telephone line if it were offered at a substantially reduced installation cost. A random sample of 500 households is selected and the results indicate that 135 of the households would purchase the additional line.

    a) Set up a 99% confidence interval estimate of the population proportion of households that would purchase the additional line.

    b) How would the manager, in charge of promotional programs concerning residential customers, use the results of part (a)?

40. A survey is planned to determine the mean annual family medical expenses of employees of a large company. The management of the company wishes to be 95% confident that the sample mean is correct to within ± \$50 of the true population mean annual family medical expenses. A previous study had established that the standard deviation is equal to \$400.

  a) How large a sample size is needed?

  b) If management wants to be correct to within ± \$25, what sample size is necessary?

41. The auditor of a large bank wishes to estimate the proportion of monthly statements for the bank's depositors that have mistakes of various types, and he specifies a confidence coefficient of 0.99 and a maximum error of 0.25 percent (or $e_{max} = 0.0025$).

  a) If no information is available on the true proportion of the monthly statements, what is the sample size required?

  b) If the auditor, according to his past experience, believes that the true proportion of statements with mistakes is $\pi = 0.01$, what is the sample size required?

42. Two groups of patients suffering from chronic headaches, A and B, consist of 200 and 100 individuals, respectively. The first group of patients are given a new kind of headache pill and the second conventional pills. The results are that 15 patients from group A, and 12 patients from group B found immediate relief. In view of their findings, can we conclude that there is a real difference in the proportions of patients who find immediate relief from these two kinds of pills? Why or why not? Construct a 99% confidence interval and comment.

SOLUTIONS

1. a) The Best Point Estimate for μ is $\overline{x}$, or $\mu = \overline{x} = 5650$.

  b) Since $n = 36 > 30$ (σ is also known) $\overline{x}$ is normally distributed with:

$$E(\overline{x}) = \mu = 5650 \text{ and } \sigma(\overline{x}) = \frac{\sigma}{\sqrt{n}} = \frac{800}{\sqrt{36}} = \frac{800}{6} = \frac{400}{3}$$

Then $P[\overline{x} - Z_{\alpha/2}\,\sigma(\overline{x}) \leq \mu \leq \overline{x} + Z_{\alpha/2}\,\sigma(\overline{x})] = 1 - \alpha$

or $P\left[5650 - 1.96\left(\frac{400}{3}\right) \leq \mu \leq 5650 + 1.96\left(\frac{400}{3}\right)\right] = 0.95$

or $P[5,388.67 \leq \mu \leq 5,911.33] = 0.95$.

  c) $n = \left[\frac{Z_{\alpha/2} \cdot \sigma}{\varepsilon_{max}}\right]^2 = \left[\frac{2.58 \cdot 800}{100}\right]^2 = (20.64)^2 = 426.0096 = 427.$

2. a) The Best Point Estimators are:
    I) for $\mu = \overline{x} = 22$, II) for $\sigma = \hat{s} = 3$ and III) for $\sigma^2 = \hat{s}^2 = (\hat{s})^2 = (3)^2 = 9$.

  b) UNBIASEDNESS, CONSISTENCY, EFFICIENCY, SUFFICIENCY.

  c) Since $n = 49 > 30$, $\overline{x}$ is Normally distributed with: $E(\overline{x}) = \mu = 22$ and

$$\sigma(\overline{x}) = \frac{\sigma}{\sqrt{n}} \approx \frac{s}{\sqrt{n}} = \frac{3}{\sqrt{49}} = \frac{3}{7}; \text{ Then}$$
$$P[\overline{x} - Z_{\alpha/2}\sigma(\overline{x}) \leq \mu \leq \overline{x} + Z_{\alpha/2}\sigma(\overline{x})] = 1 - \alpha$$

or $P\left[22 - 2.33\left(\dfrac{3}{7}\right) \le \mu \le 22 + 2.33\left(\dfrac{3}{7}\right)\right] = 0.98$

or $P[21.0014 \le \mu \le 22.9986] = 0.98$.

3. The estimator for the population parameter $\Delta\mu = \mu_1 - \mu_2$ is $\Delta\bar{x} = \bar{x}_1 - \bar{x}_2$ which, because $n_1 = 40 > 30$ and $n_2 = 56 > 30$, is Normally distributed with:
   $E(\Delta\bar{x}) = \mu_1 - \mu_2 = \Delta\mu$ and

   $$\sigma(\Delta\bar{x}) = \sqrt{\dfrac{\hat{s}_1^2}{n_1} + \dfrac{\hat{s}_2^2}{n_2}} = \sqrt{\dfrac{(2.5)^2}{40} + \dfrac{(3.1)^2}{56}} = \sqrt{0.15625 + 0.17161}$$

   $$= \sqrt{0.32786} = 0.572596$$

   Also, $\Delta\bar{x} = \bar{x}_1 - \bar{x}_2 = 20.2 - 21.0 = -0.8$

   Therefore, $P[\Delta\bar{x} - Z_{\alpha/2}\sigma(\Delta\bar{x}) \le \Delta\mu \le \Delta\bar{x} + Z_{\alpha/2}\sigma(\Delta\bar{x})] = 1 - \alpha$

   or $P[-0.8 - 2.33(0.57259) \le \Delta\mu \le -0.8 + 2.33\,(0.57259)] = 0.98$

   or $P[-0.8 - 1.334 \le \Delta\mu \le -0.8 + 1.334] = 0.98$

   or $P[-2.134 \le \Delta\mu \le 0.534] = 0.98$.

4. a) A Point Estimate for $\mu = \bar{x} = 9.87$.

   b) Since the population from which the sample is drawn is normally distributed, $\bar{x}$ will also be normal regardless of the value of n, with: $E(\bar{x}) = \mu$ and

   $$\sigma(\bar{x}) = \dfrac{\sigma}{\sqrt{n}} = \dfrac{0.27}{\sqrt{15}} = \dfrac{0.27}{3.87298} = 0.06971$$

   Therefore, $P[\bar{x} - Z_{\alpha/2}\,\sigma(\bar{x}) \le \mu \le \bar{x} + Z_{\alpha/2}\,\sigma(\bar{x})] = 1 - \alpha$

   or $P[9.87 - Z_{\alpha/2}(0.06971) \le \mu \le 9.87 + Z_{\alpha/2}\,(0.6971)] = 1 - \alpha$

   when $1 - \alpha = 0.95 \rightarrow Z_{\alpha/2} = 1.96$ and $P[9.73336 \le \mu \le 10.00664] = 0.95$

   when $1 - \alpha = 0.99 \rightarrow Z_{\alpha/2} = 2.58$ and $P[9.69015 \le \mu \le 10.04985] = 0.99$.

5. Since $n = 1200$ and $x = 645$, $p = \dfrac{x}{n} = \dfrac{645}{1200} = 0.5375$,

   and $\sigma_p = \sqrt{\dfrac{p(1-p)}{n}} = \sqrt{\dfrac{(0.5375)(0.4625)}{1200}} = 0.0144$

   Then $P\left[p - Z_{\alpha/2}\,\sigma_p \le \pi \le p + Z_{\alpha/2}\,\sigma_p\right] = 1 - \alpha$

   or $P[0.5375 - 2.33(0.0144) \le \pi \le 0.5375 + 2.33(0.0144)] = 0.98$

   or $P[0.5039 \le \pi \le 0.5711] = 0.98$

   Since $\pi > 0.5$, the President has the support of the majority of voters.

6. Because $n_1 = 100 > 30$ and $n_2 = 100 > 30$, the estimator for the population parameter $\Delta\pi = \pi_1 - \pi_2$, is $\Delta p = p_1 - p_2$ which is Normally distributed,

   with $E(\Delta p) = \Delta\pi$ and $\sigma(\Delta p) = \sqrt{\dfrac{p_1(1-p_1)}{n_1} + \dfrac{p_2(1-p_2)}{n_2}}$

   and or $\sigma(\Delta p) = \sigma_1(\Delta p) = \sqrt{\dfrac{0.60(0.40)}{100} + \dfrac{0.4(0.6)}{100}} = \sqrt{\dfrac{0.24}{100} + \dfrac{0.24}{100}} = \sqrt{\dfrac{0.48}{100}}$

   $$= \sqrt{0.0048} = 0.069282$$

Note: we could also first define: $\bar{p} = \dfrac{n_1 p_1 + n_2 p_2}{n_1 + n_2} = \dfrac{100(0.6) + 100(0.4)}{200} = 0.5$

and then $\sigma(\Delta p) = \sigma_2(\Delta p)$

$$= \sqrt{\bar{p}(1 - \bar{p})\left[\frac{n_1 + n_2}{n_1 n_2}\right]} = \sqrt{(0.5)(0.5)\left(\frac{200}{10,000}\right)}$$

$$= \sqrt{\frac{0.5}{100}} = 0.0707$$

Then $P\left[\Delta p - Z_{\alpha/2}\,\sigma(\Delta p) \le \Delta\pi \le \Delta p + Z_{\alpha/2}\,\sigma(\Delta p)\right] = 1 - \alpha$

For $\Delta p = p_1 - p_2 = 0.6 - 0.4 = 0.2$, $1 - \alpha = 0.95$ and $Z_{\alpha/2} = 1.96$

We obtain $P\left[0.2 - 1.96\,\sigma(\Delta p) \le \Delta\pi \le 0.2 + 1.96\,\sigma(\Delta p)\right] = 0.95$

For $\sigma(\Delta p) = \sigma_1(\Delta p) = 0.069282 \rightarrow$

$\quad P[0.2 - 0.13579 \le \Delta\pi \le 0.2 + 0.13579] = 0.95$

or $P[0.06421 \le \Delta\pi \le 0.33579] = 0.95$

For $\sigma(\Delta p) = \sigma_2(\Delta p) = 0.0707 \rightarrow$

$\quad P[0.2 - 0.13857 \le \Delta\pi \le 0.2 + 0.13857] = 0.95$

$\quad P[0.06143 \le \Delta\pi \le 0.33857] = 0.95$

There is, obviously, a small difference in the widths of the 2 intervals, but a very small one. In both cases the conclusion is, because the value $\Delta\pi = \pi_1 - \pi_2 = 0$ is not part of either Confidence interval, that men and women differ significantly on the divorce issue.

7. Because $n = 30$ and $n = 40$, $\bar{x}$ is normally distributed with $E(\bar{x}) = \mu$ and

$\sigma(\bar{x}) = \dfrac{\alpha}{\sqrt{n}} = \dfrac{\hat{s}}{\sqrt{n}}$; Therefore:

$P[\bar{x} - Z_{\alpha/2}\,\sigma(\bar{x}) \le \mu \le \bar{x} + Z_{\alpha/2}\,\sigma(\bar{x})] = 1 - \alpha$

a) $\bar{x} = \dfrac{\sum x_i}{n} = \dfrac{492.50}{30} = 16.417$ and

$$\hat{s}^2 = \frac{n\sum x_i - \left(\sum x_i\right)^2}{n(n-1)} = \frac{30(24,402.75) - (492.50)^2}{30(29)} = 562.6738$$

and $\sigma(\bar{x}) = \sqrt{\dfrac{\hat{s}^2}{n}} = \sqrt{\dfrac{562.6738}{30}} = \sqrt{18.7558} = 4.33$,

and $Z_{\alpha/2} = Z_{0.05} = 1.645$

Therefore $P[9.294 \le \mu \le 23.540] = 0.90$

b) $\bar{x} = 12.3125$, $\hat{s}^2 = \dfrac{40(24,402.75) - (492.50)^2}{40(39)} = 470.226762$,

$\sigma(\bar{x}) = \sqrt{\dfrac{\hat{s}^2}{n}} = 3.4286$, and $Z_{\alpha/2} = Z_{0.05} = 1.645$;

Therefore $P[6.672 \le \mu \le 17.9526] = 0.90$

c) $\bar{x} = 16.417$; $\sigma(\bar{x}) = 4.33$, and $Z_{\alpha/2} = Z = 1.96$.

Therefore $P[7.9302 \le \mu \le 24.9042] = 0.95$

8. a) $\mu = \overline{x} = 5650$;

b) $P\left[5650 - 1.96\left(\dfrac{800}{\sqrt{36}}\right) \leq \mu \leq 5650 + 96\left(\dfrac{800}{\sqrt{36}}\right)\right] = 0.95$

   or $P[5388.67 \leq \mu \leq 5911.33]$;

c) $P[5306 \leq \mu \leq 5944] = 0.99)$

9. $n = \left[Z_{\alpha/2 \cdot \sigma} / e_{max}\right]^2 = [1.96 \times 12 / 4]^2 = (1.96 \times 3)^2 = (5.88)^2 = 34.57 \approx 35$

10. a) $P\left[14.0 - 1.645\left(\dfrac{1.5}{\sqrt{225}}\right) \leq \mu \leq 14.0 + 1.645\left(\dfrac{1.5}{\sqrt{225}}\right)\right] = 0.90$ or

   $P[13.8355 \leq \mu \leq 14.1645] = 0.90$;

b) $P[13.767 \leq \mu \leq 14.233] = 0.98$

10 Classical Theory of Testing

Hypothesis Testing is a statistical procedure for checking the validity of claims, where a claim is a belief that something is true.

The claim is usually expressed as a parameter value of some population, and the solution of the problem depends in identifying the sampling distribution of the estimator of this parameter. In general, the sampling distributions of the estimators (which usually are the descriptive statistics we learned how to calculate in Chapter 3 of this book) depend on the sample size, n.

When n is large ($n \geq 30$), we speak of "Large Sample Statistics" which usually implies that the sampling distributions of the estimators of interest are normally distributed, and the normal distribution is used to solve the hypothesis testing problem.

When n is small ($n < 30$), we speak of "Small Sample Statistics" which implies that the sampling distributions of the estimators of interest are chi-square $\left(\chi^2\right)$, F, or t, and these distributions are used in the solution of the hypothesis testing problem. These distributions and their applications are discussed extensively in Chapter 11.

In this chapter, when n is large, we solve the hypothesis testing problem for claims which are expressed in terms of the population parameters: μ = population mean and π = population proportion, when sampling is performed from a single population. When sampling is performed from two separate populations and both n_1 and n_2 are large, we also solve the hypothesis testing problem which is expressed in terms of the population parameters: $\Delta\mu = \mu_1 - \mu_2 =$ difference of two population means, and $\Delta\pi = \pi_1 - \pi_2 =$ difference of two population proportions. Also discussed in this chapter are the Power and OC (Operating Characteristics) Functions and their use and application as tests, and the determination of the sample size needed to satisfy predetermined levels of Type I and Type II errors (*i.e.*, levels of α and β errors).

10.1   Introduction

In this chapter we introduce, discuss and apply a statistical decision-making procedure known as hypothesis Testing, under the assumption that the sample size n is large (*i.e.*, $n \geq 30$). The implication of this assumption is that the sampling distributions of the sample statistics used in decision-making (like $\bar{x}$, for example) become normally distributed and, as a consequence the required probability calculations are made using the standard normal distribution table (Note: When $n < 30$, we are dealing with small sample statistics, and this topic is thoroughly discussed in the following chapter, Chapter 11).

Hypothesis Testing is a procedure for testing the validity of claims, with the understanding that errors can occur because, usually, the information available is incomplete. By getting more and more information we can make the error smaller and smaller but, we can not completely eliminate the error unless we have complete (or perfect) information, and this can occur only if we are conducting a Census study but never in a sampling study. How is this testing formulated and performed? The following steps summarize the procedure:

1. Express the claim (which is usually a statement that something is true; for example: the average height of a human being is 68 inches is an example of such a claim) as a parameter value of some population. For the example above we can set $\mu = 68$, where μ is the mean height of all human beings. In the Hypothesis Testing sense we test this value against the alternative value $\mu \neq 68$, and use sample information to decide which of the two choices is better.

2. Identify the estimator of the parameter used in the claim assignment, the sampling distribution of the estimator and its Expected value and Standard deviation. For

example, if the parameter is μ, its estimator is $\bar{x}$ and when $n \geq 30$, in accordance with the Central Limit Theorem, $\bar{x}$ is normally distributed with $E(\bar{x}) = \mu$ and $\sigma(\bar{x}) = \dfrac{\sigma}{\sqrt{n}}$, where μ and σ are, respectively, the population mean and standard deviation, and n is the sample size.

3. We then divide the interval of variation of the estimator into 2 mutually exclusive regions: The Rejection region and the Non-Rejection region (or Acceptance region). The size of the Rejection region is usually equal to the error that we are willing to accept in this testing, and this guides us to select the appropriate z-values, from the standard normal table, which divide the total interval of the standard normal function into the Rejection and Non-Rejection regions. The area, or Probability of the Rejection region is equal to α, while the probability of the Non-Rejection region is equal to $1 - \alpha$. Then, for the claimed value $\mu = 68$ and its alternative, $\mu \neq 68$, as we will see later, the Rejection region will be at both ends of the normal distribution and is defined as: $Z \geq Z_{\alpha/2}$ or $Z \leq -Z_{\alpha/2}$, while the non-Rejection region will be: $-Z_{\alpha/2} \leq Z \leq Z_{\alpha/2}$, or in diagram form:

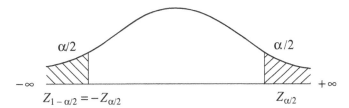

Figure 10.1 Rejection Region (Shaded Area) for H$_0$: $\mu = 68$ vs H$_1$: $\mu \neq 68$

Notes:
1. The total area under the standard normal density function $f(Z)$, and in fact under any proper probability density function, is always equal to 1.
2. For a continuous random variable,

$$P(a \leq X \leq b) \equiv P(a < X < b) \text{ because}$$

$$P(X = a) = 0 \text{ and } P(X - b) = 0 \tag{10.1}$$

But this is not the case for discrete variables where

$$P(a \leq X \leq b) > P\left(a < X < b\right) \text{ because}$$

$$P\left(X = a\right) > 0 \text{ and } P\left(X = b\right) > 0. \tag{10.2}$$

3. In Figure 10.1, α is the probability of rejecting the validity of the claim, when the claim is true. Because of the symmetry of the normal distribution, and the way the stated claim is expressed, the α value is divided into two equal parts (with value of $\alpha/2$ for each) as shown. Then $Z_{\alpha/2}$ and $Z_{1-\alpha/2}$ are the appropriate values from the Z-distribution which divide the total area under the standard normal density function (which is equal to 1) into the rejection and non-rejection regions.

4. We then calculate the value of the test statistic Z^*, where:

$$Z^* = \frac{(\text{Value of Estimator}) - (\text{Claimed Value of the Parameter})}{(\text{Standard deviation of the Estimator})} \tag{10.3}$$

$$= \frac{\bar{x} - \mu_o}{\sigma(\bar{x})} = \frac{\bar{x} - \mu_0}{\sigma/\sqrt{n}} = \frac{\bar{x} - 68}{\sigma/\sqrt{n}} \text{ (for the above example)} \tag{10.4}$$

5. We now compare the value of the test statistic ($Z*$) to the rejection region and:
   a) Accept the validity of the claim (that $\mu = 68$) if

$$-Z_{\alpha/2} < Z* < Z_{\alpha/2} \qquad (10.5)$$

   b) Reject the validity of the claim (therefore $\mu \neq 68$) if

$$Z* > Z_{\alpha/2} \text{ or if } Z* < -Z_{\alpha/2} \qquad (10.6)$$

10.2 Statistical Hypotheses Defined

A statistical hypothesis is an assumption (or claim) about the type of distribution or the parameters (*i.e.*, mean $= \mu$, variance $= \sigma^2$, etc.) of a random variable. Usually it is a statement that something is true. Statistical hypotheses can be simple or composite. A simple hypothesis is one that gives a complete specification of a probability distribution (for example X is a normally distributed variable with mean $= \mu = 50$ and variance $= \sigma^2 = 25$) or one that includes only a single value of the parameter (for example the mean of a population, μ, is equal to 50, or $\mu = 50$).

A composite hypothesis is one which does not completely define the random variable (for example X is a normally distributed random variable with $\mu = 50$ but unknown variance $= \sigma^2$) or one that includes two or more values of the parameter (for example, $\mu \geq 50$). In hypothesis testing we are usually interested in selecting one of two courses of action (a_0 and a_1), as shown in Figure 10.2 below:

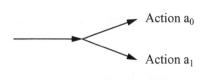

Figure 10.2 Choosing one of two courses of action

Because of this, we define two Hypotheses, H_0 or null hypothesis, and H_1 or Alternative hypothesis, where:

1. H_0, the null hypothesis, is the set of parameter values which make action a_0 better than a_1.
   and
2. H_1, the alternative hypothesis, is the set of parameter values which make action a_1 better than action a_0.

Note: The two hypotheses, H_0 and H_1, are complementary in nature because the set of parameter values in H_0 and the set of parameter values in H_1 is the entire real line, as we will shortly see below.

In the hypothesis testing procedure that we will develop later, we will be testing H_0 against H_1, under the assumption that H_0 is true. But when we do, there is always the possibility of making an error, because the testing is performed on the basis of limited information which leads to two different types of errors as we will show below. We can not eliminate these errors but we can make them smaller by using more information (or a larger sample size n).

10.3   Possible Number and Type of Hypothesis Tests

There are 3 types of possible hypothesis tests and we will illustrate them in terms of a population parameter. For this reason, we introduce the following notation:

Let θ = population parameter of interest

$\hat{\theta}$ = estimator of the population parameter θ, and $\hat{\theta}$ is normally distributed   (10.7)

$\sigma(\hat{\theta})$ = standard deviation of estimator $\hat{\theta}$, which is the estimator of the population parameter θ

The three possible tests are: 1) The Lower-Tailed Test, 2) The Double-Tailed Test, and 3) The Upper-Tailed Test, each of which is discussed below, in terms of the hypothesized parameter value, $\theta = \theta_0$.

a) The Lower-Tailed Test

In this test H_0 is defined as $H_0: \theta \geq \theta_0$ (*i.e.*, the population parameter θ is greater than or equal to the hypothesized value θ_0) while H_1 is defined as $H_1: \theta < \theta_0$ (*i.e.*, the population parameter θ is less than the hypothesized value, θ_0. This formulation of H_0 and H_1 places the Rejection region (*i.e.*, the region where H_0 is not very likely to occur) in the left (or lower tail) of the normal distribution of $\hat{\theta}$ (the estimator of the parameter θ), as shown in the diagram below:

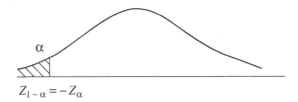

$$Z_{1-\alpha} = -Z_\alpha$$

Figure 10.3 Rejection Region (Shaded Area) of a Lower-Tailed Test

Then, $H_0: \theta \geq \theta_0$ will be rejected (and $H_1: \theta < \theta_0$ will be accepted) if and only if:

$$Z^* = \frac{\hat{\theta} - \theta_0}{\sigma(\hat{\theta})} \leq Z_{1-\alpha} \qquad (10.8)$$

Note: In Figure 10.3, α is the probability of rejecting the validity of H_0 when H_0 is true, while $Z_{1-\alpha} = -Z_\alpha$ (because of the symmetry of $f(Z)$) which divides the total area under $f(Z)$ into the rejection region (shaded area, with probability $= \alpha$) and non-rejection region with probability $= 1 - \alpha$.

b) The Double-Tailed Test

In this test H_0 is defined as $H_0: \theta = \theta_0$ (*i.e.*, the population parameter θ is equal to the hypothesized value θ_0) while H_1 is defined as $H_1: \theta \neq \theta_0$ (*i.e.*, the population parameter θ is different than the hypothesized value θ_0). This formulation of H_0 and H_1 places the rejection region at both ends of the normal distribution (*i.e.*, the rejection region is split into 2 equal parts, each with probability of rejecting H_0, when true, of $\alpha/2$) as shown below. Once again α is the probability of rejecting H_0 when true, and $Z_{\alpha/2}$ and $Z_{1-\alpha/2} = -Z_{\alpha/2}$ are the values of the standardized normal variable Z (coming from the standard normal table when α is defined) which divides the total interval of the standard normal density function into the rejection (shaded regions) and non-rejection regions, shown in Figure 10.4 below.

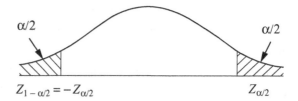

Figure 10.4 Rejection Region (Shaded Area) of a Double-Tailed Test

Then, $H_0: \theta = \theta_0$ will be rejected (and $H_1: \theta \neq \theta_0$ will be accepted) is and only if

$$Z^* = \frac{\hat{\theta} - \theta_0}{\sigma(\hat{e})} < Z_{1-\alpha/2} \quad \text{or} \quad Z^* = \frac{\hat{\theta} - \theta_0}{\sigma(\hat{\theta})} > Z_{\alpha/2}$$

Note that $Z_{1-\alpha/2} = -Z_{\alpha/2}$ because of the symmetry of the normal density function.

c) The Upper-Tailed Test

In this test H_0 is defined as $H_0: \theta \leq \theta_0$ (*i.e.*, the population parameter θ is equal to or less than the hypothesized value θ_0) while H_1 is defined as $H_1: \theta > \theta_0$ (*i.e.*, the population parameter is greater than the hypothesized value θ_0).

Such formulation of H_0 and H_1 places the rejection region at the upper tail (or right tail) of the standard normal density function, with probability of rejecting H_0 (when H_0 is true) of α, while the non-rejection region, with probability $1 - \alpha$, starts at $-\infty$ and goes up to Z_α, which is the Z-value (obtained from the standard normal table) which divides the total interval of $f(Z)$ into the rejection and non-rejection regions, for a given α value, as shown in Figure 10.5 below:

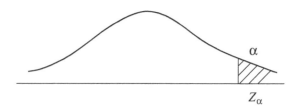

Figure 10.5 Rejection Region (Shaded Area) of an Upper-Tailed Test

Then, $H_0: \theta \leq \theta_0$ will be rejected (and $H_1: \theta > \theta_0$ will be accepted) if and only if

$$Z^* = \frac{\hat{\theta} - \theta_0}{\sigma(\theta)} > Z_\alpha \qquad (10.9)$$

10.4 Errors and Risks in Testing

We have stated previously that when testing H_0 against H_1, using limited information errors may occur; *i.e.*, we can reject H_0 when H_0 is true, or accept H_0 when H_0 is false. These errors can not be eliminated as long as we use limited information but can be made smaller and smaller as we use more and more information. The objective of this section is to show how errors in testing arise, through an example. In later sections of this chapter we will see how the type and size of these errors can be controlled.

Example 1

A Person is accused of a crime and is tried by his or her peers (*i.e.*, a jury). Under our system of justice the person is considered innocent until the evidence shows he or she is guilty. Since the evidence presented by the defense team and the prosecuting team is conflicting and incomplete (if there are no eyewitnesses to the alleged crime), it is obvious that the possibility of error (in the decision of the jury) exists. Assume also that only 2 verdicts are possible; *i.e.*, innocent and guilty (*i.e.*, no hung jury verdict is considered).

Solution To be more specific in the identification and definition of possible errors in the decision, let us formulate the hypotheses H_0 and H_1 as follows:

H_0: The accused person is innocent

and H_1: The accused person is guilty

Then, the jury on the basis of the presented evidence may find the accused person innocent (*i.e.*, it accepts or does not reject H_0) or guilty (*i.e.*, it rejects H_0). Given that the accused person is either innocent or guilty (and only the person and God know for sure, if there are no eyewitnesses), we can draw the following decision diagram:

Table 10.1 Decision Diagram for Example 1		
	Nature of Accused Person	
Jury Action	H_0: Person is Innocent	H_1: Person is guilty
Person is Innocent (Do Not Reject H_0)	Correct Decision	Do Not Reject H_0 when False β = Type II error
Person is Guilty (Reject H_0)	Reject H_0 when True α = Type I error	Correct Decision

From Table 10.1 we can see that there are 4 possible decisions for the jury and only 2 of them are correct; *i.e.*, if the accused person is innocent and the jury finds him/her innocent, or if the accused person is guilty and the jury finds him/her guilty. But there are 2 other possibilities, both of them erroneous decisions, namely:

1. The accused person is innocent but the jury finds him/her Guilty. In terms of the hypotheses H_0 and H_1 we formulated previously, this erroneous decision can be stated as: Reject H_0, when H_0 is true. The error which occurs when a true H_0 is rejected, is called a Type I error and is represented by the lower case Greek letter α, or

$$\alpha = \text{Type I error} \qquad (10.11)$$

   This is the same α which was used to define the rejection regions in Figures 10.1, 10.3, 10.4, and 10.5.

2. The accused person is Guilty but the jury finds him/her Innocent. In terms of the hypotheses H_0 and H_1 that we have formulated previously, this erroneous decision can be stated as: Do not Reject H_0, when H_0 is false. It is obvious that this error (*i.e.*, Do not Reject H_0 when H_0 is false) is different from the previous error (*i.e.*, Reject H_0 when H_0 is true). It is called a Type II error and is represented by the lower case Greek letter β, or

$$\beta = \text{Type II error} \qquad (10.12)$$

Obviously, it is desirable to keep both α and β errors as small as possible, but this is not always an easy task. For this reason, in the beginning, we will control only the α

(*i.e.*, Type I error) and accept whatever β (*i.e.*, Type II error) may occur from such an approach. But, in later sections of this chapter, we will attempt to control the size of both the α and β errors.

The probability of committing type I and type II errors are referred to as risks. The maximum probability of the type I error is called the "Level of Significance", and the most often used values of α are:

1. $\alpha = 0.05$; If, when using this α value, H_0 is rejected, the result is called "significant".
2. $\alpha = 0.01$; If, when using this α value, H_0 is rejected, the result is called "Highly Significant".

Note: If a value for α is not given in a problem, select $\alpha = 0.05$, or $\alpha = 0.01$, or both $\alpha = 0.05$ and $\alpha = 0.01$, or any other value of α. If we believe that H_0 is True, we should assign a very small value to α (like $\alpha = 0.01$). On the other hand, if we believe that H_0 is not True, we should assign to α a relatively large value (like $\alpha = 0.10$, $\alpha = 0.20$, $\alpha = 0.25$).

10.5   Test Statistics and Decision Rules

Having defined the hypotheses H_0 and H_1, the possible tests of hypothesis testing and the errors which can occur during hypothesis testing we need now to state some rules which will allow us to choose between H_0 and H_1.

First we need to select an appropriate test statistic, for the population parameter which is used to express the claim which is being tested, whose sampling distribution is known, when H_0 is true. Usually it is the estimator of the parameter, which expresses the claim, in H_0. For example if the hypothesis being tested is, H_0: $\mu = 60$ vs H_1: $\mu \neq 60$, the test statistic is $\bar{x}$, whose sampling distribution is the Normal distribution, with $E(\bar{x}) = \mu$ and $\sigma(\bar{x}) = \sigma / \sqrt{n}$, where μ and σ are the population parameters μ and σ and n is the sample size, provided that $n \geq 30$ (in accordance with the Central Limit Theorem). Knowing the sampling distribution of the test statistic makes it possible to evaluate the validity of H_0. If we let θ represent the population parameter used to express the claim being tested, and $\hat{\theta}$ represent the sample statistic, which we use as the estimator for the population parameter θ, we proceed as follows:

1. If the sample statistic $(\hat{\theta})$ differs from the hypothesized value θ_0 (*i.e.*, the value of the parameter θ being tested in H_0; for example if the hypothesis being tested is; H_0: $\mu = 60$ vs H_1: $\mu \neq 60$, the parameter $\theta = \mu$ and θ_0 is the value of 60) by a "small" quantity, the difference is interpreted as a "chance variation", due only to random fluctuations in sampling, and H_0 is not rejected.

2. If the difference between $\hat{\theta}$ and θ_0 is "large", *i.e.*, an amount which can not be attributed to random fluctuations in sampling alone, we assume that a real difference exists and H_0 is rejected.

   The decision as to whether to accept or to reject H_0 will be made on the basis of the range of variation of the estimator, $\hat{\theta}$, in a particular sample. The range of variation of $\hat{\theta}$ is divided into 2 disjoint (or mutually exclusive) subsets, or regions, namely:

   a) **The Rejection (or critical)** region, which contains the outcomes which are least favorable to the validity of H_0, and

b) **The Non-Rejection (or Acceptance)** region, which contains the outcomes which are most favorable to the validity of H_0.

The value of the estimator (or sample statistic) $\hat{\theta}$, which divides the range of variation into the rejection and non-rejection regions will be represented by $\hat{\theta} = \hat{\theta}_c$, and it is called the critical value of the estimator.

Note: The Lower and Upper Tailed Tests, which we discussed in section 10.3, each have one critical point, given respectively by $\hat{\theta}_c = Z_{1-\alpha} = -Z_\alpha$ and $\hat{\theta}_c = Z_\alpha$ (see Figures 10.3 and 10.5). The Double-Tailed test has two critical points given by: $\hat{\theta}_{c1} = Z_{1-\alpha/2} = -Z_{\alpha/2}$ and $\hat{\theta}_{c2} = Z_{\alpha/2}$ (See Figure 10.4).

The value of $\hat{\theta}_c$ depends on the following 3 factors:

i) The distribution of the test statistic $\hat{\theta}$. In this chapter $\hat{\theta}$ is assumed to be normally distributed and, therefore, $\hat{\theta}_c$ is expressed in terms of Z-values, obtained from the standard normal table, once the value of α (i.e., probability of rejecting H_0, when H_0 is true) is given. In Chapter 11 it will also be expressed in terms of values from the χ^2, F, and t distributions.

ii) The value of α, which is usually given. If an alpha value is not given, we can select $\alpha = 0.05$, or $\alpha = 0.01$, or both $\alpha = 0.05$ and $\alpha = 0.01$. Then, if the test is a lower-tailed test, the rejection region will be on the left tail of the standard normal distribution and the critical value is: $\hat{\theta}_c = Z_{1-\alpha} = -Z_\alpha$. If the test is an Upper-tailed test, the rejection region will be on the right tail of the standard normal distribution and the critical value is: $\hat{\theta}_c = Z_\alpha$. For a Double-tailed test the rejection region is split into two equal segments, each of size $\alpha/2$, at each tail of the standard normal distribution. The two critical values for this test are given by: $\hat{\theta}_{c1} = Z_{1-\alpha/2} = -Z_{\alpha/2}$ and $\hat{\theta}_{c2} = Z_{\alpha/2}$.

iii) The formulation of the H_1 hypothesis.

A) If H_1 is formulated as $H_1: \theta < \theta_0$, the rejection region will be on the left tail of the standard normal distribution, and the critical value is: $\hat{\theta}_c = Z_{1-\alpha} = -Z_\alpha$.

B) If H_1 is formulated as $H_1: \theta > \theta_0$, the rejection region will be on the right tail of the standard normal distribution, and the critical value is: $\hat{\theta}_c = Z_\alpha$.

C) If H_1 is formulated as $H_1: \theta \neq \theta_0$, the rejection region will be on both tails of the standard normal distribution, and the critical values are: $\hat{\theta}_{c1} = Z_{1-\alpha/2} = -Z_{\alpha/2}$ and $\hat{\theta}_{c2} = Z_{\alpha/2}$.

10.6   Hypothesis Testing Procedure

We can summarize the testing procedure we have been discussing above in terms of the following seven steps.

1. Formulate H_0 and H_1 in accordance with the problem statement at hand.
2. Select the value of α, if one is not given.
3. Identify the estimator $\hat{\theta}$, for the population parameter θ in H_0, its sampling distribution, and state the expected value and standard deviation of the estimator (i.e., $E(\hat{\theta})$ and $\sigma(\hat{\theta})$).
4. Construct the Rejection and Non-Rejection regions, as a function of α and H_1 and the sampling distribution of $\hat{\theta}$. It will be one of the three Rejection/Non-Rejection regions shown in Section 10.3.

5. Calculate the value of the test statistic, using the equation:

$$Z^* = \frac{(\text{Value of Estimator}) - (\text{Value of Parameter in } H_0)}{(\text{Standard Deviation of Estimator})} \tag{10.13}$$

or
$$Z^* = \frac{\hat{\theta} - \theta_0}{\sigma(\hat{\theta})} \tag{10.14}$$

or
$$Z^* = \frac{\bar{x} - \mu_0}{\sigma/n} \quad (\text{If } \theta = \mu \text{ and } \hat{\theta} = \bar{x}) \tag{10.15}$$

6. Compare Z^* to the rejection/Non-Rejection regions.
   a) Reject H_0 if Z^* falls inside the Rejection Region.
   b) Do not Reject H_0 if Z^* falls outside of the Rejection Region.
7. Express in words the mathematical conclusion of step 6.

Note: It is possible to express the statistical decision in terms of the estimator $\hat{\theta}$ rather than Z^*, as follows:

a) If H_0 is not rejected, for a given sample, and we would like to know the values of $\hat{\theta}$ for which H_0 will be rejected, assuming the sample size n and $\sigma(\hat{\theta})$ do not change then, depending on the type of test we perform, we can solve for $\hat{\theta}$ in terms of θ_0, n, $\sigma(\hat{\theta})$, and Z_{critical} and obtain:

   i) If H_0: $\theta \geq \theta_0$ vs H_1: $\theta < \theta_0$, and H_0 is not rejected, we would Reject H_0

   if $Z^* = \dfrac{\hat{\theta} - \theta_0}{\sigma(\hat{\theta})} < -Z_\alpha$, from which, solving for $\hat{\theta}$, we obtain:

   $$\hat{\theta} < \theta_0 - Z_\alpha \, \sigma(\hat{\theta}) \tag{10.16}$$

   ii) If H_0: $\theta \leq \theta_0$ vs H_1: $\theta > \theta_0$, and H_0 is not rejected, we would Reject H_0

   if: $Z^* = \dfrac{(\hat{\theta} - \theta_0)}{\sigma(\hat{\theta})} > Z_\alpha$, from which solving for $\hat{\theta}$, we obtain:

   $$\hat{\theta} > \theta_0 + Z_\alpha \, \sigma(\hat{\theta}) \tag{10.17}$$

   iii) If H_0: $\theta = \theta_0$ vs H_1: $\theta \neq \theta_0$, and H_0 is not rejected, we would reject H_0

   if $Z^* = \dfrac{(\hat{\theta} - \theta_0)}{\sigma(\hat{\theta})} < -Z_{\alpha/2}$ or if $Z^* = \dfrac{(\hat{\theta} - \theta_0)}{\sigma(\hat{\theta})} > Z_{\alpha/2}$, from which,

   solving for $\hat{\theta}$ we obtain:

   $$\hat{\theta} < \theta_0 - Z_{\alpha/2} \, \sigma(\hat{\theta}) \tag{10.18}$$

   or $\hat{\theta} > \theta_0 + Z_{\alpha/2} \, \sigma(\hat{\theta})$

b) If H_0 is rejected, for a given sample, and we would like to know the values of for $\hat{\theta}$ which H_0 will not be rejected, assuming the sample size n and $\sigma(\hat{\theta})$ do not change then, depending on the type of test we perform, we can solve for $\hat{\theta}$ in terms of θ_0, n, $\sigma(\hat{\theta})$, and Z_{critical}, and obtain:

   i) If H_0: $\theta \geq \theta_0$ vs H_1: $\theta < \theta_0$, and H_0 is rejected, we would not reject H_0 if

   $$Z^* = \frac{(\hat{\theta} - \theta_0)}{\sigma(\hat{\theta})} > -Z_\alpha \text{ from which, solving for } \hat{\theta}, \text{ we obtain:}$$

   $$\hat{\theta} > \theta_0 - Z_\alpha \sigma(\hat{\theta}) \tag{10.19}$$

ii) If H_0: $\theta \le \theta_0$ vs H_1: $\theta > \theta_0$, and H_0 is rejected, we would not reject H_0 if

$$Z^* = \frac{(\hat{\theta} - \theta_0)}{\sigma(\hat{\theta})} < Z_\alpha,\ \text{from which, solving for } \theta, \text{ we obtain:}$$

$$\hat{\theta} < \theta_0 + Z_\alpha\ \sigma(\hat{\theta}) \tag{10.20}$$

iii) If H_0: $\theta = \theta_0$ vs H_1: $\theta \ne \theta_0$, and H_0 is rejected, we would not reject H_0 if

$$Z^* = \frac{(\hat{\theta} - \theta_0)}{\sigma(\hat{\theta})} > -Z_{\alpha/2},\ \text{ or if } Z^* = \frac{(\hat{\theta} - \theta_0)}{\sigma(\hat{\theta})} < Z_{\alpha/2}\ \text{ from which,}$$

solving for $\hat{\theta}$, we obtain: $\hat{\theta} > \theta_0 - Z_{\alpha/2}\ \sigma(\hat{\theta})$ or $\hat{\theta} < \theta_0 + Z_{\alpha/2}\ \sigma(\hat{\theta})$, which

when combined, become:

$$\theta_0 - Z_{\alpha/2}\,\sigma(\hat{\theta}) < \hat{\theta} < \theta_0 + Z_{\alpha/2}\,\sigma(\hat{\theta}) \tag{10.21}$$

10.7   Tests of Significance With Fixed Sample Size *n*

We will now apply the above procedure by solving the following problem:

Example 2

A manufacturer of batteries claims that the mean life of his product will exceed 30 hours. A customer wants to buy a large quantity of these batteries if the claim is true. A random sample of 36 such batteries is tested and produces a sample mean of 34 hours. If the standard deviation is known to be: $\sigma = 5$ and H_0: $\mu \le 30$, will the batteries be purchased at $\alpha = 0.05$ and $\alpha = 0.01$?

Solution Because σ is known (and also because $n = 36 > 30$), the sampling distribution of $\overline{x}$ is normal, with $E(\overline{x}) = \mu = 30$ and $\sigma(\overline{x}) = \sigma/\sqrt{n} = 5/\sqrt{36} = \dfrac{5}{6}$, and the procedure becomes:

1. H_0: $\mu \le 30$ vs H_1: $\mu > 30$
2. $\alpha = 0.05$ and $\alpha = 0.01$
3. The Estimator for μ is $\overline{x}$ and, because σ is known (and also because $n = 36 > 30$) the sampling distribution of $\overline{x}$ is normal with $E(\overline{x}) = \mu = 30$ and $\sigma(\overline{x}) = 5/6$.
4. The Rejection/Non-Rejection regions are constructed using the normal distribution and, for the given α values, become:

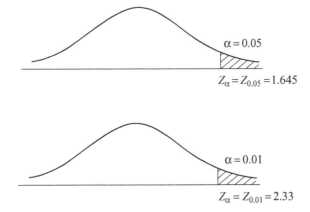

$\alpha = 0.05$

$Z_\alpha = Z_{0.05} = 1.645$

$\alpha = 0.01$

$Z_\alpha = Z_{0.01} = 2.33$

5. Value of Test Statistic $Z^* = \dfrac{\hat{\theta} - \theta_0}{\sigma(\hat{\theta})} = \dfrac{\bar{x} - \mu_0}{\sigma(\bar{x})} = \dfrac{34 - 30}{5/6} = \dfrac{4}{5/6} = \dfrac{24}{5} = 4.8$

6. Since $Z^* > Z_{0.05}$ and $Z^* > Z_{0.01}$, H_0 is rejected for both α values.

7. Rejecting the H_0 implies that $\mu > 30$, and the customer will buy the batteries.

Note: If we wanted to find out the values of $\bar{x}$ for which H_0 will not be rejected, (and the customer will not buy the batteries), we observe that H_0 will not be rejected if:

$$Z^* = \frac{\bar{x} - 30}{5/6} < Z_\alpha, \text{ or if } \bar{x} < 30 + \frac{5}{6}Z_\alpha.$$

When $\alpha = 0.05$, H_0 will not be rejected if $\bar{x} < 30 + \dfrac{5}{6}(1.645) = 30 + 1.37 = 31.37$

and when $\alpha = 0.01$, H_0 will not be rejected if $\bar{x} < 30 + \dfrac{5}{6}(2.33) = 30 + 1.9417$

$= 31.9417$.

Since the given $\bar{x}$ is equal to 34, H_0 is rejected. But, obviously, even an $\bar{x}$ value of 32 will cause the rejection of H_0.

■ ■ ■

10.7.1 Testing Hypotheses about $\Delta\mu = \mu_1 - \mu_2$

We will now illustrate the application of the testing procedure for the population parameter $\Delta\mu = \mu_1 - \mu_2$, using the example below:

Example 3

A sample of 80 steel wires produced by factory A yields a sample mean breaking strength of 1230 pounds and a sample standard deviation of 120 pounds. A sample of 100 wires produced by factory B yields a sample mean breaking strength of 1190 pounds and a sample standard deviation of 90 pounds.

Q_1: Is there a real difference in mean strengths of the 2 makers of steel wires at $\alpha = 0.05$ and $\alpha = 0.01$?

Q_2: For what values of $\Delta\bar{x}$ and $\alpha = 0.05$ will $H_0: \Delta\mu = 0$ not be rejected?

Q_3: For what values of $\Delta\bar{x}$ and $\alpha = 0.05$ will $H_0: \Delta\mu = 0$ be rejected?

Solution Because $n_1 = 80 > 30$ and $n_2 = 100 > 30$, $\Delta\bar{x} = \bar{x}_1 - \bar{x}_2$, the estimator for $\Delta\mu$, will be normally distributed with $E(\Delta\bar{x}) = E(\bar{x}_1 - \bar{x}_2) = E(\bar{x}_1) - E(\bar{x}_2) = \mu_1 - \mu_2$

$= \Delta\mu$ and $\sigma(\Delta\bar{x}) = \sqrt{\dfrac{s_1^2}{n_1} + \dfrac{s_2^2}{n_2}} = \sqrt{\dfrac{(120)^2}{80} + \dfrac{(90)^2}{100}} = \sqrt{261} = 16.15$, and the

procedure becomes:

1. $H_0: \Delta\mu = 0$ vs $H_1: \Delta\mu \neq 0$
2. $\alpha = 0.05$ and $\alpha = 0.01$
3. The estimator for $\Delta\mu$ is $\Delta\bar{x}$ and, because $n_1 > 30$ and $n_2 > 30$, it is normally distributed with $E(\Delta\bar{x}) = E(\bar{x}_1 - \bar{x}_2) = E(\bar{x}_1) - E(\bar{x}_2) = \mu_1 - \mu_2 = \Delta\mu$, and $\sigma(\Delta\bar{x}) = 16.15$.
4. The Rejection/Non-Rejection Regions are constructed from the normal distribution and become, because of the nature of H_1 and the value of α, the following:

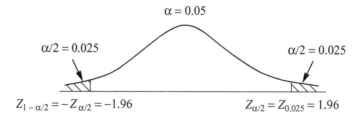

$\alpha = 0.01$

$\alpha/2 = 0.005$ $\alpha/2 = 0.005$

$Z_{1-\alpha/2} = -Z_{\alpha/2} = -2.58$ $Z_{\alpha/2} = Z_{0.005} = 2.58$

5. The value of the test statistic becomes:

$$Z^* = \frac{\hat{\theta} - \theta_0}{\sigma(\hat{\theta})} = \frac{\Delta\bar{x} - \Delta\mu_0}{\sigma(\Delta\bar{x})} = \frac{(\bar{x}_1 - \bar{x}_2) - 0}{\sigma(\Delta\bar{x})} = \frac{(1230 - 1190) - 0}{16.15} = \frac{40}{16.15}$$

$$= 2.48$$

6. Because Z^* falls inside the rejection region when $\alpha = 0.05$ H_0 is rejected, and $\Delta\mu \neq 0$. But when $\alpha = 0.01$, H_0 is not rejected.

7. Rejecting H_0 implies that, $\mu_1 \neq \mu_2$, and the two factories produce steel wires with different breaking strength. However, for $\alpha = 0.01$, H_0 is not rejected, and $\mu_1 = \mu_2$.

To find the values of $\Delta\bar{x}$ for which H_0 is not rejected, we proceed as follows:

H_0 is not rejected if $Z^* = \dfrac{\Delta\bar{x} - 0}{\sigma(\Delta\bar{x})} > -Z_{\alpha/2}$ or if $Z^* = \dfrac{\Delta\bar{x} - 0}{\sigma(\Delta\bar{x})} < +Z_{\alpha/2}$

Then H_0 is not rejected if

$$\Delta\bar{x} > -Z_{\alpha/2}\,\sigma(\Delta\bar{x}) \quad \text{or if} \quad \Delta\bar{x} < +Z_{\alpha/2}\,\sigma(\Delta\bar{x})$$

or $\Delta\bar{x} > -16.15 Z_{\alpha/2}$ or if $\Delta\bar{x} < 16.15 Z_{\alpha/2}$

Then, if $\alpha = 0.05$, do not reject H_0 if $\Delta\bar{x} > -31.654$ or if $\Delta\bar{x} < 31.654$
or Do not reject H_0, when $\alpha = 0.05$, if $-31.654 < \Delta\bar{x} < 31.654$
Clearly, because $\Delta\bar{x} = 40$ falls outside of this interval, H_0 was rejected for $\alpha = 0.05$.
To find the values of $\Delta\bar{x}$ for which H_0 is rejected, when $\alpha = 0.01$, we note that H_0 will be

rejected if $Z^* = \dfrac{\Delta\bar{x}}{\sigma(\Delta\bar{x})} > 2.58$ or if $Z^* = \dfrac{\Delta\bar{x}}{\sigma(\Delta\bar{x})} < -2.58$, from which solving for $\Delta\bar{x}$,

with $\sigma(\Delta\bar{x}) = 16.15$, we obtain:

Reject H_0 if $\Delta\bar{x} > 2.58(16.15) = 41.667$ or if $\Delta\bar{x} < -41.667$. Obviously, since the given $\Delta\bar{x} = 40$, H_0 was not rejected when $\alpha = 0.01$.

Note: When the same hypothesis is rejected for one value of α and not rejected for another α value, it is usually a good idea to obtain new and, preferably, larger samples, and solve the problem again to make sure that the ambiguous result is not due to sampling peculiarities.

10.7.2 Testing Hypotheses about π

Let us now illustrate the application of the testing procedure for the population parameter π, using the example below:

Example 4

A candidate for a certain office claims that he has the support of at least 45% of the voters. His main rival disputes this claim and conducts a random sample test of 256 voters, and finds that the front runner has the support of 103 voters, or nearly 40.23% of the voters. Is the difference of 4.77% between the claimed share of the votes and the sample result statistically significant at $\alpha = 0.05$?

Solution Because $n = 256 > 30$, the estimator of π, $p = x/n = 103/256$ will be normally distributed with: $E(p) = E\left(\dfrac{x}{n}\right) = \dfrac{1}{n}E(x) - \dfrac{1}{n}[n\pi] = \pi$ and

$$V(p) = V\left(\frac{x}{n}\right) = \frac{1}{n^2}V(x) = \frac{n\pi(1-\pi)}{n^2} = \frac{\pi(1-\pi)}{n} \text{ and } \sigma(p) = \sqrt{V(p)}$$

$$= \sqrt{\frac{\pi(1-\pi)}{n}}, \quad \text{and the procedure becomes:}$$

1. H_0: $\pi \geq 0.45$ vs H_1: $\pi < 0.45$
2. $\alpha = 0.05$
3. The estimator of the population parameter π is p and, because $n > 30$, p is normally distributed with $E(p) = \pi = \pi_0 = 0.45$ and

$$\sigma(p) = \sqrt{\frac{\pi(1-\pi)}{n}} = \sqrt{\frac{\pi_0(1-\pi_0)}{n}} = \sqrt{\frac{0.45(0.55)}{256}} = \sqrt{\frac{0.2475}{256}} = \frac{0.497494}{16}$$

$$= 0.031093$$

4. Because of the nature of H_1, the rejection region will be at the left tail of the normal distribution, as shown below:

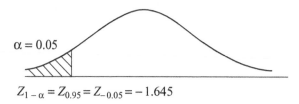

$$\alpha = 0.05$$

$$Z_{1-\alpha} = Z_{0.95} = Z_{-0.05} = -1.645$$

5. The value of the test statistic, $Z^* = \dfrac{\hat{\theta} = \theta_0}{\sigma(\hat{\theta})} = \dfrac{p - \pi_0}{\sigma(p)} = \dfrac{0.4023 - 0.45}{0.031093}$

or $Z^* = \dfrac{-0.0477}{0.03103} = -1.5341$

6. Since $Z^* > Z_{0.95}$ (*i.e.*, since $-1.5341 > -1.645$), Z^* falls outside of the rejection region and, therefore, H_0 is not rejected.
7. Therefore, the claim made (*i.e.*, 45% of voter support) cannot be rejected based on the sample observations.

10.7.3 Testing Hypotheses about the population parameter $\Delta\pi = \pi_1 - \pi_2$

We will now illustrate the application of the testing procedure for the population parameter $\Delta\pi = \pi_1 - \pi_2$, using the example below:

Example 5

In a poll conducted to determine the support of President Bush among male and female college students the following results were obtained:

From 240 male college students 108 students, or 45%, support president Bush, while from 300 female college students 150 students, or 50%, support President Bush. Is this difference of 5% in the sample proportion not sufficient to support the claim that the same percentage of female and male college students support President Bush at $\alpha = 0.05$?

Solution Because $n_1 = 240 > 30$ and $n_2 = 300 > 30$, the estimator of the population parameter $\Delta\pi = \pi_1 - \pi_2$, $\Delta p = p_1 - p_2$, is normally distributed with $E(\Delta p) = E(p_1 - p_2) = E(p_1) - E(p_2) = \pi_1 - \pi_2 = \Delta\pi$, and $V(\Delta p) = V(p_1 - p_2)$

$$= V[p_1 + (-1)p_2] = 1^2 V(p_1) + (-1)^2 V(p_2)$$

$$= V(p_1) + V(p_2), \quad \text{or} \quad V(\Delta p) = \frac{\pi_1(1 - \pi_1)}{n_1} + \frac{\pi_2(1 - \pi_2)}{n_2}, \quad \text{and}$$

$\sigma(\Delta p) = \sqrt{\dfrac{\pi_1(1 - \pi_1)}{n_1} + \dfrac{\pi_2(1 - \pi_2)}{n_2}} = \sqrt{\pi(1 - \pi)\left(\dfrac{n_1 + n_2}{n_1 n_2}\right)}$, under the assumption that $\pi_1 = \pi_2 = \pi$. But, because the population proportions are unknown, we take as the common value of π the weighted mean $\bar{p}$ of the 2 sample proportions, where

$$\bar{p} = \frac{n_1 p_1 + n_2 p_2}{n_1 + n_2} = \frac{240(0.45) + 300(0.50)}{240 + 300} = \frac{108 + 150}{540} = \frac{258}{540} = 0.4778$$

Then, replacing π by $\bar{p}$, we obtain:

$$\sigma(\Delta p) = \sqrt{(0.4778)(0.5222)\left[\frac{540}{(240)(300)}\right]} = 0.043259$$

Then, the procedure becomes:

1. $H_0: \pi_1 = \pi_2$ vs $H_1: \pi_1 \neq \pi_2$

   or $H_0: \pi_1 - \pi_2 = 0$ vs $H_1: \pi_1 - \pi_2 \neq 0$

   or $H_0: \Delta \pi = 0$ vs $H_1: \Delta \pi \neq 0$
2. $\alpha = 0.05$ (and $\alpha/2 = 0.025$)
3. The Estimator of $\Delta \pi$ is Δp which, because $n_1 > 30$ and $n_2 > 30$, is normally distributed with $E(\Delta p) = \Delta \pi (= 0)$ and $\sigma(\Delta p) = 0.043259$
4. Because of the nature of H_1, the rejection region will be on both tails of the normal distribution, as shown below:

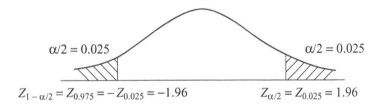

$$\alpha/2 = 0.025 \qquad\qquad\qquad\qquad \alpha/2 = 0.025$$

$$Z_{1-\alpha/2} = Z_{0.975} = -Z_{0.025} = -1.96 \qquad\qquad Z_{\alpha/2} = Z_{0.025} = 1.96$$

5. The value of the test statistic Z^* is:

$$Z^* = \frac{\hat{\theta} - \theta_0}{\sigma(\hat{\theta})} = \frac{\Delta p - \Delta \pi_0}{\sigma(\Delta p)} = \frac{(p_1 - p_2) - 0}{\sigma(\Delta p)},$$

   or $\quad Z^* = \dfrac{(0.45 - 0.50) - 0}{0.043259} = -\dfrac{0.05}{0.043259} = -1.1558$

6. Since Z^* falls outside of the rejection region, H_0 is not rejected.
7. Therefore, we conclude that $\pi_1 = \pi_2$, or that the proportion of male and female college students who support President Bush is the same.

10.8 Power and Operating Characteristic (OC) Functions

10.8.1 Introduction

Up to now the testing procedure has been presented under the assumptions of fixed sample size (n) and type I error (α). But, in situations in which the consequences of committing both type I and type II errors are serious, both α and β errors should be evaluated. But how can this be done? There are two ways of doing this

1. Fix both n and α, and determine the effect of β. This gives rise to the Power and Operating Characteristic (OC) functions and their use and application as a test, and

2. Determine the sample size which can satisfy predetermined levels of α and β errors, for selected values of the parameter.

We will discuss these two methods separately, beginning first with method one and, more specifically, by defining first the Power and OC functions.

Whenever we test a hypothesis, one and only one of the following four outcomes can occur:

a) A True H_0 may be rejected. The probability of this wrong decision is α.

b) A True H_0 may not be rejected (accepted). The probability of this correct decision is $1 - \alpha$.

3. A False H_0 may not be rejected (accepted). The probability of this wrong decision is β.

4. A False H_0 may be rejected. The probability of this correct decision is $1 - \beta$.

The probability of rejecting a false H_0, or accepting a true H_1, both of which are equal to $1 - \beta$, is called the *Power of the test* because it is the ability of the test to accept the alternative hypothesis (H_1) when true. Using the notation introduced earlier in which we let:

θ = Population parameter of interest

θ_0 and θ_1 are specific values of θ

$\hat{\theta}$ = Estimator of the population parameter θ (which is normal if $n \geq 30$)

and $\sigma(\hat{\theta})$ = standard deviation of estimator, if we are testing the hypothesis: $H_0: \theta = \theta_0$ vs $H_1: \theta = \theta_1$, the power of the test is given by:

$$\text{Power of Test} = P\left(\hat{\theta} \in R/\theta = \theta_1\right) \text{ (where } R = \text{Rejection Region)} \tag{10.22}$$

$$= \text{Probability of Rejecting } H_0 \text{ when } H_1 \text{ is True}$$

$$= 1 - \beta$$

When the hypotheses being tested are composite (rather than simple as above), the sizes of the errors are not uniquely defined but depend on the value of the parameter θ. In this case the Probability of Rejecting H_0, when it is false and should be rejected, *i.e.*, the Power of the test $= f(\theta$, with α and n fixed) is $1 - \beta$. To make this situation clear, suppose we are testing the more general hypotheses:

$$H_0: \theta \in S \text{ vs } H_1: \theta \in T, \text{ such that } S \cap T = \emptyset, \tag{10.23}$$

and S = set of all possible values of θ which make H_0 a better choice than H_1

and T = set of all possible values of θ which make H_1 a better choice than H_0

For this test, the Power Function of the test is given by:

$$PF(\theta = \theta_i) = \begin{cases} P\left(\hat{\theta} \in R/\theta = \theta_i \text{ and } \theta_i \in T\right) = 1 - \beta & \text{if } H_0 \text{ is False} \\ \\ P\left(\hat{\theta} \in R/\theta = \theta_i \text{ and } \theta_i \in S\right) = \alpha & \text{if } H_0 \text{ is True} \end{cases} \tag{10.24}$$

The complement of the Power Function is called the Operating Characteristic (OC) Function, and is defined as follows:

$$OC(\theta = \theta_i) = \begin{cases} P\left(\hat{\theta} \in A/\theta = \theta_i \text{ and } \theta_i \in S\right) = 1 - \alpha & \text{if } H_0 \text{ is True} \\ \\ P\left(\hat{\theta} \in A/\theta = \theta_i \text{ and } \theta_i \in T\right) = \beta & \text{if } H_0 \text{ is False} \end{cases} \tag{10.25}$$

where A = Acceptance or Non-Rejection region.

It is obvious that the $OC(\theta_i)$ and $PF(\theta_i)$ are Complementary functions, and

$$OC\left(\theta_i\right) = 1 - PF\left(\theta_i\right) \tag{10.26}$$

To summarize:

1. The Power of the test $= \alpha$, when H_0 is True.
2. The Power of the test $= 1 - \beta$, when H_0 is False.
3. The OC of the test $= \beta$, when H_1 is True.
4. The OC of the test $= 1 - \alpha$, when H_1 is False.

10.8.2 Power and OC Functions for Single-Tailed Tests

In this section we will investigate the Power and OC Functions, and their characteristics, for single-tailed tests, namely the following two cases:

Case 1 $H_0: \theta \geq \theta_0$ vs $H_1: \theta < \theta_0$,   and

Case 2 $H_0: \theta \leq \theta_0$ vs $H_1: \theta > \theta_0$

To be more specific, let us assume that the population parameter of interest is $\theta_0 = \mu_0 = 40$, the population standard deviation, $\sigma = 4$, and the sample size drawn from the population is $n = 64 > 30$, and $\alpha = 0.05$. Then, the estimator of $\theta = \mu$, is $\hat{\theta} = \overline{x}$, and because σ is known (and $n \geq 30$) $\overline{x}$ is normally distributed with $E(\overline{x}) = \mu = \mu_0 = 40$, and $\sigma(\overline{x}) = \sigma/\sqrt{n} = 4/\sqrt{64} = 4/8 = 0.5$ and. Use $\alpha = 0.05$.

Case 1

We are testing the hypothesis: $H_0: \mu \geq 40$ vs $H_1: \mu < 40$

If $\mu \geq 40$ and H_0 is not rejected, the correct decision is made. But, if $\mu \geq 40$ and H_0 is rejected, the wrong decision is made, and $\alpha = P(R/\mu \geq 40)$.

If $\mu < 40$ and H_0 is rejected, the correct decision is made. But, if $\mu < 40$ and H_0 is not rejected, the wrong decision is made, and $\beta = P(A/\mu < 40)$.

For this type of test (lower-tailed test), H_0 will be rejected if:

$$Z^* = \frac{\overline{x} - \mu_0}{\sigma(\overline{x})} = \frac{\overline{x} - 40}{0.5} < Z_{1-\alpha} = -Z_\alpha = -1.65, \text{ or:}$$

Reject H_0 if $\overline{x} < 40 - 1.65(0.5)$, or Reject H_0 if $\overline{x} < 40 - 0.825 = 39.175$, and do not reject H_0 if $\overline{x} > 39.175$.

To evaluate the $PF(\theta_i)$ and $OC(\theta_i)$ which, as we stated previously, are complementary functions, let us remember that, in general, for a lower-tailed test, H_0 will not be rejected, if and only if

$$\hat{\theta} > \hat{\theta}_{\text{critical}}, \tag{10.27}$$

where

$$\hat{\theta}_{\text{critical}} = \theta_0 - Z_\alpha \sigma(\hat{\theta}) \tag{10.28}$$

Therefore

$OC(\theta_i) =$ Prob(of Not Rejecting H_0 when H_0 is true)

$$= P\left(\hat{\theta} > \theta_c / \theta = \theta_i\right) = 1 - N\left(\frac{\theta_c - \theta_i}{\sigma(\hat{\theta})}\right)$$

$$= P\left(\hat{\theta} > \theta_c - Z_\alpha\, \sigma\left(\hat{\theta}\right) / \theta = \theta_i\right)$$

$$= P\left(\overline{x} > \mu_0 - Z_\alpha\, \sigma(\overline{x}) / \mu = \mu_i\right) \tag{10.29}$$

or $\qquad$ OC $(\theta_i = \mu_i) = P\left(\dfrac{\overline{x} - \mu_0}{\sigma(\overline{x})} > -Z_\alpha\right) = 1 - P\left(\dfrac{\overline{x} - \mu_0}{\sigma(\overline{x})} < Z_\alpha\right)$

or $\qquad$ OC$(\mu_0) = 1 - \alpha = 1 - N\left(\dfrac{\overline{x} - \mu_0}{\sigma(\overline{x})}\right) = 1 - N(Q),$ $\qquad$ (10.30)

where $N(Q) \equiv$ Cumulative Distribution Function of the normal density function

$$f(x) = \frac{1}{\sqrt{2n}}\,\frac{1}{\sigma}\, e^{\frac{1}{2\sigma^2}(x-\mu)^2}$$

$$N(Q) = \int_{-\infty}^{Q} f(x)\,dx$$

When

$$\mu = \mu_0 = 40,\ \text{OC}(40) = 1 - N\left(\frac{39.175 - 40}{0.5}\right) = 1 - N\left(\frac{-0.825}{0.5}\right)$$
$$= 1 - N(-1.65)$$
$$= 1 - 0.05$$
$$= 0.95$$

Since OC(θ_i) and PF(θ_i) are complementary functions (see equation 10.26), PF(40) $= 1 - \text{OC}(40) = 1 - 0.95 = 0.05$.

We will now let μ assume different values of μ_0. We will evaluate the OC(μ_i) and PF(μ_i) functions for a selected number of μ_i values, and then plot these 2 functions to obtain their characteristics shapes.

Table 10.2 Calculation of OC and PF for a Lower-Tail Test

Values of $\mu = \mu_0$	$\text{OC}\left(\mu = \mu_0\right) = 1 - N\left(\dfrac{\overline{x} - \mu_0}{\sigma(\overline{x})}\right)$ $= 1 - N\left(\dfrac{39.175 - \mu_0}{0.5}\right)$	$\text{PF}\left(\mu = \mu_0\right) = N\left(\dfrac{\overline{x} - \mu_0}{\sigma(\overline{x})}\right)$ $= N\left(\dfrac{39.175 - \mu_0}{0.5}\right)$
$\mu = \mu_0 = 40.675$	$1 - N\left(\dfrac{39.175 - 40.675}{0.5}\right) = 1 - N(-3) = 0.99865$	$N\left(\dfrac{39.175 - 40.675}{0.5}\right) = N(-3) = 0.00135$
$\mu = \mu_0 = 40.175$	$1 - N\left(\dfrac{39.175 - 40.175}{0.5}\right) = 1 - N(-2) = 0.9772$	$N\left(\dfrac{39.175 - 40.175}{0.5}\right) = N(-2) = 0.0228$
$\mu = \mu_0 = 40.000$	$1 - N\left(\dfrac{39.175 - 40}{0.5}\right) = 1 - N(-1.65) = 0.95$	$N\left(\dfrac{39.175 - 40}{0.5}\right) = N(-1.65) = 0.05$
$\mu = \mu_0 = 39.675$	$1 - N\left(\dfrac{39.175 - 39.675}{0.5}\right) = 1 - N(-1) = 0.8413$	$N\left(\dfrac{39.175 - 39.675}{0.5}\right) = N(-1) = 0.1587$

Table 10.2 Calculation of OC and PF for a Lower-Tail Test (Continued)		
$\mu = \mu_0 = 39.425$	$1 - N\left(\dfrac{39.175 - 39.425}{0.5}\right) = 1 - N(-0.5) = 0.6915$	$N\left(\dfrac{39.175 - 39.425}{0.5}\right) = N(-0.5) = 0.3085$
$\mu = \mu_0 = 39.175$	$1 - N\left(\dfrac{39.175 - 39.175}{0.5}\right) = 1 - N(0) = 0.5$	$N\left(\dfrac{39.175 - 39.175}{0.5}\right) = N(0) = 0.5$
$\mu = \mu_0 = 38.925$	$1 - N\left(\dfrac{39.175 - 38.925}{0.5}\right) = 1 - N(0.5) = 0.3085$	$N\left(\dfrac{39.175 - 38.925}{0.5}\right) = N(0.5) = 0.6915$
$\mu = \mu_0 = 38.675$	$1 - N\left(\dfrac{39.175 - 38.675}{0.5}\right) = 1 - N(1) = 0.01587$	$N\left(\dfrac{39.175 - 38.675}{0.5}\right) = N(1) = 0.8413$
$\mu = \mu_0 = 38.175$	$1 - N\left(\dfrac{39.175 - 38.175}{0.5}\right) = 1 - N(2) = 0.0228$	$N\left(\dfrac{39.175 - 38.175}{0.5}\right) = N(2) = 0.9772$
$\mu = \mu_0 = 37.675$	$1 - N\left(\dfrac{39.175 - 37.675}{0.5}\right) = 1 - N(3) = 0.00135$	$N\left(\dfrac{39.175 - 37.675}{0.5}\right) = N(3) = 0.99865$

Plotting the OC(μ) and PF(μ) values of Table 10.2 against μ, we obtain Figure 10.6.

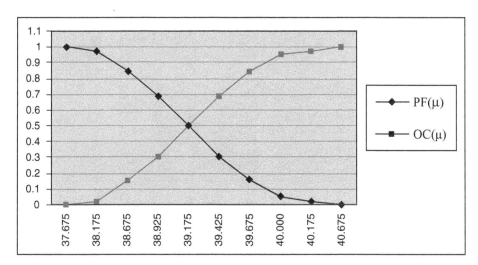

Figure 10.6 OC and Power Functions for a Lower-Tail Test

It is apparent from Figure 10.6 that the Power of the test is low for values of the parameter close to the hypothesized parameter value, and increases when the parameter value deviates more and more from the hypothesized value.

It is constructive to compare the results of Figure 10.6 against the Ideal OC and Power functions, defined for a lower-test by the equations:

$$OC(\theta = \mu) = 0, \quad \text{when } \mu < \mu_0 = 40$$
$$OC(\theta = \mu) = 1, \quad \text{when } \mu \geq \mu_0 = 40$$

$$(10.31)$$

and

$$PF(\theta = \mu) = 1, \quad \text{when } \mu < \mu_0 = 40$$

$$PF(\theta = \mu) = 0, \quad \text{when } \mu \geq \mu_0 = 40$$

(10.32)

and shown in Figure 10.7 and 10.8 below.

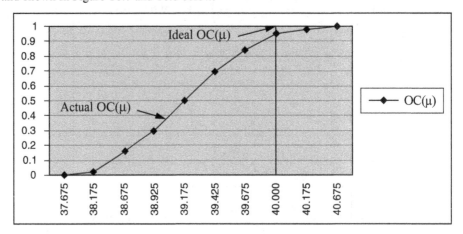

Figure 10.7 Actual and Ideal OC Function, for a Lower-Tailed Test

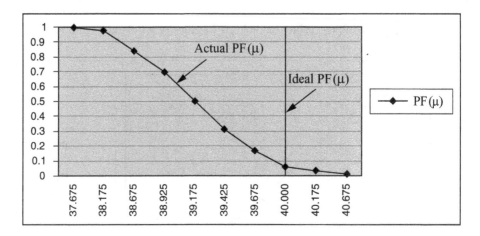

Figure 10.8 Actual and Ideal Power function, for a Lower-Tailed Test

The ideal OC and Power functions imply that if we had perfect information concerning the parameter $\theta = \mu$, we would always reject H_0 if it is not true, and never reject H_0 when it is true. However, since perfect information is never available, the ideal functions can not ever be realized, but it is interesting to see how close to the ideal the actual functions come to.

At this point we mention that if, for a given α and n, one decision rule has a power function which is higher than the power function of a second decision rule, then the first decision rule is better or more powerful than the second decision rule, for all values of the parameter included in H_1. Then, by extension, a decision rule is the Uniformly Most Powerful test if it generates the highest power function possible, for all values of the parameter included in H_1.

Case 2

Here we are testing the hypothesis $H_0: \mu \leq 40$ vs $H_1: \mu > 40$, for $\alpha = 0.05$, $n = 64$, and $\sigma(\bar{x}) = \sigma/\sqrt{n} = 4/\sqrt{64} = 4/8 = 0.5$.

If $\mu \leq 40$ and H_0 is not rejected, the correct decision is made. But, if $\mu \leq 40$ and H_0 is rejected, the wrong decision is made, and $\alpha = P(R/\mu \leq 40)$.

If $\mu > 40$ and H_0 is rejected, the correct decision is made. But, if $\mu > 40$ and H_0 is not rejected, the wrong decision is made, and $\beta = P(A/\mu > 40)$.

For this type of test (Upper-tailed test), H_0 will be rejected if

$$Z^* = \frac{\overline{x} - \mu_0}{\sigma(\overline{x})} = \frac{\overline{x} - 40}{0.5} > Z_\alpha = 1.65, \text{ or:}$$

Reject H_0 if $\overline{x} > 40 + 1.65(0.5)$, or reject H_0 if $\overline{x} > 40.825$, and do not reject H_0 if $\overline{x} < 40.825$.

To evaluate the OC(θ) and PF(θ) which, as mentioned previously are complementary functions, let us remember that, in general, for an Upper-tailed test H_0 will not be rejected, if and only if

$$\hat{\theta} < \hat{\theta}_{\text{critical}}, \tag{10.33}$$

where
$$\hat{\theta}_{\text{critical}} = \theta_0 + Z_\alpha \sigma(\hat{\theta}) \tag{10.34}$$

Therefore,

$$\text{OC}(\theta) = \text{Prob(of not Rejecting } H_0, \text{ when } H_0 \text{ is true)}$$
$$= P(\hat{\theta} \leq \theta_c / \theta = \theta_i)$$

$$\text{OC}(\theta) = N\left(\frac{\theta_c - \theta_i}{\sigma(\hat{\theta})}\right) = N\left(\frac{\overline{x} - \mu_0}{\sigma(\overline{x})}\right) = N\left(\frac{40.825 - \mu_0}{0.5}\right) \tag{10.35}$$

When $\mu = \mu_0 = 40$, $\text{OC}(40) = N\left(\frac{40.825 - 40}{0.5}\right) = N(1.65) = 0.95$ and, since OC (μ) and PF(μ) are complementary functions, $\text{PF}(40) = 1 - \text{OC}(40) = 1 - 0.95 = 0.05$

We will now let μ assume different values of μ_0 (*i.e.*, other than 40). We will evaluate the OC(μ_i) and PF(μ_i) functions for a selected number of μ_i values, and then plot these two functions to obtain their characteristic shapes.

Table 10.3 Calculation of OC and PF for an Upper-Tail Test		
Values of $\mu = \mu_0$	$\text{OC}(\mu) = N\left(\dfrac{\overline{x} - \mu_0}{\sigma(\overline{x})}\right) = N\left(\dfrac{40.825 - \mu_0}{0.5}\right)$	$\text{PF}(\mu) = 1 - N\left(\dfrac{\overline{x} - \mu_0}{\sigma(\overline{x})}\right)$ $= 1 - N\left(\dfrac{40.825 - \mu_0}{0.5}\right)$
$\mu = \mu_0 = 42.325$	$N\left(\dfrac{40.825 - 42.325}{0.5}\right) = N\left(\dfrac{-1.5}{0.5}\right) = N(-3) = 0.00135$	$1 - 0.00135 = 0.99865$
$\mu = \mu_0 = 42.075$	$N\left(\dfrac{40.825 - 42.075}{0.5}\right) = N\left(\dfrac{-1.25}{0.5}\right) = N(-2.5) = 0.0202$	$1 - 0.0202 = 0.9798$
$\mu = \mu_0 = 41.825$	$N\left(\dfrac{40.825 - 41.825}{0.5}\right) = N\left(\dfrac{-1}{0.5}\right) = N(-2) = 0.0228$	$1 - 0.0228 = 0.9772$
$\mu = \mu_0 = 41.325$	$N\left(\dfrac{40.825 - 41.325}{0.5}\right) = N\left(\dfrac{-0.5}{0.5}\right) = N(-1) = 0.1587$	$1 - 0.1587 = 0.8413$
$\mu = \mu_0 = 41.075$	$N\left(\dfrac{40.825 - 41.075}{0.5}\right) = N\left(\dfrac{-0.250}{0.5}\right) = N(-0.5) = 0.3085$	$1 - 0.3085 = 0.6915$

Table 10.3 Calculation of OC and PF for an Upper-Tail Test *(Continued)*		
$\mu = \mu_0 = 40.825$	$N\left(\dfrac{40.825 - 40.825}{0.5}\right) = N\left(\dfrac{0}{0.5}\right) = N(0) = 0.5$	$1 - 0.5 = 0.5$
$\mu = \mu_0 = 40.325$	$N\left(\dfrac{40.825 - 40.325}{0.5}\right) = N\left(\dfrac{0.5}{0.5}\right) = N(1) = 0.8413$	$1 - 0.8413 = 0.1587$
$\mu = \mu_0 = 40$	$N\left(\dfrac{40.825 - 40}{0.5}\right) = N\left(\dfrac{0.825}{0.5}\right) = N(1.65) = 0.95$	$1 - 0.95 = 0.05$
$\mu = \mu_0 = 39.825$	$N\left(\dfrac{40.825 - 39.825}{0.5}\right) = N\left(\dfrac{1}{0.5}\right) = N(2) = 0.9772$	$1 - 0.9772 = 0.0228$
$\mu = \mu_0 = 39.575$	$N\left(\dfrac{40.825 - 39.575}{0.5}\right) = N\left(\dfrac{1.250}{0.5}\right) = N(2.5) = 0.9798$	$1 - 0.9798 = 0.0202$
$\mu = \mu_0 = 39.325$	$N\left(\dfrac{40.825 - 39.325}{0.5}\right) = N\left(\dfrac{1.5}{0.5}\right) = N(3) = 0.99865$	$1 - 0.99865 = 0.00135$

Plotting the actual OC and PF functions, and their ideal functions, against μ, we obtain Figures 10.9 and 10.10 respectively.

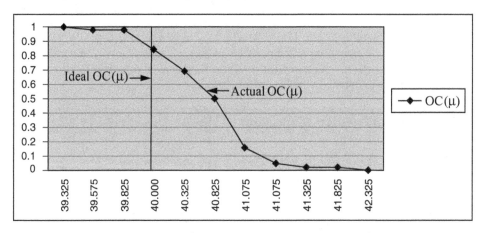

Figure 10.9 Actual and Ideal OC Functions, for an Upper-Tailed Test

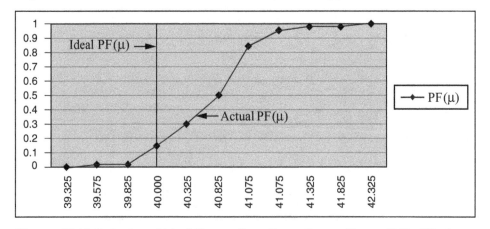

Figure 10.10 Actual and Ideal Power Functions, for an Upper-Tailed Test

When Figures 10.9 and 10.10 are compared to Figure 10.8, we see that the shape for the OC function of the lower-tail test is similar to the shape for the PF function of the Upper-tail test, and the shape of the PF function of the lower-tail test is similar to the shape for the OC function of the Upper-tail test.

10.8.3 Power and OC Functions for Double-Tailed Tests
In this section we investigate the characteristics of the Power and OC functions for a double-tailed test, *i.e.*, we are testing the hypothesis:

$$H_0: \theta = \theta_0 \quad \text{vs} \quad H_1: \theta \neq \theta_0$$

or, by using the same example as in Section 10.8.2, the hypothesis is:

$$H_0: \mu = \mu_0 = 40 \quad \text{vs} \quad H_1: \mu \neq \mu_0 \neq 40$$

For this example, $\sigma = 4$, $n = 64$ and $\alpha = 0.05$ (and $\alpha/2 = 0.025$).
Because σ is known (and $n = 64 > 36$), $\bar{x}$, the estimator for μ, is normally distributed with $E(\bar{x}) = \mu = \mu_0 = 40$ and $\sigma(\bar{x}) = \sigma/\sqrt{n} = 4/\sqrt{64} = 4/8 = 0.5$.

For this type of test (double-tail test), the rejection region is at both ends of the normal distribution, as shown below,

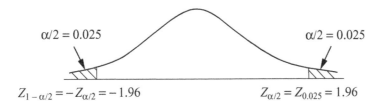

$$\alpha/2 = 0.025 \qquad\qquad\qquad \alpha/2 = 0.025$$

$$Z_{1-\alpha/2} = -Z_{\alpha/2} = -1.96 \qquad\qquad Z_{\alpha/2} = Z_{0.025} = 1.96$$

and Hypothesis H_0 will be rejected if

$$Z^* = \frac{\bar{x} - \mu_0}{\sigma(\bar{x})} = \frac{\bar{x} - 40}{0.5} < -1.96 \text{ or, if } Z^* = \frac{\bar{x} - 40}{0.5} > 1.96$$

or Reject H_0 if $\bar{x}_1 < 40 - 1.96(0.5)$ or, if $\bar{x}_2 > 40 + 0.5(1.96)$
$$\bar{x}_1 < 40 - 0.98 \qquad\qquad \bar{x}_2 > 40 + 0.98$$
$$\bar{x}_1 < 39.02 \qquad\qquad\qquad \bar{x}_2 > 40.98$$

In general, for a double-tailed test, H_0 will be accepted only if the estimator $\hat{\theta}$ is between $\hat{\theta}_{c1} \leq \hat{\theta} \leq \hat{\theta}_{c2}$ (in our case if and only if $\hat{\theta}_{c1} = 39.02 \leq \hat{\theta} = \bar{x} \leq \hat{\theta}_{c2} = 40.98$), and the OC function is defined as:

$$\text{OC}(\theta_i) = P(\hat{\theta}_{c1} \leq \hat{\theta} \leq \theta_{c2}/\theta_i) = N\left(\frac{\hat{\theta}_{c2} - \theta_i}{\sigma(\hat{\theta})}\right) - N\left(\frac{\theta_{c1} - \theta_i}{\sigma(\hat{\theta})}\right) \quad (10.36)$$

$$\text{OC}(\mu) = N\left(\frac{\bar{x}_2 - \mu_0}{\sigma(\bar{x})}\right) - N\left(\frac{\bar{x}_1 - \mu_0}{\sigma(\bar{x})}\right)$$

$$= N\left(\frac{40.98 - \mu_0}{0.5}\right) - N\left(\frac{39.02 - \mu_0}{0.5}\right)$$

Since the PF(θ_i) is complementary to the OC(θ_i) function, PF(θ_i) is defined as:

$$PF\left(\theta_i\right) = 1 - OC\left(\theta_i\right) = 1 - P\left[\theta_{c1} \le \hat{\theta} \le \theta_{c2}/\theta_i\right]$$

$$= 1 - \left[N\left(\frac{\theta_{c2} - \theta_i}{\sigma(\hat{\theta})}\right) - N\left(\frac{\theta_{c1} - \theta_i}{\sigma(\hat{\theta})}\right)\right] \qquad (10.37)$$

$$= 1 - \left[N\left(\frac{\bar{x}_2 - \mu_0}{\sigma(\bar{x})}\right) - N\left(\frac{\bar{x}_1 - \mu_0}{\sigma(\bar{x})}\right)\right]$$

$$= 1 - \left[N\left(\frac{40.98 - \mu_0}{0.5}\right) - N\left(\frac{39.02 - \mu_0}{0.5}\right)\right]$$

When $\mu = \mu_0 = 40$, OC$(\mu = \mu_0 = 40) = N\left(\frac{0.98}{0.5}\right) - N\left(\frac{-0.98}{0.5}\right) = N(1.96) - N(-1.96)$

$$= 0.975 - 0.025 = 0.95 = 1 - \alpha,$$

and PF$(\mu = \mu_0 = 40) = 1 - OC(\mu = \mu_0 = 40) = 1 - 0.95 = 0.05 = \alpha$

We will now evaluate the OC(μ) and PF(μ) for several different values of μ, and plot the results to obtain the OC(μ) and PF(μ) characteristic shapes for the double-tailed test.

When the OC(μ) column is plotted against μ, we obtain Figure 10.11, which exhibits the characteristic shape of the OC function for a Double-tailed test.

Note: The ideal OC function must satisfy the conditions:

$$OC(\mu_i) = 1, \text{ when } \mu_i = \mu_0 = 40$$

and
$$OC(\mu_i) = 0, \text{ when } \mu_i \ne \mu_0$$

Table 10.4 Calculations of OC and PF Functions for a Double-Tailed Test		
Values of $\mu = \mu_0$	$OC(\mu) = N\left(\dfrac{40.98 - \mu_0}{0.5}\right) - N\left(\dfrac{39.02 - \mu_0}{0.5}\right)$	$PF(\mu) = 1 - OC(\mu)$
$\mu = \mu_0 = 38$	$N(5.96) - N(2.04) = 1 - 0.9793 = 0.0207$	0.9793
$\mu = \mu_0 = 38.5$	$N(4.96) - N(1.04) = 1 - 0.8508 = 0.1492$	0.8508
$\mu = \mu_0 = 39$	$N(3.96) - N(0.04) = 0.99996 - 0.5160 = 0.48396$	0.51604
$\mu = \mu_0 = 39.5$	$N(2.96) - N(-0.96) = 0.9985 - 0.1685 = 0.83$	0.17
$\mu = \mu_0 = 40$	$N(1.96) - N(-1.96) = 0.9750 - 0.025 = 0.95$	0.05
$\mu = \mu_0 = 40.5$	$N(0.96) - N(-2.96) = 0.8315 - 0.0015 = 0.83$	0.17
$\mu = \mu_0 = 41$	$N-0.04 - N(-3.96) = 0.4840 - 0.00004 = 0.48396$	0.51604
$\mu = \mu_0 = 41.5$	$N-1.04 - N(-4.96) = 0.1492 - 0 = 0.1492$	0.8508
$\mu = \mu_0 = 42$	$N-2.04 - N(-5.96) = 0.0207 - 0 = 0.0207$	0.9793

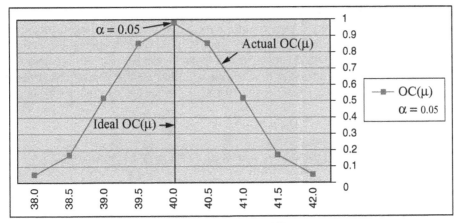

Figure 10.11 OC Function for a Double-Tailed Test

When the PF(μ) column of Table 10.4 is plotted against μ, we obtain Figure 10.12, which exhibits the characteristic shape of the PF function for a double-tailed test.

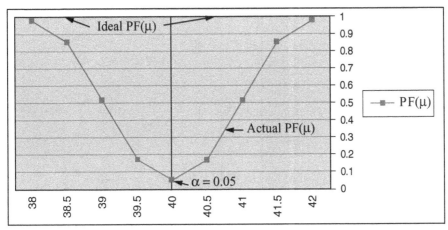

Figure 10.12 PF Function for a Double-Tailed Test

Note: The Ideal PF function must satisfy the conditions:

$$PF(\mu_i) = 0, \text{ when } \mu_i = \mu_0$$

and $\qquad\qquad\qquad PF(\mu_i) = 1, \text{ when } \mu_i \neq \mu_0$

10.9 Tests with Fixed α and β

In the previous section we evaluated the OC and Power functions by keeping both α and n fixed. In this section we will answer two questions, namely:

1. For a given level of α, how do the OC and Power functions change, if n changes? and
2. What is the appropriate sample size n, to satisfy predetermined levels of α and β errors?

10.9.1 The effect of changing n, on β

In general, as the sample size n increases, for a fixed α error, the sampling distribution of the test statistic (if we are testing μ, the test statistic is $\bar{x}$ whose sampling distribution is normal, if σ of the population is known, or if σ is not known but $n \geq 30$) becomes more compressed and results in a smaller β value. We will illustrate this general conclusion by an example, by revisiting *Case 2* of Section 10.8.2; *i.e.*, we are again testing the hypothesis:

$$H_0: \mu \leq 40 \quad \text{vs} \quad H: \mu > 40$$

with $\sigma = 4$ and $\alpha = 0.05$, but now we will let $n_1 = 36$, $n_2 = 64$, and $n_3 = 256$.

Then

$$\sigma_1(\bar{x}) = \sigma/\sqrt{n_1} = 4/\sqrt{36} = 4/6 = 2/3, \sigma_2(\bar{x}) = \sigma/\sqrt{n_2}$$
$$= 4/\sqrt{64} = 4/8 = 1/2, \text{ and } \sigma_3(\bar{x}) = \sigma/\sqrt{n_3} = 4/\sqrt{256} = 4/16 = 1/4$$

The hypothesis H_0 will be rejected if

$$Z^* = \frac{\bar{x} - \mu_0}{\sigma/\sqrt{n}} > Z_\alpha = 1.65, \text{ or if } \bar{x} > 40 + 1.65\frac{4}{\sqrt{n}}$$

1. If $n = n_1 = 36$, H_0 will be rejected if $\bar{x} > 40 + \dfrac{6.6}{\sqrt{36}} = 40 + \dfrac{6.6}{6} = 41.1$

2. If $n = n_2 = 64$, H_0 will be rejected if $\bar{x} > 40 + \dfrac{6.6}{\sqrt{64}} = 40 + \dfrac{6.6}{8} = 40.825$

3. If $n = n_3 = 256$, H_0 will be rejected if $\bar{x} > 40 + \dfrac{6.6}{\sqrt{256}} = 40 + \dfrac{6.6}{16} = 40.4125$

The calculation of the $OC(\mu)$ and $PF(\mu)$ for case (b) above is given in Table 10.3, and will not be repeated here. However, Table 10.5 gives, for the same μ values, the $OC(\mu)$ and $PF(\mu)$ for $n = n_1 = 36$, $n = n_2 = 64$, and $n = n_3 = 256$, and Tables 10.3 and 10.5 will be used to plot the $OC(\mu)$ and $PF(\mu)$ functions and observe the effect of n on β.

The calculations for Table 10.5 came from the equations:

a) For $n = n_1 = 36$, $OC(\mu) = N\left(\dfrac{41.1 - \mu_0}{0.667}\right)$, and $PF(\mu) = 1 - OC(\mu)$

b) For $n = n_2 = 64$, $OC(\mu) = N\left(\dfrac{40.825 - \mu_0}{0.5}\right)$, and $PF(\mu) = 1 - OC(\mu)$

c) For $n = n_3 = 256$, $OC(\mu) = N\left(\dfrac{40.4125 - \mu_0}{0.25}\right)$, and $PF(\mu) = 1 - OC(\mu)$

and are tabulated in Table 10.5.

Values of $\mu = \mu_0$	$N = n_1 = 36$		$N = n_2 = 64$		$N = n_3 = 256$	
	$OC(\mu) = N\left(\dfrac{41.1 - \mu_0}{0.667}\right)$	$PF(\mu) = 1 - OC(\mu)$	$OC(\mu) = N\left(\dfrac{40.825 - \mu_0}{0.5}\right)$	$PF(\mu) = 1 - OC(\mu)$	$OC(\mu) = N\left(\dfrac{40.4125 - \mu_0}{0.25}\right)$	$PF(\mu) = 1 - OC(\mu)$
42.325	$N(-1.84) = 0.0329$	0.9671	$N(-3) = 0.00135$	0.99865	$N(-7.65) \approx 0$	1.0
42.075	$N(-1.46) = 0.0721$	0.9279	$N(-2.5) = 0.0202$	0.9798	$N(-6.65) \approx 0$	1.0
41.825	$N(-1.09) = 0.1379$	0.8621	$N(-2) = 0.0228$	0.9772	$N(-5.65) \approx 0$	1.0
41.325	$N(-0.34) = 0.3669$	0.6331	$N(-1) = 0.1587$	0.8413	$N(-3.65) = 0.00013$	0.99987
41.075	$N(0.04) = 0.5160$	0.4840	$N(-0.5) = 0.3085$	0.6915	$N(-2.65) = 0.0040$	0.996
40.825	$N(0.41) = 0.6591$	0.3409	$N(0) = 0.5$	0.5	$N(-1.65) = 0.05$	0.95
40.325	$N(1.16) = 0.8770$	0.1230	$N(1) = 0.8413$	0.1587	$N(0.35) = 0.6368$	0.3632
40	$N(1.65) = 0.95$	0.05	$N(1.65) = 0.95$	0.05	$N(1.65) = 0.95$	0.05
39.825	$N(1.91) = 0.9713$	0.0287	$N(2) = 0.9772$	0.0228	$N(2.35) = 09906$	0.0094
39.575	$N(2.29) = 0.9890$	0.0110	$N(2.5) = 0.9798$	0.0202	$N(3.35) = 0.9996$	0.0004
39.325	$N(2.66) = 0.9961$	0.0039	$N(3) = 0.99685$	0.00135	$N(4.35) = 1$	0

Table 10.5 Calculation of $OC(\mu)$ and $PF(\mu)$, for an Upper-Tail Test for $n_1 = 36$, $n_2 = 64$, $n_3 = 256$

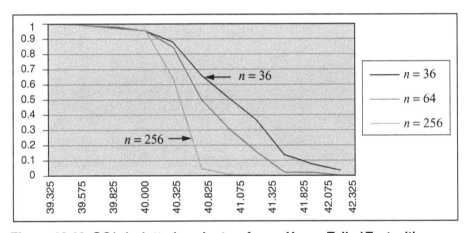

Figure 10.13 OC(μ) plotted against μ, for an Upper-Tailed Test with n as a parameter

When the $OC(\mu)$ columns of Table 10.5 are plotted against μ, as a function of n ($n = n_1 = 36$, $n = n_2 = 64$, $n = n_3 = 256$) we obtain Figure 10.13, which shows the effect of n on the $OC(\mu)$.

It is obvious that the $OC(\mu)$ function approaches its ideal form as n increases. The same conclusion can be drawn from Figure 10.14 which plots the $PF(\mu)$ against μ.

To study the effect of changing n on the $OC(\mu)$ and $PF(\mu)$ for a 2-sided test, we construct Table 10.6 and plot Figures 10.15 and 10.16 from which we observe, again, that both the $OC(\mu)$ and $PF(\mu)$ approach their ideal form as n increases.

$$H_0 \text{ will now be rejected if } \overline{X} > 40 + 1.96\,\frac{4}{\sqrt{n}} \text{ or if } \overline{X} < 40 - 1.96\,\frac{4}{\sqrt{n}}$$

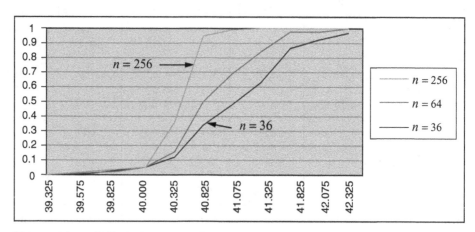

Figure 10.14 PF(μ) plotted against μ, for an Upper- Tailed Test with n as a parameter

Table 10.6 $OC(\mu)$ and $PF(\mu)$, as a function of n, for a Double-tailed test						
Values of μ	$N = n_1 = 36$		$N = n_2 = 64$		$N = n_3 = 256$	
	$OC(\mu)$	$PF(\mu) =$ $1 - OC(\mu)$	$OC(\mu)$	$PF(\mu) =$ $1 - OC(\mu)$	$OC(\mu)$	$PF(\mu) =$ $1 - OC(\mu)$
38	$N(4.96) - N(1.03)$ $= 0.1515$	0.8485	$N(5.96) - N(2.04)$ $= 0.0207$	0.9793	$N(9.96) - N(6.04)$ $= 0$	1.0
38.5	$N(4.21) - N(0.28)$ $= 0.3897$	0.6103	$N(4.96) - N(1.04)$ $= 0.1492$	0.8508	$N(7.96) - N(4.04)$ $= 0$	1.0
39	$N(3.46) - N(-0.46)$ $= 0.6769$	0.3231	$N(3.96) - N(0.04)$ $= 0.48396$	0.51604	$N(5.96) - N(2.04)$ $= 0.0207$	0.9793
39.5	$N(2.71) - N(-1.21)$ $= 0.8835$	0.1165	$N(2.96) - N(-0.96)$ $= 0.83$	0.17	$N(3.96) - N(0.04)$ $= 0.48396$	0.51604
40	$N(1.96) - N(-1.96)$ $= 0.95$	0.05	$N(1.96) - N(-1.96)$ $= 0.95$	0.05	$N(1.96) - N(-1.96)$ $=0.95$	0.05
40.5	$N(1.21) - N(-2.71)$ $= 0.8835$	0.1165	$N(0.96) - N(-2.96)$ $= 0.83$	0.17	$N(-0.04) - N(-3.96)$ $= 0.48396$	0.51604
41	$N(0.46) - N(-3.46)$ $= 0.6769$	0.3231	$N(-0.04) - N(-3.96)$ $= 0.48396$	0.51604	$N(-2.04) - N(-5.96)$ $= 0.0207$	0.9793
41.5	$N(-0.28) - N(-4.21)$ $= 0.3897$	0.6103	$N(-1.04) - N(-4.96)$ $= 0.1492$	0.8508	$N(-4.04) - N(-7.96)$ $= 0$	1.0
42	$N(-1.03) - N(-4.96)$ $= 0.1515$	0.8485	$N(-2.04) - N(-5.96)$ $= 0.0207$	0.9793	$N(-6.04) - N(-9.96)$ $= 0$	1.0

The calculation for Table 10.6 came from the equations:

1. For $n = n_1 = 36$, $OC(\mu) = N\left(\dfrac{41.31 - \mu_0}{0.667}\right) - N\left(\dfrac{38.69 - \mu_0}{0.667}\right)$

2. For $n = n_2 = 64$, $OC(\mu) = N\left(\dfrac{40.98 - \mu_0}{0.5}\right) - N\left(\dfrac{39.02 - \mu_0}{0.5}\right)$

3. For $n = n_3 = 256$, $OC(\mu) = N\left(\dfrac{40.49 - \mu_0}{0.25}\right) - N\left(\dfrac{39.51 - \mu_0}{0.25}\right)$

When the $OC(\mu)$ columns of Table 10.6 are plotted against μ, we obtain Figure 10.15, which represents the OC function, as a function of n, for a Double-tailed test. Note that the $OC(\mu)$ function approaches its ideal form as n increases.

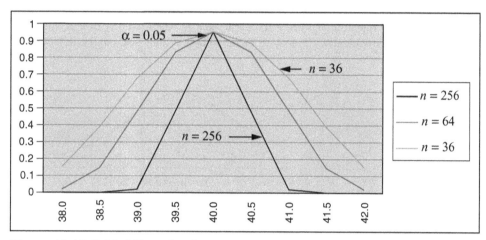

Figure 10.15 OC(μ) Function for a Double-Tailed Test, with *n* as parameter

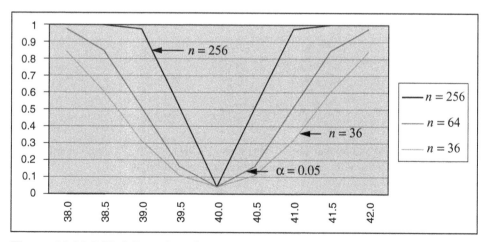

Figure 10.16 PF(μ) Function, for a Double-Tailed Test, with *n* as parameter

When the PF(μ) columns of Table 10.6 are plotted against μ, we obtain Figure 10.16, which represents the PF function, as a function of n, for a Double-tailed test. Note, again, that the PF(μ) function approaches its ideal form ($\mu = 40$) as n increases.

In summary, we can see from Figures 10.13, 10.14, 10.15, and 10.16 that the OC and PF Functions, for both one-sided and two-sided tests, approach their ideal forms as n increases.

10.9.2 Determining n for fixed α and β

In Section 10.8.2 we tested the hypotheses: $H_0 \geq 40$ vs $H_1 < 40$, $H_0 : \mu \leq 40$ vs $H_1: \mu > 40$, and in Section 10.8.3 the hypothesis: $H_0: \mu = 40$ vs $H_1: \mu \neq 40$, under the assumption that $\sigma = 4$, and with α and n fixed. Then, in section 10.9, we studied the effect of changing n on β, keeping α fixed. Now we wish to change slightly our H_0 and H_1 hypotheses, fix the α and β levels (of type I and II errors respectively), and then determine the required sample size to satisfy the α and β errors. Let us begin by assuming that we wish to test the hypothesis:

$H_0: \mu = \mu_0 = 40$ vs $H_1: \mu = \mu_1 = 35$, with $\sigma = 4$ and α and β fixed (For example, if $\alpha = 0.02$, $Z_\alpha = Z_{0.02} = 2.06$ and if $\beta = 0.05$, $Z_\beta = 1.65$). Recall that α = probability of rejecting H_0, when H_0 is true, and β = Probability of accepting H_0, when H_1 is true. Graphically, the testing of the above hypotheses, can be depicted by Figure 10.17 below:

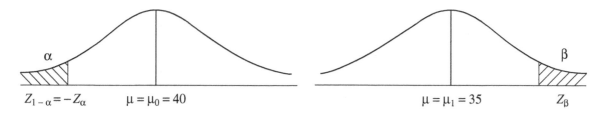

Figure 10.17 Testing the hypotheses: $H_0: \mu = \mu_0 = 40$ vs $H_1: \mu = \mu_1 = 35$

It is obvious from Figure 10.17 that H_0 will be rejected if and only if

$$Z^* = \frac{\overline{x} - \mu_0}{\sigma(\overline{x})} = \frac{\overline{x} - \mu_0}{\sigma/\sqrt{n}} < -Z_\alpha, \quad \text{or if } \overline{x} < \overline{x}_c = \mu_0 - Z_\alpha \frac{\sigma}{\sqrt{n}}, \quad (10.38)$$

and H_1 will be rejected if $Z^* = \dfrac{\overline{x} - \mu_1}{\sigma(\overline{x})} = \dfrac{\overline{x} - \mu_1}{\sigma/\sqrt{n}} > Z_\beta, \quad$ or if

$$\overline{x} > \overline{x}_c = \mu_1 + Z_\beta \frac{\sigma}{\sqrt{n}} \quad (10.39)$$

To solve for n and $\overline{x}_c$ that satisfy equations (10.38) and (10.39) simultaneously, we set the two expressions of $\overline{x}_c$ equal to each other, and solve for n, or

$$\mu_0 - Z_\alpha \frac{\sigma}{\sqrt{n}} = \mu_1 + Z_\beta \frac{\sigma}{\sqrt{n}}, \quad (10.40)$$

from which we obtain:

$$n = \left[\frac{(Z_\alpha + Z_\beta)\sigma}{\mu_0 - \mu_1}\right]^2 \tag{10.41}$$

If $\mu_0 = 40$, $\mu_1 = 35$, $\sigma = 4$, $Z_\beta = 2.06$ (when $\alpha = 0.02$) and $Z_\beta = 1.65$ (if $\beta = 0.05$), from (10.41) we obtain:

$$n = \left[\frac{(2.06 + 1.65)4}{40 - 35}\right]^2 = \left[\frac{4}{5}(3.71)\right]^2 = (2.968)^2 = 8.809 \approx 9$$

The critical value of $\bar{x}$, $\bar{x}_c$, can be obtained from either (10.38) or (10.39), and is equal to:

$$\bar{x}_c = \mu_0 - Z_\alpha \frac{\sigma}{\sqrt{n}} = 40 - 2.06\left(\frac{4}{3}\right) = 40 - 2.747 = 37.25$$

$$= \mu_1 + Z_\beta \frac{\sigma}{\sqrt{n}} = 35 + 1.65\left(\frac{4}{3}\right) = 35 + 2.25 = 37.25,$$

The decision rule now becomes: take a random sample of size $n = 9$, and compute the sample mean $\bar{x}$. If $\bar{x} < 37.25$, Reject H_0; if $\bar{x} > 37.25$, Reject H_1.

To show that the calculated values of $n = 9$ and $\bar{x} = \bar{x}_c = 37.25$, satisfy the fixed α and β levels, let us calculate the α and β levels, using their definitions and the calculated n and $\bar{x}_c$ values. We obtain:

$\alpha = P$ (Reject H_0 if H_0 is true)

$$= P(\bar{x} > 37.25 / \mu = \mu_0 = 40) = N\left(\frac{37.25 - 40}{4/3}\right) = N(-2.06) \approx 0.02$$

$\beta = P$ (Accept H_0 if H_1 is true)

$$= P(\bar{x} > 37.25 / \mu = \mu_1 = 35) = 1 - N\left(\frac{37.25 - 35}{4/3}\right) = 1 - N(1.6875)$$

$$= 1 - N(1.69) = 1 - 0.9545 = 0.0455 \approx 0.05$$

In this analysis we used only 2 values of μ, $\mu = \mu_1 = 35$, and $\mu = \mu_0 = 40$. What would happen if μ is some other value? The answer to this question is as follows:

1. If $\mu > \mu_0 = 40$, the probability of wrongly accepting H_1 will be less than α because the left normal curve of Figure 10.17 will be shifted to the right, making the left tail of the left curve smaller than α. Therefore, if $\mu \geq 40$ the maximum probability of wrongly accepting H_1 will be α.
2. If $\mu < \mu_1 = 35$, the probability of wrongly accepting H_0 will be less than β because the right normal curve of Figure 10.17 will be shifted to the left, making the right tail of the right curve smaller than β. Therefore, if $\mu \leq 35$, the maximum probability of wrongly accepting H_0 will be β.

Note: In cases 1 and 2 above the type I (α) and type II (β) errors have been kept within the desired levels.

3. However, if $35 < \mu < 40$, the α and β errors are not within the desired levels.

Note: A similar analysis, with similar results can be made if we chose to test the hypothesis: H_0: $\mu = \mu_0 = 40$ vs H_1: $\mu = \mu_2 = 45$. In this case we can represent the testing of these hypotheses by figure 10.18 below:

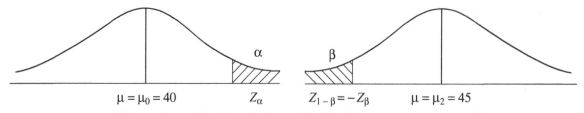

$$\mu = \mu_0 = 40 \qquad Z_\alpha \qquad Z_{1-\beta} = -Z_\beta \qquad \mu = \mu_2 = 45$$

Figure 10.18 Testing the hypothesis: $H_0: \mu = \mu_0 = 40$ vs $H_1: \mu = \mu_2 = 45$

H_0 will be rejected if $Z^* = \dfrac{\bar{x} - \mu_0}{\sigma/\sqrt{n}} > Z_\alpha$, or if $\bar{x} > \bar{x}_c = \mu_0 + Z_\alpha \dfrac{\sigma}{\sqrt{n}}$

and H_1 will be rejected if $Z^* = \dfrac{\bar{x} - \mu_{02}}{\sigma/\sqrt{n}} < -Z_\beta$, or if $\bar{x} < \bar{x}_c = \mu_2 - Z_{\alpha\beta} \dfrac{\sigma}{\sqrt{n}}$.

When the two expressions for $\bar{x}_c$ are set equal, we obtain for n:

$$n = \left[\frac{\sigma(Z_\alpha + Z_\beta)}{\mu_2 - \mu_0} \right]^2 = 9, \text{ if } \sigma = 4, Z_\alpha = 2.06, Z_\beta = 1.65, \mu_2 = 45 \text{ and } \mu_0 = 40$$

Then $\bar{x}_c = \mu_0 + Z_\alpha \dfrac{\sigma}{\sqrt{n}} = 40 + 2.06\left(\dfrac{4}{3}\right) = 40 + 2.75 = 42.75$, and the decision rule is: Take a sample size of $n = 9$. Calculate the value of $\bar{x}$. Then, if, $\bar{x} > 42.75$, Reject H_0, and if $\bar{x} < 42.75$, Reject H_1. The rest of the analysis proceeds as above.

Let us now consider a two-sided test. Suppose we wish to test the hypotheses: $H_0: \mu = \mu_0 = 40$ vs $H_1: \mu = \mu_1 = 35$ or $H_1: \mu = \mu_2 = 45$ using $\alpha = 0.02$ and $\beta = 0.05$, with $\sigma = 4$. The graphical representation of this test is shown in Figure 10.19 below:

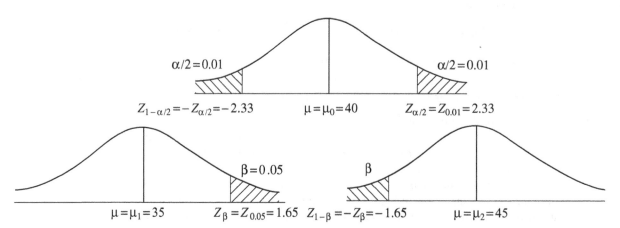

$$\alpha/2 = 0.01 \qquad\qquad\qquad \alpha/2 = 0.01$$
$$Z_{1-\alpha/2} = -Z_{\alpha/2} = -2.33 \qquad \mu = \mu_0 = 40 \qquad Z_{\alpha/2} = Z_{0.01} = 2.33$$

$$\beta = 0.05 \qquad\qquad \beta$$
$$\mu = \mu_1 = 35 \qquad Z_\beta = Z_{0.05} = 1.65 \quad Z_{1-\beta} = -Z_\beta = -1.65 \qquad \mu = \mu_2 = 45$$

Figure 10.19 Testing $H_0: \mu = 40$ vs $H_1: \mu \neq 40$, with $\alpha = 0.02$ and $\beta = 0.05$

In this case H_0 will be rejected, when true, if and only if

$$Z^* = \frac{\bar{x} - \mu_0}{\sigma/\sqrt{n}} < -Z_{\alpha/2} \text{ or if } \frac{\bar{x} - \mu_0}{\sigma/\sqrt{n}} > Z_{\alpha/2}, \text{ from which we obtain}$$

$$\bar{x} < \bar{x}_{c1} = \mu_0 - Z_{\alpha/2}\frac{\sigma}{\sqrt{n}} \tag{10.42}$$

or

$$\bar{x} < \bar{x}_{c2} = \mu_0 + Z_{\alpha/2}\frac{\sigma}{\sqrt{n}} \tag{10.43}$$

Equations (10.42) and (10.43) must be satisfied by n, $\bar{x}_{c1}$, and $\bar{x}_{c2}$, to satisfy the stated α value. H_1 will be rejected when H_0 is false (or H_0 is accepted when H_1 is true).

if $\quad Z^* = \dfrac{\bar{x} - \mu_1}{\sigma(\bar{x})} = \dfrac{\bar{x} - \mu_1}{\sigma/\sqrt{n}} > Z_\beta$, or if $\bar{x} > \bar{x}_{c1} = \mu_1 + Z_\beta\dfrac{\sigma}{\sqrt{n}} \quad$ (10.44)

and if $\quad Z^* = \dfrac{\bar{x} - \mu_2}{\sigma(\bar{x})} = \dfrac{\bar{x} - \mu_2}{\sigma/\sqrt{n}} < -Z_\beta$, or if $\bar{x} < \bar{x}_{c2} = \mu_2 - Z_\beta\dfrac{\sigma}{\sqrt{n}} \quad$ (10.45)

To obtain the required sample size, n, we solve simultaneously equations (10.42) and (10.44) or equations (10.43) and (10.45), because each of these 2 pairs of equations calculate one of the 2 critical values $\bar{x}_{c1}$ and $\bar{x}_{c2}$, respectively.

From (10.42) and (10.44) we obtain: $\mu_0 - Z_{\alpha/2}\dfrac{\sigma}{\sqrt{n}} = \mu_1 + Z_\beta\dfrac{\sigma}{\sqrt{n}}$,

or

$$n = \left[\frac{\sigma(Z_{\alpha/2} + Z_\beta)}{\mu_0 - \mu_1}\right]^2 \tag{10.46}$$

while from (10.43) and (10.45) we obtain: $\mu_0 + Z_{\alpha/2}\dfrac{\sigma}{\sqrt{n}} = \mu_2 - Z_\beta\dfrac{\sigma}{\sqrt{n}}$ from which

$$n = \left[\frac{\sigma(Z_{\alpha/2} + Z_\beta)}{\mu_2 - \mu_0}\right]^2 \tag{10.47}$$

Using the values: $\sigma = 4$, $\mu_0 = 40$, $\mu_1 = 35$, $\mu_2 = 45$, $Z_{\alpha/2} = 2.33$ and $Z_\beta = 1.65$, we obtain from (10.46): $n = \left[\dfrac{4}{5}(2.33 + 1.65)\right]^2 = 10.14 \approx 11$, and the same value for n is obtained from (10.47).

Then $\qquad \bar{x}_{c1} = \mu_0 - Z_{\alpha/2}\dfrac{\sigma}{\sqrt{n}} = 40 - 2.33\left(\dfrac{4}{\sqrt{11}}\right) = 40 - \dfrac{9.32}{3.31662479}$

$$= 40 - 2.81 = 37.19$$

and $\qquad \bar{x}_{c2} = \mu_0 + Z_{\alpha/2}\dfrac{\sigma}{\sqrt{n}} = 40 + 2.33\left(\dfrac{4}{\sqrt{11}}\right) = 40 + \dfrac{9.32}{3.31662479}$

$$= 40 + 2.81 = 42.81$$

Then the decision rule becomes: Take a random sample of $n = 11$, and calculate $\bar{x}$. Do not reject H_0 if $37.19 \leq \bar{x} \leq 42.81$, and reject H_0 if $\bar{x} < 37.19$ or if $\bar{x} > 42.81$.

10.10   Computer Solutions

In Section 9.5 of Chapter 9 (Estimation Theory) we showed how MINITAB can be used to construct Confidence Intervals for certain population parameters, namely: The population mean μ; the population difference of two means, $\Delta\mu = \mu_1 - \mu_2$, the population median, η, and the population difference of 2 population medians, $\Delta\eta = \eta_1 - \eta_2$. But there are no MINITAB commands to construct Confidence Intervals for the population parameters:

$$\pi, \Delta\pi = \pi_1 - \pi_2, \sigma^2, \text{ and } \frac{\sigma_1^2}{\sigma_2^2}.$$

For those population parameters for which MINITAB commands exist, the usual procedure is to start with one data set (when testing single population parameters against a numerical value; for example: $H_0 = \mu = 50, H_0 = \eta = 40$, etc) which is put into a named file (for example the data set for the example in section 9.5 was set into column C1, and named 'DSTAT,' and the MINITAB command MTB > DESCRIBE C1 was executed, from which we obtain the Point Estimators: $\bar{x}$ = sample mean = 83.70, sample median = $X_{0.5}$ = 84, sample unbiased standard deviation = $\hat{s}$ = 24.32, and $\hat{s} = (\hat{s})^2 = 591.4624$, and the confidence intervals for μ are calculated from:

MTB> Z INTERVAL 90, SIGMA 24.32, 'DSTAT', or

MTB> T Interval 90, 'DSTAT', depending on whether σ is known or unknown (and if $n \geq 30$ or $n < 30$).

To test the hypothesis $H_0: \mu = \mu_0$ vs $H_1: \mu \neq \mu_0$, for the same data set in file 'DSTAT', we use the commands:

MTB> Z TEST μ_0, SIGMA = 24.32, 'DSTAT' or

MTB> T TEST μ_0, 'DSTAT'

If the hypothesis being tested is: $H_0: \mu \geq \mu_0$ vs $H_1: \mu < \mu_0$, we need to use:

MTB> Z TEST μ_0, SIGMA = 24.32, 'DSTAT';

SUBC> ALTERNATIVE $-$ 1.

MTB> T TEST μ_0, SIGMA = 24.32, 'DSTAT';

SUBC> ALTERNATIVE $-$ 1.

To test the hypothesis $H_0: \mu \leq \mu_0$ vs $H_1: \mu > \mu_0$, the value of the Alternative sub-command should be changed to $+$ 1.

When comparing 2 population parameters against each other (*i.e.*, if we are testing: $H_0: \Delta\mu = \mu_1 - \mu_2 = 0$ vs $H_1: \Delta\mu \neq 0$), the 2 data sets are placed in columns C_1 and C_2 and named (for example) 'DSTAT1': and 'DSTAT2' (see example in Section 9.5), and the 90% C.I. for $\Delta\mu$ is obtained from the command:

MTB >   TWOSAMPLE $-$ T 90.0 'DSTAT1' 'DSTAT2';

SUBC> POOLED.

The hypothesis tests become:

MTB > TTEST 0.0 'DSTAT1' 'DSTAT2';
SUBC> POOLED $\quad\big\}$ if $H_0: \Delta\mu = 0$ vs $H_1: \Delta\mu \neq 0$

or   MTB> TTEST 0.0 'DSTAT1' 'DSTAT2';
      SUBC> POOLED;
      SUBC> ALTERNATIVE $+$ 1. $\quad\Big\}$ if $H_0: \Delta\mu \leq 0$ vs $H_1: \Delta\mu > 0$

or   MTB> TTEST 0.0 'DSTAT1' 'DSTAT2';
      SUBC> POOLED;
      SUBC> ALTERNATIVE $-$ 1. $\quad\Big\}$ if $H_0: \Delta\mu \geq 0$ vs $H_1: \Delta\mu < 0$

The corresponding 90% Confidence Interval and Hypothesis testing commands for the Population median, η, and using the file 'DSTAT', are:

MTB> S INTERVAL 90.0 'DSTAT'

and MTB> S TEST 84 'DSTAT' $\Big\}$ if H_0: $\eta = 84$ vs H_1: $\eta \neq 84$

or: MTB> S TEST 84 'DSTAT'; $\Big\}$ if H_0: $\eta \leq 0$ vs H_1: $\eta > 84$
SUBC> ALTERNATIVE $+$ 1

or: MTB> S TEST 84 'DSTAT'; $\Big\}$ if H_0: $\eta \geq 0$ vs H_1: $\eta < 84$
SUBC> ALTERNATIVE $-$ 1

To compare 2 population medians we use the Mann-Whitney Two-Sample Rank Sum Test, whose output includes the point Estimate, confidence Interval for the difference between population medians, and the Hypothesis Test results. The Confidence level option specifies the Confidence Coefficient. The default level is 95%.

After entering the 2 data sets in separate columns (or separate files) it is implemented by:

STAT $\rightarrow$ Nonparametrics $\rightarrow$ Mann-Whitney

The general form of the command is:

MANN-WHITNEY (CONFIDENCE LEVEL K) ON C $\cdots$ C
ALTERNATIVE K.

Example

Compare the medians of 2 exams, A and B.

Data for Exam A: 69, 80, 86, 82, 77, 78, 82, 79, 69, 77
Data for Exam B: 72, 69, 57, 72, 70, 72, 69, 61, 72, 73

Solution Enter the data in columns named Exam A and Exam B, and then issue the Commands:

1. MTB > DESCRIBE 'EXAM A' 'EXAM B', to obtain some numerical statistics
2. Test the Hypotheses:

   H_0: The medians for Exam A and Exam B are equal.

   vs

   H_1: The median for Exam A exceeds the Median for Exam B.

   This, and the construction of a 95% C.I., is accomplished by the following command:

   MTB > MANN-WHITNEY 95.0 'EXAM A' AND 'EXAM B';
   SUBC > ALTERNATIVE 1.

Note: There are no MINITAB commands available to test:

1. H_0: $\pi = \pi_0$ vs H_1: $\pi \neq \pi_0$

   or H_0: $\pi \geq \pi_0$ vs H_1: $\pi < \pi_0$

   or H_0: $\pi \leq \pi_0$ vs H_1: $\pi > \pi_0$

2. H_0: $\sigma^2 = \sigma_0^2$ vs H_1: $\sigma^2 \neq \sigma_0^2$

   or H_0: $\sigma^2 \geq \sigma_0^2$ vs H_1: $\sigma^2 < \sigma_0^2$

   or H_0: $\sigma^2 \geq \sigma_0^2$ vs H_1: $\sigma^2 > \sigma_0^2$

3. H_0: $\Delta\pi = \pi_1 - \pi_2 = 0$ vs H_1: $\Delta\pi \neq \pi_0$

   or H_0: $\Delta\pi \geq 0$ vs H_1: $\Delta\pi < 0$

   or H_0: $\Delta\pi \leq 0$ vs H_1: $\Delta\pi > 0$

4. $H_0: \sigma_1^2 = \sigma_2^2$ vs. $H_1: \sigma_1^2 \neq \sigma_2^2$
or $H_0: \sigma_1^2 \geq \sigma_2^2$ vs $H_1: \sigma_1^2 < \sigma_2^2$
or $H_0: \sigma_1^2 \leq \sigma_2^2$ vs $H_1: \sigma_1^2 > \sigma_2^2$

10.11 References

Berenson, Marc, L.; Levine, David, M.; and Krehbiel, Timothy, C.; *Basic Business Statistics*. Edition. Pearson-Prentice Hall.

Black, Ken, 2004. *Business Statistics*. 4th Edition. Wiley.

Canavos, George, C., 1984. *Applied Probability and Statistical Methods*. Little, Brown.

Carlson, William, L., and Thorne, Betty, 1997. *Applied Statistical Methods*. Prentice Hall.

Chou, Ya-lun, 1992. *Statistical Analysis for Business and Economics*. Elsevier.

Freund, John, E., and Williams, Frank, J., 1969. *Modern Business Statistics*. Revised by: Perles, Benjamin and Sullivan, Charles. Prentice Hall.

Freund, John, E., and Williams, Frank, J., 1982. *Elementary Business Statistics: The Modern approach*. Prentice-Hall.

Johnson, Robert, 1973. *Elementary Statistics*. Duxbury Press.

McClave, James, T., Benson, George, P., and Sinich, Terry, 2001. *Statistics for Business and Economics*. 8th Edition. Prentice Hall.

Salvatore, Dominick, *Theory and Problems of Statistics and Econometrics*. SCHAUM'S OUTLINE SERIES, McGraw-Hill.

Steel, Robert, G.D., and Torrie, James, H., 1976. *Introduction to Statistics*. McGraw-Hill.

10.12 PROBLEMS

1. The claim is made that "the mean carbon dioxide level of air pollution in New York City is 5.0".

   a) Does a random sample of 100 readings, which produced an $\overline{x} = 7$ and $\hat{s} = 10$, present sufficient evidence to reject this claim at $\alpha = 0.05$?

   b) Also construct a 95% CI on μ.

2. The claim is made that the average grade in a statistics class is 78.3. A sample of 38 students gave a sample mean of 74.3. The population has a standard deviation of $\sigma = 14$.

   a) Test this claim at $\alpha = 0.02$.

   b) Construct a 98% Confidence Interval for μ.

   c) Are the results in (a) and (b) the same? Why or why not? Be Specific!

   d) For what values of $\overline{x}$ will H_0 be rejected? Be specific!

3. Two state-supported universities have distinct methods of registering students. The two universities wish to compare the average time it takes students to go through registration. The registration times of 100 randomly selected students were observed at each university and the following sample information was obtained:

$$\text{University 1: } \overline{x}_1 = 50.2,\ \hat{s}_1 = 4.8,\ n_1 = 100$$

$$\text{University 2: } \overline{x}_2 = 52.9,\ \hat{s}_2 = 5.4,\ n_2 = 100$$

   a) Are the registration times of the 2 universities equal at $\alpha = 0.05$?

   b) Construct a 95% CI on the difference of mean registration times of the 2 universities.

c) Are the results in (a) and (b) the same? Why or why not? Be Specific!

d) For what values of $\Delta \bar{x}$ will H_0 be rejected? Be specific!

4. An industrial engineer has devised two methods for assembling a water pump. The first method assembled a sample of 40 units with an average of 20.2 minutes per unit and a sample standard deviation of 2.5 minutes. The second method assembled 56 units with an average of 21.0 minutes each and with a sample standard deviation of 3.1 minutes.

 a) Is there a significant difference in the time required for assembling this product between the two methods at $\alpha = 0.02$?

 b) Construct a 98% Confidence Interval for the true mean difference of required time for the two methods.

 c) What conclusion do you draw from this CI regarding the effectiveness of the two methods? Is this conclusion different from your conclusion in part (a)? Justify!

5. The President of the U.S.A. claims to "have the support of the majority of all voters". A poll of 1200 randomly selected voters was taken to test this claim and it was found that 645 voters supported the president.

 a) Does this sample result represent sufficient evidence to support the president's claim at $\alpha = 0.05$?

 b) Construct a 98% Confidence Interval for the true proportion of voters who support the president.

6. A random sample of 100 men was selected from a given state and 60 were found to be in favor of a "more modern" divorce law. A random sample of 100 women were also selected from the same state, at the same time, and revealed that 40 were in favor of such a new law. Is the proportion of men favoring the new divorce law the same as that of women, in this state, at $\alpha = 0.05$ and $\alpha = 0.01$?

7. A process, designed to fill seasoned tomatoes into cans, is said to be in control if the net weight in each can is within 16 ± 0.05 ounces. From past experience it is known that $\sigma = 0.05$ ounce. When the process is in control (*i.e.*, when the can weight is between 15.5 and 16.5 ounces) it is left alone. When the process is out of control (*i.e.*, when weight < 15.5 or weight < 16.5) adjustments are made. How large a sample must be taken, from time to time, to check and see if the process is in control, if we are willing to assume $\alpha = 0.01$ (stop the process when we do not need to) and $\beta = 0.025$ (leave the process alone when it should have been stopped)?

8. The management of a restaurant found, on the basis of a random sample of size $n = 49$, that it took its head chef on the average $\bar{x} = 15$ minutes to prepare a cooked-to-order entree, and the sample standard deviation was $\hat{s} = 5$ minutes.

 a) What can we assert, with 95% confidence about the possible size of the error when using $\bar{x} = 15$ minutes as the true average time it takes the chef to prepare this entree?

 b) Also construct a 95% Confidence Interval on μ, the true average time it takes the chef to prepare this entree.

9. A department store takes a random sample from its very extensive files and finds that the amount owed on 196 delinquent accounts have a mean of $64.00 and a standard deviation of $7.00. If $64.00 is used as the estimate of the true average amount owed on all the department stores delinquent account, with what confidence can we assert that this estimate is off by at most $1.00?

10. In a survey conducted in a retirement community it was found that a random sample of 36 senior citizens visited a physician on the average 11 times a year with a standard deviation of 3. A Health Insurance claims that the average number of visits of its senior citizen customers is 10 visits per year.

    a) Test this claim at the $\alpha = 0.05$ level.

    b) Construct a 95% Confidence Interval on μ.

    c) What is the sample size, n, needed, with 95% confidence, if the maximum error $= e_{max} = \overline{x} - \mu = 1$ visit?

11. Suppose that a company manufactures a cleaning wax which it sells in cans marked "400 grams net weight," and it knows from experience that $\sigma = 8$ grams. The cans are filled by a machine and the company considers the process to be in control if $395 < \overline{x} < 405$ and out of control if $\overline{x} < 395$ or $\overline{x} > 405$. A random sample of $n = 16$ is obtained, and the value of $\overline{x}$ is calculated.

    a) What is the probability of the type $I = \alpha$ error?

    b) What is the probability of the type $II = \beta$ error, when the actual mean is not $\mu = 400$ but $\mu = 398$?

12. In a time-motion study it is desired to test the null hypothesis $H_0: \mu \le 45$ vs $H_1: \mu > 45$ minutes on the basis of a random sample of size 40 from a population with $\sigma = 5.5$ minutes.

    a) If $\alpha = 0.05$, for what values of $\overline{x}$ will H_0 be rejected?

    b) Calculate β for $\mu = 46$ and $\mu = 48$ minutes.

13. In a study designed to test whether there is a difference in IQ between male and female applicants for a certain position, it is desired to test the hypotheses $H_0: \mu_1 = \mu_2$ vs $H_1: \mu_1 \ne \mu_2$. If $n_1 = n_2 = 50$, $\sigma_1 = 8$ and $\sigma_2 = 7.5$, and H_0 is rejected when $\Delta\overline{x} = \overline{x}_1 - \overline{x}_2 > 2$ or $\Delta\overline{x} < -2$ find:

    a) The probability of Type I error $= \alpha$

    b) The probability of Type II error $= \beta$ when $\Delta\mu = \mu_1 - \mu_2 = 1$, $\mu_2 = 1$, $\Delta\mu = 2$, $\Delta\mu = 5$

14. If we wish to test $H_0: \mu = \mu_0$ in such a way that the Type I error $= \alpha$ and the Type II error $= \beta$, for the alternative $\mu = \mu_A$, then:

$$n = \frac{\sigma^2(z_\alpha + z_\beta)^2}{(\mu_A - \mu_0)^2}$$ if the alternative is one sided,

and

$$n = \frac{\sigma^2(z_{\alpha/2} + z_\beta)^2}{(\mu_A - \mu_0)^2}$$ if the alternative is two sided.

Suppose we want to test the hypothesis $\mu = 500$ vs $H_1: \mu \ne 500$ for a population for which $\sigma = 16$. If this hypothesis is true, we want to be 95% sure of accepting it, and if the true mean differs from $500 by $10 in either direction, we want the Type II error to be 0.2.

    a) What is the required sample size?

    b) For what values of $\overline{x}$ is H_0 rejected?

15. The Police Chief of a large city claims that the mean age of bicycle thieves is 10 years old. A statistician takes a random sample of 64 cases of bicycle thieves, from the police files, and calculates a mean age of the thieves to be 12 years old, with a standard deviation of 4 years. Can the police chief's claim be substantiated at $\alpha = 0.02$?

16. A sample study was made of the number of lunches that executives claim as business expenses in a given time period. If 36 insurance executives averaged 8 lunches in this time period with a standard deviation of 2, and 64 bank executives averaged 6 lunches, with a standard deviation of 4, in the same time period, test at the $a = 0.05$ level whether the means of these 2 populations of executives are equal or not.

17. The claim is made that 68% of industrial accidents are due to unsafe working conditions. If a random sample of 250 such accidents showed that 180 were due to unsafe working conditions, test this claim at the $\alpha = 0.01$ level.

18. In a random sample of visitors to a national monument 64 of 256 men and 108 of 360 women bought souvenirs. At $\alpha = 0.05$ test the hypothesis: $H_0: \Delta\pi = \pi_1 - \pi_2 = 0$ vs $H_1: \Delta\pi \neq 0$.

19. To study the relationship between family size and intelligence, 36 "only children" were tested and found to have a mean IQ of 110 points with a standard deviation of 8, and 45 "first-born children" in three-children families had a mean IQ of 105 and a standard deviation of 6. Test at the $\alpha = 0.05$ level of significance whether the difference between these two means is significant or not.

20. In a study conducted at a large airport, 81 of 300 persons who had gotten off a plane and 32 of 200 persons who were about to board a plane admitted that they were afraid of flying. Is there a difference in the population proportions of these two populations who are afraid to fly, at $\alpha = 0.01$? $\alpha = 0.05$?

21. A researcher wants to determine the proportion of farm workers in a certain area that are illegal aliens. How large a sample is needed, if he wants to be 98% sure that his estimate will not be off by more than 0.02?

22. An airline claims that only 8 percent of all lost luggage is never found. If 20 of 160 pieces of luggage, lost by the airline, are not found:

    a) Test the null hypothesis, $H_0: \pi = 0.05$ against $H_1: \pi \neq 0.05$, at the $\alpha = 0.05$ level.

    b) Also construct a 95% Confidence Interval on π.

23. The dean of a business school claims that 60 percent of the undergraduate business students at his university will go on to graduate school.

    a) Test the validity of this claim at the $\alpha = 0.02$ level, if a random sample of 100 such students showed that 45 of them were planning to go to graduate school.

    b) Also construct a 98% Confidence Interval on π.

    c) Compare the results of the solutions of a) and b). Do they produce the same conclusions?

24. In a random sample of television viewers 80 out of 200 liked a new show. If we use the sample proportion as an estimate of the true proportion of television viewers who liked the new show, what is the size of the maximum error, if we wish to be 95% confident?

25. A study showed that 60 of 160 persons who saw a soft drink advertised during a football game and 30 out of 75 persons who saw the same soft drink advertised during a variety show, remembered the name of the soft drink five hours later.

    a) Use the $\alpha = 0.01$ to test the null hypothesis $H_0: \Delta\pi = \pi_1 - \pi_2$ vs $H_1: \Delta\pi \neq 0$

    b) Construct a 99% Confidence Interval on $\Delta\pi = \pi_1 - \pi_2$.

    c) Are the conclusions of the two solutions the same? Justify your answer!

26. An efficiency expert wants to determine the average time it takes a person to shop at a supermarket. How large a sample size will be needed, to state with 95% Confidence, that the mean of the sample will not exceed 0.5 minutes, if it is known that $\sigma = 5$?

27. A random sample of 36 small service companies (with assets under $5,000,000) showed an average profit of 2 percent, with a standard deviation of 0.5 percent, and a random sample of 40 large service companies (with assets above $5,000,000) showed a profit of 2.5 percent with a standard deviation of 0.8 percent.

a) At the 0.02 level of significance test to see if the difference between the means of these two populations $(\Delta\mu = \mu_1 - \mu_2)$ is significant or not.

b) Construct a 98% Confidence Interval on $\Delta\mu$.

c) Are the conclusions of the solutions in (a) and (b) the same? Justify.

28. Suppose the president of the United States plans to introduce health insurance legislation if sample results indicated that 60% of the voters desired it, and would not introduce the legislation if only 40% desired it. If he is willing to assume an α risk of $\alpha = 0.01$ (for $\pi = 0.6$) and a β risk of $\beta = 0.05$ (for $\pi = 0.4$), find the required sample size and state the decision rule for this test.

29. The dimensionality of a critical part in a certain design is 5 inches, with a standard deviation of 0.6 inches. The process, producing the part, is considered to be in control, if $\mu = 5$ for the critical part, and it continues. Otherwise it is considered to be out of control and it is stopped. To check whether the process is in control, a random sample of $n = 36$ is obtained every 5 hours, and the hypothesis $\mu = 5$ is tested at $\alpha = 0.05$.

a) Formulate H_0 and H_1.

b) Show the α and β risks schematically.

c) Find $\bar{x}_{c1}$ and $\bar{x}_{c2}$, and establish the decision rule.

30. A firm's packaging machinery is known to pour dry cereal into boxes with a known standard deviation of $\sigma = 2$. Two samples are taken on 2 different dates and yield the following results:

First Sample	**Second Sample**
$n_1 = 16$	$n_2 = 16$
$\bar{x}_1 = 18$	$\bar{x}_2 = 22$

Using $\alpha = 0.02$:

a) Test the hypothesis that, for the first sample, H_0: $\mu_1 = 20$.

b) Test the hypothesis that, for the second sample, H_0: $\mu_2 = 20$.

c) Test the hypothesis that, $H_0 = \Delta\mu = \mu_1 - \mu_2 = 0$.

31. A Study of naval officers showed that 15 out of 35 leading generals of the army had come from the upper 30 percent of their class at West Point. Can we conclude from this that scholastic success at West Point is helpful in becoming a leading general, at $\alpha = 0.05$?

32. Many years of experience with a University entrance examination in Mathematics has yielded a mean score of 65 and a standard deviation of 7. All the students of a certain city, of which were 49, obtained a mean score of 67. Can we claim that the students from this city are superior in Mathematics at the $\alpha = 0.05$?

33. In a study of the effects of heavy doses of vitamin C on colds, a record was kept of the number of colds caught by each individual participating in the experiment, and the following results were obtained:

Use the data to test the hypothesis that vitamin C doses had no effect on the mean number of colds, at $\alpha = 0.02$.

Groups	Number of Individuals	Mean Number of Colds	Standard Deviation of number of Colds
Vitamin Group	350	1.8	1.2
Placebo Group	400	2.1	1.3

34. In a poll of the television audience of a city, 80 out of 250 men and 98 out of 350 women disliked a certain program. Is there a real difference of opinion between men and women, at the $\alpha = 0.01$?

35. A test of 100 youths and 200 adults showed that 50 of the youths and 60 of the adults were careless drivers. Use this data to test the claim, at $\alpha = 0.05$, that the youth percentage of careless drivers is larger that the adult percentage by 10 percentage points.

36. An economist for a state agency wants to determine whether the current unemployment rates at two large urban areas of the state are the same. Based on random samples of 500 in each of the two areas, the economist finds 35 persons unemployed in one area and 25 in the other area.

    a) Is there reason to believe, at the $\alpha = 0.05$ level of significance, that the unemployment rates for the two areas are different?

    b) What is the p-value?

37. A manufacturer wishes to compare the average strength of his yarn with that of his major competitor. The strengths of 100 random yarn specimens from each factory are measured and the following data resulted:

    $$n_1 = 100, \quad \bar{x}_1 = 112, \quad \hat{s}_1 = 10$$
    $$n_2 = 100, \quad \bar{x}_2 = 108, \quad \hat{s}_2 = 12$$

    a) Is there reason to believe that a difference exists between the average strengths of the two yarns at the $\alpha = 0.05$? at $\alpha = 0.02$?

    b) What is the p-value?

38. A United Nations health organization is interested in updating its information about the proportion of female smokers, which it believes to be 40% based on previous studies. A random sample of 1500 women is selected and it is found that 525 of them are smokers.

    a) Determine whether this evidence supports the belief that the proportion of female smokers is different from 40%, at the $\alpha = 0.01$ level.

    b) What is the p-value?

39. In a certain farming state the average corn yield has been 100 bushels per acre, with a known standard deviation of 8. In a year, in which the weather was very good, 16 randomly selected large plots yielded an average of 104 bushels per acre, for the same variety of corn.

    a) Is there reason to believe that this year's yield has been better than in the past, at $\alpha = 0.05$?

    b) What is the p-value in this case?

40. According to Zero Population Growth, the average urban U.S. resident consumes 3.3 pounds of food per day. To determine whether this figure is accurate for rural U.S. residents, a random sample of 36 rural U.S. residents were selected and their average consumption per day was found to be 3.5 pounds of food with a standard deviation of $\hat{s} = 1.2$.

    a) At $\alpha = 0.05$, is the average figure for urban residents also true for rural residents on the basis of this sample data?

    b) What is the p-value in this case?

SOLUTIONS

1. a) i) $H_0: \mu = 5$ vs $H_1: \mu \neq 5$

   ii) $\alpha = 0.05$

   iii) The estimator for μ is $\bar{x}$ and, because $n = 100 > 30$, $\bar{x}$ is normally distributed with

   $$E(\bar{x}) = \mu = 5 \text{ and } \sigma(\bar{x}) = \frac{\sigma}{\sqrt{n}} = \frac{10}{10} = 1, \text{ and } \frac{\bar{x} - E(\bar{x})}{\sigma(\bar{x})} = N(0, 1)$$

   (*i.e.*, standard normal)

   iv) The rejection region is, because of the nature of H_1 and given value of α: $\pm Z_{\alpha/2} = Z_{0.025} = \pm 1.96$

   v) The value of the test statistic is $Z^* = \dfrac{\bar{x} - \mu_0}{\sigma(\bar{x})} = \dfrac{7 - 5}{1} = 2$

   vi) Since $Z^* > Z_{\alpha/2}$, H_0 is rejected

   vii) Conclusion: The mean carbon dioxide level of air pollution in New York City is different than 5.

   b) $P\left[\bar{x} - Z_{\alpha/2}\,\sigma(\bar{x}) \leq \mu \leq \bar{x} + Z_{\alpha/2}\,\sigma(\bar{x})\right] = 1 - \alpha$

   $P\left[7 - 1.96(1) \leq \mu \leq 7 + 1.96(1)\right] = 0.95$

   $P\left[5.04 \leq \mu \leq 8.96\right] = 0.95$; since $\mu = 5$ is outside of this CI, H_0 is again rejected.

2. a) i) $H_0: \mu = 78.3$ vs $H_1: \mu \neq 78.3$

   ii) $\alpha = 0.02$

   iii) The estimator for μ is $\bar{x}$ and, because $n = 38 > 30$, $\bar{x}$ is normally distributed with

   $$E(\bar{x}) = \mu = 78.3 \text{ and } \sigma(\bar{x}) = \frac{\sigma}{\sqrt{n}} = \frac{14}{\sqrt{38}} = 2.27$$

   iv) The rejection region is $\pm Z_{\alpha/2} = Z_{0.01} = \pm 2.33$

   v) $Z^* = \dfrac{\bar{x} - \mu_0}{\sigma(\bar{x})} = \dfrac{74.3 + -78.3}{2.27} = \dfrac{-4}{2.27} = -1.76$

   vi) Since $-2.33 < Z^* < 2.33$, do not reject H_0

   vii) Therefore, the average grade in this Statistics class is $\mu = 78.3$.

   b) $P\left[\bar{x} - Z_{\alpha/2}\,\sigma(\bar{x}) \leq \mu \leq \bar{x} + Z_{\alpha/2}\,\sigma(\bar{x})\right] = 1 - \alpha$

   $P\left[74.3 - 2.33(2.27) \leq \mu \leq 74.3 + 2.33(2.27)\right] = 0.98$

   $P\left[69.01 \leq \mu \leq 79.59\right] = 0.98$; since $\mu = 78.3$ falls inside this CI, H_0 is, again, not rejected.

   c) Both solutions are the same. Both solutions reject H_0.

   d) To reject H_0, $Z^* = \dfrac{\bar{x} - \mu_o}{\sigma(\bar{x})} < -2.33$ or $Z^* = \dfrac{\bar{x} - \mu_o}{\sigma(\bar{x})} > 2.33$, from which we obtain:

   Reject H_0 if $\bar{x} < \mu_0 - 2.33\,\sigma(\bar{x})$ or if $\bar{x} < 73.01$ and if $\bar{x} > \mu_0 + 2.33\,\sigma(\bar{x})$ or if $\bar{x} > 83.59$

3. a) i) $H_0: \Delta\mu = 0$ vs $H_1: \Delta\mu \neq 0$

ii) $\alpha = 0.05$

iii) The estimator for $\Delta\mu$ is $\Delta\bar{x}$ and, because $n_1 > 30$ and $n_2 > 30$, $\Delta\bar{x}$ is normally

distributed with $E(\Delta\bar{x}) = \Delta\mu$ and $\sigma(\Delta\bar{x}) = \sqrt{\dfrac{(4.8)^2}{100} + \dfrac{(5.4)^2}{100}}$

$$= \sqrt{0.522} = 0.722$$

vi) The rejection region is $\pm Z_{\alpha/2} = \pm Z_{0.025}$

$$= \pm 1.96$$

v) $Z^* = \dfrac{\Delta\bar{x} - \Delta\mu_0}{\sigma(\bar{x})} = \dfrac{(\bar{x}_1 - \bar{x}_2) - 0}{\sigma(\Delta\bar{x})} = -\dfrac{2.7}{0.722} = -3.74$

vi) Since $Z^* = -3.74 < -1.96 = -Z_{\alpha/2}$, H_0 is rejected, and we conclude that $\Delta\mu \neq 0$.

vii) Therefore, the 2 universities have different registration times.

b) $P\left[\Delta\bar{x} - Z_{\alpha/2}\,\sigma(\Delta\bar{x}) \leq \Delta\mu \leq \Delta\bar{x} + Z_{\alpha/2}\,\sigma(\Delta\bar{x})\right] = 1 - \alpha$

$P\left[-2.7 - 1.96(0.7222) \leq \Delta\mu \leq -2.7 + 1.96(0.722)\right] = 0.95$

since $\Delta\mu = 0$ is outside this CI, $H_0: \Delta\mu = 0$ is rejected.

c) The two solutions arrive at the same conclusion. Both reject H_0.

d) To not reject H_0, $-1.96 < Z^* = \dfrac{\Delta\bar{x} - 0}{\sigma(\Delta\bar{x})} = \dfrac{\Delta\bar{x}}{0.722} \leq 1.96$ from which we obtain:

$-1.415 \leq \Delta\bar{x} \leq 1.415$

4. a) i) $H_0: \Delta\mu = 0$ vs $H_1: \Delta\mu \neq 0$ $(\Delta\mu = \mu_1 - \mu_2)$

ii) $\alpha = 0.02$

iii) The estimator for $\Delta\mu$ is $\Delta\bar{x} = \bar{x}_2 - \bar{x}_1$ $(21.0 - 20.2 = 0.8)$ and, because
$n_1 = 40 > 30$ and $n_2 = 56 > 30$, $\Delta\bar{x}$ is normal with: $E(\Delta\bar{x}) = \Delta\mu = 0$, and

$$\sigma(\Delta\bar{x}) = \sqrt{\dfrac{\hat{s}_1^2}{n_1} + \dfrac{\hat{s}_1^2}{n_2}} = \sqrt{\dfrac{(2.5)^2}{40} + \dfrac{(3.1)^2}{56}} = \sqrt{0.15625 + 0.17161} = 0.5726$$

iv) The rejection region is $\pm Z_{\alpha/2} = Z_{0.01} = \pm 2.33$

v) $Z^* = \dfrac{\Delta\bar{x} - \Delta\mu_o}{\sigma(\Delta\bar{x})} = \dfrac{0.8 - 0}{0.5726} = 1.40$

vi) Since $-2.33 < Z^* < 2.33$, do not reject H_0.

vii) Therefore, there is no significant difference in the average time of assembly.

b) $P\left[\Delta\bar{x} - Z_{\alpha/2}\,\sigma(\Delta\bar{x}) \leq \Delta\mu \leq \Delta\bar{x} + Z_{\alpha/2}\,\sigma(\Delta\bar{x})\right] = 1 - \alpha$

$P\left[0.8 - 2.33(0.5726) \leq \Delta\mu \leq -0.8 + 2.33(0.5726)\right] = 0.98$

$P\left[-0.534 \leq \Delta\mu \leq 2.134\right] = 0.98$

c) Since the above C.I. includes the value of $\Delta\mu = 0$, the conclusion is the same.
There is no real difference between the two methods.

5. a) $n = 1200$, $x = 645$, $p = \dfrac{x}{n} = \dfrac{645}{1200} = .5375$; Then:

i) $H_0: \pi \leq 0.5$ vs $H_1: \pi > 0.5$

ii) $\alpha = 0.05$

iii) The estimator for π is p and, because $n = 1200 > 30$, p is normally distributed with

$$E(p) = \pi \text{ and } \sigma(p) = \sqrt{\frac{\pi(1-\pi)}{n}} = \sqrt{\frac{(0.5)(0.5)}{1200}} = 0.014434$$

iv) Rejection region $= Z_\alpha = Z_{0.05} = 1.645$

v) $Z^* = \dfrac{(p - \pi_0)}{\sigma(p)} = \dfrac{.5375 - 0.5}{0.014434} = 2.60$

vi) Since $Z^* > Z_{0.05}$, H_0 is rejected (*i.e.*, the president's support is not less than 50%).

vii) Therefore, the President has the support of the majority of voters.

b) $P\Big[p - Z_{\alpha/2}\,\sigma(p) \le \pi \le p + Z_{\alpha/2}\,\sigma(p)\Big] = 1 - \alpha$

$P\Big[.5375 - 2.33(0.014434) \le \pi \le 0.5375 + 2.33(0.014434)\Big] = 0.98$

$P\Big[.5375 - 0.03363 \le \pi \le 0.5375 + 0.03363\Big] = 0.98$

$P\Big[0.5039 \le \pi \le 0.5711\Big] = 0.98;$

6. i) $H_0: \Delta\pi = \pi_1 - \pi_2 = 0$ vs $H_1: \Delta\pi \ne 0$

ii) $\alpha = 0.05$ and $\alpha = 0.01$

iii) The estimator for $\Delta\pi$ is $\Delta p = p_1 - p_2\Big(= \dfrac{60}{100} - \dfrac{40}{100} = 0.6 - 0.4 = 0.2\Big)$

and, because $n_1 = 100 > 30$ and $n_2 = 100 > 30$ Δp is normally distributed, with

$$E(\Delta p) = \Delta\pi = 0 \text{ and } \sigma(\Delta p) = \sqrt{\overline{p}(1 - \overline{p})\Big[\frac{n_1 + n_2}{n_1 n_2}\Big]} =$$

$$\sqrt{0.5(0.5)\Big[\frac{200}{100 \times 100}\Big]} = 0.0707$$

iv) Rejection regions: a) For $\alpha = 0.05$; $\pm Z_{\alpha/2} = \pm Z_{0.025} = \pm 1.96$

b) For $\alpha = 0.01$; $\pm Z_{0.05} = \pm 2.58$

v) $Z^* = \dfrac{(\Delta p - \Delta\pi_0)}{\sigma(\Delta p)} = \dfrac{0.2 - 0}{0.0707} = 2.83$

vi) Since $Z^* > Z_{\alpha/2}$ (for both α values), H_0 is rejected.

vii) Therefore, men and women differ, concerning this new divorce law, in this state.

7. Test the hypothesis $H_0: \mu = \mu_0 = 16$ vs $H_1: \mu = \mu_1 = 15.5$ or $\mu = \mu_2 = 16.5$
$\alpha = $ Probability (of stopping process when $\mu = \mu_0 = 16$) $= 0.01$ $\beta = $ Probability (of leaving process alone when $\mu = \mu_1 = 15.5$ or $\mu = \mu_2 = 16.5$) $= 0.025$

For a 2-sided H_1, H_0 will be rejected if:

$\overline{x} < \overline{x}_{c1} = \mu_0 - Z_{\alpha/2}\,\sigma(\overline{x})$

$$= 16 - 2.58\Big(\frac{0.5}{\sqrt{n}}\Big) \tag{1}$$

or if: $\overline{x} > \overline{x}_{c2} = \mu_0 + Z_{\alpha/2}\,\sigma(\overline{x})$

$$= 16 + 2.58\Big(\frac{0.5}{\sqrt{n}}\Big) \tag{2}$$

H_0 will be accepted, when H_1 is true if:

$\overline{x} < \overline{x}_{c1} = \mu_1 - Z_\beta\,\sigma(\overline{x})$

$$= 15.5 + 1.96\Big(\frac{0.5}{\sqrt{n}}\Big) \tag{3}$$

or if: $\overline{x} > \overline{x}_{c2} = \mu_2 - Z_\beta\,\sigma(\overline{x})$

$$= 16.5 - 1.96\Big(\frac{0.5}{\sqrt{n}}\Big) \tag{4}$$

The required sample size can be obtained by either letting the 2 expressions for $\bar{x}_{c1}$ equal to each other, or letting the 2 expressions for $\bar{x}_{c2}$ equal to each other.

We obtain:

$$16 - 2.58\,\frac{0.5}{\sqrt{n}} = 15.5 + 1.96\,\frac{0.5}{\sqrt{n}}, \text{ or } 16 - 16.5 = \frac{0.5}{\sqrt{n}}(2.58 + 1.96)$$

$$\sqrt{n} = (2.58 + 1.96) = 4.54, \text{ or } n = (4.54) = 21$$

Note: The same result is obtained if we let: $16 + 2.58\,\dfrac{0.5}{\sqrt{n}} = 16.5 - 1.96\,\dfrac{0.5}{\sqrt{n}}$

Then, substituting the value of $n = 21$, in (1) and (2) above, we obtain:

$$\bar{x}_{c1} = 16 - 2.58\,\frac{0.5}{\sqrt{21}} = 16 - 0.28 = 15.72$$

and

$$\bar{x}_{c2} = 16 - 2.58\,\frac{0.5}{\sqrt{21}} = 16 + 0.28 = 16.28$$

The decision rule for the above process then becomes:

Take a random sample of $n = 21$, and calculate $\bar{x}$.

If $15.72 < \bar{x} < 16.28$, leave the process alone.

If $\bar{x} < 15.72$, or if $\bar{x} > 16.28$, stop the process and make the necessary adjustments.

8. a) The sampling error in this case is given by:

$$e_{max} = \bar{x} - \mu = Z_{\alpha/2}\,\sigma/\sqrt{n} \approx Z_{\alpha/2}\,\hat{s}/\sqrt{n} = 1.96\left(\frac{5}{\sqrt{49}}\right) = 1.96 = (5/7) = 1.4$$

Therefore with a 95% Confidence, the error is at most 1.4 minutes.

b) $P\left[\bar{x} - Z_{\alpha/2}\,\hat{s}/\sqrt{n} \le \mu \le \bar{x} + Z_{\alpha/2}\,\hat{s}/\sqrt{n}\right] = 1 - \alpha,$

or $P[15 - 1.96\left(\dfrac{5}{\sqrt{49}}\right) \le \mu \le 15 + 1.96\left(5\Big/\sqrt{49}\right) = 0.95$

or $P\left[1.5 - 1.4 \le \mu \le 15 + 1.4\right] = 0.95,$

or $P\left[13.6 \le \mu \le 16.4\right] = 0.95$

9. The maximum sampling error $e_{max} = \bar{x} - \mu = Z_{\alpha/2}\,\hat{s}/\sqrt{n} = 1$ from which we find:

$$z_{\alpha/2} = \frac{1 \cdot \sqrt{n}}{\hat{s}} = \frac{\sqrt{196}}{7} = \frac{14}{7} = 2 \text{ and}$$

$$P\left[-z_{\alpha/2} \le \mu \le z_{\alpha/2}\right] = P\left[-2 \le \mu \le 2\right] = 2(0.4772) = 0.9544$$

Therefore we can state with a 95.44% Confidence that the error of the estimate is at most $1.00.

10. a) i) $H_0: \mu = 10$ vs $H_1: \mu \ne 10$

  ii) $\alpha = 0.05$

  iii) The estimator of μ is $\bar{x}$ and because $n = 36 > 30$, $\dfrac{\bar{x} - 10}{\hat{s}/\sqrt{n}} = N(0, 1)$, with

  $E(\bar{x}) = \mu_0 = 10$ and $\sigma(\bar{x}) = \hat{s}/\sqrt{n} = 3/\sqrt{36} = 3/6 = 1/2$

  iv) Critical values: $\pm z_{\alpha/2} = \pm z_{0.025} = \pm 1.96$

  v) $z^* = \dfrac{11 - 10}{1/2} = 2(1) = 2$

vi) Since $z^* = 2 > z_{\alpha/2} = z_{0.025} = 1.96$, H_0: $\mu = 10$ is rejected, and we conclude that $u \neq 10$.

b) $P\left[\bar{x} - Z_{\alpha/2}\,\hat{s}/\sqrt{n} \leq \mu \leq \bar{x} + Z_{\alpha/2}\,\hat{s}/\sqrt{n}\right] = 1 - \alpha$,

or $P\left[11 - 1.96\left(\dfrac{1}{2}\right) \leq \mu \leq 11 + 1.96\left(\dfrac{1}{2}\right)\right] = 0.95$ or $P\left[10.02 \leq \mu \leq 11.98\right]$

$= 0.95$; since $\mu = 10$ is outside of this confidence interval, H_0: $\mu = 10$ is rejected.

c) $n = \left[Z_{\alpha/2}\,\sigma/e_{max}\right]^2 = \left[1.96\left(\dfrac{3}{1}\right)\right]^2 = (5.88)^2 = 34.5744 \approx 35$.

11 Inferential Statistics for Small Samples

When the sample size n is small ($n < 30$) the sampling distribution of the sample variance $\hat{s}^2$ (actually of $(n - 1)\hat{s}^2/\sigma^2$) is not normal but chi-square with $\delta =$ Degrees of Freedom (DOF) $= n - 1$ (or $\chi_\delta^2 = \chi_{n-1}^2$).

When $n_1 < 30$ and $n_2 < 30$, the sampling distribution of the ratio $\hat{s}_1^2 / \hat{s}_2^2$ is F-distributed, with $\delta_1 =$ DOF in the numerator $= n_1 - 1$ and $\delta_2 =$ DOF in the denominator $= n_2 - 1$. (Note: n_1 is the sample size from population 1 and n_2 is the sample size from population 2.)

When the standard deviation of the population (σ), from which the sample of observations we are analyzing came from, is not known and $n < 30$, the sampling distribution of

$$\frac{\bar{x} - \mu}{s/\sqrt{n}}$$ is no longer normal but t_{n-1}.

When we compare 2 independent samples, drawn from two populations P_1 and P_2, and σ_1 and σ_2 are not known and n_1 and n_2 are not both large (*i.e.*, if $n_1 < 30$ and $n_2 < 30$, or if $n_1 \geq 30$ but $n_2 < 30$, or if $n_1 < 30$ but $n_2 \geq 30$) the sampling distribution of $\dfrac{\Delta\bar{x}}{\sigma(\Delta\bar{x})} = \dfrac{\bar{x}_1 - \bar{x}_2}{\sigma(\Delta\bar{x})}$ is no longer normal but $t_{n_1+n_2-2}$.

In this chapter we discuss briefly the derivation and characteristics of these new distributions (*i.e.*, χ_{n-1}^2, $F_{n_2-1}^{n_1-1}$, and t_{n-1} and $t_{n_1+n_2-2}$), compare them to the normal distribution (which is the distribution used in large sample statistics, *i.e.*, when σ is known and or when $n \geq 30$ for a single population, or if σ_1 and σ_2 are known and or $n_1 \geq 30$ and $n_2 \geq 30$ for two populations), and then apply them in many business and other situations.

11.1   Large Sampling Theory and Small Sampling Theory

In descriptive statistics we learned that a data set, to be completely characterized needs 4 different types of measures, namely:

1. A measure of central tendency ($\bar{x}$, $x_{0.5}$, x_m)
2. A measure of dispersion ($\hat{s}^2$, s^2, $\hat{s}$, s, R)
3. A measure of skewness (S_{kp})
4. A measure of kurtosis or peakedness (K)

To make decisions about a population, using a set of data, we need to identify the type of distribution of each of these descriptive statistics. However, we have earlier identified as $\bar{x}$ the best measure of central tendency, $\hat{s}^2$ and $\hat{s}$ as the best measures of dispersion, and S_{kp} and K as the best measures of skewness and kurtosis respectively. Therefore, as a minimum we need to identify the sampling distributions of: $\bar{x}$, $\hat{s}^2$, S_{kp}, and K. Even though S_{kp} and K are important measures to completely characterize a data set, $\bar{x}$ and $\hat{s}^2$ are the two most important sample statistics needed in *Decision Making* and, as an *absolute minimum*, we need to obtain the sampling distributions of $\bar{x}$ and $\hat{s}^2$ before we can make inferences about μ and σ^2 of the population under study.

Note: A population consists of elements and the elements have many characteristics. If our data set measures only one of these characteristics, it is called a UNIVARIATE data set; if it measures 2 characteristics, it is called a BIVARIATE set, while if it measures 3 or more characteristics it is called a MULTIVARIATE data set. The μ and σ^2 mentioned above are the population mean (μ) and population variance (σ^2) of a univariate data set.

We have already derived the sampling distribution of $\bar{x}$ when $n \geq 30$ (large-sampling theory). In this case, and using the central limit theorem, we showed that the sampling distribution of $\bar{x}$ is normal, with:

$$E(\bar{x}) = \mu \tag{11.1}$$

$$V(\bar{x}) = \sigma^2/n \tag{11.2}$$

where
μ = population mean
σ^2 = population variance
n = sample size

This result allows us to perform all kinds of probability calculations on $\bar{x}$, which are needed in decision-making. Also, even if the sample size n is small (*i.e.*, $n < 30$), but we know in advance that the population under investigation is normal, the distribution of $\bar{x}$ is again normal, because $\bar{x} = (x_1 + x_2 + \cdots + x_n)/n$ is a linear combination of normally distributed variables $(x_1, x_2, \ldots, x_n)$.

Recall that in earlier chapters we dealt with the problems of:

1. Sampling from a single population, with parameters μ and σ^2, and:
   a) Testing the hypothesis: $H_0: \mu = \mu_0$ vs $H_1: \mu \neq \mu_0$ or $\tag{11.3}$
   b) Constructing the confidence interval

$$P\left[\bar{x} - Z_{\alpha/2} \cdot \sigma_{\bar{x}} < \mu < \bar{x} + Z_{\alpha/2} \cdot \sigma_{\bar{x}}\right] = 1 - \alpha \tag{11.4}$$

2. Sampling from two different populations, with parameters μ_1, σ_1^2, μ_2 and σ_2^2 respectively, and:
   a) Testing the hypothesis: $H_0: \mu_1 = \mu_2$ vs $H_1: \mu \neq \mu_2$ or $\tag{11.5}$
   b) Constructing the confidence interval

$$P\left[\Delta\bar{x} - Z_{\alpha/2} \cdot \sigma_{\Delta\bar{x}} < \Delta\mu = \mu_1 - \mu_2 < \Delta\bar{x} + Z_{\alpha/2} \cdot \sigma_{\Delta\bar{x}}\right] = 1 - \alpha \tag{11.6}$$

In both these cases we use the *Normal Distribution* if the Large-Sampling Theory applies (*i.e.*, if $n \geq 30$ in Problem #1, and $n_1 \geq 30$ and $n_2 \geq 30$ in Problem #2).

If the *Large-Sampling Theory* does not apply, we have to use the *Small-Sampling Theory* and find the new distribution of $\bar{x}$ (which is the estimator of μ) and $\Delta\bar{x} = \bar{x}_1 - \bar{x}_2$ (which is the estimator of $\Delta\mu = \mu_1 - \mu_2$) before we can solve the above problems. We will show that the new distribution is no longer normal, but "Student-*t*" with "$(n - 1)$ degrees of freedom" for Problem #1, and "Student-*t*" with "$(n_1 + n_2 - 2)$ degrees of freedom" for Problem #2.

Similarly, if we wish to study the variance of a population (*i.e.*, test the hypothesis: $H_0: \sigma^2 = 16$ vs $H_1: \sigma^2 \neq 16$ for example), we will need the distribution of the unbiased sample variance $\hat{s}^2$, before we can do so, because $\hat{s}^2$ is the best estimator for σ^2, and:

$$\hat{s}^2 = \frac{1}{n-1}\sum_{i=1}^{n}\left(x_i - \bar{x}\right)^2 \tag{11.7}$$

We will show that the sampling distribution of $\hat{s}^2$ is the "Chi-square Distribution with $(n - 1)$ degrees of freedom". Similarly, if we wish to compare the equality of the variance of two populations, we can formulate the hypothesis:

$$H_0: \sigma_1^2 = \sigma_2^2 \text{ vs } H_1: \sigma_1^2 \neq \sigma_2^2 \tag{11.8}$$

To solve this problem, if both $n_1 < 30$ and $n_2 < 30$ (where n_1 and n_2 are the samples obtained from populations 1 and 2 respectively), we are led to the "*F*-Distribution with $(n_1 - 1)$ degrees of freedom in the numerator and $(n_2 - 1)$ degrees of freedom in the denominator".

The "Student-t", "Chi-square", and "F" distributions are distributions assumed by sample statistics when the sample size n is small (*i.e.*, $n < 30$), are related to the Normal Distribution and are defined in terms of the "Number of Degrees of Freedom".

Note: when n is large (*i.e.*, $n \geq 30$), these distributions approach the Normal Distribution, and the normal can be used instead of them).

11.2 Degrees of Freedom

The *Degrees of Freedom* is a mathematical concept which refers to the number of linearly independent observations which occur in a sum of squares, and is defined by:

$$\text{Degrees of Freedom} = \text{D.O.F.} = \delta = n - k \tag{11.9}$$

where $n =$ sample size
$k =$ number of estimators in the given sum of squares requiring calculation, using the given data set.

Examples
Consider the following 5 sum of squares. Find the degrees of freedom associated with each sum of squares.

1. $\displaystyle\sum_{i=1}^{n} x_i^2 = x_1^2 + x_2^2 + \cdots + x_n^2$ $\tag{11.10}$

   Since there are no unknown estimators in this sum of squares, $k = 0$ and, therefore, $\delta = n - k = n - 0 = n$ degrees of freedom.

2. $\displaystyle\sum_{i=1}^{n} (x_i - \overline{x})^2 = (x_1 - \overline{x})^2 + (x_2 - \overline{x})^2 + \cdots + (x_n - \overline{x})^2$ $\tag{11.11}$

   Since there is one unknown estimator ($\overline{x}$) in this sum of squares, $k = 1$ and, therefore, $\delta = n - k = n - 1$ degrees of freedom.

3. $\displaystyle\sum_{i=1}^{n} (y_i - a - bx_i)^2 = (y_1 - a - bx_1)^2$

   $\qquad\qquad\qquad\qquad + (y_2 - a - bx_2)^2 + \cdots + (y_n - a - bx_n)^2$ $\tag{11.12}$

   (This sum of squares occurs in Bivariate Analysis when we try to fit the "Best possible linear Equation, $y = a + bx$, through a given data set (x_i, y_i), and the objective is to find the BEST values for a and b.)
   Since there are 2 unknown estimators (a, b) in this sum of squares, $k = 2$ and, therefore, $\delta = n - k = n - 2$ degrees of freedom.

4. $\displaystyle\sum_{i=1}^{n} (x_i - \mu)^2 = (x_1 - \mu)^2 + (x_2 - \mu)^2 + \cdots + (x_n - \mu)^2$ $\tag{11.13}$

   This sum of squares has $\delta = n - k = n - 0 = n$ because μ, appearing in the sum of squares, is a parameter and not an estimator, and as such is not estimated from the data.

5. $\displaystyle\sum_{i=1}^{n} \left(\frac{x_i - \mu}{\sigma}\right)^2 = \left(\frac{x_1 - \mu}{\sigma}\right)^2 + \left(\frac{x_2 - \mu}{\sigma}\right)^2 + \cdots + \left(\frac{x_n - \mu}{\sigma}\right)^2$ $\tag{11.14}$

This sum of squares has $\delta = n - k = n - 0 = n$ because μ and σ, appearing in the sum of squares, are parameters and not estimators, and as such are not estimated from the data.

■ ■ ■

11.3 The Chi-Square, *F*, and Student-*t* Distributions

11.3.1 The Chi-square Distribution
11.3.1.1 Theoretical Considerations
Suppose we had to test the hypothesis $H_0: \sigma^2 = 100$ vs $H_1: \sigma^2 \neq 100$.

Question: How would we proceed?

Answer: First, find the sampling distribution of $\hat{s}^2$, the estimator of σ^2. But, to accomplish this, we need to first discuss, briefly, the theoretical formulation of the Chi-Square Distribution.

1. Suppose $Z_1, Z_2, \ldots, Z_n$ are n independent standard normal variables, that is, each of the Z_i variables has the density function $f(z_i) = \dfrac{1}{\sqrt{2\pi}} e^{-z_i^2/2}$ $(-\infty < Z_i < \infty)$ (11.15)

Then, if we let $Y = Z_1^2 + Z_2^2 + \cdots + Z_n^2 = \sum_{i=1}^{n} z_i^2$, (11.16)

Y is said to be Chi-Square $\left(\chi^2\right)$ distributed, with DOF $= \delta = n$

2. The density function of Y, $f(y = \chi^2)$ is given by:

$$f(y = \chi^2) = \frac{\left(\chi^2\right)^{\frac{n}{2}-1} e^{-\chi^2/2}}{2^{n/2}\,\Gamma(n/2)} \qquad 0 \leq \chi^2 \leq \infty \qquad (11.17)$$

where $\qquad \Gamma(k) \equiv$ Gamma Function $= \displaystyle\int_0^\infty \chi^{k-1} e^{-x} dx$ (11.18)

and $\qquad \Gamma\left(\dfrac{1}{2}\right) = \sqrt{\pi}$

$\Gamma(1) = 1$

$\Gamma(2) = 1 \cdot \Gamma(1) = 1$

$\Gamma(n + 1) = n \cdot \Gamma(n) \qquad$ for $n > 0$

$\Gamma(n + 1) = n!$ if n is an integer (11.19)

When plotted this density function assumes the shape shown by Figure 11.1 below:

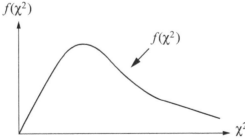

Figure 11.1 Density function of a χ^2 variable

3. Expected value of $Y = E(Y) = \int_0^\infty y \cdot f(y)dy = \mu = n = DOF$ (11.20)

4. Expected value of $Y^2 = E(Y^2) = \int_0^\infty y^2 \cdot f(y)dy = 2n + n^2$ (11.21)

5. Variance of $Y = V(Y) = E(Y^2) - [E(Y)]^2 = \sigma^2 = 2n$ (11.22)

Note: The expected value and variance of a chi-square variable depend only on the sample size n (or Degrees of Freedom).

6. If Z_1 is a standard normal variable (*i.e.*, if $Z_1 \to N(0, 1)$), then $Y = Z_1^2$ is χ^2-distributed with DOF $= \delta = n = 1$ (11.23)

7. If $Z_1 \to N(0, 1)$ and $Z_2 \to N(0, 1)$, then $Y = Z_1^2 + Z_2^2$ is χ^2-distributed with DOF $= \delta = n = 2$ (11.24)

8. If $Y = Z_1^2 + Z_2^2 + \cdots + Z_n^2$, Y is χ^2-distributed with DOF $= \delta = n$ (11.25)

9. These χ^2-distributions are positively skewed, as shown in Figure 11.2. However, as $n \to \infty$, $\chi_\delta^2 \to N\left(\mu = \delta, \sigma = \sqrt{2n}\right)$. There is a different χ^2 density function for each degree of freedom, δ.

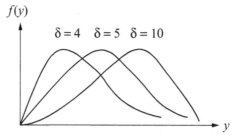

Figure 11.2 Family of χ^2 density functions

10. When $n \geq 30$, probabilities can be calculated from the normal instead of the χ^2-distribution (*i.e.*, treat $Y = \chi_\delta^2$ as a normally distributed variable with $E(Y) = E(\chi_\delta^2) = \mu = n$, and $\sigma(y) = \sigma = \sqrt{2n}$)

11. If $X_1, X_2, \ldots, X_n$ are n independent normal variables, (*i.e.*, each of the X_i variables has the density function $f(x_i) = \dfrac{1}{\sqrt{2\pi\sigma}} e^{\frac{1}{2\sigma^2}(x-\mu)^2}$ $-\infty < x_i < \infty$) (11.26)

then $Y = \left(\dfrac{X_1 - \mu}{\sigma}\right)^2 + \left(\dfrac{X_2 - \mu}{\sigma}\right)^2 + \cdots + \left(\dfrac{X_n - \mu}{\sigma}\right)^2$

$= \displaystyle\sum_{i=1}^n \left(\dfrac{X_i - \mu}{\sigma}\right)^2 = \sum_{i=1}^n Z_i^2$ (11.27)

is χ^2-distributed with DOF $= \delta = n$, since $\left(\dfrac{X_i - \mu}{\sigma}\right) = Z_i$ (11.28)

using the standard score formula, and $\left(\dfrac{X_i - \mu}{\sigma}\right)^2 = Z_i^2$ (11.29)

12. **Probability Calculations Using the Chi-Square Distribution**

To find the probability that the χ^2-variable is between the values $\chi^2 = a$ and $\chi^2 = b$ (see Figure 11.3 below), we integrate the χ^2-density function $f(y = \chi^2)$ analytically, in the interval $a \le \chi^2 \le b$. This implies that:

$$P\left(a < \chi^2 < b\right) = P\left[a \le \chi^2 \le b\right]$$
$$= \int_a^b f\left(y = \chi^2\right)d\chi^2 = g\left(\chi^2\right)\Big|_a^b = g(b) - g(a) \qquad (11.30)$$

where $g'\left(\chi^2\right) = f\left(\chi^2\right)$

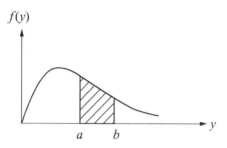

Figure 11.3 Calculating probabilities with the χ^2 density function

However, because the density function of Y, $f(y = \chi^2)$ as given by equation (11.17) is difficult to integrate analytically, we integrate **numerically** instead by using the Chi-square table found in any standard statistics text. This table has a "*df*" column, giving the degrees of freedom of the χ^2-variable under study, and several "Probability Columns" each of which is *equal to the Shaded Area under the Chi-Square distribution, on the upper right hand side of the χ^2-table*. Each entry at the intersection of the row defining the "degrees of freedom" and the column identifying the "Probability that the Chi-Square value will be exceeded", represents the value of the χ^2-variable for which the probability that the χ^2-variable between this particular value and $+\infty$ is equal to the probability of the

"Probability" column, or $\displaystyle\int_{\chi^2(\alpha,df)}^{\infty} f(\chi^2)d\chi^2 = \alpha$

To illustrate, consider the following example:

Suppose a given χ^2-variable has DOF $= \delta = 20$ associated with it. If we wish to find the values of *a* and *b* for which

$$P\left[a \le \chi^2 \le b\right] = 0.95, \qquad (11.31)$$

we proceed as follows:

1. First, notice that, for $df = 20$, Prob $(? \le \chi^2 \le \infty) = \displaystyle\int_?^{\infty} f(\chi^2)d\chi^2 = 0.975$ (11.32)

   occurs when $? = 9.59$

2. Second, notice that, for $df = 20$, Prob $(?? \le \chi^2 \le \infty) = \displaystyle\int_{??}^{\infty} f(\chi^2)d\chi^2 = 0.025$ (11.33)

   occurs when $?? = 34.71$

3. Third, notice that, for $df = 20$

   Prob $(? \le \chi^2 \le ??)$ Prob $(9.59 \le \chi^2 \le 34.17) = \displaystyle\int_{9.59}^{34.17} f(\chi^2)d\chi^2 = 0.95$ (11.34)

   For the same example as above, if DOF $= 10$ (instead of 20),

   Prob $(? \le \chi^2 \le ??) = P(3.25 \le \chi^2 \le 20.48) = 0.95$ (11.35)

   while if DOF $= 27$ (instead of 20), the corresponding values of *a* and *b* are given by:

   Prob $(? \le \chi^2 \le ??) = P(14.57 \le \chi^2 \le 43.19) = 0.95$ (11.36)

We can see from these examples that there is clearly a different Chi-Square distribution for each "degrees of freedom" value and it (*i.e.*, the Chi-Squire distribution) has a substantial effect in the calculation of probabilities.

11.3.1.2 The Sampling Distribution of the Unbiased Sample Variance ($\hat{s}^2$)

In practice we are usually interested in finding the sampling distribution of $\hat{s}^2$, which is defined by $\hat{s} = \dfrac{1}{n-1}\sum_{i=1}^{n}\left(X_i - \overline{x}\right)^2$, and can be re-written as:

$$\sum_{i=1}^{n}\left(X_i - \overline{x}\right)^2 = (n-1)\hat{s}^2 \tag{11.37}$$

We now pose the question: How is $\sum_{i=1}^{n}\left(X_i - \overline{x}\right)^2$ distributed?

(As can be seen, this Sum of Squares forms the basis for the definition of $\hat{s}^2$.)
To answer this question, we divide both sides of equation (11.37) by σ^2, and thus obtain:

$$\dfrac{\sum_{i=1}^{n}\left(X_i - \overline{x}\right)^2}{\sigma^2} = \dfrac{(n-1)\hat{s}^2}{\sigma^2} \tag{11.38}$$

But the left hand side of equation (11.38) can be re-written as:

$$\sum_{i=1}^{n}\left(\dfrac{X_i - \overline{x}}{\sigma}\right)^2 = \dfrac{(n-1)\hat{s}^2}{\sigma^2} \tag{11.39}$$

When compared to equation (11.27), where $Y = \sum_{i=1}^{n}\left(\dfrac{X_i - \mu}{\sigma}\right)^2$ was identified as a χ^2-variable with DOF $= \delta = n$, we conclude that:

$$Y = \sum_{i=1}^{n}\left(\dfrac{X_i - \overline{x}}{\sigma}\right)^2 = \dfrac{(n-1)\hat{s}^2}{\sigma^2}$$

is χ^2-distributed with DOF $= \delta = n - 1$, because of the presence of the estimator $\overline{x}$ in the sum of squares of equation (11.39).

Theoretical derivation of the sampling distribution of $\hat{s}^2$

Above we derived the sampling distribution of the variable

$$Y = \dfrac{(n-1)\hat{s}^2}{\sigma^2} = \sum_{i=1}^{n}\left(\dfrac{x_i - \overline{x}}{\sigma}\right)^2 \tag{11.40}$$

by comparing it to the variable defined by equation (11.27). But we can also derive the sampling distribution of $\hat{s}^2$ directly, as shown below:

From the definition of $\hat{s}^2$, $\hat{s}^2 = \dfrac{1}{n-1}\sum_{i=1}^{n}(x_i - \overline{x})^2$, we write

$$\sum_{i=1}^{n}(x_i - \overline{x})^2 = (n-1)\hat{s}^2 \tag{11.41}$$

But $\displaystyle\sum_{i=1}^{n}(x_i - \overline{x})^2 = \sum_{i=1}^{n}(x_i - \mu + \mu - \overline{x})^2 = \sum_{i=1}^{n}[(x_i - \mu) - (\overline{x} - \mu)]^2$ (11.42)

$$= \sum_{i=1}^{n}[(x_i - \mu)^2 - 2(x_i - \mu)(\overline{x} - \mu) + (\overline{x} - \mu)^2$$

$$= \sum_{i=1}^{n}(x_i - \mu)^2 - 2(\overline{x} - \mu)\sum_{i=1}^{n}(x_i - \mu) + \sum_{i=1}^{n}(\overline{x} - \mu)^2$$

$$= \sum_{i=1}^{n}(x_i - \mu)^2 - 2(\overline{x} - \mu) \cdot n(\overline{x} - \mu) + n(\overline{x} - \mu)^2$$

$$= \sum_{i=1}^{n}(x_i - \mu)^2 - 2n(\overline{x} - \mu)^2 + n(\overline{x} - \mu)^2$$

$$= \sum_{i=1}^{n}(x_i - \mu)^2 - n(\overline{x} - \mu)^2 \tag{11.43}$$

$$\text{or } \sum_{i=1}^{n}(x_i - \overline{x})^2 + n(\overline{x} - \mu)^2 = \sum_{i=1}^{n}(x_i - \mu)^2 \tag{11.44}$$

$$\text{or } (n - 1)\hat{s}^2 + n(\overline{x} - \mu)^2 = \sum_{i=1}^{n}(x_i - \mu)^2 \quad \text{(because of 11.41)} \tag{11.45}$$

Now divide both sides of (11.45) by the population variance σ^2 to obtain:

$$\frac{(n - 1)\hat{s}^2}{\sigma^2} + \frac{n(\overline{x} - \mu)^2}{\sigma^2} = \sum_{i=1}^{n}\frac{(x_i - \mu)^2}{\sigma^2} \tag{11.46}$$

$$\text{or} \qquad \frac{(n - 1)\hat{s}^2}{\sigma^2} + \frac{(\overline{x} - \mu)^2}{\sigma^2/n} = \sum_{i=1}^{n}\left(\frac{x_i - \mu}{\sigma}\right)^2 \tag{11.47}$$

$$\text{or} \qquad \frac{(n - 1)\hat{s}^2}{\sigma^2} + \left(\frac{\overline{x} - \mu}{\sigma^2/\sqrt{n}}\right)^2 = \sum_{i=1}^{n}\left(\frac{x_i - \mu}{\sigma^2}\right)^2 \tag{11.48}$$

The right hand side of (11.48) has already been identified as χ_n^2.

Since $\dfrac{\overline{x} - \mu}{\sigma/\sqrt{n}}$ is $Z(0, 1)$ (*i.e.,* standard normal), $\left(\dfrac{\overline{x} - \mu}{\sigma/\sqrt{n}}\right)^2 = Z^2$, which is χ_1^2.

Therefore, $\dfrac{(n - 1)\hat{s}^2}{\sigma^2}$ must be distributed as χ_{n-1}^2 for equation (11.48) to have the same number of degrees of freedom on both sides of the equation as is also stated by the theorem below.

Theorem concerning two χ^2 variables

Suppose x_1 and x_2 are two independent χ^2 variables with DOF δ_1 and δ_2 respectively. Then, if we form the sum of x_1 and x_2, the resulting variable: $y = x_1 + x_2$ is also χ^2-distributed with DOF $= \delta_1 + \delta_2$.

Then, applying this theorem to equation (11.48), we conclude that:

$\dfrac{(n - 1)\hat{s}^2}{\sigma^2}$ is a χ^2 variable with DOF $= \delta = n - 1$.

The expected value and variance of $\hat{s}^2$

Next, we are faced with the problem of finding the expected value and variance of $\hat{s}^2$, *i.e.,* we need to find $E(\hat{s}^2)$ and $V(\hat{s}^2)$.

Question: How do we proceed?
(Recall that we also had to find the $E(\overline{x})$ and $V(\overline{x})$ previously.)

Answer: We use previous results and some of the properties of the expectation and variance operators pertaining to linear functions.

If $Y = a + bX$ is a linear function of the variables X and Y and a and b are any constants, then:

$$E(Y) = E(a + bX) = E(a) + E(bX) = a + E(bX) = a + bE(X) \tag{11.49}$$

$$\text{and} \qquad V(Y) = V(a + bY) = V(a) + V(bX) = 0 + b^2V(X) \tag{11.50}$$

We showed earlier (see equations (11.20) and (11.22)) that for any χ^2-variable with DOF $= \delta = n$, $E(\chi^2) = n$ and $V(\chi^2) = 2n$. The variable of equation (11.40) is also a χ^2 variable but with DOF $= \delta = n - 1$. Then using (11.49) with $a = 0$ and $b = (n - 1)/\sigma^2$, we obtain $\quad E(Y) = E\left[\dfrac{(n-1)\hat{s}^2}{\sigma^2}\right] = (n-1),$ $\hspace{2cm}$ (11.51)

from which we conclude that: $\dfrac{(n-1)}{\sigma^2} E(\hat{s}^2) = (n-1)$ $\hspace{2cm}$ (11.52)

because $\dfrac{(n-1)}{\sigma^2}$ is a constant, and a multiplier to the E operator.

Then, from equation (11.52), solving for $E(\hat{s}^2)$, we obtain:

$$E\left(\hat{s}^2\right) = \frac{(n-1)\sigma^2}{(n-1)} = \sigma^2 \hspace{2cm} (11.53)$$

Similarly from (11.50) we obtain: $V(Y) = V\left[\dfrac{(n-1)\hat{s}^2}{\sigma^2}\right] = 2(n-1)$ $\hspace{1cm}$ (11.54)

or $\hspace{2cm} \dfrac{(n-1)^2}{\sigma^4} V\left(\hat{s}^2\right) = 2(n-1)$ $\hspace{2cm}$ (11.55)

(because $\dfrac{(n-1)}{\sigma^2}$ is a constant which is squared when it becomes a multiplier to the variance operator.)

Then from equation (11.55) we obtain: $V\left(\hat{s}^2\right) = \dfrac{2(n-1)\sigma^4}{(n-1)^2} = \dfrac{2\sigma^4}{(n-1)}$ $\hspace{1cm}$ (11.56)

Clearly, the unbiased sample variance $\hat{s}^2$, is an unbiased estimator for the population variance σ^2, because, as can be seen from equation (11.53), the expected value of $\hat{s}^2$ is equal to σ^2.

11.3.1.3 Procedures for Hypothesis Testing and Confidence Interval Construction for σ^2 and σ

Now that we have obtained the sampling distribution of $\hat{s}^2$, we are in a position to modify the hypothesis testing procedure which we used previously for the population parameter μ and adopt it to the population parameters σ and σ^2, and also derive expressions for the confidence intervals of the population parameters σ^2 (variance) and σ (standard deviation).

In both cases the appropriate statistic to use is:

$$Y = \chi^2_{n-1} = \sum_{i=1}^{n}\left(\frac{x_i - \overline{x}}{\sigma}\right)^2 = \frac{(n-1)\hat{s}^2}{\sigma^2} \hspace{2cm} (11.57)$$

which, as we have shown, is Chi-Square distributed with DOF $= \delta = n - 1$.

■ Hypothesis Testing Procedures for σ^2 and σ

1. Formulate H_0 and H_1 in accordance with the problem statement.
2. Select the value of α (if one is not given, select $\alpha = 0.01$ or $\alpha = 0.05$ or both).
3. Identify the sampling distribution of the estimator of the population parameter appearing in H_0 (and H_1). If it is σ^2, then its estimator is $\hat{s}^2$, and we have shown that $(n-1)\hat{s}^2/\sigma^2$ is Chi-Square with DOF $= \delta = n - 1$. If it is σ, we need to reformulate H_0 and H_1 in terms of σ^2, because we do not know the sampling distribution of $\hat{s}$, which is the estimator of σ.
4. Construct the rejection region, using a χ^2-table, for a χ^2-variable with DOF $= \delta = n - 1$.
5. Calculate the value of the test statistic $\chi^{*2} = \dfrac{(n-1)\hat{s}^2}{\sigma^2}$ $\hspace{2cm}$ (11.58)

6. Compare χ^{*2} to the rejection region:

   a) If χ^{*2} falls in the rejection region, *Reject* H_0;

   b) If χ^{*2} falls outside of the rejection region, *Do Not Reject* H_0.

7. Express in words the mathematical conclusion reached in step (6) above.

■ Confidence Intervals for σ^2 and σ

Because the Chi-Square distribution is positively-skewed and not symmetric, we have to obtain 2 separate values from the χ^2-table, instead of the usual one we needed from the Normal distribution, which is symmetric.

We need to introduce the following notation to help us in the construction of the confidence intervals. We let:

$\chi^2_{n-1,1-\alpha/2}$ = The value of the χ^2-variable, with DOF = $\delta = n - 1$, for which the area to the right of this value = $1 - \alpha/2$ (11.59)

$\chi^2_{n-1,\alpha/2}$ = The value of the χ^2-variable, with DOF = $\delta = n - 1$, for which the area to the right of this value = $\alpha/2$ (11.60)

These values can be better visualized in Figure 11.4 below:

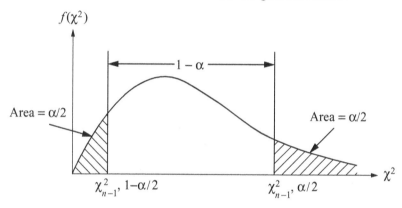

Figure 11.4 Constructing a 2-sided confidence interval for χ^2 variable

Clearly, the area between these 2 values is equal to $1 - \alpha$. We can then write the general equation below, valid for any χ^2–variable with DOF = $\delta = n - 1$, namely:

$$P[\chi^2_{n-1,1-\alpha/2} \le \chi^2_{n-1} \le \chi^2_{n-1,\alpha/2}] = 1 - \alpha \qquad (11.61)$$

But, since (11.61) is true for any χ^2-variable with DOF = $\delta = n - 1$, it is also true for $(n - 1)\hat{s}^2/\sigma^2$, which we have shown to be χ^2 with DOF = $n - 1$.

Substituting (11.57) into (11.61), we obtain:

$$P[\chi^2_{n-1,1-\alpha/2} \le \frac{(n - 1)\hat{s}^2}{\sigma^2} \le \chi^2_{n-1,\alpha/2}] = 1 - \alpha \qquad (11.62)$$

When (11.62) is solved for σ^2, by solving simultaneously, the 2 inequalities:

$$\chi^2_{n-1,1-\alpha/2} \le \frac{(n - 1)\hat{s}^2}{\sigma^2} \qquad (11.63)$$

and

$$\frac{(n - 1)\hat{s}^2}{\sigma^2} \le \chi^2_{n-1,\alpha/2} \qquad (11.64)$$

we obtain: $$P\left[\frac{(n - 1)\hat{s}^2}{\chi^2_{n-1,\alpha/2}} \le \sigma^2 \le \frac{(n - 1)\hat{s}^2}{\chi^2_{n-1,1-\alpha/2}}\right] = 1 - \alpha \qquad (11.65)$$

which is the formula to use to construct a $1 - \alpha$ two-sided confidence interval on the population parameter σ^2 (variance). Note that the left and right hand sides of (11.65) include only sample information $((n - 1), \hat{s}^2)$, and table values $\left(\chi^2_{n-1,\,\alpha/2}, \chi^2_{n-1,\,1-\alpha/2}\right)$. To obtain a $1 - \alpha$ confidence interval on σ (population standard deviation), we take the square root of all terms inside the brackets of (11.65) and obtain:

$$P\left[\sqrt{\frac{(n - 1)\hat{s}^2}{\chi^2_{n-1,\alpha/2}}} \le \sigma \le \sqrt{\frac{(n - 1)\hat{s}^2}{\chi^2_{n-1,1-\alpha/2}}}\right] = 1 - \alpha \tag{11.66}$$

Note: To obtain lower and upper one-sided $1 - \alpha$ confidence intervals on σ^2 we use the equations below:

1. Lower—Start with: $P[0 \le \chi^2_{n-1} \le \chi^2_{n-1,\alpha}] = 1 - \alpha$;

   substitute $\chi^2_{n-1} = \dfrac{(n - 1)\hat{s}^2}{\sigma^2}$, and obtain:

$$P\left[\frac{(n - 1)\hat{s}^2}{\chi^2_{n-1,\,\alpha}} \le \sigma^2 \le \infty\right] = 1 - \alpha \tag{11.67}$$

2. Upper—Start with: $P[\chi^2_{n-1,1-\alpha} \le \chi^2_{n-1} < \infty]$;

   substitute $\chi^2_{n-1} = \dfrac{(n - 1)\hat{s}^2}{\sigma^2}$, and obtain:

$$P\left[0 \le \sigma^2 \le \frac{(n - 1)\hat{s}^2}{\chi^2_{n-1,1-\alpha}}\right] = 1 - \alpha \tag{11.68}$$

11.3.1.4 Examples of Hypothesis Testing and Confidence Intervals for σ^2 & σ
Example 1 Hypothesis Testing on the Population Variance σ^2

Problem A soft drink bottling company wants to control the variance of the amount, by not allowing the variance to exceed 0.0004. Does a sample of size 28, which produced a sample variance of 0.001 indicate that the bottling process is out of control, with regard to the variance, at $\alpha = 0.05$?

Solution Applying the Hypothesis Testing procedure of Section 11.3.1.3 above, with $\sigma^2 \le 0.0004$, $\hat{s}^2 = 0.001$, and DOF $= \delta = n - 1 = 27$, we have:

1. H_0: $\sigma^2 \le 0.0004$ vs H_1: $\sigma^2 > 0.0004$,
2. $\alpha = 0.05$
3. The estimator for σ^2 is $\hat{s}^2$, and $(n - 1)\hat{s}^2/\sigma^2$ is χ^2_{27} (because $n = 28 < 30$).
4. Because of the nature of H_1, the Rejection Region will be in the upper (right hand) tail of the χ^2-distribution, as shown in Figure 11.5.

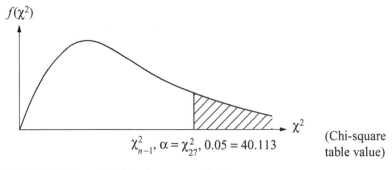

$$\chi^2_{n-1},\ \alpha = \chi^2_{27},\ 0.05 = 40.113 \qquad \text{(Chi-square table value)}$$

Figure 11.5 Rejection Region for example 1

5. Value of Test Statistic $= \chi^{2*} = \dfrac{(n-1)\hat{s}^2}{\sigma^2} = \dfrac{(27)(0.001)}{0.0004} = 67.5$.

6. Since χ^{2*} is greater than $\chi^2_{27,0.05}$ (*i.e.*, $67.5 > 40.113$), the value of the test statistic χ^{2*} falls in the *Rejection Region*, and, therefore, we *Reject* H_0.

7. The rejection of H_0 (*i.e.*, H_0: $\sigma^2 \leq 0.0004$) implies that $\sigma^2 > 0.0004$ and, therefore, the process is out of control, with regard to the variance.

■ ■ ■

Example 2 Hypothesis Testing and Confidence Intervals on σ^2 & σ

Problem In an examination with 100 total points, it has been claimed that a standard deviation of 12 points is desirable. A professor tested the above hypothesis at $\alpha = 0.05$. There were 28 students in the class, and the calculated sample standard deviation, $\hat{s}^2$, was 10.5.

1. Test the validity of this claim.
2. Construct 95% confidence intervals on σ^2 & σ.

Solution
■ Hypothesis Testing

1. H_0: $\sigma = 12$ vs H_1: $\sigma \neq 12$ or equivalently: H_0: $\sigma^2 = 144$ vs H_1: $\sigma^2 \neq 144$ (*Note*: Here we need the equivalent H_0 and H_1 statements for σ^2 because the sampling distribution of $\hat{s}$, which is the estimator of σ, is not known).

2. $\alpha = 0.05$, $\alpha/2 = 0.025$

3. The estimator for σ^2 is $\hat{s}^2$, and $\dfrac{(n-1)\hat{s}^2}{\sigma^2} = \chi^2_{n-1}$, because $n = 28 < 30$.

4. Because of the nature of H_1, the rejection region will be two-sided (with $\alpha/2 = 0.025$ on both sides) as shown below:

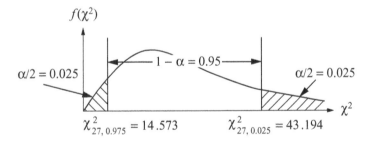

Figure 11.6 Rejection Region for Example 11.2

5. Value of test statistic $= \chi^{2*} = \dfrac{(n-1)\hat{s}_2}{\sigma^2} = \dfrac{(27)(10.5)^2}{(12)^2} = 20.67$

6. Since $14.57 < \chi^{2*} \leq 43.19$, χ^{2*} falls outside of the rejection region. Therefore, we do not reject H_0.

7. Not rejecting H_0 implies that the evidence supports the validity of the claim that the population variance is 144 (12^2) (or the population standard deviation is 12).

■ Confidence Intervals on σ^2 & σ

Using the given sample information ($n - 1 = 27$, $\hat{s}^2 = 10.5$ and $\alpha = 0.05$ (or $\alpha/2 = 0.025$)), the table values: $\chi^2_{27,0.975} = 14.573$ and $\chi^2_{27,0.025} = 43.194$, and using equations (11.65) and (11.66), we obtain by direct substitution of these values:

$$P\left[\frac{(27)(10.5)^2}{43.19} \le \sigma^2 \le \frac{(27)(10.5)^2}{14.57}\right] = 0.95$$

or
$$P[68.9 \le \sigma^2 \le 203.9] = 0.95 \tag{11.69}$$

and
$$P\left[\sqrt{68.9} \le \sigma \le \sqrt{203.9}\right] = 0.95$$

or
$$P[8.3 \le \sigma \le 14.3] = 0.95 \tag{11.70}$$

■ ■ ■

Note: Since the hypothesized value (H_0: $\sigma^2 = 144$) falls inside the confidence interval for σ^2 (clearly $68.9 \le \sigma^2 = 144 \le 203.9$), we reach the same conclusion (about not rejecting H_0) as we did when we solved the problem as a hypothesis testing problem. Obviously the two methods are equivalent and should reach the same conclusion, if both are performed correctly.

The same conclusion is drawn when we compare the H_0 value on σ (H_0: $\sigma = 12$) with the confidence interval on σ.

11.3.2 The F-Distribution
11.3.2.1 Theoretical Considerations

If we wanted to test the hypothesis that the variance of 2 populations is the same (*i.e.*, if we are testing the hypothesis: H_0: $\sigma_1^2 = \sigma_2^2$ vs H_1: $\sigma_1^2 \ne \sigma_2^2$) and the sample sizes n_1 and n_2 are small (*i.e.*, $n_1 < 30, n_2 < 30$), we must use the F-distribution to perform such a test.

Note: The equality of $\sigma_1^2 = \sigma_2^2$ is required, as we will see later, when trying to test the hypothesis: H_0: $\mu_1 = \mu_2$ vs H_1: $\mu_1 \ne \mu_2$, when n_1 and n_2 are both less than 30, and σ_1 and σ_2 are unknown!

Question: How does the F-distribution enter into the picture?

Answer: We reformulate H_0 as $\sigma_1^2/\sigma_2^2 = 1$ first; then we use the fact that $\hat{s}_1^2$ and $\hat{s}_2^2$ are the estimators of σ_1^2 and σ_2^2 respectively, and that $(n_1 - 1)\hat{s}_1^2/\sigma_1^2$ is $\chi_{n_1-1}^2$ and $(n_1 - 1)\hat{s}_2^2/\sigma_2^2$ is $\chi_{n_2-1}^2$. Then, the ratio of 2 chi-square variables, each divided by its degrees of freedom becomes an F variable with $n_1 - 1$ DOF in the numerator, and $n_2 - 1$ DOF in the denominator. But let us first briefly discuss the theoretical derivation of the F-distribution.

1. If $X_1, X_2, \ldots, X_{\delta_1}$ and $Y_1, Y_2, \ldots, Y_{\delta_2}$ are all independent standard normal variables (*i.e.*, each X_i and each Y_j is $N(0, 1)$), then the variable

$$F = \frac{\dfrac{X_1^2 + X_2^2 + \cdots + X_{\delta_1}^2}{\delta_1}}{\dfrac{Y_1^2 + Y_2^2 + \cdots + Y_{\delta_2}^2}{\delta_2}} \tag{11.71}$$

is said to have the F-distribution with (δ_1, δ_2) DOF. The F variable is a ratio of 2 chi-square variables, each divided by its own degrees of freedom, with DOF $= \delta_1$ in the numerator, and DOF $= \delta_2$ in the denominator.

2. The density function of F, $f(F)$, is given by:

$$f(F) = \left[\frac{\Gamma\left(\dfrac{\delta_1 + \delta_2}{2}\right)}{\Gamma\left(\dfrac{\delta_1}{2}\right)\Gamma\left(\dfrac{\delta_2}{2}\right)}\right]\left(\frac{\delta_1}{\delta_2}\right)^{\frac{\delta_1}{2}}\left(F^{\frac{\delta_1}{2}-1}\right)\left(1 + \frac{\delta_1}{\delta_2}F\right)^{-\left(\frac{\delta_1 + \delta_2}{2}\right)} \quad 0 \le F < \infty \tag{11.72}$$

where $\quad \Gamma(k) = $ Tabulated Gamma Function $= \displaystyle\int_0^\infty x^{k-1}e^{-x}dx \qquad (11.73)$

There is a different F distribution for each (δ_1, δ_2) combination. The bracketed quantity of Gamma functions represents the needed multiplier to keep the area of the $f(F)$ density function equal to 1, in the interval $0 \le F < \infty$, for each (δ_1, δ_2) combination.

3. Expected value of $F = E(F) = \displaystyle\int_0^\infty Ff(F)dF = \dfrac{\delta_2}{\delta_2 - 2}$

$$= 1 + \dfrac{2}{\delta_2 - 2} \ (\delta_2 > 2) \qquad (11.74)$$

4. Expected value of $F^2 = E(F^2) = \displaystyle\int_0^\infty F^2 f(F)dF \qquad (11.75)$

5. Variance of $F = V(F) = E(F^2) - [E(F)]^2$

$$= \dfrac{2\delta_2^2(\delta_1 + \delta_2 - 2)}{\delta_1(\delta_2 - 2)^2(\delta^2 - 4)} \qquad (\delta_2 > 4) \qquad (11.76)$$

Note: $E(F)$ is defined only if $\delta_2 > 2$, which $V(F)$ is defined only if $\delta_2 > 4$.

6. The density function $f(F)$ is positively skewed, and the skewness decreases as δ_1 and δ_2 increase.

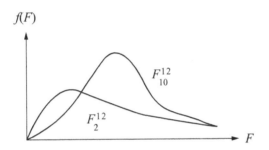

Figure 11.7 Density function of $f(F)$ for different combination of (δ_1, δ_2)

7. **Reciprocal Property of the F-distribution**

This property is unique to the F-distribution, and connects left-hand side values of the F-distribution (which are usually not tabulated) to right-hand side values of the F-distribution which are tabulated. It is given by the formula below:

$$F_{\delta_2^{\delta_1}}(1 - \alpha) = \dfrac{1}{F_{\delta_1^{\delta_2}}(\alpha)} \qquad (11.77)$$

We will discuss the use of (11.77) shortly, after we first discuss the calculation of probabilities, using the F-distribution.

8. **Probability Calculations Using the F-distribution**

To find the probability that the F-variable is between the values $F = a$ and $F = b$, we integrate the $f(F)$ density function analytically in the interval $a \le F \le b$. This implies that:

$$P[a \le F \le b] = \int_a^b f(F)dF = g(F)\big|_a^b = g(b) - g(a) \qquad (11.78)$$

(provided $g'(F) = f(F)$)

However, because the density function $f(F)$, as given by (11.72), is difficult to integrate analytically (*i.e.*, it is difficult to find a function $g(F)$ such that $g'(F) = f(F)$), we integrate numerically instead, by using the available tables of the F-distribution. These tables, because they involve 3 variables (δ_1 = DOF in the numerator, δ_2 = DOF in the denominator, probability = α) are more complicated than the chi-square table (which involved 2 variables: δ = DOF, and probability = α), and much more difficult than the normal table (probability = α). To simplify the F-tables, we fix the value of α (the usual values are: α = 0.1, 0.05, 0.025, 0.01, and 0.005) and then we have a 2-dimensional table with (δ_1 = DOF in the numerator) in the horizontal axis, and with (δ_2 = DOF in the denominator) in the vertical axis. For the given value of α, we find the value of the F variable, for which the area under the $F_{\delta_2}^{\delta_1}$ function, from this value of F to $+\infty$, is equal to the fixed value of α.

As an example, if α = 0.05 and δ_1 = 10, and δ_2 = 7, then $F_{\delta_2=7}^{\delta_1=10}(\alpha = 0.05)$=3.64. If the value of α changed to α = 0.01, with δ_1 and δ_2 unchanged (*i.e.*, with δ_1 = 10 and δ_2 = 7), then $F_{\delta_2=7}^{\delta_1=10}(\alpha = 0.01) = 6.62$.

Only right tail values are tabulated in these tables. To calculate left tail values we make use of the reciprocal property, given by (11.77). Now we learn how to use this formula.

In the example above we showed that, when α = 0.05 and δ_1 = 10 and δ_2 = 7, the value of the F variable = $F_7^{10}(0.05)$ = 3.64. Using Figure 11.8 below, this tells us that

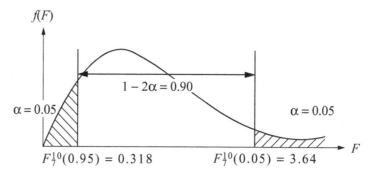

Figure 11.8 Calculating probabulities using the F density function

for this F-distribution, the area between 3.64 and $+\infty$ is equal to 0.05, as shown in the right tail of the F-distribution.

We now ask the question: How can we mark off another area, also equal to α = 0.05, but this time on the left tail of the F-distribution?

The answer is: Use the reciprocal property, as expressed by (11.75). Then we have:

$$F_{\delta_2=7}^{\delta_1=10}(1-\alpha) = F_7^{10}(0.95) = \frac{1}{F_{\delta_1=10}^{\delta_2=7}(\alpha = 0.05)} = \frac{1}{3.14} = 0.31847$$

We then conclude that $P[0.318 < F_7^{10} < 3.64] = 0.90$.

Note: The DOF of the F variable, which is in the denominator of the right hand side of (11.77) have been interchanged: *i.e.*, δ_1 now becomes the DOF in the denominator, and δ_2 becomes the DOF in the numerator.

11.3.2.2 Tests for the Equality of the Variances of 2 Populations

If we have 2 populations P_1 (with μ_1 and σ_1^2) and P_2 (with μ_2 and σ_2^2), we wish to find out through sampling, if $\sigma_1^2 = \sigma_2^2$ That is, we wish to test the hypothesis:

$$H_0: \sigma_1^2 = \sigma_2^2 \text{ vs } H_1: \sigma_1^2 \neq \sigma_2^2$$

Question: How do we proceed?
Answer: There are 2 possibilities.

1. If the sample sizes n_1 (from P_1) and n_2 (from P_2) are large, we form the difference

$$\Delta \sigma^2 = \sigma_1^2 - \sigma_2^2 \tag{11.79}$$

and treat $\Delta \sigma^2$ as a population parameter whose estimator

$$\Delta \hat{s}^2 = \hat{s}_1^2 - \hat{s}_2^2 \tag{11.80}$$

is normally distributed.

2. If the samples n_1 and n_2 are small, we reformulate H_0: $\sigma_1^2 = \sigma_2^2$ as H_0: $\sigma_1^2/\sigma_2^2 = 1$ and use the F-distribution we discussed previously.

Below we discuss each of these methods separately.

■ Test of the Equality Between Variances for Large Samples

We wish to test the hypothesis H_0: $\sigma_1^2 = \sigma_2^2$ vs H_1: $\sigma_1^2 \neq \sigma_2^2$. We rewrite H_0 as:

$$H_0: \sigma_1^2 - \sigma_2^2 = 0 \text{ vs } H_1: \sigma_1^2 - \sigma_2^2 \neq 0$$

or
$$H_0: \Delta \sigma^2 = 0 \text{ vs } H_1: \Delta \sigma^2 \neq 0 \tag{11.81}$$

Since the estimator for σ_1^2 is $\hat{s}_1^2$, and for σ_2^2 is $\hat{s}_2^2$, the estimator for $\Delta \sigma^2$ is

$$\Delta \hat{s}^2 = \hat{s}_1^2 - \hat{s}_2^2 = 1\hat{s}_1^2 + (-1)\hat{s}_2^2 \tag{11.82}$$

If n_1 and n_2 are both large (definitely n_1 and n_2 must be at least equal to or greater than 30, and preferably equal to or greater than 100), the distribution of $\Delta \hat{s}^2$ is expected to be normal with:

$$E(\Delta \hat{s}^2) = E[\hat{s}_1^2 - \hat{s}_2^2] = E[\hat{s}_1^2] - [\hat{s}_2^2] = \sigma_1^2 - \sigma_2^2 = \Delta \sigma^2 \tag{11.83}$$

and $V(\Delta \hat{s}^2) = V[\hat{s}_1^2 - \hat{s}_2^2] = V[1(\hat{s}_1^2) + (-1)\hat{s}_2^2] = (1)^2 V(\hat{s}_1^2) + (-1)^2 V(\hat{s}_2^2)$
$$= V(\hat{s}_1^2) + V(\hat{s}_2^2) \tag{11.84}$$

But, according to (11.56), $V(\hat{s}^2) = \dfrac{2\sigma^4}{(n-1)}$, then

$$V[\Delta \hat{s}^2] = \frac{2\sigma_1^4}{n_1 - 1} + \frac{2\sigma_2^4}{n_2 - 1} \tag{11.85}$$

and
$$\sigma(\Delta \hat{s}^2) = \sqrt{\frac{2\sigma_1^4}{n_1 - 1} + \frac{2\sigma_2^4}{n_2 - 1}} \approx \sqrt{\frac{2\hat{s}_1^4}{n_1 - 1} + \frac{2\hat{s}_2^4}{n_2 - 1}} \tag{11.86}$$

if σ_1 and σ_2 are not known.

Now that we have determined the nature of the sampling distribution of $\Delta \hat{s}^2$, which is the estimator of the population parameter $\Delta \sigma^2$, and obtained the expected value and standard deviation of $\Delta \hat{s}^2$ (given by (11.81) and (11.84) respectively), we can easily complete the remaining steps of the hypothesis testing procedure, and write out the expression that will provide a $1 - \alpha$ confidence interval on $\Delta \sigma^2$.

1. **Hypothesis Testing Procedure**
   a) H_0: $\Delta \sigma^2 = 0$ vs H_1: $\Delta \sigma^2 \neq 0$
   b) Select value of α (If one is not provided choose $\alpha = 0.05$ or $\alpha = 0.01$, or both)
   c) The estimator for $\Delta \sigma^2$ is $\Delta \hat{s}^2$ which is normally distributed if n_1 and n_2 are both large,

   with $E(\Delta \hat{s}^2) = \Delta \sigma^2$ and $\sigma(\Delta \hat{s}^2) = \sqrt{\dfrac{2\sigma_1^4}{n_1 - 1} + \dfrac{2\sigma_2^4}{n_2 - 1}}$

d) Construct the critical region, using the normal distribution.

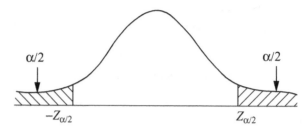

e) Calculate the value of the test statistic $= Z^* = \dfrac{\Delta \hat{s}^2 - 0}{\sigma(\Delta \hat{s}^2)} = \dfrac{\Delta \hat{s}^2}{\sigma(\Delta \hat{s}^2)}$ (11.87)

f) Compare Z^* to the critical region.
   i) Reject H_0 if Z^* is in the critical region.
   ii) Do not reject H_0, if Z^* is outside of the rejection region.
g) Express in words the mathematical conclusion of step (6).

2. Confidence Interval on $\Delta \sigma^2$

Since the estimator for $\Delta \sigma^2$, $\Delta \hat{s}^2$ is normally distributed and the normal distribution is symmetrical, we use the general equation for constructing a confidence interval for a parameter whose estimator is normally distributed, given by:

$$P[\hat{\theta} - Z_{\alpha/2}\,\sigma(\hat{\theta}) < \theta < \hat{\theta} + Z_{\alpha/2}\,\sigma(\hat{\theta})] = 1 - \alpha \qquad (11.88)$$

In our case, $\theta = \Delta \sigma^2$, $\hat{\theta} = \Delta \hat{s}^2$, and $\sigma(\hat{\theta}) = \sigma(\Delta \hat{s}^2)$. When these are substituted into (11.88) we obtain:

$$P[\Delta \hat{s}^2 - Z_{\alpha/2}\,\sigma(\Delta \hat{s}^2) < \Delta \sigma^2 < \Delta \hat{s}^2 + Z_{\alpha/2}\,\sigma(\Delta \hat{s}^2)] = 1 - \alpha \qquad (11.89)$$

3. Example 3 Hypothesis Testing and Confidence Interval on $\Delta \sigma^2 = \sigma_1^2 - \sigma_2^2$

If a random sample from population 1, produced an $\hat{s}_1^2 = 20$ when $n_1 = 41$, and a random sample of $n_2 = 33$ from population 2 produced an $\hat{s}_2^2 = 16$.
a) Test the hypothesis that $\sigma_1^2 = \sigma_2^2$, at the $\alpha = 0.05$.
b) Construct a 95% confidence interval on $\Delta \sigma^2$.

a) Hypothesis Testing Solution

i) H_0: $\sigma_1^2 = \sigma_2^2$ vs H_1: $\sigma_1^2 \neq \sigma_2^2$, or H_0: $\Delta \sigma^2 = 0$ vs H_1: $\Delta \sigma^2 \neq 0$
ii) Select α ($\alpha = 0.05$ is given)
iii) Estimator for $\Delta \sigma^2$ is: $\Delta \hat{s}^2 = \hat{s}_1^2 - \hat{s}_2^2 = (20 - 16 = 4)$, which is normally distributed (because n_1 and n_2 are large).

with $E(\Delta \hat{s}^2) = \Delta \sigma^2$

and $\quad \sigma(\Delta \hat{s}^2) \approx \sqrt{\dfrac{2(20)^2}{40} + \dfrac{2(16)^2}{32}} = \sqrt{20 + 16} = \sqrt{36} = 6$

iv) **Rejection Region:** Because of the nature of H_1, the rejection region will be at both tails of the normal distribution, and each segment will have an equal probability of $\alpha/2 = 0.025$. The value of Z, $Z_{\alpha/2}$, which separates the rejection and non-rejection regions is shown in the figure below:

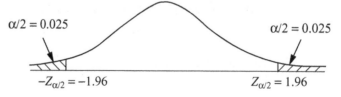

v) Value of test statistic $= Z^* = \Delta\hat{s}^2/\sigma(\Delta\hat{s}^2) = 4/6 \approx 0.67$

vi) Since Z^* is outside of the critical region, we DO NOT REJECT H_0.

vii) By not reject H_0 we conclude that the 2 populations have equal variances.

b) Confidence Interval on $\Delta\sigma^2$

Using equation (11.87) we obtain upon substitution:

$P[4 - 1.96(6) < \Delta\sigma^2 < 4 + 1.96(6)] = 0.95$

or $P[4 - 11.76 < \Delta\sigma^2 < 4 + 11.76] = 0.95$

or $P[-7.76 < \Delta\sigma^2 < 15.76] = 0.95$

Since the hypothesized value of $\Delta\sigma^2$ (*i.e.*, $\Delta\sigma^2 = 0$) is inside this C.I., once again we DO NOT REJECT H_0, and conclude that $\sigma_1^2 = \sigma_2^2$.

■ ■ ■

■ F-Test of the Equality Between Variances for Small Samples

We are testing the hypothesis H_0: $\sigma_1^2 = \sigma_2^2$ vs H_1: $\sigma_1^2 \neq \sigma_2^2$, and, when n_1 and n_2 are small, we rewrite H_0/H_1 as a ratio:

$$H_0: \frac{\sigma_1^2}{\sigma_2^2} = 1 \text{ vs } H_1: \frac{\sigma_1^2}{\sigma_2^2} \neq 1 \tag{11.90}$$

or

$$H_0: \frac{\sigma_2^2}{\sigma_1^2} = 1 \text{ vs } H_1: \frac{\sigma_2^2}{\sigma_1^2} \neq 1 \tag{11.91}$$

If $\hat{s}_1^2$ and $\hat{s}_2^2$ are the unbiased sample variances of the 2 populations (derived from 2 independent samples with $n_1 - 1$ and $n_2 - 1$ degrees of freedom respectively) whose population variances are σ_1^2 and σ_2^2 respectively, then:

1. $\hat{s}_1^2$ is an unbiased estimator for σ_1^2, and $n_1 - 1\ \hat{s}_1^2/\sigma_1^2$ is a chi-square variable with $\delta_1 = n_1 - 1$ degrees of freedom.

2. $\hat{s}_2^2$ is an unbiased estimator for σ_2^2, and $n_2 - 1\ \hat{s}_2^2/\sigma_2^2$ is a chi-square variable with $\delta_2 = n_2 - 1$ degrees of freedom.

3. The ratio of these 2 chi-square variables, each divided by its own DOF is an F variable with $\delta_1 =$ DOF in the numerator and $\delta_2 =$ DOF in the denominator, *i.e.*,

$$F_{\delta_2}^{\delta_1} = \frac{\chi_1^2/\delta_1}{\chi_2^2/\delta_2} = \frac{\dfrac{(n_1 - 1)\hat{s}_1^2/\sigma_1^2}{(n_1 - 1)}}{\dfrac{(n_2 - 1)\hat{s}_2^2/\sigma_2^2}{(n_2 - 1)}} = \frac{\hat{s}_1^2/\sigma_1^2}{\hat{s}_2^2/\sigma_2^2} = \left(\frac{\sigma_2^2}{\sigma_1^2}\right)\frac{\hat{s}_1^2}{\hat{s}_2^2} \tag{11.92}$$

$$= \frac{\hat{s}_1^2}{\hat{s}_2^2} \text{ when } H_0 \text{ is true (because then } \frac{\sigma_2^2}{\sigma_1^2} = 1) \tag{11.93}$$

Equations (11.90) and (11.91) tell us that the ratio of the unbiased sample variances of 2 populations is distributed as an F variable with δ_1 DOF in the numerator and δ_2 DOF in the denominator. We will use this fact to develop both:

a) Hypothesis Testing Procedures for H_0: $\dfrac{\sigma_1^2}{\sigma_2^2} = 1$ or H_0: $\dfrac{\sigma_2^2}{\sigma_1^2} = 1$, or both.

and

b) Confidence Interval Formulas for $\dfrac{\sigma_1^2}{\sigma_2^2}$ or $\dfrac{\sigma_2^2}{\sigma_1^2}$, or both

a) Hypothesis Testing Procedures

i) H_0: $\dfrac{\sigma_1^2}{\sigma_2^2} = 1$ vs H_1: $\dfrac{\sigma_1^2}{\sigma_2^2} \neq 1$

ii) Select α (if one is not given, choose either $\alpha = 0.05$ or $\alpha = 0.01$ or both)

iii) The estimator for $\dfrac{\sigma_1^2}{\sigma_2^2}$ is $\dfrac{\hat{s}_1^2}{\hat{s}_2^2}$ which is $F_{\delta_2}^{\delta_1}$, when H_0 is true.

iv) Construct the rejection region, using F tabulated values and the reciprocal property, as shown below:

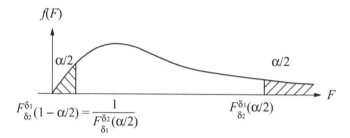

$$F_{\delta_2}^{\delta_1}(1 - \alpha/2) = \frac{1}{F_{\delta_1}^{\delta_2}(\alpha/2)} \qquad\qquad F_{\delta_2}^{\delta_1}(\alpha/2)$$

v) Calculate the value of the test statistic $= F^* = \dfrac{\hat{s}_1^2}{\hat{s}_2^2}$

vi) If F^* is in the critical region, REJECT H_0; otherwise DO NOT REJECT H_0.

vii) Express in words the mathematical conclusion of step (6) above.

Note: If H_0 is formulated as $H_0: \dfrac{\sigma_2^2}{\sigma_1^2} = 1$ $\left(\text{instead of as } H_0: \dfrac{\sigma_1^2}{\sigma_2^2} = 1\right)$, the following

changes must be made to the above procedure:

1. $H_0: \dfrac{\sigma_2^2}{\sigma_1^2} = 1$ vs $H_1: \dfrac{\sigma_2^2}{\sigma_1^2} \neq 1$

2. Select value of α (This step remains unchanged)

3. The estimator for $\dfrac{\sigma_2^2}{\sigma_1^2}$ is $\dfrac{\hat{s}_2^2}{\hat{s}_1^2}$ which is $F_{\delta_1}^{\delta_2}$.

4. Construct the rejection (critical) region, using F tabulated values and the reciprocal property, as shown below:

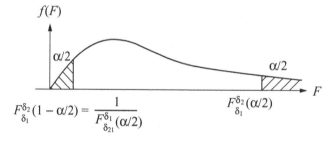

$$F_{\delta_1}^{\delta_2}(1 - \alpha/2) = \frac{1}{F_{\delta_{21}}^{\delta_1}(\alpha/2)} \qquad\qquad F_{\delta_1}^{\delta_2}(\alpha/2)$$

5. Calculate the value of the test statistic $= F^* = \dfrac{\hat{s}_2^2}{\hat{s}_1^2}$

6. If F^* falls in the rejection region, REJECT H_0; otherwise DO NOT.

7. Express in words the mathematical conclusion of step(6) above.

b) Confidence Interval Formulas for σ_1^2/σ_2^2 and σ_2^2/σ_1^2

Because the F distribution is positively skewed and not symmetric, we have to obtain 2 separate values to construct these confidence intervals. The right tail value is obtained directly form the F table. However, the left tail value is calculated using the reciprocal property (given by 11.77) and tabulated F values.

Again, as we did with the Chi-square distribution, we need to introduce the following notation to help us in the construction of the confidence intervals. We let:

$F_{\delta_2}^{\delta_1}(\alpha/2)$ = value of the F variable, with δ_1 = DOF in the numerator and δ_2 = DOF in the denominator, for which the area to the right of this value = $\alpha/2$; *i.e.*,

$$\int_{F_{\delta_2}^{\delta_1}(\alpha/2)}^{\infty} f(F)dF = \alpha/2.$$

$F_{\delta_2}^{\delta_1}(1 - \alpha/2)$ = value of the F variable, with δ_1 = DOF in the numerator and δ_2 = DOF in the denominator, for which the area to the right of this value = $1 - \alpha/2$; *i.e.*,

$$\int_{F_{\delta_2}^{\delta_1}(1-\alpha/2)}^{\infty} f(F)dF = 1 - \alpha/2.$$

These values can be better visualized in the diagram below:

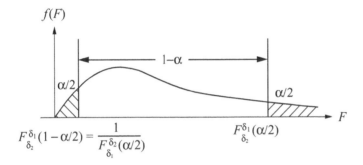

Cleary, the area between these 2 values is equal to $1 - \alpha$. We can then write the general equation shown below, valid for any F variable with δ_1 = DOF in the numerator and δ_2 = DOF in the denominator.

$$P\left[F_{\delta_2}^{\delta_1}(1 - \alpha/2) \le F_{\delta_2}^{\delta_1} \le F_{\delta_2}^{\delta_1}(\alpha/2)\right] = 1 - \alpha \tag{11.94}$$

But since equation (11.94) is valid for any F variable with (δ_1, δ_2) degrees of freedom, it is also true for the variable defined by equation (11.92), namely:

$$F_{\delta_2}^{\delta_1} = \left(\frac{\sigma_2^2}{\sigma_1^2}\right)\frac{\hat{s}_1^2}{\hat{s}_2^2} \tag{11.95}$$

When equation (11.95) is substituted into equation (11.94) we obtain:

$$P\left[F_{\delta_2}^{\delta_1}(1 - \alpha/2) \le \left(\frac{\sigma_2^2}{\sigma_1^2}\right)\frac{\hat{s}_1^2}{\hat{s}_2^2} \le F_{\delta_2}^{\delta_1}(\alpha/2)\right] = 1 - \alpha \tag{11.96}$$

Since $F_{\delta_2}^{\delta_1}(1 - \alpha/2)$ is not a tabulated function, it should be replaced by its equivalent, $1/F_{\delta_1}^{\delta_2}(\alpha/2)$, which is tabulated.

Also, if (11.96) is multiplied (inside the brackets) by the ratio $\left(\dfrac{\hat{s}_2^2}{\hat{s}_1^2}\right)$, we obtain:

$$P\left[\frac{\hat{s}_2^2}{\hat{s}_1^2}\frac{1}{F_{\delta_1}^{\delta_2}(\alpha/2)} \le \frac{\sigma_2^2}{\sigma_1^2} \le \frac{\hat{s}_2^2}{\hat{s}_1^2}F_{\delta_2}^{\delta_1}(\alpha/2)\right] = 1 - \alpha \tag{11.97}$$

Equation (11.97) gives the $1 - \alpha$ confidence interval for the ratio $\dfrac{\sigma_2^2}{\sigma_1^2}$, which corresponds

to the case of formulating the original hypothesis $H_0: \sigma_1^2 = \sigma_2^2$ as $H_0: \dfrac{\sigma_2^2}{\sigma_1^2} = 1$.

To obtain a $1 - \alpha$ confidence interval for the ration $\dfrac{\sigma_1^2}{\sigma_2^2}$ (which would correspond to the

case of formulating the original hypothesis $H_0: \sigma_1^2 = \sigma_2^2$ as $H_0: \dfrac{\sigma_1^2}{\sigma_2^2} = 1$), we must solve

equation (11.97) for $\dfrac{\sigma_1^2}{\sigma_2^2}$. This can be done by solving simultaneously the 2 inequalities below:

$$\frac{\hat{s}_2^2}{\hat{s}_1^2} \frac{1}{F_{\delta_1}^{\delta_2}(\alpha/2)} \leq \frac{\sigma_2^2}{\sigma_1^2} \tag{11.98}$$

and

$$\frac{\sigma_2^2}{\sigma_1^2} \leq \frac{\hat{s}_2^2}{\hat{s}_1^2} F_{\delta_2}^{\delta_1}(\alpha/2) \tag{11.99}$$

The result is

$$P\left[\frac{\hat{s}_1^2}{\hat{s}_2^2} \frac{1}{F_{\delta_2}^{\delta_1}(\alpha/2)} \leq \frac{\sigma_1^2}{\sigma_2^2} \leq \frac{\hat{s}_1^2}{\hat{s}_2^2} F_{\delta_1}^{\delta_2}(\alpha/2) \right] = 1 - \alpha \tag{11.100}$$

Equation (11.100) is the confidence interval for the ratio $\dfrac{\sigma_1^2}{\sigma_2^2}$, and corresponds to the case

of formulating the original $H_0: \sigma_1^2 = \sigma_2^2$ as $H_0: \dfrac{\sigma_1^2}{\sigma_2^2} = 1$.

c) Example 4 Hypothesis Testing and Confidence Interval for σ_1^2/σ_2^2 and σ_2^2/σ_1^2

1. Perform an appropriate hypothesis test to test the claim that the variance among the weights of 4th grade girls is the same as the variance among the 4th grade boys, at the $\alpha = 0.1$ level. Use the data provided by the table below.

		$\hat{s}^2$	n	
σ_1^2	Girls	136.3	25	n_1
σ_2^2	Boys	105.4	16	n_2

2. Also construct 90% confidence limits on the ratios: $\dfrac{\sigma_1^2}{\sigma_2^2}$ and $\dfrac{\sigma_2^2}{\sigma_1^2}$.

■ Hypothesis Testing Solution

1. $H_0: \sigma_1^2 = \sigma_2^2$ vs $H_1: \sigma_1^2 \neq \sigma_2^2$ or $H_0: \dfrac{\sigma_1^2}{\sigma_2^2} = 1$ vs $H_1: \dfrac{\sigma_1^2}{\sigma_2^2} \neq 1$.

2. $\alpha = 0.1$ (and $\alpha/2 = 0.05$).

3. The estimator for $\dfrac{\sigma_1^2}{\sigma_2^2}$ is $\dfrac{\hat{s}_1^2}{\hat{s}_2^2}$ which is $F_{\delta_2 = n_2 - 1}^{\delta_1 = n_1 - 1} = F_{15}^{24}$, when H_0 is true.

4. Because of the nature of H_1, the rejection region will be on both ends of the F-distribution, and is defined as shown below:

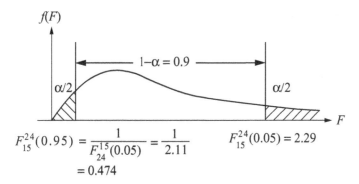

$$F_{15}^{24}(0.95) = \frac{1}{F_{24}^{15}(0.05)} = \frac{1}{2.11} \qquad F_{15}^{24}(0.05) = 2.29$$
$$= 0.474$$

5. Value of test statistic $= F^* = \dfrac{\hat{s}_1^2}{\hat{s}_2^2} = 136.3/105.4 = 1.29$

6. Since $0.474 < F^* = 1.29 < 2.29$ (*i.e.*, F^* is outside of the rejection region), we do not reject H_0.

7. Conclusion: The variance of the weights of 4th grade girls is the same as the variance of the weights of 4th grade boys when $\alpha = 0.1$.

■ Confidence Limits on σ_1^2/σ_2^2 and σ_2^2/σ_1^2

1. Confidence limits on $\dfrac{\sigma_1^2}{\sigma_2^2}$

   Use equation 11.98 with $F_{\delta_2}^{\delta_1}(\alpha/2) = F_{15}^{24}(0.05) = 2.29$,

   $F_{\delta_1}^{\delta_2}(\alpha/2) = F_{24}^{15}(0.05) = 2.11$, and $\dfrac{\hat{s}_1^2}{\hat{s}_2^2} = F^* = 1.29$

   Substituting these 3 quantities in (11.98), we obtain:

   $$P\left[(1.29)\frac{1}{2.29} \leq \frac{\sigma_1^2}{\sigma_2^2} \leq (1.29)(2.11)\right] = 0.90$$

   or $\qquad\qquad P[0.5633 \leq \dfrac{\sigma_1^2}{\sigma_2^2} \leq 2.7219] = 0.90$

Note: The hypothesized value, $\dfrac{\sigma_1^2}{\sigma_2^2} = 1$, falls inside this 90% confidence interval.

Therefore, once again we would not reject H_0.

2. Confidence limits on $\dfrac{\sigma_2^2}{\sigma_1^2}$

   Use (11.97) with: $F_{\delta_2}^{\delta_1}(\alpha/2) = F_{15}^{24}(0.05) = 2.29$, $F_{\delta_1}^{\delta_2}(\alpha/2) = F_{24}^{15}(0.05) = 2.11$, and

   $\dfrac{\hat{s}_2^2}{\hat{s}_1^2} = \dfrac{105.4}{136.3} = 0.7733$

   Substituting these values in (11.97), we obtain:

   $$P\left[0.7733\left(\frac{1}{2.11}\right) \leq \frac{\sigma_2^2}{\sigma_1^2} \leq (0.7733)(2.29)\right] = 0.90$$

or
$$P\left[0.3665 \leq \frac{\sigma_2^2}{\sigma_1^2} \leq 1.7709\right] = 0.90$$

Note: If we had stated the re-formulated H_0 and H_1 hypothesis as:

H_0: $\frac{\sigma_2^2}{\sigma_1^2} = 1$ vs H_1: $\frac{\sigma_2^2}{\sigma_1^2} \neq 1$ (instead of as H_0: $\frac{\sigma_1^2}{\sigma_2^2} = 1$ vs H_1: $\frac{\sigma_1^2}{\sigma_2^2} \neq 1$), the hypothesized

value again falls inside this 90% confidence interval. Therefore, once again, we would not reject H_0.

■■■

11.3.3 The *t*-Distribution (or Student-*t*-Distribution)

11.3.3.1 Theoretical Considerations

If we had to test a single population mean (μ) against a fixed value (*i.e.*, H_0: $\mu = 100$ vs H_1: $\mu \neq 100$) we would:

1. Use the normal distribution, if the population standard deviation (σ) is known, regardless of the sample size n.
2. Use the normal distribution, if σ is not known but $n \geq 30$ (In this case we replace σ by $\hat{s}$ and still use the normal, if $n \geq 30$).
3. However, if σ is not known and $n < 30$, we can not replace σ by $\hat{s}$ and use the normal. The appropriate distribution to use in this case is the *t*-distribution, where *t* is defined in this case by:

$$t = \frac{\overline{x} - \mu}{\hat{s}/\sqrt{n}} = \frac{\overline{x} - \mu}{\sqrt{\hat{s}^2/n}} \tag{11.101}$$

Similarly, if we had to test the equality of 2 population means (*i.e.*, H_0: $\mu_1 = \mu_2$ vs H_1: $\mu_1 \neq \mu_2$), we would:

1. Use the normal distribution, if σ_1 and σ_2 are both known, regardless of the sample sizes n_1 and n_2.
2. Use the normal distribution, if σ_1 and σ_2 are not known, but $n_1 \geq 30$ and $n_2 \geq 30$ (In this case we replace σ_1 by $\hat{s}_1$ and σ_2 by $\hat{s}_2$ and still use the normal.)
3. However, if σ_1 and σ_2 are not known and $n_1 < 30$ and $n_2 < 30$ (or $n_1 < 30$ and $n_2 \geq 30$ or $n_1 \geq 30$ and $n_2 < 30$), we can no longer use the normal distribution but we must use the *t*-distribution, where the variable *t* is defined in this case by:

$$t = \frac{(\overline{x}_1 - \overline{x}_2) - (\mu_1 - \mu_2)}{\sigma(\Delta\overline{x})} = \frac{\Delta\overline{x} - \Delta\mu}{\sigma(\Delta\overline{x})} \tag{11.102}$$

After we briefly discuss the theoretical derivation of the *t*-distribution, we will discuss the application of the *t*-distribution to the following 3 problems:

a) Inferences concerning a single population mean.
b) Inferences concerning 2 population means with independent samples.
c) Inferences concerning 2 population means with dependent samples.

1. Theoretical derivation of the *t*-distribution

   If $x_0, x_1, x_2, \ldots, x_\delta$ are $\delta + 1$ independent standard normal variables (*i.e.*, each x_i is N(0,1)), then the variable *t*, defined by:

$$t = \frac{x_0}{\sqrt{(x_1^2 + x_2^2 + \cdots + x_\delta^2)/\delta}} = \frac{Z}{\sqrt{\chi^2/\delta}} \tag{11.103}$$

   is said to be *t*-distributed with DOF = δ. The numerator and denominator, in the definition of *t* of (11.101) are independent.

2. The density function of t, $f(t)$, is given by:

$$f(t) = \left(\frac{1}{\sqrt{\delta n}}\right)\left[\frac{\Gamma\left(\frac{\delta + 1}{2}\right)}{\Gamma(\delta/2)}\right]\left(1 + \frac{t^2}{\delta}\right)^{-\frac{(\delta+1)}{2}} \qquad -\infty < t < \infty \quad (11.104)$$

The t-distribution is symmetric and has an infinite range of variation. When plotted, it looks very much like the standard normal distribution, even though it has a somewhat larger variance than the standard normal and, as a consequence, a smaller peak value (so that the area under the $f(t)$ density function remains at 1).

3. Expected value of $t = E(t) = \displaystyle\int_{-\infty}^{\infty} t \cdot f(t)dt = 0$ \qquad\qquad (11.105)

4. Expected value of $t^2 = E(t^2) = \displaystyle\int_{-\infty}^{\infty} t^2 \cdot f(t)dt = \frac{\delta}{\delta - 2}$ \qquad (11.106)

5. Variance of $t = V(t) = E(t^2) - [E(t)]^2 = E(t^2) - (0)^2 = E(t^2) = \dfrac{\delta}{\delta - 2}$

$$= 1 + \frac{2}{\delta - 2} \text{ (valid for } \delta \geq 3) \qquad\qquad (11.107)$$

We see from (11.107) that the variance of t is greater than 1 and, since the standard normal has a variance of exactly equal to 1, the t-distribution has a variance greater than the variance of the standard normal distribution.

6. When $\delta \geq 30$, the t and standard normal distributions are indistinguishable, and we treat t_δ as N(0, 1).

Note: When $\delta = 1$, the density function $f(t)$ of equation (11.104) becomes:

$$f(t) = \left(\frac{1}{\sqrt{\pi}}\right)\left[\frac{\Gamma(1)}{\Gamma(1/2)}\right](1 + t^2)^{-1} \qquad (\text{with } \Gamma(1) = 1 \text{ and } \Gamma(1/2) = \sqrt{\pi}) \quad (11.108)$$

which is the so-called Cauchy Distribution. The expected value of the density function of (11.108) is not defined.

7. **Probability Calculations Using the t-Distribution**
To find the probability that the t-variable is between the values $t = a$ and $t = b$, we need to integrate the $f(t)$ density function analytically in the interval $a \leq t \leq b$. This implies that:

$$P[a \leq t \leq b] = \int_a^b f(t)\, dt = g(t)\big|_a^b = g(b) - g(a) \qquad (11.109)$$

provided that $g'(t) = f(t)$.

However, because the density function $f(t)$, as given by equation (11.104) is difficult to integrate analytically, we integrate numerically instead, by using table values of the t-distribution. The first column of this table lists the DOF of the t-distribution which starts at $\delta = 1$ and goes to $\delta = 120$ and beyond. Then there are several other columns (marked respectively as $t_{0.100}$, $t_{0.025}$, $t_{0.010}$, $t_{0.005}$, $t_{0.001}$, $t_{0.0005}$) which represent the probability (that is equal to α) and which is marked off as a shaded area at the right tail of the t-distribution. The values found at the intersection of a fixed DOF row and a t_α column represent the numerical value of the variable t for which the area to the right of this value, and up to $+\infty$, is equal to α.

For example, if $\delta = 10$ and $\alpha = 0.025$, we find at the intersection of $DOF = 10$ and the column $t_{0.025}$ the value 2.228. This implies that:

$$\int_{2.228}^{\infty} f(t)dt = 0.025 = P[2.228 \leq t < \infty] \tag{11.110}$$

As a second example, if $\delta = 30$ and $\alpha = 0.05$, we find at the intersection of $DOF = 30$ and the column $t_{0.050}$ the value 1.697. This implies that:

$$P[1.697 \leq t < \infty] = \int_{1.697}^{\infty} f(t)dt = 0.050 \tag{11.111}$$

Note: The corresponding Z value (see entry in the t-table at $\delta = \infty$ and $\alpha = 0.05$) is $Z_{0.05} = 1.645$.

11.3.3.2 Applications of the t-Distribution
11.3.3.2.1 Inferences Concerning a Single Population Mean (μ)

As stated previously, to test a hypothesis of the type: $H_0: \mu = 100$ vs $H_1: \mu \neq 100$ (or to construct a confidence interval for μ of the type:
$P[\bar{x} - k\sigma(\bar{x}) \leq \mu \leq \bar{x} + k\sigma(\bar{x})] = 1 - \alpha$, we will use the normal distribution if:

1. σ is known, regardless of the value of n, because then $\left(\dfrac{\bar{x} - \mu}{\sigma/\sqrt{n}} \right)$ is distributed as N(0, 1).

2. σ is unknown but $n \geq 30$. In this case we replace σ by $\hat{s}$ and still use the normal, because $\dfrac{\bar{x} - \mu}{\sigma/\sqrt{n}}$ is approximately equal to $\dfrac{\bar{x} - \mu}{\hat{s}/\sqrt{n}}$ which is again distributed as N(0, 1).

3. However, if σ is unknown and $n < 30$, we cannot replace σ by $\hat{s}$ and still have a standard normal (*i.e.*, N(0, 1)) distribution. The ratio:

$$\frac{\bar{x} - \mu}{\hat{s}/\sqrt{n}} \tag{11.112}$$

is t-distributed with $DOF = n - 1$ (and the t-distribution should be used to solve such problems).

The reason for this is as follows:

From the result: $\dfrac{(n-1)\hat{s}^2}{\sigma^2} = \chi_{n-1}^2$, we get: $\hat{s}^2 = \sigma^2(\chi_{n-1}^2/n - 1)$, and then

$\dfrac{\hat{s}^2}{n} = \dfrac{\sigma^2}{n}\left(\dfrac{\chi_{n-1}^2}{n-1}\right)$, or $\dfrac{\hat{s}}{\sqrt{n}} = \dfrac{\sigma}{\sqrt{n}}\sqrt{\dfrac{\chi_{n-1}^2}{n-1}}$. Therefore, if in (11.112) we replace

$\hat{s}/\sqrt{n}$ by its equivalent, we obtain:

$$\frac{\bar{x} - \mu}{\hat{s}/\sqrt{n}} = \frac{\bar{x} - \mu}{\dfrac{\sigma}{\sqrt{n}}\sqrt{\dfrac{\chi_{n-1}^2}{n-1}}} = \frac{\dfrac{\bar{x} - \mu}{\dfrac{\sigma}{\sqrt{n}}}}{\sqrt{\dfrac{\chi_{n-1}^2}{n-1}}} = \frac{Z}{\sqrt{\dfrac{\chi_{n-1}^2}{n-1}}} = t_{n-1}$$

■ The Hypothesis Testing Problem, Using the t_{n-1} Distribution

The solution to this problem consists of the traditional 7-step procedure, except that the Z distribution is replaced by the t_{n-1} distribution, as shown below:

1. $H_0: \mu = 100$ vs $H_1: \mu \neq 100$
2. Select α
3. The estimator of μ is $\bar{x}$, and $\dfrac{\bar{x} - \mu}{\hat{s}/\sqrt{n}}$ is t_{n-1} because σ is unknown and $n < 30$.

4. To construct the rejection region, we use the t_{n-1} distribution. In this case, because of the nature of H_1, the rejection region will be at both ends of the t_{n-1} distribution with equal areas, each equal to $\alpha/2$. Because the t-distribution is symmetric the 2 critical t values (those t values which divide the range of variation of the t variable into the rejection and non-rejection regions) will be equal in value but of opposite signs, as shown below:

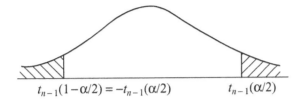

$$t_{n-1}(1-\alpha/2) = -t_{n-1}(\alpha/2) \qquad t_{n-1}(\alpha/2)$$

5. The value of the test statistic is:

$$t^* = \frac{\overline{x} - \mu_0}{\hat{s}/\sqrt{n}} \qquad (11.113)$$

6. If t^* is in the critical (or rejection) region, we **REJECT** H_0.
   If t^* is outside of the rejection region, **DO NOT REJECT** H_0.
7. Express in words the mathematical conclusion of step (6).

■ The $1 - \alpha$ Confidence Interval on μ

In the general equation for the symmetric form of a C.I. for μ, i.e.,

$$P[\overline{x} - k\sigma(\overline{x}) \le \mu \le \overline{x} + k\sigma(\overline{x})] = 1 - \alpha \qquad (11.114)$$

the multiplier k has the value:

$$k = t_{n-1}(\alpha/2) \qquad (11.115)$$

while $\sigma(\overline{x})$ is given by $\qquad \sigma(\overline{x}) = \hat{s}/\sqrt{n} \qquad (11.116)$

Therefore, the specific confidence interval on μ, using the t-distribution is given by:

$$P\left[\overline{x} - t_{n-1(\alpha/2)}\frac{\hat{s}}{\sqrt{n}} \le \mu \le \overline{x} + t_{n-1}(\alpha/2)\frac{\hat{s}}{\sqrt{n}}\right] = 1 - \alpha \qquad (11.117)$$

■ Example 5 Hypothesis Testing and Confidence Interval for μ, using the t_{n-1} distribution

The claim is made that "The mean carbon dioxide level of air pollution in New York City is 4.9".

1. Does a random sample of 25 readings (which produced an $\overline{x} = 5.1$ and $\hat{s} = 2.1$) present sufficient evidence to reject this claim? Use $\alpha = 0.05$.
2. Also construct a 95% confidence interval on μ.

■ Solution of the Hypothesis Testing Problem

1. $H_0: \mu = 4.9$ vs $H_1: \mu \ne 4.9$
2. $\alpha = 0.05$ (and $\alpha/2 = 0.025$)
3. The estimator for μ is $\overline{x}$, and $\dfrac{\overline{x} - \mu}{\hat{s}/\sqrt{n}}$ is $t_{n-1} = t_{24}$, because σ is not known and $n < 30$.
4. Rejection Region

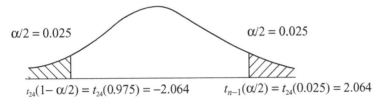

$\alpha/2 = 0.025 \qquad\qquad \alpha/2 = 0.025$

$$t_{24}(1-\alpha/2) = t_{24}(0.975) = -2.064 \qquad t_{n-1}(\alpha/2) = t_{24}(0.025) = 2.064$$

5. The value of the test statistic $= t^* = \dfrac{\bar{x} - \mu_0}{\hat{s}/\sqrt{n}} = \dfrac{5.1 - 4.9}{2.1/\sqrt{25}} = \dfrac{0.2}{2.1/5} = 0.48$

6. Since t^* is outside the rejection region, DO NOT REJECT H_0.

7. Therefore, the mean carbon dioxide level of air pollution in New York City is 4.9.

■ Solution of the Confidence Interval Problem

Use equation (11.115), with $\bar{x} = 5.1$, $t_{n-1}(\alpha/2) = t_{24}(0.025) = 2.064$, $\hat{s} = 2.1$, $n = 25$, and $1 - \alpha = 0.95$. When these quantities are substituted in (11.115), we obtain:

$$P\left[5.1 - 2.064\left(\frac{2.1}{5}\right) \le \mu \le 5.1 + 2.064\left(\frac{2.1}{5}\right)\right] = 0.95$$

or

$$P[4.2332 \le \mu \le 5.9668] = 0.95$$

Since the hypothesized value, $\mu = \mu_0 = 4.9$, is a value included in this confidence interval, once again we do not reject H_0 and conclude, as with the hypothesis testing problem, that the mean carbon dioxide level of air pollution in New York City is 4.9.

■ ■ ■

11.3.3.2.2 Inferences Concerning 2 Population Means (μ_1, μ_2) with Independent Samples

Here we wish to test the equality of the means of 2 populations (μ_1 of population 1 and μ_2 of population 2) by drawing samples from each population (n_1 from Population 1, and n_2 from Population 2), and then test the hypothesis:

$$H_0{:}\ \mu_1 = \mu_2 \text{ vs } H_1{:}\ \mu_1 \ne \mu_2$$

or

$$H_0{:}\ \mu_1 - \mu_2 = 0 \text{ vs } H_1{:}\ \mu_1 - \mu_2 \ne 0$$

or

$$H_0{:}\ \Delta\mu = 0 \text{ vs } H_1{:}\ \Delta\mu \ne 0$$

This problem can be solved using the normal distribution, if:

- σ_1 and σ_2 are both known, regardless of the sample sizes n_1 and n_2.
- σ_1 and σ_2 are not known, but $n_1 \ge 30$ and $n_2 \ge 30$. In this case we replace σ_1 by and $\hat{s}_1$ and σ_2 by $\hat{s}_2$, and still use the normal.

However, if σ_1 and σ_2 are unknown and $n_1 < 30$ and $n_2 < 30$ (or $n_1 \ge 30$ but $n_2 < 30$ or $n_1 < 30$ and $n_2 \ge 30$), the problem must be solved using the t-distribution, with Degrees Of Freedom:

$$\text{DOF} = n_1 + n_2 - 2 \tag{11.118}$$

We consider 2 cases:

  Case 1: The population variances (σ_1^2 and σ_2^2) are unknown, but are assumed to be equal (*i.e.*, $\sigma_1^2 = \sigma_2^2 = \sigma^2$).

  Case 2: The population variances are unknown and unequal ($\sigma_1^2 \ne \sigma_2^2$).

Case 1: Assume $\sigma_1^2 = \sigma_2^2 = \sigma^2$ (or $\hat{s}_1^2 = \hat{s}_2^2 = \hat{s}^2$)

I) The Hypothesis Testing Problem

It consists of the usual 7-step procedure, with the appropriate modifications to the procedure in steps 3, 4, and 5.

1. $H_0{:}\ \Delta\mu = 0$ vs $H_1{:}\ \Delta\mu \ne 0$
2. Select α
3. The estimator for $\Delta\mu = \mu_1 - \mu_2$ is: $\Delta\bar{x} = \bar{x}_1 - \bar{x}_2 = (1)\bar{x}_1 + (-1)\bar{x}_2$, with

$$E(\Delta \overline{x}) = E(\overline{x}_1) - E(\overline{x}_2) = \mu_1 - \mu_2 = \Delta\mu \tag{11.119}$$

$$\begin{aligned} V(\Delta \overline{x}) &= (1)^2 V(\overline{x}_1) + (-1)^2 V(\overline{x}_2) \\ &= V(\overline{x}_1) + V(\overline{x}_2) \\ &= \frac{\hat{s}_1^2}{n_1} + \frac{\hat{s}_2^2}{n_2} \end{aligned} \tag{11.120}$$

$$= \hat{s}^2 \left(\frac{1}{n_1} + \frac{1}{n_2} \right) \qquad \text{(because we assume that } \hat{s}_1^2 = \hat{s}_2^2 = \hat{s}^2 \text{),}$$

$$\text{or } V(\Delta \overline{x}) = \left(\frac{n_1 + n_2}{n_1 n_2} \right) \hat{s}^2 \tag{11.121}$$

The best estimator for $\hat{s}^2$ is the "pooled" variance given by:

$$\hat{s}^2 = \frac{(n_1 - 1)\hat{s}_1^2 + (n_2 - 1)\hat{s}_2^2}{n_1 + n_2 - 2} \tag{11.122}$$

Then $\qquad V(\Delta \overline{x}) = \left(\frac{n_1 + n_2}{n_1 n_2} \right) \left[\frac{(n_1 - 1)\hat{s}_1^2 + (n_2 - 1)\hat{s}_2^2}{n_1 + n_2 - 2} \right] \tag{11.123}$

and $\qquad \sigma(\Delta \overline{x}) = \sqrt{ \left(\frac{n_1 + n_2}{n_1 n_2} \right) \left(\frac{(n_1 - 1)\hat{s}_1^2 + (n_2 - 1)\hat{s}_2^2}{n_1 + n_2 - 2} \right) } \tag{11.124}$

Then $\dfrac{\Delta \overline{x}}{\sigma(\Delta \overline{x})}$ is t-distributed with

$$\text{DOF} = n_1 + n_2 - 2 \tag{11.125}$$

Note: This conclusion is obtained from a theorem on chi-square variables, which states that "the sum of 2 chi-square variables, with DOF $= \delta_1$ and δ_2 respectively is also a chi-square variable with DOF $= \delta_1 + \delta_2$". Or, in mathematical terms $\chi_1^2(\delta_1) + \chi_2^2(\delta_2) = \chi^2(\delta_1 + \delta_2)$. Then in our case:

$$\frac{(n_1 - 1)\hat{s}_1^2}{\sigma_1^2} + \frac{(n_2 - 1)\hat{s}_2^2}{\sigma_2^2} = \frac{(n_1 - 1)\hat{s}_1^2 + (n_2 - 1)\hat{s}_2^2}{\sigma^2}$$

or $\qquad \dfrac{n_1 + n_2 - 2}{\sigma^2} \left[\dfrac{(n_1 - 1)\hat{s}_1^2 + (n_2 - 1)\hat{s}_2^2}{n_1 + n_2 - 2} \right] \to \chi_{n_1 + n_2 - 2}^2 \tag{11.126}$

4. The critical region is constructed from the nature of H_1, and using a t-distribution with DOF $= n_1 + n_2 - 2$.

5. The value of the test statistic is calculated from:

$$t^* = \frac{\Delta \overline{x} - \Delta\mu_0}{\sigma(\Delta \overline{x})} = \frac{\Delta \overline{x} - 0}{\sigma(\Delta \overline{x})} = \frac{\overline{x}_1 - \overline{x}_2}{\sigma(\Delta \overline{x})} \tag{11.127}$$

where $\sigma(\Delta \overline{x})$ is given by equation (11.124).

6. Compare t^* to the rejection region. Reject H_0 if t^* falls in the rejection region. Do not reject H_0 if t^* falls outside of the rejection region.

7. Express in words the mathematical conclusion of step (6).

II) The $1 - \alpha$ Confidence Interval on $\Delta\mu$

The new population parameter here is $\Delta\mu$, whose estimator is $\Delta \overline{x} = \overline{x}_1 - \overline{x}_2$, with $\sigma(\Delta \overline{x})$ given by equation (11.124). Since $\Delta \overline{x}/\sigma(\Delta \overline{x})$ is t-distributed with DOF $= n_1 + n_2 - 2$, the $1 - \alpha$ confidence interval on $\Delta\mu$ is given by:

$$P[\Delta \overline{x} - t_{n_1 + n_2 - 2}(\alpha/2) \cdot \sigma(\Delta \overline{x}) \le \Delta\mu \le \Delta \overline{x} + t_{n_1 + n_2 - 2}(\alpha/2) \cdot \sigma(\Delta \overline{x})] = 1 - \alpha \tag{11.128}$$

III) Example 6 Hypothesis Testing and Confidence Interval for $\Delta\mu$, using the $t_{n_1+n_2-2}$ Distribution

The claim is made that the mean reported annual earnings of carpenters and house painters is the same.

  I. Use the data of the table below to test the validity of this claim, at $\alpha = 0.05$.

  II. Also construct a 95% confidence interval on $\Delta\mu$.

Carpenters	Painters
$n_1 = 12$	$n_2 = 15$
$\bar{x}_1 = 16{,}000$	$\bar{x}_2 = 15{,}400$
$\hat{s}_1^2 = 565{,}000$	$\hat{s}_2^2 = 362{,}500$

■ Solution of the Hypothesis Testing Problem

1. $H_0: \Delta\mu = 0$ vs $H_1: \Delta\mu \neq 0$

2. $\alpha = 0.05$ (and $\alpha/2 = 0.025$)

3. The estimator of $\Delta\mu$ is $\Delta\bar{x}$ ($\Delta\bar{x} = \bar{x}_1 - \bar{x}_2 = 16{,}000 - 15{,}400 = 600$), with

$$\sigma(\Delta\bar{x}) = \sqrt{\left(\frac{12 + 15}{12 \times 15}\right)\left[\frac{(11)(565{,}000) + (14)(362{,}500)}{12 + 15 - 2}\right]} = 260.26$$

and $\dfrac{\Delta\bar{x}}{\sigma(\Delta\bar{x})}$ is $t_{12+15-2} = t_{25}$

4. Rejection Region:

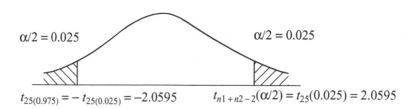

$$t_{25(0.975)} = -t_{25(0.025)} = -2.0595 \qquad t_{n1+n2-2}(\alpha/2) = t_{25}(0.025) = 2.0595$$

5. Value of test statistic $= t^* = \dfrac{\Delta\bar{x}}{\sigma(\Delta\bar{x})} = \dfrac{600}{260.26} = 2.305$

6. Since t^* is in the rejection region, we reject H_0.

7. Conclusion: The average (reported) income of carpenters and house painters is not the same.

■ Solution of the Confidence Interval Problem

Use equation (11.126) with $\Delta\bar{x} = \bar{x}_1 - \bar{x}_2 = 16{,}000 - 15{,}400 = 600$,

$t_{n1+n2-2}(\alpha/2) = t_{25}(0.025) = 2.0595$, $\sigma(\Delta\bar{x}) = 260.26$, and $1 - \alpha = 0.95$. When these quantities are substituted into equation (11.128), we obtain:

$$P[600 - 2.0595(260.26) \leq \Delta\mu \leq 600 + 2.0595(260.26)] = 0.95,$$

or
$$P[63.86 \leq \Delta\mu \leq 1{,}136.14] = 0.95$$

Since the hypothesized value, $\Delta\mu = \Delta\mu_0 = 0$, is outside of this interval, H_0 is again rejected, and we conclude that the average (reported) income of carpenters and house painters is not the same.

■ ■ ■

Case 2: Assume $\sigma_1^2 \neq \sigma_2^2$

If $\sigma_1^2 \neq \sigma_2^2$, then $\sigma(\Delta\overline{x}) = \sqrt{\dfrac{\hat{s}_1^2}{n_1} + \dfrac{\hat{s}_2^3}{n_2}}$ is not distributed as a chi-square variable. Because

$\sigma(\Delta\overline{x})$ is not chi-square, $\dfrac{\Delta\overline{x} - \Delta\mu_0}{\sqrt{\dfrac{\hat{s}_1^2}{n_1} + \dfrac{\hat{s}_2^2}{n_2}}}$ is not t-distributed. Even though we could show that

under certain conditions, the distribution of $\dfrac{\Delta\overline{x} - \Delta\mu_0}{\sqrt{\dfrac{\hat{s}_1^2}{n_1} + \dfrac{\hat{s}_2^2}{n_2}}}$ is approximately t-distributed, the

truth is that we do not know the distribution of this ratio, and, therefore, cannot solve this problem.

It should now be clear that the reason we made the assumption that $\sigma_1^2 = \sigma_2^2 = \sigma^2$ was to allow us to solve the problem, which cannot be solved without this assumption.

Note: Recall that in our discussion of the F-distribution, we tested the hypothesis

$H_0: \sigma_1^2 = \sigma_2^2$ vs $H_1: \sigma_1^2 \neq \sigma_2^2$, in anticipation of using it in this test.

11.3.3.2.3 Inferences Concerning 2 Population Means with Dependent Samples

When we compare independent samples from 2 populations, the elements of one population are not related to the elements of the other, and the sample sizes from the 2 populations can be different (*i.e.*, it is possible that $n_1 \neq n_2$). We showed in the previous section how to compare the equality of the means of the two populations under these circumstances.

However, if an observation in Population 1 is associated with some particular observation in Population 2 (*i.e.*, the samples are paired) then the samples from the 2 populations are DEPENDENT, and $n_1 = n_2 = n$.

To test the equality of the means of 2 dependent samples, we follow the same procedure as before. But, instead of the "traditional" population parameter $\Delta\mu$ which we used in the previous section, when we formulated $H_0: \Delta\mu = 0$ vs $H_1: \Delta\mu \neq 0$, we now introduce a new population parameter, μ_d, which represents the "mean difference between paired data", and we formulate our new hypothesis as:

$$H_0: \mu_d = 0 \quad \text{vs} \quad H_1: \mu_d \neq 0 \tag{11.129}$$

The estimator for this new population parameter is $\overline{d}$, where:

$$\overline{d} = \frac{\sum\limits_{i=1}^{n} d_i}{n} \tag{11.130}$$

where $d_i = x_i - y_i =$ difference between the i-th dependent samples.

Then $E(\overline{d}) = \dfrac{1}{n}\sum\limits_{i=1}^{n} E(d_i) = 0 \qquad$ (if the 2 samples are similar) $\tag{11.131}$

and $\qquad V(\overline{d}) = \dfrac{1}{n^2}\sum\limits_{i=1}^{n} V(d_i) = \dfrac{n\hat{s}_d^2}{n^2} = \dfrac{1}{n}\hat{s}_d^2 = \sigma^2(\overline{d}) \tag{11.132}$

where $\qquad \hat{s}_d^2 = \dfrac{n\sum\limits_{i=1}^{n} d_i^2 - \left(\sum\limits_{i=1}^{n} d_i^2\right)^2}{n(n-1)} \tag{11.133}$

From equation (11.132) we obtain: $\sigma(\overline{d}) = \dfrac{\hat{s}_d}{\sqrt{n}}$ (11.134)

The calculated values of $\overline{d}$ (from 11.130), and $\sigma(\overline{d})$ (from 11.134), are needed to solve the problem of testing for the equality of the means of 2 populations when the samples are dependent.

We now ask the question: Why is this new test important?

The answer to the question is: Because it allows us to eliminate from consideration many other factors (see the example on tire comparisons below) and attribute any difference that may exist to actual differences in the 2 populations.

We now proceed to formulate the hypothesis testing problem regarding the parameter μ_d, and to also construct a $1 - \alpha$ confidence interval on μ_d.

Both of these problems are formulated and solved using $\overline{d}$ and $\sigma(\overline{d})$, and their ratio:

$$t_d = \frac{\overline{d} - \mu_{d_0}}{\sigma(\overline{d})} = \frac{\overline{d} - 0}{\sigma(\overline{d})} = \frac{\overline{d}}{\sigma(\overline{d})}$$ (11.135)

which is t-distributed, with DOF $= \delta = n - 1$, for the same reasons as those stated after equation (11.112).

1) The Hypothesis Testing Problem

It consists of the usual 7-step procedure with appropriate changes, mainly in steps 3, 4 and 5.

a) H_0: $\mu_d = 0$ vs H_1: $\mu_d \neq 0$

   ($\mu_d = 0$ means that the difference between paired data $= 0$.)

b) Select α

c) The estimator for μ_d is $\overline{d}$, and $\overline{d}/\sigma(\overline{d})$ is t_{n-1}.

d) The rejection region, because of the nature of H_1, will be 2-sided.

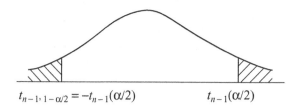

$$t_{n-1,\,1-\alpha/2} = -t_{n-1}(\alpha/2) \qquad\qquad t_{n-1}(\alpha/2)$$

e) Value of Test Statistic $= t^* = \overline{d}/\sigma(\overline{d})$.

f) If t^* is in the rejection region, reject H_0, otherwise do not reject H_0.

g) Express in words the mathematical conclusion of step (6).

2) The $1 - \alpha$ Confidence Interval Problem on μ_d

The new population parameter is μ_d, whose estimator is $\overline{d}$ with $\sigma(\overline{d})$ given by equation (11.134).

Since $\overline{d}/\sigma(\overline{d})$ is t-distributed with DOF $= \delta = n - 1$, the $1 - \alpha$ confidence interval on μ_d is given by:

$$P[\overline{d} - t_{n-1}(\alpha/2)\,\sigma(\overline{d}) \leq \mu_d \leq \overline{d} + t_{n-1}(\alpha/2)\,\sigma(\overline{d})] = 1 - \alpha$$ (11.136)

3) Example 7 Hypothesis Testing and Confidence Interval for μ_d, using the t_{n-1}-Distribution

Problem: Suppose we wish to test the "wearability" of 2 different brands of tires. If we wanted to use Independent samples, we can put tire A in Car A (actually n_1 cars) and tire B in Car B (actually n_2 cars) and measure the "wearability" of each tire separately. But, there are many important factors which affect tire "wearability", such as: Number of miles driven, car weight, car condition, road condition, driver's habits, etc. If we find a difference between the 2 brands of tires, is the difference due to differences in the 2 products or due to the factors mentioned above? We really do not know! It could be due to one or the other or a combination of both.

A better way to perform this test would be to use Dependent samples, a procedure which has a built-in ability to remove the effect of all the above mentioned other factors and thus attribute any measured differences to product differences only. To accomplish this, we put both brands of tire on the same car, thus eliminating all the other factors. We repeat this with several cars. After a car is driven for some time, the tire thread thickness of each brand is measured and the difference in the wear of the 2 brand tires is obtained, by subtracting the two measured values. When all such differences, d_i, are analyzed as explained earlier, the hypothesis testing and confidence interval problems can be solved using the procedures discussed previously.

As a numerical illustration of these procedures consider the chart below, showing the amount of wear (in thousands of an inch) that took place. One tire of each brand was placed on each of 6 cars. The position of each tire was determined randomly, to eliminate the possibility of favoring one tire over the other. (Use $\alpha = 0.05$)

Car	1	2	3	4	5	6
Brand A	125	64	94	38	90	106
Brand B	133	65	103	37	102	115

Now construct a new row to this table, with entries obtained from: $d_i = $ Brand B_i − Brand A_i, to obtain:

Car	1	2	3	4	5	6
$d_i = B_i - A_i$	8	1	9	−1	12	9

Then we have: $\sum_{i=1}^{n} d_i = 8 + 1 + 9 - 1 + 12 + 9 = 38$

$$\sum_{i=1}^{n} d_i^2 = 8^2 + 1^2 + 9^2 + (-1)^2 + 12^2 + 9^2 = 372$$

from which we calculate:

$$\bar{d} = \sum_{i=1}^{n} d_i/n = 38/6 = 6.33 \tag{11.137}$$

$$\hat{s}_d^2 = \frac{n \sum_{i=1}^{n} d_i^2 - (\sum_{i=1}^{n} d_i^2)^2}{n(n-1)} = \frac{6(372) - (38)^2}{6(5)} = 26.27$$

Then: $\sigma^2(\bar{d}) = \hat{s}^2/n = 26.27/6 = 4.3783$, and $\sigma(\bar{d}) = 2.09 \tag{11.138}$

Solution to the Hypothesis Testing Problem

1. $H_0: \mu_d = 0$ vs $H_1: \mu_d \neq 0$
2. $\alpha = 0.05$
3. The estimator for μ_d is $\bar{d}$, and $\bar{d}/\sigma(\bar{d})$ is $t_{n-1} = t_5$.
4. Rejection Region

$$t_{5(0.975)} = -t_5(0.025) = -2.5706 \qquad t_{n-1}(\alpha/2) = t_5(0.025) = 2.5706$$

5. Value of test statistic $= t^* = \overline{d}/\sigma(\overline{d}) = 6.33/2.09 = 3.03$
6. Since $t^* = 3.03$ falls in the rejection region, we reject H_0.
7. Rejecting H_0 means that there is a difference in the "wearability" of the tires. Therefore, the tires are different.

Solution to the Confidence Interval Problem

Use equation (11.136) with: $\overline{d} = 6.33$, $t_{n-1}(\sigma/2) = t_5(0.025) = 2.5706$, $\sigma(\overline{d}) = 2.09$, and $1 - \alpha = 0.95. = 0.95$. When these quantities are substituted in (11.136), we obtain:

$$P[6.33 - 2.5706(2.09) \leq \mu_d \leq 6.33 + 2.5706(2.09)] = 0.95$$

or $\qquad P[0.96 \leq \mu_d \leq 11.70] = 0.95$

Since the hypothesized value, $\mu_d = 0$, is outside of this interval, the 2 brands of tires are different!

But, can we tell which tire is better? Yes! Since the better tire wears out less, and from the d_i row we see that tire B wears out more than tire A (because of the many positive differences), we conclude that Tire A is Better!

We can also arrive at the same conclusion by calculating $\overline{x}_A$ and $\overline{x}_B$ from the data for tires A and B separately. Since $\overline{x}_A = 87.833$ and $\overline{x}_B = 94.167$ and $\overline{x}_B > \overline{x}_A$, tire B wears out more on the average than tire A and, therefore, tire A is better than tire B.

■ ■ ■

11.4 Summary of Testing Procedures

The hypothesis testing procedures and confidence intervals we discussed in this chapter can be summarized as follows:

11.4.1 Testing the Parameters of a Single Population

1. If we are testing: H_0: $\mu = \mu_0 (= 100$, for example) vs H_1: $\mu \neq \mu_0$

   a) Use the 7-step procedure and the Z distribution if:
      i) σ of the population is known, regardless of the value of n
      ii) σ of the population is not known, but $n > 30$

   The corresponding confidence intervals are:

   $$\text{i)} \quad P\left[\overline{x} - Z_{\alpha/2}\frac{\sigma}{\sqrt{n}} \leq \mu \leq \overline{x} + Z_{\alpha/2}\frac{\sigma}{\sqrt{n}}\right] = 1 - \alpha \qquad (11.139)$$

   $$\text{ii)} \quad P\left[\overline{x} - Z_{\alpha/2}\frac{\hat{s}}{\sqrt{n}} \leq \mu \leq \overline{x} + Z_{\alpha/2}\frac{\hat{s}}{\sqrt{n}}\right] = 1 - \alpha \qquad (11.140)$$

   b) Use the 7-step procedure and the t_{n-1} distribution if: σ of the population is not known and $n < 30$. The corresponding confidence interval is:

   $$P\left[\overline{x} - t_{n-1}(\alpha/2)\frac{\hat{s}}{\sqrt{n}} \leq \mu \leq \overline{x} + t_{n-1}(\alpha/2)\frac{\hat{s}}{\sqrt{n}}\right] = 1 - \alpha \qquad (11.141)$$

2. If we are testing: H_0: $\sigma_1^2 = \sigma_0^2$ ($= 64$, for example) vs H_1 $\sigma_1^2 \neq \sigma_0^2$

   a) Use the 7-step procedure and the χ_{n-1}^2 distribution if $n < 30$. The corresponding confidence interval is:

   $$P\left[\frac{(n-1)\hat{s}^2}{\chi_{n-1}^2(\alpha/2)} \leq \sigma^2 \leq \frac{(n-1)\hat{s}^2}{\chi_{n-1}^2(1-\alpha/2)}\right] = 1 - \alpha \qquad (11.142)$$

   b) Use the 7-step procedure and the Z distribution if $n \geq 30$. This means that the variable:

   $$\chi_{n-1}^2 = \frac{(n-1)\hat{s}^2}{\sigma^2} \text{ is } Z\text{-distributed, when } n \geq 30, \text{ with}$$

   $$E\left(\chi_{n-1}^2\right) = n - 1 \text{ and } V\left(\chi_{n-1}^2\right) = 2(n-1), \text{ and } \sigma\left(\chi_{n-1}^2\right) = \sqrt{2(n-1)} \qquad (11.143)$$

   Then $\dfrac{\chi_{n-1}^2 - E(\chi_{n-1}^2)}{\sigma(\chi_{n-1}^2)} = \dfrac{\dfrac{(n-1)\hat{s}^2}{\sigma^2} - (n-1)}{\sqrt{2(n-1)}} = \dfrac{\hat{s}^2 - \sigma^2}{\sigma^2\sqrt{\dfrac{2}{n-1}}} = \dfrac{\hat{s}^2 - E(\hat{s}^2)}{\sigma(\hat{s}^2)}, \qquad (11.144)$

   Where $\sigma\left(\hat{s}^2\right) = \sigma^2\sqrt{\dfrac{2}{n-1}} = \sqrt{\dfrac{2\sigma^4}{n-1}}$

   is Z-distributed $\left(\text{just as } \dfrac{\overline{x} - E(\overline{x})}{\sigma(\overline{x})} = \dfrac{\overline{x} - \mu}{\sigma/\sqrt{n}} \text{ is } Z\text{-distributed.}\right)$

   The corresponding confidence interval, assuming $\sigma\left(\hat{s}^2\right) \approx \hat{s}^2\sqrt{\dfrac{2}{n-1}}$, is given by:

   $$P\left[\hat{s}^2 - Z_{\alpha/2} \cdot \sigma(\hat{s}^2) \leq \sigma^2 \leq \hat{s}^2 + Z_{\alpha/2} \cdot \sigma(\hat{s}^2)\right] = 1 - \alpha \qquad (11.145)$$

3. If we are testing H_0: $\sigma = \sigma_0$ ($= 8$, for example) vs H_1: $\sigma \neq \sigma_0$

   Convert the given hypothesis to H_0: $\sigma^2 = \sigma_0^2$ vs H_1: $\sigma^2 \neq \sigma_0^2$, and then use the procedures in 11.4.1.2 above.

   This is necessary because we do not know the sampling distribution of the estimator for σ, $\hat{s}$, while we know the sampling distribution of the estimator for σ^2, $\hat{s}^2$ (*i.e.*, we know that: $\chi_{n-1}^2 = \dfrac{(n-1)\hat{s}^2}{\sigma^2}$ is distributed as a χ^2 variable with $n - 1$ degrees of freedom).

   To construct a confidence interval for σ, take the square root of every term inside the brackets of equation 11.140, and obtain:

   $$P\left[\sqrt{\frac{(n-1)\hat{s}^2}{\chi_{n-1}^2(\alpha/2)}} \leq \sigma \leq \sqrt{\frac{(n-1)\hat{s}^2}{\chi_{n-1}^2(1-\alpha/2)}}\right] = 1 - \alpha \qquad (11.146)$$

11.4.2 Testing the Parameters of 2 Populations

11.4.2.1 If the samples from the 2 Populations (n_1, n_2) are Independent

1. If we are testing: H_0: $\Delta\mu = 0$ vs H_1: $\Delta\mu \neq 0$

   a) Use the 7-step procedure and the Z-distribution if σ_1 and σ_2 are known regardless of the n_1 and n_2 values.

   b) Use the 7-step procedure and the Z-distribution if σ_1 and σ_2 are not known, but: $n_1 \geq 30$ and $n_2 \geq 30$.

   c) Use the 7-step procedure and the $t_{n1+n2-2}$ distribution for all other cases, under the assumption that, even though σ_1 and σ_2 are not known, they are assumed to be equal (*i.e.*, assume that $\sigma_1^2 = \sigma_2^2 = \sigma^2$, where σ^2 is unknown in value).

Note: Without the assumption that $\sigma_1^2 = \sigma_2^2$ this problem has no solution.

Therefore, before solving problem (c) above, test the hypothesis: H_0: $\sigma_1^2 = \sigma_2^2$

vs H_1: $\sigma_1^2 \neq \sigma_2^2$ Then, if this H_0 is not rejected, problem (c) can be solved. If H_0 is rejected, the solution to problem (c) cannot be obtained.

The corresponding confidence intervals are:

i) $P\left[\Delta \bar{x} - Z_{\alpha/2}\sqrt{\dfrac{\sigma_1^2}{n_1} + \dfrac{\sigma_2^2}{n_2}} \leq \Delta\mu \leq \Delta\bar{x} + Z_{\alpha/2}\sqrt{\dfrac{\sigma_1^2}{n_1} + \dfrac{\sigma_2^2}{n_2}}\right] = 1-\alpha$ (11.147)

ii) $P\left[\Delta \bar{x} - Z_{\alpha/2}\sqrt{\dfrac{\hat{s}_1^2}{n_1} + \dfrac{\hat{s}_2^2}{n_2}} \leq \Delta\mu \leq \Delta\bar{x} + Z_{\alpha/2}\sqrt{\dfrac{\hat{s}_1^2}{n_1} + \dfrac{\hat{s}_2^2}{n_2}}\right] = 1-\alpha$ (11.148)

iii) $P\left[\Delta \bar{x} - t_{n_1+n_2-2}(\alpha/2)\cdot\sigma(\Delta\bar{x}) \leq \Delta\mu \leq \Delta\bar{x} + t_{n_1+n_2-2}(\alpha/2)\cdot\sigma(\Delta\bar{x})\right]$

$= 1 - \alpha$ (11.149)

where $\sigma(\Delta\bar{x}) = \sqrt{\left(\dfrac{n_1+n_2}{n_1\cdot n_2}\right)\left[\dfrac{(n_1-1)\hat{s}_1^2 + (n_1-1)\hat{s}_2^2}{n_1+n_2-2}\right]}$ (11.150)

2. If we are testing H_0: $\sigma_1^2 = \sigma_2^2$ vs H_1: $\sigma_1^2 \neq \sigma_2^2$

    a) Use the 7-step procedure and the Z-distribution if $n_1 \geq 30$ and $n_2 \geq 30$. (preferably $n_1 \geq 100$ and $n_2 \geq 100$), by reformulating the hypothesis as:

$$H_0:\ \Delta\sigma^2\ (= \sigma_1^2 - \sigma_2^2) = 0 \text{ vs } H_1: \Delta\sigma^2 \neq 0$$

    b) Use the 7-step procedure and the $F_{\delta_2}^{\delta_1}$-distribution if:

      i) $n_1 \geq 30$ but $n_2 < 30$

      ii) $n_1 < 30$ but $n_2 \geq 30$

      iii) $n_1 < 30$ and $n_2 < 30$

    by reformulating the original hypothesis $\left(H_0: \sigma_1^2 = \sigma_2^2 \text{ vs } H_1: \sigma_1^2 \neq \sigma_2^2\right)$ as:

    i) H_0: $\dfrac{\sigma_1^2}{\sigma_2^2} = 1$ vs H_1: $\dfrac{\sigma_1^2}{\sigma_2^2} \neq 1$ or ii) H_0: $\dfrac{\sigma_2^2}{\sigma_1^2} = 1$ vs H_1: $\dfrac{\sigma_2^2}{\sigma_1^2} \neq 1$

The corresponding confidence intervals are:

a) $P\left[\Delta\hat{s}^2 - Z_{\alpha/2}\cdot\sigma(\Delta\hat{s}^2) \leq \Delta\sigma^2 \leq \Delta\hat{s}^2 + Z_{\alpha/2}\cdot\sigma(\Delta\hat{s}^2)\right] = 1 - \alpha$ (11.151)

where $\Delta\hat{s}^2 = \hat{s}_1^2 - \hat{s}_2^2$ and $\sigma(\hat{s}^2) = \sqrt{\dfrac{2\hat{s}_1^4}{n_1-1} + \dfrac{2\hat{s}_2^4}{n_2-1}}$ (11.152)

b) $P\left[\dfrac{\hat{s}_1^2}{\hat{s}_2^2}\dfrac{1}{F_{\delta_2}^{\delta_1}(\alpha/2)} \leq \dfrac{\sigma_1^2}{\sigma_2^2} \leq \dfrac{\hat{s}_1^2}{\hat{s}_2^2}F_{\delta_2}^{\delta_1}(\alpha/2)\right] = 1 - \alpha$ (11.153)

c) $P\left[\dfrac{\hat{s}_2^2}{\hat{s}_1^2}\dfrac{1}{F_{\delta_2}^{\delta_1}(\alpha/2)} \leq \dfrac{\sigma_2^2}{\sigma_1^2} \leq \dfrac{\hat{s}_2^2}{\hat{s}_1^2}F_{\delta_2}^{\delta_1}(\alpha/2)\right] = 1 - \alpha$ (11.154)

11.4.2.2 If the Samples from the 2 Populations are Dependent

In this case, $n_1 = n_2 = n$, and the data are paired. Form the difference: $d_i = x_i - y_i$, and calculate $\bar{d}$ and $\sigma(\bar{d})$. Then test the hypothesis $H_0: \mu_d = 0$ vs $H_1: \mu_d \neq 0$.

1. Use the 7-step procedure and the Z-distribution, if $n \geq 30$.
2. Use the 7-step procedure and the t_{n-1}-distribution, if $n < 30$.

The corresponding confidence intervals are:

1. $P\left[\overline{d} - Z_{\alpha/2}\ \sigma\left(\overline{d}\right) \le \mu_d \le \overline{d} + Z_{\alpha/2}\ \sigma\left(\overline{d}\right)\right] = 1 - \alpha$ (11.155)

2. $P\left[\overline{d} - t_{n-1}\left(\alpha/2\right)\ \sigma\left(\overline{d}\right) \le \mu_d \le \overline{d} + t_{n-1}\left(\alpha/2\right)\sigma\left(\overline{d}\right)\right] = 1 - \alpha$ (11.156)

where
$$\overline{d} = \frac{\sum\limits_{i=1}^{n} d_i}{n}$$ (11.157)

$$\sigma\left(\overline{d}\right) = \sqrt{\frac{\hat{s}_d^2}{n}}$$ (11.158)

and
$$\hat{s}_d^2 = \frac{n\sum\limits_{i=1}^{n} d_i^2 - \left(\sum\limits_{i=1}^{n} d_i\right)^2}{n(n - 1)}$$ (11.159)

11.5 Hypothesis Testing Using the Estimator of the Parameter in H_0 Directly

The hypothesis tests we summarized in the previous section, are performed by calculating the corresponding value of the test statistic (*i.e.*, Z^*, t^*, χ^{*2}, F^*, depending on the sampling distribution of the estimator of the parameter appearing in H_0) and comparing it to the rejection region.

The value of the test statistic, which includes the sample value of the estimator of the parameter in H_0, is a numerical value, and it is compared to another numerical value which defines the separation between rejection and non-rejection regions, and is obtained from the statistical table of the appropriate sampling distribution.

Let us perform the following example to illustrate these points again:

Example 8

Test the claim that the population mean is equal to 100, when a sample of $n = 25$ from the population produced a sample mean of $\overline{x} = 102$, when it is known that the population standard deviation is $\sigma = 5$. Use $\alpha = 0.05$,

Solution

1. H_0: $\mu = 100$ vs H_1: $\mu \ne 100$
2. $\alpha = 0.05$
3. The estimator for μ is $\overline{x}$ and, because σ is known, $\dfrac{\overline{x} - 100}{\sigma/\sqrt{n}}$ is $Z(0, 1)$
4. Rejection region:

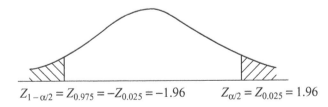

$$Z_{1-\alpha/2} = Z_{0.975} = -Z_{0.025} = -1.96 \qquad Z_{\alpha/2} = Z_{0.025} = 1.96$$

5. Value of test statistic $= Z^* = \dfrac{\overline{x} - \mu_0}{\sigma/\sqrt{n}} = \dfrac{102 - 100}{5/\sqrt{25}} = \dfrac{2}{5/5} = 2$

6. Since $Z^* = 2 > Z_{0.025} = 1.96$, H_0 is rejected.

7. The population mean is different than 100, under the stated conditions.

■ ■ ■

Now we want to restate the problem as follows: For what values of the sample mean $(\bar{x})$ is the above H_0 not rejected or rejected, (since the two are complementary events)?

To solve this revised problem, we do not substitute the numerical value for the estimator $(\bar{x})$ of the population parameter (μ) when calculating the value of the test statistic in step 5, which now becomes:

$$Z^* = \frac{\bar{x} - 100}{1} = \bar{x} - 100$$

Then we compare Z^* to the rejection region of step 4, and by inspection we conclude that:

To not reject H_0 we must have:

$$Z_{1-\alpha/2} \leq Z^* = \frac{\bar{x} - \mu_0}{\sigma/\sqrt{n}} \leq Z_{\alpha/2} \tag{11.160}$$

which, when solved for $\bar{x}$, becomes:

$$-\frac{\sigma}{\sqrt{n}} Z_{\alpha/2} \leq \bar{x} - \mu_0 \leq \frac{\sigma}{\sqrt{n}} Z_{\alpha/2}$$

and finally

$$\mu_0 - \frac{\sigma}{\sqrt{n}} Z_{\alpha/2} \leq \bar{x} \leq \mu_0 + \frac{\sigma}{\sqrt{n}} Z_{\alpha/2} \tag{11.161}$$

1. When the known numerical values $\left(\mu_0 = 100, \quad \frac{\sigma}{\sqrt{n}} = \frac{5}{\sqrt{25}} = \frac{5}{5} = 1, \right.$

$\left. Z_{\alpha/2} = Z_{0.025} = 1.96 \right)$ are substituted in (11.161), we obtain:

$100 - (1)(1.96) \leq \bar{x} \leq 100 + (1)(1.96)$ or $98.04 \leq \bar{x} \leq 101.96$

Therefore, H_0 will not be rejected if the value of $\bar{x}$ is between 98.04 and 101.96, but will be rejected if $\bar{x} > 101.96$ (as is the case for $\bar{x} = 102$) or if $\bar{x} < 98.04$.

The complementary statement to (11.161) is:

Reject H_0 if $\qquad\qquad\qquad \bar{x} > \mu_0 + \frac{\sigma}{\sqrt{n}} \tag{11.162}$

or if: $\qquad\qquad\qquad\qquad \bar{x} > \mu_0 - \frac{\sigma}{\sqrt{n}} \tag{11.163}$

Similar formulas can be written for the other hypothesis tests.

2. For instance, if in the above example, the σ of the population is not known and must be replaced by the unbiased sample standard deviation $\hat{s}$, the sampling distribution of $\frac{\bar{x} - \mu_0}{\hat{s}/\sqrt{n}}$ is t_{n-1}, because $n < 30$.

Therefore, H_0 will not be rejected if:

$$\mu_0 - \frac{\hat{s}}{\sqrt{n}} t_{n-1}(\alpha/2) \leq \bar{x} \leq \mu_0 + \frac{\hat{s}}{\sqrt{n}} t_{n-1}(\alpha/2) \tag{11.164}$$

3. The hypothesis H_0: $\sigma_1^2 = \sigma_0^2$ $(=100)$ vs H_1: $\sigma_1^2 \neq \sigma_0^2$ will not be rejected if

$$\chi^2_{n-1,\, 1-\alpha/2} \leq \frac{(n-1)\hat{s}^2}{\sigma^2} \leq \chi^2_{n-1,\, \alpha/2} \qquad (11.165)$$

from which we obtain the allowable interval of variation of $\hat{s}^2$ (and $\hat{s}$), in order for H_0 not to be rejected, and which is given by:

$$\frac{\sigma^2}{n-1}\chi^2_{n-1,\, 1-\alpha/2} \leq \hat{s}^2 \leq \frac{\sigma^2}{n-1}\chi^2_{n-1,\, \alpha/2} \qquad (11.166)$$

and
$$\sqrt{\frac{\sigma^2}{n-1}\chi^2_{n-1,\, 1-\alpha/2}} \leq \hat{s} \leq \sqrt{\frac{\sigma}{n-1}\chi^2_{n-1,\, \alpha/2}} \qquad (11.167)$$

4. The hypothesis H_0: $\Delta\mu = 0$ vs H_1: $\Delta\mu \neq 0$ will not be rejected if:

a) $-Z_{\alpha/2} \leq \dfrac{\Delta\overline{x}}{\sigma(\Delta\overline{x})} \leq Z_{\alpha/2}$ or $-Z_{\alpha/2}\,\sigma(\Delta\overline{x}) \leq \Delta\overline{x} \leq Z_{\alpha/2}\,\sigma(\Delta\overline{x})$ (11.168)

b) $-t_{n1+n2-2} \leq \dfrac{\Delta\overline{x}}{\sigma(\Delta\overline{x})} \leq t_{n1+n2-2}$ or

$\quad -t_{n1+n2-2}\,\sigma(\Delta\overline{x}) \leq \Delta\overline{x} \leq t_{n1+n2-2}\,\sigma(\Delta\overline{x})$ (11.169)

depending on whether $\dfrac{\Delta\overline{x}}{\sigma(\Delta\overline{x})}$ is $Z_{\alpha/2}$ or $t_{n1+n2-2}$. In each case the appropriate $\sigma(\Delta\overline{x})$ must be used as given in (11.148) and (11.150) respectively.

In (11.168) and (11.169), if one of the sample means $(\overline{x}_1, \overline{x}_2)$, which define $\Delta\overline{x} = \overline{x}_1 - \overline{x}_2$, is fixed to a specific numerical value, an interval of values can be obtained for the other sample mean, for H_0 not to be rejected.

5. The Hypothesis H_0: $\Delta\sigma^2 = 0$ vs H_1: $\Delta\sigma^2 \neq 0$, will not be rejected if:

$$-Z_{\alpha/2} \leq \frac{\Delta\hat{s}^2}{\sigma(\Delta\hat{s}^2)} \leq Z_{\alpha/2}$$

or $\qquad -Z_{\alpha/2}\cdot\sigma(\Delta\hat{s}^2) \leq \Delta\hat{s}^2 \leq Z_{\alpha/2}\cdot\sigma(\Delta\hat{s}^2) \qquad (11.170)$

in which $\qquad \sigma(\Delta\hat{s}^2) = \sqrt{\dfrac{2\hat{s}_1^4}{n_1-1} + \dfrac{2\hat{s}_2^4}{n_2-1}}$

Again, if one of the unbiased sample variances $(\hat{s}_1^2, \hat{s}_2^2)$ is fixed to a specific numerical value, an interval of values can be obtained for the other unbiased sample variance, for H_0 not to be rejected.

6. The hypothesis:

$$H_0\text{: } \frac{\sigma_1^2}{\sigma_2^2} = 1 \text{ vs } H_1\text{: } \frac{\sigma_1^2}{\sigma_2^2} \neq 1 \qquad \text{or} \qquad H_0\text{: } \frac{\sigma_2^2}{\sigma_1^2} = 1 \text{ vs } H_1\text{: } \frac{\sigma_2^2}{\sigma_1^2} \neq 1$$

will not be rejected if:

$$\frac{\sigma_1^2}{\sigma_2^2}\, F^{\delta_1}_{\delta_2}(1-\alpha/2) = \frac{\sigma_1^2/\sigma_2^2}{F^{\delta_2}_{\delta_1}(\alpha/2)} \leq \frac{\hat{s}_1^2}{\hat{s}_2^2} \leq F^{\delta_1}_{\delta_2}(\alpha/2)\frac{\sigma_1^2}{\sigma_2^2} \qquad (11.171)$$

or $\qquad \dfrac{\sigma_2^2}{\sigma_1^2}\, F^{\delta_2}_{\delta_1}(1-\alpha/2) = \dfrac{\sigma_2^2/\sigma_1^2}{F^{\delta_1}_{\delta_2}(\alpha/2)} \leq \dfrac{\hat{s}_2^2}{\hat{s}_1^2} \leq F^{\delta_2}_{\delta_1}(\alpha/2)\dfrac{\sigma_2^2}{\sigma_1^2} \qquad (11.172)$

In (11.171) and (11.172) if one of the unbiased sample variances ($\hat{s}_1^2$, $\hat{s}_2^2$) is fixed to a specific numerical value, an interval of values can be obtained for the other unbiased sample variance, for H_0 not be rejected.

7. The hypothesis: H_0: $\mu_d = 0$ vs H_1: $\mu_d \neq 0$, will not be rejected if:

$$-t_{n-1}(\alpha/2) \leq \frac{\overline{d}}{\sigma(\overline{d})} \leq t_{n-1}(\alpha/2)$$

or

$$-\sigma(\overline{d}) \cdot t_{n-1}(\alpha/2) \leq \overline{d} \leq \sigma(\overline{d}) \cdot t_{n-1}(\alpha/2) \qquad (11.173)$$

where $\sigma(\overline{d}) = \sqrt{\dfrac{1}{n}\left[\dfrac{n\sum\limits_{i=1}^{n}d_i^2 - (\sum\limits_{i=1}^{n}d_i)^2}{n(n-1)}\right]} = \sqrt{\dfrac{1}{n}(\hat{s}_d^2)} = \dfrac{\hat{s}_d}{\sqrt{n}}$

A similar approach can be used to calculate the interval of variation for the estimator of any population parameter we use in H_0, provided that the sampling distribution of its estimator is known.

11.6 Testing the Equality of μ and σ^2 of 3 or More Populations

The tests we have discussed up to now in this chapter concern:

1. The testing of the parameters of a single population (μ, σ^2, σ) against a fixed value (*i.e.*, $\mu = 100$, $\sigma^2 = 64$, $\sigma = 8$) or

2. The testing of the equality of the parameters of 2 populations (*i.e.*, $\mu_1 = \mu_2$, $\sigma_1^2 = \sigma_2^2$, $\sigma_1 = \sigma_2$).

However, if we need to test the equality of the parameters of 3 or more populations, we need to develop and discuss new or additional methods, as shown below:

11.6.1 Testing the Equality of the Means of 3 or More Populations

The pair of hypothesis to be tested in this case are (assuming k populations):

$$H_0: \mu_1 = \mu_2 = \mu_3 = \cdots = \mu_k \text{ vs } H_1: \text{At least 2 means are different.} \quad (11.174)$$

To complete this hypothesis test we need to develop a new and different method, which is known as the Analysis Of Variance (or ANOVA) methodology, and this methodology is discussed extensively in the next chapter.

11.6.2 Testing the Equality of the Variances of 3 or More Populations

We showed previously that to test the equality of the variances of 2 populations (*i.e.*, H_0: $\sigma_1^2 = \sigma_2^2$ vs H_1: $\sigma_1^2 \neq \sigma_2^2$), we use either:

1. The normal distribution if $n_1 \geq 30$ and $n_2 \geq 30$ (and preferably $n_1 \geq 100$ and $n_2 \geq 100$)

or 2. The $F_{n_2-1}^{n_1-1}$ distribution for all other cases.

To test the more general case that the variances of k ($k \geq 3$) populations are equal (under the assumption that the k populations are normally distributed or approximately normally distributed) we use the BARLETT TEST for HOMOGENEITY OF VARIANCES, and test the pair of hypotheses:

$$H_0: \sigma_1^2 = \sigma_2^2 = \sigma_3^3 \cdots = \sigma_k^2 \text{ vs } H_1: \text{At least 2 variances differ} \quad (11.175)$$

To complete the testing of this pair of hypotheses, we do the following:

1. Obtain independent samples of sizes: $n_1, n_2, n_3, \ldots, n_k$, from the k populations.

2. Calculate the k unbiased sample variances $(\hat{s}_1^2, \hat{s}_2^2, \hat{s}_3^2, \ldots, \hat{s}_k^2)$ from the k independent samples.

3. Calculate the Barlett Test Statistic, B, from:

$$B = \frac{\left[\sum_{i=1}^{k}(n_i - 1)\right]\ln\left[\dfrac{\sum_{i=1}^{k}(n_i - 1)\hat{s}_i^2}{\sum_{i=1}^{k}(n_i - 1)}\right] - \left[\sum_{i=1}^{k}(n_i - 1)\ln \hat{s}_i^2\right]}{1 + \dfrac{1}{3(k - 1)}\left[\sum_{i=1}^{k}\dfrac{1}{(n_i - 1)} - \dfrac{1}{\sum_{i=1}^{k}(n_i - 1)}\right]} \quad (11.176)$$

$$\text{or } B = \frac{\left[(n_1-1)+(n_2-1)+(n_3-1)+\cdots+(n_k-1)\right]\cdot\ln\left[\dfrac{(n_1-1)\hat{s}_1^2+(n_2-1)\hat{s}_2^2+(n_3-1)\hat{s}_3^2+\cdots+(n_k-1)\hat{s}_k^2}{(n_1-1)+(n_2-1)(n_3-1)+\cdots+(n_k-1)}\right]}{1+\dfrac{1}{3(k-1)}\left[\dfrac{1}{(n_1-1)}+\dfrac{1}{(n_2-1)}+\cdots+\dfrac{1}{(n_k-1)}-\dfrac{1}{(n_1-1)+(n_2-1)+\cdots+(n_k-1)}\right]}$$

$$-\frac{\left[(n_1-1)\ln\hat{s}_1^2+(n_2-1)\ln\hat{s}_2^2+(n_3-1)\ln-\hat{s}_3^2+\cdots+(n_k-1)\ln\hat{s}_k^2\right]}{1+\dfrac{1}{3(k-1)}\left[\dfrac{1}{(n_1-1)}+\dfrac{1}{(n_2-1)}+\cdots+\dfrac{1}{(n_k-1)}-\dfrac{1}{(n_1-1)+(n_2-1)+\cdots+(n_k-1)}\right]}$$

4. The test statistic B, under the H_0 hypothesis of equal variances has a sampling distribution which is chi-square with $k - 1$ degrees of freedom (*i.e.*, B is χ_{k-1}^2).
5. The rejection region, for a given α value, consists of the upper tail of the χ_{k-1}^2 distribution (*i.e.*, $\chi_{k-1}^2(\alpha)$).
6. The decision rule is:

a) Do not reject H_0 if $B \leq \chi_{k-1}^2(\alpha)$ \hfill (11.177)

b) Reject H_0 if $B > \chi_{k-1}^2(\alpha)$ \hfill (11.178)

Example 9
Testing the Equality of 3 Population Variances
Suppose we want to test the equality of the variances of 3 populations, *i.e.*, we want to test the hypothesis $H_0: \sigma_1^2 = \sigma_2^2 = \sigma_3^3$ vs H_1: The three variances are not all equal to each other. Assume that random sampling from the 3 populations produced the following results:

$$\text{Population 1: } n_1 = 16 \text{ and } \hat{s}_1^2 = 10$$
$$\text{Population 2: } n_2 = 21 \text{ and } \hat{s}_2^2 = 7$$
$$\text{Population 3: } n_3 = 26 \text{ and } \hat{s}_3^2 = 4$$

Problem Is H_0 rejected or not rejected on the basis of this sample information, when $\alpha = 0.1, 0.05, 0.025,$ 0.01, 0.005?

Solution						Calculations
Population i	n_i	$n_i - 1$	$\hat{s}_i^2$	$(n_i - 1)\hat{s}_i^2$	$\ln \hat{s}_i^2$	$(n_i - 1)\ln \hat{s}_i^2$
1	16	15	10	150	2.302585	34.538776
2	21	20	7	140	1.945910	38.918203
3	26	25	4	100	1.386294	34.657359
		$\sum_{i=1}^{3}(n_i - 1) = 60$		$\sum_{i=1}^{3}(n_i - 1)\hat{s}_i^2 = 390$		$\sum_{i=1}^{3}(n_i - 1)\ln \hat{s}_i^2 = 108.114$

$$\sum_{i=1}^{3}\frac{1}{n_i - 1} = \frac{1}{15} + \frac{1}{20} + \frac{1}{25} = \frac{20 + 15 + 12}{300} = \frac{47}{300} = 0.156667$$

and $\quad \ln\left[\dfrac{\sum_{i=1}^{k}(n_i - 1)\hat{s}_i^2}{\sum_{i=1}^{k}(n_i - 1)}\right] = \ln\left[\dfrac{\sum_{i=1}^{3}(n_i - 1)\hat{s}_i^2}{\sum_{i=1}^{3}(n_i - 1)}\right] = \ln\left[\dfrac{390}{60}\right] = \ln[6.5] = 1.87180$

Then, substituting the above quantities into equation (11.176) we obtain:

$$B = \frac{60(1.87180) - 108.114}{1 + \dfrac{1}{3(3 - 1)}\left[\dfrac{47}{300} - \dfrac{1}{60}\right]} = \frac{112.308 - 108.114}{1 + \dfrac{1}{6}\left[\dfrac{47}{300} - \dfrac{5}{300}\right]} = \frac{4.19413}{1 + \dfrac{1}{6}\left(\dfrac{42}{300}\right)}$$

$$= \frac{4.19413}{1 + \dfrac{7}{300}} = \frac{4.13413}{1 + 0.02333} = \frac{4.13413}{1.02333}$$

$$= 4.03988$$

Since $k = 3$, $\chi_{k-1}^2(\alpha) = \chi_2^2(\alpha) = 4.605 \quad$ if $\quad \alpha = 0.10$

$\hphantom{Since k = 3, \chi_{k-1}^2(\alpha) = \chi_2^2(\alpha)} = 5.991 \quad$ if $\quad \alpha = 0.05$

$\hphantom{Since k = 3, \chi_{k-1}^2(\alpha) = \chi_2^2(\alpha)} = 7.378 \quad$ if $\quad \alpha = 0.025$

$\hphantom{Since k = 3, \chi_{k-1}^2(\alpha) = \chi_2^2(\alpha)} = 9.210 \quad$ if $\quad \alpha = 0.01$

$\hphantom{Since k = 3, \chi_{k-1}^2(\alpha) = \chi_2^2(\alpha)} = 10.597 \quad$ if $\quad \alpha = 0.005$

Since $B < \chi_2^2(\alpha)$, for all these values of α, H_0 is not rejected, and we conclude that the variances of these 3 populations are equal.

Therefore, we conclude that $\sigma_1^2 = \sigma_2^2 = \sigma_3^3$.

■ ■ ■

11.7   References

Berenson, Marc, L., Levine, David, M., and Krehbiel, Timothy, C. 2004 *Basic Business Statistics*. 9th Edition, Pearson-Prentice Hall.

Black, Ken 2004 *Business Statistics*. 4th Edition, Wiley.

Canavos, George, C., 1984. *Applied Probability and Statistical Methods*. Little, Brown.

Carlson, William, L., and Thorne, Betty, 1997. *Applied Statistical Methods*. Prentice Hall.

Chou, Ya-lun, 1992. *Statistical Analysis for Business and Economics*. Elsevier.

Freund, John, E., and Williams, Frank, J., 1969. *Modern Business Statistics*. Revised by: Perles, Benjamin and Sullivan, Charles. Prentice-Hall.

Freund, John, E., and Williams, Frank, J., 1982. *Elementary Business Statistics: The Modern approach*. Prentice-Hall.

Johnson, Robert, 1973. *Elementary Statistics*. Duxbury Press.

McClave, James, T., Benson, George, P., and Sincich, Terry, 2001. *Statistics for Business and Economics*. 8th Edition. Prentice Hall.

Salvatore, Dominick, *Theory and Problems of Statistics and Econometrics*. SCHAUM'S OUTLINE SERIES, McGraw-Hill.

Steel, Robert, G.D., and Torrie, James, H., 1976. *Introduction to Statistics*. McGraw-Hill.

11.8 PROBLEMS

1. The standard deviation of the average daily wages of psychiatrists in New York is known to be $15.00 (Each psychiatrist has his own average daily wage, and the standard deviation of these is $15.00). A random sample of 100 psychiatrists, taken with replacement, yielded a mean daily wage of $160.

   Find: a) 95% confidence interval.

          b) 99% confidence interval, on the population mean μ.

2. The same vocational interest test was given to 50 salesmen of company A and to 50 of company B, and the following results were obtained:

   Company A: $\bar{x}_1 = 73.6$ and $\hat{s}_1 = 10$, $n_A = 50$

   Company B: $\bar{x}_2 = 72.4$ and $\hat{s}_2 = 8$, $n_B = 50$

   Assuming independent samples, find the 90% interval estimate for the true difference in average points scored between the salesmen in companies A and B.

3. A manufacturer of batteries claims that the mean life of his product will exceed 30 hours. A customer wants to buy a large quantity of these batteries if the claim is true. A random sample of 36 is tested, and produces a mean of 34 hours. If the standard deviation is 5 hours, and H_0: is H_0: $\mu \leq 30$, will the batteries be purchased at:

   a) $\alpha = 0.05$? b) $\alpha = 0.01$?

4. A sample of 80 steel wires produced by factory A yields a mean breaking strength of 1230 pounds, with a standard deviation of 120 pounds. A sample of 100 wires of factory B yields a mean breaking strength of 1190 pounds and a standard deviation of 90 lbs.

   a) Verify that, for this problem, $Z^* = 2.48$

   b) Is there a real difference in mean strengths of the two makes of steel wires at $\alpha = 0.05$ and $\alpha = 0.01$?

5. The claim is made that the average grade in a statistics class is 78.3. A sample of 38 students gave a sample mean of 74.3. The population has a standard deviation of $\sigma = 14$.

   a) Test this claim at $\alpha = 0.02$.

   b) Construct a 98% confidence interval for μ.

   c) Are the results in (*a*) and (*b*) the same? Why or why not? Be specific!

   d) For what values of $\bar{x}$ will H_0 be rejected? Be specific!

6. Two state-supported universities have distinct methods of registering students. The two universities wish to compare the average time it takes students to go through registration. The registration times of 100 randomly selected students were observed at each university and the following sample information was obtained.

   University 1: $\bar{x}_1 = 50.2$ and $\hat{s}_1 = 4.8$, $n_1 = 100$

   University 2: $\bar{x}_2 = 52.9$ and $\hat{s}_2 = 5.4$, $n_2 = 100$

a) Is the mean registration time of the two universities the same, based on the above sample information? Use $\alpha = 0.05$.

b) Construct a 95% confidence interval for the difference of mean registration times at the 2 universities.

c) Are the results in (a) and (b) the same? Why or why not? Be specific!

d) For what values of $\Delta \bar{x}$ is H_0 not rejected? Be specific!

7. a) Using the sample information:

$n = 10; x_1 + x_2 + \cdots + x_{10} = 492.50$ and $x_1^2 + x_2^2 + \cdots + x_{10}^2 = 24{,}402.75$
Estimate the cost of dinner in a major city, with a 90% confidence interval on μ (the mean cost).

b) How does this interval change if the sample information is:

$n = 15; x_1 + x_2 + \cdots + x_{15} = 492.50$ and $x_1^2 + x_2^2 + \cdots + x_{15}^2 = 24{,}402.75$

c) Using the information of (a) above, construct a 95% C.I. on μ.

8. Suppose that there are two products under purchase consideration. Both products have similar other characteristics, but we are not sure about their respective warm-up variances. Are they equal or not?

A sample of 64 items from products 1, yielded a variance of 16, while a sample of 36 items from product 2, yielded a variance of 12.

a) Test this claim at both $\alpha = 0.05$ and $\alpha = 0.01$.

b) Construct 95% and 99% C.I. on the appropriate population parameter.

c) Are the results in (a) and (b) the same? Why or why not? Be specific!

9. A standard machine produces 1-inch bolts with a variance of 0.0006. A random sample of 25 bolts produced by a new machine yields a sample variance of 0.0005. The manufacturer is willing to buy the new machine if he can "prove", using $\alpha = 0.05$, that it produces 1-inch bolts with equal variance.

a) Test this hypothesis at $\alpha = 0.05$.

b) Construct 95% C.I. for σ^2 and σ.

c) Are the results in (a) and (b) the same? Why or why not? Be specific!

10. Suppose there are two sources of raw materials under consideration. Both sources seem to have similar characteristics, but we are not sure about their respective variances. Are they equal or not?

A sample of 10 lots from source A yields a variance of 328, and a sample of 11 lots from source B yields a variance of 134.

a) Test this claim at both $\alpha = 0.05$ and $\alpha = 0.10$.

b) Construct C.I. (95% and 90%) for $\dfrac{\sigma_A^2}{\sigma_B^2}$ and $\dfrac{\sigma_B^2}{\sigma_A^2}$.

c) Are the results in (a) and (b) the same? Why or why not? Be specific!

11. A sample of 10 measurements of the diameter of a spherical machined part gives a mean of 4.08 inches and a standard deviation of 0.05 inch.

a) Are these results consistent with the fact that the manufacturing process is expected to produce parts with diameter $\mu = 4$ at $\alpha = 0.05$?

b) Construct 95% C.I. on μ.

c) Are the results in parts (a) and (b) the same? Why or why not? Be specific!

12. Two working designs are under consideration for adoption in a plant. A time and motion study shows that 12 workers using design A have a mean assembly time of 300 seconds, with a standard deviation of 12 seconds, and that 15 workers using design B have a mean assembly time of 335 seconds with a standard deviation of 15 seconds.

a) Test the claim that the means of the 2 designs are the same, at $\alpha = 0.01$

b) Construct a 99% C.I. on the parameter $\Delta\mu = \mu_A - \mu_B$

c) Are the results in (a) and (b) the same? Why or why not? Be specific!

13. To compare the efficiency of standard and electric type-writers, 8 typists are chosen at random, being thoroughly familiar with both kinds of typewriters. Then they are asked to type on each kind of typewriter for 10 minutes, and their speeds, measured as average number of words per minute, are observed. The results of this experiment are shown below:

Typist	1	2	3	4	5	6	7	8
Electric	75	89	79	85	102	115	97	69
Standard	79	62	54	67	81	78	66	73

a) Are the 2 types of typewriters the "same" at $\alpha = 0.01$?

b) Construct a 99% C.I. on the mean difference between the paired data.

c) Are the results in (a) and (b) the same? Why or why not? Be specific!

14. An investor wishes to compare the risks associated with 2 different stocks, A and B. The risk of a given stock is measured by the variance of the daily price changes. The investor believes that the risk associated with stock A is the same as that of stock B. Random samples of 21 daily price changes for stock A and 16 daily price changes of stock B, produced the following results:

$$\text{Stock } A: \overline{x}_A = 0.3, \ \hat{s}_A = 0.25, n_A = 21$$
$$\text{Stock } B: \overline{x}_B = 0.4, \ \hat{s}_B = 0.45, n_B = 16$$

a) Can the investor's belief be substantiated at $\alpha = 0.05$?

b) Construct a 95% C.I. on the ratio: $\dfrac{\sigma_A^2}{\sigma_B^2} = \dfrac{\sigma_1^2}{\sigma_2^2}$

c) Are the results in (a) and (b) the same? Justify!

15. In a given process the desired standard deviation should be 2. A random sample of 25 measurements of this process yielded a standard deviation of 2.8.

a) Determine, at $\alpha = 0.05$, whether the standard deviation is equal to or different from the desired value.

b) Construct a 95% C.I. on the population variance (σ^2).

c) Construct a 95% C.I. on the population standard deviation (σ).

d) Are the results in (a) and (b) the same? Why or why not? Be specific!

16. A cost-of-living survey was conducted for two large cities in a state to determine average grocery expenses for four-person families in the two cities. Twenty such families were randomly selected from each city, and their weekly grocery expenses were observed. The sample means and sample standard deviations are as follows:

$$\overline{x}_1 = 135 \ \overline{x}_2 = 122 \ n_1 = 20$$
$$\hat{s}_1 = 15 \ \hat{s}_2 = 10 \ n_2 = 20$$

If we assume that sampling is from independent normal populations with equal variances:

a) Test the hypothesis that there is no difference in the means of the two populations at $\alpha = 0.05$ and $\alpha = 0.01$ values.

b) Construct 95% and 99% C.I. estimates for the difference of the means of the two populations.

c) Are the conclusions in (a) and (b) identical? Justify your answer! Does a real difference exist between the two means?

17. The Chamber of Commerce in a large city is interested in estimating the average amount of money that people, attending conventions, spend for meals, lodging, and entertainment per day. Sixteen persons were randomly selected from various conventions taking place in this city and were asked to record their expenditures for a given day. The following information was obtained in dollars:

150, 175, 163, 148, 142, 189, 135, 174, 168, 152, 158, 184, 134, 146, 155, 163

If we assume that the amount spent per day is a normally distributed variable:

a) Determine 90%, 95%, and 98% C.I. interval estimates for the true average amount.

b) Determine a 95% C.I. estimate for the unknown variance.

18. Two machine operators are expected to produce, on the average, the same number of finished units over a period of time. The following are the observed number of finished units per day for the two workers over a week's time.

Operator 1	12	11	18	16	13
Operator 2	14	18	18	17	16

Assuming that the number of units produced daily by these workers are independent normally distributed random variables with equal variances:

a) Can you discern a difference in the means at the $\alpha = 0.01$ level? How about at $\alpha = 0.1$?

b) Can you support the contention that the variation in the daily number of finished units for Operator 2 is the same as that for Operator 1 at $\alpha = 0.05$ level?

19. The claim is made that the average grade in statistics is 80. A sample of 16 students gave a sample mean of 74 and a sample standard deviation of $\hat{s} = 8$.
a) Test this claim at $\alpha = 0.01$
b) Construct a 99% C.I. on μ
c) Are the answers in (a) and (b) the same? Why or why not? Be specific!
d) For what values of $\bar{x}$ is the above hypothesis not rejected? Be specific!

20. The standard deviation of average daily wages of psychiatrists in New York is known to be $15. A random sample of 100 psychiatrists, taken with replacement, yielded a sample mean daily wage of $160.00

a) If it is believed that the average daily wage is $162.00, test this claim at $\alpha = 0.02$

b) Construct a 98% C.I. on μ.

c) Are the answers in (a) and (b) the same? Why or why not? Be specific!

21. The specifications for the mass production of a certain spring require that the standard deviation of its compressed length should not exceed 0.04 cm. Use $\alpha = 0.05$ to test the null hypothesis: $H_0: \sigma \leq 0.04$ against $H_1: \sigma > 0.04$ on the basis of a random sample of size $n = 25$ for which $\hat{s} = 0.051$.

22. Sixteen randomly selected citrus trees of one variety have a mean height of $\bar{x}_1 = 14.8$ feet and standard deviation of $\hat{s}_1 = 1.3$ feet, while a sample of 11 randomly selected trees of another variety have a mean height of $\bar{x}_2 = 13.6$ feet and a standard deviation of $\hat{s}_2 = 1.5$ feet. Test, at the $\alpha = 0.10$ level of significance whether the 2 populations sampled have equal variances.

23. Advertisements claim that the average nicotine content of some cigarette is 0.30 milligrams. Suspecting that this figure is too low, a consumer protection service takes a random sample of 15 such cigarettes from different production lots and finds that their nicotine content has a mean of $\bar{x} = 0.33$ milligrams and $\hat{s} = 0.018$ milligrams. Use $\alpha = 0.05$ to:

a) Test the hypothesis: $H_0: \sigma = 0.01$ vs $H_1: \sigma \neq 0.01$.

b) Construct a 95% CI on σ.

24. The following values are the attendance figures in a random sample of 4 games of a minor league baseball team: 4520, 5640, 4460, and 5380.

a) Calculate $\hat{s}$, as an estimate of the standard deviation of the population sampled.

b) Use the range of the data and the following table of d values, as function of n, to

quickly calculate $\hat{s}$ from: $\hat{s} = \dfrac{\text{sample range}}{d}$ and compare the 2 values of $\hat{s}$

obtained in parts (a) and (b).

n	2	3	4	5	6	7	8	9	10	11	12
d	1.13	1.69	2.06	2.33	2.53	2.70	2.85	2.97	3.08	3.17	3.26

c) Use the value of $\hat{s}$, obtained in (b) to construct a 98% C.I. for the population standard deviation, σ.

25. In a random sample of 128 tax returns, the amount due after an audit averaged $400.00 with a standard deviation of $36.00. Use $\alpha = 0.05$ to:

a) Test the hypothesis that $\sigma = 40$ and b) Construct a 95% C.I. on σ.

26. Two different techniques of lighting a store's display window are compared by measuring the intensity of light at a selected location. Suppose a random sample of 10 measurements, using technique 1 has a variance of 2.5 foot-candles and a random sample of 16 measurements, using technique 2, has a variance of 1.25 foot-candles. Using $\alpha = 0.10$;

a) Test the hypothesis $\sigma_1^2 = \sigma_2^2$ against the alternative $\sigma_1^2 \neq \sigma_2^2$

b) Construct a 90% C.I. on the ratio σ_1^2 / σ_2^2

27. A study conducted by an airline at a certain airport showed that 100 of its passengers had to wait on the average 12 minutes with a standard deviation of 2 minutes to get their luggage

a) Test, at the $\alpha = 0.05$ the hypothesis that $\mu = 10$ minutes

b) Construct a 95% C.I. on μ.

c) Are the 2 solutions the same? Justify.

28. To study the viewing habits of its customers, a TV station wishes to estimate the average number of hours a person over 30 spends watching TV per day. If it is known that the standard deviation of this population is $\sigma = 2$, and a sample of $n = 25$ produced an average of $\bar{x} = 8$ hours:

a) Test the hypothesis that $\mu = 10$ at $\alpha = 0.05$.

b) Construct a 95% C.I. on μ.

29. A random sample of 5 is taken to decide if the fat content of a certain kind of ice cream is less than 10 percent. Can the H_0 hypothesis, where: $H_0: \mu \leq 10$ vs $H_1: \mu > 10$, be rejected at the $\alpha = 0.01$ level, if the sample produced a mean of $\bar{x} = 11$ percent and a sample standard deviation of $\hat{s} = 0.5$ percent?

30. In 9 test runs, a truck operated for 10, 12, 9, 11, 14, 12, 10, 9, and 11 miles with one gallon of a certain gasoline. Is this evidence, at the $\alpha = 0.05$ and $\alpha = 0.01$ levels of significance, that the truck is not operating at an average of 12 miles per gallon with this gasoline?

31. A soft-drink vending machine is programmed to dispense 6 ounces per cup. If the machine is tested 16 times and produced a mean cup of 5.9 ounces with a standard deviation of 0.2 ounces, is this evidence, at the $\alpha = 0.05$ level of significance, that the vending machine is underfilling the cups?

32. A department store conducted a study to determine whether the mean outstanding balance on 30-day charge accounts is the same in its 2 urban stores, and obtained the following results:

    Branch 1: $n_1 = 64; \bar{x}_1 = 128; \hat{s}_1 = 16.00$
    Branch 2: $n_2 = 72; \bar{x}_2 = 123; \hat{s}_2 = 12.00$

    a) At $\alpha = 0.05$ test the hypothesis that $\mu_1 = \mu_2$ against the alternative hypothesis that $\mu_1 \neq \mu_2$
    b) Construct a 95% C.I. on the population parameter $\Delta\mu = \mu_1 - \mu_2$
    c) How do the solutions of parts (a) and (b) compare?

33. To determine whether men and women earn comparable wages in a certain industry, two random samples were obtained and produced the following results:

    Sample 1 (Men): $n_1 = n_m = 15; \bar{x}_1 = \bar{x}_m = 560; \hat{s}_1 = \hat{s}_m = 20$
    Sample 2 (Women): $n_2 = n_w = 12; \bar{x}_2 = \bar{x}_w = 538; \hat{s}_2 = \hat{s}_w = 25$

    a) Test the hypothesis that $\Delta\mu = \mu_1 - \mu_2 = \mu_m - \mu_w = 0$ vs $H_1: \Delta\mu \neq 0$ at $\alpha = 0.01$.
    b) Construct a 99% C.I. on $\Delta\mu$.
    c) Are the results in (a) and (b) the same? Justify.

34. In an experiment with a new tranquilizer, the pulse rate of 21 patients was measured before they were given the tranquilizer and 10 minutes after they were given the tranquilizer. Their pulse rate was found to be reduced on the average by 8 beats

    $(i.e., \bar{d} = \sum d_i / n = 8)$ and a standard deviation of 2 beats

    $$(i.e., \hat{s}_d = \left(\frac{n \sum d_i^2 - \left(\sum d_i \right)^2}{n(n-1)} \right)^{1/2} = 2).$$

    a) Can we conclude, using $\alpha = 0.05$, that this tranquilizer will reduce the pulse rate on the average, by 10 beats in 10 minutes?
    b) Construct a 95% C.I. on the parameter μ_d (mean difference of paired data)
    c) Are the solutions in parts (a) and (b) the same? Why or why not? Justify.

35. To determine the effectiveness of an industrial safety program on the average weekly loss man-hours due to accidents in 10 plants "before and after" the

program was put into operation, the following data was collected over a period of one year:

	1	2	3	4	5	6	7	8	9	10
Before $= x_i$	37	45	12	72	54	34	26	13	39	79
After $= y_i$	28	46	18	59	43	29	24	15	35	75
$d_i = x_i - y_i$	9	-1	-6	13	11	5	2	-2	4	4

a) At $\alpha = 0.05$, test the hypothesis: H_0: $\mu_d = 0$ to decide whether the safety program is effective.

b) Construct a 95% C.I. on μ_d.

c) Compare the results of the solutions in (a) and (b). Are they the same? Justify!

36. In a study of television viewing habits, an investigator got the following data on the weekly number of hours a family's television set is turned on in prime time: He investigated 50 families ($n_1 = 50$) where the head of the household is not a college graduate and obtained an average of 20 hours ($\overline{x}_1$) with a standard deviation of 5 hours ($\hat{s}_1$). He also investigated 40 families ($n_2 = 40$), where the head of the household is a college graduate and obtained an average of 18 hours ($\overline{x}_2$) and a standard deviation of 4 hours ($\hat{s}_2$). Test the claim, at $\alpha = 0.05$ that if the head of the household is a college graduate, the family's television is turned on (on the average) at least 1.5 hours less per week in prime time.

37. To compare two kinds of bumper guards, 8 of each kind were mounted on cars of the same kind, were crashed into a concrete wall at a speed at 10 mph, and the following results were obtained (in dollars) for the cost of the repairs: $\overline{x}_1 = \$145.00$ and $\hat{s}_1 = 15$, and $\overline{x}_2 = \$120.00$ and $\hat{s}_2 = 12$. At $\alpha = 0.05$ test whether the difference between the mean repair costs is significant.

38. The following data were obtained to test whether or not there is a significant difference in the appraisals of 2 real estate appraisers for eight properties:

Property	1	2	3	4	5	6	7	8
Appraiser A	135,000	140,000	98,000	70,000	94,000	120,000	144,000	140,000
Appraiser B	130,000	148,000	92,000	77,000	88,000	124,000	152,000	136,000
$d_i = A_i - B_i$	5,000	-8,000	6,000	-7,000	6,000	-4,000	-8,000	4,000

Use the method of dependent samples and test at the $\alpha = 0.01$ level whether the mean paired difference is equal to zero.

39. Based on sample data from a given tennis tournament, it was found that 20 sets of tennis lasted, on the average, 30 minutes with a standard deviation of 5 minutes. Use $\alpha = 0.05$ to test the claim that σ is at most 4 minutes for the time it takes to play a set of tournament tennis.

40. Random samples of residences which had recently converted from oil heat to gas heat, in two communities, produced the following data on the total cost of the conversion (in dollars):

Community 1: $n_1 = 10, \overline{x}_1 = 3,560, \hat{s}_1 = 150$

Community 2: $n_2 = 8, \overline{x}_2 = 2,950, \hat{s}_2 = 180$

Test at the $\alpha = 0.02$ level of significance the claim that these two populations (communities) have equal variances.

41. The quality control department of a major automobile company is studying the dimensions of parts it is receiving from a factory, having 2 different production machines, and derives the following results:

1. From machine 1, a random sample of $n_1 = 25$ parts had a sample standard deviation of $\hat{s}_1 = 0.3$.

2. From machine 2, a random sample of $n_2 = 16$ parts had a sample standard deviation of $\hat{s}_2 = 0.2$ Use the sample information to:

a) Construct a 95% confidence interval for σ_1^2.

b) Construct a 95% confidence interval for σ_2^2.

c) Construct a 95% confidence interval for σ_1^2 / σ_2^2.

   If it is believed that $\sigma_1 = 0.1$ and $\sigma_2 = 0.2$, also test the hypotheses:

d) $H_0: \sigma_1^2 = 0.01$ vs $H_1: \sigma_1^2 \neq 0.01$, at $\alpha = 0.05$.

e) $H_0: \sigma_2^2 = 0.04$ vs $H_1: \sigma_2^2 \neq 0.04$, at $\alpha = 0.05$.

f) $H_0: \sigma_1^2 = \sigma_2^2$ vs $H_1: \sigma_1^2 \neq \sigma_2^2$, at $\alpha = 0.05$.

SOLUTIONS

1. a) $P[157.06 \leq \mu \leq 162.94] = 0.95$

   b) $P[156.13 \leq \mu \leq 163.87] = 0.99$

2. $P[-1.77 \leq \Delta\mu \leq 4.17] = 0.9$

3. Reject $H_0: \mu \leq 30$ for both α values. The batteries will be purchased.

4. a) $Z^* = \dfrac{\Delta\bar{x} - 0}{\sigma(\Delta\bar{x})} = \dfrac{40}{16.15} = 2.48$

   b) Reject $H_0: \Delta\mu = 0$ at $\alpha = 0.05$, but do not reject $H_0: \Delta\mu = 0$ at $\alpha = 0.01$.

5. a) Do not reject $H_0: \mu = 78.3$

   b) $P[69.01 \leq \mu \leq 79.59] = 0.98$

   c) The results are the same because both do not reject H_0.

   d) Reject $H_0: \mu = 78.3$ if $\bar{x} < 73.01$ or $\bar{x} > 83.59$

6. a) Reject $H_0: \Delta\mu = 0$

   b) $P[-4.115 \leq \Delta\mu \leq -1.285] = 0.95$

   c) The results are the same because both Reject H_0.

   d) Do not reject $H_0: \Delta\mu = 0$ if $-1.415 \leq \Delta\bar{x} \leq 1.415$

7. a) $P[46.91 \leq \mu \leq 51.59] = 0.9$

   b) $P[21.79 \leq \mu \leq 43.87] = 0.9$

   c) $P[46.36 \leq \mu \leq 52.14] = 0.95$

8. a) Do not reject $H_0: \Delta\sigma^2 = 0$ for both α values.

   b) $P[-6.43 \leq \Delta\sigma^2 \leq 14.43] = 0.99$ and

   $P[-3.93 \leq \Delta\sigma^2 \leq 11.93] = 0.95$

   c) The results are the same because both Do Not Reject H_0, at both α values.

9. a) Do not reject $H_0: \sigma^2 = 0.0006$

   b) $P[0.0003049 \leq \sigma^2 \leq 0.0009678] = 0.95$ and

   $P[0.01746 \leq \sigma \leq 0.0311] = 0.95$

   c) The results are the same because both do not Reject H_0.

10. a) Do not reject H_0: $\sigma_1^2 / \sigma_2^2 = 1$ for both α values.

b) $P[0.8105 \le \sigma_1^2 / \sigma_2^2 = \sigma_A^2 / \sigma_B^2 \le 7.6923] = 0.90$;
$P[0.6477 \le \sigma_1^2 / \sigma_2^2 \le 9.69] = 0.95$
$P[0.130 \le \sigma_2^2 / \sigma_1^2 = \sigma_B^2 / \sigma_A^2 \le 1.2338] = 0.90$;
$P[0.1032 \le \sigma_2^2 / \sigma_1^2 \le 1.544] = 0.95$

c) The results are the same because both do not Reject H_0.

11. a) Reject H_0: $\mu = 4$

b) $P[4.0442 \le \mu \le 4.1158] = 0.95$

c) The results are the same because both Reject H_0.

12. a) Reject H_0: $\Delta\mu = 0$

b) $P[-49.8534 \le -20.1446] = 0.99$

c) The results are the same because both reject H_0.

13. a) Do not reject H_0: $\mu_d = 0$

b) $P[-0.0075 \le \mu_d \le 37.7575] = 0.99$

c) The results are the same because both Do Not Reject H_0.

14. a) Reject H_0: $\sigma_1^2 / \sigma_2^2 = 1$ at $\alpha = 0.05$

b) $P[0.1118 \le \sigma_1^2 / \sigma_2^2 \le 0.7933] = 0.95$

c) The results are the same because both Reject H_0.

15. a) Reject H_0: $\sigma = 2$(or $\sigma^2 = 4$)

b) $P[4.7800 \le \sigma^2 \le 15.1730] = 0.95$

c) $P[2.186 \le \sigma \le 3.895] = 0.95$

d) The results are the same because both Reject H_0.

16. a) Reject H_0: $\Delta\mu = 0$ for both α values.

b) $P[4.86 \le \Delta\mu \le 21.14] = 0.95$ &
$P[2.08 \le \Delta\mu \le 23.92] = 0.99$

c) The conclusions are the same because both Reject H_0.

17. a) $P[151.31 \le \mu \le 165.69] = 0.90$ &
$P[149.76 \le \mu \le 167.24] = 0.95$ &
$P[147.83 \le \mu \le 169.17] = 0.98$

b) $P[147 \le \sigma^2 \le 645.75] = 0.95$ &
$P[12.15 \le \sigma \le 25.41] = 0.95$

18. a) Do not reject H_0: $\Delta\mu = 0$ at both α values.

b) Do not reject H_0: $\sigma_1^2 / \sigma_2^2 = 1$ at $\alpha = 0.05$

19. a) Reject H_0: $\mu = 80$

b) $P[68.1066 \le \mu \le 79.8934] = 0.99$

c) The results are the same because both Reject H_0.

d) Do not reject H_0 if: $74.1066 \le \bar{x} \le 85.8934$

20. a) Do not reject H_0: $\mu = 162$

b) $P[156.505 \le \mu \le 163.495] = 0.98$

c) The answers are the same because both do not reject H_0.

ANALYSIS OF VARIANCE

Chapter 12—Analysis of Variance (ANOVA)

12 Analysis of Variance (ANOVA)

To test the equality of three or more population means we use the ANOVA methodology which consists of the following basic steps:

1. Given a date set, obtain the total variance of the data set
2. Divide the total variance into the 2 components:
   a) Variance WITHIN a population, and
   b) Variance AMONG populations
3. Each of these components of variance, when divided by appropriate Degrees of Freedom, becomes a chi-square variable
4. The ratio of these two chi-square variables becomes an F-variable, thus giving us an appropriate test statistic for testing the hypotheses:

$$H_0: \mu_1 = \mu_2 = \mu_3 = \cdots = \mu_k \text{ vs } H_1: \text{ The means are not all equal}$$

5. This is so because testing the hypotheses: $H_0: \mu_1 = \mu_2 = \cdots = \mu_k$ vs H_1: The means are not all equal, is equivalent to testing the hypotheses:

$$H_0: \frac{\sigma^2_{Among}}{\sigma^2_{Within}} \leq 1 \quad \text{vs} \quad H_1: \frac{\sigma^2_{Among}}{\sigma^2_{Within}} > 1$$

6. The estimator of $\dfrac{\sigma^2_{Among}}{\sigma^2_{Within}}$ is the ratio:

$$\frac{(sum\ of\ squares\ Among\ the\ Populations)/p - 1}{(sum\ of\ squares\ Within\ the\ Populations)/p(n - 1)}$$

which is $F^{p-1}_{p(n-1)}$-distributed

12.1   Introduction

Up to now we compared the equality of 2 population means (*i.e.*, $H_0: \mu_1 = \mu_2$), using either the Z or the t tests, depending on whether σ_1 and σ_2 of the two populations are known or unknown, and whether $n_1 \geq 30$ or $n_1 < 30$, and $n_2 \geq 30$ or $n_2 < 30$.

On many occasions we have to test the equality of 3 or more population means (*i.e.*, $H_0: \mu_1 = \mu_2 = \mu_3 = \cdots = \mu_k$). How do we proceed in such a case?

Suppose $H_0: \mu_1 = \mu_2 = \mu_3$ (as an example). In this case we could use pair-wise comparisons (*i.e.*, Test: $H_0: \mu_1 = \mu_2$, $H_0: \mu_1 = \mu_3$, $H_0: \mu_2 = \mu_3$) and use the z or t tests, as appropriate. But:

1. These tests are not independent, and:
2. Even if we decide to ignore the lack of independence, the number of pair-wise comparisons increases rapidly, as k increases. For example, if $k = 10$, the number of pair-wise comparisons that need to be made, (N), is given by:

$$N = \frac{k!}{2!(k - 2)!} \tag{12.1}$$

$$= \frac{10!}{2!8!} = 45, \text{ which is a very large number}$$

Note 1: The pair-wise comparisons are not independent because the same data set is used in 2 or more comparisons. For example, when testing $H_0: \mu_1 = \mu_2$ we use the data from populations 1 and 2, and when testing $H_0: \mu_1 = \mu_3$ we use the data from populations 1 and 3; Thus the same data from population 1 is used twice, thus making the tests dependent.

Obviously what is needed is a different approach, and this is provided by the ANOVA (ANalysis Of VAriance) methodology.

Note 2: The ANOVA methodology is a very powerful tool which is capable of solving many problems from relatively simple ones (one way classification problem) to more complicated problems (two-way crossed classification problems) to very complicated problems (two-way nested classification problems with r replications). However, because this is only an introduction into the ANOVA methodology, we will cover fully only the simplest case which is solved by the one-way classification ANOVA methodology, and briefly indicate how more complicated problems can be solved.

Briefly stated, the ANOVA methodology divides the total variation of a given data set into 2 components of variance, namely:

1. Variance Within a population or class, and
2. Variance Among populations or classes.

Each of these components of variance, when divided by appropriate degrees of freedom, becomes a chi-square variable, and their ratio becomes an F-variable, thus giving us an appropriate test statistic for testing the hypothesis H_0: $\mu_1 = \mu_2 = \cdots = \mu_k$.

This is so because: testing the hypotheses,

$$H_0: \mu_1 = \mu_2 = \cdots = \mu_k \text{ vs } H_1: \text{The means are not all equal} \tag{12.2}$$

is, as we will show, equivalent to testing the hypotheses:

$$H_0: \frac{\sigma^2_{Among}}{\sigma^2_{Within}} \leq 1 \quad \text{vs} \quad H_1: \frac{\sigma^2_{Among}}{\sigma^2_{Within}} > 1 \tag{12.3}$$

or the hypotheses:

$$H_0: \sigma^2_{Among} = 0 \text{ vs } H_1: \sigma^2_{Among} \neq 0 \tag{12.4}$$

$$\text{or} \quad H_0: \sigma^2_{Among} = 0 \text{ vs } H_1: \sigma^2_{Among} > 0 \tag{12.5}$$

(since variance cannot be negative).

For a one-factor experiment, this is equivalent to testing:

H_0: The factor has no significant effect on the outcome of the experiment.

vs

H_1: The factor has a significant effect on the outcome of the experiment.

Note 3: As we will show later, a factor is an independent variable, and we are testing to see whether different values of the variable (or levels of populations) have an effect on the outcome of the experiment.

But to arrive at this conclusion, it is necessary to first introduce the following concepts and definitions:

1. Industrial experimentation.
2. Definitions of: factor, levels of a factor, treatment, response, controlled variables, and uncontrolled variables.
3. Single Factor Experiments (versus Multi-factor Experiments and Factorial or 2^n Experiments in which n factors are controlled at 2 levels only).
   a) Simplest case of a Single Factor Experiment.
   b) Data Arrangement of a single Factor Experiment.
   c) Possible models of data observation, depending on how treatments are assigned to objects.
   d) The ANOVA table.
4. Coding of the data, when the data consists of large numbers, to reduce the possibility of error due to the magnitude of the numbers.
5. Dividing the "Total Variation" into "Variance Within" and "Variance Among" populations or classes.
6. A 14-step procedure for solving the one-way classification ANOVA problem.

12.2 The Components of Variance: Variance Among Populations, Variance Within Populations and Total Variance

Before proceeding with the development of the ANOVA methodology, let us first illustrate what is meant by the components of variance: *Variance Within*, and *Variance Among*, into which the total variance of a data set is divided.

To accomplish this consider the following 3 illustrations, showing a hypothetical factor, controlled at 3 levels (I, II, III), and there are 4 observations for each level, as shown below in illustrations A, B, and C.

We are interested in testing: H_0: $\mu_1 = \mu_2 = \mu_3$ (where μ_1, μ_2, μ_3 are the population mean values of the 3 levels) vs H_1: The three population means are not all equal.

Illustration A: As we will show later, the division of the Total Variance of a data set into Variance Within and Variance Among is accomplished according to the formula:

$$\sigma_{Total}^2 = \frac{p(n-1)}{pn-1}\sigma_{Within}^2 + \frac{(p-1)}{pn-1}\sigma_{Among}^2 \qquad (12.6)$$

where p = Number of levels (3 here)

n = Number of observations per level (4 here)

pn = Total number of observations in the problem (12 here)

Table 12.1 Illustration A

Population Means	Factor Levels	Observations				SUMS	Sample Means $\bar{x} = \dfrac{\text{SUMs}}{n}$
		x_1	x_2	x_3	x_4		
μ_1	I	2	3	4	5	14	$\bar{x}_1 = 3.5$
μ_2	II	4	3	2	5	14	$\bar{x}_2 = 3.5$
μ_3	III	3	5	4	2	14	$\bar{x}_3 = 3.5$
		Grand Total = 42					
		Grand Mean = $\bar{x}$ = 42/12 = 3.5					

The most effective way of calculating the 3 variances included in equation (12.6) above is by using the ANOVA table which is part of the 14-step procedure we will discuss later, in detail, and which looks as follows:

Table 12.2 ANOVA Table for Illustration A

Source of Variation	Degrees of Freedom (DOF)	SUM of Squares (SS)	MS = SS/DOF
Variance Among Levels	$p - 1 = 2$	$SSA = 0$	$\sigma_{Among}^2 = 0$
Variance Within Levels	$p(n-1) = 9$	$SSW = 15$	$\sigma_{Within}^2 = 15/9$
Total Variance	$pn - 1 = 11$	$TSS = 15$	$\sigma_{Total}^2 = 15/11$

where SSA, SSW, and SST of this table are calculated directly from the given data using the formulas:

$$SSA = C_i - C \tag{12.7}$$
$$SSW = C_{ij} - C_i \tag{12.8}$$
$$SST = C_{ij} - C \tag{12.9}$$

and C_{ij}, C_i, and C are calculated from the data as follows:

$$C_{ij} = \text{Sum of squares of every value in the data set} = \sum_{i=1}^{p}\sum_{j=1}^{n} x_{ij} \tag{12.10}$$

$$= (2^2 + 3^2 + 4^2 + 5^2) + (4^2 + 3^2 + 2^2 + 5^2) + (3^2 + 5^2 + 4^2 + 2^2) = 162$$

$$C_i = \frac{(Row1Total)^2 + (Row2Total)^2 + (Row3Total)^2}{Number\ of\ observations\ per\ level}$$

$$= \frac{14^2 + 14^2 + 14^2}{4} = 147 \tag{12.11}$$

$$C = \frac{(GrandTotal)^2}{np} \tag{12.12}$$

$$= \frac{(Row1Total + Row2Total + Row3Total)^2}{Total\ number\ of\ observations}$$

$$= \frac{(14 + 14 + 14)^2}{12} = \frac{42^2}{12} = 147$$

Substituting (12.10), (12.11), and (12.12) into (12.7), (12.8), and (12.9), we obtain

$$SSA = 0, \quad SSW = 15, \quad SST = 15. \tag{12.13}$$

Then we enter these values in the ANOVA table above and calculate the corresponding $MS = SS/DF$ value. We obtain:

$$\sigma^2_{Among} = 0 \quad \sigma^2_{Within} = 15/9 \quad \sigma^2_{Total} = 15/11 \tag{12.14}$$

The 3 variance values of (12.14) satisfy (12.6) above, as can be verified by direct substitution.

Therefore, in this illustration, $\sigma^2_{Among} = 0$, and we would accept the hypothesis:

$H_0: \mu_1 = \mu_2 = \mu_3$, because the corresponding $\bar{x}_1$, $\bar{x}_2$ and $\bar{x}_3$ are equal, as can be seen from Illustration A and, treating $\bar{x}_1$, $\bar{x}_2$ and $\bar{x}_3$ as a data set, produces a zero variance.

But σ^2_{Among} does not have to be exactly equal to zero, to accept H_0. A "small" non-zero value of σ^2_{Among} would not reject H_0, if it is within the expected sampling error.

Illustration B: Here, because the observations in each level are identical the component of variance, $V_{Within} = 0$, while $V_{Among} > 0$, because $\bar{x}_1$, $\bar{x}_2$ and $\bar{x}_3$ are different values.

Table 12.3 Illustration B

Population Means μ	Factor Levles	Observations				SUMS	Sample Means $\bar{x} = \dfrac{SUMS}{n}$
		x_1	x_2	x_3	x_4		
μ_1	I	3	3	3	3	12	$\bar{x}_1 = 3$
μ_2	II	5	5	5	5	20	$\bar{x}_2 = 5$
μ_3	III	2	2	2	2	8	$\bar{x}_3 = 2$
		Grand Total				40	
		Grand Mean $= \bar{x} = 40/12 = 3.3$					

If we applied the same procedure we used to obtain the ANOVA table of Illustration A, the ANOVA table for Illustration B becomes:

Table 12.4 ANOVA Table for Illustration B			
Source of Variation	**Degrees of Freedom (DOF)**	**SUM of Squares (SS)**	**MS = SS/DOF**
Variance Among Levels	$p - 1 = 2$	$SSA = 56/3$	$\sigma^2_{Among} = 56/6$
Variance Within Levels	$p(n - 1) = 9$	$SSW = 0$	$\sigma^2_{Within} = 0$
Total Variance	$pn - 1 = 11$	$SST = 56/3$	$\sigma^2_{Total} = 56/33$

Where: $C_{ij} = 3^2 + 3^3 + \cdots + 2^2 = 152$
$$C_i = (12^2 + 20^2 + 8^2)/4 = 152$$
$$C = 40^2/12 \approx 133.33 = 400/3$$

Then: $SST = C_{ij} - C = 152 - 400/3 = 56/3$
$$SSW = C_{ij} - C_i = 152 - 152 = 0$$
$$SSA = C_i - C = 152 - 400/3 = 56/3$$

Therefore $\sigma^2_{Among} = 56/6$, $\sigma^2_{Within} = 0$, and $\sigma^2_{Total} = 56/33$, (12.15)
and the 3 components of variance of (12.15) satisfy (12.6), as can be verified by direct substitution.

In this illustration $\sigma^2_{Among} > 0$ *and* $\sigma^2_{Within} = 0$. The hypothesis H_0: $\mu_1 = \mu_2 = \mu_3$ will not be accepted, as we will show later.

Illustration C: Let us also consider Illustration C, which is more typical and more realistic, because both components of variance, σ^2_{Among} and σ^2_{Within}, are greater than zero.

Table 12.5 Illustration C							
Population Means μ	**Factor Levels**	**Observations**				**SUMS**	**Sample Means** $\bar{x} = \dfrac{\text{SUMS}}{n}$
		x_1	x_2	x_3	x_4		
μ_1	I	2	4	3	5	14	$\bar{x}_1 = 3.5$
μ_2	II	1	3	2	4	10	$\bar{x}_2 = 2.5$
μ_3	III	4	6	5	3	18	$\bar{x}_3 = 4.5$
		Grand Total $= 42$					
		Grand Mean $= \bar{x} = 42/12 = 3.5$					

If we apply the same procedure to Illustration C (as we did for Illustration A), we obtain the ANOVA table shown below, because:

$$C_{ij} = 2^2 + 4^2 + \cdots + 5^2 + 3^2 = 170$$
$$C_i = (14^2 + 10^2 + 18^2)/4 = 155$$
$$C = 42^2/12 = 147$$

and $SST = C_{ij} - C = 170 - 147 = 23$
$$SSW = C_{ij} - C_i = 170 - 155 = 15$$
$$SSA = C_i - C = 155 - 147 = 8$$

Table 12.6 ANOVA Table for Illustration C			
Source of Variation	**Degrees of Freedom (DOF)**	**SUM of Squares (SS)**	**MS = SS/DOF**
Variance Among Levels	$p - 1 = 2$	$SSA = 8$	$\sigma^2_{Among} = 8/2 = 4$
Variance Within Levels	$p(n - 1) = 9$	$SSW = 15$	$\sigma^2_{Within} = 15/9 = 5/3$
Total Variance	$pn - 1 = 11$	$SST = 23$	$\sigma^2_{Total} = 23/11$

$$\text{Clearly: } \sigma^2_{Among} = 4, \sigma^2_{Within} = 5/3 \text{ and } \sigma^2_{Total} = 23/11, \tag{12.16}$$

and (12.6) is satisfied. Whether $H_0: \mu_1 = \mu_2 = \mu_3$ is accepted or rejected will be determined later, after we first introduce the procedure for solving such problems.

Note 4: The 3 illustrations: A, B, C that we discussed above, show how the Total Variance (σ^2_T) of a data set is divided into the 2 components: σ^2_{Among} and σ^2_{Within}, as required by the ANOVA methodology.

We can now move from the 3 hypothetical illustrations above to a real life example. Suppose we want to study the effect of the "hours of study" factor on the students grade of an exam. In addition to obtaining a class average, regardless of the hours of study, we can divide the class into 3 groups and ask the first group to study 5 hours, the second group 8 hours, and the third group 10 hours, and compute the group averages $\overline{x}_1, \overline{x}_2, \overline{x}_3$. Then we ask the question, Are the group averages the same? Do more hours of study increase the average grade?

12.3   Definitions

We need the following definitions for the development of the ANOVA methodology:

■ Industrial Experimentation

The planning and design of industrial experiments, and the analysis of the resulting data in the presence of uncontrolled variation (error).

R.A. Fisher (the "father" of Inferential Statistics and the discoverer of the F-distribution, which was named after him) contends that: "To get meaningful inferences from the data, the experiment must be preplanned and designed very carefully".

■ Terminology

1. **Factor:** Is a feature of the experimental conditions which may be varied from one observation to another (a variable, independent variable, input variable).
2. **Levels of a Factor:** Are the values of a factor examined in an experiment (example: suppose temperature is an important factor in an experiment, and we are evaluating this factor at temperatures: 80, 100, 120; *i.e.*, we are examming the effect of 3 levels of the factor on the outcome of the experiment).
3. **Treatments:** Are the combinations of levels of factors, applied to the experimental material to obtain an observation.

   Example: Suppose temperature and pressure are 2 factors affecting the outcome of an experiment, and temperature is examined at 3 levels (T_1, T_2, T_3) and pressure at 2 levels (P_1, P_2). Then, there are 6 Treatments (combinations of levels of factors) as shown in Table 12.7 below:
4. **Response:** Is the result of a trial of the experiment with a given treatment (a dependent variable, or output).

Table 12.7 Possible Treatments of a 2-Factor Experiment with 2 and 3 Levels for Factors P and T Respectively			
Pressure	**Temperature**		
	T_1	T_2	T_3
P_1	(P_1, T_1)	(P_1, T_2)	(P_1, T_3)
P_2	(P_2, T_1)	(P_2, T_2)	(P_2, T_3)

5. **Controlled Variables:** Are the factors in the experiment.
6. **Uncontrolled Variables:** Are the variables which we know to be present, but we cannot control them, such as: amount of rain, ambient temperature, etc.

■ The 4 Design Principles

1. **Replication:** Is the repetition of the same factor on different experimental units.
2. **Cross-Classification:** Employ every unit of the experimental material with every treatment (*i.e.*, every treatment can be assigned to any experimental unit).
3. **Employ Similar Experimental Material:** The characteristics of the experimental units must remain constant.
4. **Randomization:** Assign treatments to the experimental units by chance (for statistical methodology to work).

Example 1

What is the effect of the factor "Hours of Study" on the numerical grade of the students in a statistics class?

In this example, the factor is "Hours of Study", and we may select many levels of it to study: $L_1 = H_1$ hours of study, $L_2 = H_2$ hours of study, etc, and the experimental units are students. Then:

1. By Replication, we mean the assignment of "H_1 hours of study" to several student groups.
2. By Cross Classification, we mean that the students assigned to study $H_1, H_2, \ldots, H_k$ hours are selected from the entire class.
3. By Employing Similar Experimental Material, we mean that the students taking the course have the same educational background.
4. By Randomization, we mean that the students chosen to study $H_1, H_2, \ldots, H_k$ hours, are selected by chance from the entire class.

■ ■ ■

12.4   Randomization

Every experiment involves one or more assignment(s) of treatments to experimental units (subjects, plots, segments of time, or space). There should always be an element of randomization in each such assignment for the statistical methods to work.

Example 2

Suppose we want to compare the grain yield of 3 varieties of corn (or: study the effect of 3 different drugs on a given sickness, or, determine the return on 3 different investments, etc.) We decided that 4 plots are needed for each corn variety (*i.e.*, 12 plots all together) *i.e.*, **we have 4 replicates of the basic module.** (For testing the 3 drugs we decide to use

4 sick people and for determining the return of the 3 investments we decide to ask 4 different investors, randomly selected).

Suppose the corn varieties are represented by: A, B, C. One possible assignment of treatments (corn varieties) to plots is shown below in Table 12.8a. But this layout is not so good, because the assignments are not random.

This assignment might be OK if we knew that plot fertility is the same. However, it is possible that true plot fertilities differ from the average fertility by $\varepsilon_{ij}(i = 1, \ldots, 3, j = 1, \ldots, 4)$ and ε_{ij} are unknown constants (see Table 12.8b below).

If this is the case, then differences in the grain yield could be attributed to either: grain variety, or plot fertility, or to a combination of both!

Table 12.8a Biased Treatment Assignment		
A	B	C
A	B	C
A	B	C
A	B	C

Table 12.8b Random Plot Fertilities		
ε_{11}	ε_{21}	ε_{31}
ε_{12}	ε_{22}	ε_{32}
ε_{13}	ε_{23}	ε_{33}
ε_{14}	ε_{24}	ε_{34}

Table 12.8c Completely Randomized Design Assignment		
B	C	B
A	B	A
C	A	B
A	C	C

Q: How do we get around this difficulty?

A: By assigning treatments to plots at random makes the ε_{ij} behave like random variables, thus satisfying the assumption that Z_{ij} in the ANOVA model are independent random variables. Random assignment leads to a technique of analysis known as the **"completely randomized design"**.

A possible assignment, under the "completely randomized design" approach, is shown in Table 12.8c. In this assignment, treatments are assigned to plots by chance, and there are 4 treatments for each of the 3 varieties of corn.

But suppose that plot fertility in the first horizontal strip is the same for all 3 plots in this strip. Assume also that the same is true for each of the other 3 horizontal strips. If we regard these strips as blocks of "uniform fertility", and then randomize within each block, we are led to another method of treatment assignment and analysis known as **"Randomized Block Design"**, and a possible assignment is shown below in Table 12.9. Notice that in this design each of the treatments appears only once within each of the blocks.

Table 12.9 Randomized Block Design Assignment			
Block 1 ⇒	B	A	C
Block 2 ⇒	A	B	C
Block 3 ⇒	C	B	A
Block 4 ⇒	C	A	B

The identification of blocks, even though it complicates the solution of the problem somewhat by introducing an extra term needed to be evaluated in the model of observations (as we will show shortly), it does not influence the outcome of the solution. If the blocks have an effect, it will be shown to exist. If not, we will be told to ignore blocks.

There is another possible design, called "**Latin Square**", in which you randomize within both rows and columns (*i.e.*, each treatment will appear only once in each row and each column; but for this to happen here, we must have either 3 plots for each corn variety, or bring in a fourth corn variety and have 4 plots for each; *i.e.*, Latin Square designs are possible only for $2 \times 2, 3 \times 3, 4 \times 4, \ldots, n \times n$ problems) and this design is even more complicated than the randomized block design because it not only adds an extra term in the model of observations (as we will show shortly) but it also requires the use of 3 subscripts to represent the data (x_{ijk}) (one for treatments, one for blocks, one for columns).

For a 2×2 Latin Square there are 2 possible designs $\begin{bmatrix} A & B \\ B & A \end{bmatrix}$ and $\begin{bmatrix} B & A \\ A & B \end{bmatrix}$. For a 3×3 Latin Square there are 12 possible designs, for a 4×4 Latin Square design there are 576 and for a 5×5 Latin Square there are 5760 possible designs. When one uses a Latin Square to solve a problem, one must first select randomly a design from those available.

Note 5: The use of the Randomized block Design or Latin Square Design are made with the thought that their use could lower the mean square error (σ^2) of the experiment.

Note 6: The ANOVA we construct depends on the model of treatment assignment we use. You can not test for the effect of a factor, if the factor is not included in the model.

Note 7: The ANOVA methodology is very broad and can solve many problems. It can study the simultaneous effects of many factors on a dependent variable, and it can also study the interactions among the factors. However, because of space and level of presentation constraints, we will concentrate our discussion to the simplest situation, which is represented by a completely randomized design assignment, using the one-way classification ANOVA methodology, even though we will briefly explain how the Randomized Block Design and Latin Square Design are formulated and solved. Also a brief explanation will be given of a 2-factor experiment, using the 2-way cross classification ANOVA methodology, to show how interactions between factors occur and how they are analyzed.

■ ■ ■

12.5   Single Factor Experiments

Single Factor Experiments occur when we have one variable (single factor) controlled at several (say *p*) levels (*i.e.*, we compare *p* treatments).

The simplest case occurs when we have enough homogeneous experimental material to permit the desired number of runs (*i.e.*, observations, say *n* of them) for each level. That is, we have enough for pn observations. (Note: when $n = 1$, we have a basic module of p observations to compare p treatments. This is a replication.)

The value of n is chosen on the basis of power requirements (in hypothesis testing) or accuracy of estimation (in estimation theory).

Note 8: This type of an experiment is to be contrasted with: **Multiple Factor Experiments**, in which several factors are to be tested at many levels each, and 2^n **Factorial Design Experiments**, in which n factors, at 2 levels each, are to be tested and evaluated.

A single factor experiment results in a set of data which may be analyzed by means of One-way Classification of ANalysis Of VAriance (ANOVA).

The data generated from a single factor experiment will have the structure shown in Table 12.10 below (note the use of double subscripts).

Table 12.10 Data Structure of a Single Factor Experiment with p Levels and n Observations per Level					
	Observations $1 \le j \le n$				
Treatments $1 \le i \le p$ (or Levels)	x_{11}	x_{12}	x_{13}	$\cdots$	x_{1n}
	x_{21}	x_{22}	x_{23}	$\cdots$	x_{2n}
	x_{31}	x_{32}	x_{33}	$\cdots$	x_{3n}
	$\cdots$	$\cdots$	$\cdots$	$\cdots$	$\cdots$
	x_{p1}	x_{p2}	x_{p3}	$\cdots$	x_{pn}

Q: How do these observations get generated?

A: It depends on how the treatment assignments are made (*i.e.*, whether it is a Completely Randomized Design, a Randomized Block Design, or a Latin Square Design). These observations could have come from:

1. **A Completely Randomized Design** with model of observations:

$$x_{ij} = \mu + T_i + Z_{ij} \tag{12.17}$$

where: $\mu, T_1, T_2, \dots, T_p$ are unknown constants and: $Z_{ij} \to N(0, \sigma^2)$; *i.e.*, the Z_{ij} are independent normal variables with 0 mean and unknown variance σ^2, and $T_1, T_2, \dots, T_p$ represent the treatment effects.

2. **A Randomized Block Design** with model of observations:

$$x_{ij} = \mu + T_i + B_j + Z_{ij} \tag{12.18}$$

where: μ, T_i, Z_{ij} are as above and B_j represents the effect of the blocks.

3. **A Latin Square Design** with model of observations:

$$x_{ijk} = \mu + T_i + B_j + C_k + Z_{ijk} \tag{12.19}$$

where $\mu\, T_i, B_j$ are as above; C_k represents the effect of the columns,

and $Z_{ijk} \to N(0, \sigma^2)$.

We will first make the assumption that the observations came from a "Completely Randomized Design".

12.5.1 Completely Randomized Design

There are actually 2 models of observation for the completely randomized design, namely: *Model I* which is defined by (12.17) above, and is called the "Fixed Effects" Model, and *Model II*, the "Random Effects" Model defined by $x_{ij} = \mu + Y_i + Z_{ij}$ where Y_i is assumed to be a normally distributed variable with zero mean and variance $= \omega^2$ (*i.e.*, $Y_i \rightarrow N(0, \omega^2)$) and Z_{ij} is as above (*i.e.*, $Z_{ij} \rightarrow N(0, \sigma^2)$). We will discuss first Model I, and then Model II.

12.5.1.1 Model I: The "Fixed Effects" Model

We will use the following notation to help us "break" the Total Variance of a data set, like the one represented by Table 12.10, into its components: Variance Among populations and Variance Within populations:

$x_{ij} =$ individual data entry
$\overline{x}_{i\bullet} =$ Average of Row i (*i.e.*, estimator for μ_i)
$\overline{x}_{\bullet\bullet} =$ Grand Mean (*i.e.*, estimator for μ)

Recall the definition of variance for a given data set with a single subscript: *i.e.*, if the data set is: $x_1, x_2, \ldots, x_n$, then:

$$\hat{s}^2 = \text{Total Unbiased Sample Variance} = \frac{1}{n-1} \sum_{i=1}^{n} (x_i - \overline{x})^2 \qquad (12.20)$$

Observe that to calculate the variance, we subtract from each observation x_i the sample average ($\overline{x}$), square the difference ($x_i - \overline{x}$), and then sum up all such squared differences to form $\sum_{i=1}^{n} (x_i - \overline{x})^2$, and then multiply the sum by $\left(\frac{1}{n-1}\right)$.

We will follow the same procedure with our data set, except that we will use double summations because we represent our data set in rows and columns, and we need a double subscript to identify the row and column where each data value is.

Table 12.11 below shows the data structure and organization and will be used in "breaking" the total data variation into its components: "Variance Among Levels" and "Variance Within Levels".

Table 12.11 Data Organization for "Breaking" the Total Data Variance into "Variance Among Levels" and "Variance Within Levels".

		Data $1 \leq j \leq n$					Level SUMS	Level Averages $\overline{x}_{i\bullet}$
Level 1		x_{11}	x_{12}	x_{13}	...	x_{1n}	S_1	$\overline{x}_{1\bullet}$
Level 2	$1 \leq i \leq p$	x_{21}	x_{22}	x_{23}	...	x_{2n}	S_2	$\overline{x}_{2\bullet}$
Level 3		x_{31}	x_{32}	x_{33}	...	x_{3n}	S_3	$\overline{x}_{3\bullet}$
...		...	...	...	...	...	...	...
Level p		x_{p1}	x_{p2}	x_{p3}	...	x_{pn}	S_p	$\overline{x}_{p\bullet}$
							$S_T = S_1 + \cdots + S_p$	$\overline{x}_{\bullet\bullet}$

where $S_1 = \sum_{j=1}^{n} x_{1j} = x_{11} + x_{12} + x_{13} + \cdots + x_{1n}$, and $\overline{x}_{1\bullet} = \frac{S_1}{n}$

$$S_2 = \sum_{j=1}^{n} x_{2j}, \text{ and } \overline{x}_{2\bullet} = \frac{S_2}{n}, \text{ etc.} \qquad (12.21)$$

and $S_T = S_1 + S_2 + \cdots + S_p = \sum_{i=1}^{p} \sum_{j=1}^{n} x_{ij}$, and $\overline{x}_{\bullet\bullet} = \frac{S_t}{np}$

Then we can write

$$x_{ij} - \overline{x}_{\bullet\bullet} = x_{ij} - \overline{x}_{\bullet\bullet} + (\overline{x}_{i\bullet} - \overline{x}_{i\bullet}),$$

or $\qquad x_{ij} - \overline{x}_{\bullet\bullet} = (x_{ij} - \overline{x}_{i\bullet}) + (\overline{x}_{i\bullet} - \overline{x}_{\bullet\bullet}) \qquad (12.22)$

Squaring both sides of (12.22) we obtain:

$$(x_{ij} - \overline{x}_{..})^2 = (x_{ij} - \overline{x}_{i.})^2 + (\overline{x}_{i.} - \overline{x}_{..})^2 + 2(x_{ij} - \overline{x}_{i.})(\overline{x}_{i.} - \overline{x}_{..}) \qquad (12.23)$$

Now apply double summations to both sides of (12.23) to obtain:

$$\sum_{i=1}^{p}\sum_{j=1}^{n}(x_{ij} - \overline{x}_{..})^2 = \sum_{i=1}^{p}\sum_{j=1}^{n}(x_{ij} - \overline{x}_{i.})^2 + \sum_{i=1}^{p}\sum_{j=1}^{n}(\overline{x}_{i.} - \overline{x}_{..})^2$$

$$+ \sum_{i=1}^{p}\sum_{j=1}^{n}2(x_{ij} - \overline{x}_{i.})(\overline{x}_{i.} - \overline{x}_{..}) \qquad (12.24)$$

The last term of equation (12.24) goes to zero when the 2 terms are multiplied and the double summation is applied. Then equation (12.24) becomes:

$$\sum_{i=1}^{p}\sum_{j=1}^{n}(x_{ij} - \overline{x}_{..})^2 = \sum_{i=1}^{p}\sum_{j=1}^{n}(x_{ij} - \overline{x}_{i.})^2 + \sum_{i=1}^{p}\sum_{j=1}^{n}(\overline{x}_{i.} - \overline{x}_{..})^2, \qquad (12.25)$$

or (Total Sum of Squares) = (Sum of Squares Within) + (Sum of Squares Among),

$$TSS = SSW + SSA, \qquad (12.26)$$

where $\ TSS = \sum_{i=1}^{p}\sum_{j=1}^{n}(x_{ij} - \overline{x}_{..})^2 = \sum_{i=1}^{p}\sum_{j=1}^{n}x_{ij}^2 - \dfrac{\left(\sum_{i=1}^{p}\sum_{j=1}^{n}x_{ij}\right)^2}{pn} = C_{ij} - C \qquad (12.27)$

$$SSW = \sum_{i=1}^{p}\sum_{j=1}^{n}(x_{ij} - \overline{x}_{i.})^2 = \sum_{i=1}^{p}\sum_{j=1}^{n}x_{ij}^2 - \dfrac{\sum_{i=1}^{p}\left(\sum_{j=1}^{n}x_{ij}\right)^2}{n} = C_{ij} - C_i \qquad (12.28)$$

$$SSA = \sum_{i=1}^{p}\sum_{j=1}^{n}(\overline{x}_{i.} - \overline{x}_{..})^2 = \dfrac{\sum_{i=1}^{p}\left(\sum_{j=1}^{n}x_{ij}\right)^2}{n} - \dfrac{\left(\sum_{i=1}^{p}\sum_{j=1}^{n}x_{ij}\right)^2}{pn} = C_i - C \qquad (12.29)$$

Note 9: In the simplification of the above sums of squares we have made use of the identity:

$$\sum_{i=1}^{n}(x_i - \overline{x})^2 = \sum_{i=1}^{n}x_i^2 - \dfrac{\left(\sum_{i=1}^{n}x_i\right)^2}{n}, \text{ which was developed and used in previous chapters.}$$

12.5.1.2 Relation Between Total Variance & Variance Among & Variance Within

Equation (12.26) above tells us that the Total sum of Squares in a data set is equal to the Sum of Squares Within plus the Sum of Squares Among. But these sums of squares are not variances. They become variances only when they are divided by the corresponding degrees of freedom for each sum of squares.

The Degrees of Freedom associated with the Total Sum of Squares $= pn - 1$, (12.30) because $\overline{x}_{..}$ must be evaluated from the x_{ij} data.

The Degrees of Freedom associated with the Sum of Squares Among $= p - 1$, (12.31) because $\overline{x}_{..}$ must be evaluated from the data $(\overline{x}_{1.}, \overline{x}_{2.}, \ldots, \overline{x}_{p.}$ now form the data set from which $\overline{x}_{..}$ must be evaluated).

The Degrees of Freedom associated with Sum of Squares Within $= p(n - 1)$, (12.32) because we need to use the x_{ij} data to evaluate p level means.

We now convert each sum of squares in (12.26) into variances, by dividing each sum by its corresponding degrees of freedom (actually we will first multiply and divide by its degrees of freedom, and then manipulate the terms appropriately). Then we have:

$$TSS = \left(\frac{pn - 1}{pn - 1}\right)TSS = (pn - 1)\left[\frac{TSS}{pn - 1}\right] = (pn - 1)\sigma^2_{Total} \quad (12.33)$$

$$SSW = \left(\frac{p(n - 1)}{p(n - 1)}\right)SSW = p(n - 1)\left[\frac{SSW}{p(n - 1)}\right] = p(n - 1)\sigma^2_{Within} \quad (12.34)$$

$$SSA = \left(\frac{p - 1}{p - 1}\right)SSA = (p - 1)\left[\frac{SSA}{p - 1}\right] = (p - 1)\sigma^2_{Among} \quad (12.35)$$

Now substitute equations (12.33), (12.34) and (12.35) into equation (12.26), to obtain:

$$(pn - 1)\sigma^2_{Total} = p(n - 1)\sigma^2_{Within} + (p - 1)\sigma^2_{Among} \quad (12.36)$$

which, when solved for σ^2_{Total}, becomes:

$$\sigma^2_{Total} = \left[\frac{p(n - 1)}{pn - 1}\right]\sigma^2_{Within} + \left[\frac{p - 1}{pn - 1}\right]\sigma^2_{Among}, \quad (12.37)$$

which is identically the same as equation (12.6) we stated earlier in this chapter.

12.5.1.3 Relationship Between the Mean and Variance of 2 Data Sets Which Differ by a Constant

Suppose we have a data set: $x_1, x_2, x_3, \ldots, x_n$, from which we can obtain

$$\overline{x} = \frac{\sum_{i=1}^{n} x_i}{n} \quad \text{and} \quad \hat{s}_x^2 = \frac{1}{n - 1}\sum_{i=1}^{n}(x_i - \overline{x})^2 \quad (12.38)$$

Now let us define a new data set: $y_1, y_2, y_3, \ldots, y_n$, such that

$$y_i = x_i - c \quad (12.39)$$

where c = any constant

Question: If we find $\overline{y}$ and $\hat{s}_y^2$ from the data set defined by equation (12.39), how are $\overline{y}$ and $\hat{s}_y^2$ related to $\overline{x}$ and $\hat{s}_x^2$?

Answer: By definition:

$$\overline{y} = \frac{\sum_{i=1}^{n} y_i}{n} = \frac{\sum_{i=1}^{n}(x_i - c)}{n} = \frac{\sum_{i=1}^{n} x_i - nc}{n} = \frac{\sum_{i=1}^{n} x_i}{n} - c = \overline{x} - c \quad (12.40)$$

and

$$\hat{s}_y^2 = \frac{1}{n - 1}\sum_{i=1}^{n}(y_1 - \overline{y})^2 \quad (12.41)$$

When equations (12.39) and (12.40) are substituted into (12.41) we obtain

$$\hat{s}_y^2 = \frac{1}{n - 1}\sum_{i=1}^{n}[(x_i - c) - (\overline{x} - c)]^2 = \frac{1}{n - 1}\sum_{i=1}^{n}[(x_1 - c - \overline{x} + c)]^2, \text{ from which we}$$

obtain:

$$\hat{s}_y^2 = \frac{1}{n - 1}\sum_{i=1}^{n}(x_i - \overline{x})^2 = \hat{s}_x^2 \quad (12.42)$$

Therefore, if we subtract the same constant value (c) from a given data set, the average value of the new data set is reduced by that fixed amount c (see equation (12.40)). But the variance of the new data set does not change (see (12.42)).

We intend to use this finding in our solutions because we will choose to subtract the midrange of the data set (where: Midrange = (High + Low)/2 or a whole number close to it) from each of the values in the data set. We do this to "scale down" the size of the numbers to avoid numerical errors that can result when working with large numbers. This process is called "Coding of the Data". Remember, coding changes the mean, but not the variance, and the ANOVA methodology is based on dividing the variance of the data set (which remains unchanged by coding) into the variance components of Variance Within and Variance Among.

12.5.1.4 Procedure for Problem Solution

Given a data set for comparing p treatments with n replications each, we proceed as follows:

1. **Code** if you feel comfortable working with large numbers you do not have to code the data. The values of TSS, SSW, and SSA are not affected by coding.
   If you choose not to code the data, the "ij" table is equal to the given data. The Data by subtracting the Midrange = $(H + L)/2$ (or, a whole number close to it) from each observation. This generates the "ij" table.

2. **Obtain the "i"-Table** by adding the coded observations, for each treatment, in the "ij" table.

3. **Obtain the "Grand Total"** by adding the "i-table" totals.

4. Calculate:
   a) C_{ij} = Sum of squares of each entry in the "ij-table"   (12.43)

   b) $C_i = \dfrac{(Treat\ 1\,Total)^2 + (Treat\ 2\,Total)^2 + \cdots + (Treat\ p\,Total)^2}{n}$ (12.44)

   where Treat = Treatment

   c) $C = \dfrac{(Grand\ Total)^2}{np}$ (12.45)

5. Calculate:
$$TSS = SST = C_{ij} - C \qquad (12.46)$$
$$SSW = SSW = C_{ij} - C_i \qquad (12.47)$$
$$SSA = SSA = C_i - C \qquad (12.48)$$

6. Transfer this information to an ANOVA table (see Table 12.12) and complete the ANOVA table.

Table 12.12 ANOVA Table to Compare p Treatments of a Factor with n Observations per Treatment (or Level)

Source of Variation	Degrees of Freedom (*DOF*)	Sum of Squares (*SS*)	*MS = SS/DOF*	*E(MS)*	*F*
Among Treatments Variation	$p - 1$	SSA	$\dfrac{SSA}{p-1}$	$\sigma^2 + \dfrac{n\sum\limits_{i=1}^{p} T_i^2}{p-1}$	$F^* = \dfrac{\dfrac{SSA}{p-1}}{\dfrac{SSW}{p(n-1)}}$
Within Treatments Variation	$p(n-1)$	SSW	$\dfrac{SSW}{p(n-1)}$	σ^2	
Total Variation	$pn - 1$	TSS	$\dfrac{TSS}{np-1}$		

7. Test the hypotheses:
   $H_0: \mu_1 = \mu_2 = \cdots = \mu_p$ vs H_1: the p population means are not all equal.   (12.49)
   or the equivalent hypotheses:

   or
   $$H_0: \frac{\sigma^2_{Among}}{\sigma^2_{Within}} \leq 1 \quad \text{vs} \quad H_1: \frac{\sigma^2_{Among}}{\sigma^2_{Within}} > 1 \qquad (12.50)$$

   or
   $$H_0: \sigma^2_{Among} \leq 0 \quad \text{vs} \quad H_1: \sigma^2_{Among} > 0 \qquad (12.51)$$

   But, in reality, we test the hypotheses defined by (12.50).

   To complete this test we calculate $F^* = \dfrac{\dfrac{SSA}{p-1}}{\dfrac{SSW}{p(n-1)}}$ (12.52)

   and compare it to $F^{p-1}_{p(n-1)}(\alpha)$, which is a tabulated value for a given α, $p-1$, and $p(n-1)$.

8. If we do not reject H_0, we conclude that
   $$\mu_1 = \mu_2 = \mu_2 = \cdots = \mu_p \qquad (12.53)$$

9. If we reject H_0, it means that there are at least 2 means that differ from each other. To find the pairs of means which are different we proceed as follows

10. Compute the LSD = Least Significant Difference
    $$= \sqrt{\frac{2}{n}\left[\frac{SSW}{p(n-1)}\right]}\left[F^1_{p(n-1)}(\alpha/2)\right] \qquad (12.54)$$

11. Compute the sample mean of each treatment or population $(\bar{x}_i)$, either from the coded or the original data sets, and then form the table below, by taking Absolute Values of all the possible $(\bar{x}_i - \bar{x}_j)$ differences.

Table 12.13 Sample Means of Treatments				
$\bar{x}_1$	$\bar{x}_2$	$\bar{x}_3$	...	$\bar{x}_p$
$\bar{x}_1$				
$\bar{x}_2$	$\|\bar{x}_1 - \bar{x}_2\|$			
$\bar{x}_3$	$\|\bar{x}_1 - \bar{x}_3\|$	$\|\bar{x}_2 - \bar{x}_3\|$		
...				
$\bar{x}_p$	$\|\bar{x}_1 - \bar{x}_p\|$	$\|\bar{x}_2 - \bar{x}_p\|$	$\|\bar{x}_3 - \bar{x}_p\|$	

12. Compare the differences of step 11, with the LSD value of step 10.
13. The differences which exceed the LSD are the significant ones! Mark them with an asterisk (*), for easier identification.

14. If the treatments do not have the same number of observations n (but rather: n_1, n_2, ..., n_p), the following changes are necessary in the above procedure:

a) C_i in (step 4b) should now be:

$$C_i = \frac{(Row\,1\,Total)^2}{n_1} + \cdots + \frac{(Row\,p\,Total)^2}{n_p}$$

(12.55)

b) C in (step 4c) should now be:

$$C = \frac{(Grand\,Total)^2}{n_1 + n_2 + \cdots + n_p}$$

(12.56)

c) The degrees of freedom for total variation (in Table 12.12) now is:

$$DOF_{Total\,Variation} = n_1 + n_2 + \cdots + n_p - 1 \text{ (instead of } pn-1)$$

(12.57)

d) The degrees of freedom for "Variation Within"

$$= (n_1 + n_2 + \cdots + n_p) - p$$

(12.58)

(instead of $p(n-1)$ as shown in Table 12.12)

e) An LSD has to be calculated for each pair of means $(\bar{x}_i, \bar{x}_j)$ that we wish to test to see if they are equal, from:

$$LSD_{ij} = \sqrt{\left(\frac{1}{n_i} + \frac{1}{n_j}\right)\left[\frac{SSW}{(n_1 + n_2 + \cdots + n_p) - p}\right]\left[F^1_{n_1+n_2+\cdots+n_p-p}(\alpha/2)\right]}$$

(12.59)

For example, if we are comparing 3 levels of a variable with $n_1 = 5$, $n_2 = 6$ and $n_3 = 8$, we need to calculate the following 3 LSD values for each α value of interest:

$$LSD_{1,2} = \sqrt{\left(\frac{1}{5} + \frac{1}{6}\right)\left[\frac{SSW}{5 + 6 + 8 - 3}\right]\left[F^1_{5+6+8-3}(\alpha/2)\right]}$$

(12.60)

$$LSD_{1,3} = \sqrt{\left(\frac{1}{5} + \frac{1}{8}\right)\left[\frac{SSW}{5 + 6 + 8 - 3}\right]\left[F^1_{5+6+8-3}(\alpha/2)\right]}$$

(12.61)

$$LSD_{2,3} = \sqrt{\left(\frac{1}{6} + \frac{1}{8}\right)\left[\frac{SSW}{5 + 6 + 8 - 3}\right]\left[F^1_{5+6+8-3}(\alpha/2)\right]}$$

(12.62)

Example 3

The following table of data is to be used for a comparison of the nicotine content of tobacco reported by 3 laboratories, believed to have the same variance. Do the labs differ in average reported content? Use $\alpha = 0.05$ and $\alpha = 0.10$

Table 12.14 Original Data					
Lab	**Raw Data**				
A	16	11	16	16	21
B	10	9	12	16	13
C	10	7	11	13	14

1. **Coded Data:** Subtract c = Midrange = $(21 + 7)/2 = 14$
2. i-table
3. Grand Total = -15

Table 12.15 Coded Data; i-Table; Grand Total

	ij-table					i-table	$\bar{x}$
A	2	-3	2	2	7	10	$\bar{x}_1 = 2 = 10/5$
B	-4	-5	-2	2	-1	-10	$\bar{x}_1 = -2 = 10/5$
C	-4	-7	-3	-1	0	-15	$\bar{x}_1 = -3 = -15/5$
	Grand Total = -15						

4. Calculate:

   a)
   $$C_{ij} = (2^2 + (-3)^2 + 2^2 + 2^2 + 7^2) + ((-4)^2 + (-5)^2 + (-2)^2 + 2^2 + (-1)^2) + ((-4)^2 + (-1)^2 + (-3)^2 + (-1)^2 + 0^2) = 195$$

   b) $C_i = \dfrac{(10)^2 + (-10)^2 + (-15)^2}{5} = 85$

   c) $C = \dfrac{(-15)^2}{15} = 15$

5. Calculate:

$$SST = C_{ij} - C = 195 - 15 = 180$$
$$SSA = C_i - C = 85 - 15 = 70$$
$$SSW = C_{ij} - C_i = 195 - 85 = 110$$

6. ANOVA Table

Table 12.16

Source of Variation	Degrees of Freedom (DOF)	Sum of Squares (SS)	MS = SS/DOF	E(MS)
Among Treatments	$p - 1 = 2$	$SSA = 70$	$MS = 70/2 = 35$	$\sigma^2 + \dfrac{n\sum_{i=1}^{p} T_i^2}{p - 1}$
Within Treatments	$p(n - 1) = 12$	$SSW = 110$	$MS = 110/12 = 9.17$	σ^2
Total	$p(n - 1) = 14$	$SST = 180$	$MS = 180/14 = 90/7 \approx 12.85$	

7. Test the hypothesis H_0: $\mu_1 = \mu_2 = \mu_3$ vs H_1: the means are not all equal,

   or the equivalent: H_0: $\dfrac{\sigma^2_{Among}}{\sigma^2_{Within}} \leq 1$ vs H_1: $\dfrac{\sigma^2_{Among}}{\sigma^2_{Within}} > 1$.

   The test consists of the usual 7-step procedure, shown below

   a) H_0: $\dfrac{\sigma^2_{Among}}{\sigma^2_{Within}} \leq 1$ vs H_1: $\dfrac{\sigma^2_{Among}}{\sigma^2_{Within}} > 1$

b) $\alpha = 0.05$ and $\alpha = 0.1$

c) The estimator for $\dfrac{\sigma^2_{Among}}{\sigma^2_{Within}}$ is $\dfrac{SSA / (p - 1)}{SSW / p(n - 1)}$ which is $F^{p-1}_{p(n-1)}(\alpha) = F^2_{12}(\alpha)$ distributed.

d) Rejection Region

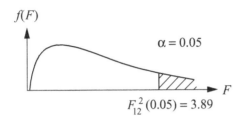

$$F^2_{12}(0.05) = 3.89$$

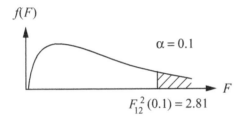

$$F^2_{12}(0.1) = 2.81$$

e) Calculate $F^* = \dfrac{SSA / (p - 1)}{SSW / p(n - 1)} = \dfrac{70 / 2}{110 / 12} = 35/9.17 = 3.82$

f) Compare F^* to the Rejection Regions; Do not reject H_0 if $\alpha = 0.05$, reject H_0 if $\alpha = 0.10$.

g) When $\alpha = 0.05$, $\mu_1 = \mu_2 = \mu_3$; when $\alpha = 0.10$, the three means are not equal.

8. a) When $\alpha = 0.05$, H_0 is not rejected because $F^* = 3.82 < 3.89$
   Conclusion: $\mu_1 = \mu_2 = \mu_3$, and the procedure stops here!

   b) When $\alpha = 0.10$, H_0 is rejected, because $F^* = 3.82 > 2.81$

9. Conclusion: The means are not equal, and the procedure continues!

10. Calculate the *LSD* from:

$$LSD = \sqrt{\frac{2}{5}\left(\frac{110}{12}\right)F^1_{12}(0.05)} = \sqrt{\left(\frac{2}{5}\right)\left(\frac{110}{12}\right)(4.75)} = 4.17$$

Note 10: The *LSD* is calculated only for the α value for which H_0 is rejected.

11. Compute $|\bar{x}_i - \bar{x}_j|$ for all possible combinations for which $i \neq j$

Table 12.17 Calculation of $|\bar{x}_i - \bar{x}_j|$ for example 3			
	$\bar{x}_1 = 2$	$\bar{x}_2 = -2$	$\bar{x}_3 = -3$
$\bar{x}_1 = 2$			
$\bar{x}_2 = -2$	$|\bar{x}_1 - \bar{x}_2| = 4$		
$\bar{x}_3 = -3$	$|\bar{x}_1 - \bar{x}_3| = 5^*$	$|\bar{x}_2 - \bar{x}_3| = 1$	

12. The only absolute value difference of the means that exceeds the *LSD* is $|\bar{x}_1 - \bar{x}_3| = 5$

13. Therefore $\mu_1 \neq \mu_3$, and these are the means which caused the rejection of H_0, when $\alpha = 0.10$

Note 11: When n is the same for all populations, the LSD is calculated from equation (12.54), namely: $LSD = \sqrt{\left(\dfrac{2}{n}\right)\left[\dfrac{SSW}{p(n-1)}\right]\left[F^1_{p(n-1)}(\alpha/2)\right]}$ and for the values of the example above, $LSD = 4.17$ when $\alpha = 0.10$, because $F^1_{3(5-1)}(0.05) = F^1_{12}(0.05) = 4.75$.

If, however, the term $F^1_{p(n-1)}(\alpha/2)$ is replaced by $F^1_{p(n-1)}(\alpha)$ in equation (12.54), its value becomes: $F^1_{12}(0.1) = 3.18$, and the corresponding $LSD = 3.41$.

When the sampled mean differences are compared against this new LSD, the paired differences: $|\bar{x}_1 - \bar{x}_3| = 4$ and $|\bar{x}_1 - \bar{x}_3| = 5$ are both greater than the $LSD = 3.41$ and, therefore, the conclusion is that $\mu_1 \neq \mu_2$ and $\mu_1 \neq \mu_3$, and these 2 pairs would be the reason for the rejection of H_0.

When we compare these new results to the results obtained previously, when only the pair $|\bar{x}_1 - \bar{x}_3|$ exceeded the $LSD = 4.17$, we come to the conclusion that $F^1_{p(n-1)}(\alpha/2)$ makes the LSD larger and, therefore, harder to exceed; or, another way of stating this is to say that $F^1_{p(n-1)}(\alpha)$ is more sensitive than $F^1_{p(n-1)}(\alpha/2)$.

■ ■ ■

12.5.2 Model II: The "Random Effects" Model

The Completely Randomized Design problem we solved above, with model of observations $x_{ij} = \mu + T_i + Z_{ij}$, is known as the "Fixed Effects" model, or Model I.

But there also exists a Model II, or "Random Effects" model which is the appropriate model to use when members of row classification are selected randomly from an infinite population.

The model of observations for this model is

$$x_{ij} = \mu + Y_i + Z_{ij} \tag{12.62}$$

in which μ and Z_{ij} are the same as for model I (See equation (12.17)) but Y_i are assumed to be independent random variables, normally distributed with: $E(Y_i) = 0$ and $V(Y_i) = \omega^2$, or $Y_i \rightarrow N(0, \omega^2)$.

An example, where this model is applicable, is in a two-stage sampling situation where primary units are randomly selected and then repeated samples are drawn within each primary unit, as shown in the diagram below

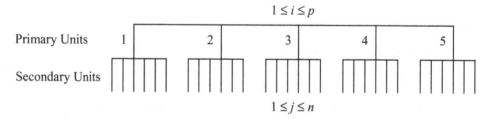

As a possible problem, suppose we are interested in the sugar content of apples in an apple farm. To solve the problem, we can first select randomly p apple trees, and then select randomly again n apples from each selected tree.

The data set for this problem looks the same as for model I (see Table 12.11) before equation (12.21), and the ANOVA table for this problem is the same as for model I (see ANOVA table 12.12 before equation (12.49)), except for the entry at the intersection of the row "Among Treatments" and column $E(MS)$ which now becomes

$$E(MS)_{Among\ Treatments} = \sigma^2 + n\omega^2 \tag{12.63}$$

instead of the original: $\sigma^2 + \dfrac{n\sum\limits_{i=1}^{p} T_i^2}{p-1}$,   used for model I.

A possible hypothesis to test here is

$$H_0: \omega^2 \le 0 \text{ vs } H_1: \omega^2 > 0 \tag{12.64}$$

which would be rejected if: $F^* = \dfrac{SSA/(p-1)}{SSW/p(n-1)} > F_{p(n-1)}^{p-1}(\alpha) \tag{12.65}$

But such a test is not of much interest or value.

Usually, in this model we want to estimate σ^2 and ω^2 which are then used to design a sampling plan which will produce desired results economically (*i.e.*, given costs for selecting primary and secondary units, obtain the optimum number of primary units (p) and secondary units per primary unit (n) to minimize the total cost). This procedure is carried out as follows:

1. From the ANOVA table we obtain the estimate for σ^2 from

$$\sigma^2 = \frac{SSW}{p(n-1)} \tag{12.66}$$

and then, since: $\sigma^2 + n\omega^2 = \dfrac{SSA}{p-1}$, we solve for ω^2 and obtain

$$\omega^2 = \frac{1}{n}\left[\frac{SSA}{p-1} - \frac{SSW}{p(n-1)}\right] \tag{12.67}$$

Note 12: It is possible to obtain a negative value for ω^2 from (12.67), because of random fluctuations. To avoid this possibility, because ω^2 is a variance and cannot be negative, we let:

$$\omega^2 = \max\left[\frac{1}{n}\left[\frac{SSA}{p-1} - \frac{SSW}{p(n-1)}\right], 0\right] \tag{12.68}$$

2. To design the sampling plan, note that there is a choice of sampling from many primary units with few samples from each primary unit, or few primary units with many samples (secondary units) per primary unit.

   For our model of observations: $x_{ij} = \mu + Y_i + Z_{ij}$, we want to estimate the value of μ, which is given by the grand mean $\bar{x}_{..}$, because $E(Y_i) = 0$ and $E(Z_{ij}) = 0$, and then minimize $V(\bar{x}_{..})$.

   By summing over both summation indices i and j we can write:

$$\bar{x}_{..} = \mu + \bar{Y}_{.} + \bar{Z}_{..} \tag{12.69}$$

and then

$$E(\bar{x}_{..}) = \mu + E(\bar{Y}_{.}) + E(\bar{Z}_{..}) = \mu + 0 + 0 = \mu \tag{12.70}$$

and $V(\bar{x}_{..}) = V(\mu) + V(\bar{Y}_{.}) + V(\bar{Z}_{..})$

$$= 0 + \frac{\omega^2}{p} + \frac{\sigma^2}{np} = \frac{1}{p}\left(\omega^2 + \frac{\sigma^2}{n}\right) \tag{12.71}$$

Let us now introduce the costs by letting

$$C_1 = \text{Cost of stage 1 sample}$$
$$C_2 = \text{Cost of stage 2 sample}$$

Then the total cost of the sampling plans, C, is given by:

$$C = (\text{Number of primary units})\, C_1 + (\text{Number of secondary units})\, C_2$$
$$= pC_1 + (np)C_2 = p(C_1 + nC_2) \tag{12.72}$$

We now ask the question: How do we choose the values of p and n so that the variance of $\overline{x}_{..}$, $V(\overline{x}_{..})$, given by (12.71), is a minimum, subject to the cost constraint given by (12.72)?

The answer to this question is: Solve the constraint for p to obtain

$$p = \frac{C}{C_1 + nC_2} \tag{12.73}$$

and then substitute the value of p into (12.71) to obtain

$$V(\overline{x}_{..}) = \frac{\sigma^2 + n\omega^2}{np} = \frac{\sigma^2 + n\omega^2}{n}\left[\frac{C_1 + nC_2}{C}\right],$$

or

$$V(\overline{x}_{..}) = \left(\frac{C_1\sigma^2}{C}\right)n^{-1} + \left(\frac{C_2}{C}\omega^2\right)n + \left(\frac{\sigma^2 C_2 + C_1\omega^2}{C}\right) \tag{12.74}$$

and then minimize $V(\overline{x}_{..})$ with respect to n.

Since

$$dV(\overline{x}_{..})/dn = -\left(\frac{C_1\sigma^2}{C}\right)n^{-2} + \left(\frac{C_2}{C}\omega^2\right)(1) + 0 \tag{12.75}$$

and

$$d^2V(\overline{x}_{..})/d^2n = 2\left(\frac{C_1\sigma^2}{C}\right)\frac{1}{n^3}, \tag{12.76}$$

the critical point of the function defined by (12.74) is:

$$-\left(\frac{C_1\sigma^2}{C}\right)n^{-2} + \left(\frac{C_2}{C}\omega^2\right) = 0 \text{ or } n^2 = \frac{C_1}{C_2}\frac{\sigma^2}{\omega^2}, \quad \text{from which we obtain}$$

$$n = n^* = \frac{\sigma}{\omega}\sqrt{\frac{C_1}{C_2}} \tag{12.77}$$

and this critical point corresponds to a local minimum because the 2nd derivative, given by (12.76), when evaluated at the critical point becomes

$$\frac{d^2V(\overline{x}_{..})}{d^2n} = 2\left(\frac{C_1\sigma^2}{C}\right)\frac{1}{n^3} = 2\left(\frac{C_1\sigma^2}{C}\right)\frac{1}{n^2}\frac{1}{n}$$

$$= 2\left(\frac{C_1\sigma^2}{C}\right)\frac{C_2}{C_1}\frac{\omega^2}{\sigma^2}\cdot\frac{\omega}{\sigma}\frac{\sqrt{C_2}}{\sqrt{C_1}} = 2\left(\frac{C_1\sigma^2}{C}\right)\frac{\omega^3 C_2^{3/2}}{\sigma^3 C_1^{3/2}}$$

$$= 2\frac{C_1}{C}\frac{\omega^3}{\sigma}\frac{C_2^{3/2}}{C_1^{3/2}} = 2\frac{\omega^3}{\sigma}\frac{1}{C}\frac{C_2^{3/2}}{C_1^{1/2}}$$

$$= 2\left(\frac{\omega^3}{\sigma}\right)\left(\frac{1}{C}\sqrt{\frac{C_2^3}{C_1}}\right) > 0 \tag{12.78}$$

Since every quantity in the right hand side of (12.78) is positive, $n^* = \dfrac{\sigma}{\omega}\sqrt{\dfrac{C_1}{C_2}}$ is the optimum number of secondary units per primary unit and the optimum number of primary units (p^*) is obtained from the constraint equation (12.72) when $n = n^*$ given by (12.73) is substituted in it. The result is

$$P^* = \frac{C}{C_1 + C_2 n^*} \tag{12.79}$$

Example 4

The percent yield in 3 samples from each of 5 batches of a chemical product is shown in the table below:

Table 12.18 Original Data Set for Example 4

Sample ($1 \leq j \leq 3 = n$)	Batch ($1 \leq i \leq 5 = p$)				
	1	2	3	4	5
1	72.8	72.4	73.6	72.7	73.4
2	73.1	72.6	74.2	72.2	72.4
3	72.6	73.2	73.7	73.8	72.8

The data were obtained to estimate the variation among batches and among samples.

1. Define an appropriate model.
2. Carry out the indicated analysis of variance.
3. Estimate the "Among Batches" and "Among Samples" components of variance.

Solution

1. The appropriate model to use here is the Completely Randomized Design, Model II (1 way of classification), where
   a) The model of observations is: $x_{ij} = \mu + Y_i + Z_{ij}\ 1 \leq i \leq 5, 1 \leq j \leq 3$
   b) $\mu = $ constant
   c) $Y_i = N(0, \omega^2)$
   d) $Z_{ij} = N(0, \sigma^2)$

2. To perform the indicated ANOVA we will first CODE the data, using the following equation:

$$\text{Coded Data} = (\text{Uncoded Data} - 73.2) \times 10 \tag{12.80}$$

   to obtain

Table 12.19 Coded Data for Example 4

-4	-8	4	-5	2
-1	-6	10	-10	-8
-6	0	5	6	-4
$S_1 = -11$	$S_2 = -14$	$S_3 = 19$	$S_4 = -9$	$S_5 = -10$

and $S = S_1 + S_2 + S_3 + S_4 + S_5 = -25$

Then

$$C_{ij} = \left[(-4)^2 + (-1)^2 + (-6)^2\right] + \left[(-8)^2 + (-6)^2 + 0\right] + \left[4^2 + 10^2 + 5^2\right]$$

$$+ \left[(-5)^2 + (-10)^2 + 6^2\right] + \left[2^2 + (-8)^2 + (-4)^2\right] = 539$$

$$C_{ij} = \frac{S_1^2 + S_2^2 + S_3^2 + S_4^2 + S_5^2}{3} = \frac{(-11)^2 + (-14)^2 + (19)^2 + (-9)^2 + (-12)^2}{3}$$

$$= \frac{859}{3} = 286.3$$

$$C = \frac{(Grand\ Total)^2}{np} = \frac{S^2}{3 \times 5} = \frac{(-25)^2}{15} = \frac{625}{15} = 41.7$$

Therefore $TSS = C_{ij} - C = 539 - 41.7 = 497.3$

$SSW = C_{ij} - C_i = 539 - 286.3 = 252.7$

$SSA = C_i - C = 286.3 - 41.7 = 244.6$

Transferring the generated information to an ANOVA Table, we obtain

Table 12.20 ANOVA for Example 4				
Source of Variation	DOF	SUM of Squares SS $\times 100^*$	Mean Square MS $= \dfrac{SS}{DOF} \times 100$	E(MS)
Variation Among Batches	$p - 1 = 5 - 1 = 4$	$SSA = 244.6$	$244.6/4 = 61.15$	$\sigma^2 + 3\omega^2$
Variation Within Batches	$p(n - 1) = 5(3 - 1) = 10$	$SSW = 252.7$	$252.7/10 = 25.27$	σ^2
Total Variation	$pn - 1 = 15 - 1 = 14$	$TSS = 497.3$	$497.3/14 = 35.52$	

* This is so because when we coded the data (see equation (12.80) we multiplied by 10 and, therefore, when the data is squared, the sum of squares are multiplied by 10^2.

3. To estimate σ^2 and ω^2, we use the ANOVA table above, but remembering that the values shown in the MS column have been multiplied by 100, we obtain:

$\sigma^2 = 25.27/100 = 0.2527$ (*i.e.*, variation within batches or among samples)

and $\sigma^2 + 3\omega^2 = 61.15/100 = 0.6115$,   from which:

$$\omega^2 = \frac{1}{3}[0.6115 - \sigma^2] = \frac{1}{3}[0.6115 - 0.2527] = \frac{1}{3}[0.3588]$$

$$= 0.1196 \text{ (\textit{i.e.}, variation among batches)}$$

12.5.3 Randomized Block Design

The Randomized Block Design is based upon the principle of grouping experimental units into blocks.

The blocks are formed with the hope that the units within each block will be more homogeneous in their response (in the absence of treatment effects) than units selected completely at random. By taking into account the differences that may exist between blocks in the analysis of variance, it is also expected that a smaller Mean Square (MS) error will be obtained for the same number of observations than if a Completely Randomized Design had been used. This is the basis for preferring the Randomized Block Design to the Completely Randomized Design, in a given application.

To analyze the data for a Randomized Block Design, we use the method of "Two-way classification with one observation per cell", and the model of observations is assumed to be

$$x_{ij} = \mu + B_i + T_j + Z_{ij} \tag{12.81}$$

where: μ = Grand mean (a Constant value)

$$T_j = \text{Treatment effects (Model I); } \sum_{j=1}^{k} T_j = 0$$

$$B_i = \text{Block effects (Model I); } \sum_{i=1}^{n} B_i = 0 \tag{12.82}$$

$$Z_{ij} = N(0, \sigma^2)$$

Note: We assume that no interaction occurs between blocks and treatments.

The hypotheses to be tested here (*i.e.*, H_0 vs H_1) are

H_0: $\mu_1 = \mu_2 = \cdots = \mu_k$ vs H_1: The means are not all equal $\tag{12.83}$

(or H_0: $T_1 = T_2 = \cdots = T_k = 0$, *i.e.*, the treatments have no effects vs H_1: Some treatments are $\neq 0$ and, therefore, have an effect.)

The analysis of variance table for this problem is as shown below.

Table 12.21 ANOVA Table for Randomised Block Design					
Source of Variation	**DOF**	**SS**	**MS**	**E(MS)**	**Where: σ_T^2 and σ_B^2 are shown below**
Variation Among Treatments	$k - 1$	SSA_T	$\dfrac{SSA_T}{k-1}$	$\sigma^2 + n\sigma_T^2$	$\sigma_T^2 = \dfrac{\sum\limits_{j=1}^{k} T_j}{k-1}$
Variations Among Blocks	$n - 1$	SSA_B	$\dfrac{SSA_B}{n-1}$	$\sigma^2 + k\sigma_B^2$	$\sigma_B^2 = \dfrac{\sum\limits_{i=1}^{k} B_i}{n-1}$
Variations Within Treatments (Error)	$(k-1)(n-1)$	SSW_T	$\dfrac{SSW_T}{(k-1)(n-1)}$	σ^2	
Total Variation	$kn - 1$	TSS	$\dfrac{TSS}{kn-1}$		

Where:

$$TSS = C_{ij} - C \qquad (12.84)$$

$$SSA_T = C_j - C \qquad (12.85)$$

$$SSA_B = C_i - C \qquad (12.86)$$

$$SSW_T = C_{ij} - C_j - C_i + C \qquad (12.87)$$

Example 5

Four types of catalysts A, B, C, and D are to be compared in their effect on the yield of an organic chemical product. Batches are produced successively in a single reactor using one of the catalysts, and a measure of the yield is obtained for each batch. A maximum of 5 batches can be produced in a day.

Table 12.22 Original Data Set for Example 5				
Catalyst (Treatments)				
Day (Blocks)	**A**	**B**	**C**	**D**
1	80	75	79	82
2	78	82	80	84
3	76	75	76	80
4	79	77	78	83
5	80	78	77	82

A preliminary investigation shows that about 5 batches (samples) using each catalyst, or 20 batches in all, should provide sufficiently precise estimates of the effectiveness of each type of catalyst.

This experiment was run as a Randomized Block Design, using days as blocks, and the data shown above (in percent yield) were obtained.

1. At the $\alpha = 0.05$ level, do the catalysts differ in effectiveness?
2. Is there a significant block effect at $\alpha = 0.05$?

Solution We will code the data, using the equation

$$\text{Coded Data} = \text{Original Data} - 79 \ (\text{where } 79 = \text{Midrange} = \frac{L + H}{2} = \frac{75 + 83}{2})$$

Table 12.23 Coded Data Set for Example 5				
Day (Blocks)	**A**	**B**	**C**	**D**
1	1	−4	0	3
2	−1	3	1	5
3	−3	−4	−3	1
4	0	−2	−1	4
5	1	−1	−2	−3
	$S_A = -2$	$S_B = -8$	$S_C = -5$	$S_D = -16$

→ Day 1 Total = $S_1 = 0$
→ Day 2 Total = $S_2 = 8$
→ Day 3 Total = $S_3 = -9$
→ Day 4 Total = $S_4 = 1$
→ Day 5 Total = $S_5 = 1$

and Grand Total $= S_A + S_B + S_C + S_D = S_1 + S_2 + S_3 + S_4 + S_5 = 1$

Then

$$C_{ij} = 1^2 + (-4)^2 + 0^2 + 3^2 + (-1)^2 + 3^2 + 1^2 + 5^2 + (-3)^2 + (-4)^2$$
$$+ (-3)^2 + 1^2 + 0^2 + (-2)^2 + (-1)^2 + 4^2 + 1^2 + (-1)^2 + (-2)^2 + 3^2$$
$$= 133$$

$$C_j = \frac{S_A^2 + S_B^2 + S_C^2 + S_D^2}{5}$$
$$= \frac{(-2)^2 + (-8)^2 + (-5)^2 + 16^2}{5} = \frac{4 + 64 + 25 + 256}{5}$$
$$= \frac{349}{5} = 69.80$$

$$C_i = \frac{S_1^2 + S_2^2 + S_3^2 + S_4^2 + S_5^2}{4}$$
$$= \frac{0^2 + 8^2 + (-9)^2 + 1^2 + 1^2}{4} = \frac{0 + 64 + 81 + 1 + 1}{4}$$
$$= \frac{147}{4} = 36.75$$

$$C = \frac{(Grand\ Total)^2}{Total\ Number\ of\ Observations} = \frac{1^2}{20} = \frac{1}{20} = 0.05$$

Therefore, the corresponding sums of squares are (using equations 12.84–12.87)

$TSS = C_{ij} - C$	$= 133.00 - 0.05$	$= 132.95$
$SSA_T = C_j - C$	$= 69.80 - 0.05$	$= 69.75$
$SSA_B = C_i - C$	$= 36.75 - 0.05$	$= 36.70$
$SSW_T = C_{ij} - C_j - C_i + C$	$= 133.00 - 69.80 - 36.75 + 0.05$	$= 26.50$

Therefore, the ANOVA table corresponding to this problem is:

Table 12.24 ANOVA Table for Example 5

Source of Variation	DOF	SS	MS = SS/DOF	E(MS)
Variation Among Treatments	$k - 1 = 4 - 1 = 3$	$SSA_T = 69.75$	$69.75/3 = 23.75$	$\sigma^2 + 5\sigma_T^2$
Variation Among Blocks	$n - 1 = 5 - 1 = 4$	$SSA_B = 36.70$	$36.70/4 = 9.175$	$\sigma^2 + 4\sigma_B^2$
Variation Within Treatments (Error)	$(k - 1)(n - 1)$ $= 3 \times 4 = 12$	$SSW_T = 26.50$	$26.50/12 = 2.21$	σ^2
Total Variation	$kn - 1 = 19$	$TSS = 132.95$	$132.95/19 = 6.997$	

Therefore, to test the hypothesis:

1. $H_0: \mu_1 = \mu_2 = \mu_3 = \mu_4$ vs H_i: The means are not all equal, (or $H_0: T_1 = T_2 = T_3 = T_4 = 0$, i.e., the catalysts have no effect), we need to form the ratio:

$$F_1^* = \frac{SSA_T / k - 1}{SSW_T / (k - 1)(n - 1)} = 23.75/2.21 = 10.747 \text{and compare it to the tabulated}$$

value: $F_{12}^3(0.05) = 3.49$ Since $F_1^* > F_{12}^3(0.05)$ we reject H_0 and conclude that the catalysts are different.

2. To see if the blocks have an effect, we test the hypothesis

$H_0: B_1 = B_2 = B_3 = B_4 = B_5 = 0$ vs H_1: The block effects are not all equal to zero.

This hypothesis is tested by forming the ratio:

$$F_2^* = \frac{SSA_B/(n-1)}{SSW_T/(k-1)(n-1)} = 9.175/2.21 = 4.15 \text{ and comparing it to the}$$

tabulated value: $F_{12}^4(0.05) = 3.26$

Since $F_2^* > F_{12}^3(0.05)$, we reject H_0 and conclude that the blocks do have an effect on the yield of this chemical product.

▪ ▪ ▪

12.5.4 Latin Square Design

In the Randomized Block Design we identified blocks (horizontal strips, for example) and then randomized the assignment of the treatments within each block, in the hope of reducing the mean square error from the error we would expect to obtain in a Completely Randomized Design. If we also identify vertical strips and also randomize within the vertical columns such that each treatment can occur only once in each row and column, we can hope for a still further reduction in the mean square error. Such a design, in which we identify both horizontal and vertical blocks and randomize within each such block so that each treatment occurs only once, is called a "Latin Square Design" and for it to be possible it is necessary that

The Number of Treatments = The Number of Replications   (12.88)

The model of observations is now given by:

$$x_{ijk} = \mu + B_i + T_j + C_k + Z_{ijk} \qquad (12.89)$$

and we need 3 indices, $i, j,$ and k to adequately describe the model.

Note that there are no interactions present in this model, but the parameters present in (12.89) represent the following

μ = Grand mean

T_j = Treatment effects; $1 \le j \le r$

B_i = Block effects; $1 \le i \le r$ (12.90)

C_k = Column effects; $1 \le k \le r$

$Z_{ijk} = N(0, \sigma^2)$

and   *the number of observations in the data set* $= r^2$ (12.91)
$\mu, T_1, T_2, \ldots, T_r$ are fixed unknown constants.

C_k and B_i are also fixed constants, and $\displaystyle\sum_{i=1}^{r} B_i = \sum_{k=1}^{r} C_k,$ (12.92)

and Model I may be assumed for all of those constants.
The hypotheses to be tested are

1. $H_0: T_1 = T_2 = T_3 = \cdots = T_r = 0$ vs H_1: The treatments are not all $= 0$
   (or:$H_0: \mu_1 = \mu_2 = \cdots = \mu_r$ vs H_1: The means are not all equal.)
2. $H_0: B_1 = B_2 = B_3 = \cdots = B_r = 0$ vs H_1: The blocks are not all $= 0$
3. $H_0: C_1 = C_2 = C_3 = \cdots = C_r = 0$ vs H_1: The columns are not all $= 0$

The ANOVA table is shown below

Table 12.25 ANOVA Table for Latin Square Design

Source of Variation	DOF	SUM of Squares SS	$MS = \dfrac{SS}{DOF}$	E(MS)
Among Treatments(j)	$r - 1$	SSA_T	$SSA_T/(r - 1)$	$\sigma^2 + r\sigma_T^2*$
Among Rows (Blocks) (i)	$r - 1$	SSA_B	$SSA_B/(r - 1)$	$\sigma^2 + r\sigma_B^2*$
Among Columns (k)	$r - 1$	SSA_C	$SSA_C/(r - 1)$	$\sigma^2 + r\sigma_C^2*$
Within Treatments (Error)	$(r - 1)(r - 2)$	SSW_T	$\dfrac{SSW_T}{(r - 1)(r - 2)}$	σ^2
Total Variation	$r^2 - 1$	TSS	$TSS/(r^2 - 1)$	

Note: σ_T^2*, σ_B^2*, and σ_C^2* are defined by

$$\sigma_T^2* = \frac{\sum\limits_{j=1}^{r} T_j^2}{r - 1}\ ; \ \sigma_B^2* = \frac{\sum\limits_{i=1}^{r} B_i^2}{r - 1}\ ; \ \sigma_C^2* = \frac{\sum\limits_{k=1}^{r} C_k^2}{r - 1}$$

The sum of the squares: SSA_T, SSA_B, SSA_C, and TSS are obtained directly from the given data (as usual) while SSW_T, the error sum of squares is obtained by subtraction, as shown below:

$$S = TSS\ = C_{ik} - C \tag{12.93}$$
$$S_j = SSA_T = C_j - C \tag{12.94}$$
$$S_i = SSA_B = C_i - C \tag{12.95}$$
$$S_k = SSA_C = C_k - C \tag{12.96}$$
$$S_E = SSW_T = S - (S_i + S_j + S_k) \tag{12.97}$$

Example 6

In a study on metal removal rate, 3 electrode shapes were studied, namely: shapes A, B, and C. For this experiment 3 holes were cut in 3 workpieces and the order of the electrodes was arranged so that each of the electrode shapes A, B, and C were used only once on each work piece and once in each position. Thus the design is a Latin Square. The time (in hours) necessary to cut the holes, was recorded as follows:

Table 12.26 Original Data Set the Example 6

Strips (Blocks/Rows)	Position (Column)		
	1	2	3
I	$A = 8$	$C = 14$	$B = 20$
II	$B = 16$	$A = 10$	$C = 16$
III	$C = 15$	$B = 9$	$A = 9$

Calculate the appropriate analysis of variance table and test for significant variation among electrodes (or treatments), strips and position.

Solution First we will code the data by subtracting 14 (the midrange value $= (20 + 8)/2$) from the original data and obtain:

Table 12.27 Coded Data for Example 6("ik" Table)			
Strips	**Position (Column)**		
(Blocks/Rows)	**1**	**2**	**3**
I	−6	0	6
II	2	−4	2
III	1	−5	−5

Table 12.27a Tables "i", "k", and "j" for Example 6		
"i" Table Sum of the values in each block	**"k"Table** Sum of the values in each position (column)	**"j"Table** Sum of the values of each treatment
0	−3	$A = -15$
0	−9	$B = 3$
−9	3	$C = 3$

and: Grand Total = Sum of all "ik" values = Sum of "i" values = Sum of "k" values
= Sum of "j" values = − 9

Then $C_{ik} = (-6)^2 + 0^2 + 6^2 + 2^2 + (-4)^2 + 2^2 + (-5)^2 + (-5)^2 = 147$

$$C_i = \frac{0^2 + 0^2 + (-9)^2}{3} = \frac{81}{3} = 27$$

$$C_k = \frac{(-3)^2 + (-9)^2 + 3^2}{3} = \frac{9 + 81 + 9}{3} = \frac{99}{3} = 33$$

$$C_j = \frac{(-15)^2 + 3^2 + 3^2}{3} = \frac{225 + 9 + 9}{3} = \frac{243}{3} = 81$$

$$C = \frac{(Grand\ Total)^2}{Total\ Number\ of\ Observations} = \frac{(-9)^2}{9} = 9$$

Therefore

$$S_i = SSA_B = C_i - C = 27 - 9 = 18$$
$$S_j = SSA_T = C_j - C = 81 - 9 = 72$$
$$S_k = SSA_C = C_k - C = 33 - 9 = 24$$
$$S = TSS = C_{ik} - C = 147 - 9 = 138$$
$$\text{and } S_E = S - (S_i + S_j + S_k) = 138 - (18 + 72 + 24) = 24$$

When this information is transferred to an ANOVA table, we obtain:

Table 12.28 ANOVA Table for Example 6				
Source of Variation	DOF	SS	$MS = \dfrac{SS}{DOF}$	E(MS)
Treatments(j)	$r - 1 = 2$	$S_j = 72$	$72/2 = 36$	$\sigma^2 + 3\sigma_T^2$
Rows(Blocks)(i)	$r - 1 = 2$	$S_i = 18$	$18/2 = 9$	$\sigma^2 + 3\sigma_B^2$
Columns (k)	$r - 1 = 2$	$S_k = 24$	$24/2 = 12$	$\sigma^2 + 3\sigma_C^2$
Error	$(r-1)(r-2) = 2$	$S_E = 24$	$24/2 = 12$	σ^2
Total Variation	$r^2 - 1 = 8$	$S = 138$	$138/8 = 17/25$	

1. To test H_0: $T_1 = T_2 = T_3 = 0$ vs H_1: The treatments are not all $= 0$, we form the

   ratio: $F_1^* = \dfrac{S_j/2}{S_E/2} = 36/12 = 3$ and compare it to the table value: $F_2^2(\alpha = 0.05)$

   $= 19.00$.

      Since $F_1^* < F_2^2(\alpha = 0.05)$, we do not reject H_0 and conclude that the treatments do not differ significantly.

2. To test the hypothesis H_0: $B_1 = B_2 = B_3 = 0$ vs H_1: The blocks are not all $= 0$, we from the ratio:

   $F_2^* = \dfrac{S_i/2}{S_E/2} = 9/12 = 0.75$ and compare it to the table value: $F_2^2(\alpha = 0.05)$
   $= 19.00$.

      Since $F_2^* < F_2^2(\alpha = 0.05)$, we do not reject H_0 and conclude that the treatments do not differ significantly.

3. To test the hypothesis H_0: $C_1 = C_2 = C_3 = 0$ vs H_1: The columns are not all $= 0$,

   we from the ratio: $F_3^* = \dfrac{S_k/2}{S_E/2} = 12/12 = 1$ and compare it to the table value:

   $F_2^2(\alpha = 0.05) = 19.00$.

      Since $F_3^* < F_2^2(\alpha = 0.05)$, we do not reject H_0 and conclude that the columns do not differ significantly.

■ ■ ■

12.6   Multifactor Experiments

In multifactor experiments the values of several factors (*i.e.*, independent variables $x_1, x_2, \ldots, x_p$, each examined at any number of desired levels) determine the response (*i.e.*, the value of a single dependent variable y), and we can write:

$$y = f(x_1, x_2, \ldots, x_p) \tag{12.98}$$

in contrast to the single factor experiments discussed previously in which the value of a single factor, examined at several levels (say p) determines the value of the dependent variable y, which we write as: $y = f(x)$.

Note: There is also another type of multifactor experiments, called *2^n factorial experiments*, in which all factors (n) are each evaluated only at 2 levels. We will not discuss 2^n factorial experiments, and our treatment of multifactor experiments will be limited to the case of 2 actors A and B, and the possible factor interaction AB, which is to be taken as a single entity and not as the product of A and B. We limit our discussion to this simple case because the more general case is much more complicated and our desire is to only illustrate how multifactor experiments are analyzed rather than provide a complete coverage of the subject material.

Such problems can be solved by using the "Two-way crossed classification with n observations per cell" method which we will discuss below. Data often arises in a 2-way classification, *i.e.*, there are 2 factors or variables of classification.

Example 7

Suppose in a fermentation experiment the 2 factors: Agitation (at 2 levels) and Organism (at 3 levels) are at work, and we observe the resulting productivity. The result is a 2 × 3 table of data, with 2 duplicate observations, as shown below:

Table 12.29 Original Data Set for Example 7				
		Organism		
		(1)	(2)	(3)
Agitation	High	56	54	55
		58	53	54
	Low	53	55	57
		53	52	54

A tentative model of observations for this problem is:

$$x_{ijk} = \mu + A_i + B_j + Z_{ijk} \tag{12.99}$$

where $i = 1, 2$ (i counts the levels of factor: Agitation)

$j = 1, 2, 3$ (j counts the levels of factor: Organism)

$k = 1, 2$ (k counts the number of duplicate observations per cell)

and $A_1 + A_2 = \displaystyle\sum_{i=1}^{2} A_i = 0$

$B_1 + B_2 + B_3 = \displaystyle\sum_{j=1}^{3} B_j = 0 \tag{12.100}$

$E[Z_{ijk}] = 0$

$V[Z_{ijk}] = \sigma^2$

Based on the tentative model defined by (12.99), which is called an Additive Model, we can estimate from the given data, the parameters μ, A_1, A_2, B_1, B_2, and B_3 and cell averages $\mu + A_i + B_j$.

To accomplish this, we first obtain the cell averages by averaging the two observations in each cell, and then obtain the Agitation level averages, and Organism level averages.

Table 12.30 Estimating Cell Averages for Example 7

		Organism			Agitation Level Averages		
		(1)	**(2)**	**(3)**			
Agitation	**High**	57	53.5	54.5	$\rightarrow \dfrac{57 + 53.5 + 54.5}{3} = \dfrac{165}{3} = 55.0$		
	Low	53	53.5	55.5	$\rightarrow 54.0$		
Organism Level Averages		↓ 55.0	↓ 53.5	↓ 55			

and

$$\text{Grand Mean} = \hat{\mu} = \frac{55 + 54}{2} = \frac{55 + 53.5 + 55}{3} = 54.5$$

Then: Since $\hat{A}_1 + \hat{\mu} = 55$ and $\hat{\mu} = 54.5$, we obtain: $\hat{A}_1 = 0.5$

Since $\hat{A}_2 + \hat{\mu} = 54$ we obtain: $\hat{A}_2 = -0.5$

Since $\hat{B}_1 + \hat{\mu} = 55$ we obtain: $\hat{B}_1 = 0.5$

Since $\hat{B}_2 + \hat{\mu} = 53.5$ we obtain: $\hat{B}_2 = -1.0$

Since $\hat{B}_3 + \hat{\mu} = 55$ we obtain: $\hat{B}_3 = 0.5$

Then, we can estimate the cell averages $\mu + A_i + B_j$, with $\hat{\mu} + \hat{A}_i + \hat{B}_j$ which are

$$\hat{\mu} + \hat{A}_1 + \hat{B}_1 = 54.5 + 0.5 + 0.5 = 55.5$$
$$\hat{\mu} + \hat{A}_2 + \hat{B}_1 = 54.5 - 0.5 + 0.5 = 54.5$$
$$\hat{\mu} + \hat{A}_1 + \hat{B}_2 = 54.5 + 0.5 - 1.0 = 54.0$$
$$\hat{\mu} + \hat{A}_2 + \hat{B}_2 = 54.5 - 0.5 - 1.0 = 53.0$$
$$\hat{\mu} + \hat{A}_1 + \hat{B}_3 = 54.5 + 0.5 + 0.5 = 55.5$$
$$\hat{\mu} + \hat{A}_2 + \hat{B}_3 = 54.5 - 0.5 + 0.5 = 54.5$$

But the additive model we have assumed is too restrictive in many cases and does not always hold true. We require a model which allows for the possibility of interaction between the factors. Such a model is the "Two-way crossed-classification with r observations per cell" with p rows, q columns, and r observations per cell.

Now the model of the observations is

$$x_{ijk} = \mu + A_i + B_j + AB_{ij} + Z_{ijk} \tag{12.101}$$

where $\mu =$ an unknown constant

$A_i = p$ unknown constants ("row effects")

$B_j = q$ unknown constants ("column effects")

$AB_{ij} = pq$ unknown constants ("interaction effects")

$$\sum_{i=1}^{p} A_i = \sum_{j=i}^{q} B_i = \sum_{i=1}^{p} AB_{ij} = \sum_{j=1}^{q} AB_{ij} = 0$$

$Z_{ijk} = N(0, \sigma^2)$, and σ^2 is an unknown constant.

The H_0/H_1 hypotheses to be tested are

1. $H_0: A_1 = A_2 = \cdots = A_p = 0$ vs H_1: The row effects are not all $= 0$

2. $H_0: B_1 = B_2 = \cdots = B_q = 0$ vs H_1: The column effects are not all $= 0$

3. $H_0: \begin{cases} AB_{11} = AB_{12} = \cdots = AB_{1q} \\ AB_{21} = AB_{22} = \cdots = AB_{2q} \\ AB_{p1} = AB_{p2} = \cdots = AB_{pq} \end{cases} = 0$ vs H_1: The interactions are not all $= 0$

Note: AB is to be regarded as a single symbol, not a product of A and B.

Note: A_i is the deviation of row i mean from the grand mean and B_j is the deviation of column j mean from the grand mean.

The ANOVA table for this case is

Table 12.31 ANOVA Table For Multifactor Experiment

Source of Variation	DOF	SUMS of Squares SS	MS = $\dfrac{SS}{DOF}$	E(MS)
Rows i	$p-1$	$S_i = rq \sum\limits_{i=1}^{p} (\bar{x}_{i\cdot\cdot} - \bar{x}_{\cdots})^2$	$\dfrac{S_i}{p-1}$	$\sigma^2 + rq\left(\dfrac{\sum\limits_{i=1}^{p} A_i^2}{p-1}\right)$
Columns j	$q-1$	$S_i = rp \sum\limits_{i=1}^{p} (\bar{x}_{\cdot j\cdot} - \bar{x}_{\cdots})^2$	$\dfrac{S_i}{q-1}$	$\sigma^2 + rp\left(\dfrac{\sum\limits_{j=1}^{q} B_i^2}{q-1}\right)$
Interaction ij	$(p-1)(q-1)$	$S_{ij} = r \sum\limits_{i=1}^{p} \sum\limits_{j=1}^{q} (\bar{x}_{ij\cdot} - \bar{x}_{i\cdot\cdot} - \bar{x}_{\cdot j\cdot} + \bar{x}_{\cdots})^2$	$\dfrac{S_{ij}}{(p-1)(q-1)}$	$\sigma^2 + r\left(\dfrac{\sum\limits_{i=1}^{p}\sum\limits_{j=1}^{q}(AB_{ij})^2}{(p-1)(q-1)}\right)$
Error $K(ij)$	$pq(r-1)$	$S_k(ij) = \sum\limits_{i=1}^{p} \sum\limits_{j=1}^{q} \sum\limits_{k=1}^{r} (\bar{x}_{ijk} - \bar{x}_{ij\cdot})^2$	$\dfrac{S_k(ij)}{pq(r-1)}$	σ^2
Total ijk	$pqr-1$	$S = \sum\limits_{i=1}^{p} \sum\limits_{j=1}^{q} \sum\limits_{k=1}^{r} (\bar{x}_{ijk} - \bar{x}_{\cdots})^2$ $= S_i + S_j + S_{ij} + S_k(ij)$	$\dfrac{S}{pqr-1}$	

The calculations for the needed sums of squares are performed using the equations:

$$S_i = C_i - C \tag{12.102}$$
$$S_i = C_i - C \tag{12.103}$$
$$S_{ij} = C_{ij} - C_i - C_j + C \tag{12.104}$$
$$S_k(ij) = C_{ijk} - C_{ij} \tag{12.105}$$
$$S = C_{ijk} - C \tag{12.106}$$

where

C_{ijk} = sum of squares of all of the given data in its coded form

(from the ijk table) $\tag{12.107}$

$$C_{ij} = \frac{(Cell_1Total)^2 + (Cell_2Total)^2 + (Cell_3Total)^2}{(Entries/Cell)}$$

$$+ \frac{(Cell_4Total)^2 + (Cell_5Total)^2 + (Cell_6Total)^2}{(Entries/Cell)} \qquad (12.108)$$

(From the ij table, obtained from the ijk table by adding the cell entries)

$$C_i = \frac{(Row_1Total)^2 + (Row_2Total)^2 + \cdots + (Row_pTotal)^2}{(Number\ of\ observations\ per\ row)} \qquad (12.109)$$

$$C_j = \frac{(Col_1Total)^2 + (Col_2Total)^2 + \cdots + (Col_qTotal)^2}{(Number\ of\ observations\ per\ column)} \qquad (12.110)$$

$$C = \frac{(Grand\ Total)^2}{Total\ Number\ of\ observations} \qquad (12.111)$$

Let us now continue with the data of example 7 above, by constructing the corresponding ANOVA table and then testing for row effects, column effects, and interaction effects.

1. Code the data by subtracting 55 (where: $55 = midrange = \dfrac{H + L}{2} = \dfrac{58 + 52}{2} = 55$

   to obtain

Table 12.32   Coded Data For Example 7

		Organism		
		(1)	**(2)**	**(3)**
Agitation	**High**	1	−1	0
		3	−2	−1
	Low	−2	0	2
		−2	−3	−1

←— ijk Table —→

Add the cell values to obtain the "ij" Table

	Organism			"i"
	1	**2**	**3**	**Table**
High	4	−3	−1	→ 0
Low	−4	−3	1	→ −6

"ij" Table

0	−6	0	→ −6

"j" Table   Grand Total

Then, using the "ijk" Table, we obtain

$$C_{ijk} = 1^2 + 3^2 + (-1)^2 + (-2)^2 + 0^2 + (-1)^2 + (-2)^2 + (-2)^2 + 0^2$$
$$+ (-3)^2 + 2^2 + (-1)^2$$
$$= 1 + 9 + 1 + 4 + 0 + 1 + 4 + 4 + 0 + 9 + 4 + 1 = 38$$

Using the "ij" Table we obtain

$$C_{ij} = \frac{4^2 + (-3)^2 + (-1)^2 + (-4)^2 + (-3)^2 + 1^2}{2(entries \, / \, cell)}$$
$$= \frac{16 + 9 + 1 + 16 + 9 + 1}{2} = \frac{52}{2} = 26$$

Using the "i" Table we obtain:

$$C_i = \frac{0^2 + (-6)^2}{(observations \, / \, Row)} = \frac{36}{6} = 6$$

Using the "j" Table we obtain

$$C_j = \frac{0^2 + (-6)^2 + 0^2}{(Observations \, / \, Columns)} = \frac{36}{4} = 9$$

Using the Grand Total value, we obtain

$$C = \frac{(Grand \, Total)^2}{Total \, Number \, of \, Observations} = \frac{(-6)^2}{12} = \frac{36}{12} = 3$$

Therefore

$S_i = C_i - C$	$= 6 - 3$	$= 3$
$S_j = C_j - C$	$= 9 - 3$	$= 6$
$S_{ij} = C_{ij} - C_i - C_j + C$	$= 26 - 6 - 9 + 3$	$= 14$
$S_k(ij) = C_{ijk} - C_{ij}$	$= 38 - 26$	$= 12$
$S = C_{ijk} - C$	$= 38 - 3$	$= 35$

and the ANOVA table becomes

Table 12.33 ANOVA Table for Example 7

Source of Variation	DOF	SS	MS = SS/DOF	E(MS)
Rows(i)	$p - 1 = 2 - 1 = 1$	$S_i = 3$	$S_i/p - 1 = 3/1 = 3$	$\sigma^2 + 6\sigma_A^2*$
Columns(j)	$q - 1 = 3 - 1 = 2$	$S_j = 6$	$S_j/q - 1 = 6/2 = 3$	$\sigma^2 + 4\sigma_B^2*$
Interaction(ij)	$(p - 1)(q - 1) = 1 \times 2 = 2$	$S_{ij} = 14$	$S_{ij}/(p - 1)(q - 1) = 14/2 = 7$	$\sigma^2 + 2\sigma_{AB}^2*$
Error k(ij)	$pq(r - 1) = 2 \times 3(2 - 1) = 6$	$S_k(ij) = 12$	$S_k(ij)/6 = 12/6 = 2$	σ^2
Total (ijk)	$pqr - 1 = (2)(3)(2) - 1 = 11$	$S = 35$	$S/11 = 35/11 = 3.181$	

* Where σ_A^2, σ_B^2 and σ_{AB}^2 and are not variances but are, respectively, equal to

$$\sigma_A^2 = \frac{1}{p - 1}\sum_{i=i}^{p} A_i^2 \, ; \sigma_B^2 = \frac{1}{q - 1}\sum_{j=1}^{q} B_i^2 \, ; \text{ and } \sigma_{AB}^2 = \frac{1}{(p - 1)(q - 1)} \sum_{i=1}^{p}\sum_{j=1}^{q}(AB)_{ij}^2$$

We are now ready to perform the tests of interest. When testing, ***test for interaction first***. If there is no interaction present, we can make a definitive statement about the effect of the factors on the response variable. If interaction exists, do not bother to look at the individual factors because the results are usually ambiguous.

To test for interaction in this problem, we form the ratio:

$$F^*_{Ineraction} = \frac{S_{ij}/(p-1)(q-1)}{S_k(ij)/pq(r-1)} = \frac{14/2}{12/6} = \frac{7}{2} = 3.5 \text{ and compare against:}$$

$$F^{(p-1)(q-1)}_{pq(r-1)}(\alpha) = F^2_6(\alpha) = \begin{cases} 5.14 \text{ if } \alpha = 0.05 \\ 3.46 \text{ if } \alpha = 0.10 \end{cases}$$

Therefore, if $\alpha = 0.10$, H_0: Interaction effects $= 0$ is rejected and we conclude that the interaction effects between the factors Agitation and Organism are significant (*i.e.*, significantly different than zero). When interaction is present, it does not make much sense to test for the significance of the individual factors. Instead, we should state the results separately for each treatment (*i.e.*, combination of levels of factors).

For example, from Table 12.30, we note that for Organism (1) changing the Agitation factor from low to high increased productivity by: $57 - 53 = 4$ units but, what we actually need here, because this is a sampling study, is a confidence interval about the value 4; but to do this we need to first obtain the standard deviation of the estimator $(\hat{\theta}_1)$ whose value is equal to 4.

We proceed as follows: we first note that the value of 57 represents the average of 2 other values ($x_1 = 56$ and $x_2 = 58$), and similarly the value of 53 represents the average of 2 other values ($x_3 = 53$ and $x_4 = 53$). Therefore, we can write:

$$\hat{\theta}_1 = \frac{x_1 + x_2}{2} - \frac{x_3 + x_4}{2} \left(= \frac{56 + 58}{2} - \frac{53 + 53}{2} = 57 - 53 = 4 \right) \quad (12.112)$$

and then

$$V(\hat{\theta}_1) = \frac{1}{4}[V(x_1) + V(x_2)] + \left(-\frac{1}{2}\right)^2 [V(x_3) + V(x_4)] \quad (12.113)$$

$$= \frac{1}{4}[V(x_1) + V(x_2) + V(x_3) + V(x_4)]$$

$$= \frac{1}{2}[\sigma^2 + \sigma^2 + \sigma^2 + \sigma^2] = \frac{1}{4}[4\sigma^2] = \sigma^2$$

Note: When using the 3 subscripts to describe each x_{ijk} value, the 4 variables (x_1, x_2, x_3, x_4) we introduced above are respectively: $x_{111}, x_{112}, x_{211}$ and x_{212}.

From the ANOVA table we have that $V(ijk) = \sigma^2 = 2$, is an estimate of the population variance based on DOF $= 6$. To obtain a 95% C.I. on the parameter (θ_1) whose estimator $\hat{\theta}_1$ has a standard deviation of $\sigma(\hat{\theta}_1) = \sqrt{2}$ and is t_6 distributed (because $n < 30$ and σ is not known but is estimated from the data), we use the equation

$$P[\hat{\theta}_1 - t_\delta(\alpha/2)\alpha(\hat{\theta}_1) \le \hat{\theta}_1 + t_\delta(\alpha/2)\sigma(\hat{\theta}_1)] = 1 - \alpha$$

or $P[4 - 2.4469(1.414) \le \theta_1 \le 4 + 2.4469(1.414)] = 0.95$

or $P[0.54 \le \theta_1 \le 7.46] = 0.95$

Similar confidence intervals can be constructed for each combination of the levels of the factors separately. This is the kind of statement one wants to make when one is asked about practical recommendations (*i.e.*, in this case, for organism 1, when agitation is increased from low to high, we expect the productivity to increase from 0.54 to 7.46, and we are 95% certain that it will do so).

On the other hand **if interactions are not significant, as is the case if = 0.05,** we can proceed to test for row and column effects as follows

1. To test for row effects, form the ratio $F^*_{Row} = \dfrac{S_i / (p-1)}{S_k (ij) / pq (r-1)} = \dfrac{3}{2} = 1.5$ and compare to:

$$F^1_6 (\alpha) = \begin{cases} F^1_6 (0.05) = 5.99 \\ F^1_6 (0.10) = 3.78 \end{cases}$$

Since $F^*_{Row} = 1.5 < F^1_6 (0.05) = 5.99$, we do not reject H_0: Row effects = 0, and conclude that row effects (*i.e.*, the factor agitation changing from low to high) are not significantly different than zero.). The same conclusion is reached for $\alpha = 0.1$.

2. To test for column effects (*i.e.*, the effect of changing organisms), form the ratio

$$F^*_{Colunm} = \dfrac{S_j / (p-1)}{S_k (ij) / pq (r-1)} = \dfrac{6/2}{12/6} = 3/2 = 1.5 \text{ and compare to}$$

$$F^2_6 (\alpha) = \begin{cases} 5.14 & if\ \alpha = 0.05 \\ 3.46 & if\ \alpha = 0.10 \end{cases}$$

Since $F^*_{Column} < F^2_6 (\alpha)$, we do not reject H_0: Column effects = 0, and conclude that column effects (*i.e.*, changing organism from 1 to 2 to 3) are not significantly different than zero.

Therefore, when $\alpha = 0.05$, no interaction is present and the 2 factors: Agitation and Organism do not have a significant effect on productivity.

12.7   The *P*-Value and Computer Solutions

12.7.1 The *P*-Value

The hypothesis tests problems we solved in Chapter 11, and the ones we solved in this chapter, all depend on the use of a "fixed level of significance", *i.e.*, on a fixed value of α which determines the rejection region, against which the "value of the test statistic" (*i.e.*, Z^*, X^*, F^*, t^*) is compared, and the decision is made to reject or not reject H_0 depending on whether the value of the test statistic falls inside or outside of the rejection region, respectively.

But there is another approach possible to hypothesis testing which uses the **p-value, which is defined as the probability of obtaining a test statistic value equal to or more extreme (i.e. greater than or less than) the result observed, provided that H_0 is true.**

The definition above has the following mathematical interpretation, depending on the population parameter being tested and the sampling distribution of its estimator, namely: (See Table 12.34 below)

For the population parameters in groups 1 (*i.e.*, $\mu, \Delta\mu, \Delta\sigma^2, Z_\rho, \alpha, \beta$) whose estimators ($\bar{x}, \Delta\bar{x}, \Delta\hat{s}^2, Z_r, a, b$) are Normally distributed, the value of the test statistic is

$Z^* = \dfrac{\hat{\theta} - \theta_0}{\sigma(\hat{\theta})}$ and the *p*–value is defined as

$$p-\text{value} = P(Z \geq Z^*) \text{ or: } p = P[Z \leq Z^*], \tag{12.114}$$

and will be calculated from the *Z*-distribution.

For the population parameters in group 2 ($(i.e., \sigma^2$ and $\sigma)$ whose estimators ($\hat{s}^2$ and $\hat{s}$) are χ^2- distributed, the value of the test statistic is $\chi^{2*} = \dfrac{(n-1)\hat{s}^2}{\sigma^2}$, and the p-value is defined as:

$$p-\text{value} = P[\chi^2 \geq \chi^{2*}] \text{ } or: p = P[\chi^2 \leq \chi^{2*}], \quad (12.115)$$

and will be calculated from the χ^2_{n-1} distribution.

For the population parameter in group 3 $\left(i.e. \dfrac{\sigma_1^2}{\sigma_2^2}\right)$ whose estimator $\left(\dfrac{\hat{s}_1^2}{\hat{s}_2^2}\right)$ is F-distributed, the value of the test statistic is $F^* = \dfrac{\hat{s}_1^2}{\hat{s}_2^2}$, and the p-value is defined as:

$$p-\text{value} = P[F \geq F^*] \text{ } or: p = P[F \leq F^*], \quad (12.116)$$

and will be calculated from the $F_{n_2-1}^{n_1-1}$ distribution.

Table 12.34 Calculation of p-value for the Parameters of Interest					
	Population Parameter (θ)	**Estimator** $(\hat{\theta})$	**Sampling Distribution**	**Value of Test Statistic**	**p-value**
1	μ	$\bar{x}$	$N(\mu, \sigma/\sqrt{n})$		
	$\Delta\mu = \mu_1 - \mu_2$	$\Delta\bar{x} = \bar{x}_1 - \bar{x}_2$	$N\left(\Delta\mu, \sqrt{\dfrac{\sigma_1^2}{n_1} + \dfrac{\sigma_2^2}{n_2}}\right)$		
	$\Delta\sigma^2 = \sigma_1^2 - \sigma_2^2$	$\Delta\hat{s}^2 = \hat{s}_1^2 - \hat{s}_2^2$	$N\left(\Delta\sigma^2, \sqrt{\dfrac{2\sigma_1^4}{n_1-1} + \dfrac{2\sigma_2^4}{n_2-1}}\right)$		
	Z_ρ	Z_r	$N(Z_\rho, \dfrac{1}{\sqrt{n-3}})$	$Z^* = \dfrac{\hat{\theta} - \theta_0}{\sigma(\hat{\theta})}$	$P[Z \geq Z^*]$ or $P[Z \leq Z^*]$
	α	a	$N\left(\alpha, \dfrac{\sigma^2}{n}\left[\dfrac{\sum_{i=1}^{n} x_i^2}{\sum_{i=1}^{n}(x_i - \bar{x})^2}\right]\right)$		
	β	b	$N\left(\beta, \sigma^2\left[\dfrac{1}{\sum_{i=1}^{n}(x_i - \bar{x})^2}\right]\right)$		
2	σ^2	$\hat{s}^2$	χ^2_{n-1}	$\chi^{2*} = \dfrac{(n-1)\hat{s}^2}{\sigma^2}$	$P[\chi^2 \geq \chi^{2\star}]$ or $P[\chi^2 \leq \chi^{2\star}]$
3	$\dfrac{\sigma_1^2}{\sigma_2^2}$	$\dfrac{\hat{s}_1^2}{\hat{s}_2^2}$	$F_{\delta_2=n_2-1}^{\delta_1=n_1-1}$	$F^* = \dfrac{\hat{s}_1^2}{\hat{s}_2^2}$	$P[F \geq F^*]$ or $P[F \leq F^*]$

(Continued)

Table 12.34 Continued

	Population Parameter (θ)	**Estimator** $(\hat{\theta})$	**Sampling Distribution**	**Value of Test Statistic**	**P-value**
4	μ	$\bar{x}$	t_{n-1}		
	μ_d	$\bar{d}$	t_{n-1}		
	$\Delta\mu$	$\Delta\bar{x} = \bar{x}_1 - \bar{x}_2$	$t_{n_1+n_2-2}$	$t^* = \dfrac{\hat{\theta} - \theta_0}{\sigma(\hat{\theta})}$	$P[t \geq t^*]$ or $P[t \leq t^*]$
	α	a	t_{n-2}		
	β	b	t_{n-2}		

For the population parameters in group 4 (*i.e.,* μ, μ_d, $\Delta\mu$, α, β) whose estimators ($\bar{x}$, $\bar{d}$, $\Delta\bar{x}$, a, b) are *t*-distributed, the value of the test statistic is $t^* = \dfrac{\hat{\theta} - \theta_0}{\sigma(\hat{\theta})}$, and the *p*-value is defined as:

$$p-\text{value} = P[t \geq t^*] \text{ or: } p = P[t \leq t^*], \qquad (12.117)$$

and will be calculated from the appropriate *t*-distribution, as shown.

The *p*-value is usually referred to as the "observed level of significance", in contrast to the α-value which is the "fixed level of significance", and represents the smallest level at which H_0 can be rejected, for a given data set. The relationship between the α-value and *p*-value tests is summarized by the following rule

1. *If* $p \geq \alpha$ Do not reject H_0 (12.118)

2. *If* $p < \alpha$ Reject H_0

If the hypothesis being tested is a one-tailed test, the p-value represents the probability in only one tail of the distribution. To illustrate the calculation of the p-value, for a one-tailed test, consider the following example:

Example 8

A manufacturer of batteries claims that the mean life of his product will exceed 30 hours. A customer wants to buy a large quantity of these batteries if the claim is true. A random sample of 36 batteries is tested and produces a sample mean of $\bar{x} = 34$ hours. If the standard deviation is $\sigma = 10$ hours, test the hypotheses: H_0: $\mu \leq 30$ vs H_1: $\mu > 30$ at $\alpha = 0.01$.

Solution Since σ is known (and $n > 30$), $\dfrac{\bar{x} - \mu_0}{\sigma/\sqrt{n}}$ is Normally distributed and the hypothesis test will consist of the following steps

1. H_0: $\mu \leq 30$ vs H_1: $\mu > 30$
2. $\alpha = 0.01$
3. The estimator for μ *is* $\bar{x}$, and $\dfrac{\bar{x} - \mu_0}{\sigma/\sqrt{n}} = \dfrac{\bar{x} - 30}{10/\sqrt{36}}$

$$= \dfrac{\bar{x} - 30}{10/6} \rightarrow N(0,1)$$

4. Rejection Region:

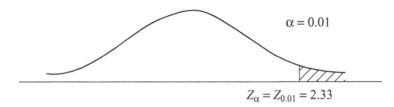

$$\alpha = 0.01$$

$$Z_\alpha = Z_{0.01} = 2.33$$

5. Value of test statistic $= Z^* = \dfrac{\hat{\theta} - \theta}{\sigma(\hat{\theta})} = \dfrac{\bar{x} - \mu_0}{\sigma(\bar{x})} = \dfrac{34 - 30}{10/6} = \dfrac{24}{10} = 2.4$

6. Since $Z^* > Z_{0.01}$, H_0 is rejected.

7. Conclusion: The mean life of the batteries is greater than 30 hours and the buyer will buy the product.

Let us now calculate the p-value of this test. According to the mathematical definition of the p-value, for parameters with Normally distributed estimators given by equation (12.114), we are looking for

$$p\text{- value} = P[Z \geq Z^*] = P[Z \geq 2.4] \int_{z^* = 2.4}^{\infty} f(Z)dZ \qquad (12.119)$$

$$= 1 - P[Z \leq 2.4] = 1 - (0.5 + 0.4918) = 0.0082$$

Since $p = 0.0082 < \alpha = 0.01$, the H_0 of example 12.8 above, is, again rejected in agreement with the rule expressed by equation (12.118).

Let us now see how we calculate the p-value using the F-distribution, for a one-tailed test.

■ ■ ■

Example 9

In exercise 1 of Chapter 12 we tested the hypotheses:

$$H_0: \frac{\sigma_{Among}^2}{\sigma_{Within}^2} \leq 1 \quad vs \quad H_1: \frac{\sigma_{Among}^2}{\sigma_{Within}^2} > 1, \text{ at } \alpha = 0.05.$$

Since $F^* = (SSA/p - 1)/[SSW/p(n - 1)] = (106/4 \ (96/15) = 4.14 > F_{15}^4 (0.05) = 3.06$, H_0 is rejected at $\alpha = 0.05$.

To find the p-value of this test, we need to find:

$$p\text{- value} = P[F > F^*] = p[F > 4.14] = \int_{F^*=4.14}^{\infty} f(F_{15}^4)dF \qquad (12.120)$$

To find this value of p, we need to look up the available F tables, when the F variable is F_{15}^4, and hope that it corresponds to one of them, or comes close to one of them, since closed-form (or analytical) integration using the F distribution (and also Z, χ^2, and t) is very difficult.

From the available F tables we obtain:

If $\alpha = 0.100 \quad F_{15}^4 (0.1) \ = 2.36$
$\quad \alpha = 0.050 \quad F_{15}^4 (0.05) \ = 3.06$
$\quad \alpha = 0.025 \quad F_{15}^4 (0.025) = 3.80$
$\quad ? \qquad\qquad F^*(\alpha = ?) = 4.14$
$\quad \alpha = 0.010 \quad F_{15}^4 (0.010) = 4.89$
$\quad \alpha = 0.005 \quad F_{15}^4 (0.005) = 5.89$

It is clear from the table above that the p-value we are looking for is between 0.010 and 0.025 (*i.e.* $0.010 < p < 0.025$), but the exact value can not be obtained from the available F-tables

Fortunately, most of the available statistical packages, including Minitab, now present the p-value as part of the output for many hypothesis testing procedures, including ANOVA, as will be illustrated below in our Computer Solutions section.

But let us first show, with a small Minitab program, how the p-value for the above example may be calculated, and then briefly discuss the p-value for a two-tailed hypothesis test.

$$\text{MTB} > \text{CDF } 4.14 \text{ K1};$$
$$\text{SUBC} > \text{F } 4.14$$
$$\text{MTB} > \text{NAME C6} = \text{'4 15'} \tag{12.121}$$
$$\text{MTB} > \text{LET "4 15"} = 1 - \text{K1}$$
$$\text{MTB} > 0.019, \text{ and this is the p-value we are looking for.}$$

If a two-tailed test is being performed, the p-value represents the probability at both tails of the distribution.

■ ■ ■

Let us illustrate the calculation of the p-value for a two-tailed test with the following example:

Example 10

A sample of 80 steel wires produced by factory A yields a sample mean breaking strength of 1230 pounds, with a sample standard deviation of 120 pounds. A sample of 100 wires, produced by factory B, yields a sample mean breaking strength of 1190 pounds and a standard deviation of 90 pounds. Are the two mean population strengths (μ_A, μ_B) equal at $\alpha = 0.01$?

Solution

1. H_0: $\Delta\mu = \mu_A - \mu_B = 0$ vs H_1: $\Delta\mu \neq 0$
2. $\alpha = 0.01$ and $\alpha/2 = 0.005$
3. The estimator for $\Delta\mu$ is $\Delta\bar{x} = \bar{x}_A - \bar{x}_B$ ($\Delta\bar{x} = 1230 - 1190 = 40$) and

$$\frac{\Delta\bar{x}}{\sigma(\Delta\bar{x})} \rightarrow N(0, 1) \text{ because } n_1 > 30 \text{ and } n_2 > 30,$$

where $\quad \sigma(\Delta\bar{x}) = \sqrt{\dfrac{\hat{s}_1^2}{n_1} + \dfrac{\hat{s}_2^2}{n_2}} = \sqrt{\dfrac{(120)^2}{80} + \dfrac{(90)^2}{100}} = \sqrt{180 + 81} = 16.15$

4. Rejection Region

$\alpha/2 = 0.005 \qquad\qquad\qquad\qquad\qquad \alpha/2 = 0.005$

$Z_{0.995} = -Z_{0.005} = -2.58 \qquad\qquad\qquad Z_{0.005} = 2.58$

5. Value of test statistic $= Z^* = \dfrac{\Delta\bar{x} - 0}{\sigma(\Delta\bar{x})} = \dfrac{40 - 0}{16.15} = 2.48$

6. Since $Z_{0.995} < Z^* < Z_{0.005}$ (*i.e.*, Z^* is outside of the rejection region), H_0 is not rejected at $\alpha = 0.01$.

7. Conclusion: The mean breaking strength of the steel wires produced by the two factories is the same.

Let us now calculate the p-value of this test, which is a two-tailed test.

We are looking for:

$$p\text{- value} = P[Z > Z^*] + P[Z < -Z^*] = \int_{Z^*}^{\infty} f(Z)dZ + \int_{-\infty}^{-Z^*} f(Z)dZ \quad (12.122)$$

Since the normal distribution is symmetric, we have:

$$P[Z < -Z^*] = P[Z > Z^*] \quad (12.123)$$

and we can write:

$$p\text{- value} = 2P[Z > Z^*] = 2\text{Prob}(Z > 2.48) = 2[1 - \text{Prob}(Z < 2.48)$$

$$= 2[1 - (0.5 + 0.4934)] = 0.0132$$

Since the p-value $= 0.0132 > \alpha = 0.01$, H_0 is not rejected, in agreement with equation (12.118).

We offer the following general comment regarding the calculation of the p-value: If we are testing for a population parameter (θ) whose estimator $(\hat{\theta})$ is normally distributed, the p-value can be calculated relatively easily, for both one-tailed and two-tailed tests, as shown above. This is so because the normal distribution is symmetrical and does not depend on the degrees of freedom.

For population parameters (θ) whose estimators $(\hat{\theta})$ are: t-distributed, χ^2-distributed and F-distributed, the calculation becomes more difficult because all 3 of these distributions depend on the degrees of freedom, even though the t-distribution is also symmetrical. For χ^2 and F distributed estimators the calculation is much more difficult because, in addition to their dependence on the degrees of freedom, they are also non-symmetric and left-tail values have to be calculated separately.

12.7.2 Computer Solutions

We have shown in this chapter how to use the ANOVA methodology to solve problems which require the testing of the hypotheses:

$$H_0: \mu_1 = \mu_2 = \ldots = \mu_k \text{ vs } H_1: \text{ The means are not all equal.}$$

In this section we will use the ANOVA methodology to solve Exercises 1 and 2 both by hand and by showing how Minitab can be used to obtain the solutions to such problems, and then point out that the 2 solutions are identical.

What is of special interest to us here is the fact that the computer solution also includes the calculation of the p-value, which is included as part of the Minitab output.

Example 11 (See Problems & Solutions, Problem 1)

Coding the given data by using the formula: Coded Data = Given Data − 9 (Mid - range), we obtain: $C_{ij} = 222$, $C_i = 126$, and $C = 20$, from which we obtain:

$TSS = C_{ij} - C = 222 - 20 = 202$; $SSA = C_i - C = 126 - 20 = 106$;

and: $SSW = C_{ij} - C_i = 222 - 126 = 96$,

and the ANOVA table is:

Table 12.35 ANOVA Table for Example 11			
Source of Variation	DOF	SS	MS = SS/DOF
Variation Among Treatments	$p - 1 = 4$	$SSA = 106$	$106/4 = 26.5$
Variation Within Treatments	$p(n - 1) = 5 \times 3 = 15$	$SSW = 96$	$96/15 = 6.4$
Total Variation	$pn - 1 = 20 - 1 = 19$	$TSS = 202$	$202/19 = 10.63$

The hypothesis being tested is: $H_0: \mu_1 = \mu_2 = \mu_3 = \mu_4 = \mu_5$ vs H_1: The means are not all equal, or the equivalent:

$$H_0: \frac{\sigma^2_{Among}}{\sigma^2_{Within}} \leq 1 \quad vs \quad H_1: \frac{\sigma^2_{Among}}{\sigma^2_{Within}} > 1$$

To fully test this hypothesis we need to follow the 7-step procedure, which is as follows:

1. $H_0: \dfrac{\sigma^2_{Among}}{\sigma^2_{Within}} \leq 1$ vs $H_1: \dfrac{\sigma^2_{Among}}{\sigma^2_{Within}} > 1$

2. Specify value of $\alpha = 0.05$

3. The estimator for $\dfrac{\sigma^2_{Among}}{\sigma^2_{Within}}$ is $\dfrac{SSA/p-1}{SSW/p(n-1)}$ which is $F^{p-1}_{p(n-1)} = F^4_{15}$

4. Rejection region:

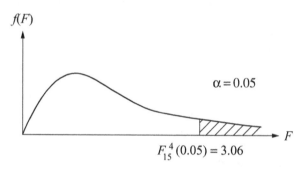

$$F^4_{15}(0.05) = 3.06$$

5. Value of test statistic $= F^* = \dfrac{SSA/p-1}{SSW/p(n-1)} = \dfrac{106/4}{96/15} = 4.14$

6. Since $F^* = 4.14 > F^4_{15}(0.05) = 3.06$, H_0 is rejected.
7. Conclusion: The 5 means are not equal.

Note: To find which paired means caused the rejection of H_0, we need to:

a) Calculate the

$$LSD = \sqrt{\frac{2}{n}[\frac{SSW}{p(n-1)}][F^1_{p(n-1)}(\alpha/2)]} = \sqrt{\frac{2}{4}[\frac{96}{15}][F^1_{15}(0.025)]} = 4.45$$

b) Calculate the absolute value of the paired sample mean differences:

$$|\bar{x}_1 - \bar{x}_2| = 4.5, |\bar{x}_1 - \bar{x}_3| = 0.5, |\bar{x}_1 - \bar{x}_4| = 5, |\bar{x}_1 - \bar{x}_5| = 1, |\bar{x}_2 - \bar{x}_3| = 5,$$

$$|\bar{x}_2 - \bar{x}_4| = 0.5, |\bar{x}_2 - \bar{x}_5| = 3.5, |\bar{x}_3 - \bar{x}_4| = 5.5, |\bar{x}_3 - \bar{x}_5| = 1.5, \text{ and}$$

$$|\bar{x}_4 - \bar{x}_5| = 1$$

c) Compare these differences to the LSD. The differences which exceed the LSD are the ones which caused the rejection of H_0.
d) Conclusion: $\mu_1 \neq \mu_2, \mu_1 \neq \mu_4, \mu_2 \neq \mu_3,$ and $\mu_3 \neq \mu_4,$

The p-value for this test was calculated previously by hand and is given in equation (12.121) where we find that: $p = 0.019$. Let us now see how this same problem can be solved by Minitab.

The Minitab page consists of 2 half windows: The Session window and the Worksheet 1 window. To use the Session window the Minitab prompt, MTB >, must be shown on the Session window. If it is not shown, go to the "Editor" and "Enable the command language", and the MTB >prompt will be generated.

We then enter the data as shown below:

> MTB > READ C1-C5
> DATA > 4 7 5 11 4
> DATA > 6 13 4 10 8
> DATA > 4 10 4 9 6
> DATA > 10 12 9 14 10
> DATA > END

The computer responds with: ***4 Rows Read.*** Then we issue the command

> MTB > AOVoneway of the data in C1 – C5

The computer responds with an ANOVA table which is exactly the same as the ANOVA table above but also includes the *p*-value which is equal to 0.019 (as previously calculated by hand), and other useful information, such as: The mean and standard deviation and the number of observations for each population, the pooled standard deviation which is given by:

$$\hat{s} = \sqrt{\left[\hat{s}_1^2 + \hat{s}_2^2 + \hat{s}_3^2 + \hat{s}_4^2 + \hat{s}_5^2\right]/5}$$

$$= \sqrt{\frac{(2.828)^2 + (2.646)^2 + (2.380)^2 + (2.160)^2 + (2.582)^2}{5}}$$

$$= \sqrt{31.995624/5} = \sqrt{6.3991248} = 2.53 \tag{12.124}$$

and 95% C.I. on each individual mean, using the pooled standard deviation given by (12.124). Note that some of these confidence intervals overlap while others do not, suggesting that some of the means are the same while others are different, and this is the same conclusion we reached by our hand solution when we identified the pairs of means which are different and caused the rejection of H_0.

The computer output for Example 11 is given in Table 12.36.

Table 12.36 Minitab Solution for Example 11

```
MTB > read c1-c5
DATA> 4 7 5 11 4
DATA> 6 13 4 10 8
DATA> 4 10 4 9 6
DATA> 10 12 9 14 10
DATA> end
      4 rows read.
MTB > aovoneway c1-c5
One-way ANOVA: C1, C2, C3, C4, C5
Analysis of Variance
Source    DOF       SS       MS       F        P
Factor     4     106.00    26.50    4.14    0.019
Error     15      96.00     6.40
Total     19     202.00

                             Individual 95% CIs For Mean
                             Based on Pooled StDev
Level      N      Mean    StDev   -+---------+---------+---------+-----
C1         4     6.000    2.828     (--------*--------)
C2         4    10.500    2.646                   (--------*--------)
C3         4     5.500    2.380   (--------*--------)
C4         4    11.000    2.160                     (--------*--------)
C5         4     7.000    2.582       (--------*--------)
                                   -+---------+---------+---------+-----
Pooled StDev =    2.530           3.0      6.0      9.0     12.0
```

Example 12 (See Problems and Solutions, Problem 2)

In this problem $n_1 = 5$, $n_2 = 7$, and $n_3 = 6$.

Coding the data by subtracting 80, we obtain

$C_{ij} = 13027$, $C_i = (61)^2/5 + (281)^2/7 + (-27)^2/6 = 12145.84$, and

$C = (315)^2/(5 + 7 + 6) = 5512.5$ from which we obtain

$TSS = C_{ij} - C = 13027 - 5512.5 = 7514.5$; $SSA = C_i - C = 12145.84 - 5512.5$

$= 6633.34$ and $SSW = C_{ij} - C_i = 13027 - 12145.84 = 881.16$

The DOF for $TSS = n_1 + n_2 + n_3 - 1 = 17$

DOF for $SSA = p - 1 = 2$

DOF for $SSW = n_1 + n_2 + n_3 - 3 = 15$

Therefore, the ANOVA table for this problem is

Table 12.37 ANOVA Table for Example 12

Source of Variation	DOF	Sum of Squares	MS = SS/DOF
Variation Among Treatments	$p - 1 = 3 - 1 = 2$	$SSA = 6633.34$	$6633.34/2 = 3316.67$
Variation Within Treatments	$n_1 + n_2 + n_3 - p =$ $5 + 7 + 6 - 3 = 15$	$SSW = 881.16$	$881.16/15 = 58.74$
Total Variation	$n_1 + n_2 + n_3 - 1 =$ $5 + 7 + 6 - 1 = 17$	$TSS = 7514.50$	$7514.5/17 = 442.03$

The hypothesis being tested is: H_0: $\mu_1 = \mu_2 = \mu_3$ vs H_1: The means are not all equal,

or the equivalent: H_0: $\dfrac{\sigma^2_{Among}}{\sigma^2_{Within}} \leq 1$ vs H_1: $\dfrac{\sigma^2_{Among}}{\sigma^2_{Within}} > 1$

and since $F^* = \dfrac{SSA/p - 1}{SSW/(n_1 + n_2 + n_3 - 3)} = \dfrac{6633.34/2}{881.16/15}$

$= 56.46 > F^2_{15}(0.05) = 3.68$, H_0 is rejected and we conclude that the 3 means are not the same, at $\alpha = 0.05$.

To find the means which caused the Rejection of H_0, we must calculate a separate LSD for each pair of sample means, namely

Since $|\bar{x}_1 - \bar{x}_2| = 27.94 > \text{LSD}_{1,2} = \sqrt{(\frac{1}{5} + \frac{1}{7})(58.74)(6.20)} = 11.17$

$\rightarrow \mu_1 \neq \mu_2$

Since $|\bar{x}_1 - \bar{x}_3| = 16.7 > \text{LSD}_{1,3} = \sqrt{(\frac{1}{5} + \frac{1}{6})(58.74)(6.20)} = 11.56$

$\rightarrow \mu_1 \neq \mu_3$

$$\text{Since } |\bar{x}_2 - \bar{x}_3| = 44.64 > \text{LSD}_{2,3} = \sqrt{(\frac{1}{6} + \frac{1}{7})(58.74)(6.20)} = 10.62$$

$$\rightarrow \mu_2 \neq \mu_3$$

Therefore, all 3 means are different from each other, at $= 0.05$.

The same conclusion can also be reached for $\alpha = 0.01$ because the corresponding LSDs are: $\text{LSD}_{1,2} = 14.75$, $\text{LSD}_{1,3} = 15.25$, and $\text{LSD}_{2,3} = 14.01$.

To solve the same problem on the computer, we first enter the given data in the Session window, as follows:

```
MTB > READ C1 − C3
DATA > 95 121 82
DATA > 87 130 73
DATA > 90 99 76
DATA > 88 119 70
DATA > 101 125 81
DATA > * 127 71
DATA > * 120 *
DATA > END
```

Note: The * indicates a missing observation, and should not be replaced by zero.

The computer responds with: 7 rows read.

Then, we issue the command: MTB > aovoneway C1 − C3

Table 12.38 Minitab Solution for Example 12

```
One-way ANOVA: C1, C2, C3


Analysis of Variance
Source      DOF        SS         MS        F         P
Factor       2      6633.3     3316.7     56.46    0.000
Error       15       881.2       58.7
Total       17      7514.5
                                   Individual 95% CIs For Mean
                                   Based on Pooled StDev
Level        N       Mean       StDev    -------+---------+---------+---------
C1           5      92.20       5.81                 (----*---)
C2           7     120.14      10.14                                (---*---)
C3           6      75.50       5.09    (---*---)
                                        -------+---------+---------+---------
Pooled StDev =     7.66                    80        96       112
```

The computer responds with an ANOVA table which is exactly the same as the ANOVA table above, but also includes the p-value which is equal to 0.000, and other useful information such as: the means, standard deviation, and the number of observations for each population (Note that in this example $n_1 = 5$, $n_2 = 7$, $n_3 = 6$), the pooled standard deviation is 7.66 and 95% confidence intervals for each individual population mean are given using the pooled standard deviation defined by (12.124). Note that there is no overlap in these intervals suggesting that the 3 means are all different from each other, a conclusion identical to the one reached when the same problem was solved by hand.

12.8   References

Berenson, Marc, L., Levine, David, M., and Krehbiel, Timothy, C., 2004. *Basic Business Statistics.* 9th Edition. Pearson-Prentice Hall.

Black, Ken, 2004. *Business Statistics.* 4th Edition. Wiley.

Canavos, George, C., 1984. *Applied Probability and Statistical Methods.* Little, Brown.

Carlson, William, L., and Thorne, Betty, 1997. *Applied Statistical Methods.* Prentice Hall.

Chou, Ya-lun, 1992. *Statistical Analysis for Business and Economics.* Elsevier.

Freund, John, E., and Williams, Frank, J., 1969. *Modern Business Statistics.* Revised by: Perles, Benjamin and Sullivan, Charles. Prentice-Hall.

Freund, John, E., and Williams, Frank, J., 1982. *Elementary Business Statistics: The Modern approach.* Prentice-Hall.

Johnson, Robert, 1973. *Elementary Statistics.* Duxbury Press.

McClave, James, T., Benson, George, P., and Sincich, Terry, 2001. *Statistics for Business and Economics.* 8th Edition. Prentice Hall.

Salvatore, Dominick, *Theory and Problems of Statistics and Econometrics.* SCHAUM'S OUTLINE SERIES, McGraw-Hill.

Steel, Robert, G.D., and Torrie, James, H., 1976. *Introduction to Statistics.* McGraw-Hill.

12.9 PROBLEMS

1. An agricultural experimental station wishes to determine the yields of 5 varieties of soybeans. Each type is planted on 4 plots of land with equal fertility. The yields, in units of 100 bushels, are as follows:

Type					
A_1	4	6	4	10
A_2	7	13	10	12
A_3	5	4	4	9
A_4	11	10	9	14
A_5	4	8	6	10

a) Construct the ANOVA table for this set of data.

b) Are the yields of the 5 varieties of soybeans the same at $\alpha = 0.05$?

c) Identify the pairs of means, if any, which are significantly different.

2. A random sample was selected from each of 3 makes of rope, and their breaking strengths were measured. The following results were obtained:

Type							
A_1	95	87	90	88	101		
A_2	121	130	99	119	125	127	120
A_3	82	73	76	70	81	71	

a) Obtain the ANOVA table for this data set.

b) Are the treatment effects significant at: $\alpha = 0.05$? at $\alpha = 0.01$?

c) Identify the pairs of means, if any, which are significantly different for both α values.

3. The following data were obtained in a test to compare the corrosion resistance of 4 types of coating material. The 16 test specimens were allotted to the coating

materials at random and weight loss recorded after a period of exposure under test conditions:

Coating Type					
	1	140	70	190	150
	2	230	110	230	220
	3	150	100	190	150
	4	110	90	130	80

a) Define an appropriate model.

b) Construct the ANOVA table for this data set.

c) Are the treatment effects significant at $\alpha = 0.05$?

d) Identify the significant pairs, if any.

4. An experiment was performed to investigate the possible effect of 4 design variations on the productivity of a certain machine. To eliminate the effect of the operator on productivity, 20 operators were used, five being randomly selected and assigned to each machine. The following data are the number of items produced in one day by each operator.

Machine Number		Observations				
	1	64	39	65	46	63
	2	41	48	41	49	57
	3	65	57	56	71	64
	4	45	51	55	48	47

a) Regarding the data as a one-way classification test, at $\alpha = 0.10$, the hypothesis that the design variations have no effect on productivity.

b) Find the machine pairs which are significantly different, if there are any.

5. Four different drugs, A_j, have been developed for the care of a certain disease. These drugs are tried on patients in 3 different hospitals. The results given below show the number of cases of recovery from the disease per 100 people who have taken the drugs. The randomized block design was used to eliminate the effects of the different hospitals.

	A_1	A_2	A_3	A_4
B_1	10	11	12	10
B_2	19	9	18	7
B_3	11	8	23	5

a) Obtain the ANOVA table for this experiment.

b) Test the hypothesis: H_0: $\mu_1 = \mu_2 = \mu_3 = \mu_4$ vs H_1: The means are not all equal, at $\alpha = 0.10$ (*i.e.*, H_0: The treatments (or drugs) are not equally effective).

c) Test H_0: $\mu_{B1} = \mu_{B2} = \mu_{B3}$ vs H_1: The hospitals are not all equal.

d) Identify the pairs of means, if any, which are significantly different.

6. In a study on metal removal rate, 4 electrode shapes were studied: shapes A, B, C, and D. The removal was accomplished by an electric discharge between the electrode

and the material being cut. For this experiment 5 holes were cut in 5 workpieces, and the order of the electrodes was arranged so that electrode shape A was used in the same position and the same workpiece twice, while shapes B, C, and D were used only once on each workpiece and once in each position. Thus the design was a Latin Square with treatment A appearing twice. The time (in hours) necessary to cut the holes was recorded as follows:

		Position (Columns)				
		1	*2*	*3*	*4*	*5*
Strips (*Blocks or Rows*)	*I*	*B*(3.5)	*A*(2.1)	*A*(2.5) or *E*	*D*(3.5)	*C*(2.4)
	II	*C*(2.6)	*B*(3.3)	*A*(2.1)	*A*(2.5) or *E*	*D*(2.7)
	III	*D*(2.9)	*C*(2.6)	*B*(3.5)	*A*(2.7)	*A*(2.9) or *E*
	IV	*A*(2.5) or *E*	*D*(2.9)	*C*(3.0)	*B*(3.3)	*A*(2.3)
	V	*A*(2.1)	*A*(2.3) or *E*	*D*(3.7)	*C*(3.2)	*B*(3.5)

a) Obtain the ANOVA for this experiment.

b) Test for significant variation among: I) Electrodes; II) Strips; III) Position, at $\alpha = 0.05$.

7. There are 2 machines of different quality and 3 different operators of possibly different skills available for the production of a certain product. Each combination of $B_i A_j$ (*i.e.*, machine and operator) produces the items for a number of hours, and 2 hourly output figures are selected at random for each $B_i A_j$ combination, as shown below:

	A_1	A_2
B_1	9	16
	10	15
B_2	6	12
	8	10
B_3	2	11
	3	10

a) Obtain the ANOVA table for this experiment.

b) Test for significant variation in: interactions, operators, and machines, at $\alpha = 0.05$ and $\alpha = 0.10$

8. The following data show the number of complaints which three television stations (Channels A,B,C) received about their programming in ten weeks:

Channel A	33	46	20	55	20	39	51	34	11	37
Channel B	28	30	22	3	25	42	13	17	28	15
Channel C	22	48	16	22	40	29	17	24	45	21

Perform an ANalysis Of VAriance (ANOVA) to test, at the $\alpha = 0.01$ level of significance, whether the difference among the means of these three sets of sample data can be attributed to chance (*i.e.*, test to see, if H$_0$: $\mu_A = \mu_B = \mu_c$ is valid)

9. The following data represent the weight losses (in milligrams of certain machine parts due to friction), when they are used with three different lubricants:

LUBRICANT A	12	11	7	13	9	11	12	9			
LUBRICANT B	10	8	7	5	6	10	7	8	11	7	8
LUBRICANT C	9	3	7	8	4	6	6	5			

Perform an Analysis of Variance to test, at the $\alpha = 0.01$ level of significance, whether the differences among the means of the three lubricants can be attributed to chance (or are due to real differences among the lubricants).

10. The following data show the yields of soybeans(in bushels per acre) planted (two inches apart) on essentially similar plots with the rows 20, 24, 28, and 32 inches apart:

A = 20 inches:	23.1	22.8	23.2	23.4	23.6	21.7
B = 24 inches:	21.7	23.0	22.4	21.1	21.9	23.4
C = 25 inches:	21.9	21.3	21.6	20.2	21.6	23.8
D = 32 inches:	19.8	20.4	19.3	18.5	19.1	21.9

Test at the $\alpha = 0.05$ level of significance whether the differences among the means of the four samples can be attributed to chance.

11. The following are the lengths of time (in minutes) it took a certain person to drive to work, along four different routes:

Route A	29	23	23	24	20
Route B	27	24	26	25	23
Route C	31	28	31	27	24
Route D	28	28	25	26	24

Perform an analysis of Variance (one-way) to test at the $\alpha = 0.05$ level of significance whether the differences among the means obtained for the different routes can be attributed to chance.

12. The following are the lengths of time(in minutes) it took a certain person to drive to work, Monday through Friday, along four different routes:

	Monday	Tuesday	Wednesday	Thursday	Friday
Route 1	29	23	23	24	20
Route 2	27	24	26	25	23
Route 3	31	28	31	27	24
Route 4	28	28	25	26	24

Perform a randomized-block Analysis of Variance(2-Way ANOVA) (using the Routes as Blocks and the Days as Treatments) to test, at the $\alpha = 0.05$ level of significance, whether the differences among the means obtained for the four routes, and the five days of the week can be attributed to chance (*i.e.*, test the Hypotheses:

a) $H_0: \mu_M = \mu_{TU} = \mu_W = \mu_{TH} = \mu_F$ vs H_1: The means of the Days are not equal
b) $H_0: \mu_1 = \mu_2 = \mu_3 = \mu_4$ vs H_1: The means of the Routes are not equal.)

13. A market research organization wants to compare four ways of promoting a breakfast food and, at the same time, study whether there are regional differences in the popularity of the breakfast food, and obtains the following data, representing one week's sales (in thousands of dollars):

Region	Discounts	Lotteries	COUPONS	Two-for One Sales
NORTHEAST	291	290	251	280
SOUTHEAST	243	205	270	245
NORTHWEST	224	198	200	189
SOUTHWEST	221	248	237	256

Perform a randomized-block Analysis of Variance (2-way ANOVA) (using the Regions as Blocks and the Methods of Breakfast promoting as Treatments) to test, at the $\alpha = 0.01$ level of significance, whether the difference among the means obtained for the four Regions and the four methods of promoting the breakfast can be attributed to chance (*i.e.*, test the Hypotheses:

a) $H_0: \mu_D = \mu_L = \mu_C = \mu_{2-1}$ vs H_1: The means are not equal, and
b) $H_0: \mu_{NE} = \mu_{SE} = \mu_{NW} = \mu_{SW}$ vs H_1: The means are not equal)

14. The sample data shown in the table are the grades in a statistics test obtained by nine college students, from 3 majors, taught by 3 different professors:

Majors	Professor A	Professor B	Professor C
Marketing	77	88	71
Finance	88	97	81
Advertising	85	95	72

Analyze this two-factor experiment, using the $\alpha = 0.05$ level of significance, using Majors as Blocks and Professors as the Treatments. Are the differences in the means due to the majors (and due to the treatments) chance variations or real differences?

15. Show that the sum of the α's, $\sum_{i=1}^{k} \alpha_i$, the treatment effects, is equal to zero.

16. A manufacturer asks his research department to show that, on the average, a gallon of his paint (Brand A) covers more square feet than those of his two principal competitions (Brands B and C). The research department tests five cans of each brand, and gets the following results (in square feet per gallon can):

Brand A	505	516	478	513	503
Brand B	512	486	511	486	510
Brand C	496	485	490	520	484

Perform an analysis of variance to test, at the $\alpha = 0.05$ level of significance, whether the differences among the mean areas covered by the three paints are significant. If they are significant (*i.e.*, if $H_0: \mu_A = \mu_B = \mu_c$ is rejected) find the paired means which are different, and caused the rejection of H_0.

17. An experiment was conducted to compare 3 methods of teaching the programming of a certain digital computer. Random samples of size 4 were taken from each of 3 groups

of students taught, respectively, by method A (*i.e.*, straight machine-instruction teaching), method B (personal instruction and some direct experience working with the computer), and method C (personal instruction but no work with the computer itself), and the following grades were obtained by the students on their achievement test:

METHOD A	76	80	70	74
METHOD B	95	85	91	89
METHOD C	77	82	81	84

Test, at the $\alpha = 0.05$ level of significance, whether the differences among the three population means are significant. If they are significant, find the pairs of means which are different, and caused the rejection of H_0.

18. To study its performance, a new motorboat was timed (in minutes) over a marked course, under three different wind and water conditions. Use the following data to test, at $\alpha = 0.05$ level of significance, the null hypothesis that the boat's performance is not affected by the difference in wind and water conditions:

A	Calm Conditions	20	17	14	24		
B	Moderate Conditions	21	23	16	25	18	23
C	Choppy Conditions	26	24	23	29	21	

If H_0 is rejected, find the pairs of means which cause the rejection of H_0.

19. To compare four different golf-ball designs, A, B, C, D, several balls of each kind were driven by a golf professional, and the following distances were measured (in yards) from the tee "to the point where the balls came to rest".

$p = 4$
$n_1 = 5$
$n_2 = 6$
$n_3 = 4$
$n_4 = 5$
$N = 20$

Design A	262	245	237	280	236	
Design B	244	216	251	263	214	228
Design C	272	265	244	259		
Design D	250	233	217	267	258	

At the $\alpha = 0.05$ level of significance, can the differences among the means be attributed to chance? If not (*i.e.*, if H_0: $\mu_A = \mu_B = \mu_C = \mu_D$ is rejected) find the pairs of means which are different and caused the rejection of H_0.

20. The following table shows the number of miles per gallon which a test driver got with four tankfuls each of five brands of gasoline:

Brand A	27	21	26	22
Brand B	24	29	27	28
Brand C	27	27	30	32
Brand D	24	21	24	23
Brand E	25	20	22	21

Perform an Analysis of Variance to test, at the $\alpha = 0.01$ level of significance, the null hypothesis that the five brands of gasoline yield the same average mileage. If the null hypothesis is rejected, find the pairs of means which are different, and cause the rejection of H_0.

21. A chemist in interested in determining the effects of storage temperature on the preservation of apples. The response in this study is the number of apples that are

rotten after a month of storage. The chemist decided to use five lots of apples as the blocks of experimental material. He selects 120 apples from each lot, divides them into four portions of equal size (*i.e.*, 30 apples in each portion), and assigns the treatments to the portions at random; where: Treatment $1 = A_1 = 50°$, $T_2 = A_2 = 55°$, $T_3 = A_3 = 60°$, $T_4 = A_4 = 70°$. The number of rotten apples obtained after a month of storage are:

Lot (Block)	A1	A2	A3	A4
	Treatments			
1	8	5	7	10
2	14	10	3	5
3	12	8	6	5
4	9	8	5	7
5	12	9	4	8

a) Derive the ANOVA Table for this randomized-block design problem.

b) Are the Block effects (*i.e.*, Lots) significant at $\alpha = 0.05$? at $\alpha = 0.01$?

c) Are the Treatment effects(*i.e.*, Temperature) significant at $\alpha = 0.05$? $\alpha = 0.01$?

d) Identify the pairs of means, if any, which are significantly different.

22. Four types of corn (A_1, A_2, A_3, A_4) and three types of fertilizer (B_1, B_2, B_3) are to be tested, and their effect be determined, and the following yields have been obtained:

	A1	A2	A3	A4
B1	12	11	13	15
B2	6	8	5	9
B3	4	3	2	4

a) Are the differences in the means among the types of corn significant at $\alpha = 0.05$? $\alpha = 0.01$?

b) Are the differences in the means among the fertilizers significant at $\alpha = 0.05$? $\alpha = 0.01$?

c) Determine the paired differences which are significant and cause the rejection of H_0, for the applicable α ($\alpha = 0.05, \alpha = 0.01$).

23. A filling operation consists of three identical machines that are set to pour a specified amount of a product into equal sized containers. Random samples are taken from the machines periodically to check for the equality of the average amount poured by each machine. For a particular time period, the following data were recorded:

Machine	A	1.6	1.5	1.5	1.4		
	B	1.8	1.9	1.9	2.0	1.9	1.9
	C	1.9	2.0	1.8	2.0	1.9	

Are there any statistically discernible differences in the average amounts poured by the 3 machines? Use $\alpha = 0.05$.

If there are any differences, find the paired means which are different and caused the rejection of H_0.

24. To determine whether there are differences in the average yield of three varieties of corn, a large homogeneous farm area is divided into 3 equal-sized plots. Each plot is then divided into five equal subplots and planted with one variety of corn. At harvest time the measurement of interest is the yield in bushels per acre. The following table shows a partial Analysis of Variance table for this problem.

Source of Variation	DOF	SS	MS	F VALUE
Treatments		64		
Error	.			
Total		100		

a) Write the model for this problem

b) State the null hypothesis to be tested

c) Complete the ANOVA table and determine if the null hypothesis can be rejected at $\alpha = 0.01$

d) If H_0 is rejected, determine the paired means which are different and caused the rejection of H_0

25. To determine if the amount of carbon used in the manufacture of steel has an effect on the tensile strength of the steel, five different percentages of carbon were investigated: $A(0.2\%)$, $B(0.3\%)$, $C(0.4\%)$, $D(0.5\%)$, and $E(0.6\%)$, and for each percentage of carbon, 5 steel specimens were randomly selected from the same batch and their strengths were measured, and produced the following results:

A(0.2%)	40	150	190	80	120
B(0.3%)	220	310	210	330	270
C(0.4%)	280	270	320	340	310
D(0.5%)	410	390	380	430	360
E(0.6%)	500	590	540	610	530

a) Determine whether the percentage of carbon has a statistically significant effect on the strength of steel, at $\alpha = 0.01$.

b) If the effect is significant, find the paired means which are different and caused the rejection of H_0.

26. Four modifications of a drug that is often used to decrease high blood pressure were given to 10 patients each, and the following information was collected:

S_1 = Sum of observations of Modification 1 = 110 $(\bar{x}_1 = 11)$

S_2 = Sum of observations of Modification 2 = 90 $(\bar{x}_2 = 9)$

S_3 = Sum of observations of Modification 3 = 140 $(\bar{x}_3 = 14)$

S_4 = Sum of observations of Modification 4 = 100 $(\bar{x}_4 = 10)$

SUM = Total sum of all observations = $\sum_{i=1}^{4} \sum_{j=1}^{10} X_{ij} = 440$

$C_{ij} = \sum_{i=1}^{4} \sum_{j=1}^{10} X_{ij}^2 = $ Total sum of squares = 6,033

a) Determine whether there are significant differences due to the four modifications, at $\alpha = 0.05$

b) If there are significant differences, find the paired differences which are different from each other, and caused the rejection of H_0.

27. Fill in the missing values in the following incomplete ANOVA table. Find the value of $F*$ and test the Hypothesis; H_0: Means of rows are equal vs H_1: The means of the rows are not all equal, at $\alpha = 0.05$

Source of Variation	DOF	SS	MS = SS/DOF	F*
Rows(Treatments)	2	$SSA = X_2$?	X_4?	X_6?
Error	9	$SSW = X_3$?	10	
Total	X_1?	$TSS = 120$	X_5?	

28. Fill in the missing values in the following ANOVA table, and test the hypotheses:

   a) H_0: The means of the rows are equal vs H_1 The means of the rows are not equal; and

   b) H_0: The means of the columns are equal vs H_1: The means of the columns are not equal, at $\alpha = 0.05$

Source of Variation	DOF	SS	MS = SS/DOF	F*
Rows	X_1?	X_4?	X_5?	X_8?
Columns	X_2?	32	16	$F_c^* = 4$
Error	X_3?	24	X_6?	
Total	11	$TSS = 62$	X_7?	

29. Three promotion schemes are tested in a marketing experiment by assigning each scheme to 3 market areas in a city that was divided into 9 market areas. The assignments were made by random selection. The sales results from this experiment, in coded units, are:

Scheme1	4	3	5
Scheme2	9	6	6
Scheme3	9	9	12

   a) Test the hypothesis that the means of the 3 schemes are the same at $\alpha = 0.05$

   b) If H_0 is rejected, find the pairs of means which are different and caused the rejection of H_0.

30. A test of 3 methods for selecting investment portfolios was made by selecting a number of alternative portfolios following each method and repeating this procedure in each quarter for a year. The table below shows the results where the numbers are coded values of the average gains of the various portfolios at the end of a year's experience.
    a) Test whether the 3 methods are equally effective.
    b) Test whether the Quarters are statistically significant.

QUARTER	METHOD		
	1	2	3
Q1	3.9	3.6	3.7
Q2	8.4	6.0	5.2
Q3	4.0	3.8	3.9
Q4	6.1	5.8	5.7

31. Two sets of 50 school children were taught to read by 2 different methods. After instruction was completed, a reading test was given and produced the following data:

Method 1; $n_1 = 50, \sum x_i = x_1 + \cdots + x_{50} = 3670;$

$$\sum x_i^2 = x_1^2 + \cdots + x_{50}^2 = 272{,}514$$

Method2; $n_2 = 50, \sum y_i = y_1 + \cdots + y_{50} = 3515;$

$$\sum y_i^2 = y_1^2 + \cdots + y_{50}^2 = 252{,}004.5$$

Test the hypothesis: H_0: $\mu_1 = \mu_2$ vs H_1: $\mu_1 \neq \mu_2$, using the ANOVA methodology with $\alpha = 0.05$.

32. The following data represent the number of units of production per day turned out by 5 workers, using 4 different types of machines.

WORKER	MACHINE TYPE			
	1	2	3	4
1	44	38	47	36
2	46	40	52	43
3	34	36	44	32
4	43	38	46	33
5	38	42	49	39

a) Test to see whether the mean productivity is the same for the 4 different machine types.

b) Test to see whether the 5 workers differ with respect to mean productivity.

33. A national advertiser of a consumer service carried out an investigation on the effectiveness of 4 programs to increase sales. They consisted of advertising alone, promotion alone, combined advertising and promotion, and no formal program. All cities in the national market were classified into one of three per capita income groups. One city was selected from each class for each program, and the following coded data was collected for analysis:

INCOME CLASS	METHOD			
	1	2	3	4
1	7.0	16.0	10.5	13.5
2	14.0	15.5	15.0	21.0
3	8.5	16.5	9.5	13.5

a) Test the hypothesis of equally effective programs, at $\alpha = 0.05$.

b) Test the hypothesis that Income classes have equal effects, at $\alpha = 0.05$.

34. A regional accounting team was instructed to compare the levels of accounts receivables for three different retail stores. Random samples were obtained from each of the three stores and the receivable values were:

Store 1	145	126	118
Store 2	110	120	128
Store 3	135	128	150

Do the 3 stores have differences in the mean receivables at $\alpha = 0.05$?

35. The same regional accounting team was also asked to compare the age (in days) of accounts receivables for three different retail stores. Random samples were obtained from each of the three stores and the receivable ages were:

Store 1	10	8	12	9
Store 2	16	17	19	15
Store 3	26	28	24	27

a) Do the three stores have differences in the age of their receivables?

b) Which stores have mean age of receivables significantly different from the other stores, at $\alpha = 0.05$?

36. A ski manufacturing company has developed a new ski-design that it intends to market, but first they tested it with 3 different age groups of skiers. As part of the survey they asked randomly selected individuals in each age group the price they would be willing to pay for the new ski, and obtained the following results:

Age group	16–25	300	320	330
Age group	6–45	200	230	50
Age group	46–60	250	60	270

a) Do the 3 age groups have different responses in terms of a market price for this new ski, at $\alpha = 0.05$?

b) Which, if any, of the age groups have a different perception of a fair market price?

37. A manufacturer receives shipments of component parts for its lawnmower assembly from four different suppliers, and their experienced inspectors rate the quality of the received parts on a scale from 1 to 20. From the most recent shipment they randomly selected 3 parts from each supplier, and the results of their rating are:

Supplier 1	18	17	16
Supplier 2	19	18	18
Supplier 3	14	15	16
Supplier 4	18	19	20

a) Is there a difference between suppliers at $\alpha = 0.05$?

b) If yes, which suppliers are different, and caused the rejection of H_0?

38. A large regional restaurant chain wanted to know if the family income levels of employees were different in three restaurants in different parts of a large urban area. Three employees were randomly selected in each of the three restaurants, and their family income was obtained, with the following results:

Restaurant 1	30,000	40,000	36,000
Restaurant 2	50,000	48,000	51,000
Restaurant 3	42,000	44,000	46,000

a) Is there a difference between employee incomes at the 3 restaurants, at $\alpha = 0.05$?

b) If yes, which restaurant employees have different incomes?

39. The following data represents the number of mistakes made in five successive days by four technicians working for a testing laboratory:

Technician 1	8	11	7	9	10
Technician 2	9	11	6	14	10
Technician 3	8	13	11	9	13
Technician 4	13	5	9	10	7

Test at the $\alpha = 0.05$ (and $\alpha = 0.01$) level of significance whether the differences among the means of the four samples can be attributed to chance.

40. The following are the numbers of defective pieces produced by four workmen operating, in turn, three different machines,

	Machine 1	Machine 2	Machine 3
Workman 1	27	29	21
Workman 2	31	30	27
Workman 3	24	26	22
Workman 4	21	25	20

Test, at the $\alpha = 0.05$ level of significance whether:

a) The differences among the means obtained for the 4 workmen can be attributed to chance.

b) The differences among the means obtained for the 3 machines can be attributed to chance.

SOLUTIONS

1. a) $p - 1 = 4$ & $SSA = 106$, $p(n - 1) = 15$ & $SSW = 96$, $pn - 1 = 19$ & $TSS = 202$

b) Since $F^* = (106/4)/(96/15) = 4.14 > F_{15}^4(0.05) = 3.06$, the yields are not the same.

c) The pairs of means which are significantly different are: $\mu_1 \neq \mu_2$, $\mu_1 \neq \mu_4$, $\mu_2 \neq \mu_3$, $\mu_3 \neq \mu_4$ (Because: $LSD = 4.45$ & ($|\bar{x}_1 - \bar{x}_2| = 4.5$, $|\bar{x}_1 - \bar{x}_4| = 5$, $|\bar{x}_2 - \bar{x}_3| = 5$, $|\bar{x}_3 - \bar{x}_4| = 5.5$)

2. a) $p - 1 = 2$ & $SSA = 6{,}633.34$, $n_1 + n_2 + n_3 - 3 = 15$ & $SSW = 881.16$, $n_1 + n_2 + n_3 - 1 = 17$ & $TSS = 7{,}514.5$

b) Since $F^* = (6{,}633.34/2)/(881.16/15) = 56.4 > F_{15}^2(0.05) = 3.68$ and $F^* > F_{15}^2(0.01) = 6.36$ H_0: $\mu_1 = \mu_2 = \mu_3$ is rejected and we conclude that the breaking strengths are not the same.

c) Because $|\bar{x}_1 - \bar{x}_2| = 27.94 > LSD\ (\alpha = 0.05) = 11.17$
and $|\bar{x}_1 - \bar{x}_2| > LSD\ (\alpha = 0.01) = 14.75$, $\Rightarrow \mu_1 \neq \mu_2$
Because $|\bar{x}_1 - \bar{x}_3| = 16.70 > LSD\ (\alpha = 0.05) = 11.56$
and $|\bar{x}_1 - \bar{x}_3| > LSD\ (\alpha = 0.01) = 15.25$, $\Rightarrow \mu_1 \neq \mu_3$
Because $|\bar{x}_2 - \bar{x}_3| = 44.64 > LSD\ (\alpha = 0.05) = 10.62$
and $|\bar{x}_2 - \bar{x}_3| > LSD\ (\alpha = 0.01) = 14.01$, $\Rightarrow \mu_2 \neq \mu_3$

3. a) $x_{ij} = \mu + T_i + Z_{ij}$; $i = 1, \ldots, 4$; $j = 1, \ldots, 4$; μ,
A_i are constants; $Z_{ij} \rightarrow N(0, \sigma^2)$

b) $p - 1 = 3$ & $SSA = 184.75$; $p(n - 1) = 12$ &
$SSW = 233.00$; $pn - 1 = 15$ & $TSS = 417.75$; $\sigma^2 = 19.42$

c) Since $F^* = (SSA/p - 1)/(SSW/p(n - 1)) = 3.17 < F_{12}^3(0.05) = 3.49$, do
not reject H_0: $\mu_1 = \mu_2 = \mu_3 = \mu_4$

d) Since H_0 is not rejected, there are no pairs which are significantly different.

4. a) $p - 1 = 3$ & $SSA = 722.8$; $p(n - 1) = 16$ & $SSW = 972.0$; $pn - 1 = 19$ &
$TSS = 1,694.8$; $\sigma^2 = 60.75$ Since $F^* = (SSA/p - 1)/(SSW/p(n - 1)) = 3.97 >$
$F_{16}^3(0.10) = 2.46$, reject H_0. Design variations have an effect on productivity.

b) $LSD = 10.445$; The pairs which are different are: $\mu_2 \neq \mu_3, \mu_3 \neq \mu_4$

5. a) Blocks (Hospitals): $DOF = 2$ & $SS_B = 13$; Treatments(Drugs): $DOF = 3$ &
$SS_T = 188$; Error: $DOF = 6$ & $SS_E = 114$; Total: $DOF = 11$ & $SS = 315$

b) Since $F_1^* = (SST/3)/(SSE/6) = 62.67/19 = 3.30 > F_6^3(0.10) = 3.29$,reject
H_0: The treatments (drugs) have an effect.

c) Since $F_2^* = (SSB/2)/(SSE/6) = 6.50/19 = 0.342 < F_6^2 = (0.10) = 3.46$, do
not reject H_0: Blocks (hospitals) have no effect.

d) $LSD = 7.135$; The pairs which are different are: $\mu_2 \neq \mu_3$ (because
$|\bar{x}_2 - \bar{x}_3| = 8.34$) and $\mu_3 \neq \mu_4$(because) $|\bar{x}_3 - \bar{x}_4| = 10.34$)

6. a) Treatments(j): $DOF = 4$ & $SST = 4.2896$ (if one of the two A_j in each strip is
replaced by E, as shown); Rows(Strips)(i): $DOF = 4$ & $SSR = 0.3136$;
Columns(Position)(k): $DOF = 4$ & $SSC = 0.5696$; Error: $DOF = 12$ & $SSE = 0.8128$; Total: $DOF = 24$ & $TSS = 5.9856$. But, because treatment A appears
twice, one of the 4 DOF of treatments can be associated with the contrast
$\bar{x}_A - \bar{x}_E$, which has a mean square error of 0.196
$(\bar{x}_A - \bar{x}_E = -3.7 - (-2.3) = -1.4$ and mean square error

$$= \frac{\left(\sum a_i T_i \right)^2}{n \sum a_i^2} = \frac{(-1.4)^2}{5(2)} = 0.196, \text{ where } \sum a_i^2 = a_A^2 + a_E^2 = (1)^2 + (-1^2) = 2).$$

Therefore, in treatments we subtract 1 DOF and 0.196 and add them to error to
obtain: Treatments: $DOF = 3$ & $SST = 4.2896 - 0.196 = 4.0936$ and Error:
$DOF = 13$ & $SSE = 0.8128 + 0.196 = 1.0088$

b) Since $F_1^* = (SST/3)/(SSE/13) = (4.0936/3)/(1.0088/13) =$
$17.6 > F_{13}^3(0.05) = 3.41$, treatments (electrodes) are significant.
Since $F_2^* = (SSR/4)/(SSE/13) = (0.3136/4)/(1.0088/13) =$
$1.01 < F_{13}^4(0.05) = 3.18$, strips (blocks or rows) are not significant.
Since $F_3^* = (SSC/4)/(SSE/13) = (0.5696/4)/(1.0088/13) =$
$1.84 < F_{13}^4(0.05) = 3.18$, positions are not significant.

7. a) Operators, B_i: $DOF = 2$ & $SSB = 72.67$; Machines, A_j: $DOF = 1$ & $SSM = 108.00$;
Interactions BA_{ij}: $DOF = 2$ & $SSI = 8$; Error: $DOF = 6$ & $SSE = 6$; Total:
$DOF = 11$ & $TSS = 194.67$

b) Since $F_1^* = (SSI/2)/(SSE/6) = (8/2)/(6/6) = 4 < F_6^2(0.05) = 5.14$, no interaction
effects exist.

Since $F_2^* = (SSB/2)/(SSE/6) = 36.33/1 = 36.33 > F_6^2 (0.01) = 10.92$, there are highly significant operator effects.

Since $F_3^* = (SSM/1)/(SSE/6) = 108/1 = 108 > F_6^1 (0.01) = 13.75$, there are highly significant machine effects.

8. Code the data by subtracting the Midrange $= \dfrac{L + H}{2} = \dfrac{11 + 55}{2} = 33$ to obtain:

											SUMS	$\overline{X}$
Channel A	0	13	−13	22	−13	6	18	1	−22	4	$S_1 = 16$	1.6
Channel B	−5	−3	−11	−30	−8	9	−20	−16	−5	−18	$S_2 = -107$	−10.7
Channel C	−11	15	−7	−11	7	−4	−16	−9	12	−12	$S_3 = -46$	−4.6
											$S = -137$	−4.567

Then,

$$C_{ij} = \left[0^2 + 13^2 + (-13)^2 + 22^2 + (-13)^2 + 6^2 + 18^2 + 1^2 + (-22)^2 + 4^2\right]$$

$$+ \left[(-5)^2 + (-3)^2 + (-11)^2 + (-30)^2 + (-8)^2 + (-9)^2 + (-20)^2 + (-16)^2\right.$$

$$+ (-5)^2 + (-18)^2\right] + \left[(-11)^2 + 15^2 + (-17)^2 + (-11)^2 + 7^2 + (-4^2) + (-16)^2\right.$$

$$+ (-9)^2 + 12^2 + (-12)^2\right] = 1{,}852 + 2{,}205 + 1{,}446 = 5{,}503$$

$$C_i = \frac{S_1^2 + S_2^2 + S_3^2}{n} = \frac{16^2 + (-107)^2 + (-46)^2}{10}$$

$$= \frac{256 + 11{,}499 + 2116}{10} = \frac{13821}{10} = 1{,}382.1$$

$$C = \frac{S^2}{np} = \frac{(-137)^2}{(10)(3)} = \frac{18{,}736}{30} = 625.63, \text{ and:}$$

$TSS = C_{ij} - C = 5{,}503 - 625.63 = 4{,}877.37$, $SSA = C_i - C = 1{,}382.1 - 625.63 = 756.47$, and $SSW = C_{ij} - C_i = 5{,}503 - 1{,}382.1 = 4{,}120.9$, and the ANOVA Table is:

Source of Variation	DOF	SUMS of Squares (SS)	Mean Square Error $MS = \dfrac{SS}{DOF}$	E(MSE)
Variation Among	$p - 1 = 2$	$SSA = 756.47$	$SSA/p - 1 = \dfrac{456.47}{2} = 378.235$	
Variation Within	$p(n - 1) = 27$	$SSW = 4{,}120.90$	$SSW/p(n - 1) = \dfrac{4{,}120.90}{27} = 152.626$	σ^2
Total Variation	$pn - 1 = 29$	$TSS = 4{,}877.37$	$TSS/pn - 1 = \dfrac{4{,}877.37}{29} = 168.185$	

Now test the hypotheses:

a) $H_0: \sigma^2_{AMONG}/\sigma^2_{WITHIN} \leq 1$ vs $H_0: \sigma^2_{AMONG}/\sigma^2_{WITHIN} > 1$

b) $\alpha = 0.01$

c) The estimator of $\sigma^2_{AMONG}/\sigma^2_{WITHIN}$ is $(SSA/p - 1)/(SSW/p(n - 1))$ which is distributed as $F_{p(n-1)}^{p-1} = F_{27}^2$

d) Rejection Region (Critical value) $F_{27}^2(0.01) = 5.49$

e) $F^* = (SSA/p - 1)/(SSW/p(n - 1) = (378.235)/(152.626) = 2.478$

f) Since $F^* = 2.487 < F_{27}^2(0.01) = 5.49$, do not reject

H_0: $\sigma_{AMONG}^2/\sigma_{WITHIN}^2 \leq 1$ (or its equivalent H_0: $\mu_A = \mu_B = \mu_C$). Therefore the differences are not significant and the sample data can be attributed to chance.

9. Because the data are relatively small in value, the data will not be coded.

Let S_1 = Sum of data of Lubricant A = 84, and $\overline{X}_1 = S_1/n_1 = 84/8 = 10.50$

S_2 = Sum of data of Lubricant B = 87, and $\overline{X}_2 = S_2/n_2 = 87/11 = 7.91$

S_3 = Sum of data of Lubricant C = 48, and $\overline{X}_3 = S_3/n_3 = 48/8 = 6.00$ and

$S = S_1 + S_2 + S_3 = 84 + 87 + 48 = 219$, and

$\overline{X} = S/n_1 + n_2 + n_3 = 219/27 = 8.11$

Then:

$$C_{ij} = \left[12^2 + 11^2 + 7^2 + 13^2 + 9^2 + 11^2 + 12^2 + 9^2\right] + \left[10^2 + 8^2 + 7^2 + 5^2\right.$$
$$\left. + 6^2 + 10^2 + 7^2 + 8^2 + 11^2 + 7^2 + 8^2\right] + \left[9^2 + 3^2 + 7^2 + 8^2 + 4^2\right.$$
$$\left. + 9^2 + 3^2 + 7^2 + 8^2 + 4^2 + 6^2 + 6^2 + 5^2\right] = 1{,}947$$

$$C_i = \frac{S_1^2}{n_1} + \frac{S_2^2}{n_2} + \frac{S_3^2}{n_3} = \frac{(84)^2}{8} + \frac{(87)^2}{11} + \frac{(48)^2}{8} = 1{,}858.09$$

$$C = \frac{S^2}{n_1 + n_2 + n_3} = \frac{(219)^2}{27} = 1{,}776.33, \text{ and}$$

TSS = $C_{ij} - C = 1{,}947 - 1{,}776.33 = 170.67$, with

DOF = $n_1 + n_2 + n_3 - 1 = 26$

SSA = $C_i - C = 1{,}858.09 - 1{,}776.33 = 81.76$, with

DOF = $p - 1 = 3 - 1 = 2$

SSW = $C_{ij} - C_i = 1{,}947 - 1{,}858.09 = 88.91$, with

DOF = $n_1 + n_2 + n_3 - 3 = 24$

To test the hypothesis: H_o: $\mu_A = \mu_B = \mu_C$ vs H_1: The means are not all equal, or the equivalent. H_0: $\sigma_{Among}^2/\sigma_{Within}^2 \leq 1$ vs H_1: $\sigma_{Among}^2 \sigma_{Within}^2 > 1$

We form: $F^* = \dfrac{(SSA/p - 1)}{(SSW/n_1 + n_2 + n_3 - 3)} = \dfrac{(81.76/2)}{(88.91/24)} = \dfrac{40.88}{3.704583} = 11.035$,

and compare to $F_{24}^2(\alpha = 0.01) = 5.61$; Since $F^* > F_{24}^2(0.01)$, Reject H_0 and conclude that the 3 means (μ_A, μ_B, μ_C,) are not equal.

Since we rejected H_0 the procedure continues to identify the means which caused the rejection of H_0, and this consists of comparing the absolute value of the sample paired means ($|\overline{x}_i - \overline{x}_i|$) to an appropriate LSD_{ij}. Because n_1, n_2, n_3 are not equal we need to compare each $|\overline{x}_i - \overline{x}_i|$ to its own LSD_{ij}; Therefore:

Since $|\overline{x}_1 - \overline{x}_2| = |10.5 - 7.91| = 2.09 < LSD_{1.2}$

$$= \sqrt{\left(\frac{1}{8} + \frac{1}{11}\right)\left(\frac{88.91}{24}\right)}(F_{24}^1(0.005)) = 2.764,$$

(where $F_{24}^1(0.005) = 9.55$), $\mu_1 = \mu_2$ or $\mu_A = \mu_B$

Since $|\overline{x}_1 - \overline{x}_3| = |10.5 - 6| = 4.5 > LSD_{1,3}$

$$= \sqrt{\left(\frac{1}{8} + \frac{1}{8}\right)\left(\frac{88.91}{24}\right)}(9.55) = 2.974.$$

$\mu_1 \neq \mu_3$ or $\mu_A \neq \mu_C$

since $|\bar{x}_2 - \bar{x}_3| = |7.91 - 6| = 1.91 < LSD_{2,3}$

$$= \sqrt{\left(\frac{1}{11} + \frac{1}{8}\right)\left(\frac{88.91}{24}\right)}(9.55) = 2.764$$

$\mu_2 = \mu_3$ or $\mu_B = \mu_C$

Therefore, $\mu_A \neq \mu_C$, and these are the means which are different and caused the rejection the H_0.

10. The data will not be coded (but it seems logical to subtract 20)

Then $S_1 = $ sum of values in "20 inches" row $= 137.8$, and $\bar{x}_1 = 137.8/6 = 22.97$

$S_2 = $ sum of values in "24 inches" row $= 133.5$, and $\bar{x}_2 = 133.5/6 = 22.30$

$S_3 = $ sum of values in "28 inches" row $= 130.4$, and $\bar{x}_3 = 130.4/6 = 21.73$

$S_4 = $ sum of values in "32 inches" row $= 119.0$, and $\bar{x}_4 = 119.0/6 = 19.83$,

and $S = S_1 + S_2 + S_3 + S_4 = 520.7$

Then

$$C_{ij} = \sum_{i=1}^{4}\sum_{j=1}^{6} x_{ij}^2 = (23.1^2 + 22.8^2 + 23.2^2 + 23.4^2 + 23.6^2 + 21.7^2) + \cdots$$
$$+ (19.8^2 + 20.4^2 + 19.3^2 + 18.5^2 + 19.1^2 + 21.9^2) = 11{,}349.39$$

$$C_i = \frac{S_1^2 + S_2^2 + S_3^2 + S_4^2}{n} = \frac{137.8^2 + 133.5^2 + 130.4^2 + 119.0^2}{6} = 11{,}329.38$$

$$C = \frac{S^2}{np} = \frac{(520.7)^2}{6(4)} = \frac{271{,}128.49}{24} = 11{,}297.02, \text{ and}$$

TSS $= C_{ij} - C = 11{,}349.39 - 11{,}297.02 = 52.37$, with

DOF $= pn - 1 = 4(6) - 1 = 23$

SSA $= C_i - C = 11{,}329.38 - 11{,}297.02 = 32.36$, with

DOF $= p - 1 = 4 - 1 = 3$

SSW $= C_{ij} - C = 11{,}349.39 - 11{,}329.38 = 20.01$, with

DOF $= p(n - 1) = 4(5) = 20$

To test the hypothesis: $H_0 = \mu_A = \mu_B = \mu_C = \mu_o$ vs H_1: The means are not all equal or, the equivalent :

$H_0: \sigma^2_{Among}/\sigma^2_{Within} \leq 1$ vs $H_1: \sigma^2_{Among}\,\sigma^2_{Within} > 1$,

we form:

$F^* = (SSA/p - 1)/(SSW/p(n - 1)) = (32.36/3)/(20.01/20) = 10.787/1 = 10.787$

and compare to $F^{p-1}_{p(n-1)}(\alpha) = F^3_{20}(0.05) = 3.10$

Since $F^* = 10.787 > F^3_{20}(0.05) = 3.10$, we reject H_0 and conclude that the four means are not equal. To find the means which are different, we compare each $|\bar{x}_i - \bar{x}_j|$ to

the LSD (Least Significant Difference) or: $LSD = \sqrt{\frac{2}{n}\left[\frac{SSW}{p(n-1)}\right]\left[F^1_{p(n-1)}(\alpha/2)\right]}$

$$= \sqrt{\frac{2}{6}\left[\frac{20.0}{20}\right][3.86]} = 1.134$$

Then

Since $|\bar{x}_1 - \bar{x}_2| = |22.97 - 22.30| = 0.67 < LSD = 1.134, \mu_1 = \mu_2$

$\quad\quad\quad |\bar{x}_1 - \bar{x}_3| = |22.97 - 21.73| = 1.24 > LSD = 1.134, \mu_1 \neq \mu_3$

$\quad\quad\quad |\bar{x}_1 - \bar{x}_4| = |22.97 - 19.83| = 3.14 > LSD = 1.134, \mu_1 \neq \mu_4$

$\quad\quad\quad |\bar{x}_2 - \bar{x}_3| = |22.30 - 21.73| = 0.67 < LSD = 1.134, \mu_2 = \mu_3$

$\quad\quad\quad |\bar{x}_2 - \bar{x}_4| = |22.30 - 19.83| = 2.47 < LSD = 1.134, \mu_2 \neq \mu_4$

$\quad\quad\quad |\bar{x}_3 - \bar{x}_4| = |21.73 - 19.83| = 1.90 > LSD = 1.134, \mu_3 \neq \mu_4$

Therefore, the pairs of means which are different, and caused the rejection of H_0, are: $\mu_1 \neq \mu_3, \mu_1 \neq \mu_4, \mu_2 \neq \mu_4,$ and $\mu_3 \neq \mu_4$.

REGRESSION AND CORRELATION ANALYSIS

13 Bivariate Analysis

Whenever possible we try to express relationships between known quantities, and other unknown quantities that are to be predicted, by constructing appropriate mathematical equations, (such as the linear $y = a + bx$, the quadratic $y = a + bx + cx^2$, etc.). Usually we use observed data between two variables X and Y (X is the known quantity and Y is the unknown quantity) to derive a mathematical equation which connects Y to X (*i.e.*, derive the function $y = f(x)$) and use it to predict the value of Y, when the X value is known.

The procedure of constructing the function $y = f(x)$, known as curve fitting, involves the following three actions:

1. Decide what kind of predicting equation is to be constructed; *i.e.*, linear ($\hat{y} = a + bx$), exponential ($\hat{y} = ke^{cx}$), quadratic ($\hat{y} = a + bx + cx^2$) or other.
2. Evaluate the unknown coefficients of each possible candidate equation, using the given observed data and the Least Squares methodology, *i.e.*, select the values of the unknown coefficients such that the sum of the squares of the residuals between the observed and predicted y-values is a minimum.
3. Test the goodness of the derived equation before using it for prediction.

In this chapter we discuss and analyze these and other issues related to the Bivariate Linear analysis which includes: Linear Regression, Correlation, and the Coefficient of Determination, which is a measure used to ascertain the goodness of the derived regression equation.

13.1   Introduction

Up to now we dealt with univariate data (*i.e.*, the analysis of a set of data describing a single characteristic of the elements of a population). It is possible, however, to measure 2 characteristics of the elements of the population and call one characteristic X (Variable $1 = V_1$) and the other Y (Variable $2 = V_2$), and then ask the question: Are the 2 variables related, and if so, how are they related?

To answer these questions we perform Bivariate Analysis, which consists of 2 distinct parts:

1. **Correlation Analysis** which attempts to answer the question: Are the 2 variables linearly related (*i.e.*, Are the 2 variables connected through a linear relationship: $y = a + bx$)? and
2. **Regression Analysis** which finds the "best" linear relationship between the 2 variables when such a relationship exists.

We will begin our bivariate analysis by discussing regression analysis first, and then correlation analysis, as most texts usually discuss bivariate analysis, even though logically it may appear that correlation analysis should be discussed first! In the final analysis, it really does not make any difference which is discussed first and which second.

13.2   Regression Analysis

13.2.1 The Linear Bivariate Model

The linear bivariate model assumes the existence of an ideal linear model (*i.e.*, a population linear model) given by:

$$y_i = \alpha + \beta x_i + v_i \tag{13.1}$$

in which   1. α and β are the population regression coefficients
2. v_i is the random (residual) disturbance
3. x_i is the independent variable which is fixed (*i.e.*, x is non-stochastic) and for each value of x there is a stochastic variable y, and
4. y_i is a dependent variable

We make the following observations on equation (13.1):

1. For the error term v_i, we assume that:
$$E(v_i) = 0, \tag{13.2}$$
which implies that:
$$E(y_i/x_i) = E(\alpha + \beta x_i + v_i)$$
$$= \alpha + \beta x_i + E(v_i)$$
$$= \alpha + \beta x_i, \quad \text{since } E(v_i) = 0 \tag{13.3}$$

Equation (13.3) represents the population regression equation of y and x, which gives the mean value of y, given a fixed value of x (μ_{yx}).

2. α is the mean value of y when $x = 0$ (*i.e.*, α is the y-intercept)

3. β measures the change in the mean value of y, for a unit change in the x value (*i.e.*, β is the slope of the regression line)

4. $V(y_i) = E[y_i - E(y_i)]^2 = $ Variance of Regression, or: \hfill (13.4)
$$V(y_i) = E[y_i - E(y_i)]^2 = E[\alpha + \beta x_i + v_i - \alpha - \beta x_i]^2$$
$$= E(v_i)^2 = E(v_i^2) = \sigma_v^2 = V(v_i) \tag{13.5}$$

We note from equation (13.5) that the variance of $y_i = V(y_i)$ is constant (because it does not depend on x). This "constant variance property" is called "homoscedasticity" as opposed to "heteroscedasticity" when the variance is not constant.

5. Summary of assumptions on the linear bivariate regression model
   a) x is fixed
   b) v_i is a random variable with: $E(v_i) = 0$ and $V(v_i) = \sigma_v^2$
   c) $V(y_i) = V(v_i) = \sigma_v^2$ (constant variance)
   d) x_i and v_i are statistically independent (This implies that: $E(x_i \cdot v_i) = E(x_i) E(v_i) = E(x_i) \cdot 0 = 0$).

6. **Notes:** a) Useful results can be obtained, even if x is not fixed.
   b) If $E(v_i) \neq 0$ for some values of x, we no longer deal with linear regression, but non-linear regression.

With the above assumptions, estimates of the unknown regression parameters can be derived, as shown below.

13.2.2 Estimation of Regression Parameters

13.2.2.1 The Sample Regression Model
The sample regression model, corresponding to the ideal linear regression model of equation (13.1) is given by:
$$\hat{y}_i = a + bx_i + \varepsilon_i \tag{13.6}$$

where $a = $ estimator for $\alpha = $ sample y-intercept when $x = 0$
   $b = $ estimator for $\beta = $ sample slope
   $\varepsilon_i = $ estimator for $v_i = $ computed "residuals", where
$$\varepsilon_i = y_i - (a + bx_i) = y_i - \hat{y}_i \left(\text{with } \sum_{i=1}^{n} e_i = 0\right), \tag{13.7}$$
and $\hat{y} = a + bx_i$ is a linear estimator of $\alpha + \beta x_i$ \hfill (13.8)

13.2.2.2 BLUE (Best Linear Unbiased Estimators) Estimators

When $y_1, y_2, \ldots, y_n$ are random variables with equal σ^2, and $x_1, x_2, \ldots, x_n$ are fixed, then the Least Squares (L.S.) method produces BLUE estimators for α and β, in accordance with the **Gauss-Markov** theorem, which states the following: "Least Square estimates are Best, Linear, Unbiased Estimators (BLUE) of the p parameters ($p = 2$ for the linear model), and:

$$Q^* = (n - p)\sigma^2, \tag{13.9}$$

where Q^* = value of Q, computed when L.S. estimates of the p parameters are substituted in Q, where Q is defined below. The terms: best, linear, and unbiased have the following meanings:

1. Best: The Least Square Estimators have minimum variance
2. Linear: The Least Square Estimators are linear combinations of the y values; *i.e.*, they are of the form: $\sum_{i=1}^{n} c_i y_i$
3. Unbiased: The expected value of each estimator = corresponding population parameter, or, in mathematical form:

$$E(\hat{\theta}_j) = \theta_j \tag{13.10}$$

where θ_j is any population parameter and $\hat{\theta}_j$ is the estimator of θ_j.

Note: When the $y_i (y_1, y_2, \ldots, y_n)$ are normally distributed, the estimates obtained by the least squares method are identical to the estimates obtained using the Maximum Likelihood method.

13.2.2.3 The Least Squares Method

Given the linear dependence between x and y, and the n pairs of observations (x_i, y_i), the least squares method derives the values of a and b in such a way that:

$$Q(a, b) = \sum_{i=1}^{n} e_i^2 = \sum_{i=1}^{n} (y_i - \hat{y}_i)^2 = \sum_{i=1}^{n} (y_i - a - bx_i)^2 \tag{13.11}$$

becomes a minimum. This implies that a and b are chosen in such a way that the sum of squares of the differences, between the actually observed values y_i, and estimated values $\hat{y}_i = a + bx_i$, is a minimum.

The procedure for deriving the least squares estimates for a and b is the *Optimization Methodology of 2 independent variables of differential calculus*, which consists of the following steps.

1. Find the partial derivatives:

$$\frac{\partial Q(a, b)}{\partial a} = 2 \sum_{i=1}^{n} (y_i - a - bx_i)(-1) \tag{13.12}$$

and

$$\frac{\partial Q(a, b)}{\partial b} = 2 \sum_{i=1}^{n} (y_i - a - bx_i)(-x_i) \tag{13.13}$$

2. Set the partial derivatives equal to zero, to obtain the system of equations:

$$-2 \sum_{i=1}^{n} (y_i - a - bx_i) = 0 \tag{13.14}$$

$$-2\sum_{i=1}^{n}(y_i - a - bx_i)(-x_i) = 0 \qquad (13.15)$$

3. Solve equations (13.14) and (13.15) simultaneously to obtain the critical point of the $Q(a, b)$ function. The function being analyzed can have: a minimum value at the critical point, a maximum value at the critical point, or a saddle point at the critical point, (or this method can not be applied to the solution of this problem), as will be shown below.

4. When (13.14) and (13.15) are simplified, they can be written as:

$$n(a) + (b)\sum_{i=1}^{n}x_i = \sum_{i=1}^{n}y_i \qquad (13.16)$$

$$(a)\sum_{i=1}^{n}x_i + (b)\sum_{i=1}^{n}x_i^2 = \sum_{i=1}^{n}x_i \cdot y_i, \qquad (13.17)$$

which are known as the "normal equations" of the linear model, and are the 2 equations that must be solved simultaneously to derive the L.S. estimates for a and b which define the critical point of the function $Q(a, b)$. The only unknowns in equation (13.16) and (13.17) are a and b, and the equations must be solved for a and b simultaneously, because every other quantity appearing in these equations are numerical values derived from the given data set, namely:

$$n = \text{Number of ordered pairs } (x_i, y_i) \qquad (13.18)$$

$$\sum_{i=1}^{n}x_i = x_1 + x_2 + \cdots + x_n = \text{Sum of } x \text{ values} \qquad (13.19)$$

$$\sum_{i=1}^{n}x_i^2 = x_1^2 + x_2^2 + \cdots + x_n^2 = \text{Sum of squared } x \text{ values} \qquad (13.20)$$

$$\sum_{i=1}^{n}x_i \cdot y_i = x_1y_1 + x_2y_2 + \cdots + x_n y_n = \text{Sum of the products } (xy) \qquad (13.21)$$

Note: We will represent the critical point values of a and b by $a*$ and $b*$ respectively.

5. Find the 2nd partial derivatives: $\qquad \dfrac{\partial^2 Q(a, b)}{\partial a^2} = 2n > 0 \qquad (13.22)$

(because n is always positive)

and $\qquad \dfrac{\partial^2 Q(a, b)}{\partial b^2} = 2\sum_{i=1}^{n}x_i^2 > 0 \qquad (13.23)$

(because the x_i values are squared)

6. Find the cross partial derivative: $\dfrac{\partial^2 Q(a, b)}{\partial a\,\partial b} = 2\sum_{i=1}^{n}x_i \qquad (13.24)$

7. Evaluate: $\dfrac{\partial^2 Q(a, b)}{a^2}, \dfrac{\partial^2 Q(a, b)}{\partial b^2}$, and $\dfrac{\partial^2 Q(a, b)}{\partial a\,\partial b}$ at the critical point values of a, b, namely: $a*$ and $b*$.

8. Let $D = \left(\dfrac{\partial^2 Q(a, b)}{\partial a^2}\right)\left(\dfrac{\partial^2 Q(a, b)}{\partial b^2}\right) - \left(\dfrac{\partial^2 Q(a, b)}{\partial a\,\partial b}\right)^2 = \begin{cases} D > 0 \\ D < 0 \\ D = 0 \end{cases} \qquad (13.25)$

Then, the critical point defined by equations (13.16) and (13.17) is:

a) A minimum, if $\dfrac{\partial^2 Q(a,b)}{\partial a^2} > 0$, and $\dfrac{\partial^2 Q(a,b)}{\partial b^2} > 0$, and $D > 0$ \hfill (13.26)

b) A maximum, if $\dfrac{\partial^2 Q(a,b)}{\partial a^2} < 0$, and $\dfrac{\partial^2 Q(a,b)}{\partial b^2} < 0$, and $D > 0$ \hfill (13.27)

c) A saddle point if $D < 0$ \hfill (13.28)

d) This method is not applicable, if $D = 0$ \hfill (13.29)

When (13.22), (13.23) and (13.24) are substituted into (13.25), we obtain:

$$D = (2n)\left(2\sum_{i=1}^{n} x_i^2\right) - \left(2\sum_{i=1}^{n} x_i\right)^2 \tag{13.30}$$

$$= 4n\sum_{i=1}^{n} x_i^2 - 4\left(\sum_{i=1}^{n} x_i\right)^2$$

$$= 4\left[n\sum_{i=1}^{n} x_i^2 - \left(\sum_{i=1}^{n} x_i\right)^2\right] \tag{13.31}$$

We need to determine whether $D > 0, D < 0$ or $D = 0$. To arrive at the proper conclusion, we note that the bracketed quantity of equation (13.31) is the numerator of the variance of a variable x:

$$V(x) = \frac{1}{n-1}\sum_{i=1}^{n}(x_i - \overline{x})^2 = \frac{n\sum_{i=1}^{n} x_i^2 - \left(\sum_{i=1}^{n} x_i\right)^2}{n(n-1)} \tag{13.32}$$

which is always a positive number.

Therefore $\left[n\sum_{i=1}^{n} x_i^2 - \left(\sum_{i=1}^{n} x_i\right)^2\right] = n(n-1)V(x) > 0,$ \hfill (13.33)

and, we can rewrite (13.31) as:

$$D = 4[n(n-1)V(x)] > 0 \tag{13.34}$$

and, since $\dfrac{\partial^2 Q(a,b)}{\partial a^2} > 0, \dfrac{\partial^2 Q(a,b)}{\partial b^2} > 0$, and $D > 0$, (from equations (13.22), (13.23), and (13.34) respectively), the function $Q(a, b)$ has a minimum at the critical point defined by equations (13.16) and (13.17), as required by the least squares method.

When the L.S. estimates of a and b are substituted into $Q(a, b)$, it becomes $Q^*(a,b)$ which is needed for the calculation of σ^2 (using the Gauss-Markov Theorem).

13.2.3 Sample Variance of Regression (σ^2)

The main purpose of deriving the linear regression equation is to use it to predict the "mean value of y given x (i.e., μ_{yx})", or the value y_i associated with a given value of $x = x_i$.

How good is the regression equation as a predictor? The answer to this question depends on the variability (variance) of y_i from $\hat{y}_i$ associated with x_i which, according to the Gauss-Markov theorem, is given by:

$$\sigma^2 = \frac{Q^*(a, b)}{n - p} = \frac{\sum\limits_{i=1}^{n}(y_i - \hat{y}_i)^2}{n - p} = \frac{\sum\limits_{i=1}^{n}\left(y_i - a_i - bx_i\right)^2}{n - 2} \quad (13.35)$$

$$= \frac{\sum\limits_{i=1}^{n} y_i^2 - (a)\sum\limits_{i=1}^{n} y_i - (b)\sum\limits_{i=1}^{n} x_i y_i}{n - 2} \quad (p = 2 \text{ for the linear function}) \quad (13.36)$$

where

$$\sum_{i=1}^{n} y_i = y_1 + y_2 + \cdots + y_n$$

$$\sum_{i=1}^{n} y_i^2 = y_1^2 + y_2^2 + \cdots + y_n^2$$

$$\sum_{i=1}^{n} x_i \cdot y_i = x_1 y_1 + x_2 y_2 + \cdots + x_n y_n$$

$n = $ number of ordered pairs (x_i, y_i)

The values for a and b are the L.S. Estimates derived from the solution of the normal equations.

This regression variance is very important because we need it for the analysis of the distributions of a, b, and $\hat{y}$, as we will show shortly.

But this variance is not the same as the "variance of the y_i observations from $\overline{y}$" $= \sigma_y^2$, which is defined by:

$$\sigma_y^2 = \frac{1}{n - 1}\sum_{i=1}^{n}(y_i - \overline{y})^2 = \sigma_v^2 \quad (13.37)$$

To find the relationship between these 2 variances (σ^2 defined by (13.36) and σ_y^2 defined by (13.37)), we make use of the following relationships:

$$(y_i - \overline{y}) = (\hat{y}_i - \overline{y}) + (y_i - \hat{y}_i) \quad (13.38)$$

$$\sum_{i=1}^{n}(y_i - \overline{y})^2 = \sum_{i=1}^{n}(\hat{y}_i - \overline{y})^2 + \sum_{i=1}^{n}(y_i - \hat{y})^2 \quad (13.39)$$

$$+ \sum_{i=1}^{n} 2(\hat{y} - \overline{y})(y_i - \overline{y})$$

where

$$\sum_{i=1}^{n}(y_i - \overline{y})^2 = \text{Total Sum of Squares} \quad (13.39a)$$

$$\sum_{i=1}^{n}(\hat{y}_i - \overline{y})^2 = \text{Regression Sum of Squares} \quad (13.39b)$$

$$\sum_{i=1}^{n}(y_i - \hat{y})^2 = \text{Error Sum of Squares} \quad (13.39c)$$

and

$$\frac{\text{Total Sum}}{\text{of Squares}} = \frac{\text{Regression Sum}}{\text{of Squares}} + \frac{\text{Error Sum}}{\text{of Squares}} \quad (13.39d)$$

or

$$\text{TSS} = \text{RSS} + \text{ESS}, \quad (13.40)$$

and Degrees of Freedom for each sum of squares is:

$$\text{DOF} = n - 1, \quad \text{for TSS} \tag{13.40a}$$
$$\text{DOF} = 1, \quad\quad \text{for RSS} \tag{13.40b}$$
$$\text{DOF} = n - 2, \quad \text{for ESS} \tag{13.40c}$$

or in equation form:

$$n - 1 = 1 + n - 2 \tag{13.41}$$

Then $\sigma_y^2 = \dfrac{\text{TSS}}{n - 1}$ and $\sigma^2 = \dfrac{\text{ESS}}{n - 2}$ $\tag{13.42}$

Then equation (13.40) can be written as:

$$(n - 1)\sigma_y^2 = \sum_{i=1}^{n}(\hat{y} - \overline{y})^2 + (n - 2)\sigma^2 \tag{13.43}$$

and finally $\quad\quad \sigma_y^2 = \dfrac{\displaystyle\sum_{i=1}^{n}(\hat{y} - \overline{y})^2}{(n - 1)} + \dfrac{(n - 2)}{(n - 1)}\sigma^2$ $\tag{13.44}$

Equation (13.44) defines the relationship between these 2 variances and $\sum_{i=1}^{n}(\hat{y} - \overline{y})^2$, which is defined as the sum of the squares that can be explained by the regression.

13.2.4 Sampling Distributions of *a*, *b*, and *y*

The 3 estimators in the sample regression equation $(a, b, \hat{y})$ are random variables, and as such, have sampling distributions which are assumed to be normal, because both a and b are linear combinations of independent and normally distributed random variables $(y_1, y_2, \ldots, y_n)$, as can be seen from the "normal equations" of the linear model (equations (13.16) and (13.17)).

Then, the sampling distribution of a, b, and $\hat{y}$ are:

1. a is normally distributed with: $E(a) = \alpha \,\&\, V(a) = \dfrac{\sigma^2}{n}\left[\dfrac{\displaystyle\sum_{i=1}^{n}x_i^2}{\displaystyle\sum_{i=1}^{n}(x_i - \overline{x})^2}\right]$ $\tag{13.45}$

    if $n \geq 30$, and t_{n-2} if $n < 30$.

2. b is normally distributed with: $E(b) = \beta \,\&\, V(b) = \dfrac{\sigma^2}{\displaystyle\sum_{i=1}^{n}(x_i - \overline{x})^2}$ $\tag{13.46}$

    if $n \geq 30$, and t_{n-2} if $n < 30$.

3. $\hat{y}$ is normally distributed with: $E(\hat{y}) = E(a + bx) = \alpha + \beta x$ $\tag{13.47}$
    (for a given value of x, say $x = x_0$) if $n \geq 30$, and t_{n-2} if $n < 30$.

    To calculate the variance of $\hat{y}$, we consider 2 separate cases:

    a) The case for estimating the mean value of $y\,(\mu_{yx})$ for which the estimate is:
    $\hat{\overline{y}}_0 = a + bx_0$ with a variance $V(\hat{y})_p$ given by: $\tag{13.48}$

$$V(\hat{y})p = \sigma^2\left[\dfrac{1}{n} + \dfrac{(x_0 - \overline{x})^2}{\displaystyle\sum_{i=1}^{n}(x_i - \overline{x})^2}\right] \tag{13.49}$$

This case is known as the Prediction Case.

b) The case for estimating a single value of $y = y_0$, associated with a value of $x = x_0$.

For this case the estimate is given by: $\hat{\bar{y}}_0 = a + bx_0$ with a variance $V(\hat{y})_F$ given by:

$$V(\hat{y})_F = \sigma^2 \left[1 + \frac{1}{n} + \frac{(x_0 - \bar{x})^2}{\sum\limits_{i=1}^{n}(x_i - \bar{x})^2} \right] \qquad (13.50)$$

This case is known as the Forecasting case.

It can be seen that: $\qquad V(\hat{y})_F = V(\hat{y})_p + \sigma^2 \qquad (13.51)$

In equations (13.45), (13.46), (13.49), and (13.50), σ^2 is the sample variance of defined by equation (13.36). The expression $\sum\limits_{i=1}^{n}(x_i - \bar{x})^2$, found in all of be evaluated easier from the expanded formula:

$$\sum_{i=1}^{n}(x_i - \bar{x})^2 = \sum_{i=1}^{n}x_i^2 - \frac{\left(\sum\limits_{i=1}^{n}x_i\right)^2}{n} \qquad (13.52)$$

e: The variance of a, $V(a)$, and the variance of b, $V(b)$, will be derived as part of the multivariate (or generalized) regression analysis that we will discuss in Chapter 15, because these derivations become easier when using matrix operations.

13.2.5 Hypothesis Testing for: α, β and y

To test the hypotheses: H_0: $\beta = \beta_0$ vs H_1: $\beta \neq \beta_0$, $\qquad\qquad (13.53)$

$\qquad\qquad\qquad\qquad H_0$: $\alpha = \alpha_0$ vs H_1: $\alpha \neq \alpha_0$, $\qquad\qquad (13.54)$

and: $\qquad\qquad\qquad H_0$: $y = \alpha + \beta x_0$ vs H_1: $y \neq \alpha + \beta x_0$, $\qquad (13.55)$

it is obvious that we need the sampling distributions of a, b, and $\hat{y}$ which are, as we stated above, normally distributed if $n \geq 30$, or t_{n-2} distributed if $n < 30$ (t_{n-2} because the sum of squares $\sum\limits_{i=1}^{n}(y_i - a - bx_i)^2$ has 2 unknown estimators, a and b, to be estimated from the data).

1. We usually let $\beta_0 = 0$, and test the hypothesis: H_0: $\beta = 0$ vs H_1: $\beta \neq 0$ which, if accepted, implies that $y = $ constant and does not depend on x (because in the linear equation $y = \alpha + \beta x$, if $\beta = 0$, $y = \alpha$).

If H_0: $\beta = 0$ vs H_1: $\beta \neq 0$ is rejected, then we conclude that y is a function of x, and that the value of x affects the value of y.

a) If $n \geq 30$, the test statistic is: $Z^* = \dfrac{b - 0}{\sigma(b)}$, $\qquad\qquad\qquad (13.56)$

and we compare Z^* against $Z_{\alpha/2}$.

b) If $n < 30$, the test statistic is: $t^* = \dfrac{b - 0}{\sigma(b)}$, $\qquad\qquad\qquad (13.57)$

and we compare t^* against $t_{n-2}(\alpha/2)$.

2. Also, we usually let $\alpha_0 = 0$, and test the hypothesis: H_0: $\alpha = 0$ vs H_1: $\alpha \neq 0$ which, if accepted, implies that the line $y = \alpha + \beta x$ goes through the origin

(because $a = 0$). If H_0: $\alpha = 0$ vs H_1: $\alpha \neq 0$ is rejected, we conclude that the y-intercept of the linear function is $\neq 0$, and the line does not go through zero.

For a given value of α (such as $\alpha = 0.05$ or $\alpha = 0.01$), the hypothesis is tested as follows:

a) If $n \geq 30$, the test statistic is $Z^* = \dfrac{a - 0}{\sigma(a)}$, $\qquad$ (13.58)

and we compare Z^* against $Z_{\alpha/2}$.

b) If $n < 30$, the test statistic is $t^* = \dfrac{a - 0}{\sigma(a)}$, $\qquad$ (13.59)

and we compare t^* against $t_{n-2}(\alpha/2)$.

3. For a given value of $x = x_0$, we test the hypothesis:

$\quad$ H_0: $y = \alpha + \beta x_0$ vs H_1: $y \neq \alpha + \beta x_0$

The hypothesis is tested as follows:

a) If $n \geq 30$, the test statistic is

$$Z^* = \frac{\hat{\bar{y}}_0 - (\alpha + \beta x_0)}{\sigma(\hat{y})_P} = \frac{(a + bx_0) - (\alpha + \beta x_0)}{\sqrt{V(\hat{y})_P}},$$ $\qquad$ (13.60)

and we compare Z^* against $Z_{\alpha/2}$.

b) If $n < 30$, the test statistic is

$$t^* = \frac{\hat{\bar{y}}_0 - (\alpha + \beta x_0)}{\sigma(\hat{y})_P} = \frac{(a + bx_0) - (\alpha - \beta x_0)}{\sqrt{V(\hat{y})_P}},$$ $\qquad$ (13.61)

and we compare t^* against $t_{n-2}(\alpha/2)$. (This is the Prediction Case.)

c) If $n \geq 30$, the test statistic is $Z^* = \dfrac{\bar{y}_0 - y_0}{\sigma(\hat{y})_F} = \dfrac{(a + bx_0) - y_0}{\sqrt{V(\hat{y})_F}}$, $\qquad$ (13.62)

and we compare Z^* against $Z_{\alpha/2}$.

d) If $n < 30$, the test statistic is $t^* = \dfrac{\bar{y}_0 - y_0}{\sigma(\hat{y})_F} = \dfrac{(a + bx_0) - y_0}{\sqrt{V(\hat{y})_F}}$, $\qquad$ (13.63)

and we compare t^* against $t_{n-2}(\alpha/2)$.
(Parts (c) and (d) represent the Forecasting Case.)

Once the regression equation has been derived, it must be tested for significance (to derive the Final Regression equation). There are 4 possibilities:

1) If H_0: $\beta = 0$ and H_0: $\alpha = 0$ are both rejected; Final equation is: $\hat{y} = a + bx$
2) If H_0: $\beta = 0$ is rejected but H_0: $\alpha = 0$ is not rejected; Final equation is: $\hat{y} = bx$
3) If H_0: $\beta = 0$ is not rejected but H_0: $\alpha = 0$ is rejected; Final equation is: $\hat{y} = a$
4) If H_0: $\beta = 0$ and H_0: $\alpha = 0$ are both not rejected; Final equation is: $\hat{y} = 0$

Note: The sample regression equation is retained as a Predictive Device, if b is found to be significant (*i.e.*, if H_0: $\beta = 0$ vs H_1: $\beta \neq 0$ is rejected). Otherwise it should be discarded.

13.2.6 Confidence Intervals for: α, β, μ_{yx_0}, y_0

The confidence intervals for the population parameters: α, β, μ_{yx_0}, y_0 can be computed as usual, using either the Z distribution or the t_{n-2} distribution, as appropriate:

1. If $n \geq 30$ we use the Z-distribution and the following equations:

$$P[a - Z_{\alpha/2} \cdot \sigma(a) < \alpha < a + Z_{\alpha/2} \cdot \sigma(a)] = 1 - \alpha$$ $\qquad$ (13.64)

$$P[b - Z_{\alpha/2} \cdot \sigma(b) < \beta < b + Z_{\alpha/2} \cdot \sigma(b)] = 1 - \alpha$$ $\qquad$ (13.65)

$$P[\hat{\bar{y}}_0 - Z_{\alpha/2} \cdot \sigma(\hat{y})_P < \mu_{yx_0} < \hat{\bar{y}}_0 + Z_{\alpha/2} \cdot \sigma(\hat{y})_P] = 1 - \alpha \qquad (13.66)$$
(where $\quad \hat{\bar{y}}_0 = a + bx_0$)

$$P[\hat{y}_0 - Z_{\alpha/2} \cdot \sigma(\hat{y})_F < y_0 < \hat{y}_0 + Z_{\alpha/2} \cdot \sigma(\hat{y})_F] = 1 - \alpha \qquad (13.67)$$
(where $\quad \hat{y}_0 = a + bx_0$)

2. If $n < 30$, we use the t_{n-2} distribution and the following equations:

$$P[a - t_{n-2}(\alpha/2) \cdot \sigma(a) < \alpha < a + t_{n-2}(\alpha/2) \cdot \sigma(a)] = 1 - \alpha \qquad (13.68)$$

$$P[b - t_{n-2}(\alpha/2) \cdot \sigma(b) < \beta < b + t_{n-2}(\alpha/2) \cdot \sigma(b)] = 1 - \alpha \qquad (13.69)$$

$$P[\hat{\bar{y}}_0 - t_{n-2}(\alpha/2) \cdot \sigma(\hat{y})_P < \mu_{yx_0} < \hat{\bar{y}}_0 + t_{n-2}(\alpha/2) \cdot \sigma(\hat{y})_P] = 1 - \alpha \quad (13.70)$$
(where $\quad \hat{\bar{y}}_0 = a + bx_0$)

$$P[\hat{y}_0 - t_{n-2}(\alpha/2) \cdot \sigma(\hat{y})_F < y_0 < \hat{y}_0 + t_{n-2}(\alpha/2) \cdot \sigma(\hat{y})_F] = 1 - \alpha \qquad (13.71)$$
(where $\quad \hat{y}_0 = a + bx_0$)

13.2.7 Example 1

A sample of 5 adult men, for whom heights and weights are measured, gives the following results:

#	H: Height	W: Weight
1	64	130
2	65	145
3	66	150
4	67	165
5	68	170
	$\Sigma H_i = 330$	$\Sigma W_i = 760$

Problem

1. Fit the equation: $\hat{y} = a + bx$
2. Test the hypothesis: H_0: $\beta = 0$ vs H_1: $\beta \neq 0$, at $\alpha = 0.05$
3. Test the hypothesis: H_0: $\alpha = 0$ vs H_1: $\alpha \neq 0$, at $\alpha = 0.05$
4. Test the hypothesis: H_0: $\mu_{yx} = 152$ vs H_1: $\mu_{yx} \neq 152$, $\alpha = 0.05$, when $x_0 = 70$
5. Test the hypothesis: H_0: $y_0 = 180$ vs H_1: $y_0 \neq 180$, at $\alpha = 0.05$, when $x_0 = 70$
6. Construct 95% C.I. on β
7. Construct 95% C.I. on α
8. Construct 95% C.I. on μ_{yx}
9. Construct 95% C.I. on y_0

Solution To solve these problems we need to first perform the following calculations:

$$\Sigma x_i = \Sigma H_i = 64 + 65 + \cdots + 68 = 330$$

$$\sum x_i^2 = \sum H_i^2 = 64^2 + 65^2 + \cdots + 68^2 = 21,790$$

$$\sum y_i = \sum W_i = 130 + 145 + \cdots + 170 = 760$$

$$\sum y_i^2 = \sum W_i^2 = 130^2 + 145^2 + \cdots + 170^2 = 116,550$$

$$\sum x_i y_i = \sum H_i W_i = (64)(130) + (65)(145) + \cdots + (68)(170) = 50,260$$

$$\sum (x_i - \bar{x})^2 = \sum x_i^2 - \frac{\left(\sum x_i\right)^2}{n}$$

$$= (64 - 66)^2 + (65 - 66)^2 + (66 - 66)^2 + (67 - 66)^2$$

$$+ (68 - 66)^2 = 10$$

Then

1. To find the equation $\hat{y} = a + bx$, we must use the normal equations (equations (13.16) and (13.17)) and substitute some of the above generated values in the equations to obtain:

$$na + b \sum_{i=1}^{n} x_i = \sum_{i=1}^{n} y_i$$

$$a \sum_{i=1}^{n} x_i + b \sum_{i=1}^{n} x_i^2 = \sum_{i=1}^{n} x_i \cdot y_i$$

or
$$5a + 330b = 760$$
$$330a + 21,790b = 50,260$$

Solving these two equations simultaneously for a and b, we obtain:

$$a = -508, \quad b = 10,$$

and the regression equation is:

$$y = -508 + 10x \tag{13.72}$$

Before we can continue with the remaining parts of the problem, we need to first calculate: σ^2, $\sigma(b)$, $\sigma(a)$, $\sigma(\hat{y})_P$, and $\sigma(\hat{y})_F$. Then:
From eq (13.36) we obtain:

$$\sigma^2 = \frac{\sum y_i^2 - a\sum y_i - b\sum x_i y_i}{n - 2} = \frac{116,550 - (-508)(760) - 10(50,260)}{3}$$

$$= \frac{116,550 + 386,080 - 502,600}{3} = \frac{30}{3} = 10 \tag{13.73}$$

From eq (13.45) we obtain:

$$V(a) = \frac{\sigma^2}{n}\left[\frac{\sum x_i^2}{\sum(x_i - \bar{x})^2}\right] = \frac{10}{5}\left[\frac{21,790}{10}\right] = 4,358, \quad \text{and}$$

$$\sigma(a) = \sqrt{V(a)} = \sqrt{4,358} = 66.015 \tag{13.74}$$

From eq (13.46) we obtain:

$$V(b) = \frac{\sigma^2}{\Sigma (x_i - \bar{x})^2} = \frac{10}{10} = 1, \quad \text{and}$$

$$\sigma(b) = \sqrt{V(b)} = 1 \tag{13.75}$$

From eq (13.49) we obtain:

$$V(\hat{y})_p = \sigma^2 \left[\frac{1}{n} + \frac{(x_0 - \bar{x})^2}{\Sigma (x_i - \bar{x})^2} \right] = 10 \left[\frac{1}{5} + \frac{(70 - 66)^2}{10} \right] = 18, \text{ at } x_0 = 70,$$

$$\text{and} \quad \sigma(\hat{y})_P = \sqrt{V(y)_P} = \sqrt{18} = 4.2426 \tag{13.76}$$

From eq(13.50) we obtain:

$$V(\hat{y})_F = \sigma^2 \left[1 + \frac{1}{n} + \frac{(x_0 - \bar{x})^2}{\Sigma (x_i - \bar{x})^2} \right] = 10 \left[1 + \frac{1}{5} + \frac{(70 - 66)^2}{10} \right] = 28, \text{ and}$$

$$\sigma(\hat{y})_F = \sqrt{V(y)_F} = \sqrt{28} = 5.2915 \tag{13.77}$$

For $\alpha = 0.05$, $\alpha/2 = 0.025$ and $n = 5$ and $p = 2$ (for the linear model) we have: $t_{n-p}(\alpha/2) = t_{5-2}(0.025) = t_3(0.025) = 3.182$, and
$t_3(0.975) = -t_3(0.025) = -3.182 \tag{13.78}$

Then:

2. From equation (13.57) we have: $t_b^* = b/\sigma(b) = 10/1 = 10$ and, when compared to $t_3(0.025) = 3.182$, we reject H$_0$: $\beta = 0$, and conclude that $\beta \neq 0$ (*i.e.*, Height affects weights)
3. From equation (13.59) we have: $t_a^* = a/\sigma(a) = (-508)/66.015 = -7.695$ and, when t_a^* is compared to $-t_3(0.025) = -3.182$, we reject H$_0$: $\alpha = 0$, and conclude that the linear equation does not go through zero.
4. When $x = x_0 = 70$, equation (13.72) produces $\hat{\hat{y}} = -508 + 10(70) = 192$. Then, from equation (13.61) we have: $t_{\hat{y}P}^* = (192 - 152)/4.2426 = 9.428$ and, when $t_{\hat{y}P}^*$ is compared to $t_3(0.025) = 3.182$, we reject H$_0$: $\mu_{yx} = 152$, and conclude that $\mu_{yx} \neq 152$.
5. When $x = x_0 = 70$, equation (13.72) produces $\hat{y}_0 = 192$. Then, from equation (13.63) we have: $t_{\hat{y}F}^* = (192 - 180)/5.2915 = 2.2678$ and, when $t_{\hat{y}F}^*$ is compared to $t_3(0.025) = 3.182$, we do not reject H$_0$: $y_0 = 180$, and conclude that the individual value of $y = y_0$, corresponding to the value of $x = x_0 = 70$, is 180.

     The confidence intervals asked for in parts: 6, 7, 8 and 9 of the problem come from equations (13.68), (13.69), (13.70) and (13.71) respectively, and are given by equations (13.79), (13.80), (13.81), and (13.82).
6. $P[a - t_3(0.025) \cdot \sigma(a) < \alpha < a + t_3(0.025) \cdot \sigma(a)] = 0.95$

   $P[-508 - 3.1824(66.015) < \alpha < -508 + 3.1824(66.015)] = 0.95$

   $P[-718.08 < \alpha < -297.92] = 0.95 \tag{13.79}$

   Since the hypothesized value $\alpha = 0$ is not in this interval, again we reject H$_0$.

7. $P[b - t_3(0.025) \cdot \sigma(b) < \beta < b + t_3(0.025) \cdot \sigma(b)] = 0.95$
   $P[10 - 3.1824(1) < \beta < 10 + 3.1824(1)] = 0.95$
   $P[6.8176 < \beta < 13.1824] = 0.95$ (13.80)
   Since the hypothesized value $\beta = 0$ is not in this interval, again we reject H_0.

8. $P\left[\hat{\bar{y}} - t_3(0.025)\, \sigma(\hat{y})_p < \mu_{yx_0} < \hat{\bar{y}} + t_3(0.025)\, \sigma(\hat{y})_p\right] = 0.95$
   $P[192 - 3.1824(4.2426) < \mu_{yx_0} < 192 + 3.1824(4.2426)] = 0.95$
   $P[178.50 < \mu_{yx_0} < 205.50] = 0.95$ (13.81)
   Since the hypothesized value $\mu_{yx_0} = 152$ is not in this interval, again we reject H_0.

9. $P[\hat{y}_0 - t_3(0.025)\, \sigma(\hat{y})_F < y_0 < \hat{y}_0 + t_3(0.025)\ \sigma(\hat{y})_F] = 0.95$
   $P[192 - 3.1824(5.2915) < y_0 < 192 + 3.1824(5.2915)] = 0.95$
   $P[175.16 < y_0 < 208.84] = 0.95$ (13.82)
   Since the hypothesized value H_0: $y_0 = 180$ falls inside this interval, again we do not reject H_0.

13.3   Correlation Analysis

13.3.1 Theoretical Considerations

Before correlation analysis can be meaningfully discussed, we need to state the following:

1. Correlation analysis answers the question: Is there a linear relationship between the two variables under consideration?

   To answer this question we first need to calculate the sample correlation coefficient, r, and then perform appropriate tests to determine if the calculated value of r is significantly different than zero, as a function of n (sample size) and α (the probability of making the wrong decision, that we are willing to accept).

   When r is significantly different than zero, we conclude that a linear relationship between the 2 variables exists, and we use regression analysis (which we discussed previously) to obtain it.

2. The sample correlation coefficient, r is the estimator for the population correlation coefficient, ρ, which is defined by the equation:

$$\rho = \frac{Cov(x, y)}{\sigma_x \cdot \sigma_y} = \frac{E(xy) - E(x)E(y)}{\sigma_x \cdot \sigma_y}$$ (13.83)

To calculate ρ, we need to make the following assumptions:

a) x and y are both random variables, with density functions $f(x)$ and $f(y)$ respectively, and there is no need to designate one of the variables as dependent and the other as independent.

b) The Bivariate density function of x and y, $f(x, y)$, and also the individual density functions of x and y, $f(x)$ and $f(y)$, are normally distributed; *i.e.*,

$$f(x, y) = \frac{1}{2\pi\sigma_x\sigma_y(1 - \rho^2)^{1/2}}\, e^{-\frac{1}{2(1-\rho^2)}\left[\frac{(x - E(x))^2}{\sigma_x^2} - \frac{2\rho[x - E(x)][y - E(y)]}{\sigma_x\sigma_y} + \frac{[y - E(y)^2]}{\sigma_y^2}\right]}$$ (13.84)

$$f(x) = \frac{1}{\sqrt{2\pi}\sigma_x}\, e^{-\frac{1}{2\sigma_x^2}[x - E(x)]^2}$$ (13.85)

$$f(y) = \frac{1}{\sqrt{2\pi}\sigma_y} e^{-\frac{1}{2\sigma_y^2}[y-E(y)]^2} \tag{13.86}$$

c) The relationship between x and y is linear.

3. Observations on ρ

   a) The definition for ρ (eq (13.83)), includes all 5 parameters of the bivariate density function $f(x, y)$, namely: $E(x)$, $E(y)$, σ_x, σ_y, ρ.

   b) ρ is symmetric with respect to x and y (i.e., interchanging x and y does not change ρ).

   c) When $\text{Cov}(x, y) \equiv$ (Covariance Between x and y) $= 0$, ρ is also equal to zero, and we conclude that no linear relationship exists between x and y (x and y are said to be *uncorrelated* in this case).

   d) When $\rho = 1$, perfect positive covariance exists between x and y (i.e., as x increases y also increases), and all the ordered pairs (x_i, y_i) lie on a straight line with positive slope.

   e) When $\rho = -1$, perfect negative covariance exists between x and y (i.e., as x increases y decreases), and all the ordered pairs (x_i, y_i) lie on a straight line with negative slope.

   f) In general: $-1 \leq \rho \leq 1$ \hfill (13.87)

   g) When $\rho = 0$, the bivariate density function $= f(x, y)$ can be written as the product of $f(x) f(y)$:

$$f(x, y) = \frac{1}{\sqrt{2\pi}\sigma_x} e^{-\frac{1}{2\sigma_x^2}[x-E(x)]^2} \frac{1}{\sqrt{2\pi}\sigma_y} e^{-\frac{1}{2\sigma_y^2}[y-E(y)]^2} \tag{13.88}$$

$$= f(x) \cdot f(y) \tag{13.89}$$

   In this case, when $\rho = 0$ and $f(x, y) = f(x) \cdot f(y)$, the variables x and y are both *uncorrelated and independent*.

   h) An example of 2 variables which are positively correlated (though not perfectly) are heights and weights of adult human beings while an example of negatively (though not perfectly) correlated variables are price of cars and age of cars.

4. Example 13.2 Calculation of ρ

Problem: Suppose a population consists of the 3 numbers: 1, 2, 3. A number is selected randomly, recorded, and returned to the box containing the population. Then, a second number is drawn.

a) Define the sample space, S, of this experiment.

b) On S, define the random variables:
   $X = $ Sum of the 2 numbers drawn
   $Y = $ Product of the 2 numbers drawn

c) Find: $E(X)$, $V(X)$, and $\sigma(X)$

d) Find: $E(Y)$, $V(Y)$, and $\sigma(Y)$

e) Find: $f(x, y) = $ Joint density function of variables (X, Y)

f) Use $f(x, y)$ to define pertinent "joint density" parameters and illustrate their computation:

   i) joint density function $[f(x, y)]$
   ii) Marginal density functions $[f(x), f(y)]$
   iii) Are X and Y independent variables?
   iv) Expected value of a function of 2 variables $h(x, y) = E[h(x, y)]$ when:

   a) $h(x, y) = x + y$
   b) $h(x, y) = x - y$
   c) $h(x, y) = xy$

       v) Variance of a sum (or difference) of 2 (or more) variables, if:
          a) The variables are independent
          b) The variables are dependent
          c) Interpretation of covariance
    g) Calculation and interpretation of ρ

Solution The sample space, S, of this experiment is given by:

a) $S = \{(1, 1), (1, 2), (1, 3), (2, 1), (2, 2), (2, 3), (3, 1), (3, 2), (3, 3)\}$, and the possible values of the random variables X and Y are:

b) $X =$ Sum: 2, 3, 4, 3, 4, 5, 4, 5, 6
   $Y =$ Product: 1, 2, 3, 2, 4, 6, 3, 6, 9

c) The PMF and the needed calculations for the random variable X are given in the table below:

X	$P(X)$	$X \cdot P(X)$	$X^2 \cdot P(X)$
2	1/9	2/9	4/9
3	2/9	6/9	18/9
4	3/9	12/9	48/9
5	2/9	10/9	50/9
6	1/9	6/9	36/9
	Sum = 1	**$E(X) = 36/9 = 4$**	**$E(X^2) = 156/9$**

$$V(X) = E(X^2) - [E(X)]^2$$
$$= 156/9 - 4^2 = 4/3$$
$$\sigma(X) = \sqrt{V(X)} = \frac{2\sqrt{3}}{3}$$

d) The PMF and the needed calculations for the random variable Y are given in the table below:

Y	$P(Y)$	$Y \cdot P(Y)$	$Y^2 \cdot P(Y)$
1	1/9	1/9	1/9
2	2/9	4/9	8/9
3	2/9	6/9	16/9
4	1/9	4/9	72/9
6	2/9	12/9	81/9
9	1/9	9/9	81/9
	Sum = 1	**$E(Y) = 36/9 = 4$**	**$E(Y^2) = 196/9$**

$$V(Y) = E(Y^2) - [E(Y)]^2$$
$$= 196/9 - 4^2 = 52/9$$
$$\sigma(Y) = \sqrt{V(Y)} = \sqrt{\frac{52}{9}} = \frac{2\sqrt{13}}{3}$$

5. The joint density function of variables X and Y ($f(x, y)$) is given by the joint occurrence of X and Y values, as can be seen from the sample space, S, and the possible values of the random variables X and Y, and it is shown in the table below:

$Y(1 \leq j \leq 6)$

		1	2	3	4	6	9	$f(x)$
	2	1/9						1/9
	3		2/9					2/9
X	4			2/9	1/9			3/9
$(1 \leq i \leq 5)$	5					2/9		2/9
	6						1/9	1/9
		1/9	2/9	2/9	1/9	2/9	1/9	$\leftarrow f(y)$

6 a) The joint density function, $f(x, y)$, given here by the entries of the above rectangle (non-entries are equal to zero) is obtained by examining the occurrence of X and Y (Part b) and when they occur jointly.

   b) Observe that the "sum of the entries in each row" produces the density function of X ($f(x)$), which is also known as the marginal density of $X = f(x)$ (see Part c).

   Similarly observe that the "sum of the entries in each column" produces the density function of Y ($f(y)$), which is also known as the marginal density of $Y = f(y)$ (see Part d).

   c) Are the variables X and Y independent?

   For X and Y to be independent, we must show that $f(x, y) = f(x) \cdot f(y)$ for every combination of (x, y) values. If we can find one such combination of (x, y) for which $f(x, y)$ is NOT equal to: $f(x) \cdot f(y)$, then the variables are dependent.

   By observation, $f(x = 2, y = 1) = 1/9$ from the table above, but $f(x = 2) \cdot f(y = 1) = (1/9)(1/9) = 1/81$, which is different than $1/9$; Therefore, X and Y are dependent.

   d) The expected value of the function $h(X, Y) = XY$ is given by:

$$E[h(x, y)] = \sum \sum h(x, y) \cdot f(x, y) = \sum_{i=1}^{5} \sum_{j=1}^{6} (x_i \, y_j) f(x_i, y_j) \qquad (13.90)$$

$$= (1 \times 2) \times (1/9) + (2 \times 3) \times (2/9) + (4 \times 3) \times (2/9)$$

$$+ (4 \times 4) \times (1/9) + (6 \times 5) \times 2/9 + (9 \times 6) \times (1/9), \text{ and:}$$

$$E(XY) = (2/9) + (12/9) + (24/9) + (16/9) + (60/9) + 54/9 = 168/9$$

   e) The variance of the sum of 2 variables is given by:

$$V(X + Y) = E[(X + Y) - (E(X) + E(Y)]^2$$

$$= E[X - E(X) + (Y - E(Y)]^2 \qquad (13.91)$$

$$V(X + Y) = V(X) + V(Y) \text{ if } X \text{ and } Y \text{ are independent} \qquad (13.92a)$$

$$V(X + Y) = V(X) + V(Y) + 2\text{Cov}(X, Y)$$

if X and Y are dependent, $\qquad (13.92b)$

where $\qquad \text{Cov}(X, Y) = E(XY) - E(X)E(Y),$ and

$$\text{Cov}(X, Y) \begin{cases} > 0 \ X \text{ and } Y \text{ are positively correlated and dependent} \\ < 0 \ X \text{ and } Y \text{ are negatively correlated and dependent} \\ = 0 \ X \text{ and } Y \text{ are uncorrelated (i.e., no linear relationship exists).} \\ \quad \text{They may or may not be independent. To show independence} \\ \quad \text{we need to show that:} \\ \quad f(x_i, y_j) = f(x_i) \cdot f(y_j) \text{ for all } (x_i, y_j) \text{ combinations.} \end{cases}$$

(13.93)

In this example: $\text{Cov}(X, Y) = 168/9 - (4)(4) = 24/9 > 0$

7. $\rho = \dfrac{Cov(X, Y)}{\sigma_x \cdot \sigma_y} = \dfrac{24/9}{\left[\dfrac{2\sqrt{3}}{3}\right]\left[\dfrac{2\sqrt{13}}{3}\right]} \approx 0.96$

The value of ρ shows that X and Y are almost perfectly positively correlated.

13.3.2 Scatter Diagram

The scatter diagram of a Bivariate set of data (x_i, y_i) is a plot of the y_i values versus the x_i values.

When the "outer perimeter" of this set of data is connected by a continuous line, it can tell us if the two variables are correlated or not. If the resulting shape is "elliptical" (with major axis $= D$, and minor axis $= d$, where: $D > d$), the two variables are correlated; They are positively correlated if the "elliptical" shape starts at the lower left hand of the coordinate system and moves upward, and negatively correlated if the "elliptical" shape starts at the upper left hand of the coordinated system and moves downward to the right.

On the other hand, if the resulting shape is "circular", with $D \approx d$, the two variables are uncorrelated, and no linear relationship exists between the variables X and Y.

The 3 plots below illustrate graphically these 3 possibilities

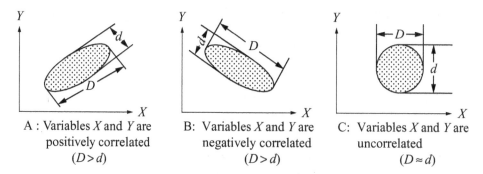

A : Variables X and Y are positively correlated ($D > d$)

B: Variables X and Y are negatively correlated ($D > d$)

C: Variables X and Y are uncorrelated ($D \approx d$)

Figure 13.1 Possible Scatter Diagram of a Bivariate Data Set

13.3.3 The Sample Correlation Coefficient, r

The estimator for the population correlation coefficient, ρ, is the sample correlation coefficient, r, which can be calculated in two ways, namely:

1. Approximately, using the equation: $r \approx \pm \left(1 - \dfrac{d}{D} \right),$ (13.94)

      where D = Major Axis of the resulting scatter diagram

             d = Minor Axis of the resulting scatter diagram

      Equation (13.94) has both: a positive, and a negative sign, and the appropriate sign is to be selected by inspection from the scatter diagram, for each situation.

      It should be "+", if the scater diagram looks like case A above, and "–", if the scatter diagram looks like case B above.

      It is obvious from equation (13.94) that if $d = D$, $r = 0$, and X and Y are uncorrelated, and no linear relationship exists between X and Y.

2. Exactly, using the equation:

$$r = \frac{n\left(\sum\limits_{i=1}^{n} x_i\, y_i \right) - \left(\sum\limits_{i=1}^{n} x_i \right)\left(\sum\limits_{i=1}^{n} y_i \right)}{\left[n\left(\sum\limits_{i=1}^{n} x_i^2 \right) - \left(\sum\limits_{i=1}^{n} x_i \right)^2 \right]^{\frac{1}{2}} \left[n\left(\sum\limits_{i=1}^{n} y_i^2 \right) - \left(\sum\limits_{i=1}^{n} y_i \right)^2 \right]^{\frac{1}{2}}}$$ (13.95)

      Note that all of the quantities involved in the calculation of r in (13.95) can be obtained from the given Bivariate data set (x_i, y_i).

3. Interpretation of the calculated value of r

      What does the calculated value of r, whether obtained from equation (13.94) or (13.95) mean? Is it large enough to be significantly different than zero and assure us that the variables X and Y are correlated and, therefore, a linear relationship exists between them (*i.e.*, X and Y), or not large enough and statistically equal to zero which would imply that X and Y are uncorrelated and, therefore, no linear relationship exists between X and Y?

These questions can be answered using Table 13.1 below. According to this table, decision points are calculated, as functions of n (= sample size), and α, and if the calculated value of r falls inside the decision points, r is assumed to be zero, the variables are uncorrelated, and no linear relationship exists between the variables. On the other hand, if the calculated value of r falls outside the decision points, r is assumed to be different than zero, the variables are correlated, and a linear relationship exists between the variables (and regression analysis should be used to obtain the linear relationship).

      The diagram below illustrzates the interpretation of the calculated value of r, using the decision points:

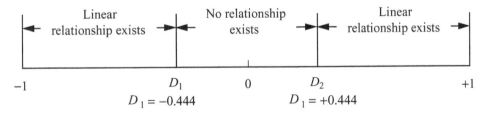

Figure 13.2 Interpretation of the Calculated Value of r

      If $n = 20$, and $\alpha/2 = 0.025$, then, using Table 13.1, the decision points are: D1 = −0.444 and D2 = 0.444. Then, if the calculated value of r is between: −0.444 and +0.444 (*i.e.*, if $-0.444 \le r \le 0.444$), then r is assumed to be equal to zero, and no linear relationship exists between the variables. On the other hand, if $-1 \le r < -0.444$ or if $0.444 < r \le 1$, the variables are assumed to be correlated, and a linear relationship exists between the variables.

Table 13.1 Calculation of Decision Points

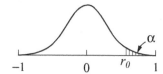

TABLE VIII Critical Values of r for Testing $\rho = 0$

For a two-sided test, α is twice the value listed at the heading of a column of critical r-values, hence for $\alpha = 0.05$ choose the 0.25 column

	α					α		
n	.05	.025	.005		n	.05	.025	.005
5	.805	.878	.959		17	.412	.482	.606
6	.729	.811	.917		18	.400	.468	.590
7	.669	.754	.875		19	.389	.456	.575
8	.621	.707	.834		20	.378	.444	.561
9	.582	.666	.798		25	.337	.396	.505
10	.549	.632	.765		30	.306	.361	.463
11	.521	.602	.735		35	.283	.334	.430
12	.497	.576	.708		40	.264	.312	.402
13	.476	.553	.684		50	.235	.279	.361
14	.457	.532	.661		60	.214	.254	.330
15	.441	.514	.641		80	.185	.220	.286
16	.426	.497	.623		100	.165	.196	.256

As an illustration, if $r = -.40$ and $n = 20$ and a two-sided test is being used, first find the .025 value corresponding to $n = 20$. It is .444; therefore the critical region for this test consists of the two intervals $r < -.444$ and $r > .444$. Since $r = -.40$ does not lie in either interval, the hypothesis H_0 that $\rho = 0$ is accepted.

13.3.4 The Sampling Distribution of r

The sample correlation coefficient r (whose numerical value in a given situation can be calculated from equations (13.94) or (13.95) is a random variable (it is also the estimator for the population correlation coefficient ρ, and to test hypotheses concerning values of ρ, or to construct confidence intervals on ρ, we need the sampling distribution of r), and as such it has a sampling distribution which is:

1. symmetric when $\rho = 0$
2. skewed when $\rho \ne 0$

The sampling distribution of r is not known, in general, but some specific "transformed" values of r have known distribution which can be used for hypothesis testing and/or construction of confidence intervals. For example:

1. When $\rho = 0$ (*i.e.*, when we wish to test the hypothesis: $H_0: \rho = 0$ vs $H_1: \rho \ne 0$), there is a transformation of the values of r, given by:

$$T(r) = \frac{r}{\sqrt{1 - r^2}} \cdot \sqrt{n - 2} \qquad (13.96)$$

which is distributed as t_{n-2}.

To test the hypothesis: $H_0: \rho = 0$ vs $H_1: \rho \neq 0$, for a given α, we calculate the value of the test statistic, t^*, from:

$$t^* = \frac{r}{\sqrt{1 - r^2}} \cdot \sqrt{n - 2} \tag{13.97}$$

and compare t^* to $t_{n-2}(\alpha / 2)$.
(r is the value of r calculated from either (13.94) or (13.95), and n is the sample size)
     The transformation given by (13.96) can NOT be used to construct a confidence interval, because it applies only for $\rho = 0$.

Note: Testing: $H_0: \rho = 0$ vs $H_1: \rho \neq 0$ and using the transformation defined by (13.96), is similar to, but not identical to the "decision point" interpretation of the calculated value of r discussed previously.

 2. When $\rho \neq 0$ (*i.e.*, when we wish to test the hypothesis: $H_0: \rho = \rho_0$ vs $H_1: \rho \neq \rho_0$ (where $\rho_0 \neq 0$), or when we wish to construct a confidence interval on ρ) we use the so-called "Z-Transformation" defined by:

$$Z_r = \frac{1}{2} \ln \left(\frac{1 + r}{1 - r} \right) \ (Z_r \text{ is normally distributed}), \tag{13.98}$$

with
$$E(Z) = Z\rho, \tag{13.99}$$

and
$$V(Z_r) = \frac{1}{n - 3} \ \left(\sigma(Z_r) = \frac{1}{\sqrt{n - 3}} \right) \tag{13.100}$$

Note: Equation (13.98) can also be solved for r in terms of Z_r, to produce:

$$r = \frac{e^{2Z_r} - 1}{e^{2Z_r} + 1} \tag{13.101}$$

     To find the value of Z_r, for a calculated value of r, we use equation (13.98) which requires the use of natural logarithms. If, on the other hand, we have the value of Z_r and wish to find the corresponding r value, we use equation (13.101) which requires the use of exponentials (with e as the base). To avoid having to use natural logarithms or exponentials in these calculations, use Table 13.2 below.
     This table does the following:

 1. For a calculated value of r, find the corresponding Z_r
    (Example: If $r = 0.95$, $Z_r = 1.832$)
 2. For a stated value of ρ, find the corresponding Z_ρ
    (Example: If $\rho = 0.90$, $Z_\rho = 1.472$)
 3. Given Z_r, use Table 13.2 to find the corresponding value of r
    (Example: If $Z_r = 1.832$, locate this value in the table, and then use the table to read $r = 0.95$ under column r)
 4. Given Z_ρ, use Table 13.2 to find the corresponding value of ρ
    (Example: If $Z_\rho = 1.472$, locate this value in the table and then use the table to read $\rho = 0.9$ under column r)

Note: To test a hypothesis about ρ (For example: $H_0: \rho = 0.9$ vs $H_1: \rho \neq 0.9$), using r, we use the test statistic:

$$Z^* = \frac{Z_r - Z_\rho}{\sigma(Z_r)} \tag{13.102}$$

Table 13.2 Relationship Between Z_r and r and also Z_ρ and ρ

Values of $Z = \left(\dfrac{1}{2}\right)\ln\left(\dfrac{1+r}{1-r}\right)$

			r(3d decimal)						r(3d decimal)		
r	.000	.002	.004	.006	.008	r	.000	.002	.004	.006	.008
.00	.0000	.0020	.0040	.0060	.0080	.50	.5493	.5520	.5547	.5573	.5600
1	.0100	.0120	.0140	.0160	.0180	1	.5627	.5654	.5682	.5709	.5736
2	.0200	.0220	.0240	.0260	.0280	2	.5763	.5791	.5818	.5846	.5874
3	.0300	.0320	.0340	.0360	.0380	3	.5901	.5929	.5957	.5985	.6013
4	.0400	.0420	.0440	.0460	.0480	4	.6042	.6070	.6098	.6127	.6155
.05	.0500	.0520	.0541	.0561	.0581	.55	.6194	.6213	.6241	.6270	.6299
6	.0601	.0621	.0641	.0661	.0681	6	.6328	.6358	.6387	.6416	.6446
7	.0701	.0721	.0741	.0761	.0782	7	.6475	.6505	.6535	.6565	.6595
8	.0802	.0822	.0842	.0862	.0882	8	.6625	.6655	.6685	.6716	.6746
9	.0902	.0923	.0943	.0963	.0983	9	.6777	.6807	.6838	.6869	.6900
.10	.1003	.1024	.1044	.1064	.1084	.60	.6931	.6963	.6994	.7026	.7057
1	.1104	.1125	.1145	.1165	.1186	1	.7089	.7121	.7153	.7185	.7218
2	.1206	.1226	.1246	.1267	.1287	2	.7250	.7283	.7315	.7348	.7381
3	.1307	.1328	.1348	.1368	.1389	3	.7414	.7447	.7481	.7514	.7548
4	.1409	.1430	.1450	.1471	.1491	4	.7582	.7616	.7650	.7684	.7718
.15	.1511	.1532	.1552	.1573	.1593	.65	.7753	.7788	.7823	.7858	.7893
6	.1614	.1634	.1655	.1676	.1696	6	.7928	.7964	.7999	.8035	.8071
7	.1717	.1737	.1758	.1779	.1799	7	.8107	.8144	.8180	.8217	.8254
8	.1820	.1841	.1861	.1882	.1903	8	.8291	.8328	.8366	.8404	.8441
9	.1923	.1944	.1965	.1986	.2007	9	.8480	.8518	.8556	.8595	.8634
.20	.2027	.2048	.2069	.2090	.2111	.70	.8673	.8712	.8752	.8792	.8832
1	.2132	.2153	.2174	.2195	.2216	1	.8872	.8912	.8953	.8994	.9035
2	.2237	.2258	.2279	.2300	.2321	2	.9076	.9118	.9160	.9202	.9245
3	.2342	.2363	.2384	.2405	.2427	3	.9287	.9330	.9373	.9417	.9461
4	.2448	.2469	.2490	.2512	.2533	4	.9505	.9549	.9549	.9639	.9684
.25	.2554	.2575	.2597	.2618	.2640	.75	0.973	0.978	0.982	0.987	0.991
6	.2661	.2683	.2704	.2726	.2747	6	0.996	1.001	1.006	1.011	1.015
7	.2769	.2790	.2812	.2833	.2855	7	1.020	1.025	1.030	1.035	1.040
8	.2877	.2899	.2920	.2942	.2964	8	1.045	1.050	1.056	1.061	1.066
9	.2986	.3008	.3029	.3051	.3073	9	1.071	1.077	1.082	1.088	1.093
.30	.3095	.3117	.3139	.3161	.3183	.80	1.099	1.104	1.110	1.116	1.121
1	.3205	.3228	.3250	.3272	.3294	1	1.127	1.133	1.139	1.145	1.151
2	.3316	.3339	.3361	.3383	.3406	2	1.157	1.163	1.169	1.175	1.182
3	.3428	.3451	.3473	.3496	.3518	3	1.188	1.195	1.201	1.208	1.214
4	.3541	.3564	.3586	.3609	.3632	4	1.221	1.228	1.235	1.242	1.249
.35	.3654	.3677	.3700	.3723	.3746	.85	1.256	1.263	1.271	1.278	1.286
6	.3769	.3792	.3815	.3838	.3861	6	1.293	1.301	1.309	1.317	1.325
7	.3884	.3907	.3931	.3954	.3977	7	1.333	1.341	1.350	1.358	1.367
8	.4001	.4024	.4047	.4071	.4094	8	1.376	1.385	1.394	1.403	1.412
9	.4118	.4142	.4165	.4189	.4213	9	1.422	1.432	1.442	1.452	1.462
.40	.4236	.4260	.4284	.4308	.4332	.90	1.472	1.483	1.494	1.505	1.516
1	.4356	.4380	.4404	.4428	.4453	1	1.528	1.539	1.551	1.564	1.576
2	.4477	.4501	.4526	.4550	.4574	2	1.589	1.602	1.616	1.630	1.644
3	.4599	.4624	.4648	.4673	.4698	3	1.658	1.673	1.689	1.705	1.721
4	.4722	.4747	.4772	.4797	.4822	4	1.738	1.756	1.774	1.792	1.812
.45	.4847	.4872	.4897	.4922	.4948	.95	1.832	1.853	1.874	1.897	1.921
6	.4973	.4999	.5024	.5049	.4075	6	1.946	1.972	2.000	2.029	2.060
7	.5101	.5126	.5152	.5178	.5204	7	2.092	2.127	2.165	2.205	2.249
8	.5230	.5256	.5282	.5308	.5334	8	2.298	2.351	2.410	2.477	2.555
9	.5361	.5387	.5413	.5440	.5466	9	2.647	2.759	2.903	3.106	3.453

Source: This table is abridged from Table 14 of the *Biomtretrika Tables for Statisticians*, Vol. 1 (1st ed.), edited by E. S. Pearson and H. O. Hartley.

13.3.5 Example 3 Hypothesis Testing on ρ

1. Suppose that in a given bivariate data set with $n = 12$, the calculated value of r is:
   $r = 0.88$

   Test, when $\alpha = 0.05$, the hypothesis: H_0: $\rho = 0$ vs H_1: $\rho \neq 0$

   a) Calculate:

   $$t^* = \frac{r}{\sqrt{1 - r^2}} \cdot \sqrt{n - 2} = \frac{0.88}{\sqrt{1 - 0.88^2}} \sqrt{12 - 2} = 5.94 \qquad (13.103)$$

   b) Compare: $t^* = 5.94$ to $t_{n-2}(\alpha/2) = t_{10}(0.025) = 2.228$ $\qquad$ (13.104)

   Since $t^* > t_{10}(0.025)$, we reject H_0, and conclude that the population correlation coefficient $\rho \neq 0$.

2. Suppose that 12 ordered pairs of values (x_i, y_i) were obtained and a value of $r = 0.95$ was calculated. Test, at the $\alpha = 0.01$ level, the hypothesis:

   H_0: $\rho = 0.9$ vs H_1: $\rho \neq 0.9$.

   a)* H_0: $\rho = 0.9$ vs H_1: $\rho \neq 0.9$

   b)* $\alpha = 0.01$ and $\alpha/2 = 0.005$

   c)* The estimator for ρ is r, but we do not know the distribution of r; therefore, we redefine H_0, using Z_ρ, whose estimator is Z_r and whose distribution is known to be normal (see (13.98), (13.99) and (13.100)), and proceed as shown below:

   i) H_0: $Z_\rho = 1.472$ vs H_1: $Z_\rho \neq 1.472$

   ii) $\alpha = 0.01$ and $\alpha/2 = 0.005 \rightarrow Z(0.005) = 2.58$

   iii) The estimator for Z_ρ is Z_r and Z_r is: $N\left[E(Z_r) = Z_\rho, \sigma(Z_r) = \dfrac{1}{\sqrt{n - 3}} \right]$

   iv) Rejection region:

   $\alpha/2 = 0.005$ $\qquad\qquad\qquad\qquad$ $\alpha/2 = 0.005$

   $Z(0.995) = -2.58$ $\qquad\qquad\qquad$ $Z(0.005) = 2.58$

   v) $Z^* = \dfrac{Z_r - Z_\rho}{\sigma(Z_r)} = \dfrac{1.832 - 1.472}{\sqrt{\dfrac{1}{12 - 3}}} = \dfrac{0.360}{1/3} = 1.08$

   (Note: When $r = 0.95$, $Z_r = 1.832$, and when $\rho = 0.9$, $Z_\rho = 1.472$)

   vi) Since Z^* is not in the rejection region, we do not reject H_0: $Z_\rho = 1.472$, and conclude that $\rho = 0.9$.

13.3.6 Confidence Intervals on ρ

The confidence interval on ρ will be found indirectly, *i.e.*, we will first find a confidence interval on Z_ρ because we know the sampling distribution of its estimator, and then we will use Table 13.2 to find the corresponding confidence interval on ρ.

1. Confidence Interval on Z_ρ

   Since the estimator of Z_ρ, Z_r, is normally distributed with $\sigma(Z_r) = \dfrac{1}{\sqrt{n-3}}$, the $1 - \alpha$ confidence interval for Z_ρ is given by:

   $$P\left[Z_r - Z_{\alpha/2} \cdot \sigma(Z_r) < Z_\rho < Z_r + Z_{\alpha/2} \cdot \sigma(Z_r)\right] = 1 - \alpha, \qquad (13.105)$$

   or $P\left[1.832 - 2.58(1/3) < Z_\rho < 1.832 + 2.58(1/3)\right] = 0.99$

   or $P\left[0.973 < Z_\rho < 2.691\right] = 0.99$

2. Confidence Interval on ρ

   Using Table 13.2, we find that when $Z_\rho = 0.973$, the corresponding value of $\rho \approx 0.75$, and when $Z_\rho = 2.691$, $\rho \approx 0.991$ (by interpolation between the values: 2.647 (corresponding to $\rho = 0.99$) and 2.759 (corresponding to $\rho = 0.992$). Then the 99% confidence interval on ρ is given by:

   $$P[0.75 < \rho < 0.991] = 0.99 \qquad (13.106)$$

   Since the hypothesized value: H_0: $\rho = 0.9$ falls inside the interval defined by equation (13.106), we do not reject H_0, and conclude that $\rho = 0.9$.

Note: To test the hypothesis: H_0: $\rho_1 = \rho_2$ vs H_1: $\rho_1 \neq \rho_2$ (*i.e.*, to test the equality of 2 population correlation coefficients using information obtained from 2 independent samples), we use the test statistic:

$$Z^* = \frac{Z_{r_1} - Z_{r_2}}{\sqrt{\sigma_{Z_1}^2 + \sigma_{Z_2}^2}} \qquad (13.107)$$

where Z_{r_1} = Estimator of Z_{ρ_1}, corresponding to ρ_1

Z_{r_2} = Estimator of Z_{ρ_2}, corresponding to ρ_2

$$\sigma_{Z_1}^2 = \frac{1}{n_1 - 3} \qquad (13.108)$$

$$\sigma_{Z_1}^2 = \frac{1}{n_2 - 3} \qquad (13.109)$$

and compare to $Z_{\alpha/2}$, for a given level of significance α.

13.4 Coefficient of Determination (R^2)

After correlation analysis revealed the existence of a linear relationship between the variables X and Y, and regression analysis was used to derive the linear equation: $\hat{y} = a + bx$, the questions that must be answered are: How good is the linear equation we derived? How well does the equation fit the data?

To answer these questions, we use R^2, the coefficient of determination. A high value for R^2 implies a good fit.

Note: In multivariate problems (*i.e.*, problems with 2 or more independent variables) in addition to a high R^2 value we must have a:

$$\text{"Durbin-Watson Statistic"} \approx 2, \qquad (13.110)$$

to make sure the variables are independent. The "Durbin-Watson Statistic" is approximately defined as: $DW \approx 2(1 - r)$; when $r = 0$, $DW \approx 2$; when $r = +1$, $DW \approx 0$, and when $r = -1$, $DW \approx 4$)

13.4.1 Derivation of R^2

To derive an expression for R^2, we will decompose the variance of y into meaningful and distinct portions (as we did in ANOVA when we decomposed the total variance into variance among, and variance within) using Figure 13.3 below as a guide.

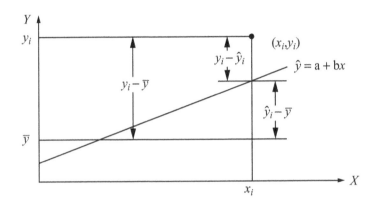

Figure 13.3 Calculating the Coefficient of Determination (R^2)

Using Figure 13.3, we can write:

$$(y_i - \overline{y}) = (y_i - \hat{y}_i) + (\hat{y}_i - \overline{y}), \qquad (13.111)$$

where $y_i - \overline{y}$ = Total Variation = Total distance of y_i from $\overline{y}$.

$\hat{y}_i - \overline{y}_i$ = "Explained Variation" = Distance of regression line ($\hat{y}$) from $\overline{y}$

$y_i - \hat{y}_i$ = "Residual Error" = Distance of an individual observation (y_i) from the regression line ($\hat{y}$)

Equation (13.111) applies to an individual observation (x_i, y_i); When summing over all the observations, we obtain (after squaring):

$$\sum_{i=1}^{n}(y_i - \overline{y})^2 = \sum_{i=1}^{n}[(\hat{y} - \overline{y}) + (y_i - \hat{y}_i)]^2 \qquad (13.112)$$

$$= \sum_{i=1}^{n}(\hat{y}_i - \overline{y})^2 + \sum_{i=1}^{n}(y_i - \hat{y}_i)^2 + 2\sum_{i=1}^{n}(\hat{y}_i - \overline{y})(y_i - \hat{y}_i) \qquad (13.113)$$

But: $$2\sum_{i=1}^{n}(\hat{y}_i - \overline{y})(y_i - \hat{y}_i) = 2\sum_{i=1}^{n}(\hat{y}_i - \overline{y})e_i$$

$$= 2\sum_{i=1}^{n}(a + bx_i - \overline{y})e_i \qquad (13.114)$$

$$= 2\left[\sum_{i=1}^{n}ae_i + b\sum_{i=1}^{n}x_ie_i - \overline{y}\sum_{i=1}^{n}e_i\right] = 0, \qquad (13.115)$$

since $\sum_{i=1}^{n} e_i = 0$, and x_i and e_i are statistically independent; Therefore, equation (13.113) can be written as:

$$\sum_{i=1}^{n}(y_i - \overline{y})^2 = \sum_{i=1}^{n}(\hat{y}_i - \overline{y})^2 + \sum_{i=1}^{n}(y_i - \hat{y}_i)^2 \qquad (13.116)$$

$$\begin{array}{ccccc} \text{Total Sum} & & \text{Regression Sum} & & \text{Error Sum} \\ \text{of Squares} & = & \text{of Squares} & + & \text{of Squares} , \end{array} \qquad (13.117)$$

or $\qquad\qquad\qquad \text{TSS} = \text{RSS} + \text{ESS} , \qquad\qquad\qquad (13.118)$

where $\qquad \text{TSS} = \sum_{i=1}^{n}(y_i - \overline{y})^2 = \sum_{i=1}^{n} y_i^2 - \dfrac{\left(\sum_{i=1}^{n} y_i\right)}{n} \qquad (\text{with dof} = n-1) \quad (13.119)$

$$\text{RSS} = \sum_{i=1}^{n}(\hat{y}_i - \overline{y})^2 = \sum_{i=1}^{n}[(a + bx_i) - (a + b\overline{x})]^2 = b^2 \sum_{i=1}^{n}(x_1 - \overline{x})^2$$

$$= b^2\left[\sum_{i=1}^{n} x_i^2 - \dfrac{\left[\sum_{i=1}^{n} x_i\right]^2}{n}\right] \qquad (\text{with dof} = 1) \qquad (13.120)$$

$$(\text{since } \hat{y} = a + bx_i, \text{ and } \overline{y} = a + b\overline{x})$$

$$\text{ESS} = \sum_{i=1}^{n}(y_i - \hat{y}_i)^2 = Q^*$$

$$= \sum_{i=1}^{n} y_i^2 - a\sum_{i=1}^{n} y_i - b\sum_{i=1}^{n} x_i y_i \qquad (\text{with dof} = n-2) \quad (13.121)$$

Note: The RSS of equation (13.120) includes only the effect of the coefficient b of the equation ($\hat{y} = a + bx_i$).

The sum of squares due to the constant $a = \text{SS}a$, is given by:

$$\text{SS}a = \dfrac{\left(\sum_{i=1}^{n} y_i\right)^2}{n}, \qquad (13.122)$$

and this term has to be included (*i.e.*, added or subtracted as is appropriate in a given situation) as we will show in the next section.

The coefficient of determination, R^2, is obtained from equation (13.118), by dividing both sides of equation (13.118) by TSS.

We obtain:

$$1 = \frac{\text{RSS}}{\text{TSS}} + \frac{\text{ESS}}{\text{TSS}} \qquad (13.123)$$

or $\qquad\qquad \dfrac{\text{RSS}}{\text{TSS}} = 1 - \dfrac{\text{ESS}}{\text{TSS}} \qquad\qquad (13.124)$

and $\qquad R^2 = \dfrac{\text{RSS}}{\text{TSS}} = \dfrac{Sum\ of\ Squares\ Explained\ by\ the\ regression}{Total\ Sum\ of\ Squares} \qquad (13.125)$

$$= 1 - \frac{\text{ESS}}{\text{TSS}}$$

13.4.2 Interpretation of R²

1. The value of R^2 can vary from $R^2 = 0$ to $R^2 = 1$.
2. When ESS = 0, $R^2 = 1$, and RSS = TSS; This implies that all the observations fall on the regression line.
3. When RSS = 0, $R^2 = 0$, and ESS = TSS; This implies that $b = 0$, and x does not affect the value of y.
4. As an example, suppose in a given problem we calculate $R^2 = 0.9$. What does this mean?
   It means that 90% of the variation in the values of y is explained (or accounted for) by the regression line (and factor x included in the regression) and only 10% is due to other factors, and we may wish to consider including another factor in the equation to increase the "explanatory" power of the regression line and bring it closer to 100%.
5. If R^2 is close to 1, we say that the "fit" of the equation to the data is good!
   It is possible to "split" ESS into 2 components (Sum of Squares due to Lack of Fit = $SS_{Lack\ of\ Fit}$, and Sum of Squares due to Pure Error = $SS_{Pure\ Error}$), and then test for "Lack of Fit". If the result is significant, we try to fit a different mode. (This is usually a topic of a more advance course in regression analysis/ANOVA).

Notes:

1. The numerical value of R^2 can be shown to be equal to: $R^2 = (r)^2$, where $r =$ Correlation coefficient defined by equations 13.94 or 13.95, but the meaning is different, as explained above.
2. There is another R^2, called the R^2 modified for degrees of freedom and represented by $\overline{R}^2$, which is defined as:

$$\overline{R}^2 = 1 - \frac{\text{ESS}/n - 2}{\text{TSS}/n - 1}$$

Computer programs usually show both R^2 and $\overline{R}^2$.

13.5 F Tests on α and β (Instead of Using z or t)

We showed how to test hypotheses about α and β, using either Z or t_{n-2}, depending on whether $n \geq 30$ or $n < 30$ (see equations (13.56, 13.57, 13.58), and the numerical example at the end of our Regression Analysis discussion.)

We will now show how to perform the same hypotheses on α and β using the ANOVA for regression and equations (13.119), (13.120), (13.121), and (13.122).

We can construct 2 "ANOVA for Regression" tables; one which does not include the Sum of Squares due to $a = SSa$, given by equation (13.122) (and can only be used to test the hypothesis $H_o: \beta = 0$ vs $H_1: \beta \neq 0$), and a second one which includes the SSa term and can be used to test both hypotheses:

1) $H_o: \beta = 0$ vs $H_1: \beta \neq 0$, and 2) $H_o: \alpha = 0$ vs $H_1: \alpha \neq 0$.

The 2 "ANOVA for Regression" tables are constructed below for the same example we used at the end of our "Regression Analysis" discussion (*i.e.*, Example 13.1). But, before we construct the 2 tables, we need to evaluate: TSS, RSS, ESS, and SSa, given by equations (13.119), (13.120), (13.121) and (13.122) respectively. Then we have:

1. $\text{TSS} = \sum_{i=1}^{5}(y_i - \bar{y})^2 = (130 - 152)^2 + (145 - 152)^2$

$$+ (150 - 152)^2 + (165 - 152)^2 + (170 - 152)^2$$

$$= (-22)^2 + (-7)^2 + (-2)^2 + (13)^2 + (18)^2$$

$$= 484 + 49 + 4 + 169 + 324 = 1030 \tag{13.126}$$

2. $\text{RSS}_b = \sum_{i=1}^{5}(\hat{y}_i - \bar{y})^2 = b^2 \sum_{i=1}^{5}(x_i - \bar{x})^2$

$$= 10^2(10) = 100(10) = 1000 \tag{13.127}$$

(Because b, from equation (13.72) is: $b = 10$,

and $\sum_{i=1}^{5}(x_i - \bar{x})^2 = (64 - 66)^2 + (65 - 66)^2 + (66 - 66)^2$

$$+ (67 - 66)^2 + (68 - 66)^2 = 10)$$

3. $\text{ESS} = \sum_{i=1}^{5}(y_i - \hat{y}_i)^2 = Q^* = \sum_{i=1}^{5}y_i^2 - a\sum_{i=1}^{5}y_i - b\sum_{i=1}^{5}x_i y_i$

$$= 116{,}550 - (-508)(760) - 10(50260) = 30 \tag{13.128}$$

4. $\text{SSa} = \dfrac{\left(\sum_{i=1}^{5}y_i\right)^2}{n} = \dfrac{(760)^2}{5} = \dfrac{577{,}600}{5} = 115{,}520 \tag{13.129}$

Table A ANOVA with SSa

Source of Variance	DF	Sum of Squares (SS)	MS = SS/DF	E(MS)
Regression $_b$ Regression $_a$	1 1	$RSS_b = 1000$ $SSa = 115{,}520$	1000/1 115,520/1	
Error	$n - 2 = 3$	$ESS = Q^* = 30$	30/3 = 10	σ^2
Total	$n = 5$	$\sum y_i^2 = 116{,}550$	116,550/5 = 23,310	

Table B ANOVA with SSa

Source of Variance	DF	Sum of Squares (SS)	MS = SS/DF	E(MS)
Regression $_b$	1	$RSS_b = 1000$	1000/1	
Error	$n - 2 = 3$	$ESS = Q^* = 30$	30/3 = 10	σ^2
Total	$n = 4$	$TSS = 1030$ $= \sum y_i^2 - \dfrac{(\sum y_i)^2}{n}$	1030/4 = 257.5	

Example 4

Then, from Table A we can test the hypothesis: $H_o: \beta = 0$ vs $H_1: \beta \neq 0$, by forming the F-ratio:

$$F_1^* = \frac{RSS_b/1}{Q^*/(n-2)} = \frac{1000/1}{10} = 100$$

and comparing it to $\qquad F_3^1(\alpha): \begin{cases} F_3^1(\alpha = 0.01) = 34.12 \\ F_3^1(\alpha = 0.05) = 10.13 \end{cases}$

For both values of α, reject H_0! Therefore, $\beta \neq 0$, and x affects the value of y.

We can also test the hypothesis: H_0: $\alpha = 0$ vs H_1: $\alpha \neq 0$ by forming the ratio:

$$F_2^* = \frac{SSa/1}{Q^*/(n-2)} = \frac{115,520/1}{10} = 11,552$$

and comparing it to $F_3^1(\alpha)$.

We reject H_0 for both $\alpha = 0.01$ and $\alpha = 0.05$, which means that the linear equation does not go through the origin (*i. e.*, $x = 0$, $y = 0$).

Table A can also be used to test the significance of the entire regression equation $\hat{y} = a + bx$.

This is accomplished by forming $F^* = \dfrac{(RSS_b + SSa)/2}{ESS/n - 2} = \dfrac{(1000 + 115,520)/2}{30/3} = 5,826$,

and comparing to $F_{n-2}^2(\alpha) = F_3^2(\alpha) = F_3^2(0.05) = 9.55$. Since $F^* = 5,826 > F_3^2(0.05) = 9.55$, the entire regression equation is significant.

From Table B we can test only the hypothesis: H_0: $\beta = 0$ vs H_1: $\beta \neq 0$ by forming the ratio:

$$F_3^* = \frac{RSS_b/1}{Q^*/(n-2)} = \frac{1000/1}{10} = 100$$

and compare it to $\qquad F_3^*(\alpha): \begin{cases} F_3^1(\alpha = 0.01) = 34.12 \\ F_3^1(\alpha = 0.05) = 10.13 \end{cases}$

The hypothesis H_0: $\beta = 0$ again, is rejected, and we conclude that $\beta \neq 0$. Therefore the factor x affects the value of variable y.

13.6 Rank Correlation Coefficient (r_s)

1. The rank correlation coefficient, r_s, is used when a random sample of n pairs is drawn from a bivariate population where observations are in ordinal measurements, instead of cardinal numbers.
   It was developed by *C.* Spearman in 1904, and it is applied to a set of ordinal rank numbers, with 1 for first, 2 for second, ..., n for last.

   Let $\quad x_i$ = Rank of Individual i on variable X

   $\qquad y_i$ = Rank of Individual i on variable Y

   and $\qquad\qquad\qquad\qquad d_i = x_i - y_i \qquad\qquad\qquad\qquad$ (13.130)

   Then $\qquad\qquad\qquad\qquad r_s = 1 - \dfrac{6 \displaystyle\sum_{i=1}^{n} d_i^2}{n(n^2 - 1)} \qquad\qquad\qquad$ (13.131)

2. Observations on r_s
   a) If the rank orders agree perfectly, each $d_i = x_i - y_i = 0$, and $r_s = 1$
   b) If the ranks are exactly the opposite, $r_s = -1$
   c) If $r_s = 0$, the conclusion drawn is that there is no relationship between the 2 sets of ranks.

d) Assume that no ties occur (if a tie does occur, each is assigned the mean of the ranks they would otherwise get).

The following examples illustrate observations (a) and (b) above and the more general case when r_s is neither equal to $+1$, nor equal to -1.

Example 5a

The math score ranking (x_i) and English score ranking (y_i) of 5 students is given below. Calculate r_s.

Student	x_i	y_i	$d_i = x_i - y_i$
1	1	1	0
2	2	2	0
3	3	3	0
4	4	4	0
5	5	5	0

Then $r_s = 1 - \dfrac{6\sum_{i=1}^{n} d_i^2}{n(n^2 - 1)} = 1 - \dfrac{6 \cdot 0}{5(5^2 - 1)} = 1$

Example 5b

Suppose the Math (x_i) and English (y_i) rankings are as shown below. Calculate r_s.

Student	x_i	y_i	$d_i = x_i - y_i$	$d_i^2 = (x_i - y_i)^2$
1	1	5	-4	16
2	2	4	-2	4
3	3	3	0	0
4	4	2	2	4
5	5	1	4	16

$$\sum_{i=1}^{n=5} d_i^2 = 40$$

Then $r_s = 1 - \dfrac{6\sum_{i=1}^{n} d_i^2}{n(n^2 - 1)} = 1 - \dfrac{6 \cdot 40}{5(5^2 - 1)} = 1 - \dfrac{240}{120} = 1 - 2 = -1$

Example 5c

Suppose the weights and heights of 5 people are given by the table below. Assign rank to the weights (x_i) and heights (y_i), and find r_s.

Person	Weight (lbs)	Height (')	$x_i (W)$	$y_i (H)$	$d_i = x_i - y_i$	$d_i^2 = (x_i - y_i)^2$
1	250	69	5	3	2	4
2	180	73	3	5	-2	4
3	150	60	1	1	0	0
4	200	72	4	4	0	0
5	160	68	2	2	0	0

$$\sum_{i=1}^{5} d_i^2 = 8$$

Then $r_s = 1 - \dfrac{6\sum\limits_{i=1}^{n} d_i^2}{n(n^2 - 1)} = 1 - \dfrac{6(8)}{5(5^2 - 1)} = 1 - \dfrac{48}{120} = 1 - 0.4 = 0.6$

3. The Sampling Distribution of r_s

The population rank correlation coefficient is ρ_s, and its estimator is r_s. Obviously, to test the hypothesis: $H_0: \rho_s = 0$ vs $H_1: \rho_s \neq 0$, we need to know the sampling distribution of r_s, which depends on the sample size n, as shown below:

a) <u>When $n \geq 20$</u>

   i) Calculate r_s, using equation   (13.131)

$$\left(i.e., r_s = 1 - \frac{6\sum\limits_{i=1}^{n} d_i^2}{n(n^2 - 1)} \right)$$

   ii) Then $\dfrac{r_s\sqrt{n - 2}}{\sqrt{1 - r_s^2}}$ is distributed as t_{n-2}.

   iii) To complete the testing of the hypothesis, let:

$$t^* = \frac{r_s\sqrt{n - 2}}{\sqrt{1 - r_s^2}} \qquad (13.132)$$

   iv) Compare t^* to $t_{n-2}(\alpha/2)$, for a given α value.

b) <u>When $8 \leq n < 20$</u>

   i) Modify equation (13.131) to correct r_s for continuity. Then the corrected r_s, $\bar{r}_s$, is defined by:

$$\bar{r}_s = 1 - \frac{\sum\limits_{i=1}^{n} d_i^2}{\dfrac{1}{6}[n(n^2 - 1)] + 1} \qquad (13.133)$$

   ii) Then $\dfrac{\bar{r}_s\sqrt{n - 2}}{\sqrt{1 - \bar{r}_s^2}}$ is distributed as t_{n-2}.

   iii) To complete the testing of the hypothesis, let:

$$t^* = \frac{\bar{r}_s\sqrt{n - 2}}{\sqrt{1 - \bar{r}_s^2}} \qquad (13.134)$$

   iv) Compare t^* to $t_{n-2}(\alpha/2)$, for a given α value.

Example 5d

Suppose in an example of ranking 27 people according to weight (x_i) and height (y_i), produced an $r_s = 0.6$. Test $H_0: \rho_s = 0$ vs $H_1: \rho_s \neq 0$ at $\alpha = 0.05$.

Then $t^* = \dfrac{r_s\sqrt{n - 2}}{\sqrt{1 - r_s^2}} = \dfrac{0.6\sqrt{27 - 2}}{\sqrt{1 - (.6)^2}} = 3.75$, and $\qquad t_{n-2}(\alpha/2) = t_{27-2}(0.025) = t_{25}(0.025) = 2.0595$

Since $t^* = 3.75 > t_{25}(0.025) = 2.0595$, the hypothesis $H_0: \rho_s = 0$ is rejected.

13.7   Computer Solutions & Exercises

We have shown in this chapter how to use the regression and correlation methodologies to manually construct linear relationships between 2 variables, when a bivariate data set is given. In this section we will use the regression and correlation methods to solve problems 1 and 2 by hand and then solve the same problems using Minitab. As can be seen from the computer (Minitab) output, these computer solutions include:

1. A scatter diagram
2. The sample correlation coefficient, r
3. The regression equation
4. The values of the estimators (a and b), their standard deviation, their t^* value (t-ratio), and the corresponding p-value.
5. An analysis of variance for regression, from which F-tests on α and β and can be performed, and
6. A list and analysis of the residual values of y.
   From this output, all of the tests discussed in this chapter, can then be performed.

Example 6
The number of defective items produced per unit of time, Y, by a certain machine is known to vary linearly with the speed of the machine X. Observations for 12 hours, selected at random from a month, yield the following results:

X	13.2	14.9	8.1	16.4	13.1	10.8	10.9	17.4	13.8	10.2	15.8	12.0
Y	9.4	12.2	6.0	11.4	9.6	7.5	5.7	12.3	9.2	7.0	9.0	7.0

1a) Construct a scatter diagram regressing Y on X for the data above.
1b) Obtain the linear regression equation $y = a + bx$
1c) Is the b obtained significant at: $\alpha = 0.05$? $\alpha = 0.01$?
1d) Construct a 95% C.I. for β.
1e) Construct a 95% C.I. for μ_{yx} and y_0 when $x = 10$.

Solutions From the given data we obtain:

$$n = 12, \sum_{i=1}^{12} x_i = 156.6, \sum_{i=1}^{12} x_i^2 = 2{,}128.76, \sum_{i=1}^{12} y_i = 106.3, \sum_{i=1}^{12} y_i^2 = 998.99,$$

$$\text{and } \sum_{i=1}^{12} x_i y_i = 1{,}448.89. \text{ Also, } \sum_{i=1}^{12} (x_i - \overline{x})^2 = \sum_{i=1}^{12} x_i^2 - \frac{\left(\sum_{i=1}^{12} x_i\right)^2}{12} = 85.13$$

1a) The scatter-diagram (a plot of Y vs X) shows two positively correlated variables which, reasonably, appear to be linearly related (see the computer-generated scatter diagram).

1b) The linear relationship $\hat{y} = a + bx$, is obtained from the solution of the normal equations for the linear model, when the appropriate data is substituted in, namely:

$$12a + 156.6b = 106.3$$
$$156.6a + 2{,}128.76b = 1{,}448.89$$

Solving simultaneously, we obtain:
$a = -0.5964$ and $b = 0.7245$ and, therefore, $\hat{y} = -0.5964 + 0.7245x$

1c) To test the hypothesis: H_0: $\beta = 0$ vs H_1: $\beta \neq 0$, we need to first obtain $\sigma(b)$, the standard deviation of b.

From (13.36) we obtain: $\sigma^2 = \dfrac{998.99 - (-0.5964)(106.3) - 0.7245(1{,}448.89)}{12 - 2}$ or,

$$\sigma^2 = 1.267,$$

and then

$$\sigma^2(b) = \frac{\sigma^2}{\displaystyle\sum_{i=1}^{12}(x_i - \bar{x})^2} = \frac{1.267}{85.13} = 0.01485961, \text{ and } \sigma(b) = 0.1219$$

Then, the hypothesis testing proceeds as follows:

i) H_0: $\beta = 0$ vs H_1: $\beta \neq 0$

ii) $\alpha = 0.05$ and $\alpha = 0.01$

iii) The estimator for β is b and, because $n < 30$, $\dfrac{b}{\sigma(b)}$ is $t_{n-2} = t_{10}$.

iv) The rejection region for $\alpha = 0.05$ is:

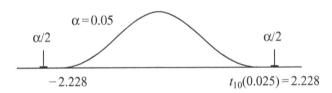

and for $\alpha = 0.01$ is

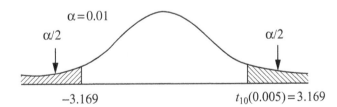

v) Value of test statistic $= t^* = \dfrac{b}{\sigma(b)} = \dfrac{0.7245}{0.1219} = 5.943$

vi) Since t^* falls in the rejection region (for both α values), H_0 is rejected.

vii) Rejecting H_0 implies that $\beta \neq 0$ and, equivalently, the variable X affects the value of the variable Y.

1d) The $1 - \alpha = 0.95$ confidence interval is obtained from the equation:

$$P[b - t_{n-2}(\alpha/2)\,\sigma(b) \le \beta \le b + t_{n-2}(\alpha/2)\,\sigma(b)] = 1 - \alpha$$

or $P[0.7245 - 2.228(0.1219) \le \beta \le 0.7245 + 2.228(0.1219)] = 0.95,$

or $P[0.453 \le \beta \le 0.996] = 0.95$

Since the hypothesized value, $\beta = 0$, is outside of this confidence interval, $H_0\colon \beta = 0$ again is rejected.

1e) To construct confidence intervals for μ_{yx} and y_o, at $x = x_0 = 10$, we first need to obtain the standard deviation for $\sigma(\hat{y})_P$ and $\sigma(\hat{y})_F$. Then, using the value of $\sigma^2 = 1.267$ and equations (13.49) and (13.50), we obtain:

$$V(\hat{y})_P = 0.244 \text{ and } \sigma(\hat{y})_P = 0.494$$

$$V(\hat{y})_F = 1.511 \text{ and } \sigma(\hat{y})_F = 1.229$$

Then $P[\hat{y} - t_{n-2}(\alpha/2)\cdot\sigma(\hat{y})_P \le \mu_{yx} \le [\hat{y} + t_{n-2}(\alpha/2)\cdot\sigma(\hat{y})_P] = 1 - \alpha$

and $P[\hat{y} - t_{n-2}(\alpha/2)\cdot\sigma(\hat{y})_F \le y_0 \le [\hat{y} + t_{n-2}(\alpha/2)\cdot\sigma(\hat{y})_F] = 1 - \alpha$

Since $\hat{y} = a + bx_0 = -0.5964 + 0.7245\,(10) = 6.6486 \approx 6.65$, when $x = x_0 = 10$, and $t_{n-2}(\alpha/2) = t_{10}(0.025) = 2.228$, we obtain:

$$P[5.55 \le \mu_{yx} \le 7.75] = 0.95$$

and $\qquad\qquad P[3.911 \le y_0 \le 9.389] = 0.95$

Example 7

For the data of problem 1) above

2a) Compute the sample correlation coefficient r.
2b) Test the hypothesis: $H_0\colon \rho = 0$ vs $H_1\colon \rho \ne 0$, at $\alpha = 0.05$
2c) Test the hypothesis: $H_0\colon \rho = 0.95$ vs $H_1\colon \rho \ne 0.95$, at $\alpha = 0.05$
2d) Construct a 95% C.I. on ρ

Solutions To solve Exercise 2, we use the same data, as for Exercise 1.

2a) Using equation (13.95) we calculate the value of the sample correlation coefficient r. We obtain: $r = 0.88268 \approx 0.883$

2b) i) $H_0\colon \rho = 0$ vs $H_1\colon \rho \ne 0$
  ii) $\alpha = 0.05$

  iii) The estimator for ρ is r, and $T(r) = \dfrac{r\sqrt{n-2}}{\sqrt{1-r^2}}$ is $t_{n-2} = t_{10}$-distributed.

  iv) The Rejection Region for $\alpha = 0.05$ is:

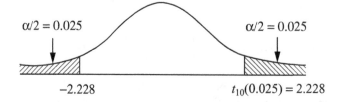

$\alpha/2 = 0.025$ $\qquad\qquad\qquad\qquad\qquad$ $\alpha/2 = 0.025$

-2.228 $\qquad\qquad\qquad\qquad\qquad$ $t_{10}(0.025) = 2.228$

v) The Value of Test Statistic $= t^* = \dfrac{r\sqrt{n-2}}{\sqrt{1-r^2}} = \dfrac{0.883\sqrt{12-2}}{\sqrt{1-(0.883)^2}} = 5.94898$

vi) Since t^* falls in the rejection region, H_0 is rejected.

vii) Therefore, $\rho \neq 0$

2c) To test the hypothesis H_0: $\rho = 0.95$ vs H_1: $\rho \neq 0.95$, we reformulate the hypothesis as: H_0: $Z_\rho = 1.832$ vs H_1: $Z_\rho \neq 1.832$ (using Table 13.2) because the estimator for Z_ρ, Z_r, is then known to be normally distributed. The hypothesis testing then proceeds as follows:

   i) H_0: $Z_\rho = 1.832$ vs H_1: $Z_\rho \neq 1.832$

   ii) $\alpha = 0.05$

   iii) The estimator for Z_ρ is Z_r, and Z_r is normally distributed with :

$$E(Z_r) = Z_\rho \text{ and } \sigma(Z_r) = \frac{1}{\sqrt{n-3}} = \frac{1}{\sqrt{12-3}} = \frac{1}{\sqrt{9}} = \frac{1}{3}$$

   iv) The Rejection Region for $\alpha = 0.05$ is:

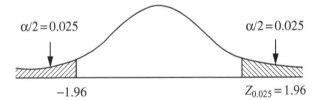

$\alpha/2 = 0.025$ $\alpha/2 = 0.025$

-1.96 $Z_{0.025} = 1.96$

   v) The Value of Test Statistic $= Z^*$

$$= \frac{Z_r - Z_\rho}{\sigma(Z_r)} = \frac{1.390 - 1.832}{1/3} = \frac{-0.442}{1/3} = -1.326$$

Note: When $r = 0.883$, $Z_r = 1.390$ (by interpolation, from Table 13.2; when $r = 0.882$, $Z_r = 1.385$ and when $r = 0.884$, $Z_r = 1.394$)

   vi) Since Z^* falls outside of the rejection region, H_0 is not rejected.

   vii) Therefore, since H_0 is not rejected, $\rho = 0.95$

2d) To construct a $1 - \alpha$ C.I. on ρ, we do it indirectly; *i.e.*, we first construct a $1 - \alpha$ C.I. on Z_ρ and then use Table 13.2 to go from Z_ρ to ρ.

Since Z_r is the estimator for Z_ρ and is normally distributed, we write:

$$p[Z_r - Z_{\alpha/2} \cdot \sigma(Z_r) \leq Z_\rho \leq Z_r + Z_{\alpha/2} \cdot \sigma(Z_r)] = 1 - \alpha$$

or $P[1.390 - 1.96(1/3) \leq Z_\rho \leq 1.390 + 1.96(1/3)] = 0.95$

or $P[0.737 \leq Z_\rho \leq 2.043] = 0.95$

Then, using Table 13.2 and interpolating we find that: when $Z_\rho = 0.7381$, $\rho = 0.628$, and when $Z_\rho = 0.7348$, $\rho = 0.626$. Therefore, when $Z_\rho = 0.737$, $\rho = 0.627$.

Similarly, when $Z_\rho = 2.029$, $\rho = 0.966$, and when $Z_\rho = 2.060$, $\rho = 0.968$. Therefore, when $Z_\rho = 2.043$, $\rho = 0.967$. Then, the $1 - \alpha = 0.95$ confidence interval for ρ is given by:

$$P[0.627 \leq \rho \leq 0.967] = 0.95$$

Since the hypothesized value, $\rho = 0.95$, is inside this *C.I.*, H_0: $\rho = 0.95$ is, again, not rejected.

Let us now see how the same problems can be solved by Minitab. The Minitab page (on the computer) consists of 2 half windows: The Session Window and the Worksheet 1 Window. To use the Session Window the Minitab prompt, MTB>, must be shown on the Session Window. If it is not shown, go to the "Editor" and "Enable the Command Language", and the MTB prompt will be generated.

We enter the data as shown below:

```
MTB> SET C1
DATA> 13.2 14.9 8.1 16.4 13.1 10.8 10.9 17.4 13.8 10.2 15.8 12.0
DATA> END
MTB> SET C2
DATA> 9.4 12.2 6.0 11.4 9.6 7.5 5.7 12.3 9.2 7.0 9.0 7.0
DATA> END
MTB> Name C1 'X' C2 'Y'
MTB> Plot X*Y            ← Obtains scatter diagram
MTB> Regress 'Y' 1 'X'   ← Obtains regression analysis
MTB> Correlate X Y       ← Obtains the sample correlation coefficient, r
```

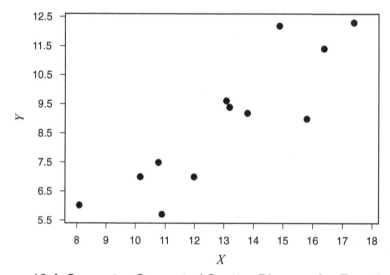

Figure 13.4 Computer-Generated Scatter Diagram for Exercise 1

The computer responds with Figure 13.4 which is Minitab's version of the scatter diagram and with Table 13.3 which includes the regression equation, the standard deviation, *t*-ratio, and *p*-value for both regression equation estimators (*a*=constant and *b*=machine), the R^2 and $\overline{R}^2$ values, and an analysis of variance for regression (this is the same as the ANOVA table without SSa, which was previously discussed) from which an *F*-test can be performed on the hypothesis: H_0: $\beta = 0$ vs H_1: $\beta \neq 0$, by comparing $F_b^* = 35.28$ against $F_{10}^1 (\alpha)$. Since the corresponding *p*-value is zero, this hypothesis will be rejected for all α values and we conclude that $\beta \neq 0$, or that the variable X (speed of machine) affects the value of Y (number of defective items).

Table 13.3 Computer-Generated Regression Analysis for Exercise 1

```
MTB > regress 'Y' 1 'X'
```

Regression Analysis: *Y* versus *X*

```
The regression equation is
Y = -0.60 + 0.724 X
```

Predictor	Coef	SE Coef	T	P
Constant	-0.596	1.625	-0.37	0.721
X	0.7245	0.1220	5.94	0.000

```
S = 1.125      R-Sq = 77.9%      R-Sq(adj) = 75.7%
```

Analysis of Variance

Source	DF	SS	MS	F	P
Regression	1	44.682	44.682	35.28	0.000
Residual Error	10	12.667	1.267		
Total	11	57.349			

Correlations: C1, C2

```
Pearson correlation of C1 and C2 = 0.883
P-Value = 0.000
```

To perform an F-test for the hypothesis $H_0: \alpha = 0$ vs $H_1: \alpha \neq 0$ we need to also construct the ANOVA table with the SSa, or recall that:

$$SSa = \frac{\left(\sum_{i=1}^{n} y_i\right)^2}{n} = \frac{(106.3)^2}{12} = 941.64. \text{ Then } F_a^* = \frac{SSA/1}{SSE/10} = \frac{941.64}{1.267} = 743.20,$$

and compare F_a^* against $F_{10}^1(\alpha)$. Because of the magnitude of F^*, $H_0: \alpha = 0$ will be rejected for all values of α, and we conclude that $\alpha \neq 0$, or that the linear equation $\hat{y} = a + bx$ does not go through the origin.

Also included in the Minitab output is a residual listing and analysis, and the value of the correlation coefficient r. In all cases it is seen that the hand and computer solutions are almost identical (except for rounding errors) and from this observation one should gain the confidence to go directly to the computer with a "large" problem because in such cases the hand solution is very inefficient.

13.8 References

Berenson, Marc, L., Levine, David, M., and Krehbiel, Timothy, C., 2004. *Basic Business Statistics*. 9th Edition. Pearson-Prentice Hall.

Black, Ken, 2004. *Business Statistics*. 4th Edition. Wiley.

Canavos, George, C., 1984. *Applied Probability and Statistical Methods*. Little, Brown.

Carlson, William, L., and Thorne, Betty, 1997. *Applied Statistical Methods*. Prentice Hall.

Chou, Ya-lun, 1992. *Statistical Analysis for Business and Economics*. Elsevier.

Freund, John, E., and Williams, Frank, J., 1969. *Modern Business Statistics*. Revised by: Perles, Benjamin and Sullivan, Charles. Prentice-Hall.

Freund, John, E., and Williams, Frank, J., 1982. *Elementary Business Statistics: The Modern approach*. Prentice-Hall.

Johnson, Robert, 1973. *Elementary Statistics*. Duxbury Press.

McClave, James, T., Benson, George, P., and Sincich, Terry, 2001. *Statistics for Business and Economics*. 8th Edition. Prentice Hall.

Salvatore, Dominick. *Theory and Problems of Statistics and Econometrics*. SCHAUM'S OUTLINE SERIES, McGraw-Hill.

Steel, Robert, G.D., and Torrie, James, H., 1976. *Introduction to Statistics*. McGraw-Hill.

13.9 PROBLEMS

1. The number of defective items produced per unit of time, Y, by a certain machine is known to vary linearly with the speed of the machine X. Observations for 12 hours, selected at random from a month, yield the following results:

X	13.2	14.9	8.1	16.4	13.1	10.8	10.9	17.4	13.8	10.2	15.8	12.0
Y	9.4	12.2	6.0	11.4	9.6	7.5	5.7	12.3	9.2	7.0	9.0	7.0

   a) Construct a scatter diagram regressing Y on X for the data above.

   b) Obtain the linear regression equation $Y = a + bX$

   c) Is the b obtained significant at: $\alpha = 0.05$? $\alpha = 0.01$?

   d) Construct a 95% C.I. for β.

   e) Construct a 95% C.I. for μ_{YX} and y_0 when $x = 10$.

2. For the data of Exercise 1 above:

   a) Compute the sample correlation coefficient.

   b) Test the Hypothesis: $H_0: \rho = 0$ agianst $H_0: \rho \neq 0$, at $\alpha = 0.05$.

   c) Test the Hypothesis: $H_0: \rho = 0.95$ $H_0: \rho \neq 0.95$, at $\alpha = 0.05$.

   d) Construct a 95% C.I. on ρ.

3. A sample of five adult men for whom heights and weights are measured, gives the following results:

Subject	1	2	3	4	5
Height: x_i	64	65	66	67	68
Weight: y_i	130	145	150	165	170

   a) Show that: SST = SSE + SSR

   b) Compute R^2. What does R^2 measure?

   c) Test the hypothesis $H_0: \beta = 0$ vs $H_1: \beta \neq 0$, using an F test.

4. The data below represents the results of a study of the relationship between productivity of workers and scores on selected aptitude tests:

Employee Number	1	2	3	4	5	6	7	8	9	10
Y: Productivity	41.5	43.0	42.5	44.0	44.5	45.2	46.0	47.5	49.0	48.0
X: Aptitude Score	110	125	140	150	165	170	190	200	210	215

From this table we obtain:

$$\sum_{i=1}^{10} x_i = 1675; \quad \sum_{i=1}^{10} x_i^2 = 292{,}375; \quad \sum_{i=1}^{10} y_i = 451.23;$$

$$\sum_{i=1}^{10} y_i = 76{,}366.5$$

   a) Find the regression equation $\hat{y} = a + bx$

   b) Calculate σ^2 and $\sigma(b)$

   c) Calculate the exact value of the sample correlation coefficient, r

d) Test the hypothesis $H_0: \beta = 0$ vs $H_1: \beta \neq 0$, at $\alpha = 0.05$

e) Test the hypothesis $H_0: \rho = 0.92$ vs $H_1: \rho \neq 0.92$, at $\alpha = 0.05$

f) Calculate the value of R^2 and comment on the "goodness" of the regression equation derived in part (a) above.

5. The moisture of the wet mix of a product is considered to have an effect on the finished product density. The moisture of the mix was controlled and finished product densities measured as shown:

Sample Number	1	2	3	4	5	6	7	8	9	10	11	12
X-Mix Moisture	4.7	5.0	5.2	5.2	5.9	4.7	5.9	5.2	5.3	5.9	5.6	5.0
Y-Density of Product	3	3	4	5	10	2	9	3	7	6	6	4

a) Find the regression equation $\hat{y} = a + bx$

b) Construct the ANOVA for regression table, without SSa, and test the hypothesis: $H_0: \beta = 0$ vs $H_1: \beta \neq 0$, *at* $\alpha = 0.05$

c) Construct $1 - \alpha = 0.95$ confidence limits on the parameter β

d) What are the 95% confidence limits on the true mean value of y when $x = 6$? (*i.e.*, find 95% C.I. on μ_{yx})

6. The midterm and final grades for ten students in a statistics class are:

X = Midterm Grades	86	93	73	66	88	96	80	70	95	63
Y = Final Grades	71	76	61	52	75	94	71	60	85	55

a) Find the regression line $\hat{y} = a + bx$

b) If $X = x = 90$, what is the estimated (predicted) value of $\hat{y}$?

c) Find the sample variance of regression, $\hat{\sigma}^2$, and $\hat{\sigma}$

d) Find 95% Confidence Limits (*i.e.*, find 95%CI) on β

7. The data below represents tensile strength (Y) and hardness (X) for die-cast aluminum.

X = Hardness	53	70	84	55	78	64	71	53	82	67	70	56
Y = Tensile Strength	293	349	368	301	340	308	354	313	322	334	377	247

a) Find the regression line $\hat{y} = a + bx$

b) Test the hypothesis: $H_0: \beta = 2.5$ vs $H_1: \beta \neq 2.5$, at $\alpha = 0.05$

c) Construct the 95% confidence interval for β

8. Catalogs listing textbooks were examined to discover the relationship between the cost of a book and the number of pages it contains, and the following data were obtained from ten books:

Pages = X	750	550	280	580	450	350	680	500	700	300
Price = Y	90	72	55	75	65	62	80	70	85	60

a) Find the regression line $\hat{y} = a + bx$

b) What would be the estimated price of a 600 page book?

c) What price increase would you expect for a book if it was decided to increase the size of the book by 100 pages?

9. In a regression problem, $n = 18$; $\sum x_i = 360$; $\sum x_i^2 = 7290$;
$\sum y_i = 540$; $\sum y_i^2 = 16{,}800$; $\sum x_i y_i = 10{,}980$.

a) Find the regression equation $\hat{y} = a + bx$

b) Find a 95% Confidence interval for β

10. For the data set below:

X	1	2	3	4	5
Y	2	5	3	8	7

a) Find the regression equation $\hat{y} = a + bx$

b) Test the hypothesis: $\alpha = 0$, at $\alpha = 0.05$

c) Test the hypothesis: $\beta = 0$, at $\beta = 0.05$

d) Construct a 95% Confidence interval for α

e) Construct a 95% Confidence interval for β

f) Construct a 95% Confidence interval on μ_{yx}, at $x_0 = 6$

g) Construct a 95% Confidence interval on y_0, at $x_0 = 6$

11. A restaurant manager is concerned about the large number of individuals who make reservations but do not show. He wants to know the relationship between the number of reservations (x) and the number of showing guests (y), which he believes to be linear. To check on his belief, he collected data for 27 nights, and obtained the following results: $n = 27$; $\sum x_i = 1080$; $\sum x_i^2 = 47{,}200$; $\sum y_i = 891$; $\sum y_i^2 = 32{,}653$; $\sum x_i y_i = 38{,}810$.

a) Find the linear regression equation $\hat{y} = a + bx$

b) If 50 reservations are made, how many can be expected to show?

c) Find the regression standard deviation, $\hat{s}$.

d) If the restaurant can accommodate at most 50 guests, is it "safe" to accept 60 reservations? Justify your answer.

12. The following pairs of numbers are the scores made by 30 students on a verbal aptitude test (x) and a mathematical aptitude test (y).

#	X	Y	#	X	Y
1	77	90	16	54	48
2	57	71	17	73	76
3	93	79	18	72	66
4	66	62	19	63	60
5	86	84	20	83	93
6	62	66	21	42	60
7	74	81	22	92	85
8	70	67	23	64	80
9	68	62	24	71	80
10	69	75	25	87	92
11	80	80	26	54	57
12	56	60	27	65	72
13	66	58	28	70	70
14	74	60	29	83	71
15	79	71	30	87	94

a) Calculate the value of r

b) Calculate the regression equation $\hat{y} = a + bx$

c) Calculate the regression standard deviation

13. Using the data from problem 13.12;

    a) Test the hypothesis: $H_0: \beta = 0$ vs $H_1: \beta \neq 0$, at $\alpha = 0.05$

    b) Construct a 95% C.I. on β

    c) Are the conclusions from (a) and (b) the same? Justify!

14. Using the data of problem 13.12;

    a) Test the hypothesis: $H_0: \alpha = 0$ vs $H_1: \alpha \neq 0$, (at $\alpha = 0.05$)

    b) Construct a 95% C.I. on α

    c) Are the conclusion from (a) and (b) the same? Justify!

15. Using the data of problem 13.12;

    a) Calculate the value of R^2 (= Coefficient of determination), and explain the meaning of the value of R^2.

    b) Test the significance of the overall regression equation, at $\alpha = 0.05$, by constructing an ANOVA for Regression table, by first calculating: TSS, RSS_b, ESS and SSa.

16. Use the data of problem 13.12 and the results of problem 13.15, to :

    a) Test the hypothesis: $H_0: \beta = 0$, at $\alpha = 0.05$, using the F-distribution

    b) Test the hypothesis: $H_0: \alpha = 0$, at $\alpha = 0.05$, using the F-distribution

17. The data below represent the scores made by students on an entrance examination (X) and a final examination (Y).

X	129	179	347	328	286	256	477	430	327	245	286	326
Y	370	361	405	302	496	323	374	332	435	165	375	466

    a) Find the equation of the regression line

    b) Find the sample regression standard deviation

    c) Test the hypothesis: $H_0: \beta = 0$ vs $H_1: \beta \neq 0$, at $\alpha = 0.05$

    d) Construct a 95% C.I. on β

    e) Are the results in (c) and (d) the same? Justify!

18. Using the data of Problem 13.17;

    a) Find the final regression equation

    b) Find a 95% C.I. for μ_{yx}, when $x_0 = 250$

    c) Find a 95% C.I. for a new observation of $y(y_0)$, when $x_0 = 250$.

19. For the following sample data:

X	4	2	1	3
Y	3	4	2	1

    a) Obtain the regression equation

    b) Calculate the value of r

20. Use the 2 data sets:

a)

X	Y
15	6
5	1

b)

X	Y
10	30
20	5

a) To find the corresponding regression equation

b) To find the corresponding correlation coefficient, r

c) Are you surprised by the values of r obtained? Explain your answer.

21. In the table below the X's are the amounts of money (in \$100,000) spent in advertising six movies and the Y's are their net earnings (in \$1,000,000):

X	4.0	1.9	1.0	3.1	2.9	1.3
Y	2.8	1.4	1.2	3.4	2.4	1.0

a) Obtain the regression equation which will enable us to predict the net earnings of a movie in terms of the amount of money spent on advertising.

b) If \$250,000 (*i.e.*, if $x = 2.5$) is spent on advertising a movie, what are its predicted net earnings?

c) Calculate σ^2, $\sigma^2(b)$, $\sigma^2(a)$, and $\sigma(b)$ and $\sigma(a)$.

22. Using the data of problem 13.21:

a) Test the hypothesis H_0: $\alpha = 0$ vs H_1: $\alpha \neq 0$, at $\alpha = 0.05$

b) Construct a 95% C.I. on α

23. Using the data of problem 13.21:

a) Test the hypothesis H_0: $\beta = 0$ vs H_1: $\beta \neq 0$, at $\alpha = 0.05$

b) Construct a 95% C.I. on β

c) What is the Final Regression equation?

24. Using the data of problem 13.21:

a) Construct a 95% C.I. on μ_{yx}, when $x = x_0 = 3$

b) Construct a 95% C.I. on y_0, when $x = x_0 = 3$

25. Using the data of problem 13.21:

a) Calculate the value of r, the sample correlation coefficient

b) Test the hypothesis H_0: $\rho = 0.95$ vs H_1: $\rho \neq 0.95$, at $\alpha = 0.05$

c) Construct a 95% C.I. on ρ

d) Calculate R^2, the Coefficient of Determination. What does the value of R^2 mean? Explain

26. In the following table, X represents the percentages of shipments of six companies that are delivered on time, and Y represents the percentages of their shipments that arrive in damaged conditions:

X	67	59	52	65	70	50
Y	12	19	14	7	6	22

a) Find the regression equation, $\hat{y} = a + bx$ which can be used to predict y in terms of x.

b) Find the standard error of regression, $\sigma = \sqrt{\sigma^2}$, and $\sigma(b)$.

c) Test the hypothesis: H_0: $\beta = 0.5$ vs H_1: $\beta \neq -0.5$, at $\alpha = 0.05$

27. In a study of the amount of irrigation applied to the soil, X, and the corresponding amount of cotton harvested, Y, the residual sum of squares $= ESS = \Sigma\left(y_i - \hat{y}\right)^2$ $= 217$, and the total sum of squares, $= TSS = \Sigma\left(y_i - \bar{y}\right)^2 = 1023$. Calculate r.

28. If two correlation studies yielded: $r_1 = 0.39$ and $r_2 = 0.87$, Compare the explanatory power of the corresponding linear regression equations.

29. Test in each case whether the given value of r is significant at the $\alpha = 0.01$ level of significance.

    a) $n_1 = 11$ and $r_1 = -0.75$

    b) $n_2 = 20$ and $r_2 = 0.48$

    c) $n_3 = 15$ and $r_3 = 0.68$

30. Test in each case whether the given value of r is significant at the $\alpha = 0.05$ level of significance:

    a) $n_1 = 27$ and $r_1 = 0.39$

    b) $n_2 = 18$ and $r_2 = -0.52$

    c) $n_3 = 52$ and $r_3 = 0.24$

31. The following are the processing times (in minutes), X, and hardness reading, Y, in a random sample of nine machine parts of a certain kind:

X	20	34	19	10	24	31	25	13	29
Y	282	275	171	142	145	340	282	105	233

   a) Find the regression equation, $\hat{y} = a + bx$, and use it to predict the value of y (hardness reading) for a part which has been hardened for 25 minutes (i.e., when $x = 25$).

   b) Find σ^2 and $\sigma(b)$

   c) Construct 99% C.I. for β

32. Use the data of problem #13.31 to find:

   a) 95% C.I. for the mean hardness of parts that have been processed for 25 minutes (i.e., find 95% C.I. on μ_{yx} when
   $$x_0 = 25 \text{ and } \bar{x} = \frac{\Sigma x_i}{n} = \frac{205}{9} = 22.7778)$$

   b) 95% C.I. for the hardness of a part that has been processed for 25 minutes (i.e., find 95% for y_0, when $x = x_0 = 25$)

33. The following table shows the assessed values and the selling prices of eight houses, constituting a random sample of all the houses sold in a given year, in a metropolitan area.

X = Assessed Value (x1000)	40.3	72.0	32.5	44.8	27.9	51.6	80.4	58.0
Y = Selling Price (x1000)	63.4	118.3	55.2	74.0	48.8	81.1	123.2	92.5

   a) Fit the regression line, $\hat{y} = a + bx$, to predict the selling price of a house in terms of the assessed value.

   b) Test the hypothesis: $H_0: \beta = 1.30$ vs. $H_1: \beta \neq 1.30$, at $\alpha = 0.05$, and $\alpha = 0.01$

   c) Construct a 99% C.I. on β

34. In a random sample of ten door-to-door salespersons, the correlation between years of experience, X, and gross sales, Y, is $r = 0.85$. If we construct the regression equation, $\hat{y} = a + bx$, what percentage of differences in sales can be attributed to differences in experience?

35. The following are the numbers of inquiries which a brokerage house received in eight weeks about municipal bonds, X, and money market funds, Y.

X	57	33	45	17	38	47	72	60
Y	88	69	50	29	53	61	85	82

   a) Find the regression equation, $\hat{y} = a + bx$

   b) Calculate r

   c) Test the hypothesis $H_0: \rho = 0$ vs $H_1: \rho \neq 0$, at $\alpha = 0.05$

   d) Calculate R^2. What percentage of the variation in the y-values is explained by the regression equation (and variable X)?

36. The following table shows the percentage of the vote predicted by a poll for seven candidates for the U.S. Senate in different states, X, and the percentage of the vote which they actually received, Y.

X: Poll	42	34	59	41	53	40	55
Y: Election	51	31	56	42	58	35	54

   Calculate r_s

37. The table below shows the 1979 final standings of the six baseball teams in the Western division of the National League, and the average salaries they paid to their players:

Team	Final Standing	Average Salary	Rank of Salaries
Los Angeles	1	$134,305	5
Cincinnati	2	165,144	6
Houston	3	73,660	1
San Francisco	4	120,737	4
San Diego	5	103,819	3
Atlanta	6	93,366	2

   Calculate r_s

38. The following table shows the grades in statistics, X, and the grades in accounting, Y, in a random sample of 18 students.

X	83	67	46	68	91	91	50	75	86	71	71	50	67	55	71	59	94	71
Y	71	68	60	81	82	87	52	77	83	82	68	68	64	64	68	61	87	66

   a) Calculate the value of r_s

   b) Test the hypothesis: $H_0: \rho_s = 0$ vs $H_1: \rho_s \neq 0$, at $\alpha = 0.05$

39. Can the consumption of water in a city be predicted by temperature? The following data represent a sample of a day's water consumption and the high temperature of that day:

Y-Water Use ($\times 10^6$ gallons)	219	56	107	129	68	184	150	112
X-Temperature (°F)	103	39	77	78	50	96	90	75

a) Develop a least squares regression line to predict the amount of water used in a day in a city by the high temperature for that day

b) What would be the predicted water usage for a temperature of 100°?

c) Evaluate the regression model by:

   i) Calculating the standard error of the regression

   ii) Testing the hypothesis:

   $H_0: \beta = 0$ vs $H_1: \beta \neq 0$, at $\alpha = 0.01$

   iii) Calculating the Coefficient of Determination, R^2. What does the calculated value of R^2 mean?

40. Use the data and partial results of problem 13.39, to:

a) Test the hypothesis: $H_0: \alpha = 0$ vs $H_1: \alpha \neq 0$, at $\alpha = 0.01$

b) Determine the final equation to be used for Forecasting purposes

c) Construct a 99% C.I. on α

d) Construct a 99% C.I. on β

e) Construct a 99% C.I. on μ_{yx} (*i.e.*, the mean value of y)

   (with $\bar{x} = \dfrac{608}{8} = 76$, at $x_0 = 96$)

f) Construct a 99% C.I. on y_0 (*i.e.*, estimate an individual value of y) when $x = x_0 = 106$

SOLUTIONS

1. a) The scatter diagram (see Figure 13.4 generated by the computer) shows 2 positively correlated variables, which appear to be linearly related.

b) $\hat{y} = a + bx = -0.5964 + 0.7245x$

c) $\sigma^2 = 1.267$ and $\sigma(b) = 0.1219$. Since $t_1^* = \dfrac{b}{\sigma(b)} = 5.943 > 2.228$ and

   $t_2^* = 5.943 > 3.169$, the hypothesis: $H_0: \beta = 0$ is rejected and we conclude that the b obtained in part (b) above is significant.

d) $P[b - t_{n-2}(\alpha/2)\cdot\sigma(b) \leq \beta \leq b + t_{n-2}(\alpha/2)\cdot\sigma(b)] = 1 - \alpha$

   or $P[0.453 \leq \beta \leq 0.996] = 0.95$

e) $p[\hat{y} - t_{n-2}\cdot\sigma(\hat{y})_P \leq \mu_{YX} \leq \hat{y} + t_{n-2}\cdot\sigma(\hat{y})_P] = 1 - \alpha$

   or $P[5.55 \leq \mu_{YX} \leq 7.75] = 0.95$ and $P[\hat{y} - t_{n-2}\cdot\sigma(\hat{y})_F \leq y_0 \leq \hat{y}$

   $+ t_{n-2}\cdot\sigma(\hat{y})_F] = 1 - \alpha$ or $P[3.911 \leq y_0 \leq 9.389] = 0.95$

2. a) $r = 0.88268 \approx 0.883$

b) Since $t^*_{n-2} = \dfrac{r\sqrt{n-2}}{\sqrt{1-r^2}} = 5.94 > t_{10}(0.025) = 2.228$, H_0: $\rho = 0$ is rejected.

c) Since $Z^* = \dfrac{Z_r - Z_\rho}{\sigma(Z_r)} = \dfrac{1.390 - 1.832}{1/3} = -1.326$, and $-1.96 < Z^* < 1.96$,

$H_0 : Z_\rho = 1.832$ (or $H_0 : \rho = 0.95$) is not rejected.

d) First construct a C.I. on Z_ρ and then, using Table 13.2, construct a C.I. on ρ.
Then $P[Z_r - Z_{\alpha/2} \cdot \sigma(Z_r) \le Z_\rho \le Z_r + Z_{\alpha/2} \cdot \sigma(Z_r)] = 1 - \alpha$,
or $P[0.737 \le Z_\rho \le 2.043] = 0.95$, and $P[0.629 \le \rho \le 0.967] = 0.95$, by
using Table 13.2 and linear interpolation.

3. a) Since TSS $= \displaystyle\sum_{i=1}^{5}(y_i - \bar{y})^2 = \sum_{i=1}^{5} y_i^2 - \dfrac{\left(\displaystyle\sum_{i=1}^{5} y_i\right)^2}{5} = 1030$

RSS $= \displaystyle\sum_{i=1}^{5}(\hat{y}_i - \bar{y})^2 = b^2\sum_{i=1}^{5}(x_i - \bar{x})^2 = 10^2(10) = 100(10) = 1000$

and ESS $= \displaystyle\sum_{i=1}^{5}(y_i - \hat{y}_i)^2 = Q^* = \sum_{i=1}^{5} y_i^2 - a\sum_{i=1}^{5} y_i - b\sum_{i=1}^{5} x_i y_i = 30$

It is obvious that TSS = SSR + SSE

Note: First use the normal equations to obtain the line $\hat{y} = a + bx = -508 + 10x$

b) R^2 = SSR/TSS = 1000/1030 = 0.97; R^2 measures the percent variation (97% here) of the y values that is explained by the variable x.

c) Construct ANOVA for regression tables, using the information in (a) above. Then

$F^*_b = \dfrac{\text{SSR}/1}{\text{TSS}} = \dfrac{1000/1}{30/3} = \dfrac{1000}{10} = 100$, and when compared to

$F^1_3(\alpha) = \begin{cases} 10.13 \text{ if } \alpha = 0.05 \\ 34.12 \text{ if } \alpha = 0.01 \end{cases}$, the hypothesis H_0: $\beta = 0$ is rejected.

4. a) $\hat{y} = a + bx = 33.910789 + 0.06692x$

b) $\sigma^2 = 0.38$; $\sigma^2(b) = \dfrac{\sigma^2}{\sum(x_i - \bar{x})^2} = \dfrac{0.38}{11{,}812.5} = 0.000032169$
and $\sigma(b) = \sqrt{\sigma^2(b)} = 0.0056718$

c) $r = 0.97$

d) Since $t^* = b/\sigma(b) = 0.06692/0.0056718 = 11.80$, and
$t^* > t_8(0.025) = 2.3060$, H_0: $\beta = 0$ is rejected.

e) Since $Z^* = (Z_r - Z_\rho)/\sigma(Z_r) = (2.092 - 1.589)/0.378 = 1.33$,
and $-1.96 < Z^* < 1.96$, H_0: $Z_\rho = 1.589$ (or, equivalently H_0: $\rho = 0.92$) is not rejected.

f) R^2 = RSS/TSS = $1 -$ ESS/TSS = $r^2 = 0.97^2 = 0.941$

(Also TSS $= \displaystyle\sum_{i=1}^{10}(y_i - \bar{y})^2 = \sum_{i=1}^{10} y_i^2 - \dfrac{\left(\displaystyle\sum_{i=1}^{10} y_i\right)^2}{5} = 55.896$;

RSS $= b^2\displaystyle\sum_{i=1}^{10}(x_i - \bar{x})^2 = (0.06692)^2(11{,}812.5) = 52.8998$

Since $R^2 = 0.941$, 94.1% of the variation in the y-values can be explained by the variable X, and only 5.9% is due to other factors. The equation is good and can be used to forecast future values of y.

5. $\sum_{i=1}^{12} x_i = 63.6$; $\sum_{i=1}^{12} x_i^2 = 339.18$; $\sum_{i=1}^{12} y_i = 62.0$; $\sum_{i=1}^{12} x_i y_i = 339.1$

a) $\hat{y} = a + bx = -21.33 + 5x$

b) $\text{TSS} = \sum_{i=1}^{12}(y_i - \bar{y})^2 = \sum_{i=1}^{12} y_i^2 - \dfrac{(\sum_{i=1}^{12} y_i)^2}{5} = 390 - \dfrac{(62)^2}{12} = 69.67$

$\text{RSS} = b^2 \sum_{i=1}^{12}(x_i - \bar{x})^2 = 2\left[339.18 - \dfrac{(63.6)^2}{12}\right] = 52.50$

$\text{ESS} = \sum_{i=1}^{12}(y_i - \hat{y}_i)^2 = Q^* = \sum_{i=1}^{12} y_i^2 - a\sum_{i=1}^{12} y_i - b\sum_{i=1}^{12} x_i y_i$

$= 390 - (-21.33)(62) - 5(339.1) = 17.17$

Then $H_0: \beta = 0$ vs $H_1: \beta \neq 0$ is rejected because:

$F^* = \dfrac{\text{RSS}/1}{\text{ESS}/n - 2} = \dfrac{52.50/1}{17.17/10} = 30.52$, and $F^* > F^1_{10}(\alpha = 0.05) = 4.96$

c) $P[b - t_{n-2}(\alpha/2)\sigma(b) \leq \beta \leq b + t_{n-2}(\alpha/2)\sigma(b)] = 1 - \alpha$

$\sigma^2 = \dfrac{\text{ESS}}{n-2} = \dfrac{17.17}{10} = 1.717$;

$\sigma^2(b) = \dfrac{\sigma^2}{\sum_{i=1}^{12}(x_i - \bar{x})^2} = \dfrac{\sigma^2}{\sum_{i=1}^{12} x_i^2 - \dfrac{(\sum_{i=1}^{12} x_i)^2}{12}}$

$= \dfrac{1.717}{339.18 - \dfrac{(63.6)^2}{12}} = \dfrac{1.717}{2.1} = 0.817619.$

and $\sigma(b) = \sqrt{\sigma^2(b)} = 0.904$
Then $P[5 - 2.228(0.904) \leq \beta \leq 5 + 2.228(0.904)] = 0.95$,
or $P[2.986 \leq \beta \leq 7.014] = 0.95$

d) $\hat{y} = a + bx = -21.33 + 5x$; Then when $x = x_0 = 6$, $\hat{y}(x_0 = 6) = 8.67$, and:
$P[\hat{y} - t_{n-2}(\alpha/2)\sigma(\hat{y})_p \leq \mu_{yx} \leq \hat{y} + t_{n-2}(\alpha/2)\sigma(\hat{y})_p] = 1 - \alpha$

or $P[8.67 - 2.228(0.7374) \leq \mu_{yx} \leq 8.67 + 2.228(0.7374)] = 0.95$

or $P[7.0721 \leq \mu_{yx} \leq 10.3121] = 0.95$

Note: Use equation (13.49) to calculate $V(\hat{y})_p$ and then $\sigma(\hat{y})_p$.

6. $n = 10$, $\sum_{i=1}^{10} x_i = 810$; $\sum_{i=1}^{10} x_i^2 = 66{,}984$; $\sum_{i=1}^{10} y_i = 700$;

$\sum_{i=1}^{10} y_i^2 = 50{,}594$; $\sum_{i=1}^{10} x_i y_i = 58{,}103$ $\sum_{i=1}^{10} y_i^2 = 50{,}594$; $\sum_{i=1}^{10} x_i y_i = 58{,}103$

Then

a) $\left.\begin{array}{l} na = b\Sigma\,x_i = \Sigma\,y_i \\ a\Sigma\,x_i + b\Sigma\,x_i^2 = \Sigma\,x_iy_i \end{array}\right\} \rightarrow \left.\begin{array}{l} 10a + 810b = 700 \\ 810a + 66{,}984b = 58{,}103 \end{array}\right\} \rightarrow \begin{array}{l} a = -12.71 \\ b = 1.0211 \end{array}$

and $\hat{y} = a + bx = -12.71 + 1.0211x$

b) When $x = 90$, $\hat{y}\,(x = 90) = -12.71 + 1.0211(90) = -12.71 + 91.899$

$$= 79.189$$

c) $\hat{\sigma}^2 = \dfrac{\Sigma\,y_i^2 - a\Sigma\,y_i - b\Sigma\,x_iy_i}{n - 2} = \dfrac{50{,}594 - (-12.71)(700) - 1.0211(58{,}103)}{10 - 2}$

$$= \dfrac{50{,}594 + 8{,}897 - 59{,}328.9733}{8}$$

$$= \dfrac{162.0267}{8} = 20.2533375\ \&\ \hat{\sigma} = 4.5$$

d) $\sigma^2(b) = \dfrac{\hat{\sigma}^2}{\Sigma\,(x_i - \bar{x})^2} = \dfrac{\hat{\sigma}^2}{\Sigma\,x_i^2 - \dfrac{\left(\Sigma\,x_i\right)^2}{n}}$

$$= \dfrac{20.2533375}{66{,}984 - \dfrac{(810)^2}{10}} = \dfrac{20.2533375}{66{,}984 - 65{,}610}$$

$$= \dfrac{20.2533375}{1374} = 0.01474\ \text{and}$$

$\sigma(b) = 0.12141$

Then

$$P\left\lfloor b - t_{n-2(\alpha/2)}\sigma\,(b) \le \beta \le b + t_{n-2(\alpha/2)}\,\sigma(b)\right\rfloor = 1 - \alpha,\ \text{or}$$

$$P\left[1.0211 - 2.306(0.12141) \le \beta \le 1.0211 + 2.306(0.12141)\right] = 0.95,\ \text{or}$$

$$P\left[0.74 \le \beta \le 1.30\right] = 0.95\ (\text{Note: } t_{8(0.025)}{=}2.306)$$

7. $n = 12;\ \Sigma\,x_i = 803;\ \Sigma\,x_i^2 = 55{,}609;\ \Sigma\,y_i = 3{,}906;\Sigma\,y_i^2 = 1{,}285{,}802;$

$\Sigma\,x_iy_i = 264{,}385$

a) $\left.\begin{array}{l} 12a + b(803) = 3906 \\ 803a + 55{,}069b = 264{,}385 \end{array}\right\}$

$\rightarrow \left.\begin{array}{l} a = 174.6869 \\ b = 2.253744 \end{array}\right\} \rightarrow \hat{y} = 174.6869 + 2.253744x$

$\sigma^2 = \dfrac{264{,}385 - (174.6869)(3906) - (2.253744)(264{,}385)}{10} = \dfrac{7618.86256}{10}$

$$= 761.886256$$

$\sigma^2(b) = \dfrac{\hat{\sigma}^2}{\Sigma\,(x_i - \bar{x})^2} = \dfrac{\hat{\sigma}^2}{\Sigma\,x_i^2 - \dfrac{\left(\Sigma\,x_i\right)^2}{n}} = \dfrac{761.886256}{55{,}069 - \dfrac{(803)^2}{12}} = \dfrac{761.886256}{1{,}334.9167}$

$$= 0.5707\ \text{and}\ \sigma(b) = 0.75545$$

b) Since $t^* = \dfrac{b - \beta_0}{\sigma(b)} = \dfrac{2.253744 - 2.5}{0.75545} = \dfrac{-0.246256}{0.75545} = -0.326$ falls outside

of the rejection region (i.e.,$-2.228 < t^* < 2.228$), H_0: $\beta = 2.5$ is not rejected.

c) $P[b - t_{n-2(\alpha/2)}\sigma(b) \leq \beta \leq b + t_{n-2(\alpha/2)}\sigma(b)] = 1 - \alpha$, or
$P[2.253744 - 2.228(0.755448) \leq \beta \leq 2.253744 + 2.228(0.755448)] = 0.95$,
or $p[0.5706 \leq \beta \leq 3.9369] = 0.95$. Since $\beta = 2.5$ falls inside this C.I.,
$H_0: \beta = 2.5$ is not rejected.

8. $n = 10;$ $\sum x_i = 5140;$ $\sum x_i^2 = 2,897,200;$ $\sum y_i = 714;$ $\sum y_i^2 = 52,128;$

$\sum x_i y_i = 383,850$

a) $\left.\begin{array}{l} 10a + 5140b = 714 \\ 5140a + 2,897,200b = 383,850 \end{array}\right\} \rightarrow \left.\begin{array}{l} a = 37,46 \\ b = 0.066 \end{array}\right\} \rightarrow \hat{y} = 37.46 + 0.066x$

b) $\hat{y}(x = 600) = 37.46 + 0.066(600) = 37.46 + 39.60 = 77.06$

c) Replace x by $x + 100$ in the regression equation, and simplify to obtain:
$\hat{y}_1 = 37.46 + 0.066(x + 100) = 37.46 + 6.60 + 0.066x = 44.06 + 0.066x$
Clearly the difference between $\hat{y}_1$ and $\hat{y}$ is: $\hat{y}_1 - \hat{y} = 6.60$

9. a) $\left.\begin{array}{l} na + b\sum x_i = \sum y_i \\ a\sum x_i + b\sum x_i^2 = \sum x_i y_i \end{array}\right\} \rightarrow \left.\begin{array}{l} 18a + 360b = 540 \\ 360a + 7290b = 10,980 \end{array}\right\} \rightarrow \left.\begin{array}{l} a = -10 \\ b = 2 \end{array}\right.$

Therefore $\hat{y} = a + bx = -10 + 2x$

b) $\hat{\sigma}^2 = \dfrac{\sum y_i^2 - a\sum y_i - b\sum x_i y_i}{n - 2} = \dfrac{16,800 - (-10)(540) - 2(10,980)}{8 - 2}$

$= \dfrac{16,800 + 5400 - 21,960}{16}$

$= \dfrac{22,200 - 21,960}{16} = \dfrac{240}{16} = 15$

$\sigma^2(b) = \dfrac{\hat{\sigma}^2}{\sum(x_i - \bar{x})^2} = \dfrac{\hat{\sigma}^2}{\sum x_i^2 - \dfrac{(\sum x_i)^2}{n}} = \dfrac{15}{7290 - \dfrac{(360)^2}{18}} = \dfrac{15}{7290 - 7200}$

$= \dfrac{15}{90} = \dfrac{1}{6} = 0.166667$

and $\sigma(b) = 0.40825$

$P[b - t_{n-2(\alpha/2)}\sigma(b) \leq \beta \leq b + t_{n-2(\alpha/2)}\sigma(b)] = 1 - \alpha$, or

$P[2 - t_{16(0.025)}(0.40825) \leq \beta \leq 2 + t_{16(0.025)}(0.40825)] = 0.95$, or

$P[2 - 2.120(0.40825) \leq \beta \leq 2 + 2.120(0.40825)] = 0.95$, or

$P[1.13451 \leq \beta \leq 2.86549] = 0.95$

10. $n = 5;$ $\sum x_i = 15;$ $\sum x_i^2 = 55;$ $\sum y_i = 25;$ $\sum y_i^2 = 151;$

$\sum x_i y_i = 88$

a) $\left.\begin{array}{l} 5a + 15b = 25 \\ 15a + 55b = 88 \end{array}\right\} \rightarrow \left.\begin{array}{l} a = 4.25 \\ b = 0.325 \end{array}\right.$ and $\hat{y} = a + bx = 4.25 + 0.325x$

$$\hat{\sigma}^2 = \frac{\sum y_i^2 - a\sum y_i - b\sum x_i y_i}{n-2} = \frac{151 - 4.25(25) - 0.325(88)}{3}$$

$$= \frac{16.15}{3} = 5.383333$$

$$\sum (x_i - \bar{x})^2 = \sum x_i^2 - \frac{(\sum x_i)^2}{n} = 55 - \frac{(15)^2}{5} = 55 - 45 = 10$$

$$\sigma^2(a) = \frac{\hat{\sigma}^2}{n}\left[\frac{\sum x_i^2}{\sum (x_i - \bar{x})^2}\right] = \frac{5.383333}{5}\left[\frac{55}{10}\right] = 5.9216663, \text{ and } \sigma(a) = 2.4334$$

$$\sigma^2(b) = \frac{\hat{\sigma}^2}{\sum (x_i - \bar{x})^2} = \frac{5.383333}{10} = 0.5383333, \text{ and } \sigma(b) = 0.7337$$

$$\sigma^2(\hat{y})p = \hat{\sigma}^2\left[\frac{1}{n} + \frac{(x_0 - \bar{x})^2}{\sum (x_i - \bar{x})^2}\right] = 5.383333\left[\frac{1}{5} + \frac{(6-3)^2}{10}\right]$$

$$= 5.921616, \text{ and } \sigma(\hat{y})p = 2.4334$$

$$\sigma^2(\hat{y})_F = \hat{\sigma}^2\left[1 + \frac{1}{n} + \frac{(x_0 - \bar{x})^2}{\sum (x_i - \bar{x})^2}\right] = 5.383333\left[1 + \frac{1}{5} + \frac{(6-3)^2}{10}\right]$$

$$= 11.3045, \text{ and}$$

$\sigma^2(\hat{y})_F = 3.3623; t_{n-p(\alpha/2)} = t_{3(0.025)} = 3.182,$ and
$\hat{y}(x = 6) = 4.25 + 0.325(6) = 6.20$

b) Since $t_a^* = \dfrac{a}{\sigma(a)} = \dfrac{4.25}{2.4334} = 1.746 < 3.182$, Do not reject H_0: $\alpha = 0$

c) Since $t_b^* = \dfrac{b}{\sigma(b)} = \dfrac{0.325}{0.7337} = 0.443 < 3.182$, Do not reject H_0: $\beta = 0$

d) $P[a - t_{3(0.025)}\sigma(a) \le \alpha \le a + t_{3(0.025)}\sigma(a)] = 1 - \alpha$, or

$P[4.25 - 3.182(2.4334) \le \alpha \le 4.25 + 3.182(2.4334)] = 0.95$, or

$P[-3.493 \le \alpha \le 11.993] = 0.95$

e) $P[b - t_{3(0.025)}\sigma(b) \le \beta \le b + t_{3(0.025)}\sigma(b)] = 1 - \alpha$, or

$P[0.325 - 3.182(0.7337) \le \beta \le 0.325 + 3.182(0.7337)] = 0.95$, or

$P[-2.01 \le \beta \le 2.66] = 0.95$

f) $P\lfloor \bar{y} - t_{3(0.025)}\sigma(\hat{y})p \le \mu_{yx} \le \bar{y} + t_{3(0.025)}\sigma(\hat{y})p \rfloor = 1 - \alpha$, or

$P[6.20 - 3.182(2.4334) \le \mu_{yx} \le 6.20 + 3.182(2.4334)] = 0.95$, or
$P[-1.543 \le \mu_{yx} \le 13.943] = 0.95$

g) $P[6.20 - 3.182(3.3623) \le y_0 \le 6.20 + 3.182(3.3623)] = 0.95$, or
$P[-4.499 \le y_o \le 16.899] = 0.95$

14 Non-Linear Regression

Sometimes two variables are related but their relationship is not linear and trying to fit a linear equation to a data set which is inherently non-linear will result in a bad-fit. But, because non-linear regression is, in general, much more difficult than linear regression, we explore in this chapter estimation methods that will allow us to fit non-linear equations to a data set by using the results of linear regression which we have already discussed.

This becomes possible by first performing logarithmic transformations of the non-linear equations, which change the non-linear into linear equations, and then using the normal equations of the linear model to generate the normal equations of the "linearized" non-linear equations, from which the values of the unknown model parameters can be obtained. In this chapter we show how the exponential model, $\hat{y} = ke^{cx}$, and the power model, $\hat{y} = ax^b$ (for $b \neq 1$) can be easily estimated by using logarithmic transformations to first derive the linearized version of the above non-linear equations, namely:

$$\ln \hat{y} = \ln k + cx \text{ and } \ln \hat{y} = \ln a + b \ln x,$$

and then comparing these to the original linear equation, $\hat{y} = a + bx$, and its normal equations.

A procedure is also discussed which allows us to fit these three models (*i.e.*, linear, exponential, power), and possibly others, to the same data set, and then select the equation which fits the data set "best".

Also discussed is the quadratic model, $\hat{y} = a + bx + cx^2$ which, even though is a non-linear model, can be discussed directly using the linear methodology. But now we have to solve simultaneously a system of 3 equations and 3 unknowns, because the normal equations for the quadratic model become:

$$na + b\sum_{i=1}^{n} x_i + c\sum_{i=1}^{n} x_i^2 = \sum_{i=1}^{n} y_i$$

$$a\sum_{i=1}^{n} x_i + b\sum_{i=1}^{n} x_i^2 + c\sum_{i=1}^{n} x_i^3 = \sum_{i=1}^{n} x_i y_i$$

$$a\sum_{i=1}^{n} x_i^2 + b\sum_{i=1}^{n} x_i^3 + c\sum_{i=1}^{n} x_i^4 = \sum_{i=1}^{n} x_i^2 y_i$$

14.1 Introduction

Non-linear estimation is, in general, more difficult than linear estimation and, because of this difficulty, we will not discuss non-linear estimation in general.

There are, however, some non-linear models which can be derived from the results we have obtained thus far for a linear model, by a simple "logarithmic transformation" of the candidate non-linear model and comparison to the linear model.

14.2 The Linear Model and its Normal Equations

Recall the linear model and the normal equation associated with it. (The normal equations of the linear model are the two equations which must be solved simultaneously to obtain the least square estimates for a and b.)

Linear Model

$$y = a + bx \tag{14.1}$$

Normal Equations

$$na + b\sum_{i=1}^{n} x_i = \sum_{i=1}^{n} y_i \qquad (14.2)$$

$$a\sum_{i=1}^{n} x_i + b\sum_{i=1}^{n} x_i^2 = \sum_{i=1}^{n} x_i\, y_i \qquad (14.3)$$

14.3   The Exponential Model

Consider now the **exponential model** which is defined by the equation:

$$y = ke^{cx} \qquad (14.4)$$

Our objective is to use the given data to find the best possible values for k and c, just as our objective in equation (14.1) was to use the data to find the best (in the least-square sense) values for a and b.

Taking natural logarithms (*i.e.*, logarithms to the base e) of both sides of equation (14.4) we obtain:

$$\ln (y = ke^{cx}) \text{ or: } \ln y = \ln (ke^{cx}) \qquad (14.5)$$

14.3.1 Logarithmic Laws

To simplify equation (14.5), we have to use some of the following laws of logarithms:

1. $\log (A \cdot B) = \log A + \log B$ (14.6)
2. $\log (A/B) = \log A - \log B$ (14.7)
3. $\log (A^n) = n \log A$ (14.8)

Then, using equation (14.6) we can re-write equation (5) as:

$$\ln y = \ln k + \ln e^{cx}, \qquad (14.9)$$

and, by applying equation (14.8) to the second term of the right hand side of equation (14.9), equation (14.9) can be written finally as:

$$\ln y = \ln k + cx\,(\ln e) \text{ or } \ln y = \ln k + cx \qquad (14.10)$$

$$(\text{Because } \ln e = \log_e e = 1)$$

Even though equation (14.4) is non-linear, as can be verified by plotting y against x, equation (14.10) is linear (*i.e.*, The logarithmic transformation changed equation (14.4) from non-linear to linear) as can be verified by plotting: $\ln y$ against x.

But, if equation (14.10) is linear, it should be similar to equation (14.1), and must have a set of normal equations similar to the normal equations of the linear model.

Question: How are these normal equations going to be derived?

Answer: We will compare the "transformed linear model", *i.e.*, equation (14.10), to the actual linear model (equation (14.1)), note the differences between these two models, and then make the appropriate changes to the normal equations of the linear model to obtain the normal equations of the "transformed linear model".

14.3.2 Logarithmic Transformation of Exponential Model

To make the comparison easier, we list below the 2 models under consideration, namely:

1. Original Linear Model: $y = a + bx$ (14.1)
2. Transformed Linear Model: $\ln y = \ln k + cx$ (14.10)

Comparing equations (14.1) and (14.10), we note the following three differences between the two models:

1. y in equation (14.1) has been replaced by **$\ln y$** in equation (14.10)
2. a in equation (14.1) has been replaced by **$\ln k$** in equation (14.10)
3. b in equation (14.1) has been replaced by c in equation (14.10)

14.3.3 Normal Equations of Exponential Model

When the three changes listed above are applied to the normal equations of the actual linear model (equations (14.2) and (14.3)), we will obtain the normal equations of the "transformed model". The normal equations of the "transformed linear model" are:

$$n(\ln k) + c\sum_{i=1}^{n} x_i = \sum_{i=1}^{n} \ln y_i \tag{14.11}$$

$$(\ln k)\sum_{i=1}^{n} x_i + c\sum_{i=1}^{n} x_i^2 = \sum_{i=1}^{n} x_i (\ln y_i) \tag{14.12}$$

In equations (14.11) and (14.12) all the quantities are known numbers, derived from the given data as will be shown later, except for $\ln k$ and c, and equations (14.11) and (14.12) must be solved simultaneously for $\ln k$ and c.

Suppose that for a given data set, the solution to equations (14.11) and (14.12) produced the solution:

$$\ln k = 0.3 \text{ and } c = 1.2 \tag{14.13}$$

If we examine the exponential model (equation (14.4)), we observe that the value of $c = 1.2$ can be substituted directly into equation (14.4), but we do not yet have the value of k; instead we have the value of $\ln k = 0.3$!

Question: If we know $\ln k = 0.3$, how do we find the value of k?

Answer: If $\ln k = 0.3$, then $k = e^{0.3} \approx (2.718281828)^{0.3} \approx 1.349859$

Therefore, now that we have both the **k** and **c** values, the non-linear model, given by equation (14.4), has been completely estimated.

14.4 The Power Model

Another non-linear model which can be analyzed in a similar manner is the Power Model defined by the equation:

$$y = ax^b \tag{14.14}$$

which is non-linear if $b \neq 1$ and, as before, we must obtain the best possible values for a and b (in the least-square sense) using the given data.

14.4.1 Logarithmic Transformation of Power Model

A logarithmic transformation of equation (14.14) produces the "transformed linear model"

$$\ln y = \ln a + b \ln x \tag{14.15}$$

When equation (14.15) is compared to equation (14.1), we note the following 3 changes:

1. y in equation (14.1) has been replaced by $\ln y$ in equation (14.15)

2. a in equation (14.1) has been replaced by $\ln a$ in equation (14.15) $\qquad$ (14.16)

3. x in equation (14.1) has been replaced by $\ln x$ in equation (14.15)

When the changes listed in (14.16) are substituted into equations (14.2) and (14.3), we obtain the normal equations for this "transformed linear model" which are given by equations (14.17) and (14.18) below.

14.4.2 Normal Equations of Power Model

$$n(\ln a) + b \sum_{i=1}^{n} \ln x_i = \sum_{i=1}^{n} \ln y_i \tag{14.17}$$

$$(\ln a) \sum_{i=1}^{n} \ln x_i + b \sum_{i=1}^{n} (\ln x_i)^2 = \sum_{i=1}^{n} (\ln x_i)(\ln y_i) \tag{14.18}$$

Equations (14.17) and (14.18) must be solved simultaneously for $(\ln a)$ and b. If $\ln a = 0.4$ then $a = e^{0.4} \approx (2.718251828)^{0.4} \approx 1.491825$ and since we have numerical values for both a and b, the non-linear model defined by equation (14.14) has been completely estimated.

14.5 Data Utilization in Estimating the 3 Models

To generate the quantities needed to estimate the 3 models:

1. The Linear Model
2. The Exponential Model
3. The Power Model

the given (x, y) bivariate data must be manipulated as shown in Tables 14.1, 14.2, and 14.3, respectively.

Table 14.1 Manipulation of Given Data to Evaluate the Linear Model			
x	y	xy	x^2
x_1	y_1	$x_1 y_1$	x_1^2
x_2	y_2	$x_2 y_3$	x_2^2
x_3	y_3	$x_3 y_4$	x_3^2
...	...	...	...
x_n	y_n	$x_n y_n$	x_n^2
$\sum_{i=1}^{n} x_i$	$\sum_{i=1}^{n} y_i$	$\sum_{i=1}^{n} x_i y_i$	$\sum_{i=1}^{n} x_i^2$
N_1	N_2	N_3	N_4

To evaluate $y = a + bx$ substitute N_1, N_2, N_3, N_4 into equations (14.2) and (14.3) and solve for a and b simultaneously.

Table 14.2 Manipulation of Given Data to Evaluate the Exponential Model				
x	y	x^2	$\ln y$	$x \ln y$
x_1	y_1	x_1^2	$\ln y_1$	$x_1 \cdot \ln y_1$
x_2	y_2	x_2^2	$\ln y_2$	$x_2 \cdot \ln y_2$
x_3	y_3	x_3^2	$\ln y_3$	$x_3 \cdot \ln y_3$
...	...	...	...	...
x_n	y_n	x_n^2	$\ln y_n$	$x_n \cdot \ln y_n$
$\sum_{i=1}^{n} x_i$	$\sum_{i=1}^{n} y_i$	$\sum_{i=1}^{n} x_i^2$	$\sum_{i=1}^{n} \ln y_i$	$\sum_{i=1}^{n} x_i \ln y_i$
N_5	N_6	N_7	N_8	N_9

To evaluate $y = ke^{cx}$ substitute N_5, N_7, N_8, N_9 into equations (14.11) and (14.12) and solve for $\ln k$ and c simultaneously.

Table 14.3 Manipulation of Given Data to Evaluate the Power Model					
x	y	$\ln x$	$(\ln x)^2$	$(\ln x)(\ln y)$	$\ln y$
x_1	y_1	$\ln x_1$	$(\ln x_1)^2$	$(\ln x_1)(\ln y_1)$	$\ln y_1$
x_2	y_2	$\ln x_2$	$(\ln x_2)^2$	$(\ln x_2)(\ln y_2)$	$\ln y_2$
x_3	y_3	$\ln x_3$	$(\ln x_3)^2$	$(\ln x_3)(\ln y_3)$	$\ln y_3$
...	...	...	...	...	...
x_n	y_n	$\ln x_n$	$(\ln x_n)^2$	$(\ln x_n)(\ln y_n)$	$\ln y_n$
$\sum_{i=1}^{n} x_i$	$\sum_{i=1}^{n} y_i$	$\sum_{i=1}^{n} \ln x_i$	$\sum_{i=1}^{n} (\ln x_i)^2$	$\sum_{i=1}^{n} (\ln x_i)(\ln y_i)$	$\sum_{i=1}^{n} \ln y_i$
N_{10}	N_{11}	N_{12}	N_{13}	N_{14}	N_{15}

To evaluate $y = ax^b$, substitute N_{12}, N_{13}, N_{14}, N_{15} into equations (14.17) and (14.18) and solve simultaneously for (ln a) and b.

14.6   Selecting the Best-Fitting Model

1. Given a data set (x_i, y_i), we have shown how to fit to such a data set three different models, namely:

   a) Linear $\hat{y}_i = a + bx_i$ (14.19)

   b) Exponential $\hat{y}_i = ke^{cx_i}$ (14.20)

   c) Power $\hat{y}_i = ax_i^b$ (14.21)

   We might decide to fit all three models to the same data set if, after examining the scatter diagram of the given data set, we are unable to decide which of the "3 models appears to fit the data "best".

   But, after we fit the 3 models, how can we tell which model fits the data best?

   To answer this question, we calculate the "variance of the residual values" for each of the models, and then "select as the best model" the one with the smallest variance of the residual values.

2. Calculating the residual values of each model and their variance.

   Use each x_i value, of the given data set (x_i, y_i), to calculate the $\hat{y}_i$ value, from the appropriate model, and then for each i, form the residual:

$$\text{Residual of observations} = (y_i - \hat{y}_i) \tag{14.22}$$

Then the variance of the residual values is defined by:

$$V(\text{Residual}) = \frac{1}{n-2}\sum_{i=1}^{n}(y_i - \hat{y}_i)^2 \tag{14.23}$$

Note: The multiplier of $(n - 2)$ in equation (14.23) is due to the fact that each of the 3 models of interest have 2 unknown quantities, in their respective sum of squares, that need to be estimated (a and b, k and c, and a and b respectively) and, as a consequence, 2 degrees of freedom are lost.

Using equation (14.23) to calculate the variance of the residuals for each of the 3 models, we obtain:

$$V(\text{Residual})_{Linear} = \frac{1}{n-2}\sum_{i=1}^{n}(y_i - a - bx_i)^2 \tag{14.24}$$

$$= \frac{1}{n-2}\sum_{i=1}^{n}\left[(y_1 - a - bx_1)^2 + (y_2 - a - bx_2)^2 + \cdots + (y_n - a - bx_n)^2\right] \tag{14.25}$$

$$V(\text{Residual})_{Exponential} = \frac{1}{n-2}\sum_{i=1}^{n}(y_i - ke^{cx_i})^2 \tag{14.26}$$

$$= \frac{1}{n-2}\sum_{i=1}^{n}\left[(y_1 - ke^{cx_1})^2 + (y_2 - ke^{cx_2})^2 + \cdots + (y_n - ke^{cx_n})^2\right] \tag{14.27}$$

$$V(\text{Residual})_{Power} = \frac{1}{n-2}\sum_{i=1}^{n}(y_i - ax_i^b)^2 \tag{14.28}$$

$$= \frac{1}{n-2}\sum_{i=1}^{n}\left[(y_1 - ax_1^b)^2 + (y_2 - ax_2^b)^2 + \cdots + (y_n - ax_n^b)^2\right] \tag{14.29}$$

After the calculation of the 3 variances from equations (14.25), (14.27) and (14.29), the model with the "smallest" variance is the model which fits the given data set "best".

We will now illustrate, through an example, how the 3 models we discussed above can be fitted to a given bivariate data set, and then how the "best" model from among them is selected.

14.7   An Example

A sample of 5 adult men for whom heights and weights are measured gives the following results:

#	X = Height	Y = Weight
1	64	130
2	65	145
3	66	150
4	67	165
5	68	170

Problem: Fit the linear, exponential, and power models to this bivariate data set and then select as the "best" the model with the smallest variance of the residual values.

14.7.1 Fitting the Linear Model $\hat{y} = a + bx$

To fit the linear model, we must extend the given bivariate data so that we can also calculate $\sum_{i=1}^{n} x_i^2$ and $\sum_{i=1}^{n} x_i y_i$, as shown below:

x^2	x	y	xy
4096	64	130	8320
4225	65	145	9425
4356	66	150	9900
4489	67	165	11055
4624	68	170	11560
$\sum_{i=1}^{5} x_i^2 = 21{,}790$	$\sum_{i=1}^{5} x_i = 330$	$\sum_{i=1}^{5} y_i = 760$	$\sum_{i=1}^{5} x_i y_i = 50{,}260$

We then substitute the generated data into the normal equations for the linear model, namely equations (14.2) and (14.3):

$$na + b\sum_{i=1}^{n} x_i = \sum_{i=1}^{n} y_i$$

$$a\sum_{i=1}^{n} x_i + b\sum_{i=1}^{n} x_i^2 = \sum_{i=1}^{n} x_i y_i,$$

and obtain the equations:

$$5a + 330b = 760$$

$$330a + 21{,}790b = 50{,}260$$

When these equations are solved simultaneously for a and b we obtain:

$$a = -508 \quad \text{and} \quad b = 10$$

Therefore, the linear model is:

$$\hat{y} = a + bx = -508 + 10x$$

The variance of the residual values for the linear model is calculated as shown below:

x	y	$\hat{y} = -508 + 10x$	$y - \hat{y}$	$(y - \hat{y})^2$
64	130	$-508 + 10(64) = 132$	-2	$(-2)^2 = 4$
65	145	$-508 + 10(65) = 142$	$+3$	$(+3)^2 = 9$
66	150	$-508 + 10(66) = 152$	-2	$(-2)^2 = 4$
67	165	$-508 + 10(67) = 162$	$+3$	$(+3)^2 = 9$
68	170	$-508 + 10(68) = 172$	-2	$(-2)^2 = 4$
				$\displaystyle\sum_{i=1}^{5}(y_i - \hat{y}_i)^2 = 30$

Therefore, the variance of the residual values, for the linear model is:

$$V(\text{Residual})_{\text{Linear}} = \frac{1}{n-2}\sum_{i=1}^{n}(y_i - \hat{y}_i)^2 = \frac{1}{5-2}(30) = 10$$

14.7.2 Fitting the Exponential Model $\hat{y} = ke^{cx_i}$

To fit the exponential model we need to extend the given bivariate data so that we can calculate, in addition to $\displaystyle\sum_{i=1}^{5} x_i = 30$ and $\displaystyle\sum_{i=1}^{5} x_i^2 = 21{,}790$, $\displaystyle\sum_{i=1}^{5}\ln y_i$ and $\displaystyle\sum_{i=1}^{5} x_i \ln y_i$ as shown below:

x^2	x	y	$\ln y$	$x \cdot \ln y$
4096	64	130	4.8675	311.5200
4225	65	145	4.9767	323.4855
4356	66	150	5.011	330.726
4489	67	165	5.1059	342.0953
4624	68	170	5.1358	349.2344
$\displaystyle\sum_{i=1}^{5} x_i^2 = 21{,}790$	$\displaystyle\sum_{i=1}^{5} x_i = 330$	$\displaystyle\sum_{i=1}^{5} y_i = 760$	$\displaystyle\sum_{i=1}^{5}\ln y_i = 25.0966$	$\displaystyle\sum_{i=1}^{5} x_i \cdot \ln y_i = 1657.0612$

We then substitute the generated data into the normal equations for the exponential model (*i.e.*, equations (14.11) and (14.12)):

$$n(\ln k) + c\sum_{i=1}^{n} x_i = \sum_{i=1}^{n} \ln y_i$$

$$(\ln k)\sum_{i=1}^{n} x_i + c\sum_{i=1}^{n} x_i^2 = \sum_{i=1}^{n} x_i (\ln y_i),$$

and obtain the equations:

$$5 \ln k + 330c = 25.0969$$

$$330 \ln k + 21{,}790c = 1657.0612$$

When these equations are solved simultaneously for $\ln k$ and c, we obtain $c = 0.06658$ and $\ln k = 0.6251$, or $k = e^{0.6251} = 1.868432$

Therefore, the exponential model is

$$\hat{y} = ke^{cx} = 1.868432e^{0.06658x}$$

Then, the variance of the residual values, for the exponential model, is calculated as shown below:

x	y	$\hat{y} = ke^{cx} = 1.868432\,e^{0.06658x}$	$y - \hat{y}$	$(y - \hat{y})^2$
64	130	$1.868432\,e^{0.06658(64)} = 132.4515$	-2.4515	6.0099
65	145	$1.868432\,e^{0.06658(65)} = 141.5703$	3.4297	11.7628
66	150	$1.868432\,e^{0.06658(66)} = 151.3169$	-1.3169	1.7324
67	165	$1.868432\,e^{0.06658(67)} = 161.7346$	3.2654	10.6630
68	170	$1.868432\,e^{0.06658(68)} = 172.8694$	-2.8694	8.2336
				$\sum_{i=1}^{5}(y_i - \hat{y}_i)^2 = 38.4035$

Therefore, the variance of the residual values, for the exponential model is

$$V(\text{Residual})_{\text{Exponential}} = \frac{1}{n-2}\sum_{i=1}^{n}(y_i - \hat{y}_i)^2 = \frac{1}{n-2}\sum_{i=1}^{n}(y_i - ke^{cx_i})^2$$

$$= \frac{1}{5-1}\sum_{i=1}^{5}\left[y_i - 1.868432e^{0.06658x_i}\right]^2$$

$$= \frac{38.4035}{3} = 12.8017$$

14.7.3 Fitting the Power Model $\hat{y} = ax^b$

To fit the power model we need to extend the given bivariate data set to generate the quantities: $\sum_{i=1}^{n} \ln x_i$, $\sum_{i=1}^{n}(\ln x_i)^2$, $\sum_{i=1}^{n} \ln y_i$ and $\sum_{i=1}^{n}(\ln x_i)(\ln y_i)$, and this is accomplished as shown below:

x	y	$\ln x$	$(\ln x)^2$	$\ln y$	$(\ln x)(\ln y)$
64	130	4.158883	17.2963085	4.867553	20.2435
65	145	4.1738727	17.42550908	4.976734	20.2435
66	150	4.189654742	17.55320686	5.010635	20.9928
67	165	4.204692619	17.67944002	5.105945	21.4689
68	170	4.219507705	17.80424527	5.135798	21.6705
		$\sum_{i=1}^{5} \ln x_i$ $= 20.9471$	$\sum_{i=1}^{5} (\ln x_i)^2$ $= 87.7581$	$\sum_{i=1}^{5} \ln y_i$ $= 25.0967$	$\sum_{i=1}^{5} (\ln x_i)(\ln y_i)$ $= 105.1505$

We then substitute the generated data into the normal equations of the power model, namely equations (14.17) and (14.18):

$$n(\ln a) + b \sum_{i=1}^{n} \ln x_i = \sum_{i=1}^{n} \ln y_i$$

$$(\ln a) \sum_{i=1}^{n} \ln x_i + b \sum_{i=1}^{n} (\ln x_i)^2 = \sum_{i=1}^{n} (\ln x_i)(\ln y_i)$$

to obtain the equations:

$$5 \ln a + 20.9471b = 25.0967$$

$$20.9471 \ln a + 87.7587b = 105.1505$$

When these equations are solved simultaneously for b and $\ln a$ we obtain $b = 2.22659$ and $\ln a = -4.3086$ or $a = e^{-4.3086} = 0.013452369$. Therefore, the power model is

$$\hat{y} = ax^b = 0.013452369x^{2.22659}$$

Then the variance of the residual values for the power model is obtained as shown below:

x	y	$\hat{y} = ax^b = \mathbf{0.013452369}x^{2.22659}$	$y - \hat{y}$	$(y - \hat{y})^2$
64	130	$0.013452369\,(64)^{2.22659} = 141.36586$	-11.36586	129.18287
65	145	$0.013452369\,(65)^{2.22659} = 146.3312$	-1.331234	1.77218
66	150	$0.013452369\,(66)^{2.22659} = 151.3911$	-1.391195	1.935422
67	165	$0.013452369\,(67)^{2.22659} = 156.5460$	8.4539	71.46887
68	170	$0.013452369\,(68)^{2.22659} = 161.796195$	8.2038	67.30241
				$\sum_{i=1}^{5}(y_i - \hat{y}_i)^2$ $= 271.6618$

Therefore, the variance of the residual values for the power model is

$$V(\text{Residual})_{Power} = \frac{1}{n-2} \sum_{i=1}^{n} (y_i - ax_i^b)^2$$

$$= \frac{271.6618}{3} = 90.5539$$

14.7.4 Summary of Results and Selection of the "Best" Model
We have fitted the 3 models linear, exponential, and power models, calculated the respective residual variances, and have obtained the following results:

1. The linear model is $\hat{y} = a + bx = -508 + 10x$, with $V(\text{Linear}) = 10$
2. The exponential model is: $\hat{y} = ke^{cx} = 1.868432e^{0.06658x}$, with $V(\text{Exponential}) = 12.8017$
3. The power model is: $\hat{y} = ax^b = 0.013452369x^{2.22659}$, with $V(\text{Power}) = 90.5539$

Since the linear model has the smallest variance, of the residual values of the 3 models fitted to the same bivariate data set, the linear model is the "best" model.

14.8   References

Berenson, Marc, L., Levine, David, M., and Krehbiel, Timothy, C., 2004. *Basic Business Statistics*. 9th Edition. Pearson-Prentice Hall.

Black, Ken, 2004. *Business Statistics*. 4th Edition. Wiley.

Canavos, George, C., 1984. *Applied Probability and Statistical Methods*. Little, Brown.

Carlson, William, L., and Thorne, Betty, 1997. *Applied Statistical Methods*. Prentice Hall.

Chou, Ya-lun, 1992. *Statistical Analysis for Business and Economics*. Elsevier.

Freund, John, E., and Williams, Frank, J., 1969. *Modern Business Statistics*. Revised by: Perles, Benjamin and Sullivan, Charles. Prentice-Hall.

Freund, John, E., and Williams, Frank, J., 1982. *Elementary Business Statistics: The Modern approach*. Prentice-Hall.

Johnson, Robert, 1973. *Elementary Statistics*. Duxbury Press.

McClave, James, T., Benson, George, P., and Sincich, Terry, 2001. *Statistics for Business and Economics*. 8th Edition. Prentice Hall.

Salvatore, Dominick. *Theory and Problems of Statistics and Econometrics*. SCHAUM'S OUTLINE SERIES, McGraw-Hill.

Steel, Robert, G.D., and Torrie, James, H., 1976. *Introduction to Statistics*. McGraw-Hill.

14.9 PROBLEMS

1. Derive the normal equations for the exponential model with base b, i.e., $\hat{y} = ab^x$.
2. Calculate the values for a and b, for the data set

x	64	65	66	67	68
y	130	145	150	165	170

3. Calculate the variance of the residual values for the exponential model with base $b = 1.068846$ and compare it to the variance of the other models: i.e., $V(\text{Linear})$, $V(\text{Exponential with base} = e)$, and $V(\text{Power model})$. Then choose the model from among these 4, which "best" fits this data set.
4. Derive the normal equations for the quadratic model, $\hat{y} = a + bx + cx^2$
5. The number of units, x, produced in a factory, and the estimated cost in dollars per unit, $\hat{y}$, are given in the table below.
   Fit a quadratic to this data set.

X	42	55	61	68	75	82	22	14	30	0	10	37	84	93	98	102	106	113
Y	7	8	2	3	5	0	13	18	12	20	22	14	3	2	0	4	3	5

6. For the Bivariate data set below:

X	5	6	7	8	9	10	11	12	13	14	15	16	17
Y	7.6	9.5	9.3	10.3	11.1	12.1	13.3	12.7	13.0	13.8	14.6	14.6	14.7

    a) Find the linear equation $\hat{y} = a + bx$.

    b) Calculate $\hat{\sigma}_L^2$ and $\hat{\sigma}_L$.

    c) Predict the value of y, when $x = 16.5$.

7. For the data set of problem 14.6:

    a) Find the quadratic equation $\hat{y} = a + bx + cx^2$.

    b) Calculate $\hat{\sigma}_Q^2$ and $\hat{\sigma}_Q$.

    c) Compare $\hat{\sigma}_Q^2$ to $\hat{\sigma}_L^2$ and $\hat{\sigma}_Q$ to $\hat{\sigma}_L$. What conclusion can we draw?

8. To estimate the total cost function $\hat{y}$ ($y = $ Cost, measured in thousands of dollars) as a function of total output x ($x = $ Quantity, measured in thousands of units) a manufacturer has obtained the following set of sample data:

Y	3.0	4.0	5.0	4.0	4.5	6.0	6.0	7.5
X	1	2	3	4	5	6	7	8

    a) Fit the exponential function: $y = ke^{cx}$.

    b) Obtain the variance of the residuals, $V(\text{res})_{\text{EXP.}} = \dfrac{1}{n-2} \sum\limits_{i=1}^{8} \left(y_i - ke^{cx_i}\right)^2$

9. Using the data of problem 8:

    a) Fit the power model $\hat{y} = ax^b$ $(b \neq 1)$.

    b) Obtain the variance of the residuals, $V(\text{Residuals})_{\text{Power}} = \dfrac{1}{n-2} \sum\limits_{i=1}^{n=8} \left(y_i - ax_i^b\right)^2.$

    c) Compare the fit of the 2 exponential models. Which model fits the data better?

10. Using the data of problem 8

    a) Fit the exponential model with base b (*i.e.*, $\hat{y} = ab^x$)

    b) Obtain the variance of the residuals,

$$V(\text{Residual})_b = \frac{1}{n-2} \sum_{i=1}^{n} \left(y_i - ab^{x_i}\right)^2$$

    c) Compare the fit of the 3 estimated models. Which model fits the data better?

11. According to economic theory, the total net investment function for a nation as a whole is assumed to be of the form: $i = ar^b$, where $i = $ total net investment (in billions of dollars) and $r = $ rate of interest.
For the sample data below:

i	10	6.5	9.5	5.0	4.5	2.5	4.0	2.5	2.2	2.8
r	3	4	3	5	6	8	7	7	9	8

a) Find the function $i = ar^b$

b) Find the value of i (in billion dollars) if $r = 5.5$.

12. Use the following Bivariate data:

x	14	9	6	21	17	15	8	5	10
y	200	74	29	456	320	247	82	21	94

a) To derive the linear regression model, $\hat{y} = a + bx$.

b) To derive a quadratic regression model, $\hat{y} = a + bx + cx^2$.

c) Compare the two models. Which one provides better predictability?

U.S.A. Population Data to be used in Problems 13–20

In the U.S.A., the Bureau of the Census, collects, tabulates and publishes census statistics about America, its people and its economy. Population (and housing) censuses are performed every 10 years.

The table below lists the Population Census results from 1790 (the first year a population census was performed) to 2000.

Year of Census	Time X (years)	Population Census Y (millions)
1790	1	3.929
1800	2	5.308
1810	3	7.240
1820	4	9.638
1830	5	12.866
1840	6	17.069
1850	7	23.192
1860	8	31.443
1870	9	39.818
1880	10	50.156
1890	11	62.948
1900	12	75.995
1910	13	91.972
1920	14	105.711
1930	15	122.775
1940	16	131.669
1950	17	150.697
1960	18	179.323
1970	19	203.302
1980	20	226.546
1990	21	249.600
2000	22	281.400

For this data set: $n = 22$; $\Sigma x_i = 253$; $\Sigma x_i^2 = 3{,}795$

$\Sigma x_i^3 = 64{,}009$; $\Sigma x_i^4 = 1{,}151{,}403$; $\Sigma \ln x_i = 48.47118$; $\Sigma (\ln x_i)^2 = 120.98842$;

$\Sigma y_i = 2{,}082.597$; $\Sigma y_i^2 = 357{,}062.4525$; $\Sigma \ln y_i = 86.31378$;

$\Sigma x_i(\ln y_i) = 1{,}171.30524$; $\Sigma (\ln x_i)(\ln y_i) = 212.55574$; $\Sigma x_i y_i = 35{,}359.379$;

$\Sigma x_i^2 y_i = 640{,}658.239$; $\Sigma(\ln y_i)^2 = 376.0101186$

13. Using the population census data:

   a) Fit the linear regression equation, $\hat{y} = a + bx$.

   b) Calculate the expected population at the next census, *i.e.*, find $\hat{y}(x = 23)$.

   c) Calculate the variance of regression residuals for the linear model.

   d) Calculate R^2. What percent of the variation in the values of y is explained by the regression equation?

14. Using the population census data:

   a) Fit the quadratic equation, $\hat{y} = a + bx = cx^2$.

   b) Calculate the expected population at the next census, *i.e.*, find $\hat{y}(x = 23)$.

   c) Calculate the variance of regression residuals for the quadratic model.

   d) Calculate R^2. What percent of the variation in the values of y is explained by the quadratic regression equation? Was the addition of the term cx^2 in the regression equation beneficial, regarding the explanatory power of the regression equation, and the predicted value $\hat{y}(x = 23)$?

15. Using the population census data:

   a) Fit the exponential regression equation, $\hat{y} = ke^{cx}$.

   b) Calculate the expected population at the next census, *i.e.*, $\hat{y}(x = 23)$.

   c) Calculate the variance of the regression residuals for the exponential model.

   d) Calculate R^2. What percent of the variation in the values of y is explained by the exponential regression equation.

16. Using the population census data:

   a) Fit the exponential model with base b, $\hat{y} = ab^x \, (b \neq 1)$.

   b) Calculate the expected population at the next census, *i.e.*, find $\hat{y}(x = 23)$.

   c) Calculate the variance of regression residuals for this model.

   d) Calculate R^2. What percent of the variation in the y-values is explained by the regression equation?

17. Using the population census data:

   a) Fit the power model, $\hat{y} = ax^b \, (b \neq 1)$.

   b) Calculate the expected population at the next census, *i.e.*, find $\hat{y}(x = 23)$.

   c) Calculate the variance of regression residuals for the Power Model.

   d) Calculate R^2. What percent of the variation in the y values is explained by the Power function regression equation?

18. Using the population Census data:

   a) Summarize the results of problems: 14.13, 14.14, 14.15, 14.16, and 14.17.

   b) Using $\hat{\sigma}^2$ (or $\hat{\sigma}$) as a criterion, which model fits the census data best?

   c) Using R^2 as a criterion, which model fits the census data best?

   d) Which model's prediction of the expected population at the next census (2010, *i.e.*, $x = 23$) seems more reasonable? Why? Justify your answer.

19. For the population Census data and the exponential model of problem 14.15:
    a) Test the hypothesis H_0: ln $k = 0$ vs H_1: ln $k \neq 0$, at $\alpha = 0.05$.
    b) Test the hypothesis H_0: $c = 0$ vs H_1: $c \neq 0$, at the $\alpha = 0.05$.
    c) Test the hypothesis H_0: The entire exponential regression is not significant.

    vs

    H_1: The entire exponential regression is significant, at $\alpha = 0.05$.

20. For the population Census data and the Power model of problem 14.17:
    a) Test the hypothesis: H_0: ln $\alpha = 0$ vs H_1: ln $\alpha \neq 0$, at $\alpha = 0.05$.
    b) Test the hypothesis: H_0: $\beta = 0$ vs H_1: $\beta \neq 0$, at the $\alpha = 0.05$.
    c) Test the hypothesis

    H_0: The entire Power function is not significant.

    vs

    H_1: The entire Power fucntion is significant, at $\alpha = 0.05$.

SOLUTIONS

1. $n(\ln a) + (\ln b) \sum_{i=1}^{n} x_i = \sum_{i=1}^{n} \ln y_i$

   $(\ln a) \sum_{i=1}^{n} x_i + (\ln b) \sum_{i=1}^{n} x_i^2 = \sum_{i=1}^{n} x_i \ln y_i$

2. Since $\sum_{i=1}^{5} x_i = 330$, $\sum_{i=1}^{5} x_i^2 = 21{,}790$, $\sum_{i=1}^{5} \ln y_i = 25.0966$, and

   $\sum_{i=1}^{5} x_i \cdot \ln y_i = 1657.0612$, ln b $= 0.06658$ or $b = e^{0.06658} = 1.068846$,

   and ln $a = 0.62552$, or $a = e^{0.62552} = 1.869218$
   Therefore, the exponential model with base $b = 1.068846$, is
   $\hat{y} = ab^x = 1.868432 \, (1.068846)^x$.

3. $V(\text{Linear}) = 10$

   $V(\text{Exponential}) = 12.8071$

   $V(\text{Power}) = 90.5539$

   $V(\text{Exponential with base } b) = \dfrac{1}{n-2} \sum_{i=1}^{1} \left(y_i - ab^{x_i}\right)^2$

   $= \dfrac{1}{5-2}\Big[(130 - 132.5076)^2 + (145 - 141.63028)^2$

   $\qquad\qquad + (165 - 161.80307)^2 + (170 - 172.94264)^2\Big]$

   $= 12.80993$
   Therefore, the linear model is still the "best" model because it has the smallest variance of the residual values of all of these 4 models.

4. Form the function $Q(a, b, c) = \sum_{i=1}^{n} \left[y_i a - bx_i - cx_i^2 \right]^2$

Now take the partial derivatives: $\dfrac{\partial Q}{\partial a}, \dfrac{\partial Q}{\partial b}, \dfrac{\partial Q}{\partial c}$, and set each equal to 0, to obtain the 3 equations needed to solve for a, b, c.

We have:

$$\frac{\partial Q}{\partial a} = +2 \sum_{i=1}^{n} \left[y_i - a - bx_i - cx_i^2 \right] (-1) = 0$$

or $\displaystyle\sum_{i=1}^{n} y_i - na - b \sum_{i=1}^{n} x_i - c \sum_{i=1}^{n} x_i^2 = 0$, or

$$na + b \sum_{i=1}^{n} x_i + c \sum_{i=1}^{n} x_i^2 = \sum_{i=1}^{n} y_i \qquad (1)$$

$$\frac{\partial Q}{\partial b} = +2 \sum_{i=1}^{n} \left[y_i - a - bx_i - cx_i^2 \right] (-x_i) = 0$$

or $\displaystyle\sum_{i=1}^{n} \left[x_i y_i - ax_i - bx_i^2 - cx_i^3 \right] = 0$ or

$$\sum_{i=1}^{n} x_i y_i - a \sum_{i=1}^{n} x_i - b \sum_{i=1}^{n} x_i^2 - c \sum_{i=0}^{n} x_i^3 = 0$$

or $a \displaystyle\sum_{i=1}^{n} x_i + b \sum_{i=1}^{n} x_i^2 + c \sum_{i=1}^{n} x_i^3 = \sum_{i=1}^{n} x_i y_i \qquad (2)$

$$\frac{\partial Q}{\partial c} = +2 \sum_{i=1}^{n} \left[y_i - a - bx_i - cx_i^2 \right] (-x_i^2) = 0$$

or $\displaystyle\sum_{i=1}^{n} \left[y_i x_i^2 - ax_i^2 - bx_i^3 - cx_i^4 \right] = 0$

or $\displaystyle\sum_{i=1}^{n} x_i^2 y_i - a \sum_{i=1}^{n} x_i^2 - b \sum_{i=1}^{n} x_i^3 - c \sum_{i=0}^{n} x_i^4 = 0$

or $a \displaystyle\sum_{i=1}^{n} x_i^2 + b \sum_{i=1}^{n} x_i^3 + c \sum_{i=1}^{n} x_i^4 = \sum_{i=1}^{n} x_i^2 y_i \qquad (3)$

5. $n = 18$, $\Sigma x_i = 1{,}092$; $\Sigma x_i^2 = 88{,}250$; $\Sigma x_i^3 = 7{,}880{,}538$; $\Sigma x_i^4 = 741{,}676{,}598$;
$\Sigma y_i = 141$; $\Sigma x_i y_i = 4{,}800$ *and* $\Sigma x_i^2 y_i = 305{,}608$.

Then, substituting in equations: (1), (2), and (3) above, we obtain:

$18a + 1{,}092b + 88{,}250c = 141$

$1{,}092a + 88{,}250b + 7{,}880{,}538c = 4{,}800$

$88{,}250a + 7{,}880{,}538b + 741{,}676{,}598c = 305{,}608$

When these 3 equations are solved simultaneously for a, b, c, we obtain:

$a = 23.163$, $b = -0.4477$ and $c = 0.002413$. Therefore, The Quadratic equation is:

$\hat{y} = a + bx + cx^2 = 23.163 - 0.4477x + 0.002413x^2$

6. $n = 13$, $\Sigma x_i = 143$; $\Sigma x_i^2 = 1755$; $\Sigma y_i = 156.6$;
$\Sigma y_i^2 = 1{,}950.24$; $\Sigma x_i y_i = 1{,}826.8$

a) From the normal equations $13a + 143b = 156.6$

$143a + 1755b = 1{,}826.8$, we obtain:

$a = 5.78$ and $b = 0.570$ or $\hat{y} = a + bx = 5.78 + 0.570x$

b) $\sigma_L^2 = \dfrac{\Sigma y_i^2 - a\Sigma y_i - b\Sigma x_i y_i}{n-2} = \dfrac{1{,}950.24 - 5.78(156.6) - 0.570(1{,}826.8)}{13-2}$

$= \dfrac{1{,}950.24 - 905.148 - 1041.276}{11} = \dfrac{3.816}{11} = 0.3469,$

and $\hat{\sigma}_L = \sqrt{0.3469} = 0.589$

c) $\hat{y}(x=16.5) = 5.78 + 0.570(16.5) = 5.78 + 9.405 = 15.185$

7. $n = 13$, $\Sigma x_i = 143$; $\Sigma x_i^2 = 1755$; $\Sigma y_i = 156.6$; $\Sigma y_i^2 = 1{,}950.24$;
$\Sigma x_i y_i = 1{,}826.8\,\Sigma x_i^3 = 23{,}309$; $\Sigma x_i^4 = 327{,}015$; $\Sigma x_i^2 y_i = 23{,}366.8$.

a) Then, from the normal equations for the quadratic model (see problem 14.4 above) we have:

$\left. \begin{array}{l} 13a + 143b + 1{,}755c = 156.6 \\ 143a + 1{,}755b + 23{,}309 = 1{,}826.8 \\ 1{,}755a + 23{,}309b + 327{,}015c = 23{,}366.8 \end{array} \right\}$ $\begin{array}{l} \textit{Solving simul}\tan\textit{ously, we obtain} \\ a = 2.212, \ b = 1.299 \ \textit{and} \ c = -0.033, \\ \textit{or} \ \hat{y} = 2.212 + 1.299x - 0.033x^2 \end{array}$

b) $\sigma^2_Q = \dfrac{\Sigma y_i^2 - a\Sigma y_i - b\Sigma x_i y_i - c\Sigma x_i^2 y_i}{n-3}$

$= \dfrac{1{,}950.24 - 2.212(156.6) - 1.249(1{,}826.8) - (-0.033)(23{,}366.8)}{13-3}$

$= \dfrac{1.932}{10} = 0.1932,$ and $\hat{\sigma}_Q = \sqrt{0.1932} = 0.4395$

c) Since $\hat{\sigma}_L^2 > \hat{\sigma}_Q^2$ (i.e., since $0.3469 > 0.1932$) and $\hat{\sigma}_L > \hat{\sigma}_Q$ (i.e., $0.589 > 0.4395$), the quadratic equation gives a better fit. The error of regression has been reduced by:

$\left| \dfrac{0.4395 - 0.589}{0.589} \times 100 \right| = |-25.382\%| = 25.382\%.$

8. a) The normal equation for the exponential model are:

$n(\ln k) + (c)\Sigma x_i = \Sigma \ln y_i$

$(\ln k)\Sigma x_i + (c)\Sigma x_i^2 = \Sigma x_i \ln y_i$

Therefore, we need to generate from the given data: n, Σx_i, Σx_i^2, $\Sigma \ln y_i$ and $\Sigma x_i \ln y_i$; $n = 8$, $\Sigma x_i = 36$, $\Sigma x_i^2 = 204$, $\Sigma \ln y_i = 12.58313828$ and $\Sigma x_i \ln y_i = 61.17717644$;   Then:

$\left. \begin{array}{l} 8 \ln k + 36c = 12.58313828 \\ 36 \ln k + 204c = 61.17717644 \end{array} \right\}$ or $\begin{array}{l} \ln k + 4.5c = 1.57289 \\ \ln k + 5.66667 = 1.699366, \end{array}$

or: $1.16667c = 0.126476$ or $c = 0.126476/1.16667 = 0.1084$ and

$\ln k = 1.57289 - 4.5c = 1.57289 - 0.48783 = 1.085055347$ and

$k = e^{1.0850} = 2.9596.$

Therefore, the estimated exponential model is: $\hat{y} = ke^{cx} = 2.9596e^{0.1084x}$

b) Calculation of residuals

x	y	$\hat{y} = 2.9596e^{0.1084x}$	Residuals $= \hat{y}_i - y_i$	(Residuals)^2 $= (y_i - \hat{y}_i)^2$
1	3.0	3.299854	0.2984548	0.089075
2	4.0	3.676106	−0.3238937	0.104907
3	5.0	4.096996	−0.903003	0.815415
4	4.0	4.5660757	0.5660757	0.32044
5	4.5	5.088861	0.08886	0.007896
6	6.0	5.6715028	−0.328497	0.107910
7	6.0	6.32085	0.32085	0.1029465
8	7.5	7.044549	−0.455451	0.2074356

Then: Sum of (Residuals)^2 = 1.300574, and:

$$V(\text{Residual})_{\text{Exponential}} = \frac{1}{8-2}(1.300574) = \frac{1}{6}(1.300574) = 0.21676$$

9. a) The normal equations for this model are:

$$n(\ln a) + b\sum_{i=1}^{n} \ln x_i = \sum_{i=1}^{n} \ln y_i$$

$$(\ln a)\sum_{i=1}^{n} \ln x_i + b\sum_{i=1}^{n}(\ln x_i)^2 = \sum_{i=1}^{n}(\ln x_i)(\ln y_i)$$

Therefore to estimate this model, we need to obtain from the given Bivariate data set: $n = 8$; $\Sigma \ln x_i$; $\Sigma(\ln x_i)^2$; $\Sigma \ln y_i$; $\Sigma(\ln x_i)(\ln y_i)$; we have: $n = 8$; $\Sigma \ln x_i = 10.6046$; $\Sigma(\ln x_i)^2 = 17.52054985$; $\Sigma \ln y_i = 12.58313828$; $\Sigma(\ln x_i)(\ln y_i) = 17.95846343$

The normal equations then become:

$8\ln a + 10.6046\,b = 12.58313828$

$10.6046 \ln a + 17.5205499\,b = 17.95846343$ or

$\ln a + 1.325575\,b = 1.572892255$

$\ln a + 1.652165\,b = 1.693459766$ or $b = \dfrac{0.12056748}{0.32659} = 0.36917$

and: $\ln a = 1.572892285 - 1.325575(0.36917)$

$= 1.572892285 - 0.489363536, = 1.08353$ and

$a = e^{1.08353} = 2.9551$; Therefore, the model is: $\hat{y} = ax^b = 2.9551x^{0.36917}$

x	y	$\hat{y} = 2.9551x^{0.3691x}$	Residuals $= \hat{y}_i - y_i$	(Residuals)^2 $= (y_i - \hat{y}_i)^2$
1	3	2.9551	−0.0449	0.002016
2	4	3.816835	−0.18316465	0.03354929
3	5	4.4331358	−0.5668642	0.321335
4	4	4.929861	0.92986	0.86464136
5	4.5	5.3531688	0.8531688	0.727897
6	6	5.72588	−0.27412	0.07514
7	6	6.0611778	−0.938822	0.881387
8	7.5	6.367455	−1.132545	1.282658

and $\Sigma(\hat{y}_i - y_i)^2 = 3.2498$; Therefore, $V(\text{Residual})_{\text{Power}} = \dfrac{1}{n-2}\Sigma(\hat{y}_i - y_i)^2$

$$= \frac{1}{6}(3.2498) = 0.54163$$

c) Since $V(\text{Residual})_{\text{EXP}} = 0.21676 < V(\text{Residual})_{\text{Power}}$ the exponential model is a better fit than the Power model.

10. a) The normal equations for this model are: $\begin{array}{l} n(\ln a) + (\ln b)\Sigma x_i = \Sigma \ln y_i \\ (\ln a)\Sigma x_i + (\ln b)\Sigma x_i^2 = \Sigma x_i \ln y_i, \end{array}$

and when the appropriate values are substituted in, we obtain:

$\begin{array}{l} 8\ln a + 36\ln b = 12.58313828. \\ 36\ln a + 204\ln b = 61.17717644, \end{array}$ or $\begin{array}{l} \ln a + 4.5\ln b = 1.572892286 \\ \ln a + 5.66667\ln b = 1.699366, \end{array}$

from which we obtain: $\ln b = \dfrac{1.699366 - 1.572892286}{5.66667 - 4.5}$

$$= \frac{0.126473714}{1.16667} = 0.1084,$$

from which we obtain $b = e^{0.1084} = 1.1145$; $\ln a$

$$= 1.572892286 - 4.5(0.1084) = 1.085092,$$

or $a = e^{1.085092} = 2.95971$; Therefore the model $\hat{y} = ab^x = 2.95971(1.1145)^{x_i}$

b) Calculating the variance of the residuals

x	y	$\hat{y} = ab^x = 2.95971(1.1145)^x$	**Residuals** $= \hat{y}_i - y_i$	$(\textbf{Residuals})^2 = (y_i - \hat{y}_i)^2$
1	3	3.298597	0.298597	0.089160
2	4	3.676286	-0.3237138	0.104790
3	5	4.09722	-0.902779	0.815010
4	4	4.566353	0.56635268	0.320755
5	4.5	5.0892	0.5892	0.347157
6	6	5.671913	-0.328086	0.107641
7	6	6.32134756	0.32134756	0.10326426
8	7.5	7.04514186	-0.45485814	0.206896

and $\Sigma(\hat{y}_i - y_i)^2 = 2.094673188$;

Therefore: $V(\text{Residual})_b = \dfrac{1}{n-2}\Sigma(\hat{y}_i - y_i)^2 = \dfrac{1}{6}(2.094673188) = 0.34911$

c) Since $V(\text{Residual})_{\text{EXP}} = 0.2176 < V(\text{Residual})_b$
$= 0.34911 < V(\text{Residual})_p = 0.54163$, the exponential with base

$b = e = 2.718\ldots$, has the best fit.

15 Generalized Regression (Multivariate)

On many occasions the value of a single (dependent) variable is determined from the values of two (or more) independent variables, or:

$$y = b_1 x_1 + b_2 x_2 + b_3 x_3 + \cdots + b_p x_p$$

To estimate such a model, we need to start with a multivariate data set which is first used to obtain numerical values for the multipliers: $b_1, b_2, b_3, \ldots, b_p$, and their standard deviations: $\sigma(b_1), \sigma(b_2), \ldots, \sigma(b_1)$. This information is then used to test for the significance of each independent variable, X_i, in determining the value of y, by testing the hypothesis

$$H_0: \beta_i = 0 \text{ vs. } H_1: \beta_i \neq 0, \text{ for } i = 1, 2, 3, \ldots, p.$$

When such a hypothesis is not rejected for a given value of i, the corresponding random variable, X_i, is assumed not to be significant in the determination of the value of y, and is dropped from the final equation (the final regression is retained and used for Prediction/Forecasting purposes).

Also tested is the significance of the entire regression, including the constant term b_1 (to have a constant term in the equation, the variable X_1 is assigned a value of 1 in each of the n observations), and also the significance of the entire regression, excluding the constant term b_1. The estimation and testing of such a model is treated best by using Matrix Algebra.

15.1   Introduction

Bivariate and Trivariate data are special cases of the Multivariate case, which can be treated best in terms of matrices. To develop the matrix model, we start by making the following observations:

1. The model of observations for the Simple Regression model is usually written as:

$$\hat{y}_i = a + b x_i + z_i \tag{15.1}$$

   or

$$\hat{y}_i = b_1 x_{1i} + b x_{i2} + z_i, \tag{15.2}$$

   where in equation (15.2) the variable x_{1i} has the value of 1 for all i.

2. Then a more general Linear Model, applicable when several independent variables $x_1, x_2, \ldots, x_p$, determine the value of a single dependent variable y, can be written as:

$$\hat{y}_i = b_1 x_{1i} + b_2 x_{2i} + \cdots + b_p x_{pi} + z_i \tag{15.3}$$

   The corresponding ideal linear model to the above model of observations is:

$$\hat{y}_i = \beta_1 x_{1i} + \beta_2 x_{2i} + \cdots + \beta_p x_{pi}, \tag{15.4}$$

   where $b_1, b_2, \ldots, b_p$, are the Least Squares Estimates of the population parameters: $\beta_1, \beta_2, \ldots, \beta_p$.

3. Generally we have n observations (i.e., $i = 1, 2, 3, \ldots, n$) at n sets of values of the x_j variables, where: $j = 1, 2, 3, \ldots, p$.

The data looks as shown below forming an $n \times p$ matrix of values for the independent variables and $n \times 1$ vector for the dependent variable:

$$
\begin{array}{cccccc}
X_1 & X_2 & X_3 & \ldots & X_p & Y \\
x_{11} & x_{21} & x_{31} & \ldots & x_{p1} & y_1 \\
x_{12} & x_{22} & x_{32} & \ldots & x_{p2} & y_2 \\
\ldots & \ldots & \ldots & \ldots & \ldots & \ldots \\
x_{1n} & x_{2n} & x_{3n} & \ldots & x_{pn} & y_n
\end{array}
\tag{15.5}
$$

where the first p columns represent the $n \times p$ matrix of values for the independent variables, and the last column represents the $n \times 1$ vector of observations for the dependent variable Y.

Note: If equation (15.3) has to have a constant term, then the values under the X_1 column in equation (15.5) (*i.e.*, $x_{11}, x_{12}, x_{13}, \ldots, x_{1n}$) are all equal to 1.

4. We seek the Least Square Estimates of the p unknown population parameters, $\beta_1, \beta_2, \ldots, \beta_p$, denoted by $b_1, b_2, b_3, \ldots, b_p$.

$$
\text{Let } \beta = \begin{bmatrix} \beta_1 \\ \beta_2 \\ \ldots \\ \beta_p \end{bmatrix} \text{ and } b = \begin{bmatrix} b_1 \\ b_2 \\ \ldots \\ b_p \end{bmatrix}
$$

be 2, $p \times 1$ vetors of the unknown population parameters β and their corresponding estimators b.

In the model of observations (equation (15.3)), we have:

$$
E(z_i) = 0
$$
$$
V(z_i) = \sigma^2
\tag{15.6}
$$
$$
E(z_i z_j) = 0
$$

for all $i \neq j$ (*i.e.*, the z_i's are uncorrelated).

5. The general Linear Model can be written in matrix form as:

$$
Y = XB + Z
\tag{15.7}
$$

with
$$
E(Z) = 0
\tag{15.8}
$$

and
$$
E(ZZ^t) = \sigma^2 I_{nxn}
\tag{15.9}
$$

Equations (15.8) and (15.9) are valid because:

$$
\text{If we let } Z = \begin{bmatrix} Z_1 \\ Z_2 \\ \ldots \\ Z_n \end{bmatrix}, \text{ then } E(Z) = \begin{bmatrix} E(Z_1) \\ E(Z_2) \\ \ldots \\ E(Z_n) \end{bmatrix} = \begin{bmatrix} 0 \\ 0 \\ \ldots \\ 0 \end{bmatrix} = 0
\tag{15.10}
$$

Let us also consider the vector product ZZ^t.

$$\text{Since } ZZ^t = \begin{bmatrix} Z_1 \\ Z_2 \\ \cdots \\ Z_n \end{bmatrix} \begin{bmatrix} Z_1 & Z_2 \cdots Z_n \end{bmatrix} = \begin{bmatrix} Z_1^2 & Z_1 Z_2 & \cdots & Z_1 Z_n \\ Z_2 Z_1 & Z_2^2 & \cdots & Z_2 Z_n \\ \cdots\cdots\cdots\cdots\cdots\cdots\cdots\cdots \\ Z_n Z_1 & Z_n Z_2 & \cdots & Z_n^2 \end{bmatrix} \quad (15.11)$$

ZZ^t is an $n \times n$ Matrix, and

$$E(ZZ^t) = \begin{bmatrix} E(Z_1^2) & E(Z_1 Z_2) & \cdots & E(Z_1 Z_n) \\ E(Z_2 Z_1) & E(Z_2^2) & \cdots & E(Z_2 Z_n) \\ \cdots\cdots\cdots\cdots\cdots\cdots\cdots\cdots\cdots\cdots\cdots\cdots \\ E(Z_n Z_1) & E(Z_n Z_2) & \cdots & E(Z_n^2) \end{bmatrix} \quad (15.12)$$

But, since

$$V(Z_i) = E(Z_i^2) - [E(Z_i)]^2 \quad (15.13)$$

for any random variable, Z_i, and $E(Z_i) = 0$ (see equation (15.6)), we can state that:

$$V(Z_i) = E(Z_i^2), \quad (15.14)$$

and we can write:

$$E(ZZ^t) = \begin{bmatrix} V(Z_1) & Cov(Z_1 Z_2) & \cdots & Cov(Z_1 Z_n) \\ Cov(Z_2 Z_1) & V(Z_2) & \cdots & Cov(Z_2 Z_n) \\ \cdots\cdots\cdots\cdots\cdots\cdots\cdots\cdots\cdots\cdots\cdots\cdots \\ Cov(Z_n Z_1) & Cov(Z_n Z_2) & \cdots & V(Z_n) \end{bmatrix} \quad (15.15)$$

$$= \begin{bmatrix} \sigma^2 & 0 & \cdots & 0 \\ 0 & \sigma^2 & \cdots & 0 \\ \cdots & \cdots & \cdots & \cdots \\ 0 & 0 & \cdots & \sigma^2 \end{bmatrix}, \text{ because of equation (15.6)}$$

$$= \sigma^2 I_{n \times n} \quad (15.16)$$

6. To find the Least Squares Estimates of the Estimators $b_1, b_2, \ldots, b_p$, of the ideal population model parameters: $\beta_1, \beta_2, \ldots, \beta_p$, we need to Minimize the Quadratic Function:

$$Q = \sum_{i=1}^{n} (y_i - b_1 x_{1i} - b_2 x_{2i} - \cdots - b_p x_{pi})^2, \quad (15.17)$$

which can be written in Matrix Form as:

$$Q = (Y - XB)^t (Y - XB) \quad (15.18)$$

or by using equation (15.7) above, as:

$$Q = Z^t \cdot Z \quad (15.19)$$

Before these functions can be minimized, it is necessary to review the optimization procedure of multivariate functions which, for a function of 2 independent variables, consists of the following steps.

15.2   Optimizing a Function of 2 or more Independent Variables

DIGRESSION 1: To minimize a non-linear function of 2 independent variables (For example: Let $Z = f(x,y) = x^3 + 2xy + y^2$), we do the following:

1. Find the Partial Derivatives: $\dfrac{\partial Z}{\partial x} = 3x^2 + 2y$, and $\dfrac{\partial Z}{\partial y} = 2x + 2y$.

2. Set the Partial Derivatives equal to zero and solve the resulting equations simultaneously,

   $i.e.$, solve $\left. \begin{array}{ll} \text{(I)} & 3x^2 + 2y = 0 \\ \text{(II)} & 2x + 2y = 0 \end{array} \right\} \rightarrow$ simultaneously.

   From equation (II) we obtain: $y = -x$; By substituting this into equation (I), we obtain: $x(3x - 2) = 0$, from which we obtain 2 solutions, namely:

   solution 1: $x = 0,\ y = 0$

   and   solution 2: $x = 2/3,\ y = -2/3$

   Note: The pairs of (x, y) values, which satisfy equations I and II simultaneously, define the Critical points of the function.

3. Find the 2nd Partial Derivatives: $fxx = \dfrac{\partial^2 Z}{\partial x \partial y} = 6x$, and $fyy = \dfrac{\partial^2 Z}{\partial y^2} = 2$

4. Find the Cross-Partial Derivative: $fxy = fyx = \dfrac{\partial^2 Z}{\partial x \partial y} = \dfrac{\partial^2 Z}{\partial y \partial x} = 2$

5. Evaluate fxx, fyy, fxy at each of the Critical Points.

	Critical Point 1 $(x = 0,\ y = 0)$	Critical Point 2 $(x = 2/3,\ y = -2/3)$
$fxx = 6x$	$6x \rightarrow 0$	$6x \rightarrow 4$
$fyy = 2$	$2 \rightarrow 2$	$2 \rightarrow 2$
$fxy = fyx = 2$	$2 \rightarrow 2$	$2 \rightarrow 2$

6. Let $D = (fxx)(fyy) - (fxy)^2$

   $= (0)(2) - (2)^2 = -4$ For Critical Point 1 $(x = 0, y = 0)$

   $= (4)(2) - (2)^2 = +4$ For Critical Point 2 $(x = 2/3, y = -2/3)$

7. If $fxx > 0$ and $fyy > 0$ and $D > 0$, the Function has a Definite Minimum at the Critical Point.

8. If $fxx < 0$ and $fyy < 0$ and $D > 0$, the Function has a Definite Maximum at the Critical Point.

9. If $D = 0$ (Regardless of the sign and values of fxx, fyy), this method is not applicable to the solution of this problem. To find the nature of the critical point, evaluate the function at the critical point, and at points adjacent to the critical point and then, by inspectional comparison, decide the nature of the critical point (Maximum or Minimum).

10. If $D < 0$ (Regardless of the sign and values of the fxx, fyy), this function has a Saddle Point at the critical point. A Saddle point is neither a Minimum nor a Maximum, but it is a Minimum along one axis, and a Maximum along a second axis.

Conclusion Therefore, the function $Z = f(x, y) = x^3 + 2xy + y^2$, has a Saddle Point at critical point 1, and a minimum at Critical Point 2.

15.3 Model Estimation

Now let us apply the Optimization Methodology discussed above to the function defined by equations (15.17), (15.18), or (15.19).

When the p-equations: $\dfrac{\partial Q}{\partial b_1} = 0, \dfrac{\partial Q}{\partial b_2} = 0, \dots, \dfrac{\partial Q}{\partial b_p} = 0$ (15.20)

are solved simultaneously and simplified, they can be written in matrix form as:

$$X^t X b = X^t Y \tag{15.21}$$

Equation (15.21) represents, in matrix form, the Normal Equations of the General Linear Model of Equation (15.3).

If we let $\left(X^t X\right)^{-1}$ represent the Inverse Matrix of Matrix $(X^t X)$, then the matrix solution to equation (15.21) is given by:

$$b = \left(X^t X\right)^{-1} X^t Y \tag{15.22}$$

Equation (15.22) provides the numerical values for the coefficients $b_1, b_2, \dots, b_p$, of equation (15.3).

Now let us apply the Expectation and Variance operators on equation (15.22) to obtain the Expected value and Variance of the b estimators.

1. Taking the Expected Value of equation (15.22), we obtain:

$$E(b) = E\left[\left(X^t X\right)^{-1} X^t Y\right] \tag{15.23}$$

$$= \left(X^t X\right)^{-1} X^t E(Y) \tag{15.24}$$

But, because of Equation (15.7), $E(Y) = E(Xb + Z) = E(Xb) + E(Z)$

$$= \beta X + 0 = \beta X \tag{15.25}$$

Therefore, Equation (15.24) can be written as:

$$E(b) = (X^tX)^{-1}X^t(\beta X)$$
$$= (X^tX)^{-1}(X^tX)\beta$$
$$= [(X^tX)^{-1}(X^tX)]\beta$$
$$= 1 \cdot \beta$$
$$= \beta \tag{15.26}$$

Therefore, the solution vector b, given by equation (15.22), is an Unbiased Estimator for the parameter vector β.

2. The Variance of Vector b, in Matrix Form, can be written as:

$$V(b) = E[(b - \beta)(b - \beta)^t] \tag{15.27}$$

(Compare this with the Algebraic Formulation: $V(b) = E[b - \beta]^2$)

or

$$V(b) = E[(X^tX)^{-1}X^tY - \beta][(X^tX)^{-1}X^tY - \beta]^t \tag{15.28}$$

(Because of (15.22))

$$= E[(X^tX)^{-1}X^t(X\beta + Z) - \beta][(X^tX)^{-1}X^t(X\beta + Z) - \beta]^t \tag{15.29}$$

(because $Y = Xb + Z$)

$$= E[(X^tX)^{-1}(X^tX)\beta + (X^tX)^{-1}X^tZ - \beta]^*$$
$$[(X^tX)^{-1}(X^tX)\beta + (X^tX)^{-1}X^tZ - \beta]^t \tag{15.30}$$
$$= E[\beta + (X^tX)^{-1}X^tZ - \beta][\beta + (X^tX)^{-1}X^tZ - \beta]^t \tag{15.31}$$
$$= E[(X^tX)^{-1}X^tZ][(X^tX)^{-1}X^tZ]^t \tag{15.32}$$

But, in Matrix Algebra:

$$(AB)^t = B^tA^t \tag{15.33}$$

Using equation (15.33) in equation (15.32), we can write:

$$V(b) = E[(X^tX)^{-1}X^tZ][Z^tX((X^tX)^{-1})^t] \tag{15.34}$$

Since X^tX is Symmetric, $(X^tX)^{-1}$ is also Symmetric, and

$$(X^tX)^{-1} = [(X^tX)^{-1}]^t \tag{15.35}$$

Then

$$V(b) = E\left[\left(X^t X\right)^{-1} X^t Z Z^t X \left(X^t X\right)^{-1}\right] \tag{15.36}$$

$$= \left[\left(X^t X\right)^{-1} X^t E\left(Z Z^t\right) X \left(X^t X\right)^{-1}\right] \tag{15.37}$$

$$= \left[\left(X^t X\right)^{-1} X^t \left(\sigma^2 I_{n \times n}\right) X \left(X^t X^{-1}\right)\right] \tag{15.38}$$

(Because $E\left(Z Z^t\right) = \sigma^2 I_{n \times n}$)

$$= \sigma^2 I_{n \times n} \left[\left(X^t X\right)^{-1} \left(X^t X\right)\left(X^t X\right)^{-1}\right] \tag{15.39}$$

$$= \left(X^t X\right)^{-1} \sigma^2 I_{n \times n} \tag{15.40}$$

$$= \left(X^t X\right)^{-1} \sigma^2 \tag{15.41}$$

(Since $I_{n \times n} = 1$ in Matrix Form)

3. When the solution vector b, given by equation (15.22), is substituted into equation (15.18), we obtain (after some initial simplification):

$$Q^* = \left(Y - Xb\right)^t \left(Y - Xb\right) = \left(Y^t - b^t X^t\right)\left(Y - Xb\right) \tag{15.42}$$

$$= Y^t Y - Y^t Xb - b^t X^t Y + b^t X^t Xb \tag{15.43}$$

But, because of equation (15.22), which we can write as $X^t Xb = X^t Y$, we obtain by finding the transposed of this matrix:

$$\left(X^t Xb\right)^t = \left(X^t Y\right)^t \tag{15.44}$$

or

$$b^t X^t X = Y^t X, \tag{15.45}$$

and the last term of equation (15.43), $b^t X^t X(b)$, becomes: $Y^t Xb$ (15.46)

Finally, equation (15.43), after canceling the resulting similar terms, becomes:

$$Q^* = Y^t Y - b^t X^t Y \tag{15.47}$$

The value of Q^* is needed to obtain an estimate of σ^2 which, according to Markov's Theorem is given by:

$$\sigma^2 = \frac{Q^*}{n - p} \tag{15.48}$$

When equation (15.48) is substituted into equation (15.41), the variance of vector b, which is the estimator of the parameter vector β, becomes:

$$V(b) = \left(X^t X^{-1}\right)^{-1}\left[\frac{Y^t Y - b^t X^t Y}{n - p}\right] \tag{15.49}$$

$$
\begin{aligned}
\text{In equation (15.47)}, Q^* &= \text{ Residual or Error Sum of Squares, with dof} = n - p \\
Y'Y &= \text{ Total Sum of Squares with dof} = n \\
b'X'Y &= \text{ Regression Sum of Squares with dof} = p
\end{aligned}
$$

15.4 Summary of Matrix Methodology

Having derived above the procedure, for solving a Multivariate Regression problem, the seven steps below represents a summary of this procedure:

1. Model of Observations (equation (15.10)): $Y = Xb + Z$ (15.50)
2. Normal Equations (equation (15.21)): $X'Xb = X'Y$ (15.51)
3. Solution to Normal Equations (equation (15.22)): $b = \left(X'X\right)^{-1}X'Y$ (15.52)
4. Expected Value of $b = E(b)$ (equation (15.26)): $E(b) = \beta$ (15.53)
5. $Q^* = $ Error Sum of Squares (equation (15.47)): $Q^* = Y'Y - b'X'Y$ (15.54)
6. Variance of Regression (equation (15.48)): $\sigma^2 = \dfrac{Q^*}{(n - p)}$ (15.55)
7. Variance of b Estimators $= V(b)$ (equation (15.49):

$$
= V(b) = \left(X^{-1}X\right)^{-1}\sigma^2 \tag{15.56}
$$

15.5 Testing for the Significance of the Generated Equation

The information generated above can be transferred to an "ANOVA Table for Regression".

Actually there are 2 such "ANOVA Tables for Regression", one which includes the effect of the Constant term b_1 (Remember: Variable X_1 is set to the value of 1 when a constant term is to be included in the model of observations (equation (15.6)), and a second table which removes the effect of the constant term.

These 2 "ANOVA Tables for Regression" are shown below, and their use will be described shortly:

1. ANOVA with the Constant Term.

Source of Variation	DF	Sum of Squares (SS)	$MS = \dfrac{SS}{DF}$	E(MS)
Regression	p	$b'X'Y$	$\dfrac{b'X'Y}{p}$	
Error	$n - p$	$Q^* = Y'Y - b'X'Y$	$\dfrac{Q^*}{n - p}$	σ^2
Total	n	$Y'Y$	$\dfrac{Y'Y}{n}$	

2. ANOVA without the Constant Term.

Source of Variation	DF	Sum of Squares (SS)	MS $= \dfrac{\text{SS}}{\text{DF}}$	E(MS)
Regression (without Constant)	$p - 1$	$b^t X^t Y - \dfrac{\left(\sum\limits_{i=1}^{n} Y_i\right)^2}{n}$ $= \textbf{SSR}$	$\dfrac{\text{SSR}}{p - 1}$	
Error	$n - p$	$Q^* = Y^t Y - b^t X^t Y$	$\dfrac{Q^*}{n - p}$	σ^2
Total	$n - 1$	$Y^t Y - \dfrac{\left(\sum\limits_{i=1}^{n} Y_i\right)^2}{n}$		

Note that the "Error" Row is the same in Both ANOVA Tables. When the effect of the constant term is excluded from the table, the Sum of Squares due to the constant term

$$\text{SSa} = \frac{\left(\sum\limits_{i=1}^{n} Y_i\right)^2}{n},$$ is subtracted from the Regression SS, and Total SS, and their

degrees of freedoms are reduced by one.

3. **Reason for constructing 2 ANOVA for Regression Tables**

The reason for constructing 2 "ANOVA Tables for Regression" is the fact that when testing for the "Significance of Regression", we may wish to test for either:

H_0: $\beta = 0$ (all β parameters including the constant term are ZERO)

$$\text{vs} \tag{15.57}$$

H_1: $\beta \neq 0$ (Not all βs are equal to ZERO)

(We use: "ANOVA with Constant", for this test)

or

H_0: $\beta_2 = \beta_3 = \cdots = \beta_\rho = 0$ (all β parameters except the Constant term are ZERO)

$$\text{vs} \tag{15.58}$$

H_1: (Not all $\beta_2, \beta_3, \ldots, \beta_\rho$ are equal to ZERO)

(We use: "ANOVA without the Constant", for this test.)

a) To test either of the above 2 Hypotheses, at some value of α we do the following

$$\text{To test the first hypothesis above, we calculate } F_1^* = \frac{\dfrac{b^t X^t Y}{p}}{\dfrac{Q^*}{n - p}} \tag{15.59}$$

and compare to $F_{n-p}^{p}(\alpha)$, using the "ANOVA with the Constant term" table for this test.

b) To test the second hypothesis above, we calculate:

$$F_2^* = \frac{\dfrac{\left[b'X'Y - \dfrac{\left(\sum_{i=1}^{n} Y_i\right)^2}{n} \right]}{p-1}}{\dfrac{Q^*}{n-p}}, \tag{15.60}$$

and compare to $F_{n-p}^{p-1}(\alpha)$, using the "ANOVA without the Constant term" table for this test.

4. Testing each parameter, β_i, individually

It is usually more useful if we can "Break" the Regression Sum of Squares $\left(RSS = b'X'Y\right)$ into Sum of Squares (SS) for individual parameters (*i.e.*, SS for β_1, SS for $\beta_2, \ldots$, SS for β_p). If this can be done, then we can test for each β_1 separately, using the F-distribution.

This cannot always be done easily, but when it can it simplifies the solution considerably. The discussion below offers some insight on the options available:

a) If the $X'X$ matrix is a Diagonal matrix, *i.e.*, if $X'X = D_1$, where:

$$D_1 = \begin{pmatrix} d_1 & 0 \\ 0 & d_2 \end{pmatrix}, \text{ or } X'X = D_2, \text{ where } D_2 = \begin{pmatrix} d_1 & 0 & 0 \\ 0 & d_2 & 0 \\ 0 & 0 & d_3 \end{pmatrix}, \text{ etc.,}$$

then there is no problem in separating $RRS = b'X'Y$ into SS due to each b_i. We simply perform the indicated matrix multiplication, and use the individual products (without adding them) as the SSb_i components.

Note: when $(X'X)$ is a diagonal matrix, it is very easy to find the Inverse Matrix $\left(X'X\right)^{-1}$, because by inspection:

i) The Inverse of the Diagonal Matrix D_1 defined above is:

$$D_1 = D_1^{-1} = \begin{pmatrix} \dfrac{1}{d_1} & 0 \\ 0 & \dfrac{1}{d_2} \end{pmatrix}, \text{ and} \tag{15.61}$$

ii) The Inverse Matrix of the Diagonal Matrix D_2 defined above is:

$$D_2^{-1} = \begin{pmatrix} \dfrac{1}{d_1} & 0 & 0 \\ 0 & \dfrac{1}{d_2} & 0 \\ 0 & 0 & \dfrac{1}{d_3} \end{pmatrix} \tag{15.62}$$

b) However, if (X^tX) is not a Diagonal Matrix, this separation of the $RSS = b^tX^tY$ into component SS, cannot be accomplished by simple multiplication, because some of the components end up with negative values, if simple matrix multiplication is used, and this is not possible, because a "Sum of Squares" can never be negative! There exists a method, called the "Forward Doolittle Method" for accomplishing this "separation", but it is rather complicated, and we will not discuss it, because easier alternative approaches exist, as shown below:

  i) One alternative approach to this problem, is to try to "transform" the data so that the matrix (X^tX) becomes Diagonal. This may not always be easy to accomplish, but, if it can be done, it eliminates a lot of the complicated calculations needed to solve this problem. A procedure that usually works is to standardize each variable $X_i (i = 1, 2, 3, \ldots, p)$ using the transformation:

$$Z_i = \frac{X_i - \overline{X_i}}{\sigma(X_i)} \tag{15.63}$$

  ii) Another alternative approach to this problem (*i.e.*, to test for each individual β_i, $H_0: \beta_i = 0$ vs: $H_1: \beta_i \neq 0$, for $i = 1, 2, \ldots, p$) is to:

  A) Use the Matrix Method to obtain the values for each b_i and $\sigma(b_i)$, and then

  B) Use Z or t_{n-p} to test for the significance of each β_i (depending on n), by testing:

$$H_0: \beta_i = 0 \text{ vs } H_1: \beta_i \neq 0, \quad \text{for } i = 1, 2, \ldots, p.$$

when $n \geq 30$; we calculate: $Z_i^* = \dfrac{b_i - 0}{\sigma(b_i)}$ \hfill (15.64)

and compare against $Z(\alpha/2)$, for a given α.

When $n < 30$; we calculate: $t_i^* = \dfrac{b_i - 0}{\sigma(b_i)}$ \hfill (15.65)

and compare against $t_{n-p}(\alpha/2)$, for a given α.

Note: To perform these tests fully, one needs to follow the traditional seven-step procedure discussed at length in Chapter 11.

  iii) Construct a C. I. for each β_i, and check to see if the value $\beta_i = 0$ is included in the interval (or not). If the value $\beta_i = 0$ is inside the interval, the corresponding hypothesis $H_0: \beta_i = 0$ is not rejected and the estimator b_i (or, correspondingly the factor X_i) is not significant to the process (or to the dependent variable, Y), and can be dropped from the Final Regression equation.

  When $n \geq 30$, the $1 - \alpha$ Confidence Interval for each β_i is calculated using the equation below:

$$P\Big[b_i - Z(\alpha/2) \cdot \sigma(b_i) < \beta_i < b_i + Z(\alpha/2) \cdot \sigma(b_i)\Big] = 1 - \alpha \tag{15.66}$$

  When $n < 30$, the $1 - \alpha$ Confidence Interval for each β_i is calculated using the equation below:

$$P\Big[b_i - t_{n-p}(\alpha/2) \cdot \sigma(b_i) < \beta_i < b_i + t_{n-p}(\alpha/2) \cdot \sigma(b_i)\Big] = 1 - \alpha \tag{15.67}$$

15.6   Variance of Y, Using Matrix Development

In addition to the Variance of Regression $= \sigma^2$, and $V(b) =$ Variance of the estimated Vector, b, of the parameters, β, we need to also obtain the Variance of Y (Y is the dependent variable defined algebraically by equation (15.3) and in Matrix form by equation (15.7)). We proceed as follows:

1. The Vector of the Fitted Values can be stated as: $\hat{Y} = Xb$ (15.68)

2. The Variance of Y, when $\hat{Y} = b_0 + b_1 X = b_1 X_1(=1) + b_2 X_2,$ (15.69)
   is obtained as follows:

   a) Let X_k be a selected value of X. Then, the Predicted Value of Y, $\hat{Y}$, for $X = X_k$ is given by: $\hat{Y}_k = b_0 + b_1 X_k$ (Algebraic Formulation)   (15.70)

   b) Let the Vector X_k be defined as:

   $$X_k^t = \left(1, X_k\right)\left(\text{because } X_1 = 1\right) \qquad (15.71)$$

   Then $\quad \hat{Y}_k = \left(1, X_k\right)\begin{bmatrix} b_0 \\ b_1 \end{bmatrix} = X_k^t b = b^t X_k = (b_0, b_1)\begin{bmatrix} 1 \\ X_k \end{bmatrix} \qquad (15.72)$

   (Matrix Formulation)

   c) Since $\hat{Y}_k$ is a Linear combination of the random variables b_0 and b_1, we have:

   $$V\left(\hat{Y}_k\right) = V\left(b_0 + b_1 X_k\right) = V(b_0) + V\left(X_k b_1\right) + 2X_k Cov\left(b_0, b_1\right) \quad (15.73)$$

   $$= \left(1, X_k\right)\begin{bmatrix} V(b_0) & Cov(b_0, b_1) \\ Cov(b_0, b_1) & V(b_1) \end{bmatrix}\begin{bmatrix} 1 \\ X_k \end{bmatrix} \qquad (15.74)$$

   $$= X_k^t\left[\left(X^t X\right)^{-1}\sigma^2\right]X_k$$

   $$= \left[X_k^t\left(X^t X\right)^{-1}X_k\right]\sigma^2 \qquad (15.75)$$

3. The Variance of Y, when $\hat{Y} = b_1 X + b_2 X_2 + \cdots + b_p X_p.$ (15.76)
   Generalizing the results stated by equations (15.68) and (15.75), we can write:

   a) Prediction of Y at X_k: $\hat{Y}_k = X_k^t b = b^t X_k$ (15.77)

   b) Variance of Y: $V\left(\hat{Y}_k\right) = \left[X_k^t (X^t X)^{-1} X_k\right]\sigma^2$ (15.78)

   Note: Only the X_k vector and the inverse Matrix $(X^t X)^{-1}$ is different in equations (15.75) and (15.78).

15.7   Finding the Inverse of a Matrix

DIGRESSION 2: When we examine the "Summary of Matrix Methodology" (see 15.4 above), we see that the calculation of b (equation (15.52)), and the calculation of $V(b)$ (equation (15.56)), depend on the Inverse of the Matrix $(X^t X) = (X^t X)^{-1}$. We have stated earlier (see equation (15.61) and (15.62) that when $(X^t X)$ is a diagonal matrix, the calculation of the Inverse Matrix $(X^t X)^{-1}$ is very simple. But, how do we calculate the Inverse of, say a 3×3 Matrix, when the Matrix is not diagonal? The 2 methods discussed below can be used to find the Inverse!

■ Finding the Inverse A Matrix

Given a system of Matrix Equations: $AX = B$ (15.79)

If the Inverse of Matrix $A = A^{-1}$ can be found, then: $X = A^{-1}B$, (15.80)

is the solution of the given System of Matrix Equations.

Problem:

Given $A = \begin{matrix} R_1 \\ R_2 \\ R_3 \end{matrix} \begin{bmatrix} a_{11} & a_{12} & a_{13} \\ a_{21} & a_{22} & a_{23} \\ a_{31} & a_{32} & a_{33} \end{bmatrix} = \begin{bmatrix} 3 & -2 & 4 \\ 6 & 4 & 5 \\ 3 & -1 & 6 \end{bmatrix} \begin{matrix} R_1 \\ R_2 \\ R_3 \end{matrix}$ (15.81)

Find $\left(A \right)^{-1}$.

Two Methods Exist for Finding the Inverse of Matrix $A = A^{-1}$

15.7.1 Gauss Elimination Method

1. Form the Augmented Matrix A/I, where I is the Identity Matrix.

   For example if $I = I_{2\times2}$, then $I = \begin{pmatrix} 1 & 0 \\ 0 & 1 \end{pmatrix}$, etc. (15.82)

2. Use Row Operations (*i.e.*, Multiply a Row by a Constant, Interchange 2 Rows, Add k times a Row to another Row) to convert the A/I to I/C. (15.83)

3. Then $C = A^{-1}$ is the Inverse Matrix $A = A^{-1}$, if $AA^{-1} = A^{-1}A = I$ (15.84)

4. To convert the A, in A/I of equation (15.81), into $I = \begin{pmatrix} 1 & 0 & 0 \\ 0 & 1 & 0 \\ 0 & 0 & 1 \end{pmatrix}$, (15.85)

   we must multiply row 1 by $1/a_{11} = 1/3$, so that the term a_{11} is changed to 1.

5. Then we use appropriate multiples of the new row 1 to force a_{21} and a_{31} to become zero.

6. Then, we multiply row 2 by $1/a_{22}$ to make $a_{22} = 1$, and then use appropriate multiples of row 2 to force a_{12} and a_{32} to become zero.

7. Finally we multiply row 3 by $1/a_{33}$ to make $a_{33} = 1$, and then use appropriate multiples of the new row 3 to force a_{13} and a_{23} to become zero.

8. When the A in A/I has been changed to I, $C = A^{-1}$, if

$$A \cdot A^{-1} = A^{-1} \cdot A = I$$ (15.86)

Example
Given Matrix A, defined by equation (15.81), find the Inverse, A^{-1}.

1. $A/I = \begin{matrix} R_1 \\ R_2 \\ R_3 \end{matrix} \begin{pmatrix} 3 & -2 & 4 & | & 1 & 0 & 0 \\ 6 & 4 & 5 & | & 0 & 1 & 0 \\ 3 & -1 & 6 & | & 0 & 0 & 1 \end{pmatrix}$

Multiply R_1 by 1/3 to change the 3 to 1 (*i.e.*, form $\dfrac{1}{3}R_1$).

2. $(A/I)_1 = \begin{array}{c} R_1 \\ R_2 \\ R_3 \end{array} \left(\begin{array}{ccc|ccc} 1 & -2/3 & 4/3 & 1/3 & 0 & 0 \\ 6 & 4 & 5 & 0 & 1 & 0 \\ 3 & -1 & 6 & 0 & 0 & 1 \end{array} \right)$

To change the "6" and "3" of column 1 into "zero",

a) Form: $-6R_1 + R_2$, and:

b) Form: $-3R_1 + R_3$.

The result is:

3. $(A/I)_2 = \begin{array}{c} R_1 \\ R_2 \\ R_3 \end{array} \left(\begin{array}{ccc|ccc} 1 & -2/3 & 4/3 & 1/3 & 0 & 0 \\ 0 & 8 & -3 & -2 & 1 & 0 \\ 0 & 1 & 2 & -1 & 0 & 1 \end{array} \right)$

Now multiply by R_2 1/8 to change the 8 to 1, and obtain:

4. $(A/I)_3 = \begin{array}{c} R_1 \\ R_2 \\ R_3 \end{array} \left(\begin{array}{ccc|ccc} 1 & -2/3 & 4/3 & 1/3 & 0 & 0 \\ 0 & 1 & -3/8 & -2/8 & 1/8 & 0 \\ 0 & 1 & 2 & -1 & 0 & 1 \end{array} \right)$

To change the "$-2/3$" of R_1 and "1" of R_3 of column 2 into "zero", form:

a) $\dfrac{2}{3}R_2 + R_1$ and b) $-R_2 + R_3$, and the result is:

5. $(A/I)_4 = \begin{array}{c} R_1 \\ R_2 \\ R_3 \end{array} \left(\begin{array}{ccc|ccc} 1 & 0 & 26/24 & 4/24 & 2/24 & 0 \\ 0 & 1 & -3/8 & -2/8 & 1/8 & 0 \\ 0 & 0 & 19/8 & -6/8 & -1/8 & 1 \end{array} \right)$

Now we need to multiply R_3 by 8/19 to change the 19/8 to 1!

6. $(A/I)_5 = \begin{array}{c} R_1 \\ R_2 \\ R_3 \end{array} \left(\begin{array}{ccc|ccc} 1 & 0 & 26/24 & 4/24 & 2/24 & 0 \\ 0 & 1 & -3/8 & -2/8 & 1/8 & 0 \\ 0 & 0 & 1 & -6/19 & -1/19 & 8/19 \end{array} \right)$

To change the "26/24" and "$-3/8$" into "zero", (in column 3), form:

a) $-\dfrac{26}{24} R_3 + R_1$, and

b) $+\dfrac{3}{8} R_3 + R_2$, and the result is:

7. $(A/I)_6 = \begin{array}{c} R_1 \\ R_2 \\ R_3 \end{array} \left(\begin{array}{ccc|ccc} 1 & 0 & 0 & 232/456 & 64/456 & -208/456 \\ 0 & 1 & 0 & -56/152 & 16/152 & 24/152 \\ 0 & 0 & 1 & -6/19 & -1/19 & 8/19 \end{array} \right)$

8. Since the "A" in "A/I" has been changed to "I", we conclude that:

$$C = \begin{bmatrix} \dfrac{232}{456} & \dfrac{64}{456} & -\dfrac{208}{456} \\[2mm] -\dfrac{56}{152} & \dfrac{16}{152} & \dfrac{24}{152} \\[2mm] -\dfrac{6}{19} & -\dfrac{1}{19} & \dfrac{8}{19} \end{bmatrix} = \dfrac{1}{456} \begin{bmatrix} 232 & 64 & -208 \\ -56(3) & 16(3) & 24(3) \\ -6(24) & -1(24) & 8(24) \end{bmatrix}$$

$$= \frac{1}{456}\begin{bmatrix} 232 & 64 & -208 \\ -168 & 48 & 72 \\ -144 & -24 & 192 \end{bmatrix} = \frac{8}{456}\begin{bmatrix} 29 & 8 & -26 \\ -21 & 6 & 9 \\ -18 & -3 & 24 \end{bmatrix}$$

is the Inverse of Matrix $A = A^{-1}$ (If $A \cdot A^{-1} = A^{-1} \cdot A = I$) , because:

$$A^{-1} \cdot A = \frac{1}{57}\begin{bmatrix} 29 & 8 & -26 \\ -21 & 6 & 9 \\ -18 & -3 & 24 \end{bmatrix} \cdot \begin{bmatrix} 3 & -2 & 4 \\ 6 & 4 & 5 \\ 3 & -1 & 6 \end{bmatrix}$$

$$= \frac{1}{57}\begin{bmatrix} 29(3) + 8(6) - 26(3) = 57 & 29(-2) + 8(4) - 26(-1) = 0 & 29(4) + 8(5) - 26(6) = 0 \\ -21(3) + 6(6) + 9(3) = 0 & -21(-2) + 6(4) + 9(-1) = 57 & -21(4) + 6(5) + 9(6) = 0 \\ -18(3) - 3(6) + 24(3) = 0 & -18(-2) - 3(4) + 24(-1) = 0 & -18(4) - 3(5) + 24(6) = 57 \end{bmatrix}$$

$$= \frac{1}{57}\begin{bmatrix} 57 & 0 & 0 \\ 0 & 57 & 0 \\ 0 & 0 & 57 \end{bmatrix} = \begin{pmatrix} 1 & 0 & 0 \\ 0 & 1 & 0 \\ 0 & 0 & 1 \end{pmatrix}$$

■ ■ ■

15.7.2 Adjoint Matrix Method

1. Given a Matrix A, construct the COFACTOR Matrix $A = \text{Cof}(A)$, where

$$\text{Cof}(A) = \begin{bmatrix} A_{11} & A_{12} & A_{13} \\ A_{21} & A_{22} & A_{23} \\ A_{31} & A_{32} & A_{33} \end{bmatrix}$$

and the elements of the COFACTOR Matrix A_{ij} are obtained from the elements of Matrix A, from the Formula:

$$A_{ij} = (-1)^{i+j} \times (\text{Minor of element } a_{ij} \text{ in Matrix } A) \tag{15.87}$$

and

Minor of element a_{ij} of Matrix A = Determinant of the sub matrix which results when Row i and column j are deleted in Matrix A. (15.88)

2. Obtain the ADJOINT Matrix $A = \text{Adj}(A) = [\text{Cof}(A)]^t$, (15.89)

where $[\text{Cof}(A)]^t$ is the **TRANSPOSED** of the COFACTOR Matrix $= [\text{Cof}(A)]^t$

(TRANSPOSED Matrix $A = A^t$ is a Matrix derived from a given Matrix A by interchanging the Rows and Columns of Matrix A)

3. Obtain the INVERSE Matrix $A = A^{-1}$, by using the Formula:

$$A^{-1} = \frac{1}{\text{Det}(A)}\text{Adj}(A) \tag{15.90}$$

where Det(A) = Determinant of Matrix A, obtained form Matrix A and Matrix Cof(A) and the expansion:

$$\text{Det}(A) = a_{11}A_{11} + a_{12}A_{12} + a_{13}A_{13} \text{ (Expansion about Row 1)} \qquad (15.91)$$

$$\text{or: Det}(A) = a_{13}A_{13} + a_{23}A_{23} + a_{33}A_{33} \text{ (Expansion about Column 3)} \qquad (15.92)$$

Note: The determinant is a Unique value which can be obtained by using an expansion about any Row or Column, as shown above.

4. **Example:** Find the Inverse of Matrix $A = A^{-1}$, for the Matrix A given by (15.81), **using the ADJOINT Matrix Method**.

$$A_{11} = (-1)^{1+1} \text{ minor of } a_{11} \text{ in } A = (-1)^2 \cdot \det\begin{pmatrix} 4 & 5 \\ -1 & 6 \end{pmatrix}$$

$$= (+1)[24 - (-5)] = 29$$

$$A_{12} = (-1)^{1+2} \text{ minor of } a_{12} \text{ in } A = (-1)^3 \cdot \det\begin{pmatrix} 6 & 5 \\ 3 & 6 \end{pmatrix}$$

$$= (-1)[36 - 15] = -21$$

$$A_{13} = (-1)^{1+3} \text{ minor of } a_{13} \text{ in } A = (-1)^4 \cdot \det\begin{pmatrix} 6 & 4 \\ 3 & -1 \end{pmatrix}$$

$$= (+1)[-6 - 12] = -18$$

In a similar manner, we find:

$$A_{21} = +8; \quad A_{22} = 6; \quad A_{23} = -3$$
$$A_{31} = -26; \quad A_{32} = +9; \quad A_{33} = 24$$

Therefore

$$\text{Cof}(A) = \begin{bmatrix} 29 & -21 & -18 \\ 8 & 6 & -3 \\ -26 & +9 & 24 \end{bmatrix};$$

Then $\text{Adj}(A) = [\text{Cof}(A)]^t = \begin{bmatrix} 29 & 8 & -26 \\ -21 & 6 & 9 \\ -18 & -3 & 24 \end{bmatrix}$

and

Det(A) = 3(29) − 2(−21) + 4(−18) = 57 (Expansion about Row 1)
Then, the Inverse of Matrix A is given by Equation (15.90), and:

$$A^{-1} = \frac{1}{57}\begin{bmatrix} 29 & 8 & -26 \\ -21 & 6 & 9 \\ -18 & -3 & 24 \end{bmatrix},$$

and we see that the 2 methods produce the same Inverse Matrix. This is as it should be, because the Inverse is unique, when it exists.

15.8 Procedure for Solving Multivariate (and Bivariate) Problems

After reviewing the theory discussed previously in this chapter, we can summarize it as the following procedure:

■ Estimate the Model

1. Given a Multivariate (or Bivariate) data set and the multivariate function, $y = b_i X_i(=1) + b_2 X_2 + b_3 X_3 + \cdots + b_p X_p$, to fit to this data set: Identify the matrix X and the vectors Y, b, and Z (which define the model of observations: $Y = Xb + Z$).

2. From matrix X calculate X^t (*i.e.*, the transposed matrix X), and then $X^t X$ and $X^t Y$.

3. Calculate the Inverse of matrix $X^t X = (X^t X)^{-1}$
   a) If $X^t X$ is a Diagonal matrix, the inverse $(X^t X)^{-1}$ is easy to find (as previously explained).
   b) If $X^t X$ is not a Diagonal matrix, the inverse $(X^t X)^{-1}$ is found by using either the Gauss Elimination Method or the Adjoint Matrix Method.

4. Calculate: $b = (X^t X)^{-1} \times (X^t Y) = \begin{bmatrix} b_1 \\ b_2 \\ b_3 \\ \cdots \\ b_p \end{bmatrix}$ (15.93)

5. Calculate:
   a) $Y^t Y$ (15.94)
   b) $b^t X^t Y$ (15.95)
   c) $Q^* = Y^t Y - b^t X^t Y$ (15.96)
   d) $SSa = \dfrac{\left(\sum\limits_{i=1}^{n} y_i \right)^2}{n}$ (15.97)

6. Calculate: $\sigma^2 = \dfrac{Q^*}{n - p}$ (15.98)

7. Calculate:

$$V(b) = (X^t X)^{-1} \sigma^2 = \begin{bmatrix} V(b_1) & Cov(b_1, b_2) & \ldots Cov(b_1, b_p) \\ Cov(b_1, b_2) & V(b_2) & \ldots Cov(b_2, b_p) \\ \ldots\ldots\ldots\ldots & \ldots\ldots\ldots\ldots & \ldots\ldots\ldots\ldots \\ Cov(b_1, b_p) & Cov(b_2, b_p) & \ldots V(b_p) \end{bmatrix}$$ (15.99)

Note that the variances of $b_1, b_2, \ldots, b_p$, are along the main diagonal of the above matrix and, from them, we can find $\sigma(b_1), \sigma(b_2), \ldots, \sigma(b_p)$ easily, since $\sigma(b_i) = \sqrt{V(b_i)}$.

The terms off the main diagonal are covariance terms and they indicate the strength of the relationship that may exist between the corresponding X_i and X_j variables appearing in the multivariate function. If some of these relationships are very strong, the problem of COLLINEARITY may arise, and we address this problem briefly in Section 15.10.

At this point we have numerical values for: $b_1, b_2, \ldots, b_p$, the standard deviations: $\sigma(b_1), \sigma(b_2), \ldots, \sigma(b_p)$, and the Sum of Squares: $\text{TSS} = Y^tY, \text{RSS} = b^tX^tY$,

$$SSa = \frac{\sum\limits_{i=1}^{n} yi^2}{n}, \text{ and ESS} = Q^* = Y^tY - b^tX^tY.$$

■ Test the Estimated Model For Significance

The model testing consists of 3 major parts, namely:

1. Testing for the significance of the entire regression equation, including the constant term.
2. Testing for the significance of the entire regression equation excluding the constant term.
3. Testing for the significance of each Factor separately.

- To test part (1), we construct an ANOVA table for Regression with SSa, as shown previously, and test the hypothesis: H_0: $\beta_1 = \beta_2 = \cdots = \beta_p = 0$ vs H_1: $\beta_1, \beta_2, \ldots, \beta_p$ are not all equal to zero, by forming:

$$F_T^* = \frac{\dfrac{b^tX^tY}{p}}{\dfrac{Q^*}{n-p}} \tag{15.100}$$

and comparing it against $F_{n-p}^{p}(\alpha)$.

    If $F_T^* > F_{n-p}^{p}(\alpha)$, the entire regression, including the constant, is significant.

- To test part (2), we construct the ANOVA table for Regression without SSa, as shown previously, and test the hypothesis: H_0: $\beta_2 = \beta_3 = \cdots = \beta_p = 0$ vs H_1: $\beta_2, \beta_3, \ldots, \beta_p$, are not all equal to zero, by forming:

$$F_{T-1}^* = \frac{\dfrac{b^tX^ty - \left(\sum\limits_{i=1}^{n} Y_i\right)^2 \Big/ n}{p-1}}{Q^* \Big/ n-p} \tag{15.101}$$

and comparing it against $F_{n-p}^{p-1}(\alpha)$.

    If $F_{T-1}^* > F_{n-p}^{n-1}(\alpha)$, the entire regression, excluding the constant, is significant.

- To test for the significance of each factor separately, we proceed as follows:

a) **If X^tX is a Diagonal Matrix**

The Total RSS can be divided into RSS for each factor separately, by simply multiplying b^t by X^tY and not adding the components together. Then the ANOVA table can also be used to test the significance of each variable (Factor) X_i separately (i.e., we can use the F-distribution for this test by forming:

$$F_i^* = \frac{\dfrac{RSS_i}{1}}{\dfrac{Q^*}{n-p}} \tag{15.102}$$

and comparing to $F_{n-p}^{1}(\alpha)$.

If $F_i^* > F_{n-p}^1(\alpha)$, the variable (Factor) X_i is significant, and should remain in the regression equation.

If $F_i^* < F_{n-p}^1(\alpha)$, the variable factor X_i is not significant (to Y) and should be dropped from the regression equation.

b) **If X^tX is not a diagonal matrix**

i) Use b_i and $\sigma(b_i)$, derived above, and either Z (if $n \geq 30$) or t_{n-p} (if $n < 30$) to:

A) Test the Hypothesis: H_0: $\beta_i = 0$ vs H_1: $\beta_i \neq 0$, by calculating

$$Z^* = \frac{b_i}{\sigma(b_i)},$$ and comparing it to $Z_{\alpha/2}$ or by calculating $t^* = \frac{b_i}{\sigma(b_i)}$ and

comparing it to $t_{n-p(\alpha/2)}$

If the hypothesis is rejected, the variable (Factor) X_i is significant and should remain in the regression equation. If the hypothesis is not rejected, the variable (Factor) X_i is not significant (to the calculation of Y) and should be dropped from the regression equation.

and

B) Construct the Confidence Intervals (C.I.):

$$P[b_i - Z_{\alpha/2}^* \sigma(b_i) \leq \beta_i \leq b_i + Z_{\alpha/2}^* \sigma(b_i)] = 1 - \alpha \qquad (15.103)$$

(if $n \geq 30$)

$$\text{or } P[b_i - t_{n-p, \alpha/2}^* \sigma(b_i) \leq \beta_i \leq b_i + t_{n-p, \alpha/2}^* \sigma(b_i)] = 1 - \alpha \qquad (15.104)$$

(if $n \geq 30$)

If the value $\beta_i = 0$ is outside this C.I., the variable (Factor) X_i is significant and should remain in the regression equation.

ii) Transform the given variables $X_2, X_3, \ldots, X_p$, by using the transformation:

$$Z_i = \frac{X_i - E(X_i)}{\sigma(X_i)}, \qquad (15.105)$$

to construct matrices Z and Z^t, to see if the matrix Z^tZ is a diagonal matrix. If Z^tZ is a diagonal matrix, proceed as in (A) above.

■ Use the Model For Prediction or Forecasting

From the estimated regression model we now construct the Final Regression equation which includes only the variables (Factors) which were found to be significant (to the calculation of the value of the dependent variable Y).

Then, for any combination of values of the significant independent variables (X_i), use the Final Regression equation to predict/forecast future values of Y.

15.9 Examples using the Procedure

The procedure summarized above will now be used to solve the following three problems:

• In example 1, we show how the matrix methodology is applied to the Bivariate problem and verify that the Algebraic and Matrix Solutions to the problem are identical. We also show how $V(a)$ and $V(b)$ are obtained, which had been postulated previously in the Algebraic solution.

• In example 2, the resulting X^tX is not a diagonal matrix, and the procedure is used to: Estimate, test, and use the regression equation. Because X^tX is not a diagonal matrix, the inverse $(X^tX)^{-1}$ is obtained using the Adjoint matrix method and, when Q^* is calculated, it becomes clear why simple matrix multiplication cannot divide the total RSS into component RSS values. The testing of the significance of the individual factors is accomplished by using the t_{n-p} distribution to test H_0: $\beta_i = 0$ vs H_1: $\beta_i \neq 0$.

- In example 3, example 2 is solved again but this time we first use the transformation: $Z_i = \dfrac{X_i - E(X_i)}{\sigma(X_i)}$ to obtain matrices Z and Z^t, and then show that Z^tZ is a diagonal matrix. Because of this fact the total RSS can be easily (by simple matrix multiplication) divided into component RSS, and the F-distribution is used to test for the significance of each variable (Factor) separately.

Note: The final regression equation for examples 2 and 3 are the same because the 2 methods are equivalent.

Example 1

Apply the Matrix Methodology to the Simple linear Regression Model

Given data:

X	Y
x_1	y_1
x_2	y_2
...	...
x_n	y_n
$\sum x_i$	$\sum y_i$

The True Model is given by:

$$y = \alpha + \beta x, \tag{15.106}$$

while the **Model of Observations** is given by:

$$\hat{y}_1 = a + bx_i + z_i \tag{15.107}$$

Then, applying the **Matrix Methodology**, we need to define:

$$Y = \begin{bmatrix} y_1 \\ y_2 \\ y_3 \\ ... \\ y_n \end{bmatrix} \qquad \beta = \begin{bmatrix} \alpha \\ \beta \end{bmatrix} \qquad b = \begin{bmatrix} a \\ b \end{bmatrix} \qquad X = \begin{bmatrix} 1 & x_1 \\ 1 & x_2 \\ 1 & x_3 \\ ... & ... \\ 1 & x_n \end{bmatrix}$$

The Y, b, and X Vectors and Matrices, are obtained when the given Bivariate data is substituted, one ordered pair at the time, to the model of Observations equation and generate the following set of n simultaneous equations:

$$\left. \begin{array}{l} y_1 = a + bx_1 + z_1 \\ y_2 = a + bx_2 + z_2 \\ \text{............................} \\ y_n = a + bx_n + z_n \end{array} \right\}, \tag{15.108}$$

which, re-written in Matrix form become:

$$\begin{bmatrix} y_1 \\ y_2 \\ ... \\ y_n \end{bmatrix} = \begin{bmatrix} 1 & x_1 \\ 1 & x_2 \\ ... & ... \\ 1 & x_n \end{bmatrix} \begin{bmatrix} a \\ b \end{bmatrix} + \begin{bmatrix} z_1 \\ z_2 \\ ... \\ z_n \end{bmatrix} \tag{15.109}$$

From it we identify the Matrices: Y, X, b, and Z, and the Model of Observations is expressed in Matrix form as:

$$Y = Xb + Z \qquad (15.110)$$

Then the Normal Equations for the Linear Model are (to obtain the Normal Equations, we need to first obtain X^tX and X^tY):

$$X^tXb = X^tY \qquad (15.111)$$

since

$$X_{(n \times 2)} = \begin{bmatrix} 1 & x_1 \\ 1 & x_2 \\ 1 & x_3 \\ \cdots & \cdots \\ 1 & x_n \end{bmatrix}, \quad \text{and} \quad \underset{(2 \times n)}{X^t} = \begin{bmatrix} 1 & 1 & 1 & \cdots & 1 \\ x_1 & x_2 & x_3 & \cdots & x_n \end{bmatrix}, \qquad (15.112)$$

then

$$\underset{(2 \times 2)}{X^t}X = \begin{bmatrix} n & \sum\limits_{i=1}^{n} x_i \\ \sum\limits_{i=1}^{n} x_i & \sum\limits_{i=1}^{n} x_i^2 \end{bmatrix}, \qquad (15.113)$$

and

$$X^tY = \begin{bmatrix} 1 & 1 & 1 & \cdots & 1 \\ x_1 & x_2 & x_3 & \cdots & x_n \end{bmatrix} \begin{bmatrix} y_1 \\ y_2 \\ \cdots \\ y_n \end{bmatrix} = \begin{bmatrix} \sum\limits_{i=1}^{n} y_i \\ \sum\limits_{i=1}^{n} x_i y_i \end{bmatrix} \qquad (15.114)$$

Then the Normal Equations become

$$\begin{bmatrix} n & \sum\limits_{i=1}^{n} x_i \\ \sum\limits_{i=1}^{n} x_i & \sum\limits_{i=1}^{n} x_i^2 \end{bmatrix} \begin{bmatrix} a \\ b \end{bmatrix} = \begin{bmatrix} \sum\limits_{i=1}^{n} y_i \\ \sum\limits_{i=1}^{n} x_i y_i \end{bmatrix}, \qquad (15.115)$$

and their solution is:

$$\begin{bmatrix} a \\ b \end{bmatrix} = \begin{bmatrix} n & \sum\limits_{i=1}^{n} x_i \\ \sum\limits_{i=1}^{n} x_i & \sum\limits_{i=1}^{n} x_i^2 \end{bmatrix}^{-1} \begin{bmatrix} \sum\limits_{i=1}^{n} y_i \\ \sum\limits_{i=1}^{n} x_i y_i \end{bmatrix} \qquad (15.116)$$

$$= \frac{1}{n \sum\limits_{i=1}^{n} x_i^2 - \left(\sum\limits_{i=1}^{n} x_i \right)^2} \begin{bmatrix} \sum\limits_{i=1}^{n} x_i^2 & -\sum\limits_{i=1}^{n} x_i \\ -\sum\limits_{i=1}^{n} x_i & n \end{bmatrix} \begin{bmatrix} \sum\limits_{i=1}^{n} y_i \\ \sum\limits_{i=1}^{n} x_i y_i \end{bmatrix} \qquad (15.117)$$

Note: The denominator in the equation (15.117) can be shown to be equal to:

$n \sum_{i=1}^{n} \left(x_i - \overline{x} \right)^2$, and we can write:

$$n \sum_{i=1}^{n} x_i^2 - \left(\sum_{i=1}^{n} x_i \right)^2 = n \sum_{i=1}^{n} \left(x_i - \overline{x} \right)^2 \qquad (15.118)$$

The Inverse Matrix is obtained by using either the Gauss Elimination or the Adjoint Matrix Methods.

■ ■ ■

Solving for *a* and *b* we obtain:

$$a = \frac{\left(\sum_{i=1}^{n} y_i \right) \left(\sum_{i=1}^{n} x_i^2 \right) - \left(\sum_{i=1}^{n} x_i \right) \left(\sum_{i=1}^{n} x_i y_i \right)}{n \sum_{i=1}^{n} x_i^2 - \left(\sum_{i=1}^{n} x_i \right)^2}$$

$$= \frac{\left(\sum_{i=1}^{n} y_i \right) \left(\sum_{i=1}^{n} x_i^2 \right) - \left(\sum_{i=1}^{n} x_i \right) \left(\sum_{i=1}^{n} x_i y_i \right)}{n \sum_{i=1}^{n} \left(x_i - \overline{x} \right)^2} \qquad (15.119)$$

and

$$b = \frac{n \sum_{i=1}^{n} x_i y_i - \left(\sum_{i=1}^{n} x_i \right) \left(\sum_{i=1}^{n} y_i \right)}{n \sum_{i=1}^{n} x_i^2 - \left(\sum_{i=1}^{n} x_i \right)^2} = \frac{n \sum_{i=1}^{n} x_i y_i - \left(\sum_{i=1}^{n} x_i \right) \left(\sum_{i=1}^{n} y_i \right)}{n \sum_{i=1}^{n} \left(x_i - \overline{x} \right)^2}, \qquad (15.120)$$

Also

$$V(a) = \frac{1}{n} \left[\frac{\sum_{i=1}^{n} x_i^2}{\sum_{i=1}^{n} \left(x_i - \overline{x} \right)^2} \right] \sigma^2 \qquad (15.121)$$

$$\left(V(a) = \frac{1}{n} \sigma^2 \text{ if } \overline{x} = 0 \right)$$

$$V(b) = \frac{1}{\sum_{i=1}^{n} \left(x_i - \overline{x} \right)^2} \sigma^2 \qquad (15.122)$$

and

$$Cov(a, b) = \left[-\frac{\sum_{i=1}^{n} x_i}{n \sum_{i=1}^{n} x_i^2 - \left(\sum_{i=1}^{n} x_i \right)^2} \right] \sigma^2 = \left[-\frac{n \sum_{i=1}^{n} x_i}{n \sum_{i=1}^{n} \left(x_i - \overline{x} \right)^2} \right] \sigma^2 \qquad (15.123)$$

Finally, the expressions for $Q*$ and σ^2 become:

$$\underset{\substack{(\text{ESS} \\ n-2df)}}{Q*} = Y'Y - b'X'Y = \underset{\substack{(\text{TSS} \\ n\,df)}}{\sum_{i=1}^{n} y_i^2} - \underset{(\text{RSS with 2df})}{(a\ b)\begin{bmatrix} \sum_{i=1}^{n} y^i \\ \sum_{i=1}^{n} x_i y_i \end{bmatrix}} \tag{15.124}$$

or

$$\text{ESS} = \text{TSS} - \text{RSS}, \tag{15.125}$$

where: ESS has $n - 2$ Degrees of Freedom
        TSS has n Degrees of Freedom
        RSS has 2 Degrees of Freedom,
and

$$\sigma^2 = \frac{Q*}{n - 2} \tag{15.126}$$

Note: $V(a)$ and $V(b)$ are identical to the formulas we used in Bivariate analysis. The procedure above shows how these variances are derived, with a minimal effort, when matrix methods are used.

Example 2
Suppose the following data represents the measurement of the yield of a process due to 2 factors X_2 (time) and X_3 (temperature).

Data

$X_2 = Time$	$X_3 = Temperature$	$Y = Yield$
1 Hour	240	43
5 Hour	240	53
1 Hour	280	59
5 Hour	280	73

Problem:

1. Estimate the equation $\hat{Y} = b_1 X_1(=1) + b_2 X_2 + b_3 X_3$.
2. Perform ANOVA for this problem. Are b_1, b_2, and b_3 jointly significant?
3. Are b_2 and b_3 jointly significant at $\alpha = 0.05$?
4. Is b_2 significant at $\alpha = 0.05$?
5. Is b_3 significant at $\alpha = 0.05$?
6. Construct 95% C.I. on β_2 and β_3.

Solutions The X, X', and Y matrices for this problem are, respectively (assuming the presence of a constant term in the equation):

$$\underset{4\times3}{X} = \begin{bmatrix} 1 & 1 & 240 \\ 1 & 5 & 240 \\ 1 & 1 & 280 \\ 1 & 5 & 280 \end{bmatrix}; \quad \underset{3\times4}{X'} = \begin{bmatrix} 1 & 1 & 1 & 1 \\ 1 & 5 & 1 & 5 \\ 240 & 240 & 280 & 280 \end{bmatrix};$$

$$\underset{3\times3}{X'X} = \begin{bmatrix} 4 & 12 & 1040 \\ 12 & 52 & 3120 \\ 1040 & 3120 & 272{,}000 \end{bmatrix}; \quad Y = \begin{bmatrix} 43 \\ 53 \\ 59 \\ 73 \end{bmatrix}$$

Since (X^tX) is not a diagonal matrix, we will not be able to use the F distribution (*i.e.*, the ANOVA Table) to "break up" the Total Regression Sum of Squares into "component" sum of squares and test for the significance of each factor separately. *But*, we will use the matrix approach to test for the "significance of the over-all equation" and to also derive the estimates for b_1, b_2, b_3, and $\sigma(b_1)$, $\sigma(b_2)$, and $\sigma(b_3)$ which we will need for the t-tests (*i.e.*, to test the hypothesis H_0: $\beta_2 = 0$ vs H_1: $\beta_2 \neq 0$, and H_0: $\beta_3 = 0$ vs H_1: $\beta_3 \neq 0$) and the construction of the Confidence Intervals for β_2 and β_3.

Using the "Adjoint Matrix Method", we find the inverse of matrix X^tX to be:

$$(X^tX)^{-1} = \frac{1}{\text{Det}(X^tX)} \text{Adj}(A) = \frac{1}{102,400} \begin{bmatrix} 4,409,600 & -19,200 & -16,640 \\ -19,200 & 6,400 & 0 \\ -16,640 & 0 & 64 \end{bmatrix},$$

and $X^tY = \begin{bmatrix} 228 \\ 732 \\ 60,000 \end{bmatrix}$

Then

$$b = \begin{bmatrix} b_1 \\ b_2 \\ b_3 \end{bmatrix} = (X^tX)^{-1}X^tY = \begin{bmatrix} -69 \\ 3 \\ 0.45 \end{bmatrix} \text{ and: } \hat{Y} = b_1 X_1(\, = 1) + b_2 X_2 + b_3 X_3, \text{ or:}$$
$$\hat{Y} = -69 + 3X_2 + 0.45X_3$$

Also

$$Q^* = Y^tY - b^tX^tY = (43 \quad 53 \quad 59 \quad 73) \begin{bmatrix} 43 \\ 53 \\ 59 \\ 73 \end{bmatrix} - (-69 \quad 3 \quad 0.45) \begin{bmatrix} 228 \\ 732 \\ 60,000 \end{bmatrix}$$

$$Q^* = 13,468 - (-15,732 + 2,196 + 27,000)$$

Note: Because this value of b^tX^tY is a negative number, the "break-up" of RSS (RSS = b^tX^tY) cannot be accomplished this way! The total RSS is correct! But the components are not correct! This is the case whenever X^tX is not a Diagonal Matrix.

or $$Q^* = 13,468 - 13,464 = 4,$$

and $$\sigma^2 = \frac{Q^*}{n-p} = \frac{4}{4-3} = \frac{4}{1} = 4$$

Finally

$$V(b) = (X^tX)^{-1}\sigma^2 = \frac{4}{102,400} \begin{bmatrix} 4,409,600^* & -19,200 & -16,640 \\ -19,200 & 6,400^{**} & 0 \\ -16,640 & 0 & 64^{***} \end{bmatrix}$$

$$= \begin{bmatrix} 172.25 & -0.75 & -0.65 \\ -0.75 & 0.25 & 0 \\ -0.65 & 0 & 0.0025 \end{bmatrix},$$

and

$$*V(b_1) = \frac{4}{102,400}(4,409,600) = 172.25 \rightarrow \sigma(b_1) = 13.1244$$

$$**V(b_2) = \frac{4}{102,400}(6,400) = 0.25 \rightarrow \sigma(b_2) = 0.5$$

$$***V(b_3) = \frac{4}{102,400}(64) = 0.0025 \rightarrow \sigma(b_3) = 0.05$$

1. ANOVA with the constant term

Source of Variation	DF	Sum of Squares (SS)	$MS = \dfrac{SS}{DF}$	E(MS)
Regression (without Constant)	$p = 3$	$b^t X^t Y = 13,464$	$13,464/3 = 4,488$	
Error	$n - p = 4 - 3 = 1$	$Q^* = 4$	$4/1 = 4$	σ^2
Total	$n = 4$	$Y^t Y = 13,468$	$13,468/4 = 3,367$	

2. ANOVA without the constant term

Source of Variation	DF	Sum of Squares (SS)	$MS = \dfrac{SS}{DF}$	E(MS)
Regression (without Constant)	$p - 1 = 2$	$b^t X^t Y - \dfrac{\left(\sum\limits_{i=1}^{n} \Sigma y_i\right)^2}{n}$ $= 13,464 - 12,996 = 468$	$468/2 = 234$	
Error	$n - p = 4 - 3 = 1$	$Q^* = 4$	$4/1 = 4$	σ^2
Total	$n - 1 = 3$	$Y^t Y - \dfrac{\left(\sum\limits_{i=1}^{n} \Sigma y_i\right)^2}{n} = 472$	$472/3 = 157.3$	

$$\text{where } SSa = \frac{\left(\sum\limits_{i=1}^{n} y_i\right)^2}{n} = \frac{(43 + 53 + 59 + 73)^2}{4} = \frac{(228)^2}{4} = \frac{51,984}{4} = 12,996$$

Then

From the "ANOVA with the constant term" we can test the significance of the overall regression" by testing the Hypothesis:

$H_0: \beta_1 = \beta_2 = \beta_3 = 0$ vs H_1: not all β's are equal to zero

by forming: $F_T^* = \dfrac{\dfrac{13,464}{3}}{\dfrac{4}{1}} = \dfrac{4.488}{4} = 1,122$ & comparing it against

$$F_1^3(\alpha = 0.05) = 215.7$$

Since $F_T^* > F_1^3(\alpha = 0.05)$, we reject H_0 and conclude that the "overall regression is significant". From the "ANOVA without the constant" we can test the "significance of factors X_2 and X_3 jointly" by testing the hypothesis:

$H_0: \beta_2 = \beta_3 = 0$ vs $H_1: \beta_1$ and β_3 are not both equal to zero.

This is accomplished by calculating:

$$F^*_{T-1} = \frac{\dfrac{468}{2}}{\dfrac{4}{1}} = \frac{234}{4} = 58.5 \text{ and comparing it against } F^2_1(\alpha = 0.05) = 199.5$$

Since $F^*_{T-1} < F^2_1(\alpha = 0.05)$, we do not reject H_0 and conclude that the two factors (time and temperature) are not significant jointly!

To test for the significance of each factor separately, we test the hypotheses:

$$\left.\begin{array}{l} H_0: \beta_1 = 0 \text{ vs } H_1: \beta_1 \neq 0 \\ H_0: \beta_2 = 0 \text{ vs } H_1: \beta_2 \neq 0 \\ \text{and } H_0: \beta_3 = 0 \text{ vs } H_1: \beta_3 \neq 0 \end{array}\right\} \text{ using the } t\text{-rest, since } n = 4 < 30$$

Since the values of the corresponding test statistics are:

$$t^*_1 = \frac{b_1}{\sigma(b_1)} = -\frac{69}{13.124} = -5.2574,$$

$$t^*_2 = \frac{b_2}{\sigma(b_2)} = -\frac{3}{0.5} = 6, \text{ and}$$

$$t^*_3 = \frac{b_3}{\sigma(b_3)} = -\frac{0.45}{0.05} = 9$$

we compare all three against $t_{n-p(\alpha/2)} = t_{4-3(0.05/2)} = t_1(0.025) = 12.706$.

Since: $t^*_1 = -5.2574 > -12.706$ and $t^*_2 = 6 < 12.706$ and $t^*_3 = 9 < 12.706$, all three H_0 hypotheses are not rejected, and we conclude that each factor X_1, X_2, X_3, is not individually significant to the process!

CONFIDENCE INTERVALS for β_1, β_2 and β_3 are constructed from the formula:

$$P\left\{(b_i - t_{n-p}(\alpha/2)\sigma(b_i) < \beta_i < b_i + t_{n-p}(\alpha/2)\sigma(b_i)\right\} = 1 = \alpha$$

Then
$$P\left\{(b_1 - t_{1(0.025)}\sigma(b_1) < \beta_1 < b_1 + t_{1(0.025)}\sigma(b_1)\right\} = 0.95$$

$$P\left\{(-69 - 12.706(13.124) \leq \beta_1 \leq -69 + 12.706(13.124)\right\} = 0.95$$

$$P\left\{(-235.7535 \leq \beta_1 \leq 97.7535\right\} = 0.95$$

Since $\beta_1 = 0$ falls inside this interval, the Hypothesis $H_0: \beta_1 = 0$ is not rejected!

$$P\left\{(b_2 - t_{1(0.025)}\sigma(b_2) < \beta_2 < b_2 + t_{1(0.025)}\sigma(b_2)\right\} = 0.95$$

$$P\left\{(3 - 12.706(0.5) \leq \beta_2 \leq 3 + 12.706(0.5)\right\} = 0.95$$

$$P\left\{(3 - 6.353 < \beta_2 \leq 3 + 6.353\right\} = 0.95$$

$$P\left\{-3.353 \leq \beta_2 \leq 9.353\right\} = 0.95$$

Since $\beta_2 = 0$ falls inside this interval, the Hypothesis H_0: $\beta_2 = 0$ is not rejected!

$$P\left\{(b_3 - t_{1(0.025)}\sigma(b_3) < \beta_3 < b_3 + t_{1(0.025)}\sigma(b_3)\right\} = 0.95$$

$$P\left\{(0.45 - 12.706(0.05) \le \beta_3 \le 0.45 + 12.706(0.05)\right\} = 0.95$$

$$P\left\{(0.45 - 0.6353 \le \beta_3 \le 0.45 + 0.6353\right\} = 0.95$$

$$P\left\{-0.1853 \le \beta_3 \le 1.0853\right\} = 0.95$$

Since $\beta_3 = 0$ falls inside this interval, the Hypothesis H_0: $\beta_3 = 0$ is not rejected!

Note: Since the overall regression is significant but each of the individual factors is not significant, it may be the interaction among the factors which is responsible for the significance of the overall regression.

■ ■ ■

Example 3

But we can also solve the same problem by first "transforming the data" to force the (X^tX) matrix to become diagonal. This can be accomplished in this problem by introducing the linear transformations:

$$Z_2 = \frac{X_2 - E(X_2)}{\sigma(X_2)} = \frac{Time - 3}{2} \quad \text{and} \quad Z_3 = \frac{X_3 - E(X_3)}{\sigma(X_3)} = \frac{Temparature - 260}{20}$$

which "standardize" each variable and make the time values of 1 and 5 equal to -1 and $+1$ respectively and the temperature values of 240 and 280 equal to -1 and $+1$ respectively. Then the X, X^t, and X^t, X matrices become respectively: Z, Z^t, and Z^t, Z, where:

$$\underset{(4\times3)}{Z} = \begin{bmatrix} 1 & -1 & 1 \\ 1 & 1 & -1 \\ 1 & -1 & 1 \\ 1 & 1 & 1 \end{bmatrix}; \quad \underset{(3\times4)}{Z^t} = \begin{bmatrix} 1 & 1 & 1 & 1 \\ -1 & 1 & -1 & 1 \\ -1 & -1 & 1 & 1 \end{bmatrix}; \quad \underset{(3\times3)}{Z^t Z} = \begin{bmatrix} 4 & 0 & 0 \\ 0 & 4 & 0 \\ 0 & 0 & 4 \end{bmatrix}$$

Since matrix (Z^tZ) is now diagonal, the problem of separating RSS $= b^tZ^tY$ into components is easy, as is shown below.

The inverse of matrix (Z^tZ) is, by inspection:

$$(Z^tZ)^{-1} = \begin{pmatrix} 1/4 & 0 & 0 \\ 0 & 1/4 & 0 \\ 0 & 0 & 1/4 \end{pmatrix}, \quad \text{and} \quad (Z^tY) = \begin{pmatrix} 228 \\ 24 \\ 36 \end{pmatrix}$$

Then:

$$b = (Z^tZ)(Z^tY) = \begin{pmatrix} b_1 \\ b_2 \\ b_3 \end{pmatrix} = \begin{pmatrix} 1/4 & 0 & 0 \\ 0 & 1/4 & 0 \\ 0 & 0 & 1/4 \end{pmatrix}\begin{pmatrix} 228 \\ 24 \\ 36 \end{pmatrix} = \begin{pmatrix} 57 \\ 6 \\ 9 \end{pmatrix},$$

and $\qquad b^t = (57 \quad 6 \quad 9)$,

and the estimated model is: $\hat{y} = b_1 Z_1(= 1) + b_2 Z_2 + b_3 Z_3 = 57 + 6Z_2 + 9Z_3$***
(in terms of the new variables introduced by the linear transformations).
***This new estimated equation can be shown to be identical to the equation derived in
example 15.2. by bringing back the original variables, as shown below:

$$\hat{y} = 57 + 6Z_2 + 3Z_3,$$

or $\hat{y} = 57 + 6\left[\dfrac{X_2 - 3}{2}\right] + 9\left[\dfrac{X_3 - 260}{20}\right] = 57 + 3(X_2 - 3) + 0.45(X_3 - 260)$

$$= (57 - 9 - 117) + 3X_2 + 0.45X_3 = -69 + 3X_2 + 0.45X_3,$$

which is the result obtained in example 15.2.

$$Q^* = \text{ERROR SUM OF SQUARES} = Y'Y - b'Z'Y$$

$$Q^* = Y'Y - b'Z'Y = (43 \quad 53 \quad 59 \quad 73)\begin{pmatrix} 43 \\ 53 \\ 59 \\ 73 \end{pmatrix} - (57 \quad 6 \quad 9)\begin{pmatrix} 228 \\ 24 \\ 36 \end{pmatrix}$$

$$Q^* = \underbrace{13{,}468}_{\text{total sum of squares}} - \left(\underbrace{\underbrace{12{,}996}_{\text{sum of squares due to constant }(b_1)} + \underbrace{144}_{\text{sum of squares due to }(b_2)} + \underbrace{324}_{\text{sum of squares due to }(b_3)}}_{\text{regression sum of squares} = \text{RSS} = b'X'Y = 13{,}464}\right)$$

$$= 13{,}468 - 13{,}464 = 4$$

Note that now all 3 components into which RSS is divided are positive, and represent the correct sum of squares due to each factor. Also, the total RSS of 13,464 is the same as in problem 15.2.

Then $$\sigma^2 = \frac{Q^*}{n - p} = \frac{4}{4 - 3} = \frac{4}{1} = 4,$$

And $$V(b) = (Z'Z)^{-1}\sigma^2 = \begin{pmatrix} 1/4 & 0 & 0 \\ 0 & 1/4 & 0 \\ 0 & 0 & 1/4 \end{pmatrix}(4) = \begin{pmatrix} 1 & 0 & 0 \\ 0 & 1 & 0 \\ 0 & 0 & 1 \end{pmatrix},$$

and
$$V(b_1) = 1, so \ \sigma(b_1) = 1$$
$$V(b_2) = 1, so \ \sigma(b_2) = 1$$
$$V(b_3) = 1, so \ \sigma(b_3) = 1$$

We will use the ANOVA Table with the constant term to test the hypotheses:

1. $H_0: \beta_1 = \beta_2 = \beta_3 = 0$ vs H_1: not all β's are equal to 0
2. $H_0: \beta_2 = \beta_3 = 0$ vs $H_1: \beta_2$ and β_3 are not both equal to zero
3. $H_0: \beta_1 = 0$ vs $H_1: \beta_1 \neq 0$
4. $H_0: \beta_2 = 0$ vs $H_1: \beta_2 \neq 0$
5. $H_0: \beta_3 = 0$ vs $H_1: \beta_3 \neq 0$

To test hypothesis 1, calculate F_1^* and compare to $F_1^3(\alpha = 0.05)$ where

Source of Variation	DF	Sum of Squares (SS)	$MS = \dfrac{SS}{DF}$
Regression$_{TOTAL}$	$p = 3$	13,464	$13,464/3 = 4,488$
due to b_1	1	12,996	$12,996/1 = 12,996$
due to b_2	1	144	$144/1 = 144$
due to b_3	1	324	$324/1 = 324$
Error	$n - p = 1$	$Q^* = 4$	$4/1 = 4$
Total	$n = 4$	$TSS = 13,468$	$13,468/4 = 3,367$

$$F_1^* = \frac{\dfrac{13,464}{3}}{\dfrac{4}{1}} = \frac{4,488}{4} = 1,122 \quad \text{and} \quad F_1^3(0.05) = 215.7$$

Since $F_1^* > F_1^3 (0.05)$, H_0 is rejected and we conclude that the entire regression equation, including the constant, is significant.

To test hypothesis 2, calculate:

$$F_2^* = \frac{\left[\dfrac{b^t z^t y - \left[\sum y_i\right]^2/n}{p - 1}\right]}{Q^* \Big/ n - p} = \frac{\dfrac{(13,464 - 12,996)}{2}}{\dfrac{4}{1}} = \frac{\dfrac{468}{2}}{\dfrac{4}{1}} = \frac{234}{4} = 58.5$$

and compare against $F_1^2\left(\alpha = 0.05\right) = 199.5$

Since $F_2^* < F_1^2 (\alpha = 0.05)$, H_0 is not rejected. Therefore the transformed factors Z_2 and Z_3 (and original factors X_2 and X_3) are not jointly significant.

Note: To test hypothesis 2 we can also obtain the sum of the squares directly from the above ANOVA table by adding $SS_{b2} + SS_{b3} = 144 + 324 = 468$, and this sum of squares now has 2 Degrees of Freedom; one due to b_2 and one due to b_3 for a total of 2.

Then
$$F_2^* = \frac{\dfrac{(SS_{b2} + SS_{b3})}{2}}{\dfrac{Q^*}{n - p}} = 58.5 \quad \text{as before.}$$

To test hypotheses 3, 4, 5 form:

$$F_3^* = \frac{\dfrac{12,996}{1}}{\dfrac{4}{1}} = 3,249$$

$$F_4^* = \frac{144/1}{4/1} = 36$$

$$F_5^* = \frac{324/1}{4/1} = 81$$

and compare each against $F_1^1(0.05) = 161.4$. Clearly, b_1 is significant, but b_2 and b_3 are not!

Note that these conclusions are identical to those we reached in problem 15.2 when we worked with the original data.

15.10   Minitab Solutions to Problems 2 and 3

Let us now see how the same problems (problem 2 and problem 3) can be solved by Minitab. The Minitab page (on the computer) consists of 2 half windows: The Session Window and the Worksheet 1 Window. To use the Session Window, the Minitab prompt, MTB > 0, must be shown on the Session Window.

If the prompt is not shown, go to the "Editor" and "Enable the Command Language", and the prompt will be generated.

To solve problem 2 by Minitab, enter the data as shown below:

MTB> SET C1
DATA> 43 53 59 73
DATA> END
MTB> SET C2
DATA> 1 5 1 5
DATA> END
MTB> SET C3
DATA> 240 240 280 280
DATA> END
MTB> PRINT C1 C2 C3
MTB> REGRESS C1 on 2 independent variables in C2 C3

Note 1: If this last command does not work, try the one below:

MTB> REGRESS C1 2 C2 C3;
SUBC> CONSTANT;
SUBC> BRIEF2.

Note 2: You can also use the "Worksheet 1" window of Minitab. You need to type values for X_2, X_3, and Y on separate columns, and then follow the steps indicated.

The computer responds with Table 15.1, which is the Minitab solution to problem 2.

Minitab Solution for 2

MTB> SET C1
DATA> 43 53 59 73
DATA> END
MTB> SET C2
DATA> 1 5 1 5
DATA> END
MTB> SET C3
DATA> 240 240 280 280
DATA> END
MTB> PRINT C1 C2 C3

Data Display

Row	C1	C2	C3
1	43	1	240
2	53	5	240
3	59	1	280
4	73	5	280

MTB> Regress C1 2 C2 C3;
SUBC> Constant;
SUBC> Brief 2

Regression Analysis: C1 versus C2, C3

Table 15.1A Minitab Solution for Example 2

```
The regression equation is
C1 = -69.0 + 3.00 C2 + 0.450 C3
```

Predictor	Coef	SE Coef	T	P
Constant	-69.00	13.12	-5.26	0.120
C2	3.0000	0.5000	6.00	0.105
C3	0.45000	0.05000	9.00	0.070

```
S = 2   R-Sq = 99.2%   R-Sq(adj) = 97.5%
Analysis of Variance
```

Source	DF	SS	MS	F	P
Regression	2	468.00	234.00	58.50	0.092
Residual Error	1	4.00	4.00		
Total	3	472.00			

Source	DF	Seq SS
C2	1	144.00
C3	1	324.00

To solve this equation using Microsoft Excel:

1. Input the data:

Data Display

Row	C1	C2	C3
1	43	1	240
2	53	5	240
3	59	1	280
4	73	5	280

2. Highlight the three data columns (A, B, and C) with the mouse.
3. Select the "Tools" Menu bar at the top of the page. Drag down the cursor and select "Data Analysis". Scroll down until you can see the "regression" option and select it.

4. Select column A as the "Y" range by highlighting the data in column A with the mouse.
5. Select columns B and C as the "X" range by highlighting the data in columns A and B with the mouse.
6. Select "OK". The default settings for all other information (confidence intervals, Constant is Zero, etc.) will remain unchanged unless otherwise instructed.
7. The data will appear on a new sheet looking as follows:

Table 15.1B Excel Solution for Example 2

	Coefficients	Standard Error	t Stat	P-value	Lower 95%	Upper 95%	Lower 95.0%	Upper 95.0%
Intercept	−69	13.1244	−5.25738	0.119661	−235.761	97.76066	−235.761	97.76066
X Variable 1	3	0.5	6	0.105137	−3.35308	9.353075	−3.35308	9.353075
X Variable 2	0.45	0.05	9	0.070447	−0.18531	1.085308	−0.18531	1.085308

Summary Output

Regression Statistics	
Multiple R	0.995754
R Square	0.991525
Adjusted R Square	0.974576
Standard Error	2
Observations	4

ANOVA

	df	SS	MS	F	Significance F
Regression	2	468	234	58.5	0.092057
Residual	1	4	4		
Total	3	472			

Tables 15.1A and 15.1B give us the estimated regression equation, the values of the b estimates, their standard deviations, their t-ratios, and the corresponding p-values which can be used to ascertain immediately which of the factors are individually significant and which are individually insignificant.

The Analysis of Variance table is the one without the SSa, and can be used to test for the significance of the "entire regression equation excluding the constant." Below the ANOVA table, Minitab divides the total Regression SSR into component SSR, thus making it possible to use the F-distribution to test for significance or insignificance of the individual factors. The Minitab is, perhaps, using the Forward Doolittle Method to accomplish this. Unfortunately Minitab does not give us the "ANOVA with SSa" which is capable of testing for the significance of the "entire regression equation, including the constant", but this ANOVA table can be easily constructed from the one given by Minitab, by doing the following:

1. In the "Regression" row, under DF add one (1), under SS add SSa, MS is now equal to $\dfrac{SS + SSa}{DF + 1}$, where DF and SS are the degrees of freedom and Regression SS of the Minitab ANOVA, and $SSa = \dfrac{\left(\sum\limits_{i=1}^{n} y_i\right)^2}{n}$

2. In the "Total" row, under DF add one (1) and under SS add SSa.
    To solve problem 3 by Minitab, we enter the data as shown below:

    MTB> SET C1
    DATA> 43 53 59 73
    DATA> END
    MTB> SET C2
    DATA> − 1 1 −1 1
    DATA> END
    MTB> SET C3
    DATA> −1 −1 1 1
    DATA> END
    MTB> PRINT C1 C2 C3
    MTB> REGRESS C1 on 2 INDEPENDENT VARIABLES IN C2 C3

    $$\left[\begin{array}{l} or: \quad MTB > REGRESS\ C1\ 2\ C2\ C3; \\ \qquad SUBC > CONSTANT; \\ \qquad SUBC > BRIEF \end{array} \right]$$

    The computer responds with Table 15.2, which is the Minitab solution to problem 3.

    Minitab Solution for 15.3

    MTB> SET C1
    DATA> 43 53 59 73
    DATA> END
    MTB> SET C2
    DATA> −1 −1 1 5
    DATA> END
    MTB> SET C3
    DATA> −1 −1 1 1
    DATA> END
    MTB> PRINT C1 C2 C3

    Data Display

Row	C1	C2	C3
1	43	−1	−1
2	53	1	−1
3	59	−1	1
4	73	1	1

    MTB> Regress C1 2 C2 C3;
    SUBC> Constant;
    SUBC> Brief 2

Regression Analysis: C1 versus C2, C3

Table 15.2A   Minitab Solution for Example 3

```
The regression equation is
C1 = 57.0 + 6.00 C2 + 9.00 C3
```

Predictor	Coef	SE Coef	T	P
Constant	57.000	1.000	57.00	0.011
C2	6.000	1.000	6.00	0.105
C3	9.000	1.000	9.00	0.070

```
S = 2.000   R-Sq = 99.2%   R-Sq(adj) = 97.5%
Analysis of Variance
```

Source	DF	SS	MS	F	P
Regression	2	468.00	234.00	58.50	0.092
Residual Error	1	4.00	4.00		
Total	3	472.00			

Source	DF	Seq SS
C2	1	144.00
C3	1	324.00

To solve this equation using Microsoft Excel:

1. Input the data:

Data Display

Row	C1	C2	C3
1	43	−1	−1
2	53	1	−1
3	59	−1	1
4	73	1	1

2. Highlight the three data columns (A, B, and C) with the mouse.
3. Select the "Tools" Menu bar at the top of the page. Drag down the cursor and select "Data Analysis". Scroll down until you can see the "regression" option and select it.
4. Select column *A* as the "*Y*" range by highlighting the data in column *A* with the mouse.
5. Select columns *B* and *C* as the "*X*" range by highlighting the data in columns *A* and *B* with the mouse.
6. Select "OK". The default settings for all other information (confidence intervals, Constant is Zero, etc.) will remain unchanged unless otherwise instructed.
7. The data will appear on a new sheet looking as follows:

Summary Output

Regression Statistics	
Multiple R	0.99575
R Square	0.99153
Adjusted R Square	0.97458
Standard Error	2
Observations	4

ANOVA

	df	SS	MS	F	Significance F
Regression	2	468	234	58.5	0.09206
Residual	1	4	4		
Total	3	472			

Table 15.2B Excel Solution for Example 3

	Coefficients	Standard Error	t Stat	P-value	Lower 95%	Upper 95%	Lower 95.0%	Upper 95.0%
Intercept	57	1	57	0.01117	44.29385	69.70615	44.29385	69.70615
X Variable 1	6	1	6	0.10514	−6.70615	18.70615	−6.70615	18.70615
X Variable 2	9	1	9	0.07045	−3.70615	21.70615	−3.70615	21.70615

Some observations on the Hand and Minitab solutions for Examples 2 and 3:

1. The derived equations for examples 2 and 3 are different, because of the different variables used.
   For example 2 the derived equation is: $\hat{y} = -69 + 3X_2 + 0.45X_3$ (1)
   For example 3 the derived equation is: $\hat{y} = 57 + 6Z_2 + 9Z_3$ (2)
   However, if we replace Z_2 and Z_3 by $Z_2 = \dfrac{X_2 - 3}{2}$ and $Z_3 = \dfrac{X_3 - 260}{20}$ and
   simplify the 2 equations become identical.
2. The ANOVA Tables for examples 2 and 3 are identical. Both generate the ANOVA without SSa and because the p-value for regression (*i.e.*, b_2 and b_3 jointly) is $0.092 > \alpha = 0.05$, the hypothesis: $H_0: \beta_2 = \beta_3 = 0$ will not be rejected.
3. There is, however, a puzzling observation that can be made from these two examples, the following:
   Examining the p-values in example 2, since each is greater than $\alpha = 0.05$, each of the hypothesis: $H_0: \beta_i = 0$ will not be rejected. However in example 3, the p-value for the constant term is less than $\alpha = 0.05$, which implies that $H_0: \beta_1 = 0$ is rejected while the other two (*i.e.*, $H_0: \beta_2 = 0$ and $H_0: \beta = 0$) are not rejected.

QUESTION: Why does this difference occur?

15.11 Multicollinearity

One of the basic assumptions of multivariate regression analysis is that there is no exact linear relationship between the predictor variables in the model. But a frequent problem in multivariate linear regression is that some of the predictor variables (*i.e.*, X_2, X_3, …, X_p) are correlated. If the correlation is slight, the consequences are minor. But, if two or more variables are highly correlated, it becomes very difficult, if not impossible, to separate the influences of these highly correlated variables and obtain a precise estimate of their effects. *Multicollinearity* is the name given to the problem in multivariate regression when some of the predictor variables are highly correlated. Recall that in our matrix methodology, the estimating procedure is:

$$b = (X^t X)^{-1}(X^t Y) \tag{15.127}$$

and

$$V(b) = (X^t X)^{-1}\sigma^2 \tag{15.128}$$

This estimating procedure will break down if it is impossible to derive the inverse matrix $(X^tX)^{-1}$ which, using the Adjoint Matrix Method, is given by:

$$(X^tX)^{-1} = \frac{1}{\det(X^tX)}\left[\text{Cof}(X^tX)\right]^t \qquad (15.129)$$

As can be seen from equation 15.129 the inverse cannot be obtained if det $(X^tX)=0$, and this is precisely what would happen is there is an *exact* linear relationship between the predictor variables. A less extreme but much more likely case occurs when the values of the predictor variables are highly correlated but not perfectly correlated. In this case it will be possible to obtain the least squares estimates of the regression coefficients but the interpretation of these coefficients will be very difficult. As a general rule, in multivariate regression analysis, the regression coefficients become less reliable as the correlation between the predictor variables increases.

A "rule of thumb" exists which claims that if there are only two predictor variables in the model, Multicollinearity will become a problem if the correlation between the two predictor variables is larger than the correlation of one or both of the predictor variables with the dependent variable. But this rule is not very reliable in the general case when there are p (and $p > 2$) predictor variables.

But what can be done if Multicollinearity is uncovered? Because Multicollinearity depends directly on the sample observations, not very much can be done to resolve it, unless more information of the process becomes available.

One approach has been to add observation points, for the collinear variables, if this is possible, because this action tends to lessen the severity of the correlation.

Another approach is to simply delete one or more of the collinear variables, thus reducing the variability of the regression coefficients of the remaining variables.

The easiest way to tell if Multicollinearity is causing problems is to examine the standard errors of the regression coefficients. If the standard deviation of these coefficients is high and deleting one or more variables from the regression equation lowers the standard deviation of the remaining variables, Multicollinearity is present and will cause interpretation problems on the effects of the predictor variables on the dependent variable Y.

Note: When two variables X_2 and X_3 each is highly significant in a simple regression (*i.e.*, $Y_1 = a_2 + b_2X_2$ and $Y_2 = a_3 + b_3X_3$), and in a multiple regression (*i.e.*, $Y_3 = b_1 + b_2X_2 + b_3X_3$) X_2 and X_3 are jointly very significant but individually they are not significant, this apparent contradiction is usually due to the fact that the predictor variables X_2 and X_3 are highly correlated.

15.12   References

Berenson, Marc, L., Levine, David, M., and Krehbiel, Timothy, C., 2004. *Basic Business Statistics*. 9th Edition. Pearson-Prentice Hall.

Black, Ken, 2004. *Business Statistics*. 4th Edition. Wiley.

Canavos, George, C., 1984. *Applied Probability and Statistical Methods*. Little, Brown.

Carlson, William, L., and Thorne, Betty, 1997. *Applied Statistical Methods*. Prentice Hall.

Chou, Ya-lun, 1992. *Statistical Analysis for Business and Economics*. Elsevier.

Freund, John, E., and Williams, Frank, J., 1969. *Modern Business Statistics*. Revised by: Perles, Benjamin and Sullivan, Charles. Prentice-Hall.

Freund, John, E., and Williams, Frank, J., 1982. *Elementary Business Statistics: The Modern approach*. Prentice-Hall.

Johnson, Robert, 1973. *Elementary Statistics*. Duxbury Press.

McClave, James, T., Benson, George, P., and Sincich, Terry, 2001. *Statistics for Business and Economics*. 8th Edition. Prentice Hall.

Salvatore, Dominick, *Theory and Problems of Statistics and Econometrics.* SCHAUM'S OUTLINE SERIES, McGraw-Hill.

Steel, Robert, G.D., and Torrie, James, H., 1976. *Introduction to Statistics.* McGraw-Hill.

15.13 PROBLEMS

1. The sales manager of a certain firm believes that sales ability depends on a salesman's verbal reasoning ability and vocational interest. To verify this belief, 10 salesmen were selected at random from his staff and given 2 tests: One for verbal reasoning ability, the other for vocational interest. The results are shown below:

Observation	1	2	3	4	5	6	7	8	9	10
Y_2: Average Sales in a month	1	1	1	2	2	4	3	5	6	6
X_2: Verbal Reasoning Ability	1	1	2	2	3	3	4	4	5	5
X_3: Vocational Interest	2	1	1	3	2	4	3	5	4	6

a) estimate the regression equation: $\hat{y} = b_1 X_1(=1) + b_2 X_2 + b_3 X_3$

b) Obtain the ANOVA Table for Regression, with SSa

c) Obtain the ANOVA Table for Regression, without SSa

d) Find $\sigma(b_1)$, $\sigma(b_2)$, and $\sigma(b_3)$

e) Test the hypotheses:
   $H_0: \beta_1 = 0$ vs $H_1: \beta_1 \neq 0$
   $H_0: \beta_2 = 0$ vs $H_1: \beta_2 \neq 0$
   $H_0: \beta_3 = 0$ vs $H_1: \beta_3 \neq 0$, at $\alpha = 0.05$

f) Construct 95% C.I.'s on: β_1, β_2 and β_3

g) Test the hypothesis $H_0: \beta_1 = \beta_2 = \beta_3 = 0$ vs $H_1: \beta_1, \beta_2, \beta_3$ are not all zero at $\alpha = 0.01$

h) Test the hypothesis: $H_0: \beta_2 = \beta_3 = 0$ vs $H_1: \beta_2, \beta_3$ are not both zero at $\alpha = 0.01$

i) What is the final regression equation?

j) Calculate R^2 and $\overline{R}^2$

2. Given the following trivariate data set, linking the dependent variable Y to the independent variables X_2 and X_3:

Y	3	3	0	0	2	0	0	2	1
X_2	0	0	$\sqrt{3}/2$	$\sqrt{3}/2$	$-\sqrt{3}/2$	$-\sqrt{3}/2$	0	0	0
X_3	1	1	−0.5	−0.5	−0.5	−0.5	0	0	0

a) Estimate the regression equation:
   $\hat{y} = b_1 X_1(=1) + b_2 X_2 + b_3 X_3$

b) Test for the significance of the entire regression equation, including the constant, at $\alpha = 0.05$.

c) Test for the significance of the entire regression equation, excluding the constant, at $\alpha = 0.05$.

d) Are X_2 and X_3 significant regression factors, individually, at $\alpha = 0.05$?

e) What is the final regression equation of Y? Be specific!

3. Suppose Y (the number of units of a certain product produced) as a function of X_2 (labor input in hours) and X_3 (total variable cost in tens of dollars) is given by the following multivariate data:

Observations	1	2	3	4	5	6	7	8	9	10
Y	7	5	11	10	8	6	3	9	5	11
X_2	6	4	8	9	7	6	4	7	3	8
X_3	24	23	20	25	23	26	23	20	22	23

a) Estimate the regression equation:
$\hat{y} = b_1 X_1(=1) + b_2 X_2 + b_3 X_3$

b) Test for the significance of the entire regression equation, including the constant, at $\alpha = 0.05$.

c) Test for the individual significance of X_1, X_2, and X_3, at $\alpha = 0.05$.

d) What is the final regression equation?

e) Find the value of Y when $X_1 = 1$, $X_2 = 10$, and $X_3 = 25$

4. Given the following trivariate data set, linking the dependent variable Y to the independent variables X_2 and X_3:

Observations	1	2	3	4	5	6	7	8	9	10	11
Y	6	8	1	0	5	3	2	−4	10	−3	5
X_2	1	4	9	11	3	8	5	10	2	7	6
X_3	8	2	−8	−10	6	−6	0	−12	4	−2	−4

a) Using Least Squares Procedures estimate the model
$\hat{y} = b_1 X_1(=1) + b_2 X_2 + b_2 X_3$

b) Using $\alpha = 0.05$, determine if the overall regression is significant.

c) Calculate R^2. What portion of the total variation is explained by the 2 variables X_2 and X_3?

d) Are variables X_1, X_2, and X_3 individually significant?

e) What is the final regression equation?

f) What is the variance of the predicted value of $\hat{y}$, for the point:
$X_1 = 1$, $X_2 = 3$, $X_3 = 5$?

5. Eight runs were made, at different combinations of values of the independent variables X_2 and X_3, to generate the response Y, shown in the table below:

Observations	1	2	3	4	5	6	7	8
Y	66	43	36	23	22	14	12	7.6
X_2	38	41	34	35	31	34	29	32
X_3	47.5	21.3	36.5	18	29.5	14.2	21	10

a) Using Least Squares Procedures estimate the model:
$\hat{y} = b_1 X_1(=1) + b_2 X_2 + b_3 X_3$

b) Using $\alpha = 0.05$, determine if the overall regression, including the constant is significant.

c) Using $\alpha = 0.05$, determine if the overall regression, excluding the constant is significant.

d) Calculate R^2. What portion of the total variation is explained by X_2 and X_3?

e) Are variables X_1, X_2, and X_3 individually significant at $\alpha = 0.05$?

f) Construct 95% C.I. on β_1, β_2, β_3.

6. A sample of 5 adult men for whom heights and weights are measured, gives the following results:

X = Height	64	65	66	67	68
Y = Weight	130	145	150	165	170

Using Matrix Algebra,

a) Fit the equation $\hat{y} = a + bx = b_1 x_1 (=1) + b_2 x_2$.

b) Find $\hat{\sigma}^2$, $\sigma(a)$, $\sigma(b)$.

c) Test the hypothesis: $H_0: \alpha = 0$ vs. $H_1: \alpha \neq 0$ and $H_0: \beta = 0$ vs. $H_0: \beta \neq 0$.

d) Construct confidence intervals for α and β.

e) Compare the conclusions drawn from Hypothesis Testing and Confidence Intervals.

7. Using the data of problem (15.6):

a) Test for the significance of the entire regression equation, including the constant term.

b) Calculate the Coefficient of determination, R^2. What percentage of the variation in the values of y is explained by the regression equation?

8. Using the data of problem (15.6):

a) Fit the quadratic equation $y = a + bx + cx^2$ to this data set.

b) Find $\hat{y}$ when $x = 70$.

c) Calculate $\hat{\sigma}^2$, $\sigma(a)$, $\sigma(b)$, and $\sigma(c)$.

9. Using the data of problem (6) and the results of problem (8):

a) Test for the significance of each factor separately by testing the hypothesis:

   i) $H_0: \alpha = 0$ vs. $H_1: \alpha \neq 0$, at $\alpha = 0.05$
   ii) $H_0: \beta = 0$ vs. $H_1: \beta \neq 0$, at $\alpha = 0.05$
   iii) $H_0: \gamma = 0$ vs. $H_1: \gamma \neq 0$, at $\alpha = 0.05$

b) Construct 95% Confidence intervals for α, β, γ.

c) Compare the results of (1) and (2). Are the conclusions the same?

10. Using the data of problem (6) and the results of problem (8):

a) Test for the significance of the entire regression, including the constant.

b) Test for the significance of the entire regression, excluding the constant.

c) Calculate the R_Q^2 for the quadratic model and compare to R_L^2, for the linear model.

What is now the explanatory power of the quadratic equation?

11. For the following data:

X_2	1	7	6	2	5	2	8	3	7	6
X_3	4	6	8	0	1	5	8	8	3	0
Y	11	21	23	7	13	18	30	18	21	20

a) Find the linear regression $\hat{y}_2 = a_2 + bx_2$

b) Find the standard error of regression, $\hat{\sigma}_2$

c) Find the linear regression $\hat{y}_3 = a_3 + b_3x_3$

d) Find the standard error of regression $\hat{\sigma}_3$

e) Find the multivariate regression $\hat{y} = b_1x_1(=1) + b_2x_2 + b_3x_3$

f) Find the standard error of regression, $\hat{\sigma}_m$

g) Compare the 3 models. Which of the 3 models is the best?

12. For the census data and problem (14.12) for which:
$n = 22$, $\Sigma x_i = 253$, $\Sigma x_i^2 = 3{,}795$, $\Sigma x_i^3 = 64{,}009$,

$\Sigma x_i^4 = 1{,}151{,}403$, $\Sigma y_i = 2{,}082.597$, Σy_i^2

$= 357{,}062.4525$,

$\Sigma x_i y_i = 35{,}359.379$, and $\Sigma x_i^2 y_i = 640{,}658.239$

a) Find the inverse of matrix $X^t X$, and obtain vector $X^t Y$

b) Estimate the model $\hat{y} = b_1x_1(=1) + b_2x_2 + b_3x_3$,
   where $x_3 = x_2^2$

c) Test the hypotheses: H_0: $\beta_i = 0$ vs. H_1: $\beta_i \neq 0$, for $i = 1, 2, 3$ at $\alpha = 0.05$

13. For the census data and problem 12:

a) Test the hypothesis:

   H_0: The entire regression equation (including the constant) is not significant

   vs

   H_1: The entire regression equation (including the constant) is significant, at
   $\alpha = 0.05$

b) Test the hypothesis:

   H_0: The entire regression equation (excluding the constant) is not significant vs:

   H_1: The entire regression equation (excluding the constant) is significant, at
   $\alpha = 0.05$

c) What is the Final regression equation, and why?

14. The following sample data were collected to determine the relationship between 2
processing variables and the current gain of a certain electronic component:

Diffusion Time $= X_2$ (hours)	1.5	2.5	0.5	1.2	2.6	0.3	2.4	2.0	0.7	1.6
Sheet Resistance $= X_3$ (ohm-cm)	66	87	69	141	93	105	111	78	66	123
Current Gain $= Y$	5.3	7.8	7.4	9.8	10.8	9.1	8.1	7.2	6.5	12.6

For this data set:

$n = 10$; $\Sigma x_2 = 15.3$; $\Sigma x_2^2 = 29.85$; $\Sigma x_3 = 939$; $\Sigma x_3^2 = 94.131$; $\Sigma y_i = 84.6$;
$\Sigma y_i^2 = 757.64$; $\Sigma x_2 x_3 = 1{,}458.9$; $\Sigma x_2 y_i = 132.27$; $\Sigma x_3 y_i = 8{,}320.2$

a) Fit the equation: $\hat{y} = b_1x_1(=1) + b_2x_2 + b_3x_3$

b) Estimate the expected current gain corresponding to a diffusion time of 2.2 hours and
   a sheet resistance of 90 ohm-cm.

15. Use the data of problem (14)

a) Calculate the sample variance of regression, $\hat{\sigma}^2$

b) Calculate $\sigma(b_1)$, $\sigma(b_2)$, $\sigma(b_3)$

    c) Test the hypotheses: H_0: $\beta_i = 0$ vs $H_1 = \beta_i \neq 0$, for $i = 1, 2, 3$, at $\alpha = 0.05$

    d) Construct 95% Confidence Intervals for β_i, for $i = 1, 2, 3$

16. Using the data of problem (14):

    a) Calculate R^2. What percent of the variation in the y values is explained by the regression equation?

    b) Test the hypothesis:

        H_0: The entire regression (including the constant) is not significant

            vs

        H_1: The entire regression (including the constant) is significant, at $\alpha = 0.05$

    c) Test the hypothesis:

        H_0: The entire regression (excluding the constant) is not significant

            vs

        H_1: The entire regression (excluding the constant) is significant, at $\alpha = 0.05$

    d) What is the Final regression equation?

17. The following data show the number of bedrooms, the number of baths, and the prices at which eight one family houses sold recently in a certain community.

X_2 = # of Bedrooms	3	2	4	2	3	2	5	4
X_3 = # of Baths	2	1	3	1	2	2	3	2
Y = Price (dollars)	488,000	443,000	538,000	442,000	497,000	449,000	584,000	529,000

    a) Construct the multivariate function $\hat{y} = b_1 X_1 (= 1) + b_2 X_2 + b_3 X_3$, to help us predict the average sale price of a one-family house in the given community in terms of the number of bedrooms and the number of baths.

    b) Predict the price of a house with $X_2 = 3$ (bedrooms) and $X_3 = 2$ (baths)

    c) Using the resulting equation: How much does each extra bedroom and each extra bath add to the sale price of a house?

18. Using the data of problem (15.17):

    a) Calculate the variance of regression, $\hat{\sigma}^2$

    b) Calculate $\sigma(b_1)$, $\sigma(b_2)$, $\sigma(b_3)$,

    c) Test the hypotheses: H_0: $\beta_i = 0$ vs H_1: $\beta_i \neq 0$, for $i = 1, 2, 3$, at the $\alpha = 0.05$

    d) Find the Final regression equation

19. Using the data of problem (15.17):

    a) Calculate R^2. What percent of the variation in the y-values is explained by the regression equation?

    b) Test the hypothesis:

        H_0: The entire regression (including the constant) is not significant

            vs

        H_1: The entire regression (including the constant) is significant

    c) Test the hypothesis:

        H_0: The entire regression (excluding the constant) is not significant

            vs

        H_1: The entire regression (excluding the constant) is significant

20. The following sample data show the demand for a product (in thousands of units) and its price (in cents) charged in six different market areas:

X(Price)	19	23	21	15	16	18
Y(Demand)	55	7	20	123	88	76

a) Calculate the correlation coefficient, r, and $R^2 = (r)^2$

b) Use the matrix approach to fit the least squares line which will enable us to predict the demand (for the product), in term of its price.

c) Use the equation obtained to predict the demand for the product in the market area where it is priced at 15 cents.

d) Calculate the variance of regression, $\hat{\sigma}^2$.

21. Use the data of problem (15.20) to:

a) Test the hypothesis: $H_0: \beta_i = 0$ vs $H_1: \beta_i \neq 0$, for $i = 1,2$, at $\alpha = 0.05$

b) Construct 95% Confidence Intervals for $\alpha = \beta_1$ and $\beta = \beta_2$

c) Are the conclusion of the solutions in (a) and (b) the same? Justify

22. Use the data of problem (20) to:

a) Calculate R^2, the Coefficient of Determination. What percent of the variation in the y-values is explained by the regression equation?

b) Test the hypothesis:

H_0: The entire regression (including the constant) is not significant

vs

H_1: The entire regression (including the constant) is significant Use $\alpha = 0.05$

c) Determine the final regression equation

23. Suppose the estimated regression equation, relating the dependent variable y to two predictor (independent) variables X_1 and X_2 is: $y = 15 + 6x_1 - 2x_2 - 1.5x_1x_2$

a) When $X_2 = 2$, what is the effect on y for a unit change in X_1?

b) When $X_1 = 1$, what is the effect on y for a unit change in X_2?

24. A government agency wants to estimate family expenditures for food (y) based on family income(X_2) and family size (X_3) for a given geographic region, using the following data of 15 families which were randomly selected (monthly data):

X_2 (×1000)	X_3	Y(×1000)
2.1	3	0.43
1.1	4	0.31
0.9	5	0.32
1.6	4	0.46
6.2	4	1.25
2.3	3	0.44
1.8	6	0.52
1.0	5	0.29
8.9	3	1.29
2.4	2	0.35
1.2	4	0.35
4.7	3	0.78
3.5	2	0.43
2.9	3	0.47
1.4	4	0.38

a) Obtain the regression equation $\hat{y} = b_1 x_1 (=1) + b_2 x_2 + b_3 x_3$, using matrices.

b) Estimate the monthly average food expenses for a family of four, with a monthly income of \$2,500 (*i.e.*, $X_2 = 2.5$)

25. Use the data of problem (24) to :

a) Find the variance of regression, $\hat{\sigma}^2$

b) Find $\sigma(b_1)$, $\sigma(b_2)$, $\sigma(b_3)$

c) Test the hypotheses: $H_0: \beta_i = 0$ vs $H_1: \beta_i \neq 0$, for $i = 1, 2, 3$, at $\alpha = 0.01$

d) Construct 99% C.I.'s for $\beta_1, \beta_2, \beta_3$

e) Determine the final regression equation

26. Use the data of problem (15.24) to

a) Find R^2. What percent of the variation in the y-values is explained by the regression equation?

b) Test the hypothesis:

H_0: The entire regression (including the constant) is not significant

vs

H_1: The entire regression (including the constant) is significant, at $\alpha = 0.01$

c) Test the hypothesis:

H_0: The entire regression (excluding the constant) is not significant

vs

H_1: The entire regression (excluding the constant) is significant, at $\alpha = 0.01$

27. Forty students were selected at random from a large group of students and their grade-point averages(y), intelligence test scores(X_2) and reading rates(X_3) were recorded. The regression equation on those data was found to be:
$\hat{y} = -1.20 + 0.016 x_2 - 0.009 x_3$, where $0 \leq y_i \leq 4$, $110 \leq x_2 \leq 295$, and $10 \leq x_3 \leq 45$.

   If two students have the same reading rate score but one student scores 20 points more than the other on his intelligence test, how much would his GPA be expected to exceed that of the other student?

28. The following sample data show the average annual yield of wheat (in bushels per acre) in a given county and the annual rainfall (in inches):

X = Rainfall	8.8	10.3	15.9	13.1	12.9	7.2	11.3	18.6
Y = Yield of Wheat	39.6	42.5	69.3	52.4	60.5	26.7	50.2	78.6

a) Fit the linear regression, $\hat{y} = a + bx = b_1 x_1 (=1) + b_2 x_2$, using the matrix method, to predict the yield of wheat in this county, in terms of the rainfall.

b) Use the derived regression equation to predict the annual yield of wheat when the annual rainfall is 9.0 inches.

c) Calculate the variance of regression, $\sigma^2 = \text{ESS}/ n - p$

29. Use the data of problem (28) to:

a) Test the hypothesis: $H_0: \beta = \beta_2 = 0$ vs $H_1: \beta = \beta_2 \neq 0$, at $\alpha = 0.01$

b) Test the hypothesis: $H_0: \beta = \beta_2 = 5$ vs $H_1: \beta = \beta_2 \neq 5$, at $\alpha = 0.01$

c) Construct a 99% C.I. on $\beta = \beta_2$

d) Compare the results of (a), (b), and (c).

30. Use the data of problem (28) to:

a) Determine R^2. What percentage of the variation in the y-values is explained by the regression equation?

b) Determine whether the entire regression equation (including the constant) is significant at $\alpha = 0.01$

c) Determine the final equation.

31. The following are data on the average weekly net profits (in $1,000) of five restaurants, their seating capacities, and the average daily traffic (in thousands of cars) which passes their location:

X_2 – Seating Capacity	120	200	150	180	240
X_3 – Traffic Count	19	8	12	15	16
Y – Weekly Net Profit	23.8	24.2	22.0	26.2	33.5

a) Derive the regression equation $\hat{y} = b_1 x_1(=1) + b_2 x_2 + b_3 x_3$

b) Use the derived regression equation to predict the average weekly net profit for a restaurant with a seating capacity of 210 at a location where the daily traffic count averages 14,000 cars.

c) Calculate R^2. What percent of the variation in the y-values is explained by the regression equation?

32. Use the data of problem (31) to:

a) Test the hypothesis: H_0: $\beta_i = 0$ vs H_1: $\beta_i \neq 0$, for $i = 1, 2, 3$, at $\alpha = 0.05$

b) Test:

H_0: The entire regression, including the constant, is not significant

vs

H_1: The entire regression, including the constant, is significant, at $\alpha = 0.05$

c) Test:

H_0: The entire regression, excluding the constant, is not significant

vs

H_1: The entire regression, excluding the constant, is significant, at $\alpha = 0.05$

d) Determine the final regression equation

33. The following sample data were obtained from a moving company on the weights of six shipments, the distances they were moved, and the damage that was incurred:

X_2 = Weight (1000 pounds)	4.0	3.0	1.6	1.2	3.4	4.8
X_3 = Distance (1000 miles)	1.5	2.2	1.0	2.0	0.8	1.6
Y = Damage (dollars)	160	112	69	90	123	186

a) Fit the regression equation $\hat{y} = b_1 x_1(=1) + b_2 x_2 + b_3 x_3$

b) Use the derived regression equation to predict the damage when a shipment weighing 2400 lbs is moved 1,200 miles.

c) Calculate R^2. What percent of the y-values variation is explained by the regression equation?

34. Use the data of problem (33) to:

a) Construct a 95% Confidence Interval for β_1, β_2, and β_3

b) Test the hypothesis: H_0: $\beta_i = 0$ vs H_1: $\beta_i \neq 0$, for $i = 1, 2, 3$, at $\alpha = 0.05$

c) Test: H_0: The entire regression, including the constant, is not significant

vs

H_1: The entire regression, including the constant, is significant, at $\alpha = 0.05$.

d) Determine the final regression equation

35. The following sample data were collected to determine the relationship between two processing variables and the current gain of an electronic component:

X_2 = Diffusion Time (hours)	1.5	2.5	0.5	1.2	2.6	0.3	2.4	2.0	0.7	1.6
X_2 = Sheet Resistance (Ohm-cm)	66	87	69	141	93	105	111	78	66	123
Y = Current Gain	5.3	7.8	7.4	9.8	10.8	9.1	8.1	7.2	6.5	12.6

a) Fit the regression equation $\hat{y} = b_1 x_1 (=1) + b_2 x_2 + b_3 x_3$

b) Use the derived regression equation to estimate the expected current gain for a component with a diffusion time if 2.2 hours and 90 ohm-cm sheet resistance.

c) Calculate R^2. What percent of the variation in the y-values is explained by the regression equation?

36. Use the data of problem (35) to:

a) Test the hypothesis: H_0: $\beta_i = 0$ vs H_1: $\beta_i \neq 0$, for $i = 1, 2, 3$, at $\alpha = 0.05$

b) Test the hypothesis:

H_0: The entire regression, including the constant, is not significant, vs.

H_1: The entire regression, including the constant, is significant, at $\alpha = 0.05$

c) Test the hypothesis:

H_0: The entire regression, excluding the constant, is not significant, vs

H_1: The entire regression, excluding the constant, is significant, at $\alpha = 0.05$

d) Derive the final regression equation

37. The following are sample data on family income, family size, and percentage of income saved:

X_2 = Family Income ($1000)	50	28	42	25	37
X_3 = Family Size	3	5	4	3	4
Y = % of Income Saved	7.6	3.5	5.8	3.4	5.5

a) Derive the regression equation $\hat{y} = b_1 x_1 (=1) + b_2 x_2 + b_3 x_3$

b) Use the derived regression equation to estimate the percentage of income that a family with $40,000 income and family size of 4 is expected to save.

c) Calculate R^2. What percent of the variation in the y values is explained by the regression equation?

38. Use the data of problem (37) to:

   a) Test the hypothesis: H_0: $\beta_i = 0$ vs H_1: $\beta_i \neq 0$, for $i = 1, 2, 3$, at $\alpha = 0.05$

   b) Test the hypothesis:

      H_0: The entire regression, including the constant, is not significant,

vs

      H_1: The entire regression, including the constant, is significant, at $\alpha = 0.05$

   c) Test the hypothesis:

      H_0: The entire regression, excluding the constant, is not significant,

vs

      H_1: The entire regression, excluding the constant, is significant, at $\alpha = 0.05$

39. The following are data on the ages and incomes of a random sample of executives working for a large multinational company, and the number of years each went to college:

X_2 = Age	37	45	38	42	31
X_3 = Years of College	4	0	5	2	4
Y = Income (Dollars)	41,200	36,800	45,000	40,300	35,400

   a) Fit the regression equation $\hat{y} = b_1 x_1 (=1) + b_2 x_2 + b_3 x_3$

   b) Use the derived regression equation to estimate the average income of a 40 year old executive with 4 years of college, working for this company.

   c) Calculate R^2. What percent of the variation in the y values is explained by the regression equation?

40. The following sample data was obtained to study the relationship between the grades students get in a certain examination, their IQ's, and the number of hours they study for the test:

X_2 = Number of Hours Studied	8	5	11	13	10	5	18	15	2	8
X_3 = IQ	98	99	118	94	109	116	97	100	99	114
Y = Grade in Examination	56	44	79	72	70	54	94	85	33	65

   a) Fit the regression equation $\hat{y} = b_1 x_1 (=1) + b_2 x_2 + b_3 x_3$

   b) Use the derived regression equation to predict the grade of a student who studied 12 hours (*i.e.*, $X_2 = 12$) and has an IQ of 105 (*i.e.*, $X_3 = 105$).

   c) Calculate R^2. What percent of the variation in the y values is explained by the regression equation?

SOLUTIONS

1. $(X^t X) = \begin{bmatrix} 10 & 30 & 31 \\ 30 & 110 & 111 \\ 31 & 111 & 121 \end{bmatrix}$, $X^t Y = \begin{bmatrix} 31 \\ 118 \\ 124 \end{bmatrix}$,

and: $(X^t X)^{-1} = \dfrac{1}{1740} \begin{bmatrix} 989 & -189 & -80 \\ -189 & 249 & -180 \\ -80 & -180 & 200 \end{bmatrix}$

a) $b = \begin{bmatrix} b_1 \\ b_2 \\ b_3 \end{bmatrix} = (X^t X)^{-1} X^t Y = \begin{bmatrix} -1563/1740 \\ 1203/1740 \\ 1080/1740 \end{bmatrix} \approx \begin{bmatrix} -0.8982 \\ 0.6913 \\ 0.6207 \end{bmatrix}$

b) and c)

$$\text{TSS} = Y^t Y = \sum_{i=1}^{10} \sum y_i^2 = 133.000;$$

$$\text{RSS} = b^t X^t Y = (-0.8982 \quad 0.6913 \quad 0.6207) \begin{pmatrix} 31 \\ 118 \\ 124 \end{pmatrix} = 130.7047$$

$$Q^* = \text{TSS} - \text{RSS} = Y^t Y - b^t X^t Y = 133.000 - 130.7047 = 2.2953$$

$$\text{SS}a = \left(\sum_{i=1}^{n} y_i \right)^2 \bigg/ n = (31)^2/10 = 96.1$$

b) ANOVA Table with SSa

Source of Variation	DOF	SS	MS = SS/DOF
SSR$_b$ & SSa	$p = 2 + 1 = 3$	$34.6047 + 96.1 = 130.7047$	$130.7047/3 = 43.5682$
SSE	$n - p = 10 - 3 = 7$	$Q^* = 2.2953$	0.3279
Total	$n = 10$	133	13.3

c) ANOVA Table without SSa

Source of Variation	DOF	SS	MS = SS/DOF
SSRb	$p - 1 = 2$	34.6047	17.30235
SSE	$n - p = 7$	$Q^* = 2.2953$	0.3279
Total	$n - 1 = 7$	$133 - 96.1 = 36.90$	4.1

d) $V(b_1) = \dfrac{989}{1740}\sigma^2 = \dfrac{989}{1740}\left[\dfrac{Q^*}{n-3}\right] = \dfrac{989}{1740}(0.3279) = 0.1864$ and

$\sigma(b_1) = 0.4316$

$V(b_2) = \dfrac{249}{1740}\sigma^2 = \dfrac{249}{1740}(0.3279) = 0.0469$ and $\sigma(b_2) = 0.2163$

$V(b_3) = \dfrac{200}{1740}\sigma^2 = \dfrac{200}{1740}(0.3279) = 0.0377$ and $\sigma(b_3) = 0.1942$

e) • Since $t_1^* = \dfrac{b_1}{\sigma(b_1)} = \dfrac{-0.8982}{0.4316} = -2.081 > -t_{n-p}\left(\dfrac{\alpha}{2}\right) = -t_7(0.025) = -2.365$,

the hypothesis: $H_0 = \beta_1 = 0$ is not rejected. This implies that the constant term ($X_1 = 1$) is removed from the regression equation.

• Since $t_2^* = \dfrac{b_2}{\sigma(b_2)} = \dfrac{+0.6913}{0.2163} = 3.192 > 2.365$, the hypothesis $H_0 = \beta_2 = 0$ is

rejected. This implies that the variable X_2 remains in the regression equation.

• Since $t_3^* = \dfrac{b_3}{\sigma(b_3)} = \dfrac{0.6207}{0.1942} = 3.196 > 2.365$, the hypothesis H_0: $\beta_3 = 0$ is rejected.

This implies that the variable X_3 remains in the regression equation.

f) $P[b_i - t_{n-p}(\alpha/2)^*\sigma(b_i) \le \beta_i \le b_i + t_{n-p}(\alpha/2)^*\sigma(b_i)] = 1 - \alpha$ or

$P[b_i - 2.365^*\sigma(b_i) \le \beta_i \le b_i + 2.365^*\sigma(b_i)] = 0.95$

• For $\beta_1; b_1 = -0.8982$ and $\sigma(b_1) = 0.4316 \rightarrow P[-1.9189 \le \beta_1 \le 0.1225] = 0.95$

Since $\beta_1 = 0$ is inside this C.I., do not reject H_0: $\beta_1 = 0$

• For $\beta_2; b_2 = 0.6913$ and $\sigma(b_2) = 0.2163 \rightarrow P[0.1799 \le \beta_2 \le 1.202] = 0.95$

Since $\beta_2 = 0$ is outside this C.I., reject Ho: $\beta_2 = 0$

• For $\beta_3; b_3 = 0.6207$ and $\sigma(b_3) = 0.1942 \rightarrow P[.1614 \le \beta_3 \le 1.0800] = 0.95$

Since $\beta_3 = 0$ is outside this C.I., reject H_0: $\beta_3 = 0$

g) From the ANOVA Table with SSa:

Form $F_1^* = \dfrac{43.5682}{0.3279} = 132.87$, and compare against $F_7^3(0.01) = 8.45$

Since $F_1^* > F_7^3(0.01)$, reject the hypothesis: H_0: $\beta_1 = \beta_2 = \beta_3 = 0$, and conclude that the entire regression, including the constant, is significant.

h) From the ANOVA Table without SSa:

Form $F_2^* = \dfrac{17.30235}{0.3279} = 52.64$, and compare against $F_7^2(0.01) = 9.55$

Since $F_2^* > F_7^2(0.01)$, reject the hypothesis: H_0: $\beta_2 = \beta_3 = 0$, and conclude that the variables X_2 and X_3 are jointly significant (or, the entire regression, excluding the constant, is significant).

i) The final regression equation is: $y = b_2X_2 + b_2X_3 = 0.6913X_2 + 0.6207X_3$

j) Using the ANOVA table without SSa (which is the one Minitab uses in its calculations and thus allows for a comparison of the results), we obtain:

$$R^2 = \frac{\text{RSS}}{\text{TSS}} = 1 - \frac{\text{ESS}}{\text{TSS}} = 1 - \frac{2.2953}{36.90} = 0.9377$$

$$\overline{R}^2 = 1 - \frac{\text{ESS}/n - p}{\text{TSS}/n - 1} = 1 - \frac{2.2953/7}{36.90/9} = 1 - \frac{0.3279}{4.1} = 0.9199$$

Minitab Solution for 15.1

MTB > SET C1

DATA > 1 1 1 2 2 4 3 5 6 6

DATA > END

MTB > SET C2

DATA > 1 1 2 2 3 3 4 4 5 5

DATA > END

MTB > SET C3
DATA > 2 1 1 3 2 4 3 5 4 6
DATA > END
MTB > PRINT C1 C2 C3

Data Display

Row	C1	C2	C3
1	1	1	2
2	1	1	1
3	1	2	1
4	2	2	3
5	2	3	2
6	4	3	4
7	3	4	3
8	5	4	5
9	6	5	4
10	6	5	6

MTB > Regress C1 2 C2 C3;
SUBC > Constant;
SUBC > Brief 2

Regression Analysis: C1 versus C2, C3

```
The regression equation is
C1 = − 0.898 + 0.691 C2 + 0.621 C3


Predictor        Coef      SE Coef         T        P
Constant      −0.8983       0.4320     −2.08    0.076
C2             0.6914       0.2168      3.19    0.015
C3             0.6207       0.1943      3.20    0.015


S = 0.5730      R−Sq = 93.8%      R−Sq(adj) = 92.0%


Analysis of Variance


Source           DF          SS         MS        F        P
Regression        2      34.602     17.301    52.69    0.000
Residual Error    7       2.298      0.328
Total             9      36.900
Source      DF      Seq SS
C2           1      31.250
C3           1       3.352


Unusual Observations


Obs       C2          C1         Fit     SE Fit    Residual    St Resid
  9     5.00       6.000       5.041      0.359       0.959       2.15R

R denotes an observation with a large standardized residual
```

To solve this problem using Microsoft Excel:

1. Input the data:

Data Display

Row	C1	C2	C3
1	1	1	2
2	1	1	1
3	1	2	1
4	2	2	3
5	2	3	2
6	4	3	4
7	3	4	3
8	5	4	5
9	6	5	4
10	6	5	6

2. Highlight the three data columns (A, B, and C) with the mouse.

3. Select the "Tools" Menu bar at the top of the page. Drag down the cursor and select "Data Analysis". Scroll down until you can see the "regression" option and select it.

4. Select column A as the "Y" range by highlighting the data in column A with the mouse.

5. Select columns B and C as the "X" range by highlighting the data in columns B and C with the mouse.

6. Select "OK". The default settings for all other information (confidence intervals, Constant is Zero, etc) will remain unchanged unless otherwise instructed.

7. The data will appear on a new sheet looking as follows:

SUMMARY OUTPUT	
Regression Statistics	
Multiple R	0.96836
R Square	0.93772
Adjusted R Square	0.91992
Standard Error	0.57300
Observations	10

ANOVA					
	df	SS	MS	F	Significance F
Regression	2	34.60172	17.30086	52.69430	0.00006
Residual	7	2.29828	0.32833		
Total	9	36.9			

	Coefficients	Standard Error	t Stat	P-value	Lower 95%	Upper 95%	Lower 95.0%	Upper 95.0%
Intercept	−0.89828	0.43199	−2.07938	0.07615	−1.91977	0.12322	−1.91977	0.12322
X Variable 1	0.69138	0.21676	3.18962	0.01528	0.17883	1.20393	0.17883	1.20393
X Variable 2	0.62069	0.19426	3.19508	0.01517	0.16133	1.08005	0.16133	1.08005

2.

$$(X^tX) = \begin{bmatrix} 9 & 0 & 0 \\ 0 & 3 & 0 \\ 0 & 0 & 3 \end{bmatrix}, X^tY \begin{bmatrix} 11 \\ -\sqrt{3} \\ 5 \end{bmatrix}, \text{ and } (X^tX)^{-1} = \begin{bmatrix} 1/9 & 0 & 0 \\ 0 & 1/3 & 0 \\ 0 & 0 & 1/3 \end{bmatrix}$$

a) $b = \begin{bmatrix} b_1 \\ b_2 \\ b_3 \end{bmatrix} = (X^tX)^{-1} X^tY = \begin{bmatrix} 1/9 & 0 & 0 \\ 0 & 1/3 & 0 \\ 0 & 0 & 1/3 \end{bmatrix}\begin{bmatrix} 11 \\ -\sqrt{3} \\ 5 \end{bmatrix} = \begin{bmatrix} 11/9 \\ \sqrt{3}/3 \\ 5/3 \end{bmatrix};$

and $\hat{y} = \dfrac{11}{9} - \dfrac{\sqrt{3}}{3}X_2 + \dfrac{5}{3}X_3$

b) and c) $Y^tY = \displaystyle\sum_{i=1}^{n} y_i^2 = 27;$

$$b^t X^t Y = \left(11/9 \quad -\sqrt{3}/3 \quad \frac{5}{3} \right)\begin{pmatrix} 11 \\ -\sqrt{3} \\ 5 \end{pmatrix}$$

$$= \underbrace{\frac{121}{9}}_{SS_{b1}} + \underbrace{\frac{1}{1}}_{SS_{b2}} + \underbrace{\frac{25}{3}}_{SS_{b3}} = \frac{205}{9} \approx 22.8,$$

and $Q^* = Y^tY = b^t X^t Y = 27 - \dfrac{205}{9} = \dfrac{38}{9} = 4.222$

Also $SSa = SSb_1 = \dfrac{(\sum_{i=1}^{n} y_i^2)}{n} = \dfrac{(11)^2}{9} = \dfrac{121}{9}$, and this checks the SSb, obtained

from the "split" of the total RSS. (This is the case because X^tX is a diagonal Matrix.)

b) ANOVA Table with SSa

Source of Variation	DOF	SS	MS = SS/DOF
RSS_b & SSa	$P = 2 + 1 = 3$	205/9	$\dfrac{205/9}{3} = \dfrac{205}{27} \approx 7.593$
ESS	$n - p = 9 - 3 = 6$	$Q^* = 38/9$	0.753
Total	$n = 9$	$Y'Y = \displaystyle\sum_{i=1}^{n} y_i^2 = 27$	$27/9 = 3$

c) ANOVA Table without SSa

Source of Variation	DOF	SS	MS = SS/DOF
SSR$_b$	$p - 1 = 2$	28/3	$\dfrac{28/3}{2} = \dfrac{14}{3} \approx 4.667$
ESS	$n - p = 9 - 3 = 6$	$Q^* = 38/9$	0.703
Total	$n - 1 = 8$	$27 - \dfrac{121}{9} = \dfrac{122}{9} \approx 13.56$	$\dfrac{122/9}{8} = 1.694$

To test for the significance of the entire regression, including the constant, we test the hypothesis (using the ANOVA table with SSa):

$H_0: \beta_1 = \beta_2 = \beta_3 = 0$ vs $H_1 : \beta_1, \beta_2, \beta_3$ are not all zero

To test it we calculate: $F_T^* = \dfrac{b^t X^t Y / p}{Q^* / n - p} = \dfrac{205/27}{19/27}$ and

compare it to $F_{n-p}^p(\alpha) = F_6^3(0.05) = 4.76$.

Since $F_T^* = \dfrac{205}{19} = 10.79 > 4.76$, H_0 is rejected and we conclude that the entire

regression equation, including the constant, is significant.

To test for the significance of the entire regression, excluding the constant, we test the hypothesis (using the ANOVA table without SSa):

$H_0: \beta_2 = \beta_3 = 0$ vs $H_1: \beta_2, \beta_3$ are not both zero

To test it we calculate: $F_{T-b_i}^* = \dfrac{14/3}{19/27} = \dfrac{126}{19} = 6.631$ and compare it to
$F_6^2(0.05) = 5.14$.

Since $F_{T-b_i}^* = \dfrac{126}{19} = 6.631 > 5.1$, H_0 is rejected and we conclude that the two

variables, X_2 and X_3, are jointly significant (or the entire equation, without the constant, is significant).

d) To test for the significance of X_2 and X_3 individually, we can test the hypotheses:

$H_0: \beta_2 = 0$ vs $H_1: B_2 \neq 0$ and $H_0: \beta_3 = 0$ vs $H_1: \beta_3 \neq 0$

To test these hypothesis, we need to form $t_2^* = \dfrac{b_2}{\sigma(b_2)}$ and $t_3^* = \dfrac{b_3}{\sigma(b_3)}$ and
compare them to: $t_{n-p}(\alpha/2) = t_{9-3}(0.025) = t_6(0.025) = 2.4469$.

We know the values of b_2 and b_3 $\left(b_2 = \dfrac{\sqrt{3}}{3} \text{ and } b_3 = 5/3 \right)$ and their standard

deviations can be found from: $V(b_2) = \dfrac{1}{3}\left(19/27 \right) = 0.234568$, and then
$\sigma(b_2) = 0.4843$

Similarly: $V(b_3) = \dfrac{1}{3}\left(19/27 \right) = 0.234568$, and $\sigma(b_3) = 0.4843$

Therefore, since $t_2^* = \dfrac{b_2}{\sigma(b_2)} = \dfrac{-\sqrt{3}/3}{.4843} = -1.192$ and $t_2^* > -2.4469$

H_0: $\beta_2 = 0$ is not rejected, and the variable X_2 is not significant, and should be dropped from the equation.

Also, since $t_3^* = \dfrac{b_3}{\sigma(b_3)} = \dfrac{5/3}{0.4843} = 3.4414$ and $t_3^* > 2.4469$, H_0: $\beta_3 = 0$ is rejected, and the variable X_3 is significant and stays in the equation.

But these hypotheses can also be tested using the F-distribution, and the ANOVA tables above, because the $X'X$ matrix is diagonal.

To test H_0: $\beta_2 = 0$ vs H_1: $\beta \neq 0$, we form the ratio:

$$F_2^* = \frac{SS_{b_2}\Big/1}{Q^*\Big/n - p} = \frac{1}{0.703} = 1.4225 \text{ and compare to } F_6^1(0.05) = 5.99.$$

Since $F_2^* < 5.99$, H_0 is not rejected, and X_2 is not significant.

Similarly to test the hypothesis: H_0: $\beta_3 = 0$ vs H_1: $\beta \neq 0$, we form the ratio:

$$F_3^* = \frac{SS_{b_3}\Big/1}{Q^*\Big/n - p} = \frac{25/3\Big/1}{19\Big/27} = \frac{25}{3} * \frac{27}{19} = \frac{25*9}{19} = 11.8421 \text{ and compare it to}$$

$F_6^1(0.05) = 5.99.$

Since $F_1^* > 5.99$, the hypothesis is rejected, and factor X_3 is significant.

e) Before we can derive the final equation, we need to test for the significance of the constant term individually, by testing the hypothesis: H_0: $\beta_1 = 0$ vs H_1: $\beta_1 \neq 0$. This can be accomplished by forming:

$$F_1^* = \frac{SS_{b_1}\Big/1}{Q^*\Big/n - p} = \frac{(121/9)\Big/1}{(38/9)\Big/6} = \frac{121}{9} \times \frac{27}{19} = 19.1053, \text{ and comparing it}$$

to $F_6^1(0.05) = 5.99.$

Since $F_1^* > 5.99$, H_0: $\beta_1 = 0$ is rejected and the constant term is significant and must stay in the regression equation. Therefore, the final regression equation is $\hat{y} = (11/9) + (5/3)X_3$.

3. $(X'X) = \begin{pmatrix} 10 & 62 & 229 \\ 62 & 420 & 1420 \\ 229 & 1420 & 5277 \end{pmatrix}$, $X'Y = \begin{bmatrix} 75 \\ 510 \\ 1705 \end{bmatrix}$, and

$(X'X)^{-1} = \dfrac{1}{11,712}\begin{bmatrix} 199,940 & -1994 & -8140 \\ -1994 & 329 & -2 \\ -8140 & -2 & 356 \end{bmatrix}$

a) $b = \begin{pmatrix} b_1 \\ b_2 \\ b_3 \end{pmatrix} = \left(X^t X \right)^{-1} \left(X^t Y \right) = \begin{bmatrix} 99,860/11,712 \\ 14,830/11,712 \\ -4,540/11,712 \end{bmatrix} = \begin{bmatrix} 8.5263 \\ 1.2662 \\ -0.3876 \end{bmatrix}$

For parts b, c, and d:

TSS $= Y^t Y = 631$; $b^t X^t Y = 624.3255$; $Q^* = Y^t Y - b^t X^t Y = 6.6745$;

$SSa = \dfrac{\left(\sum\limits_{i=1}^{10} y_i \right)^2}{n} = \dfrac{(75)^2}{10} = 562.5$; $\sigma^2 = Q^* \Big/ n - p = \dfrac{6.6745}{10-3} = \dfrac{6.6745}{7}$

$\quad = 0.9535$

b) Form: $F_T^* = \dfrac{b^t X^t Y / p}{Q^* / n - p} = \dfrac{624.3255/3}{6.6745/7} = 218.2574$ and compare to

$F_1^3(0.05) = 4.35$

Since $F_T^* > 4.35$, the entire regression, including the constant, is significant.

c) Test: H_0: $\beta_i = 0$ vs H_1: $\beta_i \neq 0$, by forming: $t_1^* = \dfrac{b_i}{\sigma(b_i)}$, $t_2^* = \dfrac{b_2}{\sigma(b_2)}$,

$t_3^* = \dfrac{b_3}{\sigma(b_3)}$ and compare them against $t_{n-p}(\alpha/2) = t_{10-3}(0.025) = t_7(0.025)$

$\quad = 2.3646$

But: $\sigma(b_1) = \sqrt{\dfrac{199,940}{11,722} \sigma^2} = 4.0345$; $\sigma(b_2) = \sqrt{\dfrac{329}{11,722} \sigma^2} = .1637$;

$\sigma(b_3) = \sqrt{\dfrac{356}{11,722} \sigma^2} = 0.17024$;

Then: since $t_1^* = \dfrac{b_1}{\sigma(b_1)} = \dfrac{8.5263}{4.0345} = 2.1133 < 2.3646$, Do not reject H_0: $\beta_1 = 0$.

Since $t_2^* = \dfrac{b_2}{\sigma(b_2)} = \dfrac{1.2662}{0.1637} = 7.7349 > 2.3646$, Reject H_0: $\beta_2 = 0$.($X2$ stays in the equation)

Since $t_3^* = \dfrac{b_3}{\sigma(b_3)} = \dfrac{-0.3876}{0.17024} = -2.2768 < -2.3646$, Do not reject H_0: $\beta_3 = 0$.

d) $\hat{y} = b_2 X_2 = 1.2662 X_2$

e) $\hat{y}(X_1 = 1, X_2 = 10, X_3 = 25) = \hat{y}(X_2 = 10) = \hat{y} = 1.2662(10) = 12.662$

4. $(X^t X) = \begin{bmatrix} 11 & 66 & -22 \\ 66 & 506 & -346 \\ -22 & -346 & 484 \end{bmatrix}$; $X^t Y = \begin{bmatrix} 33 \\ 85 \\ 142 \end{bmatrix}$, and

$$(X^t X)^{-1} = \begin{bmatrix} 4.3705 & -0.8495 & -0.4086 \\ -0.8495 & 0.1690 & 0.0822 \\ -0.4086 & 0.0822 & 0.0422 \end{bmatrix}$$

a) $b = \begin{pmatrix} b_1 \\ b_2 \\ b_3 \end{pmatrix} = (X^t X)^{-1}(X^t Y) = \begin{bmatrix} 13.9978 \\ -1.996 \\ -0.5044 \end{bmatrix} \approx \begin{bmatrix} 14 \\ -2 \\ -1/2 \end{bmatrix}$

b) TSS $= Y^t Y = \sum_{i=1}^{n} y_i^2 = 289;\ b^t X^t Y = (14 - 2 - 1/2) \begin{pmatrix} 33 \\ 85 \\ 142 \end{pmatrix}$

$$= (462 - 170 - 71) = 221$$

SS$a = \dfrac{\left(\sum_{i=1}^{n} y_i\right)^2}{n} = \dfrac{(33)^2}{11} = 99,\ Q^* = Y'Y - b'X'Y = 289 - 221 = 68$

and $b'X'Y - \text{SS}a = 221 - 99 = 122;\ \sigma^2 = \dfrac{Q^*}{n-p} = \dfrac{68}{11-3} = \dfrac{68}{8} = 8.5$

Then Form: $F_T^* = \dfrac{b^t X^t Y / p}{Q^*/n - p} = \dfrac{221/3}{68/8} = \dfrac{73.6667}{8.5} = 8.6667$ and compare to:

$F_{n-p}^p(\alpha) = F_8^3(0.05) = 4.07$; Since $F_T^* > 4.07$, the entire regression, including the constant, is significant.

c) $R^2 = \dfrac{b^t X^t Y - \text{SS}a}{\text{TSS} - \text{SS}a} = \dfrac{221 - 99}{289 - 99} = \dfrac{122}{190} = 64.21\%$

d) Test H$_0$: $\beta_i = 0$ vs H$_1$: $\beta_i \neq 0$, by forming $t_1^* = \dfrac{b_1}{\sigma(b_1)},\ t_2^* = \dfrac{b_2}{\sigma(b_2)}$,

$t_3^* = \dfrac{b_3}{\sigma(b_3)}$,and compare them to $t_{n-p}\ (\alpha/2) = t_{11-3} = (0.025)$

$= t_8(0.025) = 2.3060$

But, $\sigma(b_1) = \sqrt{4.3705\sigma^2} = \sqrt{4.3705 \ast 8.5} = 6.095$;

$\sigma(b_2) = \sqrt{0.1690 \ast 8.5} = 1.199$, and $\sigma(b_3) = \sqrt{0.0422 \ast 8.5} = 0.599$

Since $t_1^* = \dfrac{14}{6.095} = 2.297 < 2.3060$, H$_0$: $\beta_1 = 0$ is not rejected.

Since $t_2^* = \dfrac{-2}{1.199} = -1.668 < -2.3060$, H$_0$: $\beta_2 = 0$ is not rejected.

Since $t_3^* = \dfrac{-0.5}{0.599} = -0.835 < -2.3060$, H$_0$: $\beta_3 = 0$ is not rejected.

e) $\hat{y} = 0$

f) Since $X_k^t = (1\quad 3\quad 5)$ and $V(\hat{Y}_k) = X_k^t(X^t X)^{-1}X_k \ast \sigma^2$, we obtain:

$$V(Y_k) = (1 \quad 3 \quad 5) \begin{bmatrix} 4.3705 & -0.8495 & -0.4086 \\ -0.8495 & 0.1690 & 0.0822 \\ -0.4086 & 0.0822 & 0.0422 \end{bmatrix} \begin{bmatrix} 1 \\ 3 \\ 5 \end{bmatrix} (\sigma^2)$$

$$= 0.2295\sigma^2 = 0.2295(8.5) = 1.95075.$$

5. $n = 8$;

$$\sum_{i=1}^{8} y_i = 223.6; \quad \sum_{i=1}^{8} y_i^2 = 8,911.76; \quad \sum_{i=1}^{8} X_{2i} = 274; \quad \sum_{i=1}^{8} X_{2i}^2 = 9,488; \quad \sum_{i=1}^{8} X_{3i} = 198;$$

$$\sum_{i=1}^{8} X_3^2 i = 5,979.08; \quad \sum_{i=1}^{8} (X_2 Y)_i = 8,049.2; \quad \sum_{i=1}^{8} (X_3 Y)_i = 6,954.7;$$

$$\sum_{i=1}^{8} (X_2 X_3)_i = 6,875.6$$

Then:

$$\left(X^t X \right) = \begin{bmatrix} 8 & 274 & 198 \\ 274 & 9,488 & 6,875.6 \\ 198 & 6,875.6 & 5,979.08 \end{bmatrix}; \quad \left(X^t Y \right) = \begin{bmatrix} 223.6 \\ 8,049.2 \\ 6,954.7 \end{bmatrix},$$

and $\left(X^t X \right)^{-1} = \dfrac{1}{822,225.76} \begin{bmatrix} 9,455,635.38 & -276,899,12 & 5,290.4 \\ -276,899.12 & 8,628.64 & -752.8 \\ 5,290.40 & -752.8 & 828 \end{bmatrix}$

a) $b = \begin{pmatrix} b_1 \\ b_2 \\ b_3 \end{pmatrix} = (X^t X)^{-1}(X^t Y) = \dfrac{1}{822,225.76} \begin{pmatrix} -77,743,114.12 \\ 2,303,507.70 \\ 881,987.28 \end{pmatrix}$

$$= \begin{pmatrix} -94.5520 \\ 2.8016 \\ 1.0727 \end{pmatrix}$$

For parts b, c, and d:

$$\text{TSS} = Y^t Y = \sum_{i=1}^{8} y_i^2 = 8,911.76;$$

$$\text{SS}a = \dfrac{\left(\sum_{i=1}^{8} y_i \right)^2}{n} = \dfrac{(223.6)^2}{8} = 6,249.62$$

$$\text{RSS}b = b^t X^t Y = (-94.5520 \quad 2.8016 \quad 1.0727) \begin{pmatrix} 223.6 \\ 8,049.2 \\ 6,954.7 \end{pmatrix}$$

$$= (-21,141.83 + 22,550.64 + 7,460.31) = 8,870.12;$$

$$Q^* = Y^t Y - b^t X^t Y^t = 8,911.76 - 8,870.12 = 41.64$$

$$\sigma^2 = \dfrac{Q^*}{n - p} = \dfrac{41.64}{8 - 3} = \dfrac{41.64}{5} = 8.33$$

b) Form $F_T^* = \dfrac{b'X'Y/p}{Q^*/n-p} = \dfrac{8,870.12/3}{41.64/5} = \dfrac{2956.71}{8.33} = 354.95$ and compare to:

$F_5^3(0.05) = 5.41$; Since $F_T^* > 5.41$ the entire regression, including the constant, is significant

c) Form:

$$F_{T-b_1}^* = \frac{(b'X'Y - SSa)/p - 1}{Q^*/n-p} = \frac{(8,870.12 - 6,249.62)/2}{41.64/5} = \frac{2,620.5/2}{8.33}$$

$$= \frac{1,310.25}{8.33} = 157.29, \text{ and compare to:}$$

$F_5^2(0.05) = 5.79$; Since $F_{T-b_1}^* > 5.79$ the entire regression equation, excluding the constant, is significant.

d) $R^2 = \dfrac{b'X'Y - SSa}{Y'Y - SSa} = \dfrac{2620.5}{2662.14} = 98.44\%$

e) Test: $H_0: \beta_i = 0$ vs $H_1: \beta_i \neq 0$, by forming the ratios: $t_1^* = \dfrac{b_1}{\sigma(b_1)}, t_2^* = \dfrac{b_2}{\sigma(b_2)}$,

$t_3^* = \dfrac{b_3}{\sigma(b_3)}$ and comparing them to: $t_{n-p}(\alpha - 2) = t_{8-3}(0.025) = 2.5706$

But $\sigma(b_1) = \sqrt{\dfrac{9,455,635.68}{822,225.76}\sigma^2} = \sqrt{11.50*8.33} = \sqrt{95.7954} = 9.7875$,

$\sigma(b_2) = \sqrt{\dfrac{8,628.64}{822,225.76}\sigma^2} = \sqrt{0.0104942*8.33} = \sqrt{0.087417} = 0.2957$,

and: $\sigma(b_3) = \sqrt{\dfrac{828}{822,225.76}\sigma^2} = \sqrt{0.001007*8.33} = \sqrt{0.00838850} = 0.0916$

Then: $t_1^* = \dfrac{b_1}{\sigma(b_1)} = \dfrac{-94.5520}{9.7875} = -9.66$, and since

$t_1^* < -2.5706$, $H_0: \beta_1 = 0$ is rejected; The constant stays in the regression equation.

$t_2^* = \dfrac{b_2}{\sigma(b_2)} = \dfrac{2.8016}{.2957} = 9.47$, and since $t_2^* > 2.5706$, $H_0: \beta_2 = 0$ is rejected;

The variable X_2 stays in the regression equation.

$t_3^* = \dfrac{b_3}{\sigma(b_3)} = \dfrac{1.0727}{0.0916} = 11.71$, and since $t_3^* > 2.5706$, $H_0: \beta_3 = 0$ is rejected;

The variable X_3 stays in the regression equation, and the final equation is:
$\hat{y} = -94.5520 + 2.8016X_2 + 1.0727X_3$

f) $P\left[b_i - t_{n-p}(\alpha/2)\sigma(b_i) \leq b_i + t_{n-p}(\alpha/2)\sigma(b_i)\right] = 1 - \alpha$

$P\left[b_i - 2.5706\sigma(b_i) \leq B_i \leq b_i + 2.5706\sigma(b_i)\right] = 0.95$

$P[-94.552 - 2.5706(9.7875) \leq \beta_i \leq -94.552 + 2.5706(9.7875)] = 0.95$

$P[-94.552 - 25.160 \leq \beta_i \leq -94.552 + 25.160] = 0.95$

$P[-119.71 \le \beta_1 \le -69.39] = 0.95$

Since the hypothesized value, $\beta_1 = 0$, is outside of this C.I., H_0: $\beta_1 = 0$ is, again, rejected.

$P\left[2.8016 - 2.5706(0.2957) \le \beta_2 \le 2.8016 + 2.5706(0.2957)\right] = 0.95$

$P[2.8016 - 0.7601 \le \beta_2 \le 2.8016 + 0.7601] = 0.95$

$P[2.0415 \le \beta_2 \le 3.5617] = 0.95$

Since the hypothesized value, $\beta_2 = 0$, is outside of this C.I., H_0: $\beta_2 = 0$ is, again, rejected.

$P\left[1.0727 - 2.5706(0.0916) \le \beta_3 \le 1.0727 + 2.5706(0.0916)\right] = 0.95$

$P[1.0727 - 0.2355 \le \beta_3 \le 1.0727 + 0.2355] = 0.95$

$P[0.8372 \le \beta_3 \le 1.3082] = 0.95$

Since the hypothesized value, $\beta_3 = 0$, is outside of this
C.I., H_0: $\beta_3 = 0$ is, again, rejected.

6. a) $n = 5$, $\sum_{i=1}^{5} x_i = 330$: $\sum_{i=1}^{5} x_i^2 = 21{,}790$; $\sum_{i=1}^{5} y_i = 760$; $\sum_{i=1}^{5} y_i^2 = 116{,}550$;

$$\sum_{i=1}^{5} x_i y_i = 50{,}260, \text{ and: } n\sum(x_i - \bar{x})^2 = n\left[\sum x_i^2 - \frac{(\sum x_i)^2}{n}\right]$$

$$= 5\left[21{,}790 - \frac{(330)^2}{5}\right] = 5(10) = 50$$

From equations (15.116) and (15.117) we find that the inverse of matrix

$$X^t X = \begin{bmatrix} n & \sum_{i=1}^{n} x_i \\ \sum_{i=1}^{n} x_i & \sum_{i=1}^{n} x_i^2 \end{bmatrix} \text{ is } (X^t X)^{-1} = \frac{1}{n\sum_{i=1}^{n}(x_i - \bar{x})^2}\begin{bmatrix} \sum_{i=1}^{n} x_i^2 & -\sum_{i=1}^{n} x_i \\ -\sum_{i=1}^{n} x_i & n \end{bmatrix}, \text{ or:}$$

$$(X^t X)^{-1} = \frac{1}{50}\begin{bmatrix} 21{,}790 & -330 \\ -330 & 5 \end{bmatrix} = \begin{bmatrix} 435.8 & -6.6 \\ -6.6 & 0.1 \end{bmatrix}, \text{ and the solution is:}$$

$$\begin{pmatrix} b_1 \\ b_2 \end{pmatrix} = \begin{pmatrix} a \\ b \end{pmatrix} = (X^t X)^{-1}(X^t Y)$$

$$= \begin{bmatrix} 435.8 & -6.6 \\ -6.6 & 0.1 \end{bmatrix}\begin{bmatrix} \sum y_i = 760 \\ \sum x_i y_i = 50{,}260 \end{bmatrix} = \begin{bmatrix} -508 \\ 10 \end{bmatrix}, \text{ where:}$$

$$X^t Y = \begin{pmatrix} 1 & 1 & 1 & 1 & 1 \\ 64 & 65 & 66 & 67 & 68 \end{pmatrix}\begin{pmatrix} 130 \\ 145 \\ 150 \\ 165 \\ 170 \end{pmatrix} = \begin{bmatrix} \sum y_i = 760 \\ \sum x_i y_i = 50{,}260 \end{bmatrix}.$$

b) $\hat{\sigma} = \dfrac{\text{ESS}}{n-2} = \dfrac{\Sigma y_i^2 - a\Sigma y_i - b\Sigma x_i y_i}{n-2}$

$= \dfrac{116{,}550 - (-508)(760) - 10(50{,}260)}{5-2} = \dfrac{30}{3} = 10$

$V(b) = (X^tX)^{-1}\hat{\sigma}^2 = \begin{bmatrix} 435.8 & -6.6 \\ -6.6 & 0.1 \end{bmatrix}(10) = \begin{bmatrix} 4358 & -66 \\ -66 & 1 \end{bmatrix}$, from which

we obtain: $V(b_1) = V(a) = 4358$, and $\sigma(a) = \sqrt{4358} = 66.015149$, and:

$V(b_2) = V(b) = 1$, and $\sigma(b) = \sqrt{1} = 1$.

c) Since $t_a^* = \dfrac{a}{\sigma(a)} - \dfrac{508}{66.015149} = -7.695 < t_3(0.975) = -3.1824$, reject

$H_0: \alpha = 0$, and conclude that $\alpha \neq 0$(Therefore the term a, in $\hat{y} = a + bx$ stays
in the final equation)

Since $t_b^* = \dfrac{b}{\sigma(b)} = \dfrac{10}{1} = 10 > t_3(0.025) = 3.1824$, Reject $H_0: \beta = 0$, and conclude that $\beta \neq 0$ (Therefore the term bx, in the regression equation $\hat{y} = a + bx$,
stays in the final equation.)

d) $P[a - t_3(0.025)\sigma(a) \leq \alpha \leq a + t_3(0.025)\sigma(a)] = 1 - \alpha$ or:
$P[-718.086 \leq \alpha \leq -279.914] = 0.95$.

Since $\alpha = 0$ falls outside of this Confidence Interval, the hypothesis: $H_0: \alpha = 0$
is Rejected.

$P[b - t_3(0.025)\sigma(b) \leq \beta \leq b + t_3(0.025)\sigma(b)] = 1 - \alpha$ or:
$P[6.818 \leq \beta \leq 13.182] = 0.95$.

Since $\beta = 0$ falls outside of this Confidence Interval, the hypothesis: $H_0: \beta = 0$,
is rejected.

e) The Hypothesis Testing and Confidence Interval solutions are the same because
both solutions reject the corresponding hypothesis.

7. a) $\text{TSS} = \displaystyle\sum_{i=1}^{n}(y_i - \bar{y})^2 = \sum_{i=1}^{n} y_i^2 - \dfrac{\left(\displaystyle\sum_{i=1}^{n} y_i\right)^2}{n}$

$= 116{,}550 - \dfrac{(760)^2}{5} = 116{,}550 - 115{,}520 = 1030$

$\text{RSS}_b = b^2 \displaystyle\sum_{i=1}^{n}(x_{i-x})^2 = (10)^2(10) = 1000$

$\text{ESS} = \displaystyle\sum_{i=1}^{n} y_i^2 - a\sum_{i=1}^{n} y_i - b\sum_{i=1}^{n} x_i y_i = 30$

$\text{SSa} = \dfrac{\left(\displaystyle\sum_{i=1}^{n} y_i\right)^2}{n} = \dfrac{(760)^2}{5} = 115{,}520$

To test the hypothesis $H_0: \alpha = \beta = 0$ vs $H_1: \alpha$ and β are not both equal to zero, or

H_0: The Entire Regression is not significant   vs
H_1: The Entire Regression is significant,

form

$$F^*_{TOTAL} = \frac{(RSS_b + SSa)/p}{ESS/(n-p)} = \frac{(1000 + 115,520)/2}{30/3} = \frac{116,520/2}{30/2}$$

$$= \frac{58,260}{10} = 5,826, \text{ and compare to } F^P_{n-p}(\alpha) = F^2_3(\alpha = 0.05) = 9.55;$$

Since $F^*_{TOTAL} = 5,826 > F^2_3(\alpha = 0.05) = 9.55$, reject H_0; Therefore, the entire regression equation is significant.

b) $R^2 = \dfrac{RSS_b}{TSS} = \dfrac{1000}{1030} = 0.971$; Therefore the regression equation explains 97.1% of the variation in the values of y, and only 2.9% is due to other factors.

8. a) The normal equations for the quadratic are:

$$na + b\Sigma x_i + c\Sigma x_i^2 = \Sigma y_i$$
$$a\Sigma x_i + b\Sigma x_i^2 + c\Sigma x_i^3 = \Sigma x_i y_i$$
$$a\Sigma x_i^2 + b\Sigma x_i^3 + c\Sigma x_i^4 = \Sigma x_i^2 y_i$$

We already have values for:

$$n = 5, \sum_{i=1}^{5} x_i = 330; \sum_{i=1}^{5} x_i^2 = 21,790; \sum_{i=1}^{5} y_i = 760; \sum_{i=1}^{5} y_i^2 = 116,550;$$

$\sum_{i=1}^{5} x_i y_i = 50,260$, We need the additional summations: Σx_i^3, Σx_i^4, and $\Sigma x_i^2 y_i$, and they are given by: $\Sigma x_i^3 = 1,439,460$; $\Sigma x_i^4 = 95,135,074$; and

$\Sigma x_i^2 y_i = 3,325,270$.

Then the normal equations become: Solving simultaneously, we find:

$$\left.\begin{array}{r} 5a + 330b + 21,790c = 760 \\ 330a + 21,790b + 1,439,460c = 50,260 \\ 21,790a + 1,439460b + 95,135,074c = 3,325,270 \end{array}\right\}$$

$$a = -\frac{25,326}{7} = -3,618$$

$$b = \frac{730}{7} \approx 104.2857143, \text{ and}$$

$$c = -\frac{5}{7} \approx -0.7142857,$$

and $\hat{y} = a + bx + cx^2 = -3,618 + \dfrac{730}{7}x - \dfrac{5}{7}x^2$

b) $\hat{y} = a + bx + cx^2 = -3,618 + \dfrac{730}{7}(70) - \dfrac{5}{7}(70)^2 = 182$, when $x = 70$

c) We first set up the matrices X^tX and X^tY, where

$$(X^tX) = \begin{bmatrix} 1 & 1 & 1 & 1 & 1 \\ 64 & 65 & 66 & 67 & 68 \\ 4096 & 4225 & 4356 & 4489 & 4624 \end{bmatrix} \begin{bmatrix} 1 & 64 & 4096 \\ 1 & 65 & 4225 \\ 1 & 66 & 4356 \\ 1 & 67 & 4489 \\ 1 & 68 & 4624 \end{bmatrix} = \begin{bmatrix} 5 & 330 & 21,790 \\ 330 & 21,790 & 1,439,460 \\ 21,790 & 1,439,460 & 95,135,674 \end{bmatrix},$$

$$\text{and } X^tY = \begin{bmatrix} 760 = \Sigma y_i \\ 50{,}260 = \Sigma x_i y_i \\ 3{,}325{,}270 = \Sigma x_i^2 y_i \end{bmatrix}, \text{ and then find}$$

$$(X^tX)^{-1} = \begin{bmatrix} 1{,}354{,}529.8 & -41{,}058.6 & 311 \\ -41{,}058.6 & 1{,}244.67143 & -9.428571 \\ 311 & -9.428571 & 0.07142857 \end{bmatrix},$$

Also $\hat{\sigma}^2 = \dfrac{(\Sigma(y_i) - a - bx_i - cx_i^2)^2}{n-3} = \dfrac{\Sigma y_i^2 - a\Sigma y_i - b\Sigma x_i y_y - c\Sigma x_i^2 y_i}{5-3}$

$$= \dfrac{116{,}550 - (-3618)(760) - \dfrac{730}{7}(50{,}260) - \left(-\dfrac{5}{7}\right)(3{,}325{,}270)}{2}$$

$$= \dfrac{22.85714}{2} = 11.42857, \text{ and } \hat{\sigma} = 3.3806168 \approx 3.381$$

Then:

$V(b) = \left(X^tX\right)^{-1}\hat{\sigma}^2$, and:

$V(b_1) = 1{,}354{,}529.8(11.42857) = 15{,}480{,}338.64$, and: $\sigma(b_1) = \sigma(a) = 3934.5061$

$V(b_2) = 1{,}244.67143(11.42857) = 14{,}224.81456$, and: $\sigma(b_2) = \sigma(b) = 119.2678$

$V(b_3) = 0.07142857(11.42857) = 0.816326412$, and: $\sigma(b_3) = \sigma(c) = 0.9035$

9. a) i) Form $t_a^* = \dfrac{a}{\sigma(a)} = \dfrac{-3{,}618}{3934.5061} = -0.9196$ and compare to

$\pm t_2(0.025) = \pm 4.303$

Since $t_a^* = -0.9196 > -t_2(0.025) = -4.303$, do not reject H_0: $\alpha = 0$

ii) Form $t_b^* = \dfrac{b}{\sigma(b)} = \dfrac{730/7}{119.2678} = \dfrac{104.2857143}{119.2678} = 0.8744$ and compare to

$t_2(0.025) = 4.303$;

Since $t_b^* < t_2(0.025)$, do not reject H_0: $\beta = 0$.

iii) Form $t_c^* = \dfrac{c}{\sigma(c)} = \dfrac{-5/7}{0.9035} = -0.79058$, and compare to

$\pm t_2(0.025) = \pm 4.303$

Since $t_c^* = -0.79058 > -t_2(0.025) = -4.303$, do not reject H_0: $\gamma = 0$

b) i) $P[a - t_2(0.025)\sigma(a) \le \alpha \le a + t_2(0.025)\sigma(a)] = 1 - \alpha$, or:

$P[-3{,}618 - 4.303(3934.50061) \le \alpha \le -3{,}618$

$+4.303(3934.5061)] = 0.95$, or:

$P[-20{,}548.18 \le \alpha \le 13{,}312.18] = 0.95$; Do not reject H_0: $\alpha = 0$, because $\alpha = 0$ falls inside this Confidence interval.

ii) $P[b - t_2(0.025)\sigma(b) \le \beta \le b + t_2(0.025)\sigma(b)] = 1 - \alpha$, or:

$P[104.2857 - 4.303(119.2678) \le \beta \le 104.2857 + 4.303(119.2678)]$

$= 0.95$, or:

$P[-408.92 \leq \beta \leq 617.50] = 0.95$; Do not reject H_0: $\beta = 0$, because $\beta = 0$ falls inside this Confidence interval.

iii) $P[c - t_2(0.025)\sigma(c) \leq \gamma \leq c + t_2(0.025)\sigma(c)] = 1 - \alpha$, or

$P[-0.714286 - 4.303(0.9035) \leq \gamma \leq -0.714286 + 4.303(0.9035)] = 0.95$, or

$P[-4.602 \leq \gamma \leq 3.173] = 0.95$; Do not reject H_0: $\gamma = 0$, because $\gamma = 0$ falls inside this Confidence interval.

c) The results of (1) and (2) are the same. In each case the hypothesis H_0: $\beta_i = 0$ (where $\beta_1 = \alpha$, $\beta_2 = \beta$, $\beta_3 = \gamma$) is not rejected.

10. TSS $= \displaystyle\sum_{i=1}^{n}(y_i - \bar{y})^2 = \sum_{i=1}^{n} y_i^2 - \frac{\left(\displaystyle\sum_{i=1}^{n} y_i\right)^2}{n}$

$= 116{,}550 - \dfrac{(760)^2}{5} = 116{,}550 - 115{,}520 = 1030$

$SSa = \dfrac{\left(\Sigma y_i\right)^2}{n} = 155{,}520$

$RSS = b^t X^t Y = \begin{pmatrix} -3618 & 730/7 & -5/7 \end{pmatrix} \begin{pmatrix} 760 \\ 50{,}260 \\ 3{,}325{,}270 \end{pmatrix}$

$= \left(-2{,}749{,}680 + \dfrac{36{,}689{,}800}{7} - \dfrac{16{,}626{,}350}{7}\right)$

$= \left(-2{,}749{,}680 + \dfrac{20{,}063{,}450}{7}\right)$

$= -2{,}749{,}680 + 2{,}866{,}207.142 = 116.527.1420,$

ESS $= Y^t Y - b^t X^t Y = 116{,}550 - 116{,}527.1429 = 22.8571$

a) $F^*_{TOTAL} = \dfrac{b^t X^t Y / p}{ESS/n - p} = \dfrac{116{,}527.1429/3}{22.8571/2} = \dfrac{38{,}842.38097}{11.42857} = 3398.7088$

and compare to $F^p_{n-p}(\alpha) = F^2_3 = (\alpha = 0.05) = 19.2$.

Since $F^*_{TOTAL} = 3398.7088 > F^2_3(0.05) = 19.2$, Reject H_0 (*i.e.*, the entire regression is significant) and conclude that the entire regression, (including the constant) is significant.

b) Form $F^*_{TOTAL-b_1} = \dfrac{(b^t X^t Y - SSa)/p - 1}{ESS/n - p} = \dfrac{(116{,}527.1429 - 115{,}520)/2}{(22.8571)/2}$

$= \dfrac{(1{,}007.1429)/2}{(22.8571)/2} = \dfrac{503.57145}{11.42857} = 44.0625$, and compare to

$F^{p-1}_{n-p}(\alpha) = F^2_2(0.05) = 19.0$

Since $F^*_{TOTAL-b_1} = 44.0625 > F^2_2(0.05) = 19.0$, Reject H_0 (*i.e.*, the entire regression, not including the constant) and conclude that the entire regression, excluding the constant, is significant.

c) $R_Q^2 = \dfrac{\text{RSS}}{\text{TSS}} = 1 - \dfrac{\text{ESS}}{\text{TSS}} = 1 - \dfrac{22.8571}{1030} = 1 - 0.0222 = 0.9778$

Since $R_L^2 = 0.971$, $R_Q^2 = 0.9778 > R_L^2 = 0.971$; Therefore the explanatory power of the regression equation increased from 97.1 to 97.8 when a quadratic equation was fitted to the same data set. (Also $\text{RSS}_Q = 1{,}007.14$ while and $\text{RSS}_L = 1000$, and $\text{ESS}_Q = 22.86$ while $\text{ESS}_L = 30.00$).

PART VI

Time Series Analysis & Forecasting

16 Time Series Analysis

A time series portrays the variations of a variable through time, and a set of observations for the same variable, taken over a period of time, is called a time series.

But samples taken over a period of time often do not behave like (independent) random variables and, therefore, the standard statistical techniques cannot be applied to their analysis. When studying time series the first question which needs to be answered is whether the time series really depends on time. The serial correlation test can be used to answer this question. For series which are not obviously time-dependent, it is necessary to apply some statistical test for randomness, such as those discussed in the Non-Parametric statistics chapter (Chapter 18), before one is justified in proceeding further in the analysis of a series. The natural alternative to randomness in a time series is dependence on time, which may consist of a long time trend (which can be obtained by using regression methods), a seasonal variation (*i.e.*, a variation which completes itself in a 12-month period) and can be obtained using a twelve-month moving average, and cyclical variations, which usually exceed one year in length. After the major question of the time dependence of a series has been settled, the next problem is to determine whether the resulting relationship can be used to predict the future course of the series with some reliability, which is the ultimate desire of every statistical analyst.

Many statistical techniques have been proposed for making such predictions, with various degrees of success, and some of these techniques are discussed in this chapter.

16.1 Introduction

A time series portrays the changes of a variable through time. It is studied for the purpose of learning how to perform "Statistical Forecasting", *i.e.*, how to predict future values of the time series.

In a Time Series the data analyzed is dependent (*i.e.*, the current value depends on one or more of the previous values of the time series, in contrast to the **cross sectional data** we had been analyzing up to now which is independent (*i.e.*, the current value does not depend on any of the previous values).

We will discuss "Time Series Analysis" in the following order:

1. Goal of time series analysis.
2. Methods of forecasting.
3. Discussion of "Select Methods" of forecasting.
4. Other Forecasting Methods.

16.2 Goal of Time Series Analysis

The main aim of Time Series analysis is Forecasting, which is used for planning purposes.

Forecasting is the basis for rational decision making in both the private sector and in Government.

Question:	But how is Forecasting performed?
Answer:	We use the past to forecast the future!
	The assumption is made that the future is some extension of the past, but not an exact replica of the past. Because of this fact, Forecasting is difficult!

However, we can state that: successful forecasting consists of expert blending of:

1. Economic theory,
2. Statistical expertise, and
3. Thorough familiarity with the relevant statistical data.

   i.e., Forecasting is an art, rather than a science.

16.3   Methods of Forecasting

There are many Forecasting techniques available (see the attached Table 16.1 which compares 7 such techniques, using several "Criteria of Goodness"), but they are usually grouped into 3 main categories:

■ The Naïve Category
The techniques in this category lack mathematical rigor, but they are easy to understand.

   The Basic Assumption of these techniques is that "The Future will resemble the Past".

   The best-known Naïve category methods are

Table 16.1 Comparison of Forecasting Methods							
Factor	Simple Exponential Smoothing	Holt-winters	Decom-position	Box-Jenkins	Mltiple Regression	Econometrics	Multivariate Box-Jenkins
Lead Time							
Immediate	x	x	x	x	–	–	–
Short term	x	x	x	x	x	x	x
Medium term	–	–	–	–	x	x	x
Long term	–	–	–	–	x	x	x
Time to prepare forecast							
(1–shortest; 7–longest)	1	2	3	5	4	7	6
Pattern of data							
Horizontal	x	–	x	x	–	–	x
Trend	–	x	x	x	x	x	x
Seasonal	–	x	x	x	x	x	x
Cyclical	–	–	x	–	x	x	–
Date requirements	10	15	30	30	30	Few	60
(S: period of seasonality)		2(S)	6(S)	6(S)	6(S)	100	8(S)
Ease of understanding							
(1 - easiest; 7 - hardest)	1	2	3	4	5	7	6
Cost							
(1 - least costly;							
7 - most costly)	1	2	3	5	4	7	6

1. The Exponential Smoothing Method, and
2. The Decomposition Method.

Both of these methods will be discussed and analyzed later in this chapter.

■ The Barometric Category

(see Appendix 16B for a more detailed discussion)

In these techniques we seek to discover past statistical behavior, which seems to be regularly associated with fluctuations in particular series, and use as the basis for Forecasting.

The basic assumption here is that "Past Historical patterns tend to repeat. The Future can be predicted from certain happenings in the Past".

The most important and best known representatives of this category are:

1. The Statistical Indicators, and
2. The Diffusion Index

1. **The Statistical Indicators** are based on the Lead-Lag approach (which attempts to determine the approximate lapse of time between the movements of one particular Time Series and the movements of General Business Conditions) and consist of:

    a) **Leading Indicators** which "signal in advance" a change in the basic performance of the economy as a whole. Examples of Time Series that can be classified as Leading Indicators are: a) Average Work week, b) Unemployment Claims, and c) Net Business Formation

    b) **Lagging Indicators**

    Lagging Indicators move in a direction opposite to that of the Leading Indicators (*i.e.*, they "trail" the performance of the economy as a whole).

    Examples of Time Series that can be classified as Lagging Indicators are: a) Unemployment Rate, b) Unit Labor Costs, and c) Bank Loans Interest Rate.

    c) **Coincident Indicators**

    Coincident Indicators inform us whether the economy as a whole is currently experiencing a boom or a slowdown. Examples of Time Series that can be classified as Coincident Indicators are: a) Non-Agricultural Employment, b) GNP (in dollars), and c) Personal Income.

    The Statistical Indicator approach to Forecasting attempts to derive the broad general framework of what the "whole economy is doing", from "what its sections are doing", and then moves on to "evaluate any particular segment" within this framework.

2. **The Diffusion Index**

    The Diffusion Index represents an attempt to describe and forecast Business Cycles (*i.e.*, the Turning Points and Amplitudes of the Variations of a Time Series) by measuring such changes in the "diversity of experience" that underlines cyclical fluctuations.

■ The Analytical Category

(see Appendix 16C for a more detailed discussion)

The techniques in this category require detailed analysis of the causative forces operating currently on the variable to be predicted.

The main representative techniques of this category are:

1. **Regression Analysis**

    This is the same Regression Analysis that we have discussed extensively previously.

    But here, the Regression Analysis results must be modified to account for the correlation that usually exists between Time Series data.

2. **Econometric Models**

    The Econometric Models approach seeks to discover and measure the Quantitative aspects of an Economic System for the purpose of making forecasts.

The "Econometric Models" approach to Forecasting consists of the following major steps:

a) Build the model
b) Estimate the parameters of the model
c) Use the model for prediction

16.4 Naïve Category Forecasting Techniques

Since this is only an Introduction into Time Series Analysis, rather than an exhaustive coverage of the topic, we will select and discuss extensively only 2 of the many Forecasting techniques which are available. Later on, in section 16.5 we will briefly discuss some additional Forecasting techniques. The techniques we have chosen for thorough discussion and analysis are the "Naïve Category" techniques:

1. Simple Exponential Smoothing Method, and
2. Decomposition Method

The main reason for their selection is their "relative" simplicity, and our aim to show how Forecasting Methods work in a way which is as quick and efficient as possible.

16.4.1 The Exponential Smoothing Method and Model Definition

This technique is useful in "short-term" Forecasting (of Sales and Inventory, as examples), and is based on the following functional relationship:

$$S_t = \text{Forecast at time } t \text{ for period } t + 1$$
$$= f(S_{t-1}, y_t), \tag{16.1}$$

where S_{t-1}: Forecast at Time $t - 1$ for period t, and
y_t: Actual value of series, for time t.

The functional relationship of (16.1) tells us that the value of the Forecast we are making now (at time t), for the next time period (time $t + 1$), S_t, depends on the previously forecasted value (S_{t-1}), and the current measurement of the time series of interest (y_t). The usual form assigned to the functional relationship (16.1) is the linear form, namely:

$$S_t = \beta \cdot S_{t-1} + \alpha \cdot y_t \tag{16.2}$$

where: $\qquad\qquad \alpha > 0, \beta > 0, \text{ and } \alpha + \beta = 1 \tag{16.3}$

Small values of α place more weight on S_{t-1}, while large values of α place more weight on y_t, when Forecasting S_t.

Because of equation (16.3) (*i.e.*, because $\alpha + \beta = 1$), equation (16.2) can be re-written as:

$$S_t = (1 - \alpha)S_{t-1} + \alpha \cdot y_t \tag{16.4}$$

(in terms of the single parameter α)

16.4.1.1 Observations on the Model

1. S_{t-1} represents the "Total Experience" of the series to date.
2. At time t, a new observation, y_t, becomes available for the time series.
3. S_t is a Linear Combination of *all* past observations, because:

at time 1: $\quad S_1 = \alpha \cdot y_1 + \beta \cdot S_0 \tag{16.5}$

at time 2: $\quad S_2 = \alpha \cdot y_2 + \beta \cdot S_1 = \alpha \cdot y_2 + \beta[\alpha \cdot y_1 + \beta \cdot S_0]$

$$= (\alpha)y_2 + (\alpha\beta)y_1 + (\beta^2)S_0 \tag{16.6}$$

at time 3: $S_3 = \alpha \cdot y_3 + \beta \cdot S_2 = \alpha \cdot y_2 + \beta[\alpha \cdot y_2 + \alpha\beta \cdot y_1 + \beta^2 S_0]$

$$= (\alpha)y_3 + (\alpha\beta)y_2 + (\alpha\beta^2)y_1 + \beta^3 S_0 \qquad (16.7)$$

etc.

Note that S_3 is a linear combination of the time series observations y_3, y_2, and y_1, with weights: α_1, $\alpha\beta_1$, and $\alpha\beta_2$, respectively.

4. The weights given to past observations "decrease exponentially" with the age of the data (*i.e.*, "older" data is given less weight but *all* past and current data contribute to the forecast). This is so because $\alpha > \alpha\beta > \alpha\beta^2$ etc, because of (16.3). It is this "Exponential decrease" of the weight of the data that is mainly responsible for the name of this Forecasting technique.

5. Small values of α place more weight on the value of S_{t-1} when determining the new value for S_t, while large values of α place more weight on the y_t value.

6. In practice, the actual value assigned to α is determined by simulation, and it is the value of α which Minimizes the Variance of $S_t = V(S_t)$.

7. Usual (or Typical) values for α are: $0 < \alpha < 0.6$ $\qquad\qquad$ (16.8)

16.4.1.2 Procedure for using the "Exponential Smoothing" Model for Prediction

1. Find $\qquad S_t = \alpha y_t + \beta S_{t-1}$ $\qquad\qquad\qquad\qquad\qquad\qquad$ (16.9)
2. Find $\qquad \Delta S_t = S_t - S_{t-1}$ $\qquad\qquad\qquad\qquad\qquad\qquad$ (16.10)
   (*i.e.*, use differences between successive forecasts as "Trend" estimates)
3. Let: $\qquad T_t = \alpha \cdot \Delta S_t + \beta \cdot T_{t-1}$ $\qquad\qquad\qquad\qquad\qquad$ (16.11)
   (*i.e.*, Estimate a "New Trend")
4. Then $\qquad S'_t = S_t + \left(\dfrac{\beta}{\alpha}\right) \cdot T_t$ $\qquad\qquad\qquad\qquad\qquad\qquad$ (16.12)

   a) **For Annual data,**
      S'_t is the Final Forecast (for the time series y_t), for period $t + 1$.

   b) **For Monthly data,**
      the Final Forecast is $\qquad S^*_t = (S'_t) \cdot I_{t+1}$, $\qquad\qquad\qquad$ (16.13)
      where I_{t+1} is the Seasonal Index for period $t + 1$ (To be discussed later, in the Decomposition Method)

5. **Accuracy of Forecasts**
   a) For Annual Data $e_{t+1} = S'_t - y_{t+1}$ $\qquad\qquad\qquad\qquad\qquad$ (16.14)
   b) For Monthly Data $e_{t+1} = S^*_t - y_{t+1}$ $\qquad\qquad\qquad\qquad\qquad$ (16.15)

Note: To start the "Exponential Smoothing" Method, we need to specify:

a) The Initial Smoothed Value S_0 (by assigning S_0 to the "first" given data value)
b) The Initial Trend Value T_0 (by assigning $T_0 = 0$)

Example

Suppose we are given the following data values of a time series y_t

$$y_0 = 100$$
$$y_1 = 110$$
$$y_2 = 105$$
$$y_3 = 120$$
$$\text{etc.,}$$

and the values of $\alpha = 0.4$, and $\beta = 1 - \alpha = 0.6$

Use the given data to see how well the Simple Exponential Model "Predicts" the given values of the time series and to Predict Future values for the Time Series y_t.

Solution Applying the above described procedure (with $S_0 = y_0 = 100$, and $T_0 = 0$), we obtain:

1. $S_1 = \alpha \cdot y_1 + \beta \cdot S_0 = 0.4(110) + 0.6(100) = 44 + 60 = 104$
2. $\Delta S_1 = S_1 - S_0 = 104 - 100 = 4$
3. $T_1 = \alpha \cdot \Delta S_1 + \beta \cdot T_0 = 0.4(4) + 0.6(0) = 1.6 + 0 = 1.6$
4. $S'_1 = S_1 + \left(\dfrac{\beta}{\alpha}\right) \cdot T_1 = 104 + \left(\dfrac{0.6}{0.4}\right)1.6 = 104 + 2.4 = 106.4$
5. **Accuracy of Forecast** $= e_2 = S_1 - y_2 = 106.4 - 105 = 1.4$

This ends the "First Round" of forecasting! To go to the "Second Round", we need to "carry" the values: $S_1 = 104$ and $T_1 = 1.6$, from the first to the second round. Then we obtain:

1. $S_2 = \alpha \cdot y_2 + \beta \cdot S_1 = 0.4(105) + (0.6)(104) = 42.0 + 62.4 = 104.4$
2. $\Delta S_2 = S_2 - S_1 = 104.4 - 104 = 0.4$
3. $T_2 = \alpha \cdot \Delta S_2 + \beta \cdot T_1 = 0.4(0.4) + 0.6(1.6) = 0.16 + 0.96 = 1.12$
4. $S'_2 = S_2 + \left(\dfrac{\beta}{\alpha}\right) \cdot T_2 = 104.4 + \left(\dfrac{0.6}{0.4}\right)1.12 = 104.4 + 1.68 = 106.08$
5. **Accuracy of Forecast** $= e_3 = S_2 - y_3 = 106.08 - 120 = -13.92$

This ends the "Second Round". If we had more data on the Time Series $y_t(y_4, y_5, y_6, \ldots, y_n)$, and wanted to continue with our forecasting calculations, we would move on to the "Third Round", but we need to "carry" from round two the values: $S_2 = 104.4$ and $T_2 = 1.12$
Then the procedure continues as shown above.

16.4.2 The Decomposition Method
This Forecasting method assumes that the actual numerical value of a Time Series, y_t, is a "composition" of 4 different types of economic change, namely: The Trend Component (T), The Seasonal Component (S), The Cyclical Component (C), and The Random Component (I), and these 4 components are combined either through Addition (Additive Model: $y_t = T + S + C + I$) or through Multiplication (Multiplicative Model: $y_t = TSCI$) to generate the "Total" observed value y_t.

The Decomposition method consists of the following 3 general steps:

1. Decompose the given series, y_t, into its 4 components (T, S, C, I).
2. Project each component individually into the future
3. Re-compose (*i.e.*, synthesize the projected components to form a single value again) the series, by using either the additive or the multiplicative model (it must be the same model used in the decomposition step).

The procedure is based on our belief that it is more accurate to project (*i.e.*, forecast) each component separately, than it is to project (*i.e.*, forecast) the entire series.
In the discussion that follows, we will explain how the steps of this procedure are carried out.

1. Decompose the series y_t into its 4 components (T, S, C, I)
   a) The Trend Component (T) is obtained either by using *Regression Analysis* methods to fit a model to the given data (Linear: $y_t = a + bx$, Exponential $= ke^{cx}$, Power $= ax^b$, or Quadratic: $y_t = a + bx + cx^2$; see Appendix 16A for details) or by using *Moving Averages (MA)*. We have already discussed how to use Regression Methods to fit models to data sets (see Chapters 13 and 14), and will not repeat this discussion here. However, we have not discussed Moving Averages

before, and we will do so now because the Moving Average method, even though it is not very useful for calculating the Trend component, it is the method used to obtain the Seasonal component.

■ **Moving Averages**

Moving Averages are artificially constructed time series, in which each period's actual value is replaced by the mean value of "that period's value, and the values of a number of preceding and succeeding periods".

The procedure for calculating the Moving Average (MA) of a given time series, y_t, is best explained by using the attached Table 16.2, in which a 3-year and 5-year Moving Averages are calculated for a hypothetical data set (having 5-year cycles with Uniform Duration and Amplitude). Column (1) of Table 16.2 lists the 20 values (years) of the data set, column (2) gives the value of the Time Series y_t (Original Value), column (3) gives the "3-year Moving Total", mt, which consists of the sum of 3 values (the current value, the value before the current value, and the value after the current value).

Note: The first value, under column (3), is for year 2, and it consists of the sum of the values: 1(for year 1) + 2(for year 2) + 3(for year 3) = 6.

(Note also, that there is no value listed for year 1 and year 20, because the 3 values needed to form the sum are not available). Column (4), represents the

Table 16.2 * Computation of Three-year and Five-year Moving Averages for Hypothetical Data having Five-year Cycles with Uinform Duration and Amplitude					
Year (1)	Original value (2)	Three-year mt (3)	Three-year ma (4)	Five-year mt (5)	Five-year ma (6)
1	1	–	–	–	–
2	2	6	2.0	–	–
3	3	7	2.3	9	1.8
4	2	6	2.0	10	2.0
5	1	5	1.7	11	2.2
6	2	6	2.0	12	2.4
7	3	9	3.0	13	2.6
8	4	10	3.3	14	2.8
9	3	9	3.0	15	3.0
10	2	8	2.7	16	3.2
11	3	9	3.0	17	3.4
12	4	12	4.0	18	3.6
13	5	13	4.3	19	3.8
14	4	12	4.0	20	4.0
15	3	11	3.7	21	4.2
16	4	12	4.0	22	4.4
17	5	15	5.0	23	4.6
18	6	16	5.3	24	4.8
19	5	15	5.0	–	–
20	4	–	–	–	–

Source; Adapted from: Chou, Ya-lun; "Statistical Analysis"; Sceond Edition, 1975 Holt, Rinehart, and Winston.

"3-year Moving Average" = *ma*, which is obtained for each year by dividing the column (3) entry by 3. Columns (5) and (6) show how the "5-year Moving Totals" and "5-year Moving Averages" are calculated. The procedure is the same as the one used to calculate the "3-year" moving totals and moving averages, the only difference being the fact that now we use 5 values instead of 3 (current value, 2 values before the current value, and 2 values after the current value).

Note that because of this requirement, there are no values for years 1, 2, and 19, 20 (under column (5) and (6)) because we do not have available the 5 needed values.

When the given (original) data of the hypothetical time series y_t is plotted together with the 3-year and 5-year Moving Average Trends, the result is Figure 16.1.

Note that the fluctuations of the 3-year Moving Average are considerably less than the fluctuations of the original data, while the fluctuations have completely disappeared in the 5-year Moving Average. We can, then, ask the Question: When can the Moving Average be used as a measure of Trend?

1. **Characteristics of Moving Averages (MA) exhibited by Figure 16.1**
   a) If the data show a Uniform Periodic Variation, a MA of length equal to that period will completely eliminate the Periodic Variation.
   b) If a series changes by a constant amount per unit of time, and its fluctuations are periodic, a MA of length equal to the period of the fluctuations will be Linear.
   c) A MA of length different than the length of the period does not completely eliminate the fluctuations in the original data, but it does make the fluctuations smaller.

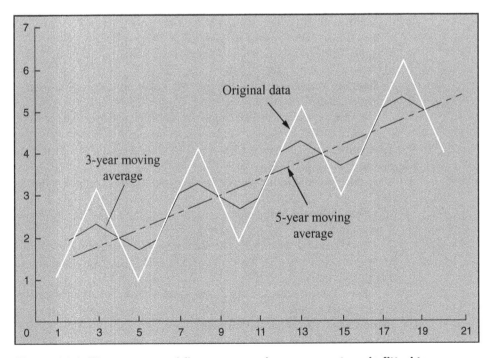

Figure 16.1 Three-year and five-year moving average trends fitted to a hypothetical data set, having five-year cycles with uniform duration and amplitude.

2. **Moving Averages (MA) used as measures of Trend**

Using the above characteristics as a basis, we can make the following statement: "A Moving Average may constitute a Satisfactory Trend for a Time Series which is basically Linear and whose Cycles are regular in Duration and Amplitude". Unfortunately these are characteristics that very rarely, if ever, are exhibited by economic Time Series.

3. **Disadvantages in using Moving Averages (MA) as a measure of Trend**

a) When computing the MA, depending on its length, we lose one or more years of data at each end of the series.

b) The MA is not represented by some particular Mathematical function (as for example the "Exponential Smoothing" method is) and is therefore not capable of objective projection into the future.

Since the main objective of Trend Analysis is Forecasting, and the MA does not have this capability, it is no longer used as a Trend measure.

But, Moving Averages still have their uses! The MA is the basic tool used in analyzing the Seasonal component of a Time Series, through the construction of a "Centered, 12-month Moving Average" as we will show below.

■ **The Seasonal Component, S**

1. The seasonal component of a Time Series is obtained by constructing a "centered, 12-month moving average" which is an estimate of TC (*i.e.*, the product of the Trend and Cyclical components).

By the seasonal component of a Time Series (or Seasonal Variation of a Time Series) we refer to the fluctuations which complete a whole cycle within a year and have about the same pattern year after year. Annual data do not exhibit seasonal variations, but Monthly and Quarterly data do! For example, the price of fresh vegetables changes from season to season (or month to month), and it is usually High in January and Low in July.

The seasonal variations can exhibit one of 2 patterns:

a) **A Stable Pattern** which remains stable over a number of years and is relatively easy to measure.

b) **A Changing Pattern** in which the seasonal variations change from year to year, and it is difficult to measure.

To measure the Seasonal Component of a Time Series we construct a "Seasonal Index" by using a "centered, 12-month MA" as shown below:

2. **The Seasonal Index** consists of 12 numbers, one for each month of the year, and may be Specific or Typical.

a) **A Specific Seasonal Index** refers to the seasonal changes during a particular year.

b) **A Typical Seasonal Index** is obtained by averaging a number of Specific Seasonal Indeces.

By observing several specific seasonals, one can determine whether the seasonal pattern of a Time Series is stable, changing gradually, or changing abruptly.

For a Typical Seasonal Index to be representative, the specific Seasonal Indeces must be stable.

3. **Calculation of a Typical Seasonal Index**

a) Assume a Multiplicative Model for the Time Series Components (*i.e.*, assume that $y_t = TSCI$).

b) Construct a "Centered, 12-month MA", which is a measure of TC, because it eliminates all of the Seasonal (*S*) and most Irregular (*I*) influences.

To show how this is done, we will use Table 16.3, which shows the "Stocks of frozen vegetables, in cold storage, at the end of each month, for the years 1952–1958", whose columns have the following meanings

Year and month	Stock (1)	12-month moving total (2)	12-month moving average (3)	Centered 12-month moving average (4)	Ratio to moving average (percent) (5)
1952					
Jan	444	–	–	–	–
Feb	399	–	–	–	–
Mar	348	–	–	–	–
Apr	314	–	–	–	–
May	302	–	–	–	–
Jun	337			–	–
		5204	434		
Jul	385			436.0	88.3
		5255	438		
Aug	463			440.0	105.2
		5306	442		
Sep	530			445.0	119.1
		5378	448		
Oct	577			451.0	127.9
		5448	454		
Nov	570			456.5	124.9
		5507	459		
Dec	535			461.0	116.1
1953					
		5554	463		
Jan	495			466.5	106.1
		5637	470		
Feb	450			474.5	94.8
		5748	479		
Mar	420			485.5	86.5
		5906	492		
Apr	384			499.0	77.0
		6066	506		
May	361			512.0	70.5
		6218	518		
Jun	384			525.0	73.1
		6388	532		
Jul	468			538.0	87.0
		6524	544		
Aug	574			548.5	104.6
		6638	553		
Sep	688			557.0	123.5
		6731	561		
Oct	737			564.5	130.6
		6817	568		
Nov	722			571.5	126.3
		6902	575		
Dec	705			577.5	122.1
1954					
		6962	580		
Jan	631			581.0	108.6
		6987	582		
Feb	564			583.5	96.7
		7015	585		
Mar	513			585.0	87.7
		7025	585		
Apr	470			584.0	80.5
		6998	583		
May	446			581.5	76.7
		6965	580		
Jun	444			578.0	76.8
		6909	576		
Jul	493			573.5	86.0
		6855	571		
Aug	602			568.5	105.9

Table title: **Table 16.3*   Frozen Vegetable, Stocks, Cold Storage, End of the Month, 1952–1958**

Year and month	12-month Stock (1)	moving total (2)	12-month moving average (3)	Centered 12-month moving average (4)	Ratio to moving average (percent) (5)
1954					
Sep	698	6796	566		
				564.0	123.8
Oct	710	6740	562		
				560.0	126.8
Nov	689	6697	558		
				556.0	123.9
Dec	649	6647	554		
				553.0	117.4
1955					
Jan	577	6622	552		
				551.5	104.6
Feb	505	6612	551		
				551.0	91.7
Mar	457	6615	551		
				550.0	83.1
Apr	427	6590	549		
				548.5	77.8
May	396	6573	548		
				547.0	72.4
Jun	419	6547	546		
				545.0	76.9
Jul	483	6522	544		
				543.0	89.0
Aug	605	6503	542		
				541.5	111.7
Sep	673	6494	541		
				541.0	124.4
Oct	693	6487	541		
				540.5	128.2
Nov	663	6484	540		
				541.0	122.6
Dec	624	6503	542		
				544.5	114.6
1956					
Jan	558	6565	547		
				551.5	101.2
Feb	496	6670	556		
				562.0	88.3
Mar	450	6816	568		
				576.0	78.1
Apr	424	7012	584		
				593.5	71.4
May	415	7234	603		
				613.0	67.7
Jun	481	7476	623		
				633.0	76.0
Jul	588	7710	643		
				652.5	90.1
Aug	751	7939	662		
				671.0	111.9
Sep	869	8165	680		
				689.0	126.1
Oct	915	8380	698		
				708.0	129.2
Nov	905	8612	718		
				726.5	124.6
Dec	858	8822	735		
				742.5	115.6
1957					
Jan	787	8998	750		
				755.5	104.2
Feb	722	9137	761		
				766.5	94.2
Mar	665	9260	772		
				776.5	85.6
Apr	656	9376	781		
				784.5	83.6
May	625	9454	788		
				790.0	79.1
Jun	657	9506	792		
				793.0	82.8

Table 16.3* Frozen Vegetable, Stocks, Cold Storage, End of the Month, 1952–1958 (continued)

Table 16.3* Frozen Vegetable, Stocks, Cold Storage, End of the Month, 1952–1958 (continued)

Year and month	12-month Stock (1)	moving total (2)	12-month moving average (3)	Centered 12-month moving average (4)	Ratio to moving average (percent) (5)
1957					
Jul	727	9530	794	794.0	91.6
Aug	874	9524	794	793.0	110.2
Sep	985	9500	792	790.0	124.7
Oct	993	9457	788	784.5	126.6
Nov	957	9378	781	777.5	123.1
Dec	882	9289	774	769.5	114.6
1958					·
Jan	781	9182	765	762.0	102.5
Feb	698	9106	759	755.5	92.4
Mar	622	9025	752	747.0	83.3
Apr	577	8901	742	738.0	78.2
May	536	8812	734	732.0	73.2
Jun	550	8754	730	728.5	75.5
Jul	651	8719	727	–	–
Aug	793	–	–	–	–
Sep	861	–	–	–	–
Oct	904	–	–	–	–
Nov	899	–	–	–	–
Dec	847	–	–	–	–

*Source; Adapted from: Chou, Ya-lun; "Statistical Analysis", Second Edition, 1975 Holt, Rinehart, and Winston.

α) **Column (1)** is the Total Value of the y_t series.

β) **Column (2)** is a "12-month Moving Total", *i.e.*, each of the values of Column 2 is the sum of 12 values of the y_t series.

   The first value of Column (2), 5204, is the sum of the 12 monthly values of 1952. Notice that this value (5204) is placed between June and July of 1952 (the mid-point of the 12 months we are adding together).

   The next value of Column (2), 5255, is the sum of the monthly values: February 1952 + March 1952 + $\cdots$ + January 1953, and similarly for the other values of Column (2).

γ) **Column (3)** is obtained by dividing the corresponding entry in Column (2) by 12 (*i.e.*, 434 ≈ 5204/12 = 433.67)

δ) **Column (4)** is the numerical average of 2 successive values of Column (3), with the result placed "between these 2 values", thus "centering" the result to a particular month (Recall that the entries of both Columns (2) and (3) are "between" months).

   For example the first entry of Column (4), 436.0, is obtained from: (434 + 438)/2 = 436, and is placed "between" 434 and 438, thus making the July 1952 value = 436. The other values of Column (4) are obtained similarly.

   The entries of Column (4) are estimates of *TC* (*i.e.*, the product of the Trend and Cyclical Components. Therefore, by dividing the y_t value

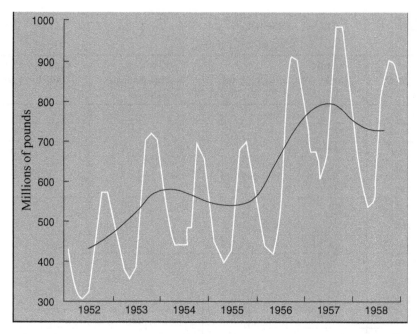

Figure 16.2 Stock of frozen vegetables in the United States, 1952–1958, and twelve-month moving average.

(Column (1)), by the *TC* value (Column (4)), we obtain an estimate of *SI* (in percent form), which is shown in Table 16.3 as Column (5).

    When the values of both column (1) and column (4) are plotted in the same graph against time, Figure 16.2 is obtained from which it can be seen that the 12–month MA is a smooth curve which no longer exhibits the seasonal Highs and Lows of the original data (column (1)). The "12–month MA" is an estimate of *TC* because seasonal variations have a Fixed Periodicity of 12 months and, therefore, a 12–month MA is expected to eliminate all of the seasonal component (The I component is assumed to be a Normally distributed random variable with Expected Value = 0, and an Unknown Variance = σ^2).

ε) **Column (5)** is obtained by dividing the Column (1) value by the corresponding Column (4) value and multiplying by 100. For example, the first value of Column (5), 88.3, is obtained from: (385/436) × 100. The other values of Column (5) are obtained similarly. Then, for each calendar year, the 12 monthly entries of column (5) are the Specific Seasonal Indeces for that year, and are estimates of *SI* (since the entries of column (4) are estimates of *TC* and were divided into $y_t = TSCI$ (Column (1)).

Note: Six (6) monthly values were lost at each end of the series.

4. **Check the Stability of the Specific Seasonal Indeces**

Before proceeding with the construction of a Typical Seasonal Index, we must determine if the Specific Seasonal Indeces (constructed above) are stable and, therefore, suitable for constructing a Typical Seasonal Index. To check the stability of the Specific Seasonal Indeces we tabulate them as shown in Table 16.4, and plot them as shown in Figure 16.3. Their stability is determined by examining Figure 16.3.

Table 16.4 Specific Seasonals for end-of month stock of frozen vegetables 1952–1958

Month	Year						
	1952	1953	1954	1955	1956	1957	1958
Jan		106.1	108.6	104.6	101.2	104.2	102.5
Feb		94.8	96.7	91.7	88.3	94.2	92.4
Mar		86.5	87.7	83.1	78.1	85.6	83.3
Apr		77.0	80.5	77.8	71.4	83.6	78.2
May		70.5	76.7	72.4	67.7	79.1	73.2
Jun		73.1	76.8	76.9	76.0	82.8	75.5
Jul	88.3	87.0	86.0	89.0	90.1	91.6	
Aug	105.2	104.6	105.9	111.7	111.9	110.2	
Sep	119.1	123.5	123.8	124.4	126.1	124.7	
Oct	127.9	130.6	126.8	128.2	129.2	126.6	
Nov	124.9	126.3	123.9	122.6	124.6	123.1	
Dec	116.1	122.1	117.4	114.6	115.6	114.6	

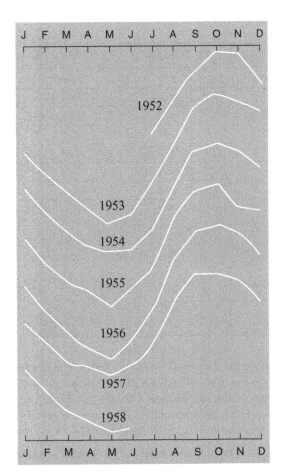

Figure 16.3 Specific Seasonal patterns for end-of month stock of frozen vegetables, in tier-graph form.

Table 16.4 shows 6 Specific Seasonal Indeces for each month, while Figure 16.3 shows their graphs in a tier-form.

All the Specific Seasonal Indeces have identical Turning Points (May is low, and October is high), and show a high-degree of Uniformity.

Therefore, the Seasonal pattern is Stable, and we should proceed with the construction of a Typical Seasonal Index, as shown below

5. **Eliminate the Irregular Movements (*i.e.*, Eliminate the I component)**
   Under the assumption that I, in the SI product (obtained by dividing y_t by TC, when $y_t = TSCI$), is Normally distributed with Expected Value $= 0$ and Variance $= \sigma^2$, we will eliminate I by the following Averaging process:

   a) **Rank the values of Table 16.4**, which shows monthly SI components, from Lowest to Highest, to obtain Table 16.5.

   b) **In Table 16.5, eliminate the smallest and largest value** of each of the 6 monthly SI components (*i.e.*, remove the Extreme observations).

   c) **Compute "Modified Means"**, as shown in Table 16.5, by first obtaining the Average of the remaining 4 central values for each month, and then dividing by 4. For example, for the month of January, after eliminating the smallest value (101.2), and the largest value (108.6), the sum of the 4 central values is $= 102.5 + 104.2 + 104.6 + 106.1 = 417.4$, and the Modified Mean for January $= 417.4/4 = 104.35 \approx 104.4$

Table 16.5 Computation of the Seasonal Index for the stock of frozen vegetables, 1952–1958												
Rank	**Jan**	**Feb**	**Mar**	**Apr**	**May**	**Jun**	**Jul**	**Aug**	**Sep**	**Oct**	**Nov**	**Dec**
1	101.2	88.3	78.1	71.4	67.7	73.1	86.0	104.6	119.1	126.6	122.6	114.6
2	102.5	91.7	83.1	77.0	70.5	75.5	87.0	105.2	123.5	126.8	123.1	114.6
3	104.2	92.4	83.3	77.8	72.4	76.0	88.3	105.9	123.8	127.9	123.9	115.6
4	104.6	94.2	85.6	78.2	73.2	76.8	89.0	110.2	124.4	128.2	124.6	116.1
5	106.1	94.8	86.5	80.5	76.7	76.9	90.1	111.7	124.7	129.2	124.9	117.4
6	108.6	96.7	87.7	83.6	79.1	82.8	91.6	111.9	126.1	130.6	126.3	122.1
Total of four central items	417.4	373.1	338.5	313.5	292.8	305.2	354.4	433.0	496.4	512.1	496.5	463.7
Modified mean	104.4	93.3	84.6	78.4	73.2	76.3	88.6	108.2	124.1	128.0	124.1	115.9
Adjusted seasonal index	104.5	93.4	84.7	78.4	73.2	76.3	88.7	108.3	124.2	128.1	124.2	116.0

d) **Calculate the Adjusted Seasonal Index** The sum of the 12 values in a Seasonal index should add up to 1200, or an average of 100.0 per month. The sum of the "12 Modified Means" of Table 16.5 is equal to 1199.1, and not 1200, as it should be. Therefore, to obtain the desired sum of 1200, we Adjust the 12 Modified Means by multiplying each by the ratio: $\frac{1200}{1199.1} \approx 1.00075$, and obtain the "Adjusted Seasonal Index" for this data set which appears as the last line of Table 16.5.

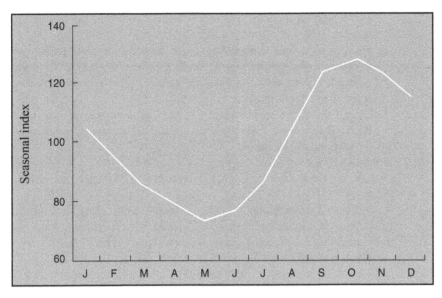

Figure 16.4 Season Index of frozen vegetables stock in the United States, 1952–1958.

A graph of the Seasonal Index appears in Figure 16.4, which shows that the Seasonal pattern of our illustrative series is quite pronounced, with a seasonal Low associated with May, which is about 27 percent below the average of 100, and a seasonal High associated with October, which is more than 28 percent above the average of 100.

6. **Using the Seasonal Index**

Forecasts of Total Annual Values (sales for Example) are first transformed into monthly forecasts (this is done by dividing the Annual data by 12), and then the monthly forecasts are multiplied by the Seasonal Index, constructed as shown above, to obtain the corresponding monthly data.

■ The Cyclical Component, C

1. Definition of Cycles

By the Cyclical Component of a Time Series, we refer to a repeated sequence of fluctuations of different Durations and Amplitudes.

Cycles of a Time Series show a broad pattern of some repetition, but

a) There are differences in Duration of these variations, and
b) There are differences in Amplitude of these variations

These variations are different than the Seasonal Variations and/or Periodic Variations.

This lack of Uniformity in these Variations implies that

c) It is possible to isolate Cycles, and
d) It is almost Impossible to Project them into the future (*i.e.*, it is very difficult to Forecast Cycles)

But, for Time Series affected by Cyclical Factors (such as: Durable goods and Investment Goods) Projecting the Cyclical movement becomes extremely important.

Unfortunately, no objective way exists of accurately Forecasting Cyclical Turning Points and Amplitudes, which are the main characteristics of Cyclical Fluctuations. But sometimes the following approaches may be taken:

e) Sine or Cosine functions are fitted to the data. But such an approach assumes the existence of periodicities in the data (remember that the Trigonometric functions of Sine and Cosine are periodic – *i.e.*, they repeat themselves) that no economic series meets.

f) Extend the Cycle subjectively! But such an approach implies the use of Personal judgment, and requires a substantial amount of familiarity with the particular Time Series.

2. **Isolate Cycles**

Q: How do we isolate the Cyclical Component, C, when a time series, y_t is given?

A: It depends on whether the data is Annual or Monthly, and whether an Additive or Multiplicative Model is assumed for the way the 4 components of the Time Series are combined to produce the Time Series

a) **From Annual Data**

It is relatively simple to isolate cycles from annual data because Annual data consists basically of 2 components only: The Trend and the Cycle, because

Seasonal Variations do not show up in Annual data, and Irregular movements, which are short-run influences compared to an entire year, produce negligible effects upon annual data, because Positive and Negative influences (remember: Irregular movements are Normally distributed variables, with Expected Value = 0) offset each other.

With Annual data, the Trend value is considered the **normal annual growth**, or the "Statistical Normal", while the Cyclical variations are considered as Deviations from the Normal values.

Then, depending on whether an Additive or Multiplicative Model is assumed, we proceed as follows:

i) **Assuming an Additive Model** $y_t = T + C$

α) Use Regression Analysis to first find T

β) Subtract T, from y_t, to find C, or: $C = y_t - T$ (16.16)

ii) **Assuming a Multiplicative Model** $y_t = TC$

α) Use Regression Analysis to first find T

β) Divide y_t by T, to find C, or $C = y_t / T$ (16.17)

However, Annual data obscure 2 critical aspects of cycles, namely:

α) The Location of Turning Points, and

β) The Amplitude of fluctuations between Turning Points

Because of this, it is desirable to use Monthly (or Quarterly) data to isolate the Cycles. But, when we do this, Seasonal and Irregular movements enter the picture.

Therefore, to measure Cycles from monthly data, we must remove the Seasonal Variations (S) and the Trend (T), thus Estimating CI.

b) **From Monthly Data** (assuming a Multiplicative Model: $y_t = TSCI$)

α) Obtain T from Regression Analysis

β) Obtain S from a 12-month centered MA

γ) Obtain the "Statistical Normal" which for Monthly data is defined as the product TS.

δ) Obtain CI, by dividing TS into y_t, or: $CI = y_t / TS$ (16.18)

These calculations are made clear by using Table 16.6, which shows the Cyclical-Irregular Movements for US Factory Production of

Table 16.6* Cyclical-Irregular Movements for United States Factory Production of Cheese, 1947–1955

Year and month	Production y (millions of pounds) (1)	Trend[a] y_t (T) (2)	Seasonal[b] index S (as ratios) (3)	Statistical normal TS (4)	Cyclical-irregulae movements y/TS (percent) (5)
1947					
Jan	74.3	93.3	0.780	72.774	102.1
Feb	78.3	93.5	0.770	71.995	108.8
Mar	100.2	93.6	0.968	90.605	110.6
Apr	114.1	93.8	1.099	103.086	110.7
May	140.6	94.0	1.410	132.540	106.1
Jun	148.1	94.1	1.416	133.246	111.1
Jul	133.3	94.3	1.233	116.272	114.6
Aug	104	94.4	1.096	103.462	100.5
Sep	87.7	94.6	0.933	88.262	99.4
Oct	80.9	94.8	0.839	79.537	101.7
Nov	60.9	94.9	0.712	67.569	90.1
Dec	60.4	95.1	0.744	70.754	85.4
1948					
Jan	63.7	95.3	0.780	74.334	85.7
Feb	65.2	95.4	0.770	73.458	88.8
Mar	80.3	95.6	0.968	92.541	86.8
Apr	94.0	95.8	1.099	105.284	89.3
May	129.8	95.9	1.410	135.219	96.0
Jun	131.9	96.1	1.416	136.078	96.9
Jul	114.7	96.3	1.233	118.738	96.6
Aug	108.5	96.4	1.096	105.654	102.7
Sep	89.4	96.6	0.933	90.128	99.2
Oct	81.5	96.8	0.839	81.215	100.4
Nov	67.3	96.9	0.712	68.993	97.5
Dec	72.1	97.1	0.744	72.242	99.8

a $y_t = 93.29 + 0.165x$ (Origin, January 1947).
b Modified means of 4 central ratios of actual values to centered 12-month moving averages for 1947–1955.

Source: Adapted from: Chou, Ya-lun; "Statistical Analysis", Second Edition, 1975 Holt, Rinehart, and Winston.

Cheese for the year 1947 – 1955 (only computations for 1947 and 1948 are shown in Table 16.6).

α) **Column (1)** of Table 16.6 is the original data of the Time Series.

β) **Column (2)** contains the Numerical value of the Trend equation $y_t = 93.29 + 0.165x$, (with origin January 1947)

γ) **Column (3)** contains the Seasonal Indeces, computed by modified means of 4 central values (obtained by a centered 12-month MA)

δ) **Column (4)** contains the "Statistical Normal" value $= TS$

ε) **Column (5)** contains the *CI* estimate, in percent form, which is obtained by dividing the original data (Column (1)) value by the corresponding *TS* value (Column (4)), and multiplying by 100.

For example, the first value of Column (5) of Table 16.6 is obtained from: $(74.3/72.774) \times 100 = 102.1$, and the other values of Column (5) are calculated in a similar manner.

When the values of Column (1) are plotted against Time, Figure 16.5 is obtained (upper part) which in addition to the original data, also shows the Trend. The Seasonal variations are so pronounced that the original data do not reveal any cyclical movements at all.

The Lower part of Figure 16.5 is a plot of the *CI* product (values of Table 16.6) versus time, and tells quite a different story by revealing a strong Cyclical Component, and making it necessary to eliminate the Seasonal Component from the original data before we can hope to extract any cyclical pattern of variation that may be present.

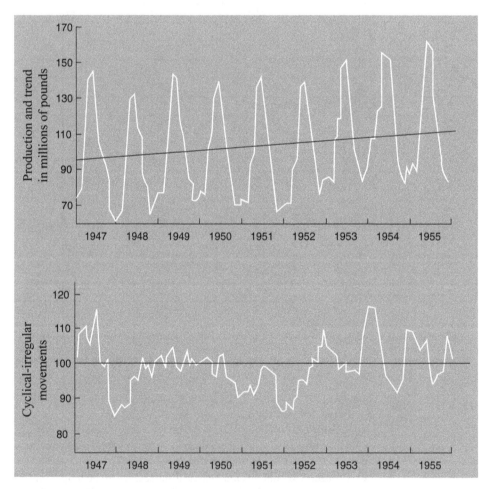

Figure 16.5 United States Factory Cheese Production, with Trend and Cyclical-Irregular movements, 1947–1955.

■ The Random (or Irregular) Component (*I*)

As we have said previously, the *I* component is assumed to be Normally distributed, with Expected Value $= 0$ and Variance $= \sigma^2$, which is unknown.

It is natural to wish to eliminate the *I* component from the *CI* product, and various attempts have been made towards this goal.

1. One approach is to "smooth" the *CI* curve with "free-hand" drawing.
2. Another approach is to calculate a MA of *CI* to estimate *C*. Terms used are often 3 or 5 months. An odd number of terms makes the computations easier (there is no need for "centering" the MA as is the case when an even number of terms is selected). The selection of 3 or 5 terms is also desirable because they avoid "smoothing out too much" of the cycles.

    However, there is no satisfactory method of removing Irregular Variations (the 2 approaches mentioned above are, in general, not satisfactory). This has led to the practice of analyzing Cyclical and Irregular fluctuations as a single entity.

We have now finished discussing the first step of the Decomposition Method. At this stage we should have available the components of the series: *T*, *S*, and *CI* (or *C* and *I* if we use one of the 2 methods mentioned above).

1. Second step of the Decomposition Method consists of Projecting each of these components to the "Time Frame" of interest either by using an equation (for the Trend), or a Multiplier (for the Seasonal Component – use the Seasonal Index as a multiplier) or pattern extrapolation (to determine the Cyclical Component *C*, or the combined *CI* component).
2. Then, the third (3rd) and Final step of the Decomposition method consists of Re-combining the projected components (at the Time of interest), by using the same model we used in the Decomposition step (Additive or Multiplicative). The Re-combined Series is the Forecasted value of the Time Series, y_t, according to the Decomposition method.

16.5   Other Forecasting Methods

Table 16.1 lists and compares certain characteristics of seven Forecasting methods, among them the Simple Exponential Smoothing and Decomposition methods which we have discussed, in some detail, above.

We now turn our attention to a brief discussion of the other five Forecasting methods listed in Table 16.1, namely: Holt-Winters, Box-Jenkins, Multiple Regression, Econometrics, and Multivariate Box-Jenkins.

16.5.1 Holt-Winters Forecasting Method

This method is a more sophisticated version of the Exponential Smoothing method. Recall that the Exponential Smoothing method is used only for short-term forecasting. However, the more elaborate Holt-Winters method also allows the study of Trend patterns in the data, by using intermediate and/or long-term forecasting.

To use the H-W method at any time period, *t*, we need to continuously estimate the Level of the time series, L_t, and the Trend of the time series, T_t, using the equations below

$$L_t = C_1(L_{t-1} + T_{t-1}) + (1 - C_1)Y_t \tag{16.19}$$

$$T_t = C_2 T_{t-1} + (1 - C_2)(L_t - L_{t-1}), \tag{16.20}$$

where

$$L_t = \text{Level of the given time series, computed at time } t$$
$$L_{t-1} = \text{Level of the given time series, computed at time } t - 1$$
$$T_t = \text{Trend of the given time series, computed at time } t$$
$$T_{t-1} = \text{Trend of the given time series, computed at time } t - 1$$
$$Y_t = \text{Observed value of the given time series, in period } t$$
$$C_1 = \text{Smoothing constant, subjectively assigned } (0 < C_1 < 1)$$
$$C_2 = \text{Smoothing constant, subjectively assigned } (0 < C_2 < 1)$$

To begin computations, we let

$$L_2 = Y_2 \tag{16.21}$$

and

$$T_2 = Y_2 - Y_1, \tag{16.22}$$

and choose the smoothing constants C_1 and C_2.

To use the H-W method for forecasting, the assumption is made that all future trends will continue from the most recent L_t value ($L_t = L_n$).

Therefore, to forecast k years into the future, we let

$$\hat{Y}_{n+k} = L_n + kT_n, \tag{16.23}$$

where

$$\hat{Y}_{n+k} = \text{Forecasted value, } k \text{ years into the future}$$
$$k = \text{Number of years into the future}$$
$$L_n = \text{Most recently computed Level value (when } t = n)$$
$$T_n = \text{Most recently computed Trend value (when } t = n)$$

To illustrate the Holt-Winters method, suppose we have the following values for a time series, Y_t:

Y_1	Y_2	Y_3	Y_4	Y_5	Y_6	Y_7	Y_8	Y_9	Y_{10}
3.8	4.0	4.5	5.0	5.6	6.0	6.4	7.0	8.0	9.0

Choosing smoothing constants $C_1 = 0.4$ and $C_2 = 0.6$ and substituting into equations (16.19) and (16.20) we obtain

$$L_t = 0.4(L_{t-1} + T_{t-1}) + 0.6Y_t$$

and

$$T_t = 0.6T_{t-1} + 0.4(L_t - L_{t-1})$$

From these equations, when $t = 3$ and using equations (16.21) and (16.22) we obtain:

$$L_3 = 0.4(L_2 + T_2) + 0.6Y_3 = 0.4[Y_2 + (Y_2 - Y_1)] + 0.6Y_3$$
$$= 0.4[4.0 + 0.2] + 0.6(4.5) = 0.4(4.2) + 0.6(4.5) = 1.68 + 2.70 = 4.38$$

and $T_3 = 0.6T_2 + 0.4(L_3 - L_2) = 0.6(0.2) + 0.4(4.38 - 4.0) = 0.12 + 0.4(0.38)$
$$= 0.12 + 0.152 = 0.272$$

If we continue in this manner, the values of L_3 and T_3 will be used in equations (16.19) and (16.20) to obtain L_4 and T_4, etc.

To use the Holt-Winters method for forecasting, we use the latest estimates of current level (L_t) and trend (T_t) and equation (16.23), in which we set $k = 1, 2, \ldots$, depending on how many years ahead we wish to forecast. Let us suppose that in the above example

$L_{10} = 12$ and $T_{10} = 1.2$

Then from equation (16.23) we would obtain:

$k = 1$; one year ahead: $\hat{Y}_{10+1} = \hat{Y}_{11} = L_{10} + (1)T_{10} = 12 + (1)(1.2) = 13.2$

$k = 2$; two years ahead: $\hat{Y}_{10+2} = \hat{Y}_{12} = L_{10} + (2)T_{10} = 12 + (2)(1.2) = 14.4$

$k = 3$; three years ahead: $\hat{Y}_{10+3} = \hat{Y}_{13} = L_{10} + (3)T_{10} = 12 + (3)(1.2) = 15.6$,

and so on, for other values of k.

16.5.2 The Box-Jenkins Method

This method studies an entire class of models known as ARMA (or: Auto Regressive Moving Average) models. From the behavior of the given data an appropriate ARMA model is selected, and used to make forecasts.

The main advantage of the Box-Jenkins method is that it provides the most accurate forecasts for short term forecasting.

The main disadvantage of the Box-Jenkins method is that the process of identifying the correct model from the class of possible models is difficult to understand and time consuming.

16.5.3 Multiple Regression Method

This method uses the Least Squares method to determine the coefficients of the regression equation, which is the relationship connecting the dependent variable (y) to one or more independent variables ($x_1, x_2, \ldots, x_p$). The regression equation is then used to forecast future values of the dependent variable. For more details of this method, see Chapter 15.

16.5.4 The Econometrics Method

This method describes the behavior of an economic system by a system of interrelated regression equations. The coefficients of the equations, which make up the system of these regression equations, are obtained using the Least Squares method.

The main disadvantage of Econometric models is that they are more difficult to understand and more costly than other models, because of the costs involved in developing a model and collecting and analyzing the required data. Another disadvantage of these models is the fact that they require forecasts of future values of the independent variables in the regression equations.

For a more detailed discussion of the Econometrics Method see Appendix 16C.

16.5.5 The Multivariate Box-Jenkins Method

The Multivariate Box-Jenkins method is an extension of the univariate Box-Jenkins method (discussed in section 16.4.2 above) in which past values of a single variable are used to forecast future values of that variable. In the Multivariate Box-Jenkins method the assumption is made that independent variables exist which are related to the dependent variable, which is to be forecasted, and the method attempts to relate these independent variable to the dependent variable by means of Transfer Functions.

16.6 Appendix 16a

■ **Use Bivariate Data (x_i, y_i) to Fit a Quadratic (Least Squares)**

When discussing the Decomposition Method of Forecasting a Time Series, we mentioned that the calculation of the Trend (T) component requires us to use Regression Analysis methods to fit either:

1. A Linear Model
2. An Exponential Model
3. A Power Model
4. A Quadratic Model

We have already discussed how to fit Linear, Exponential, and Power Models to Bivariate Date (see chapters 13 and 14), but we have not before shown how to fit the Quadratic Model:

$$y = a + bx + cx^2, \tag{16A1}$$

to a set of Bivariate data, and we do so below.

■ **FITTING A QUADRATIC MODEL TO BIVARIATE DATA**

1. **Interpretation of the constants**
   a) The y-intercept, $y = a$, occurs when $x = 0$

   b) The Critical point of this function (*i.e.*, the value of x at which the Quadratic has either a Maximum value, or a Minimum value) occurs when

   $$x = x^* = -b/2c \tag{16A2}$$

   c) The Critical point is a Maximum, if $c < 0$
   d) The Critical point is a Minimum, if $c > 0$

2. **Deriving the Numerical Values of: a, b, c, using Least Squares**
   a) Start with the function

   $$Q(a, b, c) = \sum_{i=1}^{n}(y_i - a - bx_i - cx_i^2)^2 \tag{16A3}$$

   b) Find the Partial Derivatives: $\partial Q/\partial a$, $\partial Q/\partial b$, $\partial Q/\partial c$

   c) Set $\dfrac{\partial Q}{\partial a} = 0, \dfrac{\partial Q}{\partial b} = 0, \dfrac{\partial Q}{\partial c} = 0,$ \hfill (16A4)

   and solve the system of resulting equations simultaneously.
   d) The result is

   $$na + b\sum_{i=1}^{n}x_i + c\sum_{i=1}^{n}x_i^2 = \sum_{i=1}^{n}y_i \tag{16A5}$$

   $$a\sum_{i=1}^{n}x_i + b\sum_{i=1}^{n}x_i^2 + c\sum_{i=1}^{n}x_i^3 = \sum_{i=1}^{n}x_iy_i \tag{16A6}$$

   $$a\sum_{i=1}^{n}x_i^2 + b\sum_{i=1}^{n}x_i^3 + c\sum_{i=1}^{n}x_i^4 = \sum_{i=1}^{n}x_i^2y_i \tag{16A7}$$

e) Equations (16A5), (16A6), and (16A7), are the Normal equations of the Quadratic function. All of the Summations in these equations, and the value of n, can be obtained from the given Bivariate set of data (x_i, y_i).

f) When these equations are solved simultaneously, the Least Squares values for a, b, c are obtained, and are designated as: a^*, b^*, c^*.

g) This solution for (a^*, b^*, c^*) corresponds to a Minimum $Q(a, b, c)$ value, which we designate as: $Q(a^*, b^*, c^*)$ or $Q^*(a, b, c)$.

16.7   Appendix 16b—Barometric Methods

The Barometric methods assume that past Historical Patterns tend to repeat themselves in the Future, and that the Future can be predicted from certain happenings in the Present/Past.

Past Statistical Behavior, therefore, that appears to be regularly associated with fluctuations in Particular Series or General Business Conditions, is discovered and used as the basis for Forecasting.

Specific Series are identified, whose behavior can be used as a "Barometer of future changes in other Specific Series or General Business Conditions".

Therefore, the Barometric Methods involve the use of Statistical Indicators that will provide an indication of the direction in which a Specific Time Series or the Aggregate Economy is heading.

The Barometric Methods discussed in this Appendix are:

1. Statistical Indicators, and
2. Diffusion Index

■ Statistical Indicators

Their use in Forecasting is an outgrowth of studying the Lead-Lag relationships among different time series.

The Lead-Lag approach attempts to determine the approximate lapse of time between the movements of one series and the movements of general business conditions.

As an example, if one or more series can be found such that their Turning points lead by a Number of Months, with Substantial Regularity, the Turning points of General Business in the Past, it is only logical to use these leading series to Predict what is going to happen to General Business Activity in the future.

The most important list of Statistical Indicators started in 1937–1938, and was revised in 1950, 1960, and 1966.

A relatively recent list, consisting of 26 Indicators appears in "Indicators of Business Expansion and Contraction" published by NBER (National Bureau of Economic Research) in 1967.

The selection of the NBER Indicators has been made using the following 2 principles:

1. The Indicator must play a significant role in the accepted theory of Business Cycles.
2. A Selected Series must be closely correlated empirically with Fluctuations in General Economic Activity (*i.e.*, it must: Lead, Coincide with, or Lag Aggregate Economic activity consistently).

Among the current 26 NBER Statistical Indicators, 12 are classified as Leading Series, 8 as coincident series, and 6 as lagging series.

Up-to-date figures of these Indicators are published monthly in "Business Conditions Digest" and Weekly in "Statistical Indicator Reports".

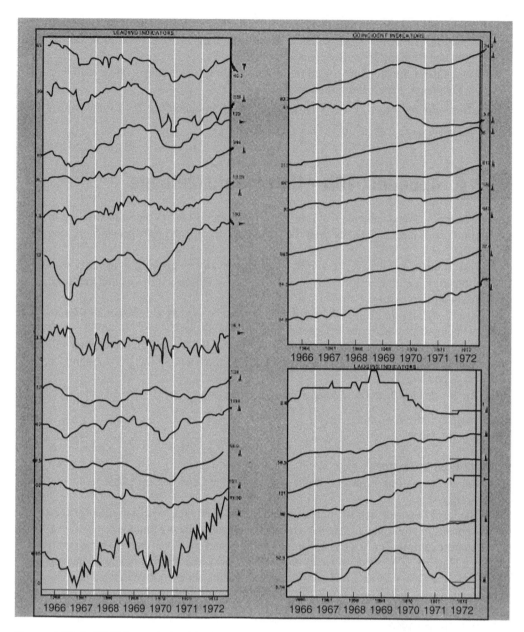

Figure16B.1 NBER statistical indicators (SOURCE: Statistical Indicators Associates, North Egremont, Mass., February 14, 1973).

Figure 16B.1 above is the graphical representation of these Indicators for the period 1966–1972.

i) **Leading Indicators** signal in advance a change in the basic performance of the economy as a whole.

The 12 Leading Indicators are:

1. Average Work Week-Manufacturing
2. Unemployment claims
3. Net Business Formation
4. New Orders-Durable Goods
5. Housing Permits
6. Plant and Equipment Contracts and Orders
7. Manufacturing and Trade Inventory Change

   8. Industrial Materials Prices
   9. Common Stock Prices
  10. Net Corporate Profits
  11. Ratio of Price to Unit Labor Cost
  12. Change in Consumer Debt

ii) **Coincident Indicators** are those whose movements roughly coincide with (and provide a measure of) the current performance of Aggregate Economic Activity.

   The 8 Coincident Indicators are:

   1. Non-Agricultural Employment
   2. Unemployment Rate
   3. Gross National Product (GNP) in current dollars
   4. GNP in 1958 dollars
   5. Industrial Production
   6. Personal Income
   7. Manufacturing and Trade sales
   8. Retail sales

iii) **Lagging Indicators** are those whose movements are in a direction opposite to the direction of the Leading Indicators, throughout various phases of Business Cycles.

   The 6 Lagging Indicators are:

   1. Unemployment Rate
   2. Plant and Equipment Expenditures
   3. Manufacturing and Trade Inventories
   4. Unit Labor Cost
   5. Commercial and Industrial Loans
   6. Bank Loans Interest Rate

The Statistical indicator approach to Forecasting attempts to derive the "Broad general framework of what the whole economy is doing" from what its sections are doing, and then moves on to evaluate any particular segment within this framework.

To facilitate reading of these indicators, NBER constructs an Index for each class of Indicators. Individual Indicators are weighted and adjusted so that all the indicators would have the same opportunity to influence the index, irrespective of their differences in amplitude.

Figure 16B.2 shows a graphical representation of such Composite Indeces.

Statistical Indicators are Most useful in Forecasting Turning Points, where most other methods tend to break down. Below is a list of 6 guidelines, suggested by: Leonard H. Lempert, director of "Statistical Indicator Reports", which help to gain insight into the timing of Turning Points:

1. Apply Maximum or Minimum leads (rather than average leads) to the Most Recent Highs (or Lows) in the Leading Indicators.
2. Apply Average, Maximum, or Minimum leads to subsequent Highs (or Lows) rather than to Initial peaks, in the Leading Indicators.
3. Relate the relative change in current and previous upswings (or downswings) after a comparable number of months have passed to ultimate lengths of upswings (or downswings).
4. Assume a Peak date in the Future, and study the resulting segment by segment progress of the upswing (or downswing) relative to the Usual Business Cycle.
5. Assume a Peak date at some point in the Future, and study Individual Indicators in the current and previous upswings (or downswings) at a corresponding number of months prior to a peak.
6. Compare the changes in the Indicators in the most recent 6 months to those in the preceding 6 months to often obtain a perspective for judging the progress of the upswing (or downswing).

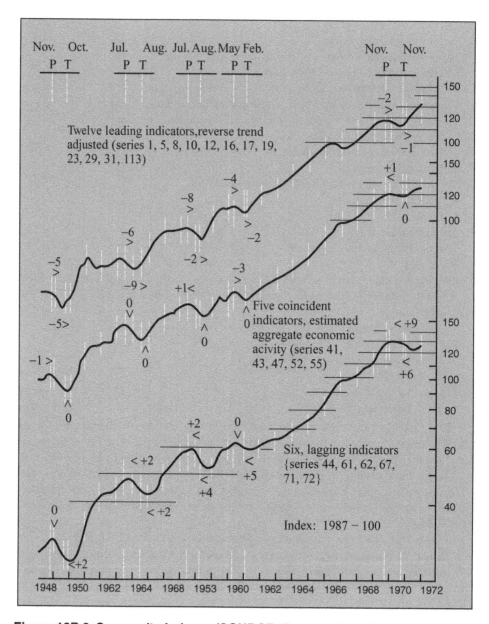

Figure 16B.2 Composite indexes (SOURCE: Bureau of the Census) Dates at the top of the chart are reference peak and trough dates when expansion ended and recession began (P) and when recession ended and expansion began (T). Numbers on the chart are length of lead (−) or lag (+), in months, from index peak or trough to reference peak or trough.

The record of NBER Indicators in Forecasting "Turning Points" is quite good. However, they cannot forecast Cyclical Amplitudes, and should be used together with other methods, which can Forecast Cyclical Amplitudes.

■ DIFFUSION INDEX

Diffusion Indices represent an effort to describe and Forecast Business Cycles.

A Diffusion Index is constructed around a known aggregate by determining the number of parts of the aggregate that are rising, and expressing that as a percent (%) of the total number of parts.

By the way they are constructed, diffusion indeces resemble "rates of change" of the aggregate; hence they tend to change direction well before the change in direction of the aggregate itself. Therefore, the movements of a Diffusion Index can be employed to Forecast the movements of the aggregate from which the Diffusion Index was constructed.

The most Comprehensive Diffusion Index (constructed by the NBER) includes some 400 series that are generally in conformity with business-cycle patterns. This Diffusion Index and the general Business Activity are shown in Figure 16B.3.

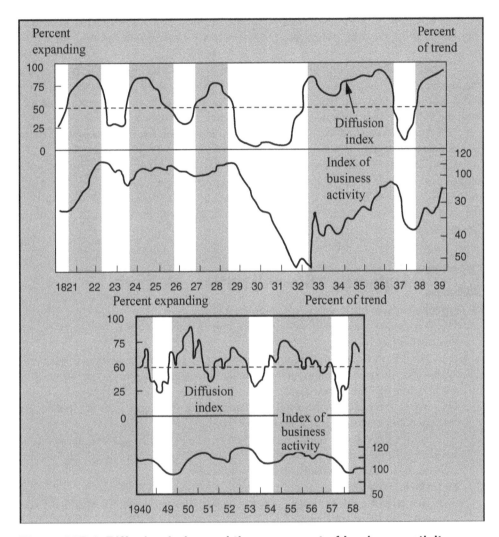

Figure 16B.3 Diffusion index and the movement of business activity (SOURCE: G.H. Moore, "The 1957–58 Business Contraction: New Model or Old?" American Economic Review, Vol. 49, May 1959, p. 298).

Because of its broad coverage the NBER diffusion index shows the tendency of all sectors of the economy to respond to the aggregate demand at different time sequences. At any given time, some series are expanding while others are contracting. Some are reaching their peaks, while others are moving toward their low points. However, after an upswing of General Business Activity gets into full force, almost all sectors of the economy will be expanding with it. After a certain period of time some sectors, and then more and more, will run into difficulties and start to contract.

Evidently the movement of the Diffusion Index is related to that of the General Business Activity.

But the peaks and throughs of the Diffusion Index are not the same as the peaks and throuhgs of the Business Cycles.

As long as more than 50% of the series are expanding, the economy as a whole is in the process of expansion. Consequently, it is not until the Diffusion Index has crossed the 50% line from above, that the peak of Business Cycle is reached.

Similarly, as long as less than 50% of the series are expanding, General Business must be in a state of contraction. Therefore, the Business as a whole reaches its trough, and starts to expand only when the Diffusion Index has crossed the 50% line from below.

It can be seen from Figure 16B.3 that there is a lead and lag relationship between the movements of the Diffusion Index and those of Business Activity. When the Diffusion Index reaches its peak and begins to turndown, the whole economy continues to expand until the Diffusion Index, decreasing, crosses the 50% line from above.

Now more sectors of the economy are contracting, and the downswing of General Business commences.

The Diffusion Index provides perfectly persistent leads, though of irregular duration, to the Index of Business Activity. It seems to be an excellent device for Forecasting the Turns in Business Cycles. But it does have its shortcomings, especially in the delays in waiting until it crosses the 50% line, to be able to Forecast a Turn in the Business Cycles.

16.8   Appendix 16c—Analytical Methods

■ Regression Analysis with Time—Series Data

The Forecasting techniques we introduced up to now pertain to Broad Economic Forecasts (Macro-Economics).

For Micro-Economic Level Forecasting (*i.e.*, suitable for particular business), Regression Analysis is important, even though the assumption of independence does not hold *true* in Time-Series data.

When the assumption of independence of the stochastic term is violated, the residual errors are *serially* correlated.

In this case, the *least squares* method will not provide *efficient* and *unbiased* estimators for the Regression Coefficients, and the "Sample Variance of Regression" may seriously underestimate the Population Variance.

a) Serial Correlation

A simple, but quite common form of serial correlation is the Linear First-Order Serial Correlation, in which:

$$e_i = re_{i-1} + v_i, \tag{16C.1}$$

where: r is the sample Correlation Coefficient, which is an estimator of ρ, the Population Coefficient of serial correlation, defined by:

$$r = \frac{\sum\limits_{i=2}^{n} e_i e_{i-1}}{\sum\limits_{i=2}^{n} e_{i-1}^2} \tag{16C.2}$$

and v_i are independent variables, with zero mean and constant variance.

Note: In (16C.1), the variable e_i depends on the value of the variable in the previous time frame (e_{i-1}), in addition to depending on the values of r and v_i. When $r = 0$ (*i.e.*, when linear first-order serial correlation is equal to zero),

$$e_i = v_i \qquad (16C.3)$$

This is the case of the independent stochastic terms.

The sample Correlation Coefficient r, is a random variable which can be positive or negative in value, and its interval of variation is:

$$-1 \leq r \leq 1 \qquad (16C.4)$$

b) The Durbin-Watson Test for Serial Correlation

Unfortunately, the sampling distribution of r, defined by (16C.2) above is generally not known and, therefore, tests on the Population Coefficient of Serial Correlation cannot be performed directly.

Fortunately another test Statistic, known as the Durbin-Watson d-statistic and defined by:

$$d = \frac{\sum_{i=2}^{n} (e_i - e_{i-1})^2}{\sum_{i=2}^{n} e_i^2} \qquad (16C.5)$$

has a known distribution, which can be used to test ρ.

It can be shown that $\qquad d \approx 2(1 - r), \qquad (16C.6)$

and, since: $\qquad -1 \leq r \leq 1, \ 0 \leq d \leq 4 \qquad (16C.7)$

The exact distribution of d depends on:

  i) The Sample Size n, and the

  ii) Number of Independent Variables, k, in the Regression Equation.

  However, given n and k and assuming that the v_i are distributed as $N(0, \sigma^2)$, the distribution of d always lies between the distributions of d_L and d_U (see attached Tables for $\alpha = 0.05$, and $\alpha = 0.025$; p. 709 & p. 710).

The Figure below shows the Rejection and Acceptance regions of the D-W test, which can be summarized as follows:

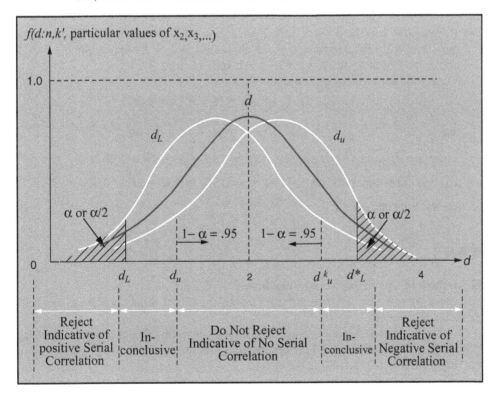

Figure 16C.1 The relation between the sampling distributions of d, d_L, and d_U.

    i) If we are testing: $H_0: \rho \leq 0$ vs. $H_1: \rho > 0$, H_0 will be Rejected if $d =$ (computed value of D-W) $< d_L$, and conclude that there is *significant positive serial correlation.*

    ii) If we are testing: $H_0: \rho \geq 0$ vs. $H_1: \rho < 0$, H_0 will be Rejected if $d =$ (computed value of D-W) $> 4 - d_L$, and conclude that there is *significant negative serial correlation.* (Note: $d_L^* = 4 - d_L$)

    iii) If we are testing: $H_0: \rho = 0$ vs. $H_1: \rho \neq 0$, H_0 will be Rejected if $d < d_L$ or $d > 4 - d_L$, and conclude that there is *significant serial correlation* (either positive or negative).

Note: As is shown in Figure 16C.1 above, there are 2 regions where the test is inconclusive. These 2 regions occur when:

$$d_L < d < d_U \text{ and } d_U^*(= 4 - d_U) < d < d_L^*(= 4 - d_L) \tag{16C.8}$$

EXAMPLE 16C.1

Suppose we are running a Regression Analysis with $k = 3$ and $n = 30$.

    i) If we wish to test: $H_0: \rho \leq 0$ vs. $H_1: \rho > 0$, at $\alpha = 0.05$ we find from the attached table that: $d_L = 1.21$ and $d_U = 1.65$ (p. 710, n = 30, k = 3, and $\alpha = 0.05$)
Thus H_0 will be Rejected if $d < d_L = 1.21$;
        H_0 will not be Rejected if $d > d_U = 1,65$; and:
        the test is inconclusive if $d_L = 1.21 \leq d \leq d_U = 1.65$

    ii) If we wish to test: $H_0: \rho \geq 0$ vs. $H_1: \rho < 0$, at p. 710, n = 30, k = 3, and $\alpha = 0.05$,

Then H_0 will be Rejected if $d > d_L^* = 4 - d_L = 4 - 1.21 = 2.79$;

H_0 will not be Rejected if $d < d_U^* = 4 - d_U = 4 - 1.65 = 2.35$; and:

the test is inconclusive if $d_U^* = 2.35 \leq d \leq d_L^* = 2.79$

    iii) If we wish to test: $H_0: \rho = 0$ vs. $H_1: \rho \neq 0$, at $\alpha = 0.05$, the critical points are found in the $\alpha/2 = 0.025$ attached table, from which we find, for $k = 3$ and $n = 30$: $d_L = 1.12$ and $d_U = 1.54$ (see page 709, n = 30, k = 3, and $\alpha/2 = 0.025$)
Then; from these values we calculate:

$$d_L^* = 4 - d_L = 4 - 1.12 = 2.88$$

and $$d_U^* = 4 - d_U = 4 - 1.54 = 2.46.$$

Therefore H_0 will be Rejected if $d < d_L = 1.12$ or $d > d_L^* = 2.88$;

H_0 will not be Rejected if $d_U = 1.54 \leq d \leq d_U^* = 2.46$; and:

the test is inconclusive if

$$d_L^* = 1.12 \leq d \leq d_U = 1.54 \text{ or } d_U^* = 2.46 \leq d \leq d_L^* = 2.88$$

■ ■ ■

■ Methods of Correcting Serial Correlation

Assuming that we have detected the existence of significant serial correlation, can it be corrected or removed?

    Several methods have been suggested towards answering this question, all of which depend on the transformation of the observations (variables). Below we discuss some of the simpler and more practical such methods.

a) **Regression with Serially Correlated Error Terms**

Under the assumption that First Order Serial Correlation exists, we have in a sample of size n (see equation (16C.1))

$$e_i = re_{i-1} + v_i$$

An efficient estimation procedure is one which *minimizes* the sum of squared error terms v_i. Namely, we wish to use the Least Squares method to minimize:

$$Q = \sum_{i=2}^{n} v_i^2 = \sum_{i=2}^{n} (e_i - re_{i-1})^2 \qquad (16C.9)$$

For example, if we have a set of Bivariate data (x_i, y_i), and we use the Least Squares method to fit the Linear Model $\hat{y}_i = a + bx_i$, then e_i is defined by:

$$e_i = y_i - \hat{y}_i = y_i - a - bx_i = re_{i-1} + v_i \qquad (16C.10)$$

If the observed values of y, y_i, are assumed to be generated by the Linear Model, for a given value x_i, we have

$$y_i = a + bx_i + e_i, \qquad (16C.11)$$

from which we obtain

$$e_i = y_i - a - bx_i \qquad (16C.12)$$

We can also write: $y_{i-1} = a + bx_{i-1} + e_{i-1}$ \qquad (16C.13)

and $ry_{i-1} = ra + rbx_{i-1} + re_{i-1}$, \qquad (16C.14)

from which we obtain $re_{i-1} = ry_{i-1} - ra - rbx_{i-1}$ \qquad (16C.15)

Then, by subtracting (16C.15) from (16C.12) we obtain:

$$v_i = e_i - re_{i-1} = (y_i - a - bx_i) - (ry_{i-1} - ra - rbx_{i-1}) \qquad (16C.16)$$

$$= (y_i - ry_{i-1}) - a(1 - r) - b(x_i - rx_{i-1}) \qquad (16C.17)$$

Then

$$Q = \sum_{i=2}^{n} v_i^2 = \sum_{i=2}^{n} \left[(y_i - ry_{i-1}) - a(1 - r) - b(x_i - rx_{i-1}) \right]^2, \qquad (16C.18)$$

where r is defined by equation (16C.2).

If we now introduce new variables (*i.e.*, Transformed Variables),

$$y_i' = y_i - ry_{i-1} = (a + bx_i) - r(a + bx_{i-1}) = a(1 - r) + bx_i' \qquad (16C.19)$$

where $x_i' = x_i - rx_{i-1}$, \qquad (16C.20)
equation (16C.18) can be re-written as

$$Q = \sum_{i=2}^{n} v_i^2 = \sum_{i=2}^{n} \left[y_i' - a(1 - r) - bx_i' \right]^2 \qquad (16C.21)$$

If we follow the usual optimization procedure (see our discussion of Linear Regression Analysis in Chapter 13 in which for

$$Q = \sum_{i=1}^{n} (y_i - a - bx_i)^2$$ we obtained the Normal equations for the Linear Model:

$$na + b\sum_{i=1}^{n} x_i = \sum_{i=1}^{n} y_i$$

$$a\sum_{i=1}^{n} x_i + b\sum_{i=1}^{n} x_i^2 = \sum_{i=1}^{n} x_i y_i, \tag{16C.21a}$$

the Normal equations for the transformed model of (16C.21) are (by comparison)

$$n\left[a(1 - r)\right] + b\sum_{i=1}^{n} x_i' = \sum_{i=1}^{n} y_i'$$

$$\left[a(1 - r)\right]\sum_{i=1}^{n} x_i' + b\sum_{i=1}^{n} (x_i')^2 = \sum_{i=1}^{n} x_i' \, y_i', \tag{16C.22}$$

or

$$na' + b'\sum_{i=1}^{n} x_i' = \sum_{i=1}^{n} y_i'$$

$$a'\sum_{i=1}^{n} x_i' + b'\sum_{i=1}^{n} (x_i')^2 = \sum_{i=1}^{n} x_i' y_i' \tag{16C.23}$$

Comparing equations (16C.22) and (16C.23) we observe that

$$a(1 - r) = a' \tag{16C.24}$$

$$b = b', \tag{16C.25}$$

and from these we obtain

$$a = \frac{a'}{1 - r} \tag{16C.26}$$

$$b = b' \tag{16C.27}$$

where (a, b) are the coefficients of the Linear Model with $r = 0$, and (a', b') are the coefficients of the revised model, with $r \neq 0$.

The procedure above can also be applied to situations where more than one independent variable is involved. For example, given that

$$\hat{y}_i = b_1 + b_2 x_{i2} + b_3 x_{i3}, \tag{16C.28}$$

the corresponding regression equation in terms of serially correlated terms becomes

$$\hat{y}_i = b_1 + b_2 x_{i2} + b_3 x_{i3} = \frac{b_1'}{1 - r} + b_2' x_{i2} + b_3' x_{i3} \tag{16C.29}$$

We now ask the question

How do we use this method, assuming a Linear Function between X and Y?

We can answer this question as follows

Given a set of Bivariate data (x_i, y_i), use the following procedure to fit a Linear function $(\hat{y} = a' + b'x)$, if $r \neq 0$:

1. Use equations (16C.21a) to calculate a and b, thus defining

$$\hat{y}_i = a + bx_i, \text{ for } r = 0. \tag{16C.30}$$

2. Calculate $e_i = y_i - \hat{y}_i = y_i - a - bx_i$ (using (16C.10))
3. Calculate r, using equation (16C.2)
4. Use equations (16C.23) to solve for: a' and b'

5. Then
$$\hat{y}_i = \frac{a'}{1 - r} + b'x_i \tag{16C.31}$$

b) **Regression with Detrended Data**

The presence of significant trends in time series introduces dependence in successive observations and tends to produce serial correlations in the regression residuals (*i.e.*, $e_i = re_{i-1} + v_i$)This dependence can be corrected by "Regressing Detrended Data." This method consists of the following 3 steps:

   i) Determine the Trends in the Original Series
   ii) Eliminate Trends from the Original Set of Data
   iii) Apply the Least Squares Method to "Deviations from Trends" to establish the Regression equation

A simpler way to achieve the same result is to work with the original data (observations), but with *time* (*t*) as an additional explanatory variable, as shown below

   a) Given a sample Regression of the form

$$\hat{y}_i = b_1 + b_2 x_{i2} + b_3 x_{i3} \tag{16C.32}$$

whose residuals ($e_i = y_i - \hat{y}_i$) are dependent due to the existence of a Trend.

   b) The dependence can be corrected by constructing a new model

$$\hat{y}_i = b_1 + b_2 x_{i2} + b_3 x_{i3} + b_4 t_i \tag{16C.33}$$

where t = denotes time, with a defined origin, and appropriate units of time (year, for example)

   c) One way to determine b_4 is to determine e_i for (16C.32), then plot e_i against time, and determine a "time Trend" for e_i.
   d) Incorporate this time Trend into (16C.32) to produce (16C.33).

Note: The dependent variable (y_i) is always Linear in "*t*", even though it may not have to be linear in the other explanatory variables. Thus, we may have for example:

$$\hat{y}_i = b_1 + b_2 \log x_{i2} + b_3 e^{x_{i3}} + b_4 t_i \tag{16C.34}$$

c) **Dummy Variables**

Another problem in Regressing Time-Series data, is the effect of Heterogeneous Historical Influences on the behavior of a series. For example, War, Inflation, and Recession, may produce unusually large distortions in the relationship between two series.

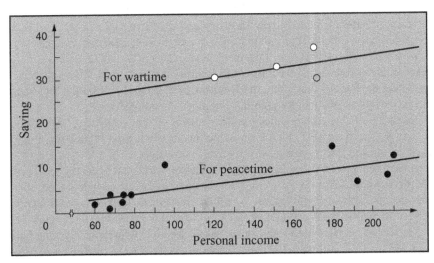

Figure 16C.2 Regression lines of savings on personal income for peace and war.

Consider, for example, the scatter diagram below, showing personal savings on Personal Income in the United States from 1935 to 1949.

War time savings (circles in the diagram) are at a much higher level than peace time savings (dots in the diagram), corresponding to various levels of personal income.

This phenomenon can be explained as follows:

i) During Wartime because of rationing, which tends to reduce consumption, and Patriotism, which tends to increase the purchase of Government Savings Bonds, a greater portion of personal income is saved.

ii) During Peacetime people tend to increase consumption and therefore a smaller portion of personal income is saved.

To 'capture' the effect of such 'non-homogeneous' influences and to improve the Forecast we apply Regression Analysis with 'Dummy Variables'.

A Dummy Variable is a "switching" variable whose value can be switched "On" or "Off" arbitrarily.

In the example above, when the Variable is switched 'On', indicating Wartime, it assumes a value of 1, and when it is switched "Off", indicating Peacetime, it assumes a value of 0.

YEAR	1935	1936	1937	1938	1939	1940	1941	1942	1943	1944	1945	1946	1947	1948	1949
Y	2	4	4	1	3	4	11	28	33	37	30	15	7	13	9
X	60	69	74	68	73	78	96	123	151	165	171	179	191	210	207
W	0	0	0	0	0	0	0	1	1	1	1	0	0	0	0

Consider the data of the table above, to estimate the Regression equation of Personal Savings (Y), on Personal Income (X), and we have introduced the Dummy Variable (W), for the years 1935 to 1949.

The resulting multiple Linear Regression equation becomes:

$$\hat{y} = a + bx_i + cw_i$$

$$= -0.415022 + 0.059437x_i + 23.350885w_i \qquad (16C.35)$$

The Regression coefficients are obtained in the usual manner, using the Least Square method, and equation (16A.5), (16A.6), and (16A.7), of Appendix 16A.

d) Forecasts of Sales Demand for the Industry and the Firm

With Regression Analysis, the level of Industry Sales is usually forecasted first, and the company Forecast is then made on the basis of the predicted behavior of the whole Industry.

The procedure of forecasting the Sales of an Industry consists of the following steps:

i) Select the Factors that affect the Demand for the Industry's output, but keep the Number or Factors as small as possible (*i.e.*, employ "Parsimony").

The demand for many commodities usually depends on a multiplicity of Aggregate economic variables, such as: GNP, Real Disposable Income, Industrial Production, Population, Employment, and Prices, which are sometimes correlated.

The problem here is with assumed Independent Variables, which may be highly correlated.

A) Perfect correlation (*i.e.*, $r = \pm 1$) between a pair of assumed Independent Variables, makes it impossible to find a *unique, best-fitting* plane (*i.e.*, there will be an *infinite* number of best-fitting planes). A consequence of this is that it is impossible to calculate the Regression Coefficients at all, and the attempt to find the Multiple Regression equation fails completely.

B) If the assumed Independent Variables are highly correlated but not perfectly correlated, the best-fitting plane is uniquely determined, but inferences to the population plane (*i.e.*, the variables defining the plane) are severely affected, because the standard errors of the coefficients b_i and b_j are very large if x_i and x_j are highly correlated.

RULE OF THUMB: For each pair of Independent Variables in a Multiple Regression, calculate their correlation coefficient r. If $r < -0.95$ or $r > 0.95$, *discard* one of the two variables.

ii) Regress the Industry's past sales on the selected Demand Factors (or Factor). The resulting equation is an approximate Forecasting equation.

However, Residuals may still remain which cannot be explained by the Independent Variables selected. This can be due to the following 3 reasons:

A) Inaccuracies may exist in the data used.

B) Other types of technical errors may have been introduced.

C) Other factors which affect sales may have been excluded.

But, if reasons a) and b) have been, after analysis, removed from consideration, and the residual errors are attributable mainly to the third reason, a 'catch-all' time-trend variable may be introduced.

This is accomplished by plotting the Residual errors from the Regression line as a time series and fitting to it a Trend line, using Least Squares.

iii) Incorporate in the regression equation the estimated time Trend to improve the accuracy of its Prediction capability.

After the Forecast for the whole Industry is made, the Forecast of the firm's sales may be based on the Industry's Forecast, usually as a percentage of the Total Market.

iv) The use of Regression Analysis for Forecasting involves a number of additional considerations that must be observed in order to provide Maximum Reliability.

A) The Time Series may need some prior adjustment or Transformation in order to provide compatibility, avoid spurious correlation, and improve accuracy of Forecasts (For example the original data may need to be deflated by appropriate price indeces before regression is applied).

B) It may be necessary to break down the Industry's total sales into homogeneous groups of output, and carry out a separate regression for each group, because they may have different important factors.

C) In general, to establish the *best relationship* possible requires that information other than statistical considerations be brought to bear on the problem.

It is important to remember that the final purpose of the Regression function is to provide the *best set of future estimates,* not to Minimize the average estimate of error of the past observations, even though usually the two occur simultaneously.

e) Econometric Models

Econometrics views the behavior of an economic system as the interaction of variables whose interrelationships can be expressed by a set of simultaneous equations. The variables are either: *endogenous* (*i.e.*, they are within the Economic System. Examples of such variables are: Income, Production, Employment, Prices, Rent, Interest, etc.) or *exogenous* (*i.e.*, they are outside of the Economic System. Examples of such variables are: Politics, Customs, Institutions, Nature, etc.).

Econometrics seeks to discover and measure the Quantitative aspects of the actual operation of the economic system in order to Forecast the course of certain economic magnitudes with a specific level of Probability.

The procedure in Forecasting by Econometric methods starts with *Model Building,* which consists of postulating the interrelationships between the variables under investigation, and expressing these relationships in mathematical terms, usually in the form of equations or inequalities.

For example, we may construct a model for the Gross National Product (GNP), as follows:

a) The GNP, in any accounting period, is made up of three components: *consumption, gross investment, and government expenditure.*

If we let $Y_t =$ GNP, $C_t =$ Consumption, $I_t =$ Gross Investment, and;

$G_t =$ Government Expenditure, in a given time period, we can write

$$Y_t = C_t + I_t + G_t, \tag{16C.36}$$

which is referred to as a *definitional equation.*

b) Next, we must develop an expression for each of the variables on the right side of equation (16C.36), showing how these variables are related functionally. Mathematical expressions for these variables are called *behavior* equations because they describe the responses in these variables due to the stimuli from other variables.

i) Consumption

We assume that consumption in a given period depends on the GNP of the previous period $(GNP_{t-1} = Y_{t-1})$, which is a LAGGED ENDOGENOUS variable, in such a way that equal increments in *GNP* (irrespective of the level of *GNP* from which we start) always bring equal increments in consumption.

This relationship is called the MARGINAL PROPENSITY TO CONSUME, and it is denoted by m.

In addition, we assume that there is a MINIMUM CONSUMPTION, denoted by a, even if $GNP = 0.$

Then the Mathematical function for consumption may be written as

$$C_t = a + mY_{t-1} \tag{16C.37}$$

ii) Gross Investment

Is the sum of induced private Investment and Autonomous Investment.

Induced Private Investment, in any time period, is proportional to the increase in consumption of that period over the preceding period. The constant of proportionality is called the RELATION, and is represented by i.

Since the Increase in consumption is given by $C_t - C_{t-1}$, the size of the Induced Private Investment is equal to $i(C_t - C_{t-1})$

Autonomous Investment refers to capital formation for Replacement and the Application of Innovations. It is assumed to be Independent of the consumption level, and is represented by k. Therefore, the function for the entire Gross Investment can be written as:

$$I_t = k + i(C_t - C_{t-1}) \tag{16C.38}$$

iii) Government Expenditure

Is an Exogenous variable which is assumed to be a given known constant, and is represented by G_0.

Therefore, $\qquad\qquad G_t = G_0 \qquad\qquad$ (16C.39)

c) The system of these 4 equations (16C.36), (16C.37), (16C.38), (16C.39)

$$Y_t = C_t + I_t + G_t$$
$$C_t = a + mY_{t-1}$$
$$I_t = k + i(C_t - C_{t-1})$$
$$G_t = G_0$$

constitutes our model for *GNP*. These equations are now re-arranged so that a single equation is derived for the variable that we intend to forecast.

By substituting equations (16C.37), (16C.38), and (16C.39) into equation (16C.36) and simplifying, we obtain the following Forecasting equation for the GNP

$$Y_t = m(1 + i)Y_{t-1} - imY_{t-2} + a + k + G_0 \tag{16C.40}$$

d) After the Forecasting equation has been derived, the next step is to estimate the parameters in the equation (m, i, a, k), using past data.

e) A Forecast made from an Econometric model is not exact because the estimates of the model parameters are subject to sampling errors. More serious is the possibility that the theoretical relationships in the model may not be correct. The model may need to be revised if new information becomes available.

Table 16C.1 The Durbin-Waston *d* Statistic Significance points of d_L and d_U: 2.5%

	k' = 1		k' = 2		k' = 3		k' = 4		k' = 5	
n	d_L	d_U	d_L	d_U	d_L	d_U	d_L	d_U	d_L	d_U
15	0.95	1.23	0.83	1.40	0.71	1.61	0.59	1.84	0.48	2.09
16	0.98	1.24	0.85	1.40	0.75	1.59	0.64	1.80	0.53	2.03
17	1.01	1.25	0.90	1.40	0.79	1.58	0.68	1.77	0.57	1.98
18	1.03	1.26	0.93	1.40	0.82	1.56	0.72	1.74	0.62	1.93
19	1.06	1.28	0.96	1.41	0.86	1.55	0.76	1.72	0.66	1.90
20	1.08	1.28	0.99	1.41	0.89	1.55	0.79	1.70	0.70	1.87
21	1.10	1.30	1.01	1.41	0.92	1.54	0.83	1.69	0.73	1.84
22	1.12	1.31	1.04	1.42	0.95	1.54	0.86	1.68	0.77	1.82
23	1.14	1.32	1.06	1.42	0.97	1.54	0.89	1.67	0.80	1.80
24	1.16	1.33	1.08	1.43	1.00	1.54	0.91	1.66	0.83	1.79
25	1.18	1.34	1.10	1.43	1.02	1.54	0.94	1.65	0.86	1.77
26	1.19	1.35	1.12	1.44	1.04	1.54	0.96	1.65	0.88	1.76
27	1.21	1.36	1.13	1.44	1.06	1.54	0.99	1.64	0.91	1.75
28	1.22	1.37	1.15	1.45	1.08	1.54	1.01	1.64	0.93	1.74
29	1.24	1.38	1.17	1.45	1.10	1.54	1.03	1.63	0.96	1.73
30	1.25	1.38	1.18	1.46	1.12	1.54	1.05	1.63	0.98	1.73
31	1.26	1.39	1.20	1.47	1.13	1.55	1.07	1.63	1.00	1.72
32	1.27	1.40	1.21	1.47	1.15	1.55	1.08	1.63	1.02	1.71
33	1.28	1.41	1.22	1.48	1.16	1.55	1.10	1.63	1.04	1.71
34	1.29	1.41	1.24	1.48	1.17	1.55	1.12	1.63	1.06	1.70
35	1.30	1.42	15.2	1.48	1.19	1.55	1.13	1.63	1.07	1.70
36	1.31	1.43	1.26	1.49	1.20	1.55	1.15	1.63	1.09	1.70
37	1.32	1.43	1.27	1.49	1.21	1.56	1.16	1.62	1.10	1.70
38	1.33	1.44	1.28	1.50	1.23	1.56	1.17	1.62	1.12	1.70
39	1.34	1.44	1.29	1.50	1.24	1.56	1.19	1.63	1.13	1.69
40	1.35	1.45	1.30	1.51	1.25	1.57	1.20	1.63	1.15	1.69
45	1.39	1.48	1.34	1.53	1.30	1.58	1.25	1.63	1.21	1.69
50	1.42	1.50	1.38	1.54	1.34	1.59	1.30	1.64	1.26	1.69
55	1.45	1.52	1.41	1.56	1.37	1.60	1.33	1.64	1.30	1.69
60	1.47	1.54	1.44	1.57	1.40	1.61	1.37	1.65	1.33	1.69
65	1.49	1.55	1.46	1.59	1.43	1.62	1.40	1.66	1.36	1.69
70	1.51	1.57	1.48	1.60	1.45	1.63	1.42	1.66	1.39	1.70
75	1.53	1.58	1.50	1.61	1.47	1.64	1.45	1.67	1.42	1.70
80	1.54	1.59	1.52	1.62	1.49	1.65	1.47	1.67	1.44	1.70
85	1.56	1.60	1.53	1.63	1.51	1.65	1.49	1.68	1.46	1.71
90	1.57	1.61	1.55	1.64	1.53	1.66	1.50	1.69	1.48	1.71
95	1.58	1.62	1.56	1.65	1.54	1.67	1.52	1.69	1.50	1.71
100	1.59	1.63	1.57	1.65	1.55	1.67	1.53	1.70	1.51	1.72

Table 16C.2 The Durbin-Waston d Statistic Significance points of d_L and d_U : 5%									
	$k' = 1$		$k' = 2$		$k' = 3$		$k' = 4$		$k' = 5$	
n	d_L	d_U	d_L	d_U	d_L	d_U	d_L	d_U	d_L	d_U
15	1.08	1.36	0.95	1.54	0.82	1.75	0.69	1.97	0.56	2.21
16	1.10	1.37	0.98	1.54	0.86	1.73	0.74	1.93	0.62	2.15
17	1.13	1.38	1.02	1.54	0.90	1.71	0.78	1.90	0.67	2.10
18	1.16	1.39	1.06	1.53	0.93	1.69	0.82	1.87	0.71	2.06
19	1.18	1.40	1.08	1.53	0.97	1.68	0.86	1.85	0.75	2.02
20	1.20	1.41	1.10	1.54	1.00	1.68	0.90	1.83	0.79	1.99
21	1.22	1.42	1.13	1.54	1.03	1.67	0.93	1.81	0.83	1.96
22	1.24	1.43	1.15	1.54	1.05	1.66	0.96	1.80	0.86	1.94
23	1.26	1.44	1.17	1.54	1.08	1.66	0.99	1.79	0.90	1.92
24	1.27	1.45	1.19	1.55	1.10	1.66	1.01	1.78	0.93	1.90
25	1.29	1.45	1.21	1.55	1.12	1.66	1.04	1.77	0.95	1.89
26	1.30	1.46	1.22	1.55	1.14	1.65	1.06	1.76	0.98	1.88
27	1.32	1.47	1.24	1.56	1.16	1.65	1.08	1.76	1.01	1.86
28	1.33	1.48	1.26	1.56	1.18	1.65	1.10	1.75	1.03	1.85
29	1.34	1.48	1.27	1.56	1.20	1.65	1.12	1.74	1.05	1.84
30	1.35	1.49	1.28	1.57	1.21	1.65	1.14	1.74	1.07	1.83
31	1.36	1.50	1.30	1.57	1.23	1.65	1.16	1.74	1.09	1.83
32	1.37	1.50	1.31	1.57	1.24	1.65	1.18	1.73	1.11	1.82
33	1.38	1.51	1.32	1.58	1.26	1.65	1.19	1.73	1.13	1.81
34	1.39	1.51	1.33	1.58	1.27	1.65	1.21	1.73	1.15	1.81
35	1.40	1.52	1.34	1.58	1.28	1.65	1.22	1.73	1.16	1.80
36	1.41	1.52	1.35	1.59	1.29	1.65	1.24	1.73	1.18	1.80
37	1.42	1.53	1.36	1.59	1.31	1.66	1.25	1.72	1.19	1.80
38	1.43	1.54	1.37	1.59	1.32	1.66	1.26	1.72	1.21	1.79
39	1.43	1.54	1.38	1.60	1.33	1.66	1.27	1.72	1.22	1.79
40	1.44	1.54	1.39	1.60	1.34	1.66	1.29	1.72	1.23	1.79
45	1.48	1.57	1.43	1.62	1.38	1.67	1.34	1.72	1.29	1.78
50	1.50	1.59	1.46	1.63	1.42	1.67	1.38	1.72	1.34	1.77
55	1.53	1.60	1.49	1.64	1.45	1.68	1.41	1.72	1.38	1.77
60	1.55	1.62	1.51	1.65	1.48	1.69	1.44	1.73	1.41	1.77
65	1.57	1.63	1.54	1.66	1.50	1.70	1.47	1.73	1.44	1.77
70	1.58	1.64	1.55	1.67	1.52	1.70	1.49	1.74	1.46	1.77
75	1.60	1.65	1.57	1.68	1.54	1.71	1.51	1.74	1.49	1.77
80	1.61	1.66	1.59	1.69	1.56	1.72	1.53	1.74	1.51	1.77
85	1.62	1.67	1.60	1.70	1.57	1.72	1.56	1.75	1.52	1.77
90	1.63	1.68	1.61	1.70	1.59	1.73	1.57	1.75	1.54	1.78
95	1.64	1.69	1.62	1.71	1.60	1.73	1.58	1.75	1.56	1.78
100	1.65	1.69	1.63	1.72	1.61	1.74	1.59	1.76	1.57	1.78

16.9   References

Berenson, Marc, L., Levine, David, M., and Krehbiel, Timothy, C., 2004. *Basic Business Statistics*. 9th Edition. Pearson-Prentice Hall.

Black, Ken, 2004. *Business Statistics*. 4th Edition. Wiley.

Canavos, George, C., 1984. *Applied Probability and Statistical Methods*. Little, Brown.

Carlson, William, L., and Thorne, Betty, 1997. *Applied Statistical Methods*. Prentice Hall.

Chou, Ya-lun, 1992. *Statistical Analysis for Business and Economics*. Elsevier.

Freund, John, E., and Williams, Frank, J., 1969. *Modern Business Statistics*. Revised by: Perles, Benjamin and Sullivan, Charles. Prentice-Hall.

Freund, John, E., and Williams, Frank, J., 1982. *Elementary Business Statistics: The Modern approach*. Prentice-Hall.

Johnson, Robert, 1973. *Elementary Statistics*. Duxbury Press.

McClave, James, T., Benson, George, P., and Sincich, Terry, 2001. *Statistics for Business and Economics*. 8th Edition. Prentice Hall.

Salvatore, Dominick, *Theory and Problems of Statistics and Econometrics*. SCHAUM'S OUTLINE SERIES, McGraw-Hill.

Steel, Robert, G.D., and Torrie, James, H., 1976. *Introduction to Statistics*. McGraw-Hill.

16.10 PROBLEMS

1. Using the following data, determine the values of Mean Absolute Deviation (MAD) and Mean Square Error (MSE). Which of these measurements of error seems to yield the best information about the forecasts? Why?

Period	1	2	3	4	5	6
Value of Series	19.4	23.6	24.0	26.8	29.2	35.5
Forecast Value	16.6	19.1	22.0	24.8	25.9	28.6

2. Use the following time series data to:

Time Period	1	2	3	4	5	6	7	8	9	10
Value	27	31	58	63	59	66	71	86	101	97

   a) Develop forecasts for periods 5 through 10, using 4-month moving averages.

   b) Develop forecasts for periods 5 trough 10, using 4-month moving averages, but: Weight the most recent month by a factor of 4, the previous month by 2, and the other months by 1.

   c) Compute the error of the forecast in parts (a) and (b) and compare the differences in the errors by the two different techniques.

3. The total units of new privately owned housing started between 1984 and 1999 in the United States are given in the table below.

   a) Use exponential smoothing to forecast the value of each time period, using $\alpha = 0.8$ and the value of 1984, 1750, as the value for S_0 (*i.e.*, $S_0 = 1750$).

Year	Unit (x 100)	Year	Unit (x 100)
1984	1,750	1995	1,354
1985	1,742	1996	1,477
1986	1,805	1997	1,474
1987	1,620	1998	1,617
1988	1,488	1999	1,666
1989	1,376		
1990	1,193		
1991	1,014		
1992	1,200		
1993	1,288		
1994	1,457		

   b) Also calculate the errors of forecast, and then calculate MAD and MSE

4. The table below shows the GNP of a hypothetical country.

   a) Fit the exponential equation $y = ke^{cx}$ to this data

   b) Use the derived equation to calculate the forecasted values

   c) Calculate the errors of the forecasts, and then calculate the MSE.

X	1	2	3	4	5	6	7
Decade	1940	1950	1960	1970	1980	1990	2000
Y	2	5	10	18	40	90	170

5. The table below shows the new plant and equipment expenditures in the United States for a 12 year period (the annual sales are in billions of dollars):

Year(X)	1	2	3	4	5	6	7	8	9	10	11	12
Y	37.0	30.5	32.5	35.7	34.4	37.3	39.2	44.9	52.0	60.6	61.7	65.2

   a) Fit a second degree polynomial to the above data set

   b) Use the derived quadratic equation to calculate the forecasted values

   c) Calculate the errors of the forecasts, and then calculate the MSE

   d) What is the forecasted value when $x = 13$?

6. The following values represent the gross incomes from sales of a corporation for a 5-year period: 4.5, 6.0, 7.1, 8.8, and 9.5 billions of dollars.

   a) Calculate the correlation coefficient, r.

   b) Fit a least squares linear equation to this data.

   c) Modify the equation by shifting the origin of x to the 5th year.

7. The equation of a least-squares trend line to fit the total amount of brandy distributed in the United States in a 10-year period is given by: $\hat{y} = 5.65 + 0.54x$, where: origin is in year 1, x units $= 1$ year, and y is in millions of gallons.

   a) Shift the origin to year 5 (of the ten year period)

   b) Modify the trend equation to use with monthly data

8. Using the formula for the exponential smoothing technique, $S_t = \alpha y_t + (1 - \alpha)S_{t-1}$

   a) Express S_4 in terms of α, y_1, y_2, y_3, and y_4

   b) Calculate the value of S_4 when $\alpha = 0.2$, $y_1 = 9.9$,

$y_2 = 22.2$, $y_3 = 11.4$, $y_4 = 14.8$, and $y_0 = S_0 = 10$

9. The following series shows the annual production of aspirin, in million pounds, in the United States, for years 1967 to 1996: 12, 11, 10, 11, 14, 13, 14, 14, 15, 17, 18, 21, 18, 24, 23, 27, 28, 28, 29, 34, 30, 31, 37, 35, 32, 35, 32, 33, 25, 29.

   a) Construct a 3-year moving total, and then a 3-year moving average.

   b) Construct a 5-year moving total, and then a 5-year moving average.

10. The following series shows the number of requests for a particular kind of service at a bank window on 12 consecutive working days: 20, 39, 18, 25, 30, 12, 21, 27, 15, 35, 30, and 17.

   a) Smooth this series using $\alpha = 0.2$

   b) Smooth this series using $\alpha = 0.5$

11. a) In an exponential smoothing process with $\alpha = 0.2$, what is the equivalent number of terms being averaged in a conventional moving average?

   b) In an exponential smoothing process, for what value of α, is such a process equivalent to a 19-term moving average?

   Note: By "equivalency" we mean the variability of the two processes, and not corresponding terms in the two series.

12. For an eight-year period (1987–1994) a country's Index of Consumer Prices (with $1987 = 100$) were: 100, 116, 125, 142, 191, 303, 486, 604. Fit the equation $y = ab^x$ to this data set.

13. Choose the best mathematical description of the trend of the given series below, and then fit the least-squares trend:

   a) In 2000 and 2001 a real estate firm sold 10 and 20 estates at prices of $1 million.

   b) In 2000, 2001, and 2002, another real estate firm sold 1, 4, and 16 estates at prices of $1 million.

14. A small research and development firm has received the following contract awards (in thousands of dollars) for the past 15 years: 95, 106, 93, 102, 119, 135, 210, 200, 198, 197, 245, 240, 275, 325, and 340.

   a) Fit a quadratic equation of the form $\hat{Y} = a + bx + cx^2$

   b) What is the trend value when $x = 8$? $x = 10$? $x = 15$?

15. The following data show the monthly sales (in thousands of dollars) of a manufacturer of home warm-air furnaces for the 5-year period 1971 to 1975, a period the manufacturer considers to be typical of these sales:

Year	Jan	Feb	Mar	Apr	May	June	July	Aug	Sept	Oct	Nov	Dec
1971	61.0	51.5	60.2	59.5	59.3	70.5	71.4	102.5	130.0	114.1	77.6	43.5
1972	55.1	52.2	56.5	56.1	64.0	83.6	79.1	110.4	140.5	132.4	100.5	75.3
1973	71.2	68.8	77.2	80.1	83.2	102.2	109.3	134.7	154.1	155.6	102.5	68.8
1974	59.2	61.0	63.7	67.8	69.4	88.3	80.0	113.1	128.5	120.6	80.8	54.4
1975	57.5	59.6	61.7	62.2	71.4	88.9	85.3	110.2	129.1	133.8	80.1	66.7

   Compute a seasonal index for this series by the ratio-to-moving average method, and using the median (and not the adjusted average) to average the percentages of moving average for the individual months.

16. Use the Seasonal Index of problem 15 to de-seasonalize the 1971–1975 sales data of problem 16.15.

17. Use the data of problem 16.15 to:

a) Fit a least squares trend line to the total annual furnace sales for the years 1971–1975.

b) Modify this equation and use it, and the season index (computed in problem 16.15 and used in problem 16.16) to forecast the monthly dollar sales of home furnaces in the year 1980.

18. A large manufacturer of furniture estimates total 2005 sales to be $44,400,000. The company's seasonal index for furniture sales is (January-December): 78, 75, 100, 126, 138, 121, 101, 104, 99, 103, 80, and 75. Ignoring the possible existence of a trend in sales, calculate a tentative 2005 sales budget for the company.

19. Suppose that there is an upward trend in the sales of the furniture manufacturer of problem (16.18) and given by the trend equation:
$\hat{Y} = a + bx = 30,000,000 + 2,880,000x$ (origin: 2000; x = units of year 1, and y = total annual sales in dollars)

a) Modify this equation, to calculate the trend values for monthly sales for the 12 months of 2005.

b) Calculate a revised monthly sales budget for 2005 which takes into account the trend in furniture sales.

20. In calculating a seasonal index for a production company, a statistician has arrived at the following median values: 58.1, 60.1, 73.8, 95.2, 116.8, 125.3, 120.6, 126.1, 123.1, 108.0, 103.1, and 71.8. Complete the calculation of the seasonal index.

21. a) Obtain the linear regression equation, using the Least Squares method for the following data:

t	-9	-8	-7	-6	-5	-4	-3	-2	-1	0	1	2	3	4	5	6	7	8	9
y	12.55	11.60	11.30	11.60	10.65	10.65	10.15	9.55	9.15	8.9	8.6	8.2	7.65	6.9	6.55	6.15	5.45	5.15	5

b) Compute the equation-derived values of y

c) Find the variance of the residuals

d) What is the projected trend value for this series when: $t = 10$? $t = 11$?

22. a) Fit a second degree polynomial to the following data, using Least Squares:

t	-5.5	-4.5	-3.5	-2.5	-1.5	-0.5	0.5	1.5	2.5	3.5	4.5	5.5
y	37	30.5	32.5	35.7	34.4	37.3	39.2	44.9	52	60.6	61.7	65.2

b) Compute the equation-derived values of y

c) Find the variance of the residuals

d) What is the projected trend value when $t = 6.5, t = 7.5, t = 8.5$?

23. a) Fit an exponential with base b (i.e., $y = ab^t$) to the following data set, using "linearized" regression analysis:

t	-8.0	-7.0	-6.0	-5.0	-4.0	-3.0	-2.0	-1.0	0.0	1.0	2.0	3.0	4.0	5.0	6.0	7.0	8.0
y	190.8	196.4	192.9	207.0	218.1	218.1	204.1	214.1	214.1	218.3	222.9	229.0	232.1	237.3	253.0	268.0	277.4

b) Complete the equation-derived values of y

c) Find the variance of the residuals

d) What is the projected trend value when $t = 10$?

e) What is the constant rate of increase per year, for this series?

24. a) Fit the exponential model $y = ke^{ct}$, using the "Linearized" Least Square method, to the following data:

t	−3	−2	−1	0	1	2	3
y	2	5	10	18	40	90	170

b) Compute the equation derived values of y

c) Find the Variance of the Residuals

d) What is the projected Trend value for $t = 5$?

25. a) Apply simple exponential smoothing to the data of the series below by using $\alpha = 0.25$, an initial smoothed value of 38 and an initial Trend value of 1.

b) Repeat step (a), above but use $\alpha = 0.50$, an Initial smoothed value of 38, and an initial Trend Value of 0

c) Compare the forecasting results of (a) and (b) and comment on the differences.

t	1986	1987	1988	1989	1990	1991	1992	1993	1994	1995
y	40.5	42.6	39.8	42.9	44.7	43.5	45.1	47.2	48.0	46.4

26. The table below shows a Bivariate data set relating the output of a firm (y) and the labor input (x) for the past 15 years:

Year	1	2	3	4	5	6	7	8	9	10	11	12	13	14	15
x	4	3	8	6	5	3	7	10	12	14	14	16	15	13	18
y	18	14	26	24	18	5	27	29	33	43	47	66	63	49	78

a) Obtain the simple linear regression of Y on X, i.e., obtain $\hat{Y} = a + bx$

b) Is the b obtained significant?

c) Construct a 95% C.I. on the population parameter β

d) Calculate the value of the Durbin-Watson d-statistic Test for the significance of d. Is there serial correlation present?

SOLUTIONS

1. The error of the individual forecast is the difference between the actual value and the forecast of that value, or:

$$e_t = x_{t_a} - x_{t_f}$$

Therefore, e_t is:

$e_t = x_{t_a} - x_{t_f}$	2.8	4.5	2.0	2.0	3.3	6.9

Then

$$\text{Mean Absolute Deviation=(MAD)} = \frac{\Sigma|e_t|}{Number\ of\ Forecasts}$$

$$= \frac{|2.8| + |4.5| + |2.0| + |2.0| + |3.3| + |6.9|}{6}$$

$$= \frac{21.5}{6} = 3.583,$$

and Mean Square Error $= \text{MSE} = \dfrac{(2.8)^2 + (4.5)^2 + (2.0)^2 + (3.3)^2 + (6.9)^2}{6}$

$$= \frac{94.59}{6} = 15.765,$$

and $\qquad\qquad \sqrt{MSE} = \sqrt{15.765} = 3.97$

MAD has the same units as the given data but MSE does not have the same units, but its square root does. The MAD value of 3.58 is comparable to the $\sqrt{MSE} = 3.97$, and both convey similar information.

2. a) Forecasted value for period 5 $= \dfrac{(27 + 31 + 58 + 63)}{4} = \dfrac{179}{4} = 44.75$

Forecasted value for period 6 $= \dfrac{(31 + 58 + 63 + 59)}{4} = \dfrac{211}{4} = 52.75$

Forecasted value for period 7 $= \dfrac{(58 + 63 + 59 + 66)}{4} = \dfrac{246}{4} = 61.50$

Forecasted value for period 8 $= \dfrac{(63 + 59 + 66 + 71)}{4} = \dfrac{259}{4} = 64.75$

Forecasted value for period 9 $= \dfrac{(59 + 66 + 71 + 86)}{4} = \dfrac{282}{4} = 70.50$

Forecasted value for period 10 $= \dfrac{(66 + 71 + 86 + 101)}{4} = \dfrac{324}{4} = 81.00$

b) Forecasterecasted value for period 5

$$= \frac{1(27) + 1(31) + 2(58) + 4(63)}{Sum\ of\ Weights} = \frac{426}{8} = 53.25$$

Forecasted value for period 6

$$= \frac{[1(31) + 1(58) + 2(63) + 4(59)]}{8} = \frac{451}{8} = 56.375$$

Forecasted value for period 7

$$= \frac{[1(58) + 1(63) + 2(59) + 4(66)]}{8} = \frac{503}{8} = 62.875$$

Forecasted value for period 8

$$= \frac{[1(63) + 1(59) + 2(66) + 4(71)]}{8} = \frac{538}{8} = 67.25$$

Forecasted value for period 9

$$= \frac{[1(59) + 1(66) + 2(71) + 4(86)]}{8} = \frac{611}{8} = 76.375$$

Forecasted value for period 10

$$= \frac{[1(66) + 1(71) + 2(86) + 4(101)]}{8}$$

$$= \frac{713}{8} = 89.125$$

c) Errors of forecast = Actual value − Forecasted value

i) e_1 = Actual value- Forecasted value in part (a)

ii) e_2 = Actual value- Forecasted value in part (b)

Then: $e_{1.5} = 59 - 44.75 = 14.25$ and $e_{2.5} = 59 - 53.25 = 5.75$

$e_{1.6} = 66 - 52.75 = 13.25$ and $e_{2.6} = 66 - 56.375 = 9.625$

$e_{1.7} = 71 - 61.50 = 8.50$ and $e_{2.7} = 71 - 62.875 = 8.125$

$e_{1.8} = 86 - 64.75 = 21.25$ and $e_{2.8} = 86 - 67.25 = 18.75$

$e_{1.9} = 101 - 70.50 = 30.50$ and $e_{2.9} = 101 - 76.375 = 24.625$

$e_{1.10} = 97 - 81.0 = 16.00$ and $e_{2.10} = 101 - 89.125 = 7.875$

Obviously the errors of the forecast for method (b) are smaller than the corresponding errors for method (a) because in each case $e_{2.i} < e_{1.i,}$ for $i = 5, 6, 7, 8, 9, 10$

3. a) The exponential smoothing forecasting method depends on the formula
$S_t = \alpha y_t + (1 - \alpha)S_{t-1}$, where α = smoothing coefficient, y_t = current value of times series, S_{t-1} = smoothed value for period t which was made in period $t - 1$, and S_1 = smoothed value for period $t + 1$ which was made in period t.

Then the values obtained are:

$S_1 = 0.8y_1 + 0.2S_0 = 0.8(1742) + 0.2(1750)$
   $= 1743.6,$

$S_2 = 0.8y_2 + 0.2S_1 = 0.8(1,805) + 0.2(1743.6)$
   $= 1792.7,$

and

$S_3 = 1,654.5, S_4 = 1,521.3, S_5 = 1,405.1, S_6 = 1,235.4, S_7 = 1,058.3,$
$S_8 = 1,171.7, S_9 = 1,264.7, S_{10} = 1,418.5, S_{11} = 1,366.9, S_{12} = 1,455.0,$
$S_{13} = 1,470.2, S_{14} = 1,587.6, S_{15} = 1,650.3,$

b) The errors of forecast are:

e_t = Actual value − Forecast value = $y_t - S_t$
$e_0 = y_0 - S_0 = 1,750 - 1,750 = 0,$
$e_1 = y_1 - S_1 = 1,742 - 1,743.6 = -1.6,$
$e_2 = y_2 - S_2 = 1,805 - 1,792.7 = 12.3,$
$e_3 = y_3 - S_3 = 1,620 - 1,654.5 = -34.5,$
$e_4 = y_4 - S_4 = 1,488 - 1,521.3 = -33.3,$
$e_5 = y_5 - S_5 = 1,376 - 1,401.5 = -29.1,$

$$e_6 = y_6 - S_6 = 1{,}193 - 1{,}235.4 = 42.4,$$
$$e_7 = y_7 - S_7 = 1{,}014 - 1{,}058.3 = -44.3,$$
$$e_8 = y_8 - S_8 = 1{,}200 - 1{,}171.7 = 28.3,$$
$$e_9 = y_9 - S_9 = 1{,}288 - 1{,}264.7 = 23.3,$$
$$e_{10} = y_{10} - S_{10} = 1{,}457 - 1{,}418.5 = 38.5,$$
$$e_{11} = y_{11} - S_{11} = 1{,}354 - 1{,}366.9 = -12.9,$$
$$e_{12} = y_{12} - S_{12} = 1{,}477 - 1{,}455.0 = 22.0,$$
$$e_{13} = y_{13} - S_{13} = 1{,}474 - 1{,}470.2 = 3.8,$$
$$e_{14} = y_{14} - S_{14} = 1{,}617 - 1{,}587.6 = 29.4,$$
$$e_{15} = y_{15} - S_{15} = 1{,}666 - 1{,}650.3 = 15.7,$$

Then

$$\text{MAD} = \frac{\Sigma |e_t|}{n}$$

$$= \frac{0 + |-1.6| + 12.3 + |-34.5| + |-33.3| + |-29.1| + 42.4 + |-44.3| + 28.3}{Number\ of\ Forecasts}$$

$$\frac{+\ 23.3 + 38.5 + |-12.9| + 22.0 + 3.8 + 29.4 + 15.7}{Number\ of\ Forecasts}$$

$$= \frac{371.4}{16} = 23.2125$$

$$\text{MSE} = \frac{\Sigma e_t^2}{n} = \frac{11{,}661.78}{16} = 728.86, \quad \text{and} \quad \sqrt{MSE} = 26.9974 \approx 27$$

4. a) The normal equations corresponding to the exponential equation, are:

$$n(\ln k) + (c)\Sigma x_i = \Sigma \ln y_i$$
$$\Sigma x_i (\ln k) + (c)\Sigma x_i^2 = \Sigma x_i \ln y_i$$

For the above data set we have: $n = 7$, $\Sigma x_i = 28$, $\Sigma x_i^2 = 140$, $\Sigma \ln y_i = 20.82003$, and $\Sigma x_i \ln y_i = 103.775511$. Then the normal equations become:

$$7(\ln k) + 28(c) = 20.82003$$
$$28(\ln k) + 140(c) = 103.775511,$$

and their solution is: $c = 20.4711/28 = 0.73111$, and $\ln k = (220.82003 - 28c)/7$, or: $\ln k = 0.049847$,

and then: $k = e^{0.049847} = 1.05111$, and the exponential equation becomes:
$\hat{y} = ke^{cx} = 1.05111e^{0.73111x}$

b) $\hat{y}(x = 1) = 1.05111e^{0.73111(1)} = 1.05111(2.077385) = 2.18356$

$\hat{y}(x = 2) = 1.05111e^{0.73111(2)} = 1.05111e^{1.46222}$
$$= (1.05111)(4.315529) = 4.5361$$

$\hat{y}(x = 3) = 1.05111e^{0.73111(3)} = 1.05111e^{2.19333}$
$$= (1.05111)(8.9650) = 9.4232$$

$\hat{y}(x = 4) = 1.05111e^{0.73111(4)} = 1.05111e^{2.92444}$
$$= (1.05111)(18.6238) = 19.5757$$

$\hat{y}(x = 5) = 1.05111e^{0.73111(5)} = 1.05111e^{3.65555}$
$$= (1.05111)(38.68879) = 40.6662$$

$$\hat{y}(x = 6) = 1.05111e^{0.73111(6)} = 1.05111e^{4.38666}$$
$$= (1.05111)(80.37153) = 84.4793$$
$$\hat{y}(x = 7) = 1.05111e^{0.73111(7)} = 1.05111e^{5.11777}$$
$$= (1.05111)(166.96263) = 175.4961$$

c) e_t = error of forecast

= Actual value − Forecasted value $e_1 = 2 - 2.18356 = -0.18356$,

$e_2 = 5 - 4.5361 = 0.4639$, $e_3 = 10 - 9.4232 = 0.5768$,

$e_4 = 18 - 19.5757 = -1.5757$, $e_5 = 40 - 40.6622 = -0.6622$,

$e_6 = 90 - 84.4793 = 5.5207$, $e_7 = 170 - 175.4961 = -5.4961$

$$\text{MSE} = \frac{\Sigma e_t^2}{n}$$

$$= \frac{1}{7}\Big[(-0.18356)^2 + (0.4639)^2 + (0.5768)^2 + (-1.5757)^2$$

$$+ (-0.6622)^2 + (5.5207)^2 + (-5.4961)^2\Big] = \frac{64.4119}{7} = 9.2017$$

5. a) The normal equation for the quadratic model $\left(\hat{y} = a + bx + cx^2\right)$ are:

$$na + b\Sigma x_i + c\Sigma x_i^2 = \Sigma y_i$$
$$a\Sigma x_i + b\Sigma x_i^2 + c\Sigma x_i^3 = \Sigma x_i y_i$$
$$a\Sigma x_i^2 + b\Sigma x_i^3 + c\Sigma x_i^4 = \Sigma x_i^2 y_i$$

For this data set: $n = 12$, $\Sigma x_i = 78$; $\Sigma x_i^2 = 650$;

$\Sigma x_i^3 = 6084$; $\Sigma x_i^4 = 60{,}710$;

$\Sigma y_i = 531$; $\Sigma y_i^2 = 25{,}191.58$; $\Sigma x_i y_i = 3{,}902.8$; $\Sigma x_i^2 y_i = 35{,}146.4$; and the normal

equations become: $\begin{cases} 12a + 78b + 650c = 531 \\ 78a + 650b + 6{,}084c = 3{,}902.8 \\ 650a + 6084b + 60{,}710c = 35{,}146.4 \end{cases}$, and the solution

to them is

$a = 35.4865$, $b = -1.87977$, and $c = 0.38736$, and the quadratic equation becomes:

$$\hat{y}(x) = a + bx + cx^2 = 35.4865 - 1.87977x + 0.38736x^2$$

b) $\hat{y}(x = 1) = 35.4865 - 1.87977(1) + 0.38736(1)^2 = 33.99409$

$\hat{y}(x = 2) = 35.4865 - 1.87977(2) + 0.38736(2)^2 = 33.2764$

$\hat{y}(x = 3) = 35.4865 - 1.87977(3) + 0.38736(3)^2 = 33.3334$

$\hat{y}(x = 4) = 35.4865 - 1.87977(4) + 0.38736(4)^2 = 34.1652$

$\hat{y}(x = 5) = 35.4865 - 1.87977(5) + 0.38736(5)^2 = 35.77165$

$\hat{y}(x = 6) = 35.4865 - 1.87977(6) + 0.38736(6)^2 = 38.15284$

$\hat{y}(x = 7) = 35.4865 - 1.87977(7) + 0.38736(7)^2 = 41.30875$

$\hat{y}(x = 8) = 35.4865 - 1.87977(8) + 0.38736(8)^2 = 45.23938$

$\hat{y}(x = 9) = 35.4865 - 1.87977(9) + 0.38736(9)^2 = 49.94473$

$\hat{y}(x = 10) = 35.4865 - 1.87977(10) + 0.38736(10)^2 = 55.4248$

$\hat{y}(x = 11) = 35.4865 - 1.87977(11) + 0.38736(11)^2 = 61.67959$

$\hat{y}(x = 12) = 35.4865 - 1.87977(12) + 0.38736(12)^2 = 68.7091$

c) Error of Forecast $= e_t =$ Actual value$-$Forecasted value

$e_1 = 37.0 - 33.99409 = 3.00591$; $e_2 = 30.5 - 33.2764 = -2.7764$;

$e_3 = 32.5 - 33.3334 = -0.8334$; $e_4 = 35.7 - 34.1652 = 1.5348$;

$e_5 = 34.4 - 35.77165 = -1.37165$; $e_6 = 37.3 - 38.15284 = -0.85284$;

$e_7 = 39.2 - 41.30875 = -2.10875$; $e_8 = 44.9 - 45.23938 = -0.33938$;

$e_9 = 52.0 - 49.94473 = 2.05527$; $e_{10} = 60.6 - 55.4248 = 5.1752$;

$e_{11} = 61.7 - 61.67959 = 0.02041$; $e_{12} = 65.2 - 68.7091 = -3.5091$;

and $MSE = \dfrac{\sum e_t^2}{\text{Number of Forecasts}} = \dfrac{e_1^2 + e_2^2 + \cdots + e_{12}^2}{12}$

$= \dfrac{70.28585281}{12} = 5.8571544$

d) $\hat{y}(x = 13) = 35.4865 - 1.87977(13) + 0.38736(13)^2 = 76.51333$

6. $n = 5 \ \sum x_i = 1 + 2 + 3 + 4 + 5 = 15; \ \sum x_i^2 = 55;$

$\sum y_i = 35.9; \ \sum y_i^2 = 274.35; \ \sum x_i y_i = 120.5$

a) $r = \dfrac{n\sum x_i y_i - (\sum x_i)(\sum y_i)}{\left[n\sum x_i^2 - (\sum x_i)^2\right]^{1/2}\left[n\sum y_i^2 - (\sum y_i)^2\right]^{1/2}}$

$= \dfrac{5(120.5) - (15)(35.9)}{\left[5(55) - (15)^2\right]^{1/2}\left[5(270.35) - (35.9)^2\right]^{1/2}}$

$= \dfrac{602.5 - 538.5}{\left[275 - 225\right]^{1/2}\left[1371.75 - 1288.1\right]^{1/2}}$

$= \dfrac{64}{\left(50\right)^{1/2}\left(82.94\right)^{1/2}} = \dfrac{64}{\left[50 \times 82.94\right]^{1/2}}$

$= \dfrac{64}{\left(4147\right)^{1/2}} = \dfrac{64}{64.3972} = 0.9938$

b) $\begin{array}{l} na + b\sum x_i = \sum y_i \\ a\sum x_i + b\sum x_i^2 = \sum x_i y_i \end{array}$ or $\begin{array}{l} 5a + 15b = 35.9 \\ 15a + 55b = 120.5 \end{array}$ or $\begin{array}{l} a = 3.24 \\ b = 1.28 \end{array}$

Therefore, $\hat{y} = a + bx = 3.34 + 1.28x$

c) The value of $\hat{y}$, when $x = 5$, is equal to: $\hat{y}(x = 5) = 3.34 + 1.28(5) = 9.74$

Therefore, shifting the origin to the fifth year, we obtain: $\hat{y} = 9.74 + 1.28x$

7. a) $\hat{y}(x = 5) = 5.65 + 0.54x = 5.65 + 2.70 = 8.35$ Therefore, the equation is $\hat{y} = a + bx = 8.35 + 0.54x$

b) To change the equation to monthly data, we divide the a value by 12 and the b value by 144, and obtain

$\hat{y} = \dfrac{a}{12} + \dfrac{b}{144}x = \dfrac{8.35}{12} + \dfrac{0.54}{144}x = 0.6958 + 0.00375x$

8. a) From the exponential smoothing equation, when $t = 1$, we obtain:
$S_1 = \alpha y_1 + (1 - \alpha)S_0$.

Also $S_2 = \alpha y_2 + (1 - \alpha) S_1$
$\quad\quad = \alpha y_2 + (1 - \alpha)[\alpha y_1 + (1 - \alpha) S_0]$
$\quad\quad = a y_2 + \alpha(1 - \alpha)y_1 + (1 - \alpha)^2 S_0$.

Then $S_3 = \alpha y_3 + (1 - \alpha) S_2$
$\quad\quad = \alpha y_3 + (1 - \alpha) \lfloor \alpha y_2 + \alpha(1 - \alpha)y_1$
$\quad\quad\quad + (1 - \alpha)^2 S_0 \rfloor$
$\quad\quad = a y_3 + \alpha(1 - \alpha)y_2$
$\quad\quad\quad + \alpha(1 - \alpha)^2 y_1 + (1 - \alpha)^3 S_0$, and

$\quad S_4 = \alpha y_4 + (1 - \alpha) S_3$
$\quad\quad = \alpha y_4 + (1 - \alpha) \lfloor \alpha y_3$
$\quad\quad\quad + \alpha(1 - \alpha) y_2 + \alpha(1 - \alpha)^2$
$\quad\quad\quad + (1 - \alpha)^3 S_0 \rfloor$
$\quad\quad = \alpha y_4 + \alpha(1 - \alpha)y_3$
$\quad\quad\quad + \alpha(1 - \alpha)^2 y_2$
$\quad\quad\quad + \alpha(1 - \alpha)^3 y_1 + (1 - \alpha)^4 S_0$

b) $S_4 = 0.2(14.8) + 0.2(0.8)(11.4)$
$\quad\quad + 0.2(0.8)^2(22.2)$
$\quad\quad + 0.2(0.8)^3(9.9) + (0.8)^4(10)$
$\quad = 2.92 + 1.824 + 2.8416$
$\quad\quad + 1.01376 + 4.096 = 12.69536$

9. a) The 3-year moving totals are $12 + 11 + 10 = 33$, $11 + 10 + 11 = 32$, $10 + 11 + 14 = 35$, 38, 41, 41, 43, 46, 50, 56, 57, 63, 65, 74, 78, 83, 85, 91, 93, 95, 98, 103, 104,102, 99, 100, 90, 87, and the 3-year moving averages are $\frac{33}{3} = 11$, $\frac{32}{3} = 10.67$, 11.67, 12.67, 13.67, 13.67, 14.33, 15.33, 16.67, 18.67, 19.21, 21.67, 24.67, 26, 27.67, 28.33, 30.33, 31, 31.67, 32.67, 34.33, 34.67, 34, 33, 33.33, 30, 29.

b) The 5-year moving totals are 58, 59, 62, 66, 70, 73, 78, 85, 89, 98, 104, 113, 120, 130, 135, 146, 149, 152, 161, 167, 165, 170, 171, 167, 157, 154, and the 5-year moving averages are $\frac{58}{5} = 11.6$, 11.8, 12.4, 13.2, 14, 14.6, 15.6, 17, 17.8, 19.6, 20.8, 22.6, 24, 26, 27, 29.2, 29.8, 30.4, 32.2, 33.4, 33, 34, 34.2, 33.4, 31.4, 30.8

10. $S_t = \alpha y_t + (1 - \alpha)S_{t-1}$; Let $S_0 = y_0 = 20$, $y_0 = 20$, $y_1 = 39$, $y_2 = 18$, $y_3 = 25$, etc. Then

a) $S_t = 0.2 y_t + 0.8 S_{t-1}$;

$\quad S_1 = \alpha y_1 + (1 - \alpha)S_0 = 0.2(39) + 0.8(20)$
$\quad\quad = 7.8 + 16 = 23.8$

$\quad S_2 = 0.2 y_2 + 0.8 S_1 = 0.2(18) + 0.8(23.8)$
$\quad\quad = 3.6 + 19.04 = 22.64$

$\quad S_3 = 0.2 y_3 + 0.8 S_2 = 0.2(25) + 0.8(22.64)$
$\quad\quad = 5 + 18.112 = 23.112$

$$S_4 = 0.2y_4 + 0.8S_3 = 0.2(30) + 0.8(23.112)$$
$$= 6 + 18.4896 = 24.4896$$
$$S_5 = 0.2y_5 + 0.8S_4 = 0.2(12) + 0.8(24.4896)$$
$$= 2.4 + 19.59168 = 21.99168$$
$$S_6 = 0.2y_6 + 0.8S_5 = 0.2(21) + 0.8(21.99168)$$
$$= 4.2 + 17.593344 = 21.793344$$
$$S_7 = 0.2y_7 + 0.8S_6 = 0.2(27) + 0.8(21.793344)$$
$$= 5.4 + 17.43475 = 22.834675$$
$$S_8 = 0.2y_8 + 0.8S_7 = 0.2(15) + 0.8(22.834675)$$
$$= 3 + 18.26774 = 21.26774$$
$$S_9 = 0.2y_9 + 0.8S_8 = 0.2(35) + 0.8(21.26774)$$
$$= 7 + 17.014192 = 24.014192$$
$$S_{10} = 0.2y_{10} + 0.8S_9 = 0.2(30) + 0.8(24.014192)$$
$$= 6 + 19.211354 = 25.211354$$
$$S_{11} = 0.2y_{11} + 0.8S_{10} = 0.2(17) + 0.8(25.211354)$$
$$= 3.4 + 20.16908 = 23.56908$$

b) $S_t = 0.5y_t + 0.5S_{t-1} = 0.5(y_t + S_{t-1}); \ S_0 = 20$

$$S_1 = 0.5(39 + 20) = 29.5;$$
$$S_2 = 0.5(18 + 29.5) = 0.5(47.5) = 23.75;$$
$$S_3 = 0.5(25 + 23.75) = 0.5(48.75)$$
$$= 24.375; \ S_4 = 0.5(30 + 24.375)$$
$$= 0.5(54.375) = 27.1875;$$
$$S_5 = 0.5(12 + 27.1875) = 0.5(39.1875)$$
$$= 19.59375; \ S_6 = 0.5(21 + 19.59375)$$
$$= 0.5(40.59375) = 20.2969;$$
$$S_7 = 0.5(27 + 20.2969) = 0.5(47.2969)$$
$$= 23.648; \ S_8 = 0.5(15 + 23.648)$$
$$= 0.5(38.648) = 19.324;$$
$$S_9 = 0.5(35 + 19.324) = 0.5(54.324)$$
$$= 27.162; \ S_{10} = 0.5(30 + 27.162)$$
$$= 0.5(57.162) = 28.581;$$
$$S_{11} = 0.5(17 + 28.581) = 0.5(45.581) = 22.791;$$

17 Index Numbers

There are many concepts in the sciences that can be measured directly in a satisfactory manner, but there are also many others for which this cannot be done. For example, the percentage of unemployed workers in a city can be measured directly very easily, but it is not very clear how to measure the level of the stock market.

For things that do not lend themselves to direct measurement, it is necessary to introduce some surrogate quantities which are used to represent them quantitatively. For example, economists use the Dow-Jones Industrial Average to describe the level of the stock market.

These indirect measures are called Index Numbers, and their main objective is to relate a variable (or variables) in a given period to the same variable (or variables) in another period, called the base period.

The motivation for using Index Numbers is our desire to reduce data to an easier-to-use form. Index Numbers are widely used around the world to relate information about stock markets, inflation, sales, exports and imports, agriculture, and many other things.

In this chapter we will explain the nature of Index Numbers, present some desirable properties that Index Numbers should possess and may be useful in their construction, point out some of the practical problems that can complicate their construction, and describe some of the more important Index Numbers which are now used in everyday and business life.

17.1   Introduction

One of the most important problems, when studying Economics and Business, is how to measure the quantity of some heterogeneous aggregate. The aggregate may be a physical quantity (such as the number of stocks in a portfolio, or number of errors in an income statement) or it may be a list of prices paid for the purchase of various items from a store. In each of these cases, the problem of measurement is to derive a single figure, which is descriptive of the entire aggregate through time, or from place to place.

The statistical devices used for such measurements are called *Index numbers,* and they relate a variable (or variables) in a given time period to the same variable (or variables) in another time period called the base period. An index number, which is computed from a single variable, is called a *Univariate Index,* while an index number, which is computed from a group of variables, is called a *Composite Index.* A Univariate Index can be constructed easily and its meaning is very apparent. On the other hand, composite indices are difficult to construct and interpret.

The main function of a Univariate Index number (see Index A in the table below) is to transform the absolute quantities of a variable into relative numbers so that, comparisons of the changes in the variable through time, can be easily made. In Table 17.1 below the Univariate Index A is constructed from the equation:

$$\textbf{INDEX A} = \textbf{(YEAR/1966)} * \textbf{100} \tag{17.1}$$

in which the base period is year 1966. The Index Numbers are in percentages.

Table 17.1 Construction of a Univariate Index										
Year	**1960**	**1961**	**1962**	**1963**	**1964**	**1965**	**1966**	**1967**	**1968**	**1969**	**1970**
Production (× 100)	8.5	12.5	9.4	10.7	13.6	15.3	13.5	12.8	14.7	16.7	18.0
Index A = (Year/1966) × 100	63	93	70	79	101	113	100	95	109	124	133

For example, the index number of 133 for 1970, means that production in 1970 was 133 percent of the 1966 production.

Composite Indices are of many types (price, quantity, cost) and may be constructed in many different ways (see for example the Laspeyres Index, Paache Index, Fisher Index). Below we will discuss some of the more frequently used indices in Economics and Business.

To avoid repetition we define here the symbols which are used in our discussion of indices:

p = price of a single commodity

q = quantity of a single commodity

p_o = base-period price of a commodity

q_o = base-period quantity of a commodity

t = given-period price of commodity ($t = \ldots, -3, -2, -1, 0, 1, 2, 3, \ldots$)

q_t = given-period quantity of a commodity

i = a particular commodity (ex. Poi = price of i-th commodity in base period; $i = 1, 2, 3, \ldots$)

K = number of commodities

P = a price index

Q = a quantity index

P_b = a price index, derived by using base-period quantities as weights

P_t = a price index, derived by using given-period quantities as weights

Q_b = a quantity index, derived by using base-period prices as weights

Q_t = a quantity index, derived by using given-period prices as weights

V = a value index

E = a productivity index

To simplify our numerical illustrations, we will use the hypothetical data of Table 17.2 below to construct Composite Indices for Price, Quantity, and Cost.

Table 17.2 Hypothetical Data for the construction of Composite Indices for Price, Quantity and Cost

Item	Prices			Quantities	
	1965 P_o	1970 P_t	Price Relative $(P_t/P_o \times 100)$	1965 q_o	1970 q_t
Steak (lb)	1.00	1.15	115	40	50
Pepper (lb)	2.00	2.20	110	1	1
Bread (loaf)	0.20	0.27	135	100	90

17.2 Price Indices

To construct the simplest possible price index we will use the data in Table 17.2 above. The problem is to describe, with a single index number, "how this basket of goods" has changed.

Note: For convenience an index value of 100 is assigned to the base period (*i.e.,* index numbers are expressed in percentage form, requiring the multiplication by 100).

1. One way to construct such an index would be to:
   a) Sum all the 1970 prices and call this sum S_t.
   b) Sum all the 1965 prices (1965 is assumed to be the base period) and call this sum S_o.
   c) Divide S_t by S_o.
   d) Multiply the ratio (S_t/S_o) by 100.

Since $S_t = 1.15 + 2.20 + 0.27 = 3.62$ and $S_o = 1.00 + 2.00 + 0.20 = 3.20$, the Price index P, is given by:

$$P = \text{Price Index} = S_t/S_o \times 100 = (3.62/3.20) \times 100 = 113.12 \qquad (17.2)$$

The conclusion based on this index, is that on the average, prices have risen by about 13% from 1965 to 1970.

But is this a good estimate? The answer is **no**, because this calculation depends on the arbitrary choice of units in which each commodity is measured. Thus, if pepper were measured in ounces instead of pounds it would have a much less dominant role in the calculation of the Price Index, P, of equation (17.2). Similarly, if steak were measured in tons instead of pounds, the resulting index would be almost 115 and would be completely dominated by the price of the steak.

2. A simple way to avoid this problem is to calculate the "price relative" of each item, as it is done in table 17.2 above. In this case the Price Index, P, is defined as:

$$P = \frac{\sum\limits_{i=1}^{k}\left(\dfrac{P_t}{P_o}\right)_i \times 100}{k} = \frac{\left(\dfrac{P_t}{P_o}\right)_1 \times 100 + \left(\dfrac{P_t}{P_o}\right)_2 \times 100 + \left(\dfrac{P_t}{P_o}\right)_3 \times 100}{3} \qquad (17.3)$$

$$= \frac{\left(\dfrac{1.15}{1.00}\right) \times 100 + \left(\dfrac{2.20}{2.00}\right) \times 100 + \left(\dfrac{0.27}{0.20}\right) \times 100}{3}$$

$$= \frac{115 + 110 + 135}{3} = \frac{360}{3} = 120$$

Note: The price index given by equation (17.3) is sometimes referred to as the "Simple Average of Relatives" Index, as opposed to the "Simple Aggregative" Price Index given by equation (17.2).

3. **The Laspeyres and Paache Price Indices**

Although the price index of equation (17.3) is an improvement over the one given in equation (17.2), because it is independent of the units of measurement of the items, it retains one major flaw because each item is assigned equal weights, when in fact some items are more important than others. (For example bread and steak are more important than pepper in any normal expenditure pattern).

An appropriate index should be a "weighted average of the price changes", with the weights being the quantities consumed.

But one question still remains: Which quantities do we use as weights? The quantities of the Base Period (Q_o) or the Weights in the Comparison Period Q_t?

a) If the quantities of the Base Period (Q_o) are used as weights, the index is called the LASPEYRES PRICE INDEX and it is defined as:

$$
\begin{aligned}
\textit{Laspeyres Index}(\star\,100) &= \frac{\sum\limits_{i=1}^{n}(P_t Q_o)_i}{\sum\limits_{i=1}^{n}(P_o Q_o)_i} \\[2mm]
&= \frac{(P_t Q_o)_1 + (P_t Q_o)_2 + (P_t Q_o)_3}{(P_o Q_o)_1 + (P_o Q_o)_2 + (P_o Q_o)_3} \\[2mm]
&= \frac{(1.15 \times 40) + (2.20 \times 1) + (0.27 \times 100)}{(1.00 \times 40) + (2.00 \times 1) + (0.20 \times 100)} \\[2mm]
&= \frac{75.20}{62} = 1.2129 \ \text{ or } \ 121.29
\end{aligned}
\qquad (17.4)
$$

b) If the Quantities of the Comparison Period (Q_t) are used as weights, the index is called the *Paasche Price Index* and it is defined as:

$$\textbf{Paasche Price Index}(\times\textbf{100}) = \frac{\sum\limits_{i=1}^{n}(P_tQ_t)_i}{\sum\limits_{i=1}^{n}(P_oQ_t)_i}$$

$$= \frac{(P_tQ_t)_1 + (P_tQ_t)_2 + (P_tQ_t)_3}{(P_oQ_t)_1 + (P_oQ_t)_2 + (P_oQ_t)_3} \qquad (17.5)$$

$$= \frac{(1.15 \times 50) + (2.20 \times 1)(0.27 \times 90)}{(1.00 \times 50) + (2.00 \times 1)(0.20 \times 90)}$$

$$= \frac{84}{70} = 1.2 \ \text{ or } \ 120$$

Even though there is no theoretical reason for preferring one index over the other, practically speaking the **Laspeyres Index** is easier to calculate by hand (when calculating an Index for several comparison periods) because it uses the same **base period** values (*i.e.,* the denominator of equation (17.4) remains fixed), while the **Paasche Index** involves changing weights for each calculation.

When constructing the **Laspeyres Index**, the selection of a base year becomes a crucial issue. Great care must be taken that the base year is a "typical" year, free of disasters or other unusual events that would distort consumption patterns.

4. **Fisher's Ideal Index: a Geometric Mean**

The Geometric Mean is the appropriate measure to use in describing the Average of rates or percentages (see Chapter 3) and is defined as the *"nth* root of the product of *n* items". Therefore, given *n* items: $X_1, X_2, \ldots, X_n$, their geometric mean is:

$$\overline{X}_G = (X_1 \times X_2 \times X_3 \cdots X_n)^{1/n} \qquad (17.6)$$

Example

To illustrate the calculation of the Geometric Mean, consider Table 17.3 below to describe the average rate of increase, in population, per decade.

Table 17.3 Average Population Increase per Decade		
Decade	**Population**	**Increase Per Decade**
1950	1,000	–
1960	2,000	2 Times (Between 1950–1960)
1970	16,000	8 Times (Between 1960–1970)
Overall Increase (Between 1950 and 1970) = 16 Times		

Note that the population increased by a factor of 2 between 1950 and 1960 and by a factor of 8 between 1960 and 1970. Therefore, the overall increase between 1950 and 1970 is 16-fold.

The Arithmetic Average of the two increases = $(2 + 8)/2 = 5$, but this is not the appropriate measure to use because, a 5-fold increase per decade, for 2 successive decades, would result in a 25-fold increase.

On the other hand, the Geometric Average of the two increases $= [(2)(8)]^{1/2} = 4$, is the appropriate measure to use because a 4-fold increase per decade, for 2 successive decades, would result in a 16-fold increase.

Fisher's Index is defined as the Geometric Mean of the Laspeyres and Paasche Indices, since they measure rates of change.

Therefore,

Fisher's Ideal Price Index $= [(\text{Laspeyres Index}) \times (\text{Paasche Index})]^{1/2}$ $\qquad$ (17.7)

$$= \left[\left(\frac{\sum_{i=1}^{n} (P_t Q_o)_i}{\sum_{i=1}^{n} (P_o Q_o)_i} \right) \left(\frac{\sum_{i=1}^{n} (P_t Q_t)_i}{\sum_{i=1}^{n} (P_o Q_t)_i} \right) \right]^{1/2}$$

$$= [1.2129 \times 1.2]^{1/2} = [1.45548]^{1/2} = 1.20643 \text{ or } 120.64$$

17.3   Quantity Indices: They Calculate Changes in the Physical Quantity of Goods Consumed

Prices will be used as weights in calculating a Quantity Index, just as quantities were previously used as weights in calculating a Price Index.

Therefore, by using similar reasoning as in Section 17.2, we obtain:

1. **Laspeyres Quantity Index** $= \dfrac{\sum_{i=1}^{n} (Q_t P_o)_i}{\sum_{i=1}^{n} (Q_o P_o)_i}$ $\qquad$ (17.8)

$$= \frac{(Q_t P_o)_1 + (Q_t P_o)_2 + (Q_t P_o)_3}{(Q_o P_o)_1 + (Q_o P_o)_2 + (Q_o P_o)_3}$$

$$= \frac{50(1.00) + 1(2.00) + 90(0.20)}{40(1.00) + 1(2.00) + 100(0.20)}$$

$$= \frac{70}{62} = 1.1290 \text{ or } 112.90$$

2. **Paasche Quantity Index** $= \dfrac{\sum_{i=1}^{n} (Q_t P_t)_i}{\sum_{i=1}^{n} (Q_o P_t)_i} = \dfrac{(Q_t P_t)_1 + (Q_t P_t)_2 + (Q_t P_t)_3}{(Q_o P_t)_1 + (Q_o P_t)_2 + (Q_o P_t)_3}$ $\qquad$ (17.9)

$$= \frac{50(1.15) + 1(2.20) + 90(0.27)}{40(1.15) + 1(2.20) + 100(0.27)}$$

$$= \frac{84}{75.2} = 1.1170 \text{ or } 111.70$$

3. **Fisher's Ideal Quantity Index** $= [(\text{Laspeyres Index})$

$\times (\text{Paasche Index})]^{1/2}$ $\qquad$ (17.10)

$$= [(1.1290 \times (1.117)]^{1/2} = (1.261117021)^{1/2}$$

$$= 1.12299 \text{ or } 112.3$$

17.4   Cost Index

Up to now we have defined price and quantity indices only. Now we will attempt to measure total cost (*i.e.*, monetary value) of the consumer's purchases.

Since the cost of one item is: **Item Cost = (Price of Item) × (Quantity)** (17.11)

and the cost of all items purchased is: **Total Cost** $= \sum_{i=1}^{n} (PQ)_i$ (17.12)

the total costs in the 2 time periods of Table 17.2 may be compared by forming their ratio. Thus we obtain the **Cost Index** defined by:

$$\textbf{Cost Index} = \frac{\sum_{i=1}^{n} (P_t Q_t)_i}{\sum_{i=1}^{n} (P_o Q_o)_i} = \frac{(P_t Q_t)_1 + (P_t Q_t)_2 + (P_t Q_t)_3}{(P_o Q_o)_1 + (P_o Q_o)_2 + (P_o Q_o)_3}$$

$$= \frac{1.15(50) + 2.20(1) + 0.27(90)}{1.00(40) + 2.00(1) + 0.20(100)} = \frac{84}{62} = 1.35484$$

$$= 135.484 \approx 135.5$$

If our indices of price, quantity and cost are "good" indices, they should follow a relationship similar to equation (17.11), which individual items satisfy; that is we want to check and see if the product of the Price Index times the Quantity Index is equal to the Cost Index or in equation form:

$$\textbf{(Price Index)} \times \textbf{(Quantity Index)} \overset{?}{=} \textbf{(Cost Index)} \qquad (17.14)$$

For example, if the Price Index increases by a factor of 2 and the Quantity Index increases by a factor of 3, then the Cost Index, according to equation 17.11 should increase by a factor of 6; if this is not the case then something must be wrong with the Price and/or Quantity Indices. Unfortunately this test known as the **"Factor-Reversal Test"** is usually not satisfied, as the following calculations show:

Q1: Is the Factor Reversal Test satisfied by the Laspeyres Indices?

$$\textbf{(Price Index)} \times \textbf{(Quantity Index)} \overset{?}{=} \textbf{(Cost Index)} \qquad (17.15)$$

or $$(1.2129)(1.129) \overset{?}{=} 1.3548$$

Since $$(1.2129)(1.129) = 1.3694$$

and $$1.3694 > 1.3548$$

or $$136.94 > 135.48$$

it is obvious that the Factor Reversal Test is not satisfied by the Laspeyres indices, with the product of Price and Quantity Indices being higher than the Cost Index.

Q2: Is the factor Reversal Test satisfied by the Paasche Indices?

Since $$(1.20)(1.117) = 1.3404 \qquad (17.16)$$

and $$1.3404 < 1.3548$$

or $$134.04 < 135.48$$

obviously the Factor Reversal Test is not satisfied by the Paasche Indices, with the product of Price and Quantity Indices being lower than the Cost Index.

Q3: Is the Factor Reversal Test satisfied by Fisher's Ideal Indices?

Since $$(1.2064)(1.123) = 1.3548 \tag{17.17}$$

and $$1.3548 = 1.3548$$

or $$135.48 = 135.48$$

obviously the Factor Reversal Test is satisfied by Fisher's Ideal Indices.

It is easy to show that Fischer's Index always satisfies the **"Factor-Reversal Test"**, and this is one of the properties that have earned this Index the name **"ideal"**.

The proof can be accomplished by multiplying Fischer's Ideal Price Index given by equation (17.7), by Fischer's Ideal Quantity Index given by equation (17.10). After cancellation of similar terms the result is:

$$\frac{\sum_{i=1}^{n}(P_t Q_t)_i}{\sum_{i=1}^{n}(P_o Q_o)_i}, \tag{17.18}$$

which is, by definition the **Cost Index** given by equation (17.13).

Comparing equations (17.15), (17.16) and (17.17), we note the following:

1. **Laspeyres Indices** (both Price and Quantity) are larger than the corresponding Ideal Indices and their product is larger than the Cost Index. **Hence Laspeyres Index overstates.**
2. **Paasche Indices** (both price and quantity) are smaller than the corresponding Ideal Indices and their product is smaller than the Cost Index. **Hence Paasche Index understates.**
3. **Fischer's Ideal Indices** Since the product of Fischer's Ideal Price and Quantity Indices is **always** equal to the Cost Index, being the Geometric Mean of the Laspeyres and Paasche Indices (see equation (17.7)), it is a very useful compromise.

Note 1: A **PRICE INDEX** is popularly known as a **"COST OF LIVING"** Index.

Note 2: A **QUANTITY INDEX** is often called a **"STANDARD OF LIVING"** Index or **"REAL INCOME"** Index.

17.5 Desirable Properties of Index Numbers

We have, up to now discussed several indices with varying degrees of computational difficulty. For an index to be considered a "Good" index, it must be easy to calculate and satisfy certain "Criteria of Goodness", one of which is the "Factor Reversal Test" which requires that the product of a price index and the quantity index should equal the corresponding cost (or value) index. This test was shown to be satisfied by Fisher's ideal index but not by the Laspeyres and Paasche indices. Other criteria of goodness of selecting between index numbers are: 1) The Units Test, 2) The Time Reversal Test and 3) The Circular Test. The *Units Test* requires that an index be independent of the units in which prices and quantities are expressed in. All the indices discussed in this chapter satisfy this test except for the simple aggregate indices.

The *Time Reversal Test* requires that if one object is twice as big as a second object, then the second object must be half as big as the first object. Another way to state this is to require that the index number for period 0, relative to the period n, is the reciprocal of the index number for period n, relative to period 0. Mathematically this can be stated as:

$$I_{o,n} \times I_{n,o} = 1 \qquad (17.19)$$

To determine whether an index satisfies the time reversal test we need to interchange the subscripts 0 and n in the formula for the index under question and then substitute into equation (17.19). It turns out that the simple aggregate and cost indices satisfy this test, but none of the other indices discussed in this chapter satisfy it.

The Circular Test is an extension of the time reversal test and it is useful because it enables us to adjust the index values from period to period without referring each time to the original base. For example, if the 2000 index with 1990 as the base is 3.0 and the 1990 index with 1980 as the base is 2.0, then the 2000 index with 1980 as the base, must be 6.0. Or in equation form:

$$I_{2000,\,1990} \times I_{1990,\,1980} = I_{2000,\,1980} \qquad (17.20)$$

All of the weighted aggregate indices fail the circular test if the weights differ from one computation to another (using the same equation) but satisfy the test when the weights are the same for all computations. The fact that most of the indices we discussed do not satisfy these tests does not make these indices useless, because these indices do have logically desirable properties. The Laspeyres and Paasche indices, even though they do not satisfy all of these desirable tests, they do provide satisfactory answers to specific questions. Perhaps, at some time in the future, an index will be constructed which meets all of the desirable tests and at the same time provides good answers to specific questions. But, until then, we must use the available indices, even though they are imperfect.

17.6   Some Problems in Constructing Indices

Up to now out main concern was how to construct index numbers. Now, we will examine the validity of the assumptions that we made and the accuracy of the developed formulas for the indices. We will examine the following problems:

1) sampling, 2) selection of base period, 3) selection of weights, 4) selection of average, 5) changing of products and 6) accuracy of formulas.

Indices are usually constructed from samples selected by the designer of the index and therefore, how representative the sample and index are depend on his/her judgment and knowledge of the data under analysis. Obviously the sample is not random. Is the fact that the sample is not random and its representativeness is questionable a serious problem in the construction of the index? It depends on what the aim of the index is. For example, if the aim is to describe the movements of general business activity, we would want to include many items and the index becomes more representative as more items are included.

Mathematically speaking, it should not matter at all which period is selected as the base. However, since the base period is used in the computation of relatives and as a basis for comparing index numbers, the base period value should be typical, *i.e.,* neither too high nor too low relative to the values of other periods. Also, the base period should be relatively recent because our interest is in comparing current fluctuations relative to a base similar to the current situation.

Selecting the appropriate weight for each variable, according to their economic importance, is a difficult task, but it can be made easier if one is familiar with economic theory. If we change the weights, the meaning of the index may also change. Therefore, the weights we want to use depend on the question we want to answer.

Theoretically any measure of Central Tendency (Median, Mode, Mean, mid-range, etc) can be used as the average of the weighted aggregative quantities. However, the arithmetic mean is the most frequently used average in constructing indices because such indices are easy to compute and have simple economic meaning. In a fast changing world old products are continuously improved or replaced by new products. How are such developments handled by an index which wants to retain its significance? Price levels over long periods of time are confined to staple commodity prices (such as grains and metals) that remain much the same from age to age. Since different formulas usually produce different results, when evaluated using the same price and/or quantity data, we naturally ask the question: which formula is the most accurate? The accuracy of the formulas depends on whether or not the formula or index meets certain mathematical tests (Factor Reversal Test, Units Test, Time Reversal Test, Circular Test), which were discussed in Section 17.5 above.

Since most of our indices do not meet any or most of these tests, we can not expect to find any index that is "most accurate" every time. Knowledge of the data and the purpose for which the index is constructed should guide one to select the most appropriate index.

17.7   Some Important Current Indices

Two of the most important indices are constructed by the United States Bureau of Labor Statistics (BLS) and they are: The *Wholesale Price Index (WPI)* and the *Consumer Price Index (CPI)*.

The BLS Wholesale Price Index was first calculated in 1920. It is based on a large sample of about 2000 commodity prices selected from 15 major groups and about 90 subgroups of commodities grouped by product. The objective of the large sample is to provide sufficient data for the computation of price indices for commodity subgroups.

The BLS Wholesale Price Index is constructed by a modified version of the Laspeyres formula. The weights used in the index are reviewed and revised every time complete Census data become available.

The BLS Consumer Price Index measures the average change in the price of a "fixed market basket" of goods and services purchased by families of urban wage earners and salaried clerks. This index was initiated during WWI (1914–1918). In its current formulation the index is constructed from a collection of about 400 retail prices which include sales taxes. It is computed by a modified Laspeyres formula. The BLS CPI is not strictly a Laspeyres index because weight revisions (which are made periodically to accommodate the shifting importance of items) do not always occur at the same time as the shift of the base.

An important quantity index is the **Federal Reserve Board (FRB)** Index of Industrial production which is in existence since 1927. Its main objective is to measure changes in the volume of manufacturing and mineral production and in the output of gas and electricity industries. In its present form, it is a weighted average of relative indices of more than 200 different series, each of which represents the output of a particular product (or industry) or the man-hours worked in that industry.

The GNP (Gross National Product) Index is the standard measure of the output of an economy. It appears quarterly in the Survey of Current Business, in both current and constant dollars.

The IPD (Implicit Price Deflator) Index is also published in the Survey of Current Business along with the GNP. It is used as the average measure of price inflation (or deflation) of an economy. It is obtained by dividing the GNP (expressed in current dollars) by the corresponding GNP (expresses in constant dollars) and multiplied by 100.

The Dow-Jones Average of 30 Industrial Stocks (D-J) is the best-known index for measuring common stock prices. It was established in 1897 at which time it was based on 12 stocks, but, eventually it was expanded to include 30 stocks. To calculate the D-J index, one sums up the closing prices of the 30 stocks making up the index, on a particular date and then divides this sum not by 30 (as one would expect because we are calculating the average of 30 stocks) but by another value which is the result of stock splits and dividends over the years. Although the 30 stocks contained in the D-J index are not a random sample of the many stocks (over 1000) that make up the New York Stock Exchange listing, they were very judiciously selected and appear to represent the entire listing, as evidenced by the fact that the Index has survived quite well against a lot of competition by other indices (such as the *Standard and Poor's 500 Index* and the *New York Stock Exchange price* of an average share based on all issues).

17.8   Some Applications of Price Indices

Over the years indices and in particular price indices, have played an important role in many decisions by private industry, labor unions and government. Below we discuss five important applications of price indices.

■ Purchasing Power

The traditional function of a price index is to measure the purchasing power of money. Intuitively we know that the higher the prices, the lower the purchasing power of money or, stated in another way, the purchasing power of money is the reciprocal of the price index. This can be written in equation form as:

$$\text{Purchasing Power of Money} = \frac{1}{\text{Price Index}} \qquad (17.21)$$

For example, if the CPI in a given year is 133.3 (or 1.333) then the purchasing power of the dollar is $= 1/1.33 = 1/(4/3) = 0.75$. Therefore, the purchasing power of the consumer dollar for this year has decreased by 25 percent from the base period.

■ Real Wages

Since real wages are the purchasing power of money wages, a Real Wage Index can be constructed to show the changes in the purchasing power of money wages of workers. Such an Index is defined by equation (17.22) below:

$$\text{Real Wage Index} = \frac{\text{Index of Money Wages}}{\text{Consumer Price Index}} \qquad (17.22)$$

in which both the numerator and denominator indices are constructed relative to the same base period. For example, if the Index of Money Wages for a particular union and a particular year, relative to a specific base year, was 140 and the CPI was 120 (for the same union and year and same base period), then the Real Wage Index for the Union Workers is equal to: $140/120 = 1.167$ or 116.7. This implies that the workers real wages had increased by 16.7% only and not by 40% as would be implied by the Index of Money Wages above.

■ Escalator Clauses

An escalator clause provides for an automatic amount of wage change, in collective bargaining agreements, for a given change in the Consumer Price Index (CPI). The reason for such a clause is to protect the workers standard of living from price changes.

■ Terms of Exchange

We have previously defined Real Wages as ratios of the Index of Money Wage to the CPI. In a similar way we define the terms of exchange of one (or more) commodity as ratios of the price index of that commodity to the price index of another commodity or in equation form:

$$\left(\begin{array}{c}\text{Index of relative price of Commodity} A \\ \text{in terms of Commodity } B\end{array}\right) = \frac{\text{Price Index of Commodity } A}{\text{Price Index of Commodity } B} \quad (17.23)$$

The concept of "terms of trade" provides another application of Terms of Exchange and represents the ratio at which commodities are traded internationally. When only 2 commodities are traded, the "terms of trade" is defined as the ratio of the Index of Import prices to the Index of Export prices. According to this definition, the "terms of trade" may be thought of as the quantity of imports obtained for one unit of exports. When the average price of a country's imports increases more rapidly than the average price it receives from its exports, the nation's "terms of trade" have become less favorable, since a smaller amount of imports can now be obtained per unit of exports. The parity ratio, defined by:

$$\text{Parity ratio} = \frac{\text{Index of Price Received by Farmers}}{\text{Index of Prices Paid by Farmers}} \quad (17.24)$$

has, for many years, been the basic guideline of American agricultural policy, which stipulates that farmers who conform to certain requirements can sell their crops to the government at a price which is a given percentage of parity. Obviously, when the "prices received" index is higher than the "Index of Prices Paid," agricultural prices are above parity while when the converse is true, agricultural prices are below parity.

■ The Constant Dollar

Since the value of an aggregate of goods is the product of price and quantity, it is obvious that the value of the aggregate can change because of changes in the prices of the items in the aggregate or changes in the quantities of the items or changes in both prices and quantities. Often we are interested in determining what the value of goods and services would be if their prices had not changed or if the value of money had remained constant. This is achieved by using *Statistical Deflation,* a procedure by which the effects of changes in prices, on the value of a list of commodities, are removed and which is defined by the expression:

$$\text{Physical Volume in Constant Dollars} = \frac{Volume\ in\ Current\ Dollars}{Appropriate\ Price\ Index} \quad (17.25)$$

in which, since the denominator is a pure number, makes the units of the right-hand side of (17.25) dollars which, however, have now been transformed in constant dollars. The Price Index used in statistical deflation is called the Deflator.

17.9 An Example

Given the following prices and quantities of 3 commodities purchased by a family for the years 1998 and 1999, use them to calculate the increase or decrease in prices from 1998 to 1999, if:

1. The simple Average of Relatives Index is used.
2. The Laspeyres Index is used.

3. The Paasche Index is used.
4. The Fishers Ideal Index is used.
5. Check to see if Cost Index = (Price Index) × (Quantity Index), in parts (2) and (3).
6. Verify numerically that Cost Index = (Price Index) × (Quantity Index), is satisfied in part (4).

	Year 1998		Year 1999	
Commodity	**Quantity** (Q_o)	**Price** (P_o)	**Quantity** (Q_t)	**Price** (P_t)
Bread	200 (loaves)	1.35	180 (loaves)	1.40
Meat	300 (pounds)	1.90	250 (pounds)	2.00
Eggs	100 (dozen)	0.90	150 (dozen)	0.80

Solutions

1. $P = \dfrac{\sum_{i=1}^{k} \left(\dfrac{P_t}{P_o}\right)_i \times 100}{k} = \dfrac{\left(\dfrac{P_t}{P_o}\right)_1 \times 100 + \left(\dfrac{P_t}{P_o}\right)_2 \times 100 + \left(\dfrac{P_t}{P_o}\right)_3 \times 100}{3}$

$= \dfrac{1}{3}\left[\dfrac{140}{135} + \dfrac{200}{190} + \dfrac{80}{90}\right] \times 100$

$= \dfrac{1}{3}[1.0370 + 1.0526 + 0.8888] \times 100 = \dfrac{1}{3}(2.9785) \times 100 = 99.28\%$

hence a decrease of 0.72 percent

2. Laspeyres Price Index $= \dfrac{\sum_{i=1}^{n}(P_tQ_o)_i}{\sum_{i=1}^{n}(P_oQ_o)_i} = \dfrac{(P_tQ_o)_1 + (P_tQ_o)_2 + (P_tQ_o)_3}{(P_oQ_o)_1 + (P_oQ_o)_2 + (P_tQ_o)_3} \times 100$

$= \dfrac{200(140) + 300(200) + 100(80)}{200(135) + 300(190) + 100(90)}$

$= \dfrac{28,000 + 60,000 + 8,000}{27,000 + 57,000 + 9,000}$

$= \dfrac{96,000}{93,000} = 1.0323$ or 103.23%

hence an increase of 3.23 percent

3. Paasche Price Index $= \dfrac{\sum_{i=1}^{n}(P_tQ_t)_i}{\sum_{i=1}^{n}(P_oQ_t)_i} = \dfrac{180(140) + 250(200) + 150(80)}{180(135) + 250(190) + 150(90)}$

$= \dfrac{25,200 + 500,00 + 12,000}{24,300 + 47,500 + 13,500} = \dfrac{87,200}{85,300} = 1.0223$ or 102.23%

hence an increase of 2.23 percent

4. Fisher's Ideal Price Index $= \sqrt{(Laspeyres\ Index) \times (Paasche\ Index)}$

$= \sqrt{(103.23)(102.23)} = \sqrt{105.532029}$

$= 102.7288$, or an increase of 2.73 percent

5. Cost Index $= \dfrac{\sum\limits_{i=1}^{n}(P_tQ_t)_i}{\sum\limits_{i=1}^{n}(P_0Q_0)_i} = \dfrac{(180 \times 140) + (250 \times 200) + (150 \times 80)}{(200 \times 135) + (300 \times 190) + 100(90)}$

$= \dfrac{25{,}200 + 50{,}000 + 12{,}000}{27{,}000 + 57{,}000 + 9{,}000} = \dfrac{87{,}200}{93{,}000} = 0.9376$

Laspeyres Quantity Index $= \dfrac{\sum\limits_{i=1}^{n}(Q_tP_0)_i}{\sum\limits_{i=1}^{n}(Q_0P_0)_i} = \dfrac{180(135) + 250(190) + 150(90)}{200(135) + 300(190) + 100(90)}$

$= \dfrac{24{,}300 + 47{,}500 + 13{,}500}{27{,}000 + 57{,}000 + 9{,}000} = \dfrac{85{,}300}{93{,}000} = 0.9172$

Since the Laspeyres Price Index = 1.0323 (see part (2)), and (Laspeyres Quantity Index) × (Laspeyres Price Index) = (0.9172 × 1.0323) = 0.9468 and 0.9468 > 0.9376, the relationship:

$$Cost\ Index = (Price\ Index) \times (Quantity\ Index)$$

is not satisfied for part (2).

Paasche Quantity Index $= \dfrac{\sum\limits_{i=1}^{n}(Q_tP_t)_i}{\sum\limits_{i=1}^{n}(Q_oP_t)_i} = \dfrac{180(140) + 250(200) + 150(180)}{200(140) + 300(200) + 100(80)}$

$= \dfrac{25{,}200 + 50{,}000 + 12{,}000}{28{,}000 + 60{,}000 + 8{,}000} = \dfrac{87{,}200}{96{,}000} = 0.9083$

Since the Paasche Price Index = 1.0223 (see part 3) and (*Paasche Quantity Index*) × (*Paasche Price Index*) = (0.9083 × 1.0223) = 0.9286 and 0.9286 < 0.9376, the relationship:

$$Cost\ Index = (Price\ Index) \times (Quantity\ Index)$$

is not satisfied for part (3).

6. Fisher's Ideal Quantity Index

$= \sqrt{(Laspeyres\ Quantity\,Index) \times (Paasche\ Quantity\,Index)}$

$= \sqrt{(0.9172) \times (0.9083)} = \sqrt{0.8330923} = 0.9127$

Since Fisher's Ideal Price Index = 1.02729 (see part (4)), and *(Fisher's Ideal Quantity Index)* × *(Fisher's Ideal Price Index)* = (0.9127 × 1.02729) = 0.9736, the relationship

$$Cost\ Index = (Price\ Index) \times (Quantity\ Index)$$

is satisfied in part (4) of the problem.

17.10   References

Berenson, Marc, L., Levine, David, M., and Krehbiel, Timothy, C., 2004. *Basic Business Statistics*. 9th Edition. Pearson-Prentice Hall.

Black, Ken, 2004. *Business Statistics*. 4th Edition. Wiley.

Canavos, George, C., 1984. *Applied Probability and Statistical Methods*. Little, Brown.

Carlson, William, L., and Thorne, Betty, 1997. *Applied Statistical Methods*. Prentice Hall.

Chou, Ya-lun, 1992. *Statistical Analysis for Business and Economics*. Elsevier.

Freund, John, E., and Williams, Frank, J., 1969. *Modern Business Statistics*. Revised by: Perles, Benjamin and Sullivan, Charles. Prentice-Hall.

Freund, John, E., and Williams, Frank, J., 1982. *Elementary Business Statistics: The Modern approach*. Prentice-Hall.

Johnson, Robert, 1973. *Elementary Statistics*. Duxbury Press.

McClave, James, T., Benson, George, P., and Sincich, Terry, 2001. *Statistics for Business and Economics*. 8th Edition. Prentice Hall.

Salvatore, Dominick, *Theory and Problems of Statistics and Econometrics*. SCHAUM'S OUTLINE SERIES, McGraw-Hill.

Steel, Robert, G.D., and Torrie, James, H., 1976. *Introduction to Statistics*. McGraw-Hill.

17.11 PROBLEMS

1. A manufacturer is interested in measuring changes in costs and physical volumes of his purchases which consist of the five types of materials: A, B, C, D, E. The prices paid and the quantities bought are given in the table below for the years 1992 and 1995.

Items	Units	Year 1992		Year 1995	
		Price (P_o)	Quantity (Q_o)	Price (P_t)	Quantity (Q_t)
A	Pound	$0.50	4500	$0.65	4000
B	Ton	$50.00	50	$52.00	65
C	Gallon	$1.50	1250	$2.00	1500
D	Yard	$4.00	400	$5.50	350
E	Ounce	$0.25	80,000	$0.15	120,000

a) Using 1992 as the base, construct:

   i)   A simple aggregative price index

   ii) A simple average-of-relatives price index

   iii) A simple average-of-relatives quantity index

   iv) A Laspeyres Price Index

   v)   A Paasche Price Index

   vi) A Laspeyres Quantity index

   vii) A Paasche Quantity index

b) Using 1995 as the base, construct:

   i)   A Laspeyres Price Index

   ii) A Paasche Quantity Index

2. Consider a microeconomy consisting of only the 4 commodities shown and which is represented by the table below, and is extending over 4 periods of time, instead of the 2 periods we used up to now in discussing the various indices.

Time Period	Commodity	Unit	Quantity (q)	Price (p)	Value V = pq
1	Bread	Loaf	1000	0.25	250
	Meat	Pound	500	0.75	375
	Vegetables	Pound	500	1.00	500
	Wine	Bottle	1000	1.25	1250
					2375
2	Bread	Loaf	900	0.25	225
	Meat	Pound	600	0.70	420
	Vegetables	Pound	500	1.00	500
	Wine	Bottle	900	1.20	1080
					2225
3	Bread	Loaf	1000	0.20	200
	Meat	Pound	600	0.80	480
	Vegetables	Pound	600	1.15	690
	Wine	Bottle	900	1.20	1080
					2450
4	Bread	Loaf	900	0.30	270
	Meat	Pound	700	0.75	525
	Vegetables	Pound	550	1.30	715
	Wine	Bottle	1000	1.30	1300
					2810

a) Characterize the economy by means of its Gross National Product (GNP) and determine how much of the GNP is due to price inflation or deflation

b) Construct a Cost of Living Index in this economy, for a particular family type.

3. The following table shows average retail prices of selected dairy products in the years 1972, 1973, 1974, and 1980.

Dairy Products	1972	1973	1974	1980
Milk (Fresh), $\frac{1}{2}$ gallon	60	65	78	92
Ice Cream, $\frac{1}{2}$ gallon	86	91	108	229
Butter, pound	87	92	95	199
Cheese (American), $\frac{1}{2}$ pound	54	60	73	129
SUMS	287	308	354	649

a) Calculate the 1972, 1973, 1974, and 1980 values of a simple aggregative index, with 1972 = 100 for the overall price change of these items.

b) Find the arithmetic mean of the price relatives comparing the 1980 prices with those of 1972.

4. The total 1998 and 1999 factory shipments of selected appliances (in thousands of units) were:

Appliances	1998	1999
Refrigerators	5,890	5,701
Freezers	1,521	1,859
Electric Ranges	3,217	3,003
Gas Water Heaters	2,921	2,887
Dishwashers	3,558	3,488
Food Waste Disposers	3,312	3,316
Room Air Conditioners	4,037	3,749
SUMS	24,456	24,003

a) Calculate a sample aggregative index comparing the 1999 shipments of these goods with those of 1998.

b) Find the arithmetic mean of the seven relatives, comparing the 1999 shipments of these goods with those of 1998.

5. a) Write the general formula for the Ideal Index.

b) If a Laspeyres Index for a set of data is 134.0 and a Paasche Index, calculated from the same data, is 132.5, find the Ideal Index for this specific comparison.

6. The table below shows the annual average prices (in dollars per pound) of three selected imported metals:

Metals	1990	1995	1996	1997	1998
Copper	0.63	0.53	0.58	0.58	0.58
Nickel	1.30	1.88	2.07	2.15	1.93
Tin	1.66	3.35	3.31	4.37	5.52
SUMS	3.59	5.76	5.96	7.10	8.03

a) Find the 1995, 1996, 1997, and 1998 values of a simple aggregative index with 1990 = 100.

b) Find a simple aggregative index comparing the 1998 prices with those of 1996.

c) Find for 1997 and 1998 the arithmetic mean of the price relatives using 1990 = 100.

d) Compare the 1998 prices of copper and nickel with those of 1996 by finding:
   i) The arithmetic mean of the price relatives.
   ii) The geometric mean of the price relatives.

7. The table below shows the 1976, 1977, and 1978 prices (in cents per can) and production (in millions of cans) of selected canned fruits and vegetables.

a) Use 1976 quantities to construct aggregative indices comparing the 1977 and 1978 prices with those of 1976.

b) Use the 1977 quantities as weights to construct aggregative indices comparing the 1977 and 1978 prices with those of 1976.

Canned	Prices			Quantities		
Fruit and Vegetables	1976	1977	1978	1976	1977	1978
Fruit Cocktail	46.0	47.8	48.8	13.6	13.0	11.1
Green Peas	38.6	38.3	37.7	31.9	30.2	25.3
Tomatoes	35.1	37.6	38.0	42.8	54.1	49.2

8. Use the data of problem 7, and do the following:

   a) Use 1978 quantities as weights to construct an aggregative index comparing the 1978 prices with those of 1976.

   b) Use the means of the 1976 and 1978 quantities as weights to construct an aggregative index comparing the 1978 prices with those of 1976.

   c) With 1976 = 100, calculate for 1978 the weighted arithmetic mean of price relatives, using base-year values as weights. Compare this result with the 1978 index number calculated in problem 7a.

   d) With 1976 = 100, calculate for 1978 the weighted arithmetic mean of the price relatives, using given-year (*i.e.*, 1978) values as weights.

9. The following table contains prices received by fishermen (in cents per pound) and the quantities of catch (in millions of pounds) of four selected species of fish:

Fish	Prices			Quantity		
Type	1974	1975	1978	1974	1975	1978
Cod	18.8	23.3	22.9	59	56	87
Sole	26.8	33.5	44.8	156	162	181
Tuna	41.0	33.8	59.8	386	393	409
Haddock	28.8	26.8	27.3	8	16	39

   a) Use the 1974 quantities as weights and 1974 = 100 to find weighted aggregative indexes for the 1975 and 1978 prices.

   b) Calculate a weighted aggregative index comparing the 1978 prices of the fish with those of 1974, using the 1978 quantities as weights.

   c) Calculate a weighted aggregative index comparing the 1978 prices of the fish with those of 1974, using the averages of the 1975 and 1978 quantities as weights.

10. Use the data of problem #9, and do the following:

    a) With 1974 = 100, calculate for 1978 the weighted arithmetic mean of price relatives, using the base-year values as weights.

    b) With 1974 = 100, calculate for 1978 the weighted arithmetic mean of price relatives, using the given-year values as weights.

    c) Interchanging the p's and q's in the formula used in part (b), construct as index comparing the 1978 catch of the four species with that of 1974.

11. a) If the average of the quantities for the first 2 periods, q_0 and q_1, are to be used as weights, how should the formula for the Laspeyres price index be stated?

    b) If the average of the prices of the first 3 periods, p_0, p_1, and p_2, is used as the base-period price, how should the Laspeyres price index formula be stated?

12. a) If the average of the prices for the first 3 periods is used as the base-period price and the average of the quantities of the first three periods is to be used as the weight, how should the Laspeyres price index be stated?

   b) Given the following index, with 1990 as the base, shift the base to 1991, and then to 1993.

Year	Index
1990	100
1991	110
1992	125
1993	115

13. If money wages go up 50 percent and the Consumer Price Index (CPI) goes up 25 percent:

   a) What is the percent increase in real wages?

   b) What percent change has occurred in the value of the dollar as far as the wage earner is concerned?

14. From 1990 to 1995 the average weekly wages of a city's maintenance workers increased from $498.60, to $548.60. Over the same period an index of consumer prices in that city increased 24.0 percent. Calculate the real average weekly wages of these employees for 1995.

15. For the months of January through April of 1995, the average weekly hours per workers in durable-goods manufacturing in the United States were: 40.8 hours for January, 40.6 hour for February, 40.4 hours for March, and 40.1 hours for April.

   a) Construct an index with January 1995 = 100 to measure changes in the hours worked.

   b) Shift the base of this index to April 1995.

16. The following table shows the production (in thousands of tons) and the farm value (in millions of dollars) of pears and cherries in 1996 and 1998:

	Production		Value	
Fruit Type	**1996**	**1998**	**1996**	**1998**
Pears	821	727	102	158
Cherries	168	155	64	108

Construct a simple aggregative index measuring the change in the overall prices of these 2 items, from 1996 to 1998.

17. Suppose that in 1995 the average factory wages in one geographic region were 125 percent of what they were in 1990, and a consumer price index for that region was 80 in 1990. Using 1995 = 100, did wages keep up with inflation?

18. In 1998 the average weekly earnings of department store employees in a certain area were $270, and in 2000 the corresponding earnings were $310. A regional cost of living index was 285 for 1998, and 325 for 2000. Using 1998 = 100, express the 2000 dollar wages of these department store employees in terms of constant 1998 dollars.

19. When we deflate the value of a single commodity in year (say) 2000 to (say) 1995 prices, we divide its values by an index expressing the 2000 price of the commodity as a relative of the 1995 price. Show in equation form that this process leads to the value of the commodity in 2000 at 1995 prices.

20. In a large metropolitan area the 1995 through 1999 gross average weekly earnings of certain type of workers were: $310.25, $337.82, $363.40, $394.18, and $440.57. Also, for the same years, 1995 through 1999, the "cost of living" index values for the same area were: 159.8, 168.9, 182.1, 195.0, and 216.7, with 1997 = 100.

   a) Shift the base index to 1995, and then use these index values to express the actual earnings in constant 1995 dollars
      (*i.e.,* deflate the actual earnings).

   b) Construct an index of the purchasing power of the dollar for this period, with 1995 = 100.

   c) What were the percentage changes from 1995 to 1999 in: I) Money earnings, II) Real earnings, III) Living costs, and IV) Purchasing power?

SOLUTIONS

1. a)

i) $P = \dfrac{\sum_{i=1}^{n}(P_t)_i}{\sum_{i=1}^{n}(P_o)_i} = \dfrac{0.65 + 52.00 + 2.00 + 5.50 + 0.15}{0.50 + 50.00 + 1.50 + 4.00 + 0.25} = \dfrac{60.30}{56.25} = 1.072$

ii) $P = \dfrac{\sum_{i=1}^{n}\left(P_t/P_o\right)_i}{n} = \dfrac{1}{5}\Big[\left(0.65/0.50\right) + \left(52/50\right) + \left(2/1.50\right)$

$\qquad\qquad\qquad + \left(5.50/4\right) + \left(0.15/0.25\right)\Big] = \dfrac{5.648}{5} = 1.1296$

iii) $Q = \dfrac{\sum_{i=1}^{n}\left(Q_t/Q_o\right)_i}{n} = \dfrac{1}{5}\Big[\left(4000/4500\right) + \left(65/50\right) + \left(1500/1250\right)$

$\qquad\qquad\qquad + \left(350/400\right) + \left(120{,}000/80{,}000\right)\Big]$

$\qquad\qquad = \dfrac{0.8888 + 1.3 + 1.2 + 0.875 + 1.5}{5}$

$\qquad\qquad = \dfrac{5.7638}{5} = 1.1528$

iv) $P_L = \dfrac{\sum_{i=1}^{n}(P_tQ_o)_i}{\sum_{i=1}^{n}(P_oQ_o)_i}$

$\quad = \dfrac{0.65(4500) + 52(50) + 2(1250) + 5.5(400) + 0.15(80{,}000)}{0.50(4500) + 50(50) + 1.5(1250) + 1.5(1250) + 4(400) + 0.25(80{,}000)}$

$$= \frac{2925 + 2600 + 2500 + 2200 + 12{,}000}{2250 + 2500 + 1875 + 1600 + 20{,}000} = \frac{22{,}225}{28{,}225} = 0.7874$$

v) $P_p = \dfrac{\sum\limits_{i=1}^{n}(P_t Q_t)_i}{\sum\limits_{i=1}^{n}(P_o Q_t)_i}$

$$= \frac{0.65(4000) + 52(65) + 2(1500) + 5.50(350) + 0.15(120{,}000) + 5.50(350) + 0.15(120.000)}{0.5(4000) + 50(65) + 1.5(1500) + 4(350) + 0.25(120{,}000) + 4(350) + 0.25(120{,}000)}$$

$$= \frac{2600 + 3380 + 3000 + 1925 + 18{,}000}{2000 + 3250 + 2250 + 1400 + 33{,}000} = \frac{28{,}905}{38{,}900} = 0.743$$

vi) $Q_L = \dfrac{\sum\limits_{i=1}^{n}(Q_t P_o)_i}{\sum\limits_{i=1}^{n}(Q_o P_o)_i} = \dfrac{38{,}900}{28{,}225} = 1.378$

vii) $Q_P = \dfrac{\sum\limits_{i=1}^{n}(Q_t P_t)_i}{\sum\limits_{i=1}^{n}(Q_o P_t)_i} = \dfrac{28{,}905}{22{,}225} = 1.3006$

b) i) $P_L = \dfrac{\sum\limits_{i=1}^{n} P_{1992} \times P_{1992}}{\sum\limits_{i=1}^{n} P_{1995} \times P_{1995}} = \dfrac{\sum\limits_{i=1}^{n}(P_o Q_t)_i}{\sum\limits_{i=1}^{n}(P_t Q_t)_i} = \dfrac{38{,}900}{28{,}905} = 1.3458$

ii) $Q_p = \dfrac{\sum\limits_{i=1}^{n} P_{1992} * P_{1995}}{\sum\limits_{i=1}^{n} P_{1992} * P_{1995}} = \dfrac{\sum\limits_{i=1}^{n}(P_o Q_o)_i}{\sum\limits_{i=1}^{n}(P_o Q_t)_i} = \dfrac{28{,}225}{38{,}900} = 0.7256$

2. a) The GNP for each year is obtained as the sum of the values of the 4 commodities for that year. To solve problem 1 we construct the table below which, in addition to giving the GNP in current dollars, also presents the GNP relative to year 1 GNP, the GNP in terms of constant year 1 dollars, the Real GNP and a Price Deflator Index.

Year	GNP (Current)	GNP (Relative) $= \dfrac{GNP_t}{GNP_1}*100$	GNP Year 1 (constant dollars)	Real GNP ($\times$ 100) $= \dfrac{GNP_t}{GNP_1}$ $\left(\begin{array}{c}\text{both in constant} \\ \text{dollars}\end{array}\right)$	Implicit Price Deflation ($\times$ **100**) $= \dfrac{\text{GNP current}}{\text{GNP constant}}$
1	2375	100	2375	100	100
2	2225	93.68	2300	96.84	96.74
3	2450	103.16	2425	102.11	101.03
4	2810	118.32	2550	107.37	110.2

cd = constant dollars

To determine how much of the GNP is due to real production, the GNP for the 4 years is expressed in terms of constant dollars, which are the prices for year 1. To accomplish this, we use the year 1 prices and the quantities for each year of interest, as shown below.

GNP for year 2, constant dollars = (Quantity of bread for year 2) × (Price of bread for year 1) + ⋯ + (Quantity of wine for year 2) × (Price of wine for year 1)

= (900)(0.25) + (600)(0.75)

+ (500)(1.00) + (900)(1.25)

= 225 + 450 + 500 + 1,125 = 2,300

GNP for year 3, constant dollars = 1000(0.25) + 600(0.75) + 600(1.00) + 900(1.25)

= 250 + 450 + 600 + 1,125 = 2,425

GNP for year 4, constant dollars = 900(0.25) + 700(0.75) + 550(1.00) + 1000(1.25)

= 225 + 525 + 550 + 1,250 = 2,550

The Real GNP Column is obtained by dividing the GNP in constant dollars, for each year, by the constant dollar GNP for year 1. The entries of the last column, called *Implicit Price Deflator* indices, are obtained by dividing the GNP in Current dollars, by the corresponding GNP in year 1 constant dollars, and multiplying by 100. These indices show that there was a slight deflation in year 2, a slight inflation in year 3, and a strong inflation in year 4.

b) To construct a Cost of Living Index for this economy, for a particular family type, we need to assume a consumer basket for this family. Suppose such a family consumed: 20 loaves of bread, 5 pounds of meat, 30 pounds of vegetables and 2 bottles of wine. How well did this particular family do when compared to the whole economy?

To answer this question we construct the table below, using the consumer basket stated above for q_1 and the prices (p_1, p_2, p_3, p_4) for the 4 years given in the table describing the economy. The results are:

Item	q_1	p_1	p_2	p_3	p_4	$q_1 p_1$	$q_2 p_2$	$q_3 p_3$	$q_4 p_4$
Bread	20	0.25	0.25	0.20	0.30	5.00	5.00	4.00	6.00
Meat	5	0.75	0.70	0.80	0.75	3.75	3.50	4.00	3.75
Vegetables	30	1.00	1.00	1.15	1.30	30.00	30.00	34.50	39.00
Wine	2	1.25	1.20	1.20	1.30	2.50	2.40	2.40	2.60
						$\sum_{i=1}^{4}(q_1 p_1)_i$ $= 41.25$	$\sum_{i=1}^{4}(q_2 p_2)_i$ $= 40.90$	$\sum_{i=1}^{4}(q_3 p_3)_i$ $= 44.90$	$\sum_{i=1}^{4}(q_4 p_4)_i$ $= 51.35$

Then, the resulting index values, using year 1 as the reference, become:

For year 1: 41.25/41.25 × 100 = 100.00

For year 2: 40.90/41.25 × 100 = 99.15

For year 3: 44.90/41.25 × 100 = 108.85

For year 4: 51.35/41.25 × 100 = 124.48

Comparing these values with the index values of 100, 96.74, 101.03, and 110.20, it can be seen that this particular family type did worse than the entire nation as a whole.

3. a) For 1972, 1973, 1974, and 1980 the values of the index are:

$$I_{1972} = \frac{287}{287} \times 100 = 100, \quad I_{1973} = \frac{308}{287} \times 100 = 107.3,$$

$$I_{1974} = \frac{350}{287} \times 100 = 123.3, \quad \text{and } I_{1980} = \frac{649}{287} \times 100 = 226.1$$

b) $P = \dfrac{\displaystyle\sum_{i=1}^{k=4}(p_t/p_o)_i \times 100}{k}$

$$= \frac{(92/60) \times 100 + (229/86) \times 100 + (199/87) \times 100 + (129/54) \times 100}{4}$$

$$= \frac{100}{4}(1.533 + 2.663 + 2.287 + 2.389) = \frac{100}{4}(8.8719) = 221.8$$

4. a) $I = \left(\dfrac{24{,}003}{24{,}450}\right) \times 100 = 98.15$

b) $I = \dfrac{100}{7}\left(\dfrac{5701}{5890} + \dfrac{1859}{1521} + \dfrac{3003}{3217} + \dfrac{2887}{2921} + \dfrac{3488}{3558} + \dfrac{3316}{3312} + \dfrac{3749}{4037}\right)$

$$= \frac{100}{7}(7.02216) = 100.32$$

5. a) Fisher's Ideal Index $= \left[\left(\dfrac{\displaystyle\sum_{i=1}^{n}P_tQ_o}{\displaystyle\sum_{i=1}^{n}P_0Q_0}\right)\left(\dfrac{\displaystyle\sum_{i=1}^{n}P_tQ_t}{\displaystyle\sum_{i=1}^{n}P_oQ_o}\right)\right]^{1/2}$

b) Fisher's Ideal Index $= (134.0 \times 132.5)^{1/2} = (17{,}755)^{1/2} = 133.25$

6. a) $I_{1995} = \dfrac{5.76}{3.59} \times 100 = 160.4, \quad I_{1996} = \dfrac{5.96}{3.59} \times 100 = 166.0,$

$$I_{1997} = \frac{7.10}{3.59} \times 100 = 197.8, \quad \text{and } I_{1998} = \frac{8.03}{3.59} \times 100 = 223.7$$

b) $I_{1998-1996} = \dfrac{8.03}{5.96} \times 100 = 134.7$

c) $I_{1997} = \dfrac{1}{3}\left[\left(\dfrac{0.58}{0.63}\right) \times 100 + \left(\dfrac{2.15}{1.30}\right) \times 100 + \left(\dfrac{4.37}{1.66}\right) \times 100\right]$

$$= \frac{5.2069 \times 100}{3} = 173.6$$

$$I_{1998} = \frac{1}{3}\left[\left(\frac{0.58}{0.63}\right) \times 100 + \left(\frac{1.93}{1.30}\right) \times 100 + \left(\frac{5.52}{1.66}\right) \times 100\right]$$

$$= \frac{5.7305 \times 100}{3} = 191.02$$

d) i) $I = \dfrac{\left(\dfrac{0.58}{0.58}\right) \times 100 + \left(\dfrac{1.93}{2.07}\right) \times 100}{2} = \dfrac{100}{2}(1 + 0.9324) = 96.62$

ii) $\sqrt{\left(\dfrac{0.58}{0.58} \times 100\right) \cdot \left(\dfrac{1.93}{2.07} \times 100\right)} = \sqrt{(100)(93.24)} = \sqrt{9324} = 96.56$

7. $\Sigma\left(P_{1976} \cdot Q_{1976}\right)_i$

$= (46.0)(13.6) + (38.6)(31.9) + (35.1)(42.8) = 625.6 + 1{,}231.34 + 1{,}502.28$

$= 3{,}359.22$

$\Sigma\left(P_{1977} \cdot Q_{1976}\right)_i$

$= (47.8)(13.6) + (38.3)(31.9) + (37.6)(42.8) = 650.08 + 1{,}221.77 + 1{,}609.28$

$= 3{,}481.13$

$\Sigma\left(P_{1978} \cdot Q_{1976}\right)_i$

$= (48.8)(13.6) + (37.7)(31.9) + (38.0)(42.8) = 663.68 + 1{,}202.63 + 1{,}626.4$

$= 3{,}492.71$

Then

a) $I_{1977} = \dfrac{\Sigma(P_{1977} \times Q_{1976})_i}{\Sigma(P_{1976} \times Q_{1976})_i} = \dfrac{3{,}481.13}{3{,}359.22} = 103.63$, and

$I_{1978} = \dfrac{\Sigma(P_{1978} \times Q_{1978})_i}{\Sigma(P_{1976} \times Q_{1976})_i} = \dfrac{3{,}492.71}{3{,}359.22} = 103.97$

$\Sigma\left(P_{1977} \cdot Q_{1977}\right)_i$

$= (47.8)(13.0) + (38.3)(30.2) + (37.6)(54.1)$

$= 621.4 + 1{,}556.66 + 2{,}034.16 = 3{,}812.22$

$\Sigma\left(P_{1978} \cdot Q_{1977}\right)_i$

$= (48.8)(13.0) + (37.7)(30.2) + (38.0)(54.1)$

$= 634.4 + 1{,}138.54 + 2{,}055.8 = 3{,}828.74$

$\Sigma\left(P_{1978} \cdot Q_{1978}\right)_i$

$= (48.8)(11.1) + (37.7)(25.3) + (38.0)(54.1)$

$= 541.68 + 953.81 + 1{,}869.6 = 3{,}365.09$

$\Sigma\left(P_{1976} \cdot Q_{1977}\right)_i$

$= (46.0)(13.0) + (38.6)(30.2) + (35.1)(54.1)$

$= 598.0 + 1{,}165.72 + 1{,}898.91 = 3{,}662.63$

Then:

b) $I_{1977} = \dfrac{\Sigma(P_{1977} \times Q_{1977})_i}{\Sigma(P_{1976} \times Q_{1977})_i} = \dfrac{3{,}812.22}{3{,}662.63} \times 100 = 104.08$,

and $I_{1978} = \dfrac{\Sigma(P_{1978} \times Q_{1978})_i}{\Sigma(P_{1976} \times Q_{1977})_i} = \dfrac{3{,}365.09}{3{,}662.63} \times 100 = 104.54$

8. a) $I = \dfrac{\Sigma(P_{1978} \times Q_{1978})_i}{\Sigma(P_{1976} \times Q_{1978})_i} = \dfrac{3{,}365.09}{3{,}214.1} \times 100 = 104.7$, where

$\Sigma\left(P_{1978} \times Q_{1978}\right)_i = 3{,}365.09$ (see solution of problem 7 above), and

$$\Sigma\left(P_{1976} \cdot Q_{1978}\right)_i = (46.0)(11.1) + (38.6)(25.3) + (35.1)(49.2)$$
$$= 510.6 + 976.58 + 1,726.92 = 3,214.1$$

b) Weights for: Fruit Cocktail $= (q_{1976} + q_{1978})/2 = (13.6 + 11.1)/2 = 12.35$

   Green Peas $= (31.9 + 25.3)/2 = 28.6$, and Tomatoes $= (42.8 + 49.2)/2 = 46.0$

Then: $I = \dfrac{\Sigma\left(P_{1978} \times Q_{Average}\right)_i}{\Sigma\left(P_{1976} \times Q_{Average}\right)_i} = \dfrac{48.8(12.35) + 37.7(28.6) + 38.0(46)}{46(12.35) + 38.6(28.6) + 35.1(46)}$

$$= \frac{3428.9}{3286.66} \times 100 = 104.33$$

c) $I = \dfrac{\Sigma\left(\dfrac{P_{1978}}{P_{1976}}\right)_i \left(P_{1976} \times Q_{1976}\right)_i}{\Sigma\left(P_{1976} \times Q_{1976}\right)_i}$

$$= \frac{\left(\dfrac{48.8}{46.0}\right)(46.0 \times 13.6) + \left(\dfrac{37.7}{38.6}\right)(38.6 \times 31.9) + \left(\dfrac{38.0}{35.1}\right)(35.1 \times 42.8)}{(4.60 \times 13.6) + (38.6 \times 31.9) \qquad + (35.1 \times 42.8)}$$

$$= \frac{\Sigma(P_{1978} \times Q_{1976})_i}{\Sigma(P_{1976} \times Q_{1976})_i} = \frac{(48.8 \times 13.6) + (37.7 \times 31.9) + (38.0 \times 42.8)}{3,359.22}$$

$$= \frac{653.68 + 1,202.63 + 1,626.4}{3,359.22} = \frac{3,492.71}{3,359.22} = 1.0397 \text{ or } 103.97;$$

or using the weights shown:

$$= \frac{1}{3,359.22}\left[1.06087(625.6) + 0.977(1,231.34) + 1.083(1502.28)\right]$$

$$= \frac{3493.6249}{3,359.22} = 1.04,$$

where $\left(\dfrac{P_{1978}}{P_{1976}}\right)_{F.C} = \dfrac{48.8}{46.0} = 1.06087,$ $\left(\dfrac{P_{1978}}{P_{1976}}\right)_{G.P} = \dfrac{37.7}{38.6} = 0.977,$

$\left(\dfrac{P_{1978}}{P_{1976}}\right)_{T} = \dfrac{38.0}{35.1} = 1.083$ and $\left(P_{1976} \cdot P_{1976}\right)_{F.C} = (46.0)(13.6) = 625.6,$

$\left(P_{1976} \cdot Q_{1976}\right)_{G.P} = (38.6)(31.9) = 1,231.34,$ and

$\left(P_{1976} \cdot P_{1976}\right)_{T} = (35.1)(42.8) = 1,502.28$

d) $I = \dfrac{\Sigma\left(\dfrac{P_{1978}}{P_{1976}}\right)_i \left(P_{1978} \times Q_{1978}\right)_i}{\Sigma\left(P_{1978} \times Q_{1978}\right)_i}$

$$= \frac{1.0608(541.68) + 0.977(953.81) + 1.083(1,869.6)}{541.686 + 953.81 + 1,869.6}$$

$$= \frac{3531.263314}{3,365.09} = 1.0494 \text{ or } 104.94$$

9. a) $I_{1975} = \dfrac{\Sigma P_{1975}Q_{1974}}{\Sigma P_{1974}Q_{1974}} = \dfrac{19,861.9}{21,364.4} \times 100 = 92.967$, and

$I_{1978} = \dfrac{\Sigma P_{1978}Q_{1974}}{\Sigma P_{1974}Q_{1974}} = \dfrac{31,641.1}{21,364.4} \times 100 = 148.102$, where

$\Sigma P_{1974}Q_{1974} = 18.8(59) + 26.8(156) + 41.0(386) + 28.8(8)$
$= 1,109.2 + 4,180.8 + 15,826.0 + 230.4 = 21,346.4$,

$\Sigma P_{1975}Q_{1974} = 23.3(59) + 33.5(156) + 33.8(386) + 26.8(8)$
$= 1,374.7 + 5,226.0 + 13,046.8 + 214.4 = 19,861.9$, and

$\Sigma P_{1978}Q_{1974} = 22.9(59) + 44.8(156) + 59.8(386) + 27.3(8)$
$= 1,351.1 + 6,988.8 + 23,082.8 + 218.4 = 31,641.1$

b) $I = \dfrac{\Sigma P_{1978}Q_{1978}}{\Sigma P_{1974}Q_{1978}} = \dfrac{35,624.0}{24,378.6} \times 100 = 146.13$, where

$\Sigma P_{1978}Q_{1978} = 22.9(87) + 44.8(181) + 59.8(409) + 27.3(39)$
$= 1,992.3 + 8,108.8 + 24,458.2 + 1,064.7 = 35,624.0$, and

$\Sigma P_{1974}Q_{1978} = 18.8(87) + 26.8(181) + 41.0(409) + 28.8(39)$
$= 1,635.6 + 4,850.8 + 16,769.0 + 1,123.2 = 24,378.6$

c) $I = \dfrac{\Sigma P_{1978}Q_{AVE}}{\Sigma P_{1974}Q_{AVE}} = \dfrac{34,051.1}{23,173.4} \times 100 = 146.94$, where

$Q_{AVE} = \dfrac{q_{1975} + q_{1978}}{2} \Rightarrow \dfrac{56 + 87}{2} = 71.5, \quad \dfrac{162 + 181}{2} = 171.5,$

$\dfrac{393 + 409}{2} = 401, \quad \dfrac{16 + 39}{2} = 27.5,$

$\Sigma P_{1978}Q_{AVE} = 22.9(71.5) + 44.8(171.5) + 59.8(401) + 27.3(27.5)$
$= 1,637.35 + 7,683.2 + 23,979.8 + 750.75 = 34,051.1$, and

$\Sigma P_{1974}Q_{AVE} = 18.8(71.5) + 26.8(171.5) + 41.0(401) + 28.8(27.5)$
$= 1,344.2 + 4,596.2 + 16,441.0 + 792.0 = 23,173.4$

10. a) $I = \dfrac{\Sigma\left(\dfrac{P_{1978}}{P_{1974}}\right)(P_{1974}Q_{1974})}{\Sigma P_{1974}Q_{1974}} = \dfrac{\Sigma P_{1978}Q_{1974}}{\Sigma P_{1974}Q_{1974}} = \dfrac{31,641.1}{21,364.4} \times 100 = 148.227$, or

$I = \dfrac{\left(\dfrac{22.9}{18.8}\right)(1,109.2) + \left(\dfrac{44.8}{26.8}\right)(4,180.8) + \left(\dfrac{59.8}{41.0}\right)(15,826.0) + \left(\dfrac{27.3}{28.8}\right)(230.4)}{1,109.2 + 4,180.8 + 15,826.0 + 230.4}$

$= \dfrac{31,641.1}{21,364.4}$

b) $I = \dfrac{\Sigma\left(\dfrac{P_{1978}}{P_{1974}}\right)(P_{1978}Q_{1978})}{\Sigma P_{1978}Q_{1978}}$

$$= \frac{\left(\frac{22.9}{18.8}\right)(1{,}992.3) + \left(\frac{48.8}{26.8}\right)(8{,}108.8) + \left(\frac{59.8}{41.0}\right)(24{,}458.2) + \left(\frac{27.3}{28.8}\right)(1{,}064.7)}{1{,}992.3 + 8{,}108.8 + 24{,}458.2 + 1{,}064.7}$$

$$= \left(\frac{52{,}664.2263}{35{,}624.0}\right) \times 100 = 147.834$$

c) $I = \dfrac{\Sigma\left(\dfrac{Q_{1978}}{Q_{1974}}\right)(P_{1978}Q_{1978})}{\Sigma P_{1978}Q_{1978}}$

$$= \frac{\left(\frac{87}{59}\right)(1{,}992.3) + \left(\frac{181}{156}\right)(8{,}108.8) + \left(\frac{409}{386}\right)(24{,}458.2) + \left(\frac{39}{8}\right)(1{,}064.7)}{1{,}992.3 + 8{,}108.8 + 24{,}458.2 + 1{,}064.7}$$

$$= \left(\frac{43{,}452.05187}{35{,}624.0}\right) \times 100 = 121.974$$

## PART VII

NON-PARAMETRIC STATISTICS

Chapter 18–Non-Parametric Statistics

18 Non-Parametric Statistics

Even if we do not know the nature (or type) of the distribution from which our samples come from, we can still perform a number of tests to analyze such data. These tests can be grouped in 5 categories and they, and the individual tests discussed under each category, are summarized below:

1. Tests for Randomness
   a) Runs Test
   b) Runs Above and Below the Median
   c) Runs Up and Down
   d) The Von Newmann Ratio Test for Independence
2. Chi-Square Tests
   a) Tests on Frequencies
   b) Tests on Independence—Contingency Tables
   c) Tests on Homogeneity
   d) Tests on Goodness of Fit
   e) Kolmogorov-Smirnoff Statistic
3. Tests for Matched Pairs
   a) Sign Test
   b) Wilcoxon Sign Test
   c) Friedman Test for k Paired Samples
4. Tests to Compare 2 or More Independent Populations
   a) Wald-Wolfowitz Test
   b) Mann-Whitney U Test
   c) Kruskal-Wallis H Test
5. Correlation
   a) Spearman's Rank Correlation Coefficient

This chapter discusses the theory, formulation, and application of these tests (called nonparametric tests) and, where possible, compares them against the corresponding and equivalent parametric tests. MINITAB solutions are also given for several problems.

18.1   Introduction

Most of the statistical methods we have discussed up to now are referred to as Parametric Statistics and the term is used to indicate that we have knowledge of the nature of the population from which the sample data set: $X_1, X_2, X_3, \ldots, X_n$, we are about to analyze, came from. For example, when we discussed the EMPIRICAL RULE in chapter 3, we made the assumption that our sample data came from a normal distribution.

However, also in chapter 3, we discussed Chebychev's inequality, namely:

$$P[\,\overline{x} - k\widehat{s} \le X \le \overline{x} + k\widehat{s}\,] \ge 1 - \frac{1}{k^2}, \text{ for } k > 1 \tag{18.1}$$

which states that the probability that a random variable X is between k standard deviations of the mean ($\overline{x}$) is at least $1 - 1/k^2$, without specifying the density function of X, and the result of equation (18.1) is valid for all possible distributions of the random variable X.

Such a "distribution-free" result, and similar others that we will discuss in this chapter are called nonparametric statistics. In these nonparametric tests the parameters of the distribution continue to be important. What is not important is the nature of the distribution of the population from which the sample came from. That is, these tests are valid whether the population distribution is Normal, Binomial, Uniform, Exponential, etc.

As we elaborate on the availability and development of nonparametric methods, we will discuss several tests which are equivalent to parametric tests that we have discussed previously. When this is the case it is natural to ask which test is preferable, the parametric or nonparametric one? The answer is: the parametric test, because for the nonparametric methods to achieve the same results (*i.e.*, the same power) require a much larger sample (*i.e.*, nonparametric methods are less efficient than parametric methods).

But there are many situations in which the form (or nature) of the population distribution is not well known and the nonparametric method is the only meaningful alternative. This is also the case when no parametric alternative exists. However, even though the computations on nonparametric statistics are usually less complicated than those for parametric statistics, for large samples the calculations for many nonparametric statistics can become very tedious.

Another disadvantage of most nonparametric methods is the fact that the null hypothesis (H_0) being tested is less precise than in the parametric methods and the conclusions drawn may be somewhat vague. But, even with all these drawbacks, nonparametric statistics are very useful and we will discuss the nonparametric tests shown in Table 18.1 below.

These tests are grouped, as shown in Table 18.1, in 5 categories depending either on what the objective of each test is or on what the underlying test statistic used is (Chi-square test, for example).

Table 18.1 Non-Parametric Tests and Some Corresponding Parametric Tests	
Non-Parametric Tests	**Corresponding Parametric Tests**

1. **TESTS FOR RANDOMNESS**
    a) Runs Tests
        i) Small Sample Runs test
        ii) Large Sample Runs test
    b) Runs above and below the Median
    c) Runs Up and Down
    d) The Von Newmann Ratio Test for Independence	

2. **CHI-SQUARE TESTS**
    a) Tests on Frequencies
        i) Tests on the Frequency of 2 classes
        ii) Tests on the Frequency of more than 2 classes
    b) Tests on Independence—Contingency Tables
    c) Tests on Homogeneity—Are 2 or more Independent
                              random samples drawn from
                              the same population?
    d) Tests on Goodness of Fit
        i) For the Uniform Distribution
        ii) For the Normal Distribution
    e) **Kolmogorov-Smirnoff Statistic**—A more appropriate
                              goodness of Fit test (than χ^2)	

3. **TESTS FOR MATCHED PAIRS**
    a) The Sign test—Uses only the sign
                    of the difference
    b) The Wilcoxon Signed test—Uses both sign
                              of difference and rank
        i) Small sample ($n < 16$)
        ii) Large Sample ($n \geq 16$)
    c) Friedman test for k paired samples
	t-test for paired data
	
	Randomized block design

(Continued)

Non-Parametric Tests	**Corresponding Parametric Tests**

4. **TESTS TO COMPARE 2 (OR MORE) INDEPENDENT POPULATIONS**
a) The Wald-Wolfowitz test
b) The Mann-Whitney U test
  i) Small Sample Case
  ii) Large Sample Case
c) The Kruskal-Wallis H test for comparing k $(k < 2)$ independent random samples
	t-test to compare 2 independent samples from 2 different populations
	
	One-Way ANOVA

5. **CORRELATION** a) Spearman's Rank Correlation Coefficient (for ordinal data)	Pearson Product-Moment Correlation Coefficient

18.2   Tests For Randomness

The objective of the non-parametric tests belonging to this category is to determine whether a sequence of observations in a sample can be considered as "random". Since most of these tests are identified as "Runs tests" let us state that a "run" is a succession of observations that have a particular characteristic, and a "Runs test" examines the number of "runs" of 2 possible characteristics that are present in our sample items. For example, when flipping a coin, the outcome of 4 tails would constitute a run. Similarly an outcome of 6 heads would constitute a second run.

Then the "Runs tests", taking into consideration the size of the sample, n, and the number of observations in the sample having each characteristic, n_1 and n_2, attempt to find out "what number of runs", R would be reasonable for the sample to be considered random. If the sample size is n, the minimum number of runs is 2 (if both characteristics are to appear at least once) and the maximum number of runs R, is n (if the 2 characteristics alternate in each item).

Therefore, we can write:

$$2 \leq R = \text{number of runs} \leq n \tag{18.2}$$

In a random sample, the number of runs, R, will be somewhere between the two limits of (18.2) and the tests we will discuss below attempt to define the value of R which would be considered reasonable for a random sample (obviously, R is a random variable).

18.2.1 Runs Tests

To test for randomness, we test the pair of hypotheses:

H_0: The observations in the sample are randomly generated

$$\text{vs} \tag{18.3}$$

H_1: The observation in the sample are not randomly generated, and the test is conducted differently for small and large samples, as stated below.

In the small-sample runs test table 18.2 is used to obtain the critical value of R, while in the large-sample runs test R is treated as a normally-distributed random variable and the z-distribution is used to test the validity of H_0.

■ Small-Sample Runs test

This test is appropriate when $n_1 \leq 20$ and $n_2 \leq 20$, and the test is carried out by comparing the observed number of runs, R, to the critical values of runs for the given values of n_1 and n_2 given in table 18.2 below.

Table 18.2 Critical Values of R for the Runs Test: Lower Tail

n_1 \ n_2	2	3	4	5	6	7	8	9	10	11	12	13	14	15	16	17	18	19	20
2											2	2	2	2	2	2	2	2	2
3				2	2	2	2	2	2	2	2	2	2	3	3	3	3	3	3
4			2	2	2	3	3	3	3	3	3	3	3	3	4	4	4	4	4
5		2	2	3	3	3	3	3	4	4	4	4	4	4	4	4	5	5	5
6	2	2	3	3	3	3	4	4	4	4	5	5	5	5	5	5	6	6	
7	2	2	3	3	3	4	4	5	5	5	5	5	6	6	6	6	6	6	
8	2	3	3	3	4	4	5	5	5	6	6	6	6	6	7	7	7	7	
9	2	3	3	4	4	5	5	5	6	6	6	7	7	7	7	8	8	8	
10	2	3	3	4	5	5	5	6	6	7	7	7	7	8	8	8	8	9	
11	2	3	4	4	5	5	6	6	7	7	7	8	8	8	9	9	9	9	
12	2	2	3	4	4	5	6	6	7	7	7	8	8	8	9	9	9	10	10
13	2	2	3	4	5	5	6	6	7	7	8	8	9	9	9	10	10	10	10
14	2	2	3	4	5	5	6	7	7	8	8	9	9	9	10	10	10	11	11
15	2	3	3	4	5	6	6	7	7	8	8	9	9	10	10	11	11	11	12
16	2	3	4	4	5	6	6	7	8	8	9	9	10	10	11	11	11	12	12
17	2	3	4	4	5	6	7	7	8	9	9	10	10	11	11	11	12	12	13
18	2	3	4	5	5	6	7	8	8	9	9	10	10	11	11	12	12	13	13
19	2	3	4	5	6	6	7	8	8	9	10	10	11	11	12	12	13	13	13
20	2	3	4	5	6	6	7	8	9	9	10	10	11	12	12	13	13	13	14

$\alpha = 0.025$

Source: Adapted from F.S. Swed and C. Eisenhart, Ann. Math. Statist., vol. 14, 1943, pp. 83–86

Critical Values of R for the Runs Test: Upper Tail

n_1 \ n_2	2	3	4	5	6	7	8	9	10	11	12	13	14	15	16	17	18	19	20
2																			
3																			
4				9	9														
5			9	10	10	11	11												
6			9	10	11	12	12	13	13	13	13								
7				11	12	13	13	14	14	14	14	15	15	15					
8				11	12	13	14	14	15	15	16	16	16	16	17	17	17	17	17
9					13	14	14	15	16	16	16	17	17	18	18	18	18	18	18
10					13	14	15	16	16	17	17	18	18	18	19	19	19	20	20
11					13	14	15	16	17	17	18	19	19	19	20	20	20	21	21
12					13	14	16	16	17	18	19	19	20	20	21	21	21	22	22

$\alpha = 0.025$

(Continued)

Critical Values of R for the Runs Test: Upper Tail

n_2						$\alpha = 0.025$													
13						15	16	17	18	19	19	20	20	21	21	22	22	23	23
14						15	16	17	18	19	20	20	21	22	22	23	23	23	24
15						15	16	18	18	19	20	21	22	22	23	23	24	24	25
16							17	18	19	20	21	21	22	23	23	24	25	25	25
17							17	18	19	20	21	22	23	23	24	25	25	26	26
18							17	18	19	20	21	22	23	24	25	25	26	26	27
19							17	18	20	21	22	23	23	24	25	26	26	27	27
20							17	18	20	21	22	23	24	25	25	26	27	27	28

Any observed value of R, which is less than or equal to the critical value of the lower tail, or greater than or equal to the critical value of the upper tail, will result in the rejection of the above null (H_0) hypothesis and the conclusion that the sample data are not random.

Example 1

Test the following sequence of observations by using the runs test and $\alpha = 0.05$ to determine whether the process, which generated these observations, produced random results:

$$\underbrace{XXX}_{1} \quad \underbrace{Y}_{2} \quad \underbrace{XX}_{3} \quad \underbrace{YYY}_{4} \quad \underbrace{X}_{5} \quad \underbrace{Y}_{6} \quad \underbrace{X}_{7} \quad \underbrace{Y}_{8} \quad \underbrace{XX}_{9} \quad \underbrace{YYYY}_{10} \quad \underbrace{X}_{11}$$

Here $n = 20 = n(x) + n(y) = 10 + 10$, $n_1 = n(x) = 10$, $n_2 = n(y) = 10$, and $R = 11$, as can be seen from above by identifying the runs of X and Y symbols, and the testing of the hypothesis is performed as follows:

1. H_0: The observations are random vs. H_1: The observations are not random
2. $\alpha = 0.05$
3. $n_1 = 10$ and $n_2 = 10$
4. With $n_1 = 10$ and $n_2 = 10$, the critical value for $R_L = 6$ (Table 18.2, lower tail) and $R_U = 16$ (Table 18.2, upper tail)
5. The sample data is given as shown above.
6. The number of runs, R, is $R = 11$
7. Because the value of $R = 11$ falls between the critical values of $R_L = 6$ and $R_U = 16$, H_0 is not rejected and we conclude that not enough evidence exists to decide that the data is not random.

■■■

Note: MINITAB can be used to analyze data, using the runs test (Section 18.7 shows how it is done and presents the MINITAB output for solved problem 18.1). The output includes the number of runs, R, the expected number of runs, the value of k (where k is the average of the observations), the number of observations above and below the value of k, and the significance level of the test.

The MINITAB runs test is a 2-tailed test and the reported significance of the test is equivalent to a p-value.

■ Large-Sample Runs Test

When $n_1 > 20$ and $n_2 > 20$, Table 18.2 can not be used to test H_0 and H_1 because the Table is limited to combinations of values for $n_1 \leq 20$ and $n_2 \leq 20$. However, the random variable R can be shown to be approximately normally distributed with:

$$E(R) = \mu_R = \frac{2n_1 n_2}{n_1 + n_2} + 1 \tag{18.4}$$

and
$$\sigma(R) = \sqrt{\frac{2n_1 n_2 (2n_1 n_2 - n_1 - n_2)}{(n_1 + n_2)^2 (n_1 + n_2 - 1)}}, \tag{18.5}$$

and this fact allows us to test the H_0 and H_1 hypothesis, for these combinations of n_1 and n_2 values.

The actual procedure used is as follows:

1. H_0: The observations are random vs. H_1: The observations are not random
2. $\alpha = 0.05$
3. The test statistic is $z = \dfrac{R - E(R)}{\sigma(R)}$, where $E(R)$ and $\sigma(R)$, are defined by equations (18.4) and (18.5).
4. For $\alpha = 0.05$, the rejection region is:

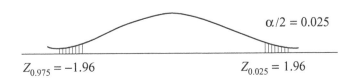

$$\alpha/2 = 0.025$$

$$Z_{0.975} = -1.96 \qquad\qquad Z_{0.025} = 1.96$$

5. Value of test statistic $= z^* = \dfrac{R - E(R)}{\sigma(R)}$

6. Compare z^* to the rejection region.
7. Do not reject H_0 if z^* falls outside of the rejection region.

Example 2

Test the following sequence of observations by using the Large-Sample Runs test and $\alpha = 0.05$ to determine whether the process produced random results.

$$\underbrace{MM}_{1} \quad \underbrace{NNNNN}_{2} \quad \underbrace{MMMMM}_{3} \quad \underbrace{NN}_{4} \quad \underbrace{MMMMM}_{5} \quad \underbrace{N}_{6} \quad \underbrace{MM}_{7}$$

$$\underbrace{NNNNNNNNNNNNN}_{8} \quad \underbrace{MMMMMMMMMMMM}_{9}$$

In this sequence of observations $n = 47$, $n_1 = n(M) = 26$, $n_2 = n(N) = 21$, and $R = 9$. Then

$$E(R) = \frac{2n_1 n_2}{n_1 + n_2} + 1 = \frac{2(26)(21)}{26 + 21} + 1 = \frac{1092}{47} + 1 = \frac{1139}{47} = 24.234$$

$$\sigma(R) = \sqrt{\frac{2(26)(21)[2(26)(21) - 26 - 21]}{(26 + 21)^2 (26 + 21 - 1)}} = \sqrt{\frac{1092(1092 - 47)}{(47)^2 (46)}}$$

$$= \sqrt{\frac{1092 \times 1045}{47 \times 47 \times 46}} = \sqrt{\frac{1{,}141{,}140}{(2209)(46)}} = \sqrt{\frac{1{,}141{,}140}{101{,}614}}$$

$$= \sqrt{11.23014545} = 3.35114$$

and

$$z^* = \frac{R - E(R)}{\sigma(R)} = \frac{9 - 24.234}{3.35114} = \frac{-15.234}{3.35114} = -4.5459$$

Since $z^* = -4.5459 < -z_{\alpha/2} = -1.96$, H_0 is rejected, and we conclude that the sequence of observations in example 18.2 are not random.

■ ■ ■

18.2.2 Runs above and Below the Median

Given a sample of n observations, $X_1, X_2, X_3, \ldots, X_n$, rank the data to obtain the ranked data set: $V_1, V_2, V_3, \ldots, V_n$ (in which $V_1 <= V_2 <= V_3 <= V_4 <= \ldots V_n$) and calculate the median. (If n is an odd number the median is the $\dfrac{n+1}{2}$ value in the ranked data set, or Median Value $= V_{n+1/2}$. If n is an even number, the median value is the arithmetic average of the $V_{n/2}$ and $V_{n+1/2}$. values of the ranked data set, or Median Value $= (V_{n/2} + V_{n+2/2}/2$

Then we compare each given observation, X_i, to see if it is greater than the median (or above the median value) or lower than the median (or below the median value).

1. If the observation is above the median value, we replace its numerical value by "a"
2. If the observation is below the median value, we replace its numerical value by "b"
3. If the observation is equal to the median value, eliminate this observation from consideration. In this case the sample size is reduced and the number of runs may also be reduced.

Each sequence of a's and b's, which is not interrupted by the other letter is a run. The number of runs above and below the median, R_1, is a random variable with:

$$E(R_1) = \frac{n+2}{2} \tag{18.6}$$

and

$$\sigma(R_1) = \sqrt{\frac{n(n-2)}{4(n-1)}} \tag{18.7}$$

Under the null hypothesis that the data are randomly generated, R_1 is approximately normally distributed for $n \geq 25$, and this fact can be used to test the validity of H_0 against H_1, where H_1 is stated as H_1: The data are not randomly generated.

Then, the testing procedure, for a two-sided test is as follows:

1. H_0: The data are randomly generated.

   vs

   H_1: The data are not randomly generated.
2. Specify the α value.

3. The test statistics is $z = \dfrac{R_1 - E(R_1)}{\sigma(R_1)}$

4. The rejection region is:

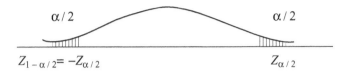

$$Z_{1-\alpha/2} = -Z_{\alpha/2} \qquad\qquad Z_{\alpha/2}$$

5. Value of test statistic $= z^* = \dfrac{R_1 - E(R_1)}{\sigma(R_1)}$.

6. Compare z^* to the rejection region.

7. Reject H_0 if z^* falls inside the rejection region, and conclude that the data are not randomly generated.

Example 3

Suppose we have the sample of $n = 27$ observations listed below.

| 100 | 97 | 89 | 25 | 81 | 11 | 83 | 16 | 96 | 44 | 32 | 98 | 19 | 68 |

| 33 | 25 | 54 | 74 | 85 | 17 | 49 | 33 | 22 | 62 | 20 | 92 | 80 |

Using the "Runs Above and Below the Median" method to determine whether this data set is randomly generated. Use $\alpha = 0.05$.

Ranking the data set, we obtain:

| 100 | 98 | 97 | 96 | 92 | 89 | 83 | 82 | 81 | 80 | 74 | 68 | 62 | 54 | 49 |

| 44 | 33 | 33 | 32 | 25 | 25 | 22 | 20 | 19 | 17 | 16 | 11 |

Then the median value is Median $= V_{(n+1)/2} = V_{(27+1)/2} = V_{14} = 54$

Comparing the given data set against the value of the median, we obtain the sequence of a's and b's:

$$a\,a\,a - b - a - b - a - b - a - bb - a - b - a - bb - \text{equal} -$$

$$- a\,a - b\,b\,b\,b - a - b - a\,a$$

The number of runs R_1 here is $R_1 = 17$ and, because of an equal value to the median, we eliminate the observation of 54, and the sample size is now $n = 27 - 1 = 26$.

Then, $E(R_1) = \dfrac{n+2}{2} = \dfrac{26+2}{2} = \dfrac{28}{2} = 14$

and

$$\sigma(R_1) = \sqrt{\dfrac{n(n-2)}{4(n-1)}} = \sqrt{\dfrac{26(24)}{4(25)}} = \sqrt{\dfrac{24}{4}\dfrac{26}{25}} = \sqrt{6 \times \dfrac{26}{25}} = \sqrt{\dfrac{156}{25}} = \sqrt{6.24}$$

$$= 2.498$$

and $z^* = \dfrac{R_1 - E(R_1)}{\sigma(R_1)} = \dfrac{17-14}{2.498} = \dfrac{3}{2.498} = 1.20$

Since $-Z_{\alpha/2} = -1.96 < z^* < z_{\alpha/2} = z_{0.25} = 1.96$, H_0 is not rejected, and we conclude that the data observations are randomly generated.

■ ■ ■

18.2.3 Runs Up and Down

The "Runs Up and Down" test is similar to the "Runs Above and Below the Median" test but, instead of comparing the observations against the median to generate the number of runs, now we place a plus sign $(+)$ or a minus sign $(-)$ between each pair of successive observations, depending on whether the later (second) observation is greater or smaller than the preceding (first) observation. Then, each string of "+"s and "−"s, uninterrupted by the other sign is counted as a run. The random variable, R_2, which counts the number of these runs is a random variable which, when $n \geq 20$, is approximately normally distributed with:

$$E(R_2) = \frac{1}{3}(2n - 1) \tag{18.8}$$

and
$$\sigma(R_2) = \sqrt{\frac{1}{90}(16(n - 29)} \tag{18.9}$$

and this fact is used to test the pair of hypotheses:

H_0: The observations in the sample are randomly generated.

vs

H_1: The observations are not randomly generated.

Note 1:   There are $(n - 1)$ signs for a sample of n observations.

Note 2:   If 2 successive observations have the same numerical value, instead of "+" or "−", we place a zero and reduce the given sample size n by the number of zeros, when evaluating (18.8) and (18.9).

Then, the testing procedure for a 2-sided test is similar to the testing procedure listed in 18.2.2, except that R_1, $E(R_1)$, and $\sigma(R_1)$ are replaced by R_2, $E(R_2)$, and $\sigma(R_2)$ which are defined as shown above.

Example 4

Let us solve example 18.3 again, this times using the "Runs Up and Down" test. Then, the sequence of "+"s and "−"s signs, according to our discussion above, is:

There are $R_2 = 19$ runs of "+" and "−" symbols, and there are $n - 1 = 26$ such signs.

Then
$$E(R_2) = \frac{1}{3}(2n - 1) = \frac{1}{3}\Big[2 \times 27 - 1\Big] = \frac{1}{3}(54 - 1)$$

$$= \frac{53}{3} = 17.667$$

$$\sigma(R_2) = \sqrt{\frac{1}{90}(16n - 29)} = \sqrt{\frac{1}{90}(16 \times 27 - 29)} = \sqrt{\frac{1}{90}(403)} = \sqrt{4.4777}$$

$$= 2.116$$

and $z^* = \dfrac{R_2 - E(R_2)}{\sigma(R_2)} = \dfrac{19 - 17.667}{2.116} = \dfrac{1.333}{2.116} = 0.63$

Since $-Z_{\alpha/2} = -1.96 < Z^* < Z_{\alpha/2} = Z_{0.25} = 1.96$ (for a 2-tailed test, when $\alpha = 0.05$), H_0 is not rejected, and we conclude that the observations are randomly generated. This is the same conclusion as the one reached when the same problem was solved using the "Runs Above and Below the Median" test.

■ ■ ■

■ The Von Newmann Ratio Test for Independence

Business and economic data, expressed as time series data, is usually dependent data because a current observation may be statistically dependent on one or more previous values of the variable. The dependence between successive terms of a time series is called serial correlation.

To test for the lack of serial correlation in time series data we need to show that

$$P\big(x_{i+1} = b/x_i = a\big) = P(x_{i+1} = b), \text{ for all } i \tag{18.10}$$

That is, if the conditional probability that $x_{i+1} = b$, given that $x_i = a$, is equal to the unconditional probability that $x_{i+1} = b$, for all values of i, there is no serial correlation.

A more general version of (18.10) is to write:

$$P\Big[x_{i+j} = b/x_i = a\Big] = P\Big[x_{i+j} = b\Big], \text{ for all } i, j, \text{ and } j \geq 1 \tag{18.11}$$

If, for any values of i and j the conditional probability on the left-hand side of (18.11) is not equal to the unconditional probability of the right-hand side of (18.11), serial correlation is present. If serial correlation is present it can be either positive or negative.

Positive serial correlation occurs when a high observation value is likely to be followed by another high observation value, or a low observation value is likely to be followed by another low observation value.

Negative serial correlation occurs when a high observation value is likely to be followed by a low observation value, or a low observation value is likely to be followed by a high observation value.

In view of our discussion above we conclude that a test for independence is similar to tests of randomness. In this section we will discuss the Von Newmann ratio test for testing independence or randomness in time-series data.

The Von Newmann ratio, K, is essentially the ratio of 2 variances, and is defined by:

$$K = \frac{\delta^2}{s_y^2}, \tag{18.11a}$$

where

$$\delta^2 = \frac{1}{n-1}\sum_{i=1}^{n}(y_{i+1} - y_i)^2 \tag{18.12}$$

and

$$s^2 = \frac{1}{n}\sum_{i=1}^{n}(y_i - \bar{y})^2 \qquad (18.13)$$

Equation (18.13) is the usual biased sample variance of the y values, while the δ^2 defined by (18.12) is the variance of the differences between successive observations. When the $y_{i+1} - y_i$ differences are small, the values of K will be small and that is an indication of the existence of positive serial correlation. However, when the $y_{i+1} - y_i$ differences are large, the value of K will be large and that is an indication of the existence of negative serial correlation.

Therefore, if the value of K is very small or very large, we reject the hypotheses that the time series data is random or independent. The actual hypotheses we are testing are:

H_0: The time series data is random (or independent).

vs

H_1: The time series data is non-random (or is dependent).

To perform this test, we make use of Table 18.3, which gives the 5% and 1% points of the distribution of K.

For each level of significance (α) and each sample size (n) the table gives 2 critical values, k and k', and the interpretation of the table values regarding the rejection/non-rejection of H_0 is as follows, for a given n (the table values for n are: $4 \leq n \leq 60$) and α:

1. If $K < k$, K is significant and H_0 is rejected, and we conclude that positive serial correlation exists.
2. If $K > k'$, K is significant and H_0 is rejected, and we conclude that negative serial correlation exists
3. If $k < K < k'$, K is not significant and H_0 is not rejected, and we conclude that the time series data is random (independent)

Example 5

Use the data of the time series below to determine whether it is random or not.

(1) Year	(2) y_i	(3) $(y_i - \bar{y})^2$	(4) $(y_{i+1} - y_i)^2$
1	$y_1 = 4$	$(y_1 - \bar{y})^2 = (4 - 9)^2 = 25$	—
2	$y_2 = 5$	$(y_2 - \bar{y})^2 = (5 - 9)^2 = 16$	$(y_2 - y_1)^2 = (5 - 4)^2 = 1$
3	$y_3 = 7$	$(y_3 - \bar{y})^2 = (7 - 9)^2 = 4$	$(y_3 - y_2)^2 = (7 - 5)^2 = 4$
4	$y_4 = 6$	$(y_4 - \bar{y})^2 = (6 - 9)^2 = 9$	$(y_4 - y_3)^2 = (6 - 7)^2 = 1$
5	$y_5 = 10$	$(y_5 - \bar{y})^2 = (10 - 9)^2 = 1$	$(y_5 - y_4)^2 = (10 - 6)^2 = 16$
6	$y_6 = 10$	$(y_6 - \bar{y})^2 = (10 - 9)^2 = 1$	$(y_6 - y_5) = (10 - 10)^2 = 0$
7	$y_7 = 9$	$(y_7 - \bar{y})^2 = (9 - 9)^2 = 0$	$(y_7 - y_6)^2 = (9 - 10)^2 = 1$
8	$y_8 = 11$	$(y_8 - \bar{y})^2 = (11 - 9)^2 = 4$	$(y_8 - y_7)^2 = (11 - 9)^2 = 4$
9	$y_9 = 12$	$(y_9 - \bar{y})^2 = (12 - 9)^2 = 9$	$(y_9 - y_8)^2 = (12 - 11)^2 = 1$
10	$y_{10} = 16$	$(y_{10} - \bar{y})^2 = (16 - 9)^2 = 49$	$(y_{10} - y_9) = (16 - 12)^2 = 16$
	$\sum_{i=1}^{10} y_i = 90$	$\sum_{i=1}^{10}(y_i - \bar{y})^2 = 118$	$\sum_{i=1}^{10}(y_{i+1} - y_i)^2 = 44$

The given time series is given by columns (1) and (2). From the total of column (2)

and the fact that $n = 10$, we calculate $\bar{y} = \dfrac{\sum\limits_{i=1}^{n} y_i}{n} = \dfrac{90}{10} = 9$, which is then used to calculate column (3) and its total. Then, column (4) and its total are obtained. Then, using formulas (18.12) and (18.13) and the totals of the table above we obtain:

$$\delta^2 = \frac{1}{n-1}\sum_{i=1}^{n}(y_{i+1} - y_i)^2 = \frac{1}{9}(44) = 4.8889$$

$$s^2 = \frac{1}{n}\sum_{i=1}^{n}(y_i - \bar{y})^2 = \frac{1}{10}(118) = 11.8,$$

and

$$K = \frac{\delta^2}{s^2} = \frac{4.8889}{11.8} = 0.4143$$

Then, from Table 18.3, for $n = 10$ and $\alpha = p = 0.01$, $k = 0.8353$ and $k' = 3.6091$
$n = 10$ and $\alpha = p = 0.05$, $k = 1.1803$ and $k' = 3.2642$

Table 18.3 5% and 1% Significance Points for the Ratio of the Mean Square Successive Difference to the Variance

Values of $K = \dfrac{\delta^2}{s^2}$ for Different Levels of Significance

	Values of k		Values of k'			Values of k		Values of k'	
n	$P=0.01$	$P=0.05$	$P=0.95$	$P=0.99$	n	$P=0.01$	$P=0.05$	$P=0.95$	$P=0.99$
4	.8341	1.0406	4.2927	4.4992	31	1.2469	1.4746	2.6587	2.8864
5	.6724	1.0255	3.9745	4.3276	32	1.2570	1.4817	2.6473	2.8720
6	.6738	1.0682	3.7318	4.1262	33	1.2667	1.4885	2.6365	2.8583
7	.7163	1.0919	3.5748	3.9504	34	1.2761	1.4951	2.6262	2.8451
8	.7575	1.1228	3.4486	3.8139	35	1.2852	1.5014	2.6163	2.8324
9	.7974	1.1524	3.3476	3.7025					
10	.8353	1.1803	3.2642	3.6091	36	1.2940	1.5075	2.6068	2.8202
					37	1.3025	1.5135	2.5977	2.8085
11	.8706	1.2062	3.1938	3.5294	38	1.3108	1.5193	2.5889	2.7973
12	.9033	1.2301	3.1335	3.4603	39	1.3188	1.5249	2.5804	2.7865
13	.9336	1.2521	3.0812	3.3996	40	1.3266	1.5304	2.5722	2.7760
14	.9618	1.2725	3.0352	3.3458					
15	.9880	1.2914	2.9943	3.2977	41	1.3342	1.5357	2.5643	2.7658
					42	1.3415	1.5408	2.5567	2.7560
16	1.0124	1.3090	2.9577	3.2543	43	1.3486	1.5458	2.5494	2.7466
17	1.0352	1.3253	2.9247	3.2148	44	1.3554	1.5506	2.5424	2.7376
18	1.0566	1.3405	2.8948	3.1787	45	1.3620	1.5552	2.5357	2.7289
19	1.0766	1.3547	2.8675	3.1456					
20	1.0954	1.3680	2.8425	3.1151	46	1.3684	1.5596	2.5293	2.7205
					47	1.3745	1.5638	2.5232	2.7125
21	1.1131	1.3805	2.8195	3.0869	48	1.3802	1.5678	2.5173	2.7049
22	1.1298	1.3923	2.7982	3.0607	49	1.3856	1.5716	2.5117	2.6977
23	1.1456	1.4035	2.7784	3.0362	50	1.3907	1.5752	2.5064	2.6908
24	1.1606	1.4141	2.7599	3.0133					
25	1.1748	1.4241	2.7426	2.9919	51	1.3957	1.5787	2.5013	2.6842
					52	1.4007	1.5822	2.4963	2.6777
26	1.1883	1.4336	2.7264	2.9718	53	1.4057	1.5856	2.4914	2.6712

(Continued)

	Values of k		*Values of* k'			*Values of k*		*Values of* k'	
27	1.2012	1.4426	2.7112	2.9528	54	1.4107	1.5890	2.4866	2.6648
28	1.2135	1.4512	2.6969	2.9348	55	1.4156	1.5923	2.4819	2.6585
29	1.2252	1.4594	2.6834	2.9177					
30	1.2363	1.4672	2.6707	2.9016	56	1.4203	1.5955	2.4773	2.6524
					57	1.4249	1.5987	2.4728	2.6465
					58	1.4294	1.6019	2.4684	2.6407
					59	1.4339	1.6051	2.4640	2.6350
					60	1.4384	1.6082	2.4596	2.6294

Frieda S. Swed and C. Eisenhart, "Tables for testing randomness of grouping in a sequence of alternatives. *Annals of Mathematical Statistics*. Vol. XIV, March, 1943 pp. 70–87.

Since $K = 0.4143 < k = 0.8353$, H_0 is rejected at $\alpha = 0.01$, and
Since $K = 0.4143 < k = 1.1803$, H_0 is also rejected at $\alpha = 0.05$
Therefore, we conclude that positive serial correlation exists.

18.3 Chi-Square Tests

We have used the chi-square distribution in Chapter 11 where we solved hypothesis test problems and constructed confidence intervals for the population parameters σ^2 (population variance) and σ (population standard deviation) because it was shown there that $\hat{s}^2$ (the unbiased sample variance) is χ^2_{n-1} (*i.e.*, $\hat{s}^2$ is distributed as a chi-square variable with $n - 1$ degrees of freedom).

But the chi-square distribution is a very versatile distribution and has many other applications some of which are discussed here. But these chi-square tests, such as tests on Frequencies, Goodness-of-fit tests, Contingency-Table tests, and tests for Homogeneity are non-parametric or "distribution-free" statistics in contrast to the parametric chi-square statistic used in Chapter 11.

With the non-parametric chi-square test statistic we follow, in general, the following procedure:

1. We formulate H_0 under which theoretical (or expected) frequencies are determined.
2. We analyze sample data to establish observed frequencies.
3. We compare the two sets of frequencies by taking corresponding differences.
4. We specify, on the basis of these differences, a decision criterion to determine whether the observed frequencies differ (or not) significantly from the expected frequencies.
5. If the differences are small and can be attributed to chance variation in random sampling, H_0 is not rejected. On the other-hand if the differences are large and cannot be attributed to chance variation in random sampling H_0 is rejected.

If we let o_i and e_i represent observed and expected frequencies, respectively, then the variable Y is chi-square distributed with DOF $= \delta$, and

$$Y = \chi^2_\delta = \sum_{i=1}^{k} \frac{(o_i - e_i)^2}{e_i} \tag{18.14}$$

where $\delta = k - 1 - m$
and $k =$ number of classes

$$m = \text{the number of estimators evaluated before expected frequencies are}$$
$$\text{calculated } (m = 0, 1, 2, \dots)$$

If $m = 0$, then $\delta = k - 1$ if we can compute expected frequencies without having to estimate any population parameters from their sample statistics (or estimators).

To use (18.14) we must make sure that:

1. The o_i and e_i are absolute and not relative frequencies.
2. There are at least five (5) items in each theoretical frequency class, so that the chi-square approximation is valid.

   If one or more classes have expected frequencies of less than 5 items we combine classes before calculating the differences $o_i - e_i$. Also the degrees of freedom, δ, is determined after the regrouping of classes.

   For example if we start out with 7 classes and 2 of these classes have small theoretical frequencies, we can combine those 2 class and form one. Thus the total number of classes is now $k = 6$, and the degrees of freedom is $\delta = k - 1 = 6 - 1 = 5$.
3. When $\delta = 1$, equation (18.14) is modified by introducing a continuity correction factor of 1/2 in computing the value of the variable, namely:

$$Y = \chi_\delta^2 = \begin{cases} \displaystyle\sum_{i=1}^{k} \frac{(|o_i - e_i| - 1/2)^2}{e_i} & \text{if } |o_i - e_i| \geq \frac{1}{2} \\[2ex] 0 & \text{if } |o_i - e_i| < \frac{1}{2} \end{cases} \qquad (18.15)$$

18.3.1 Tests on Frequencies

In this section we use the chi-square statistic to test hypotheses about frequencies. We discuss 2 separate cases: tests on the frequencies of 2 classes, and tests on the frequencies of more than two classes.

▪ Test on the frequencies of two classes

We will discuss this case with the following example:

A candidate for public office claims to have the support of 40 percent of the electorate. The sample data showed that of the 500 voters surveyed 215 were supporters of the candidate. We want to verify if 4 out of every 10 voters are in support of the candidate. To verify this claim, we proceed as follows:

1. H_0: The voters are distributed in the ratio 4:6 vs H_1: the ratio is not 4:6
2. Level of significance $\alpha = 0.05$
3. Test statistic $\chi_\delta^2 = \chi_1^2 = \displaystyle\sum_{i=1}^{k=2} \frac{(|o_i - e_i| - 1/2)^2}{e_i}$, with $k = 2$ and $\delta = k - 1 = 1$
4. Rejection Region

$$\alpha = 0.05$$
$$\chi_{1,\,0.05}^2 = 3.841$$

Note: The rejection region must be the upper end of the chi-square distribution because any departure from the ratio 4:6 will result in an increased value for chi-square.

5. The value of the test statistic, χ^2_δ, is obtained with the help of the table below:

Voters	Observed	Expected	$\lvert o_i - e_i \rvert - 1/2$	$\dfrac{(\lvert o_i - e_i \rvert - 1/2)^2}{e_i}$
Favorable	2 1 5	2 0 0	14.5	$(14.5)^2/200 = \dfrac{210.25}{200} = 1.05125$
Unfavorable	2 8 5	3 0 0	14.5	$(14.5)^2/300 = \dfrac{210.25}{300} = 0.70083$
Total	5 0 0	5 0 0	—	$\sum\limits_{i=1}^{n}\left(\dfrac{(\lvert o_i - e_i \rvert - 1/2)^2}{e_i}\right) = 1.75208$

6. **Decision** Since the computed chi-square value (1.75208) is less then the tabulated value of $\chi^2_1 (0.05) = 3.841$, the H_0 hypothesis cannot be rejected. This is so because the sample data doesn't provide sufficient evidence to doubt the candidate's claim.

■ Test on the Frequencies of more than Two Classes

In the test on the Frequencies of two classes, the H_0 can also be written as:
H_0: $p = p_0 = 0.4$ vs H_1: $p \neq 0.4$ which can then be solved using the normal distribution because:

$$\frac{p - E(p)}{\sigma(p)} = \frac{p - n\pi}{\sqrt{\dfrac{\pi(1 - \pi)}{n}}} = Z, \text{ and the two solutions are equivalent.}$$

But, when there are more then 2 classes it is more convenient to use the chi-square test than a multinomial test.

Consider the following example:

Three coins are tossed 100 times for the purpose of determining whether all 3 coins are fair, and the following results were obtained by counting the number of times we obtained 0, 1, 2, 3 heads.

x	0	1	2	3
$n(x)$	14	34	36	16

Then we perform the following test to check the validity of the claim:

1. H_0: The distribution of heads is the same as that produced by 3 fair coins.

vs

H_1: The distribution of heads is different from that produced by 3 fair coins.

2. Level of significance $= \alpha = 0.05$

3. Test statistic $\chi^2_\delta = \chi^2_3 = \sum\limits_{i=1}^{k=4} \dfrac{(o_i - e_i)^2}{e_i}$ with $k = 4$ and $\delta = k - 1 = 3$.

4. Rejection Region

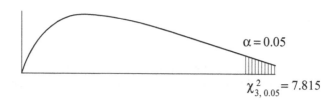

$\alpha = 0.05$

$\chi^2_{3, 0.05} = 7.815$

5. The value of the test statistic, χ_δ^2, is obtained with the help of the table below:

# of Heads	Observed #	$b(x_j, n = 3, 0.5)$	Expected # = **100** $b(x)$	$(o - e_i)^2/e_i$
0	14	1/8	100 (1/8) = 12.5	$(14 - 12.5)^2/12.5 = 0.18$
1	34	3/8	100 (3/8) = 37.5	$(34 - 37.5)^2/37.5 = 0.32667$
2	36	3/8	100 (3/8) = 37.5	$(36 - 37.5)^2/37.5 = 0.06$
3	16	1/8	100 (1/8) = 12.5	$(16 - 12.5)^2/12.5 = 0.98$
Total	100	1.00	100.0	$\sum_{i=1}^{4}(o_i - e_i)^2/e_i = 1.54667$

6. **Decision** Since the calculated chi-square value (1.54667) is less than the tabulated value of $\chi_3^2 (0.05) = 7.815$, the H_0 hypothesis cannot be rejected. Therefore we can conclude that the 3 coins are fair because the sample data does not provide sufficient information to reject the claim that the distribution of heads is the same as that provided by 3 fair coins.

18.3.2 Tests on Independence-Contingency Tables

In the test on frequencies we discussed above populations and samples are classified by a single characteristic. Such analysis is referred to as "one-way classification table" analysis because the observed frequencies occupy a single row or a single column and, because the observed frequencies are distributed in k classes, one-way classification tables are also called $1 \times k$ or $k \times 1$ tables, depending on whether the data is listed in a row or in a column. When populations or samples are classified by two (or more) characteristics we want to use "tests of independence" to determine whether the characteristics are statistically independent or not.

For example we may want to know whether income level of a family and type of college chosen by the family children are independent or not.

In general, the type of hypotheses being tested here are:

H_0: The two characteristics are independent.

$$\text{vs} \tag{18.16}$$

H_1: The two characteristics are dependent.

Tests for independence are also called "Contingency-Table tests".

In such tests the observed frequencies may occupy 2 rows and 2 columns (smallest possible contingency table test) or **r** rows and **c** columns (in general).

For each observed frequency in an $r \times c$ contingency table there is a corresponding expected frequency which is defined by the null hypothesis being tested.

The total frequencies in each row or column are called "marginal frequencies", while the observed and/or expected frequencies of each cell of the contingency table are called "cell frequencies".

To test the hypotheses in (18.16) we use the same χ^2 test statistic we used in the frequency tests, namely:

$$\chi_\delta^2 = \sum_{i=1}^{rc} \frac{(o_i - e_i)^2}{e_i}, \tag{18.17}$$

with Degrees of Freedom $= \delta = (r - 1)(c - 1)$. $\tag{18.18}$

When the contingency table is 2×2 (*i.e.*, when $r = 2$ and $c = 2$),

$$\delta = (r - 1)(c - 1) = (2 - 1)(2 - 1) = 1$$

The continuity correction factor of $1/2$, discussed previously in our tests on frequencies, should be used in (8.17), for small samples. However, when the samples are large, the continuity correction factor can be ignored.

Example 6

To test the hypothesis that high-income families choose to send their children to private universities and low-income families to state universities, 2000 families were selected at random, nationwide, and the following results were obtained (Observed Data):

Income Level	University Type		
	Private	**Public**	**Total**
Low	632	618	1,250
High	548	202	750
Total	1,180	820	2,000

From this table it is obvious that a greater proportion of high-income families $(548/750 = 0.73)$ send their children to private universities than low-income families $(632/1250 = 0.51)$. To determine whether this proportional difference is statistically significant or not, we will use the chi-square test for independence.

Before we can complete the test, however, we must construct a table of Expected Data, based on our assumption that Income Level and Type of University are independent. Under this assumption we would expect the proportion of all families that send their children to private universities to be equal to $1,180/2000 = 0.59$.

Then the expected number of low-income families that send their children to private universities should be equal to:

$$\left(\frac{1,180}{2,000}\right) \times 1250 = (0.59) \times 1250 = 737.5 \approx 738$$

We can calculate the other cell values in a similar manner but, since the marginal frequencies of the Expected Data must agree with the marginal frequencies of the Observed Data, once one of the cell values has been found the other cell values can be calculated by inspection. This statement explains why the degrees of freedom $= \delta = 1$ for a 2×2 contingency table.

Then the Expected Data for our example 18.6 become:

Income Level	University Type		
	Private	**Public**	**Total**
Low	738	512	1,250
High	442	308	750
Total	1,180	820	2,000

Our test of independence then proceeds as follows:
1. H_0: Income level and university choice are independent

vs

H_1: Income level and university choice are dependent

2. Level of significance $= \alpha = 0.05$.

3. Test statistic $\chi_\delta^2 = \sum_{i=1}^{rc} \frac{(o_i - e_i)^2}{e_i}$, with $\delta = (r - 1)(c - 1) = (2 - 1)(2 - 1) = 1$

4. Rejection Region

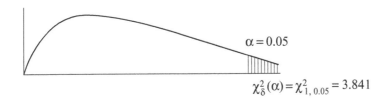

$$\chi_\delta^2(\alpha) = \chi_{1,\,0.05}^2 = 3.841$$

(For other α values the critical $\chi_\delta^2(\alpha)$ values are:

$$\chi_{1,0.1}^2 = 2.706; \ \chi_{1,0.025}^2 = 5.024; \ \chi_{1,0.01}^2 = 6.635; \ \chi_{1,0.005}^2 = 7.874)$$

5. Value of test statistic

$$\chi^{*2} = \frac{(632 - 738)^2}{738} + \frac{(618 - 512)^2}{512} + \frac{(548 - 442)^2}{442} + \frac{(202 - 308)^2}{308}$$
$$= 15.225 + 21.945 + 25.421 + 36.481 = 99.072$$

6. Since χ^{*2} falls in the rejection region, H_0 is rejected and we conclude that family income level and type of university selection are not independent.

(**Note:** The continuity correction factor was not used because the sample size is large).

■ ■ ■

18.3.3 Tests on Homogeneity

In this section we want to answer the question: Are 2 or more independent random samples drawn from the same population or from different populations

Note: When we say things are homogeneous we mean that: they have something in common, they are the same or they are equal.

These tests are an extension of the chi-square test for independence. These 2 types of tests are both concerned with the analysis of cross-classified data and the same test statistic, $\chi_\delta^2 = \sum_{i=1}^{rc} \frac{(o_i - e_i)^2}{e_i}$, is used in both tests. But, besides having these similarities, these 2 tests also have their differences which mainly are due to the types of problems solved in each case. In tests of independence a single sample is obtained from one population and the problem is to determine whether two characteristics of the elements of the population, from which the sample came from, are independent of each other. However, in tests of homogeneity we are dealing with two or more independent samples and the problem is to determine whether these samples come from the same population or from different populations.

We will illustrate the test of homogeneity using the following example.

Example 7

Three random samples of students are taken at a university. The first sample consists of 100 graduate students, the second of 100 seniors, and the third of 100 sophomore students.

Each group is asked to grade the course instruction they are receiving at the university as Excellent, Good, or Average.

The following results were obtained:

	Student Classification	Instruction Quality			Total
		Excellent	Good	Average	
Observed Data	Graduate	77	12	11	100
	Senior	73	7	20	100
	Sophomore	85	10	5	100
	Total	235	29	36	300

The H_0 to be tested here is: H_0: the 3 samples come from the same population, *i.e.*, the 3 classifications of students are homogeneous in their opinion about quality of instruction.

If this null hypothesis is true, then the best estimates for the proportions specifying "Excellent instruction", "Good instruction", and "Average instruction", respectively, should be: 235/300, 29/300, and 36/300.

Therefore, for the 100 graduate students, the expected frequencies for the categories become: (235/300)(100) = 78.33; (29/300)(100) = 9.67; (36/300)(100) = 12,   and similarly for the 100 senior and 100 sophomore students. Therefore, the expected data for the whole problem becomes:

	Student Classification	Instruction Quality			Total
		Excellent	Good	Average	
Expected Data	Graduate	78.33	9.67	12.00	100
	Senior	78.33	9.67	12.00	100
	Sophomore	78.33	9.67	12.00	100
	Total	234.99	29.01	36.00	300

Then, following our general testing procedure, the test for homogeneity becomes:

1. H_0: The 3 samples are drawn from the same population

vs

H_1: The 3 samples are drawn from different populations.

2. Level of significance = $\alpha = 0.05$

3. Test statistic = $\chi^2_\delta = \sum_{i=1}^{rc} \dfrac{(o_i - e_i)^2}{e_i} = \sum_{i=1}^{rc} \dfrac{(o^2 i - 2o_ie_i + e^2 i)}{e}$

$$= \sum_{i=1}^{rc} \frac{o^2 i}{e_i} - \sum_{i=1}^{rc} 2o_i + \sum_{i=1}^{rc} e_i = \sum_{i=1}^{rc} \frac{o^2 i}{e_i} - 2n + n = \sum_{i=1}^{rc} \frac{o^2 i}{e_i} - n \quad (18.19)$$

In this example $\delta = (r - 1)(c - 1) = (2)(2) = 4$

4. Rejection Region

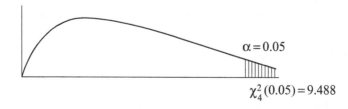

$\alpha = 0.05$

$\chi^2_4(0.05) = 9.488$

5. Value of test statistic

$$\chi_4^{2*} = \left(\frac{77^2}{78.33} + \frac{12^2}{9.67} + \frac{11^2}{12.0} \right) + \left(\frac{73^2}{78.33} + \frac{7^2}{9.67} + \frac{20^2}{12.0} \right) + \left(\frac{85^2}{78.33} + \frac{10^2}{9.67} + \frac{5^2}{12} \right) - n$$

$$= (75.69 + 14.89 + 10.08) + (68.03 + 5.07 + 5.07 + 33.33)$$
$$+ (92.24 + 10.34 + 2.08) - 300$$
$$= (100.66) = (106.43) + (104.66) - 300 = 311.75 - 300 = 11.75$$

6. **Decision** Since $\chi_4^{*2} = 11.75 > \chi_4^2(0.05) = 9.488$, H_0 is rejected and we conclude different "level" students have different opinions concerning the quality of instruction at the university.

Notes

1. The calculation of χ_4^{*2} was performed using (18.19) which is shown above to be identical to equation (18.17) and somewhat easier to use because it avoids having to take the differences between observed and expected frequencies before squaring.
2. If the level of significance was selected as $\alpha = 0.01$, then $\chi_4^2(0.01) = 13.277$, H_0 is not rejected and we would conclude that the 3 samples came from the same population (or that the 3 classification of students are homogeneous in their opinion about the quality of instruction).

■ ■ ■

18.3.4 Tests On Goodness of Fit

On many occasions it appears that the population under investigation follows a specific probability model, such as: Uniform, Normal, Exponential, etc. But it is much better if a statistical procedure existed and could be used to verify the validity of preliminary conclusions like that. Such a procedure does exist, it is called a "Goodness of Fit" test and consists of the following steps:

1. Formulate the null hypothesis that a given population has a specific probability model (such as Uniform, Normal, Poisson, Exponential, Binomial, etc.).
2. Obtain a random sample from the population and analyze it to derive the observed frequencies.
3. Use the theoretical distribution, specified in H_0, to generate expected frequencies, by multiplying the probability values for the classes by the sample size.
4. After these preliminary steps, the chi-square test for goodness-of-fit test becomes similar to the procedure used in the test for frequencies.

In this section we will discuss the goodness-of-fit test for:
a) The discrete uniform distribution and
b) The normal distribution

■ Testing the Fit of a Discrete Uniform Distribution

A very useful and simple goodness-of-fit test is that of a discrete uniform distribution, such as the toss of a coin or the throw of a die. We will illustrate this test using the following example:

Example 8

Suppose a die is tossed 120 times and the following results are obtained:

Number Showing	1	2	3	4	5	6	Total
Observed Occurrences	10	19	30	29	21	11	120

Is this result consistent with the hypothesis that the die is fair at $\alpha = 0.05$? $\alpha = 0.01$?

Then, following our general testing procedure, the goodness-of-fit test becomes:

1. H_0: The number showing is uniformly distributed (or the die is fair)

vs

H_1: The number showing is not uniformly distributed (or the die is not fair)

2. $\alpha = 0.05$ and $\alpha = 0.01$

3. The test statistic is: $\chi_\delta^2 = \displaystyle\sum_{i=1}^{k} \frac{(o_i - e_i)^2}{e_i}$, with $\delta = k - 1 = 6 - 1 = 5$

The observed data, o_i, comes from the table of the observed data above while the expected data comes from the assumed Uniform distribution, which makes: $P(1) = P(2) = P(3) = P(4) = P(5) = P(6) = 1/6$, and the expected number of occurrences of each number equal to:

$$120\,P(1) = 120\,P(2) = 120\,P(3) = 120\,P(4) = 120\,P(5) = 120\,P(6) = 20$$

4. Rejection Region

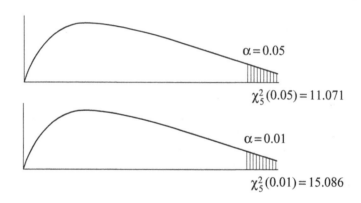

$$\chi_5^2(0.05) = 11.071$$

$$\chi_5^2(0.01) = 15.086$$

5. Calculate the value of the test statistic

$$
\begin{aligned}
\chi_5^{*2} &= \frac{(10 - 20)^2}{20} + \frac{(19 - 20)^2}{20} + \frac{(30 - 20)^2}{20} + \frac{(29 - 20)^2}{20} \\
&\quad + \frac{(21 - 20)^2}{20} + \frac{(11 - 20)^2}{20} \\
&= \frac{10^2}{20} + \frac{(-1)^2}{20} + \frac{10^2}{20} + \frac{9^2}{20} + \frac{1^2}{20} + \frac{(-9)^2}{20} \\
&= \frac{100 + 1 + 100 + 81 + 1 + 81}{20} = \frac{364}{20} = 18.2
\end{aligned}
$$

6. **Decision** Since $\chi^{*2} = 18.2 > \chi_5^2(\alpha)$ for both α values, the null hypothesis that the die is fair is rejected at both $\alpha = 0.05$ and $\alpha = 0.01$.

■ ■ ■

■ Testing the Fit of a Normal Distribution

Given a sample of observed data, $X_1, X_2, \ldots, X_n$, we proceed to calculate $\bar{x}$ and $\hat{s}$, and then test the hypothesis that the population from which the sample is drawn is normal. To accomplish this, we use the calculated $\bar{x}$ and $\hat{s}$, as the estimators for μ and σ in the normal distribution to calculate the expected number of data values in each desired interval. Then, once the observed and expected data is available, the value of the test statistic

$\chi_\delta^2 = \sum_{i=1}^{\kappa} \frac{(o_i - e_i)^2}{e_i}$ can be calculated as usual, except that now:

$$\delta = k - 1 - m = k - 1 - 2 = k - 3, \qquad (18.20)$$

where m is the number of estimators to be calculated from the data ($\overline{x}$ and $\widehat{s}$ therefore $m = 2$).

The number of intervals (k) selected, under the normal density function depends on the investigator but the entire number line should be utilized. The first interval should be from $-\infty$ to n_1, the second from n_1 to $n_2, \ldots$ and the last from n_q to $+\infty$, where the numbers $n_1, n_2, \ldots, n_q$ are selected by the researcher and may or may not be a function of $\overline{x}$ and $\widehat{s}$.

We will illustrate this test and procedure using the example below:

Example 9

It is believed that grades are usually assigned, to large university classes, according to the "normal curve".

Suppose grades of 162 students in a statistics class, in a given year, are as shown in the table below:

Class	Between 30 but below 40	40 bb* 50	50 bb 60	60 bb 70	70 bb 80	80 bb 90	90 bb 100
Frequency	5	10	28	52	31	26	10

*where bb stands for but below

Assuming that these grades constitute a random sample, can we conclude that this sample has been drawn from a population of grades which are normally distributed at $\alpha = 0.05$ and $\alpha = 0.01$?

Note: If $2 < e_i < 5$, for some class, we do not need to combine classes to meet the requirement that e_i should be ≥ 5; it is close enough).

Then, following our general testing procedure, the goodness-of-fit test becomes:

1. H_0: The population from which the sample is drawn is normal

vs

H_1: The population from which the sample is drawn is not normal

2. $\alpha = 0.05$ and $\alpha = 0.01$

3. The test statistic is $\chi_\delta^2 = \sum_{i=1}^{k} \frac{(o_i - e_i)^2}{e_i}$, with $\delta = k - 1 - m$, where k is the number of classes and $m =$ the number of estimates to be calculated from the data ($m = 2$ here because we need to calculate $\overline{x}$ and $\widehat{s}$ from the data) and $\delta = 7 - 1 - 2 = 4$.

4. Rejection regions

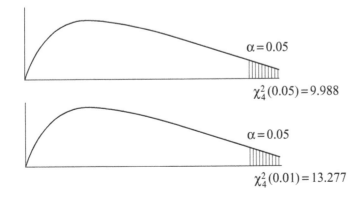

$\alpha = 0.05$

$\chi_4^2(0.05) = 9.988$

$\alpha = 0.05$

$\chi_4^2(0.01) = 13.277$

5. **Calculate the value of the test statistic**

We will assume that we have $k = 7$ classes, as shown below but, for the calculation of probability under the normal curve we will assume that the first class extends from $-\infty$ to 39.5 and the last one from 89.5 to ∞:

Class	Midpoint (m_i)	Observed Frequency (f_i)	Probability[*]	Expected Frequency $= 162^*\text{Prob}$	$\dfrac{(o_i - e_i)^2}{e_i}$
30–40	35	5	0.0233	3.77	0.401
40–50	45	10	0.0764	12.38	0.458
50–60	55	28	0.1840	29.81	0.110
60–70	65	52	0.2674	43.32	1.739
70–80	75	31	0.2478	40.14	2.081
80–90	85	26	0.1399	22.66	0.492
90–100	95	10	0.0606	9.82	0.003
		$n = \sum\limits_{i=1}^{n} f_i = 162$	$0.9994 \approx 1.0$	$161.9 \approx 162$	$\sum\limits_{i=1}^{n} \dfrac{(o_i - e_i)^2}{e_i} = 5.284$

From the midpoint (m_i) and observed frequency data (f_i) we calculate $\bar{x}$ and $\hat{s}$ using the grouped data formulas:

$$\bar{x} = \frac{\sum\limits_{i-1}^{k} m_i f_i}{n} = \frac{35(5) + 45(10) + 55(28) = 65(25) + 75(31) + 85(26) + 45(10)}{162}$$

$$= \frac{11{,}030}{162} = 68.09$$

and

$$\hat{s}^2 = \frac{n \sum\limits_{i=1}^{k} f_i m_i^2 - \left(\sum\limits_{i-1}^{k} f_i m_i\right)^2}{n(n-1)} = \frac{162(783{,}250) - (11{,}030)^2}{26{,}082}$$

$$= \frac{126{,}886{,}500 - 121{,}660{,}900}{26{,}082} = \frac{5{,}225{,}600}{26{,}082} = 200.3527$$

Then $\quad \hat{s} = \sqrt{\hat{s}^2} = \sqrt{200.3527} = 14.15$

Note: $\sum\limits_{i=1}^{k} f_i m_i^2 = 35^2(5) + 45^2(10) + 55^2(28) + 65^2(52) + 75^2(31) + 88^2(26)$

$$+ \, 95^2(10) = 783{,}250.$$

[*]The probability for each class will be calculated from a normal distribution with $\bar{x} = \widehat{\mu} = 68.09$ and $\widehat{s} = \widehat{\sigma} = 14.15$.

a) $P(X < 40) = P\left(z < \dfrac{40 - 68.09}{14.15}\right) = P(z < -1.98) = 0.0233$

b) $P(40 < X < 50) = P(-1.98 < z < -1.28) = (-1.28 < z < 1.98)$

$$= 0.0764$$

c) $P(50 < X < 60) = P(-1.28 < z < -0.57) = (0.57 < z < 1.28)$

$$= 0.1840$$

d) $P(60 < X < 70) = P(-0.57 < z < 0.13) = 0.2674$

e) $P(70 < X < 80) = P(0.13 < z < 0.84) = 0.2478$

f) $P(80 < X < 90) = P(0.84 < z < 1.55) = 0.1399$

g) $P(X > 90) = P(z > 1.55) = 0.0606$

Therefore, the computed χ^{*2} value $= 5.284$, as shown in the table above.

6. **Decision** Since $\chi^{*2} < \chi_4^2(\alpha)$ for both α values, H_0 is not rejected. This data set suggests that professors tend to grade large classes according to the normal distribution.

Note: We have shown how to test the goodness-of-fit for the discrete uniform distribution and the normal distribution. If we wanted to test the goodness-of-fit of other distributions (such as: Exponential, Poisson, Binomial, etc.) we follow the same procedure; *i.e.*, from the given data set we calculate numerical values for the unknown parameters of the distribution under consideration. Once the parameters have been estimated, we use the distribution with these parameters to calculate probabilities for the classes into which we have divided the range of variation of the distribution, and then we convert these probabilities into expected frequencies by multiplying the probability of each class by the sample size.

Once observed and expected frequencies are available the procedure continues as previously described (*i.e.*, we calculate the value of the test statistic $\chi_\delta^{*2} = \sum_{i=1}^{k} \frac{(o_i - e_i)^2}{e_i}$,

where $\delta = k - 1 - m$, and compare against $\chi_\delta^2(\alpha)$.

18.3.5 Kolmogorov-Smirnoff (K-S) Statistic—Another goodness-of-fit test

The Kolmogorov-Smirnoff statistic is a more appropriate goodness-of-fit test than the chi-square, because it does not require grouping the observed data into a finite number of classes (or class intervals) as is the case with the chi-square test. It is also applicable for small sample sizes while the chi-square test requires a relatively large sample.

On the other hand, the K-S statistic is limited, to some extend, because it requires that the distribution claimed in H_0 be completely specified.

It is based on a comparison between the observed cumulative distribution function of the ordered sample and the assumed distribution in H_0. If such a comparison shows a large difference between the sample and assumed distribution functions, then the null hypothesis is rejected.

Let us assume that our H_0 and H_1 have the form:

$$H_0: F_1(x) = F_0(x) \quad \text{vs} \quad H_1: F_1(x) \neq F_0(x) \tag{18.21}$$

where $F_0(x)$ is completely specified.

If $X_1, X_2, X_3, \ldots, X_n$ is a random sample and $V_1, V_2, V_3, \ldots, V_n$ is the ordered (or ranked) sample of the same observations, we can define the sample cumulative distribution function as:

$$S_n(x) = \begin{cases} 0 & \text{if} \quad X < V_1 \\ \dfrac{k}{n} & \text{if} \quad V_k \leq X \leq V_{k+1} \\ 1 & \text{if} \quad X \geq V_n \end{cases} \tag{18.22}$$

Equation (18.22) tells us that $S_n(x)$ is the proportion of the number of sample values less then or equal to x, for any ordered value x.

Table 18.4 Upper $1 - \alpha$ values of the Kolmogorov-Smirnov Statistic D_n					
	$1 - \alpha$				
n	0.80	0.85	0.90	0.95	0.99
1	0.900	0.925	0.950	0.975	0.995
2	0.684	0.726	0.776	0.842	0.929
3	0.565	0.597	0.642	0.708	0.828
4	0.494	0.525	0.564	0.624	0.733
5	0.446	0.474	0.510	0.565	0.669
6	0.410	0.436	0.470	0.521	0.618
7	0.381	0.405	0.438	0.486	0.577
8	0.358	0.381	0.411	0.457	0.543
9	0.339	0.360	0.388	0.432	0.514
10	0.322	0.342	0.368	0.410	0.490
11	0.307	0.326	0.352	0.391	0.468
12	0.295	0.313	0.338	0.375	0.450
13	0.284	0.302	0.325	0.361	0.433
14	0.274	0.292	0.314	0.349	0.418
15	0.266	0.283	0.304	0.338	0.404
16	0.258	0.274	0.295	0.328	0.392
17	0.250	0.266	0.286	0.318	0.381
18	0.244	0.259	0.278	0.309	0.371
19	0.237	0.252	0.272	0.301	0.363
20	0.231	0.246	0.264	0.294	0.356
25	0.21	0.22	0.24	0.27	0.320
30	0.19	0.20	0.22	0.24	0.290
35	0.18	0.19	0.21	0.23	0.270
Formula for large n	$\dfrac{1.07}{\sqrt{n}}$	$\dfrac{1.14}{\sqrt{n}}$	$\dfrac{1.22}{\sqrt{n}}$	$\dfrac{1.36}{\sqrt{n}}$	$\dfrac{1.63}{\sqrt{n}}$

Source: F. J. Massey, Jr., *The Kolmogorov-Smirnov test for goodness of fit*, J. Amer. Statistical Assoc. 46 (1951), 68–78.

Since $F_0(x)$ is completely specified, it can be evaluated for any desired value of x and compared to the corresponding $S_n(x)$ value, by forming the difference between the two distributions at the given x value. If H_0 is true, such differences should be small, and the K-S statistic is defined as:

$$D_n = \text{maximum over all } x \text{ values } |S_n(x) - F_0(x)| \qquad (18.23)$$

The D_n statistic has a distribution that does not depend on the model specified in H_0, and the D_n distribution can be evaluated as a function of the sample size only and then be compared to any specified $F_0(x)$.

Table 18.4 shows the upper $1 - \alpha$ values of the distribution of the K-S statistic as a function of $(1 \le n \le 35)$ and also presents a formula for large values of n, for each $1 - \alpha$ value.

When the level of significance, α, is specified, the rejection region is defined as:

$$P\left[D_n > \frac{c}{\sqrt{n}}\right] = \alpha, \qquad (18.24)$$

where the value of $\dfrac{c}{\sqrt{n}}$ can be obtained directly from Table 18.4, when α (or $1 - \alpha$) is specified.

Then H_0 will be rejected if, for some x value, the D_n value falls inside the rejection region.

Example 10

It is believed that the grades in a statistics class can be represented by a normally-distributed variable X with $E(X) = \mu = 75$ and $\sigma(X) = \sigma = 10$.

The current statistics class of 20 students had the following grades (arranged in order of magnitude): 45, 50, 58, 62, 65, 68, 70, 72, 74, 75, 78, 80, 82, 84, 85, 88, 90, 92, 95, 98.

Based on this sample, is there reason to believe that a change in the distribution of the grades in statistics has occurred at $\alpha = 0.05$? $\alpha = 0.01$?

Solution   The hypothesis to be tested is:
H_0: $F(x) = F_0(x) = $ the grades follow a normal distribution with $\mu = 75$ and $\sigma = 10$ (or $N(\mu = 75, \sigma = 10)$)

vs

H_1: $F(x) \ne F_0(x) = $ the grades do not follow the $N(\mu = 75, \sigma = 10)$ distribution

Because $n = 20 < 30$ (*i.e.*, n is small) we will use the K-S statistic to test the validity of H_0.

The sample distribution, $S_n(x)$, will be obtained using equation (18.22), and it simply involves the addition of the increment $\dfrac{1}{n} = \dfrac{1}{20} = 0.05$ to the previous value of the sample distribution.

The corresponding values of the hypothesized normal distribution are obtained by first converting the X values into Z values $\left(i.e., \text{ letting } Z_i = \dfrac{X_i - \mu}{\sigma} \right)$ and then using the table of the standard normal distribution.

The calculations needed for the determination of the D_n statistic, defined by equation (18.23), are shown in the table below:

#	Ordered Values	$S_n(x)$	$F_0(x) = N(\mu = 75, \sigma = 10)$	$dS_n(x) - F_0(x)$
1	45	$1/20 = 0.05$	$P(X \leq 45) = P(z \leq -3) = 0.0013$	0.0487
2	50	$2/20 = 0.10$	$P(X \leq 50) = P(z \leq -2.5) = 0.0062$	0.0938
3	58	$3/20 = 0.15$	$P(X \leq 58) = P(z \leq -1.7) = 0.0446$	0.1054
4	62	$4/20 = 0.20$	$P(X \leq 62) = P(z \leq -1.3) = 0.0968$	0.1032
5	65	$5/20 = 0.25$	$P(X \leq 65) = P(z \leq -1) = 0.1587$	0.0913
6	68	$6/20 = 0.30$	$P(X \leq 68) = P(z \leq -0.7) = 0.2420$	0.0580
7	70	$7/20 = 0.35$	$P(X \leq 70) = P(z \leq -0.5) = 0.3085$	0.0415
8	72	$8/20 = 0.40$	$P(X \leq 72) = P(z \leq -0.3) = 0.3821$	0.0179
9	74	$9/20 = 0.45$	$P(X \leq 74) = P(z \leq -0.1) = 0.4602$	0.0102
10	75	$10/20 = 0.50$	$P(X \leq 75) = P(z \leq 0) = 0.5000$	0
11	78	$11/20 = 0.55$	$P(X \leq 78) = P(z \leq 0.3) = 0.6179$	0.0679
12	80	$12/20 = 0.60$	$P(X \leq 80) = P(z \leq 0.5) = 0.6915$	0.0915
13	82	$13/20 = 0.65$	$P(X \leq 82) = P(z \leq 0.7) = 0.7580$	0.1080
14	84	$14/20 = 0.70$	$P(X \leq 84) = P(z \leq 0.9) = 0.8159$	0.1159 (max)
15	85	$15/20 = 0.75$	$P(X \leq 85) = P(z \leq 1) = 0.8143$	0.0913
16	88	$16/20 = 0.80$	$P(X \leq 88) = P(z \leq 1.3) = 0.9032$	0.1032
17	90	$17/20 = 0.85$	$P(X \leq 90) = P(z \leq 1.5) = 0.9332$	0.0832
18	92	$18/20 = 0.90$	$P(X \leq 92) = P(z \leq 1.7) = 0.9554$	0.0554
19	95	$19/20 = 0.95$	$P(X \leq 95) = P(z \leq 2) = 0.9772$	0.0272
20	98	$20/20 = 1.00$	$P(X \leq 98) = P(z \leq 2.3) = 0.9893$	0.0107

From this table we observe that the maximum absolute difference is 0.1159. Then from the table values for D_n of Table 18.4, we obtain for $n = 20$ and $\alpha = 0.05$: $D_{20}(\alpha = 0.05) = 0.294$ and $D_{20}(\alpha = 0.01) = 0.356$.

Since $D_n = \max$ over all $x |S_n(x) - F_0(x)| = 0.1159 < D_{20}(\alpha)$, for both α values, the H_0 hypothesis cannot be rejected, and we conclude that no change in the grades of this statistics class, from the hypothesized distribution $F_0(x) = N(\mu = 75, \sigma = 10)$ can be detected in this sample of grades.

■ ■ ■

18.4 Tests for Matched Pairs

In Chapter 11, among other tests we discussed, we compared the means of two populations when the observations are paired to remove the effect of outside factors. In this section we will discuss 2 non-parametric methods which are equivalent to the t-test for paired data. These tests are: a) The Sign test, which uses only the sign of the differences of the given paired data, and b) The Wilcoxon Sign Rank test, which uses both the sign of the differences of the given paired data and the rank of such differences among the many differences, in the problem.

Also, we will discuss the non-parametric Friedman test for k paired samples which can be considered equivalent to the Randomized Block Design of Analysis of Variance.

18.4.1 The Sign Test for Matched Paired Data

The sign test is based on the signs of the differences between paired observations of two random variables X and Y. If $(x_1, y_1), (x_2, y_2), \ldots, (x_n, y_n)$ are n paired sample observations, then we form the difference, $d_i = x_i - y_i$, for all i values and note the sign of the d_i difference. If $x_i > y_i$, a "+" sign is recorded for the d_i difference, while if $x_i < y_i$ a "−" sign is recorded. If $x_i = y_i$ and $d_i = 0$, the pair of observations is disregarded and the value of n is reduced by the number of $d_i = 0$ differences that we disregard.

It should be noted that for the sign test to be applicable it is not necessary for X and Y to be identically distributed, as is the case for the t test, which requires that the differences, d_i, are identically distributed. If we let $P(X > Y) = p$, then if the null hypothesis is that X and Y are identically distributed, p must be equal to 0.5 ($p = 0.5$ whether X and Y are or are not identically distributed).

The null and alternative hypotheses being tested for the sign test are:

$$H_0: p = 0.5 \quad \text{vs} \quad H_1: p \neq 0.5 \tag{18.25}$$

If H_0 is true, we would expect almost half of the n pairs to have a "+" sign.

If we let S be the test statistic which denotes the number of times the less frequent sign occurs in the sequence of d_i then S is binomially distributed with $p = 1/2$. The critical value for (18.25), at $\alpha = 0.05$, can be obtained from:

$$R = \frac{n - 1}{2} - 0.98\sqrt{n}, \tag{18.26}$$

which is derived from a chi-square goodness-of-fit test of a binomial distribution. In (18.26) n is the number of paired differences minus the number of differences for which $d_i = 0$.

The H_0 of (18.25) will be rejected if $S \leq R$ \hfill (18.27)

Example 11

Twelve newly married couples were randomly selected and each husband and wife were asked separately how many children they would like to have. The following answers were obtained:

Couple	1	2	3	4	5	6	7	8	9	10	11	12
X = Wife	1	2	3	2	2	0	0	1	2	2	2	1
Y = Husband	2	0	2	3	2	2	0	2	1	3	1	1

Using the sign test, can we conclude from this data set that wives and husbands want the same number of children, at $\alpha = 0.05$?

Forming the difference: $d_i = x_i - y_i$, we obtain:

Couple	1	2	3	4	5	6	7	8	9	10	11	12
Sign	−	+	+	−	0	−	0	−	+	−	+	0

Since there are 3 differences equal to zero, the effective value of $n = 12 - 3 = 9$.

Also since there are 4 "+" signs and 5 "−" signs, the value of the statistic $S = 4$, and under H_0

S is binomially distributed with $n = 9$ and $p = 0.5$. Then, using the Binomial Cumulative Distribution function we find that:

$$P(S \leq 4) = 0.5$$

Since this probability is higher than $\alpha = 0.05$, H_0 is not rejected, and, therefore, we conclude that wives and husbands want the same number of children.

If we use (18.26) to construct the critical value, we obtain:

$$R = \frac{n-1}{2} - 0.98\sqrt{n} = 4 - 0.98(3) = 4 - 2.94 = 1.06, \quad \text{when} \quad n = 9, \quad \text{and,}$$

using this critical value, H_0: $p = 0.5$, will not be rejected because $S = 4 > R = 1.06$

Therefore, once gain we arrive at the same conclusion, namely: husbands and wives want the same number of children.

■ ■ ■

18.4.2 The Wilcoxon Sign Rank Test

The sign test we discussed above ignored the fact that observations have not only a difference, $d_i = x_i - y_i$, but also a rank among all such differences.

When n paired observations are given, *i.e.*, if $(x_1, y_1), (x_2, y_2), \dots, (x_n, y_n)$ are given, we form n differences, $d_i = x_i - y_i$, for $i = 1, 2, \dots, n$, take the absolute value of the differences, and then rank them according to their magnitude. The smallest absolute difference is assigned rank 1, and the largest absolute difference is assigned rank n. Then the sign of each difference is attached to the rank for that difference.

The test statistic for this test is represented by T and is found as follows: we compute 2 sums of ranks, S^+ and S^-, where S^+ is the sum of the positive ranks and S^- is the sum of the negative ranks but both S^+ and S^- are considered positive. Then

$$T = \text{minimum } (S^+, S^-) \tag{18.28}$$

Note: When ties of the type $d_i = 0$ occur in this test, they are dropped and n is adjusted (downward) by the number of such ties. When ties of the type, say $d_i = -8$ and $d_i = +8$ occur, and if their ranks are 5 and 6, we assign a rank of $\left(\dfrac{5+6}{2}\right) = 5.5$ to each. Then, for -8 the rank becomes -5.5 and for $+8$ the rank becomes $+5.5$.

The null and alternative hypotheses are:

$$H_0: F(x) = G(x) \text{ vs } H_1: F(x) \neq G(x), \tag{18.29}$$

where $F(x)$ = cumulative distribution function for S^+ and $G(x)$ = cumulative distribution function for S^-, for all values of X. When the null hypothesis is true, each of the possible 2^n sets of signed ranks (which will be obtained by arbitrarily assigning "+" and "−" to each of the n pairs) have an equal chance to occur, and this permits the derivation of the exact distribution of T to be found. It has been found and it is tabulated but it can also be adequately approximated by the normal distribution, for $n \geq 16$.

Then, for $n \geq 16$ to test (18.29) the approximate critical value for T can be calculated from:

$$T_c \approx -Z_{\alpha/2}\sqrt{\frac{n(n+1)(2n+1)}{24}} + \frac{n(n+1)}{4} - \frac{1}{2} \tag{18.30}$$

and H_0 will be rejected if $T < T_c$.

Then for $n \geq 16$ (large sample) the sampling distribution of T is approximately normal with:

$$E(T) = \frac{n(n + 1)}{4} \tag{18.31}$$

and

$$\sigma(T) = \sqrt{\frac{n(n + 1)(2n + 1)}{24}} \tag{18.32}$$

and the test statistic becomes:

$$Z^* = \frac{T - E(T)}{\sigma(T)}, \tag{18.33}$$

or

$$Z^* = \frac{T + \dfrac{1}{2} - E(T)}{\sigma(T)}, \text{ if a continuity correction factor is used.} \tag{18.34}$$

However if $n < 16$ (small sample), the following special Table 18.5 of critical values of T for the Wilcoxon Sign Rank test should be used:

Table18.5 Critical Values of T for the Wilcoxon Sign Rank Test (Small Sample)									
(n = number of pairs) →	7	8	9	10	11	12	13	14	15
$\alpha = 0.05$; Reject H_0 if $T \leq R$	$R = 2$	$R = 2$	$R = 6$	$R = 8$	$R = 11$	$R = 14$	$R = 17$	$R = 21$	$R = 25$
$\alpha = 0.01$; Reject H_0 if $T \leq R$	$R = 0$	$R = 0$	$R = 2$	$R = 3$	$R = 5$	$R = 7$	$R = 10$	$R = 13$	$R = 16$

Example 12

Two auditing procedures are compared, using 10 pairs of auditors, and the number of accounts audited per day are given in rows 2 and 3 of the table below. Is there a significant difference in the methods of auditing at $\alpha = 0.05$ and $\alpha = 0.01$?

Pairs of Auditors	1	2	3	4	5	6	7	8	9	10
Procedure 1	109	100	77	69	59	69	87	88	88	91
Procedure 2	61	78	57	64	60	75	85	84	85	83
Difference $= d_i = P_1 - P_2$	48	22	20	5	−1	−6	2	4	3	8
Signed Rank of $\lvert d_i \rvert$	10	9	8	5	−1	−6	2	4	3	7

Then

$$S^+ = 10 + 9 + 8 + 5 + 2 + 4 + 3 + 7 = 48$$
$$S^- = 1 + 6 \qquad\qquad\qquad\qquad = 7$$

and

$$T = \text{minimum}(S^+, S^-) = \text{minimum}(48, 7) = 7$$

■ ■ ■

■ Large Sample Solution

Even though $n = 10$ (and not large enough to use the large-sample procedure) let us use it anyway to illustrate the procedure. We will also obtain the small sample solution, and compare the results.

Then $E(T) = \dfrac{n(n+1)}{4} = \dfrac{10(11)}{4} = \dfrac{110}{4} = 27.5$

and $\sigma(T) = \sqrt{\dfrac{n(n+1)(2n+1)}{24}} = \sqrt{\dfrac{10(11)(21)}{24}} = \sqrt{96.25} = 9.81$

Therefore, $z^* = \dfrac{T + \dfrac{1}{2} - E(T)}{\sigma(T)} = \dfrac{7 + \dfrac{1}{2} - 27.5}{9.81} = -\dfrac{20}{9.81} = -2.04$

Then, $P(T \le 7) = P(z < -2.04) = 0.0207$

Since, at $\alpha = 0.05$ $P(T \le 7) = 0.0207 < \dfrac{\alpha}{2} = 0.025$, H_0 is rejected

However, at $\alpha = 0.01$ $P(T \le 7) = 0.0207 > \dfrac{\alpha}{2} = 0.005$, and H_0 is not rejected

Note: If we used (18.30) to calculate the critical value T_c we obtain:

1. For $\alpha = 0.05$

$$T_c = -1.96\sqrt{\dfrac{10(11)(21)}{28}} + \dfrac{10(11)}{4} - \dfrac{1}{2} = -1.96(9.81) + 27.5 - 0.5$$

$= 27 - 19.23 = 7.77$, and since $T = 7 < T_c = 7.77$ H_0 will be rejected

2. For $\alpha = 0.01$ $T_c = -2.58(9.81) + 27.5 - 0.5 = 27 - 25.31 = 1.69$

and H_0 will not be rejected since $T = 7 > T_c = 1.69$

▪ Small Sample Solution

Since $n = 10 < 16$, the appropriate solution for this example is the small-sample solution.

   Since $T = 7$ using Table 18.5 we find that when $\alpha = 0.05$ and $n = 10$ and $R = 8$; then because $T = 7 < R = 8$, H_0 is rejected at $\alpha = 0.05$.

   When $\alpha = 0.01$ and $n = 10$, $R = 3$ and since $T = 7 > R = 3$, H_0 is not rejected at $\alpha = 0.01$.

18.4.3 Friedman Test for *k* paired Samples

The Wilcoxon test we discussed above is the equivalent of the *t*-test for paired comparisons, or for the ANOVA procedure for comparing the equality of two treatments in a randomized block design. When the number of treatments to be compared, for a single factor, is three or more ($k \ge 3$) the appropriate nonparametric method to use is the Friedman test, which was developed by M. Friedman in 1937 and is the nonparametric alternative to the randomized block design discussed in chapter 12. When the basic assumption of the randomized block design (*i.e.*, observations are drawn from normal populations) is not satisfied, the Friedman test can be used.

   The Friedman test is based on the following 3 assumptions:

1. The blocks are independent.
2. No interaction is present between blocks and treatments.
3. Observations within each block can be ranked.

   A block is created for each of *n* conditions of the factor, and each block contains one observation of each of *k* treatments, which are randomly assigned to each block. The *nk* observations are arranged in *n* rows (blocks) and *k* columns (Treatments).

   The hypotheses being tested are:

   H_0: Treatment effects are the same vs H_1: Treatment differences exist.

The Friedman test is based on ranks, and consists of the following steps:

1. For each Block (row) rank the observations from smallest (1) to largest (k).
2. Sum the ranks of each treatment, and let $R_j = $ sum of ranks for treatment j.
3. If treatment effects are equal, R_j should be about the same for all j.
4. The Friedman test determines when an observed difference among the R_j is large enough to reject H_0.

The Friedman Statistic is given by:

$$S = \frac{12}{nk(k+1)}\left[\sum_{i=1}^{k}R_j^2\right] - 3n(k+1), \qquad (18.35)$$

where $n = $ number of blocks (rows)

$k = $ number of treatments (columns)

$j = $ particular treatment level (column) $(1 \le j \le k)$

$R_j = $ sum of ranks for Treatment j

The distribution of S is approximately chi-square distributed with degrees of freedom $= k - 1$ if:

a) $k > 4$

or if: b) $k = 3$ and $n > 9$

or if: c) $k = 4$ and $n > 4$

The critical region of size α, is the upper tail of the chi-square distribution, with $k - 1$ degrees of freedom. The null hypothesis, H_0, is rejected if $S > \chi_{k-1}^2, \alpha$ (18.36)

Example 13

Three persons judge a competition involving 10 finalist competitors. Using the 10 competitors as blocks and the 3 judges as the treatments, the scores received are shown in the table below. (Note 10 is the highest possible score)

	Judge		
Competitor	1	2	3
1	8.5 (rank = 2)	8.2 (rank = 1)	8.7 (rank = 3)
2	9.4 (rank = 1)	9.6 (rank = 2)	9.8 (rank = 3)
3	8.1 (rank = 1)	8.4 (rank = 2)	8.6 (rank = 3)
4	9.0 (rank = 3)	8.5 (rank = 1.5)	8.5 (rank = 1.5)
5	8.7 (rank = 2)	8.1 (rank = 1)	9.2 (rank = 3)
6	8.4 (rank = 1)	8.6 (rank = 2)	8.9 (rank = 3)
7	8.8 (rank = 2)	8.2 (rank = 1)	9.5 (rank = 3)
8	9.5 (rank = 3)	9.1 (rank = 1.5)	9.1 (rank = 1.5)
9	8.4 (rank = 1)	8.9 (rank = 3)	8.7 (rank = 2)
10	8.5 (rank = 3)	8.3 (rank = 1)	8.4 (rank = 2)
$n = 10$ $k = 3$	$R_1 = 2 + 1 + 1 + 3 + 2 + 1$ $+ 2 + 3 + 1 + 3 = 19$	$R_2 = 1 + 2 + 2 + 1.5 + 1 + 2$ $+ 1 + 1.5 + 3 + 1 = 16$	$R_3 = 3 + 3 + 3 + 1.5 + 3 + 3$ $+ 3 + 1.5 + 2 + 2 = 25$

The ranks of the observations within each block (*i.e.*, the ranked scores received by each competitor, from the 3 judges, are shown in parenthesis next to each score. Also shown in the table are the sum of the ranks by each judge ($R_1 = 19, R_2 = 19, R_3 = 25$). Then we compute the value of the Friedman statistics from (18.35) and obtain:

$$S = \frac{12}{10(3)(4)}\left[R_1^2 + R_1^2 + R_1^2\right] - 3(10)(4) = \frac{12}{120}(19^2 + 16^2 + 25^2) - 120$$

$$= \frac{1}{10}(361 + 256 + 625) - 120 = \frac{1}{10}(1242) - 120$$

$$= 124.2 - 120 = 4.2$$

For $\alpha = 0.01$, the critical region is given by $\chi^2_{k-1}, \alpha = \chi^2_2, 0.01 = 9.22$, and for $\alpha = 0.05$, the critical region is: $\chi^2_2, 0.05 = 5.991$.

Since $S < \chi^2_{k-1}, \alpha$, the null hypothesis (H_0) that the treatment effects are the same is not rejected and we conclude that differences in the scoring among the judges is not evident.

18.5   Tests to Compare 2 or More Independent Populations

In this section we first discuss 2 nonparametric tests: (1) The Wald-Wolfowitz test and 2) The Mann-Whitney U test, which compare the distributions of 2 populations (*i.e.*, are the 2 distributions the same), using 2 independent samples, on the basis of runs and then discuss a third nonparametric test (The Kruskal-Wallis test) which is capable of testing the equality of 2 or more populations and, as such, is equivalent to the ANOVA procedures discussed in Chapter 12, while the first 2 tests of this section are equivalent to the *t*-test for testing the equality of the means of 2 independent populations.

18.5.1   The Wald-Wolfowitz Test

Assume that $X_1, X_2, X_3, \ldots, X_{n1}$ and $Y_1, Y_2, Y_3, \ldots, Y_{n2}$ are independent random samples from 2 populations, with continuous distributions. For this test the null hypothesis is that the 2 independent random samples come from populations with identical distributions, or:

$$H_0: f_1(x) = f_2(x) \tag{18.37}$$

versus

$$H_1: f_1(x) \neq f_2(x)$$

where $f_1(x)$ and $f_2(x)$ are the corresponding probability functions.

The alternative hypothesis H_1 is very broad and suggests that a difference between the 2 density functions may be in central tendency, dispersion, skewness or kurtosis.

The test begins by ranking the observations in the two samples, with n_1 observations in sample 1 and n_2 observations in sample 2, in a single array. In this array we will represent an observation by X if it comes from sample 1 and by Y if it comes from sample 2.

In such an array we then count the number of runs, *i.e.*, the number of X and Y alternating sequences. In such an ordering of observations from two samples the minimum number of runs is 2 and the maximum number of runs is $n_1 + n_2$.

If the 2 samples are drawn independently from 2 populations with identical distributions the observations, when ranked, will be well mixed, and the number of runs should be large. But, if the samples are drawn from 2 populations with different distributions, the number of runs should be small. If we let R represent the number of runs observed in an ordered sequence of $n_1 + n_2$ observations, R is a random variable and its probability mass function ($PMF(R)$) is given by:

$$
P(R) = \begin{cases} \dfrac{2\dbinom{n_1 - 1}{\frac{R}{2} - 1}\dbinom{n_2 - 1}{\frac{R}{2} - 1}}{\dbinom{n_1 + n_2}{n_1}} & \text{if } R \text{ is an even number} \\[3em] \dfrac{\dbinom{n_1 - 1}{\frac{R}{2} - \frac{1}{2}}\dbinom{n_2 - 1}{\frac{R}{2} - \frac{3}{2}} + \dbinom{n_1 - 1}{\frac{R}{2} - \frac{3}{2}}\dbinom{n_2 - 1}{\frac{R}{2} - \frac{1}{2}}}{\dbinom{n_1 + n_2}{n_1}} & \text{if } R \text{ is an odd number} \end{cases}
$$
(18.38)

where
$$
\binom{n_1 + n_2}{n_1} = \frac{(n_1 + n_2)!}{n_1![n_1 + n_2 - n_1]!} = \frac{(n_1 + n_2)!}{n_1! n_2!}
$$
(18.39)

and
$$
\binom{n_1 - 1}{\frac{R}{2} - 1} = \frac{(n_1 - 1)!}{\left(\frac{R}{2} - 1\right)!\left[n_1 - 1 - \frac{R}{2} + 1\right]!}
$$

$$
= \frac{(n_1 - 1)!}{\left(\frac{R}{2} - 1\right)!\left(n_1 - \frac{R}{2}\right)!}
$$
(18.40)

The possible values of R are: 2, 3, 4, 5, 6, ..., ($n_1 + n_2$).

The Expected value of $R = E(R)$ and standard deviation of $R = \sigma(R)$, have been derived and are given by:

$$
E(R) = \frac{2n_1 n_2}{n_1 + n_2} + 1
$$
(18.41)

$$
\sigma(R) = \sqrt{\frac{2n_1 n_2 (2n_1 n_2 - n_1 - n_2)}{(n_1 + n_2)^2 (n_1 + n_2 - 1)}}
$$
(18.42)

To test the H_0 given by (18.37), at some α value we need to find an integer R_0 such that:

$$
\sum_{R=2}^{R_0} P(R) = \alpha, \text{ as closely as possible.}
$$
(18.43)

H_0 will be rejected if R, the observed number of runs, is equal to or less than R_0; $i.e.$, reject H_0 if $R \leq R_0$. Because of this, the rejection region is the lower one-sided region because H_0 should be rejected when the number of runs is small.

When $n_1 \geq 10$ and $n_2 \geq 10$, R is approximately normally distributed with $E(R)$ and $\sigma(R)$ given by (18.41) and (18.42) respectively. Therefore, when the samples are large, the Wald-Wolfowitz test can be performed using the test statistic Z^* in the usual manner, where:

$$
Z^* = \frac{R - E(R)}{\sigma(R)}
$$
(18.44)

Note: A problem arises in the application of this test when ties occur among observations that belong to different groups, because ties, and the way they are treated, affect the number of runs. The suggested way to treat ties is to order them in such a way as to help accepting H_0. But, if there are too many ties, the validity of the test is questionable.

Example 14

Suppose we have the 2 samples:

$$X = \text{sample 1: 18, 25, 30, 35, 38, 40, 45, 52, 60, 68, 74, 80} \quad (n_1 = 12)$$
and $$Y = \text{sample 2: 11, 16, 22, 23, 27, 39, 42, 44, 55, 65} \quad (n_2 = 10)$$

and wish to test to see if these observations come from populations with identical distributions (Note: the X and Y observations have been ranked purposely, to make the costruction of the combined ordered sequence of X and Y easier).

Combining these observations into a single array and representing an observation from sample 1 by X and an observation from sample 2 by Y, we obtain:

Y	Y	X	Y	Y	X	Y	X	X	X	Y	X	Y	Y	X	X	Y	X	Y	X	X	X
11	16	18	22	23	25	27	30	35	38	39	40	42	44	45	52	55	60	65	68	74	80

The observed number of runs, $R = 14$, and with $n_1 = 12$ and $n_2 = 10$, we obtain

$$E(R) = \frac{2(12)(10)}{12 + 10} + 1 = \frac{2(120)}{22} + 1 = \frac{120}{11} + 1 = 10.9 + 1 = 11.9$$

$$\sigma(R) = \sqrt{\frac{2(12)(10)[2(12)(10) - 12 - 10]}{(12 + 10)^2(12 + 10 - 1)}}$$

$$= \sqrt{\frac{240(240 - 22)}{(22)^2(21)}} = \sqrt{5.1476} = 2.269$$

Then, since $n_1 = 12 \geq 10$ and $n_2 = 10 \geq 10$, R is approximately normal, with

$$Z^* = \frac{R - E(R)}{\sigma(R)} = \frac{14 - 11.9}{2.269} = \frac{2.1}{2.269} = 0.926$$

If $\alpha = 0.05$, $Z_{\text{critical}} = -1.65$ (the rejection region is in the lower tail) and since $Z^* > Z_{\text{critical}}$, H_0 is not rejected and we conclude that the X and Y observations come from identical distributions. We can also state the rejection of H_0 directly in terms of R, by:

$$\text{Reject } H_0 \text{ if } \frac{R - E(R)}{\sigma(R)} \leq -Z_\alpha \qquad (18.45)$$

or $\quad R \leq E(R) - Z_\alpha\sigma(R)$, or $R \leq 11.9 - 1.65(2.269)$,

or, if $\quad R \leq 11.9 - 3.74$ or if $R \leq 8.16$

Since the observed R is 14, H_0 is not rejected.

■ ■ ■

18.5.2 The Mann-Whitney U test

This test is similar to the Wald-Wolfowitz test and is a nonparametric equivalent of the 2 sample t-test discussed in chapter 11.

But it is also different from the Wald-Wolfowitz test in the following 3 points:

1. A rank is assigned to the ordered sequence of the $n_1 + n_2$ observations coming from the X and Y observations.
2. The alternative hypothesis may be either two-sided or one-sided, and
3. The alternative hypothesis implies a difference only in the central tendency of one distribution relative to the other and does not suggest a difference in dispersion or skewness or kurtosis, as is the case with the Wald-Wolfowitz test.

Therefore, the Mann-Whitney U test should be used if we wish to compare only the central tendencies of 2 distributions, and the Wald-Wolfowitz test if broader comparisons are to be made.

The 2-tailed hypotheses being tested here are as follows:

H_0: The 2 populations are identical vs H_1: The 2 populations are not identical

To implement the Mann-Whitney U test we begin by combining the n_1 obsrevations from population 1 (X_i sample values) and n_2 obsrevations from population 2 (Y_i sample values) to form a single set, consisting of $n_1 + n_2$ observations. These observations are arranged in order of magnitude, from smallest to highest. Then a rank is assigned to each observation, starting with 1 and ending with $n_1 + n_2$. If ties occur in the ordered sequence, the average of the ranks is assigned to the tied observations. For example if the values for the 4th, 5th, and 6th observations are the same, then each of these observations is assigned the rank of $5 = \left(\dfrac{4 + 5 + 6}{3} \right)$.

The sum of the ranks of values from population 1 is computed and designated as R_1, and the sum of the ranks of values from population 2 is computed and designated as R_2. The Mann-Whitney U test determines if an observed arrangement of ranks can lead us to the conclusion that the 2 sets of observations (X and Y) come from populations which have the same central tendency (do no reject H_0) or different central tendency (reject H_0).

The Mann-Whitney U test is implemented differently for small and large samples. If $n_1 \leq 10$ and $n_2 \leq 10$, the samples are considered small. However when both $n_1 > 10$ and $n_2 > 10$, the samples are considered large, and the U variable is approximately normally distributed, and the normal distribution can be used to test the validity of the H_0 hypothesis.

■ Small Sample Case

The next step in the procedure, when the samples are small and R_1 and R_2 have been calculated as explained above, is to calculate:

$$U_1 = n_1 n_2 + \frac{n_1(n_1 + 1)}{2} - R_1 \qquad (18.46)$$

and

$$U_2 = n_1 n_2 + \frac{n_2(n_2 + 1)}{2} - R_2 \qquad (18.47)$$

and then let $U = $ minimum (U_1, U_2). $\qquad (18.48)$

The exact distribution of U has been derived and is tabulated (see attached table 18.6). This table contains p-values for U. To determine the p-value from the table, for a calculated U value, we let $n_1 = $ min(sample size 1, sample size 2) and $n_2 = $ max(sample size 1, sample size 2), locate the calculated U value under the U_0 column of the Table, and at the intersection of $U = U_0$ and n_1, for the specified n_2 value, read of the p-value for a *one-tailed test*. For a *2-tailed test the value shown in the table should be doubled.*

If the p-value is less than the selected α value, H_0 is rejected.

Example 15

A large corporation is conducting a study to determine if male and female employees of similar backgrounds receive equivalent compensation. A random sample of 8 female and 9 male employees were selected and their annual salaries were recorded as:

Females	32,500	29,800	30,600	34,700	33,200	29,200	28,700	30,900	
Males	31,900	31,600	32,400	34,000	34,100	33,400	31,200	33,900	30,500

Is there reason to believe that these random samples come from populations with different distributions, at $\alpha = 0.05$?

Combining the 2 sample sets to form a single set of $8 + 9 = 17$ ordered salaries, the ranks assigned to them are.

F	F	F	M	F	F	M	M	M	M	F	F	M	M	M	M	F
28.7	29.2	29.8	30.5	30.6	30.9	31.2	31.6	31.9	32.4	32.5	33.2	33.4	33.9	34.0	34.1	34.7
1	2	3	4	5	6	7	8	9	10	11	12	13	14	15	16	17

Then

$$R_1 = 1 + 2 + 3 + 5 + 6 + 11 + 12 + 17 = 57$$
$$R_2 = 4 + 7 + 8 + 9 + 10 + 13 + 14 + 15 + 16 = 96 \text{, and}$$
$$U_1 = n_1 n_2 + \frac{n_1(n_1 + 1)}{2} - R_1 = 8(9) + \frac{8(9)}{2} - 57 = 72 + 36 - 57 = 51$$

$$U_2 = n_1 n_2 + \frac{n_1(n_2 + 1)}{2} - R_2 = 8(9) + \frac{9(10)}{2} - 96 = 72 + 45 - 96 = 21$$

Therefore, $U = \min(U_1, U_2) = \min(51, 21) = 21 = U_2$.

Then, from Table 18.6, with $n_2 = 9$ and $U = 21$ and $n_1 = 8$, we obtain the p-value of 0.0836 which, for a 2-tailed test becomes $2(0.0836) = 0.1672$. Because $p = 0.1672 > \alpha = 0.05$, H_0 is not rejected and we conclude that the two random samples come from populations with identical distributions (or, to be more exact, with identical central tendencies).

■ ■ ■

■ Large Sample Case

When $n_1 > 10$ and $n_2 > 10$, the statistic U is approximately normally distributed with:

$$E(U) = \frac{n_1 n_2}{2} \tag{18.49}$$

and

$$\sigma(U) = \sqrt{\frac{n_1 n_2 (n_1 + n_2 + 1)}{12}} \tag{18.50}$$

Therefore, when the 2 samples are large, the Mann-Whitney U test can be performed using the Z^* test statistic in the usual manner, where

$$Z^* = \frac{U - E(U)}{\sigma(U)}, \tag{18.51}$$

where $U = \text{minimum}(U_1, U_2)$ is defined by (18.48), and the rejection region for a double-tailed test is: $\geq Z_{\alpha/2}$, and $\leq -Z_{\alpha/2}$, for a given α value.

Example 16

Two random samples were obtained from 2 populations to determine whether the values of population 1 are the same as the values of population 2, at $\alpha = 0.05$ (Note the values within each sample have been ranked, to make the combining of the two samples easier).

Sample 1	Sample 2	Ranks of Combined Observations			
216	203	203	s2, 1	231	s1, 16
217	208	208	s2, 2	232	s2, 17
222	209	209	s2, 3	236	s2, 18
224	211	211	s2, 4	240	s1, 19
231	214	214	s2, 5	241	s1, 20
240	218	216	s1, 6	248	s1, 21
241	219	217	s1, 7	255	s1, 22
248	223	218	s2, 8	256	s1, 23
255	227	219	s2, 9	283	s1, 24
256	229	222	s1, 10		
283	230	223	s2, 11		
	232	224	s1, 12		
	236	227	s2, 13		
$n_1 = 11$	$n_2 = 13$	229	s2, 14		
		230	s2, 15		

where, for example, s1, 6 = sample 1, rank 6 and s2, 1 = sample 2, rank 1

Then, R_1 = Sum of Ranks in Sample 1
$$= 6 + 7 + 10 + 12 + 16 + 19 + 20 + 21 + 22 + 23 + 24 = 180$$
and R_2 = Sum of Ranks in Sample 2
$$= 1 + 2 + 3 + 4 + 5 + 8 + 9 + 11 + 13 + 14 + 15 + 17 + 18 = 120$$

Then
$$U_1 = n_1 n_2 + \frac{n_1(n_1 + 1)}{2} - R_1 = (11)(13) + \frac{11(12)}{2} - 180$$
$$= 143 + 66 - 180 = 29$$
$$U_2 = n_1 n_2 + \frac{n_2(n_2 + 1)}{2} - R_2 = (11)(13) + \frac{13(14)}{2} - 120$$
$$= 143 + 91 - 120 = 114$$

and $U = \min(U_1, U_2) = \min(29, 114) = 29$. Also

$$E(U) = \frac{n_1 n_2}{2} = \frac{(11)(13)}{2} = \frac{143}{2} = 71.5,$$

and $\sigma(U) = \sqrt{\dfrac{n_1 n_2 (n_1 + n_2 + 1)}{12}} = \sqrt{\dfrac{143(11 + 13 + 1)}{12}} \sqrt{\dfrac{143(25)}{12}}$

$$= \sqrt{\frac{3575}{12}} = \sqrt{297.9166} = 17.26$$

Then $Z^* \dfrac{U - E(U)}{\sigma(U)} = \dfrac{29 - 71.5}{17.26} = \dfrac{-42.4}{17.26} = -2.46$. Since for $\alpha = 0.05$ the rejection regions are (for a 2-tailed test): $Z_{c1} = -1.96$ and $Z_{c2} = +1.96$ and $Z^* < Z_{c1}$, H_0 is rejected, and we conclude that the values of the samples are different.

Table 18.6 *p*-values for Mann-Whitney U Statistic Small Samples ($n_1 \leq n_2$)

$n_2 = 3$	U_0	n_1 1	2	3		
	0	0.2500	0.1000	0.0500		
	1	0.5000	0.2000	0.1000		
	2		0.4000	0.2000		
	3		0.6000	0.3500		
	4			0.5000		
$n_2 = 4$	U_0	n_1 1	2	3	4	
	0	0.2000	0.0667	0.0286	0.0143	
	1	0.4000	0.1333	0.0571	0.0286	
	2	0.6000	0.2667	0.1143	0.0571	
	3		0.4000	0.2000	0.1000	
	4		0.6000	0.3143	0.1714	
	5			0.4286	0.2429	
	6			0.5714	0.3429	
	7				0.4429	
	8				0.5571	
$n_2 = 5$	U_0	n_1 1	2	3	4	5
	0	0.1667	0.0476	0.0179	0.0079	0.0040
	1	0.3333	0.0952	0.0357	0.0159	0.0079
	2	0.5000	0.1905	0.0714	0.0317	0.0159
	3		0.2857	0.1250	0.0556	0.0278
	4		0.4286	0.1964	0.0952	0.0476
	5		0.5714	0.2857	0.1429	0.0754
	6			0.3929	0.2063	0.1111
	7			0.5000	0.2778	0.1548
	8				0.3651	0.2103
	9				0.4524	0.2738
	10				0.5476	0.3452
	11					0.4206
	12					0.5000

$n_2 = 6$	U_0	n_1 1	2	3	4	5	6
	0	.1429	.0357	.0119	.0048	.0022	.0011
	1	.2857	.0714	.0238	.0095	.0043	.0022
	2	.4286	.1429	.0476	.0190	.0087	.0043
	3	.5714	.2143	.0833	.0333	.0152	.0076
	4		.3214	.1310	.0571	.0260	.0130
	5		.4286	.1905	.0857	.0411	.0206
	6		.5714	.2738	.1286	.0628	.0325
	7			.3571	.1762	.0887	.0465
	8			.4524	.2381	.1234	.0660
	9			.5476	.3048	.1645	.0898
	10				.3810	.2143	.1201
	11				.4571	.2684	.1548
	12				.5429	.3312	.1970
	13					.3961	.2424
	14					.4654	.2944
	15					.5346	.3496
	16						.4091
	17						.4686
	18						.5314

$n_2 = 7$	U_0	n_1 1	2	3	4	5	6	7
	0	.1250	.0278	.0083	.0030	.0013	.0006	.0003
	1	.2500	.0556	.0167	.0061	.0025	.0012	.0006
	2	.3750	.1111	.0333	.0121	.0051	.0023	.0012
	3	.5000	.1667	.0583	.0212	.0088	.0041	.0020
	4		.2500	.0917	.0364	.0152	.0070	.0035
	5		.3333	.1333	.0545	.0240	.0111	.0055
	6		.4444	.1917	.0818	.0366	.0175	.0087
	7		.5556	.2583	.1152	.0530	.0256	.0131
	8			.3333	.1576	.0745	.0367	.0189
	9			.4167	.2061	.1010	.0507	.0265
	10			.5000	.2636	.1338	.0688	.0364
	11				.3242	.1717	.0903	.0487
	12				.3939	.2159	.1171	.0641
	13				.4636	.2652	.1474	.0825
	14				.5364	.3194	.1830	.1043
	15					.3775	.2226	.1297
	16					.4381	.2669	.1588
	17					.5000	.3141	.1914
	18						.3654	.2279
	19						.4178	.2675
	20						.4726	.3100
	21						.5274	.3552
	22							.4024
	23							.4508
	24							.5000

$n_2 = 8$	U_0	1	2	3	n_1 4	5	6	7	8
	0	0.1111	0.0222	0.0061	0.0020	0.0008	0.0003	0.0002	0.0001
	1	0.2222	0.0444	0.0121	0.0040	0.0016	0.0007	0.0003	0.0002
	2	0.3333	0.0889	0.0242	0.0081	0.0031	0.0013	0.0006	0.0003
	3	0.4444	0.1333	0.0424	0.0141	0.0054	0.0023	0.0011	0.0005
	4	0.5556	0.2000	0.0667	0.0242	0.0093	0.0040	0.0019	0.0009
	5		0.2667	0.0970	0.0364	0.0148	0.0063	0.0030	0.0015
	6		0.3556	0.1394	0.0545	0.0225	0.0100	0.0047	0.0023
	7		0.4444	0.1879	0.0768	0.0326	0.0147	0.0070	0.0035
	8		0.5556	0.2485	0.1071	0.0466	0.0213	0.0103	0.0052
	9			0.3152	0.1414	0.0637	0.0296	0.0145	0.0074
	10			0.3879	0.1838	0.0855	0.0406	0.0200	0.0103
	11			0.4606	0.2303	0.1111	0.0539	0.027	0.0141
	12			0.5394	0.2848	0.1422	0.0709	0.0361	0.0190
	13				0.3414	0.1772	0.0906	0.0469	0.0249
	14				0.4040	0.2176	0.1142	0.0603	0.0325
	15				0.4667	0.2618	0.1412	0.076	0.0415
	16				0.5333	0.3108	0.1725	0.0946	0.0524
	17					0.3621	0.2068	0.1159	0.0652
	18					0.4165	0.2454	0.1405	0.0803
	19					0.4716	0.2864	0.1678	0.0974
	20					0.5284	0.3310	0.1984	0.1172
	21						0.3773	0.2317	0.1393
	22						0.4259	0.2679	0.1641
	23						0.4749	0.3063	0.1911
	24						0.5251	0.3472	0.2209
	25							0.3894	0.2527
	26							0.4333	0.2869
	27							0.4775	0.3227
	28							0.5225	0.3605
	29								0.3992
	30								0.4392
	31								0.4796
	32								0.5204

$n_2 = 9$	U_0	1	2	3	4	5	6	7	8	9
					n_1					
	0	0.1000	0.0182	0.0045	0.0014	0.0005	0.0002	0.0001	0.0000	0.0000
	1	0.2000	0.0364	0.0091	0.0028	0.0010	0.0004	0.0002	0.0001	0.0000
	2	0.3000	0.0727	0.0182	0.0056	0.0020	0.0008	0.0003	0.0002	0.0001
	3	0.4000	0.1091	0.0318	0.0098	0.0035	0.0014	0.0006	0.0003	0.0001
	4	0.5000	0.1636	0.0500	0.0168	0.0060	0.0024	0.0010	0.0005	0.0002
	5		0.2182	0.0727	0.0252	0.0095	0.0038	0.0017	0.0080	0.0004
	6		0.2909	0.1045	0.0378	0.0145	0.0060	0.0026	0.0012	0.0006
	7		0.3636	0.1409	0.0531	0.0210	0.0088	0.0039	0.0019	0.0009
	8		0.4545	0.1864	0.0741	0.0300	0.0128	0.0058	0.0028	0.0014
	9		0.5455	0.2409	0.0993	0.0415	0.0180	0.0082	0.0039	0.0020
	10			0.3000	0.1301	0.0559	0.0248	0.0115	0.0056	0.0028
	11			0.3636	0.1650	0.0734	0.0332	0.0156	0.0076	0.0039
	12			0.4318	0.2070	0.0949	0.0440	0.0209	0.0103	0.0053
	13			0.5000	0.2517	0.1199	0.0567	0.0274	0.0137	0.0071
	14				0.3021	0.1489	0.0723	0.0356	0.0180	0.0094
	15				0.3552	0.1818	0.0905	0.0454	0.0232	0.0122
	16				0.4126	0.2188	0.1119	0.0571	0.0296	0.0157
	17				0.4699	0.2592	0.1361	0.0708	0.0372	0.0200
	18				0.5301	0.3032	0.1638	0.0869	0.0464	0.0252
	19					0.3497	0.1942	0.1052	0.0570	0.0313
	20					0.3986	0.2280	0.1261	0.0694	0.0385
	21					0.4491	0.2643	0.1496	0.0836	0.0470
	22					0.5000	0.3035	0.1755	0.0998	0.0567
	23						0.3445	0.2039	0.1179	0.0680
	24						0.3878	0.2349	0.1383	0.0807
	25						0.4320	0.2680	0.1606	0.0951
	26						0.4773	0.3032	0.1852	0.1112
	27						0.5227	0.3403	0.2117	0.1290
	28							0.3788	0.2404	0.1487
	29							0.4185	0.2707	0.1707
	30							0.4591	0.3029	0.1933
	31							0.5000	0.3365	0.2181
	32								0.3715	0.2447
	33								0.4074	0.2729
	34								0.4442	0.3024
	35								0.4813	0.3332
	36								0.5187	0.3652
	37									0.3981
	38									0.4317
	39									0.4657
	40									0.5000

$n_2=10$	U_0				n_1						
		1	2	3	4	5	6	7	8	9	10
	0	0.0909	0.0152	0.0035	0.0010	0.0003	0.0001	0.0001	0.0000	0.0000	0.0000
	1	0.1818	0.0303	0.0070	0.0020	0.0007	0.0002	0.0001	0.0000	0.0000	0.0000
	2	0.2727	0.0606	0.0140	0.0040	0.0013	0.0005	0.0002	0.0001	0.0000	0.0000
	3	0.3636	0.0909	0.0245	0.0070	0.0023	0.0009	0.0004	0.0002	0.0001	0.0000
	4	0.4545	0.1364	0.0385	0.0120	0.0040	0.0015	0.0006	0.0003	0.0001	0.0001
	5	0.5455	0.1818	0.0559	0.0180	0.0063	0.0024	0.0010	0.0004	0.0008	0.0001
	6		0.2424	0.0804	0.0270	0.0097	0.0037	0.0015	0.0007	0.0003	0.0002
	7		0.3030	0.1084	0.0380	0.0140	0.0055	0.0023	0.0010	0.0005	0.0002
	8		0.3788	0.1434	0.0529	0.0200	0.0080	0.0034	0.0015	0.0007	0.0004
	9		0.4545	0.1853	0.0709	0.0276	0.0112	0.0048	0.0022	0.0011	0.0005
	10		0.5455	0.2343	0.0939	0.0376	0.0156	0.0068	0.0031	0.0015	0.0008
	11			0.2867	0.1199	0.0496	0.0210	0.0093	0.0043	0.0021	0.0010
	12			0.3462	0.1518	0.0646	0.0280	0.0125	0.0058	0.0028	0.0014
	13			0.4056	0.1868	0.0823	0.0363	0.0165	0.0078	0.0038	0.0019
	14			0.4685	0.2268	0.1032	0.0467	0.0215	0.0103	0.0051	0.0026
	15			0.5315	0.2697	0.1272	0.0589	0.0277	0.0133	0.0066	0.0034
	16				0.3177	0.1548	0.0736	0.0351	0.0171	0.0086	0.0045
	17				0.3666	0.1855	0.0903	0.0439	0.0217	0.0110	0.0057
	18				0.4196	0.2198	0.1099	0.0544	0.0273	0.0140	0.0073
	19				0.4725	0.2567	0.1317	0.0665	0.0338	0.0175	0.0093
	20				0.5275	0.2970	0.1566	0.0806	0.0416	0.0217	0.0116
	21					0.3393	0.1838	0.0966	0.0506	0.0267	0.0144
	22					0.3839	0.2139	0.1148	0.0610	0.0326	0.0177
	23					0.4296	0.2461	0.1349	0.0729	0.0394	0.0216
	24					0.4765	0.2811	0.1574	0.0864	0.0474	0.0262
	25					0.5235	0.3177	0.1819	0.1015	0.0564	0.0315
	26						0.3564	0.2087	0.1185	0.0667	0.0376
	27						0.3962	0.2374	0.1371	0.0782	0.0446
	28						0.4374	0.2681	0.1577	0.0912	0.0526
	29						0.4789	0.3004	0.1800	0.1055	0.0615
	30						0.5211	0.3345	0.2041	0.1214	0.0716
	31							0.3698	0.2299	0.1388	0.0827
	32							0.4063	0.2574	0.1577	0.0952
	33							0.4434	0.2863	0.1781	0.1088
	34							0.4811	0.3167	0.2001	0.1237
	35							0.5189	0.3482	0.2235	0.1399
	36								0.3809	0.2483	0.1575
	37								0.4143	0.2745	0.1763
	38								0.4484	0.3019	0.1965
	39								0.4827	0.3304	0.2179
	40								0.5173	0.3598	0.2406
	41									0.3901	0.2644
	42									0.4211	0.2894
	43									0.4524	0.3153
	44									0.4841	0.3421
	45									0.5159	0.3697
	46										0.3980
	47										0.4267
	48										0.4559
	49										0.4853
	50										0.5147

18.5.3 The Kruskal-Wallis H test for Comparing $k(k > 2)$ Independent Samples

The Kruskal-Wallis test is the nonparametric equivalent to the one-way analysis of variance (ANOVA) discussed in Chapter 12, where we were interested in testing the null hypothesis

$$H_0: \ \mu_1 = \mu_2 = \mu_3 = \cdots = \mu_k$$

$$\text{vs} \tag{18.52}$$

$$H_1: \ \mu_1 \neq \mu_2 \neq \mu_3 \neq \cdots \neq \mu_k$$

based on k mutually independent random samples, drawn from k populations which were assumed to be normally distributed. The Kruskal-Wallis test can be used to analyze k ordinal data sets and does not depend on any assumption about the shape of the populations from which the data was drawn from. But it does depend on the assumption that the k groups (or data sets) are independent and that the individual items of each group are obtained randomly.

The Kruskal-Wallis procedure tests the following H_0 / H_1 hypotheses:

$$H_0: \text{the } k \text{ populations are identical}$$

$$\text{vs} \tag{18.53}$$

$$H_1: \text{At least one of the } k \text{ populations is different}$$

However, the Kruskal-Wallis test is particularly sensitive to differences in central tendency and, as such, it is regarded as an extension of the Mann-Whitney U test, which compares the "identicality" of 2 populations while the Kruskal-Wallis H test is capable of comparing the "identicality" of k populations, where $k > 2$.

We let n_1 be the sample size from population 1, n_2 the sample size of population $2, \ldots, n_1$ the sample size of population i, and n_k the sample size of population k, with:

$$N = n_1 + n_2 + \cdots + n_i + \cdots + n_k = \sum_{i=1}^{k} n_i \tag{18.54}$$

where N is the total number of all observations from the k populations. The procedure for computing a Kruskal-Wallis H statistic begins by combining all observations in the k samples to form a single set of N observations, which are then ranked in order of increasing magnitude. The smallest value is given the rank of 1, and the highest the rank of N. When ties occur in ranking, we assign the average of the adjoining ranks to each of the tied observations. For example if 2 observations are tied and their ranks should be 9 and 10, we assign to both of these observations the rank of $(9 + 10)/2 = 9.5$. Similarly, if 3 observations are tied and their ranks should be 12, 13, and 14, we assign to all 3 observations the rank of $\dfrac{12 + 13 + 14}{3} = 13$.

Under the assumption that the k samples come from populations with identical distributions, the Kruskal-Wallis H statistic is defined by:

$$H = \frac{12}{N(N + 1)} \left[\sum_{i=1}^{k} \frac{T_i^2}{n_i} \right] - 3(N + 1) \tag{18.55}$$

where $\quad$ k = number of populations being compared
$\quad$ N = total number of observations from the k populations
$\quad$ T_i = total (sum) of ranks in population (group) i
$\quad$ n_i = number of observations in population i
$\quad$ H = Kruskal-Wallis Test statistic

The H, defined by (18.55), is approximated by a chi-square distribution with DOF = Degrees of Freedom = $k - 1$ as long as $n_i \geq 5$ for all populations.

In testing the validity of (18.53), for a specified value of α, the rejection region is the upper tail of the chi-square distribution and H_0 will be rejected if $H > \chi^2_{k-1}(\alpha)$.

If the number of tied observations is large (in the combined single set of N observations), an adjusted value of H, defined by (18.55) should be calculated and used. If we let H_{adj} represent the adjusted H value, we define H_{adj} by:

$$H_{adj} = \frac{H}{M} \tag{18.56}$$

where

$$M = 1 - \frac{\sum_{j=1}^{c} t_j^3 - t_j}{N^3 - N} \tag{18.57}$$

where $\quad$ c = number of tied sets
$\quad$ t_j = number of tied observations in set j
$\quad$ N = total number of observations from the k populations
$\quad$ M = correction factor

As can be seen from (18.57) and (18.56) the effect of the correction factor M is to always increase the value of H defined in (18.55) because M is always less than 1. But this effect is usually small, even if there is a large number of ties, as the following situation illustrates:

Suppose in a given problem there are 4 sets of 2 tied observations, 2 sets of 3 tied observation, and one set of 4 tied observations, and $N = 40$.

Then, from (18.57) $\qquad$ $M = 1 - \left[\dfrac{4(2^3 - 2) + 2(3^3 - 3) + 1(4^3 - 4)}{40^3 - 40} \right]$

$$= 1 - \frac{132}{63,960} = 1 - 0.002 = 0.998,$$

and $\qquad$ $H_{adj} = \dfrac{H}{M} = \dfrac{H}{0.998} \approx 1.002H$

The H test compares well with the F test in the Analysis of Variance. However, if the samples are large, the ranking of the samples is a tedious job, unless a computer is used to sort the data.

Example 17

To determine whether a student's undergraduate field of study has an effect on the students performance in law school, a random sample of 30 students is selected from the graduating class of a certain law school. The law school class ranking and the undergraduate field of study are shown for each student in the table below. Also shown in parenthesis are the rankings of these observations for the entire sample of 30 students. At $\alpha = 0.05$, use the Kruskal-Wallis H test to determine whether the undergraduate field of study has an effect on law school performance.

Business	Science	Liberal Arts	Other
9 (5)	3 (2)	2 (1)	14 (7)
22 (10)	7 (4)	4 (3)	34 (16)
24 (12)	10 (6)	15 (8)	48 (21)
31 (15)	18 (9)	26 (14)	52 (23)
47 (20)	23 (11)	38 (17)	59 (25)
65 (28)	25 (13)	43 (18)	63 (26)
		45 (19)	67 (27)
		49 (22)	72 (29)
		55 (24)	79 (30)
$n_1 = 6$	$n_2 = 6$	$n_3 = 9$	$n_4 = 9$
$T_1 = 90$	$T_2 = 45$	$T_3 = 126$	$T_4 = 204$

For this data set $N = n_1 + n_2 + n_3 + n_4 = 6 + 6 + 9 + 9 = 30$, and

$$S = \text{sum of the ranks} = T_1 + T_2 + T_3 + T_4 = \frac{N(N+1)}{2} = \frac{30(31)}{2} = \frac{930}{2} = 465,$$

$$\text{and } H = \frac{12}{30(31)}\left[\frac{90^2}{6} + \frac{45^2}{6} + \frac{126^2}{9} + \frac{204^2}{9}\right] - 3(31)$$

$$= \frac{12}{930}[1350 + 337.5 + 1764 + 4624] - 93 = \frac{12}{930}[8075.5] - 93 = 11.2$$

Since there are no tied observations, there is no need to calculate H_{adj}, and $H = 11.2$ should be compared to $\chi^2_{k-1}(\alpha) = \chi^2_3(0.05) = 7.815$.

Since $H = 11.2 > \chi^2_3(0.05) = 7.815$ H_0 is rejected and we conclude that the result is significant, and the population distributions are not all identical.

■ ■ ■

18.6 Spearman Rank Correlation Coefficient

In Chapter 13 we discussed the sample correlation coefficient r as a technique to measure the amount of association between two variables X and Y when the values of X and Y are given by cardinal numbers, and r was defined by:

$$r = \frac{n\sum_{i=1}^{n} X_i Y_i - \left(\sum_{i=1}^{n} X_i\right)\left(\sum_{i=1}^{n} Y_i\right)}{\left[n\sum_{i=1}^{n} X_i^2 - \left(\sum_{i=1}^{n} X_i\right)^2\right]^{1/2}\left[n\sum_{i=1}^{n} Y_i^2 - \left(\sum_{i=1}^{n} Y_i\right)^2\right]^{1/2}} \tag{18.58}$$

where $-1 \leq r \leq 1$.

Also briefly discussed in Chapter 13 was the rank correlation coefficient r_s, developed by C. Spearman in 1904, which is used to determine the amount of association between two variables X and Y when their values are ordinal rank numbers, with 1 for first, 2 for second, ..., and n for the last.

If we let X_i = rank of individual i on variable X

$\qquad\qquad Y_i$ = rank of individual i on variable Y

and $\qquad\qquad d_i = X_i - Y_i,$ (18.59)

then r_s was defined as:

$$r_s = 1 - \frac{6 \sum_{i=1}^{n} d_i^2}{n(n^2 - 1)}$$ (18.60)

where $-1 \leq r_s \leq 1$.

In that brief discussion we also identified the sampling distribution of r_s as t_{n-2} and used several small examples to test hypotheses about ρ_s, the population parameter for which r_s can be considered as its estimator.

Here we wish to add a few more comments to emphasize that r_s is a nonparametric measure of linear association between the ranks of X and Y while r is a parametric measure because X and Y were assumed to be bivariate normally distributed random variables.

The interpretation of r_s values is similar to the interpretation of r values. If r_s is near $+1$, high positive correlation exists between the variables and indicates that high values of one variable are associated with high values of the other variable. If r_s is near -1, high negative correlation exists between the variables and indicates that high values of one variable are associated with low values of the other variable. If r_s is near 0 the 2 variables have little association between them. The process of calculating r_s begins by assigning ranks to the X and Y values, and then using equation (18.60) above, which is derived from (18.58) as follows, assuming that there are no ties in the ranks:

1. Since the ranks of X and Y values are arrangements of the first n integers and

$$1 + 2 + 3 + \cdots + n = \sum_{i=1}^{n} i = \frac{n(n + 1)}{2}, \text{ we can write}$$

$$\sum_{i=1}^{n} X_i = \frac{n(n + 1)}{2}$$ (18.61)

and $\qquad\qquad \sum_{i=1}^{n} Y_i = \frac{n(n + 1)}{2}$ (18.62)

2. Also, since $1^2 + 2^2 + 3^2 + \cdots + n^2 = \sum_{i=1}^{n} i^2 = \frac{n(n + 1)(2n + 1)}{6}$

we can write:

$$\sum_{i=1}^{n} X_i^2 = \frac{n(n + 1)(2n + 1)}{6}$$ (18.63)

and $\qquad\qquad \sum_{i=1}^{n} Y_i^2 = \frac{n(n + 1)(2n + 1)}{6}$ (18.64)

3. To obtain an expression for $\sum_{i=1}^{n} X_i Y_i$, we begin with the equation

$$\sum_{i=1}^{n} (X_i - Y_i)^2 = \sum_{i=1}^{n} (X_i^2 + Y_i^2 - 2X_i Y_i) = \sum_{i=1}^{n} X_i^2 + \sum_{i=1}^{n} Y_i^2 - 2 \sum_{i=1}^{n} X_i Y_i \quad (18.65)$$

from which, solving for $\sum\limits_{i=1}^{n} X_i Y_i$, we obtain:

$$\sum_{i=1}^{n} X_i Y_i = \frac{1}{2}\left[\sum_{i=1}^{n} X_i^2 + \sum_{i=1}^{n} Y_i^2 - \sum_{i=1}^{n}(X_i - Y_i)^2\right] \qquad (18.66)$$

$$= \frac{1}{2}\left[\sum_{i=1}^{n} X_i^2 + \sum_{i=1}^{n} Y_i^2\right] - \frac{1}{2}\sum_{i=1}^{n}(X_i - Y_i)^2$$

$$= \frac{n(n+1)(2n+1)}{6} - \frac{1}{2}\sum_{i=1}^{n} d_i^2 \qquad (18.67)$$

when equations (18.63), (18.64), and (18.59) are substituted into (18.66).
4. If we now substitute equations (18.61), (18.62), (18.63), (18.64), and (18.67) into (18.58) we obtain equation (18.60), after some algebraic simplifications.

Example 18

Compute a Spearman's rank correlation for the variable X and Y, and then test the hypothesis: $H_0: \rho_s = 0$ at $\alpha = 0.05$.

	1	2	3	4	5	6	7	8	9	10	11
X	23	41	37	29	25	17	33	41	40	28	19
rank of X values	3	10.5	8	6	4	1	7	10.5	9	5	2
$d_i = (X_i - Y_i)_{rank}$	1	−0.5	1	−2	−2	−2	2	1.5	−1	1	1
$d_i^2 = (X_i - Y_i)^2$	1	0.25	1	4	4	4	4	2.25	1	1	1
rank of Y values	2	11	7	8	6	3	5	9	10	4	1
Y	201	259	234	240	231	209	229	246	248	227	200

From the given X and Y values we obtain the ranks of the X and Y values, then $d_i = X_i - Y_i$ and $d_i^2 = (X_i - Y_i)^2$; therefore

$$\sum_{i=1}^{n} d_i^2 = 23.50, \text{ and } r_s = 1 - \frac{6\sum\limits_{i=1}^{n} d_i^2}{n(n^2 - 1)} = 1 - \frac{6(23.50)}{11(11^2 - 1)} = 1 - \frac{141}{11(120)}$$

$$= 1 - \frac{141}{1320} = 1 - 0.1068 = 0.893$$

From our discussion on Chapter 13 we find that if $8 \leq n \leq 20$, we need to correct r_s for continuity by using the equation:

$$\bar{r}_s = 1 - \frac{\sum\limits_{i=1}^{n} d_i^2}{\frac{1}{6}\left[n(n^2 - 1)\right] + 1} \qquad (18.68)$$

from which we obtain

$$\bar{r}_s = 1 - \frac{23.50}{\frac{1}{6}(1320) + 1} = 1 - \frac{23.50}{220 + 1} = 1 - \frac{23.50}{221}$$

$$= 1 - 0.10633 = 0.89367 \approx 0.894$$

Then, $\dfrac{\bar{r}_s \sqrt{n-2}}{\sqrt{1 - \bar{r}_s^2}}$ is distributed as t_{n-2}.

To complete the testing of the hypothesis, we let $t^* = \dfrac{\bar{r}_s \sqrt{n-2}}{\sqrt{1 - \bar{r}_s^2}}$ and compare it to $t_{n-2}(\alpha/2)$.

H_0 will be rejected if $t^* \geq t_{n-2}(\alpha/2)$.

When $\bar{r}_s = 0.894$, $t^* = \dfrac{\bar{r}_s \sqrt{n-2}}{\sqrt{1 - \bar{r}_s^2}} = \dfrac{0.894\sqrt{11-2}}{\sqrt{1 - (0.894)^2}} = \dfrac{0.894\sqrt{9}}{\sqrt{1 - 0.799236}}$

$= \dfrac{0.894(3)}{\sqrt{0.200164}} = \dfrac{2.682}{0.448} = 5.9866$

and for $\alpha = 0.05$ and $n = 11$, $t_{n-2}(\alpha/2) = t_9(0.025) = 2.262$.

Since $t^* \geq t_{n-2}(\alpha/2)$, H_0 is rejected and we conclude that $\rho_s \neq 0$.

■ ■ ■

18.7   MINITAB Solutions for Nonparametric Statistics

MINITAB can be used to exercise several of the non-parametric techniques discussed in this chapter.

The non-parametric techniques supported by MINITAB are the following:

1. 1-sample sign test
2. 1-sample Wilcoxon test
3. Mann-Whitney U test
4. Kruskal-Wallis H test
5. Mood's Median test
6. Friedman test for k paired samples
7. Runs test of Randomness
8. Pairwise Averages
9. Pairwise Differences
10. Pairwise Slopes

To implement these techniques follow the procedure:

1. Go to MINITAB.
2. Go to STAT on the menu bar.
3. Select NONPARAMETRICS.
4. Select DESIRABLE Test.
5. Follow Directions on how to run the test.

As an illustration consider the following example, exercising the "Runs Test for Randomness". Suppose 26 cola drinkers are randomly sampled to determine whether they prefer diet or regular cola. The random sample contains 8 diet cola drinkers (*D*) and 18 regular cola drinkers (*R*). If we assume that the sequence of sampled cola drinkers is given by:

$$D\,R\,R\,R\,R\,R\,D\,R\,R\,D\,R\,R\,R\,R\,D\,R\,D\,R\,R\,R\,D\,D\,D\,R\,R\,R,$$

is this sequence of cola drinkers random or non-random?

Solution We have $n(R) = 18$, $n(D) = 8$, and $N = n(R) + n(D) = 26$, and the hypotheses being tested are:

$$H_0: \text{The observations are randomly generated.}$$

vs

$$H_1: \text{The observations are not randomly generated.}$$

We enter the data into MINITAB using the code:

1. Diet cola drinkers $= D = 1$
2. Regular cola drinkers $= R = 2$

The MINITAB runs test is a two-tailed test and the reported significance of the test is equivalent to a p-value. Because the test is significant at 0.9710 (see the MINITAB output of this example below), the decision is to not Reject H_0.

The MINITAB output for this example is given by the table below, which shows how the data is entered in the sessions window and what the output is for the Runs test:`

```
MTB > set c1
DATA > 1  2  2  2  2  2  1  2  2  1  2  2  2  2  1  2  1  2  2  2
       2  1  1  1  2  2  2
DATA > end
MTB > Runs C1.
```

Runs Test: C1

```
      C1

      K = 1.6923
      The observed number of runs = 12
      The expected number of runs = 12.0769
      18 Observations above K 8 below
*N Small — The following approximation may be invalid
              The test is significant at 0.9710
              Cannot reject at alpha = 0.05
```

Similar procedures are used to exercise the other non-parametric statistical techniques supported by MINITAB, as shown below:

■ Mann-Whitney U Test

Enter the data in columns C_1 and C_2 in the Sessions Window (or worksheet 1 window). You will be asked to supply the column location of samples 1 and 2, the confidence level, and the form of the Alternative hypothesis (not equal, less than, greater than).

The output will include: sample sizes, medians, a confidence interval, W, p-value, and decision information about rejecting the null hypothesis.

Applying this procedure to problem 17, we enter the data as follows:

```
MTB  > Set C_1
DATA > 47 49 50 52 53
DATA > END
MTB  > Set C_2
DATA > 46 48 55 56 58
DATA > END
```

Then, from the Non-parametric Menu select Mann-Whitney, and supply the information asked for (*i.e.*, column location of first sample, column location of second sample, confidence level (90%, 95%, 98%, 99% $\rightarrow$ 0.90, 0.95, 0.98, 0.99)

(↑ use this)

and the form of the alternative hypothesis ($H_1 \neq$, $H_1 <$, $H_1 >$).

(↑ use this)

The MINITAB output for this example is given by the table below:

```
MTB > Mann-Whitney 95.0 c1 c2;
SUBC > Alternative 0.
```

■ Mann-Whitney Test and CI: C1, C2

```
C1              N = 5          Median = 50.000
C2              N = 5          Median = 55.000
Point estimate for ETA1-ETA2 is -3.000
96.3 Percent CI for ETA1-ETA2 is (-9.003,5.002)
W = 24.0
Test of ETA1 = ETA2 vs ETA1 not = ETA2 is significant at 0.5309

Cannot reject at alpha = 0.05
```

■ Wilcoxon Matched Pairs Signed Rank Test

Enter the 2 related samples in columns C_1 and C_2. Then generate a third column C_3 whose elements are the difference of the corresponding elements in C_1 and C_2.

From the Non-parametric menu select 1- Sample Wilcoxon. Under variables, list the column where the differences are located (C_3).

If you are testing a 0.0 median, the 1-Sample Wilcoxon will default to the zero value. To test any other value of the median, list the value under Test Median.

For hypothesis testing the three options for the Alternative Hypothesis are:

$\neq 0, <, >$.

($\uparrow$ use this)

The output includes a statement of the hypotheses, the number of differences, the Wilcoxon statistic, and the p-value.

Applying this procedure to problem 13, we enter the data as follows:

MTB > Set C_1
DATA > 79 94 76 86 65 52 78 82 85 64 85
DATA > END
MTB > Set C_2
DATA > 82 85 63 89 59 55 74 81 87 50 73
DATA > END
MTB > Set C_3
DATA > −3 9 13 −3 6 −3 4 1 −2 14 12
DATA > END

Then, from the Non-parametric menu select 1-Sample Wilcoxon and under variables, enter C_3 (The column which contain the differences) and follow the other directions as listed previously.

The MINITAB output for this example is given by the Table below, using the MTB command:

MTB > WInterval 95.0 C3.

Wilcoxon Signed Rank CI: C3

	N	Estimated Median	Achieved Confidence	Confidence Interval
C3	11	4.8	95.5	(-1.0, 9.5)

■ Kruskal-Wallis Test

Enter the observations from all treatment levels to one column (C_1) and in a second column (C_2) list the treatment levels to match the observations of column C_1.

From the Non-parametric menu, select Kruskal-Wallis and, when asked for the location of the RESPONSE variable, enter C_1, and when asked for the location of the FACTOR variable, enter C_2 (*i.e.*, the column with the treatment levels).

The output includes treatment numbers, treatment means, the average rank for a treatment, an H value, degrees of freedom, and a p-value.

Applying this procedure to problem 19, we enter the data as follows:

MTB > Set C_1
DATA > 7.7 6.8 8.5 9.0 11.0 8.9 10.1 9.5 8.7 9.2 10.5 9.8 11.4
DATA > 12.6 10.9 9.9 10.7 9.8 12.5 11.4 10.8 13.5 14.1 12.7
DATA > END
MTB > Set C_2
DATA > 1 1 1 1 1 1 1 1 2 2 2 2 2 2 2 2 2 3 3 3 3 3 3 3 3
DATA > END

From the Non-parametric menu select Kruskal-Wallis and enter C_1 for the RESPONSE variable and C_2 for the FACTOR variable.

The MINITAB output for this example is given by the Table below:

MTB > Kruskal-Wallis C1 C2.

Kruskal-Wallis Test: C1 versus C2

Kruskal-Wallis Test on C1

C2	N	Median	Ave Rank	Z
1	8	8.950	6.8	-2.82
2	8	10.200	12.5	0.00
3	8	11.950	18.3	2.82
Overall	24		12.5	

H = 10.58 DF = 2 P = 0.005
H = 10.59 DF = 2 P = 0.005 (adjusted for ties)

■ Friedman Test

Enter all of the observations in column C_1 and the treatment levels in column C_2 (as it was done in the Kruskal-Wallis test) and the BLOCKS in column C_3.

From the Non-parametric menu select FRIEDMAN and when asked, enter: C_1 for the RESPONSE variable and C_2 for the TREATMENT, and C_3 for BLOCKS. (We have the option of storing the residuals and also storing the fits by clicking on those boxes.)

The output will include an S-value, degrees of freedom, and the p-value. The output also provides information about the treatment levels (including the value of n), estimated median, and the sum of ranks. The grand median is also outputed.

Applying this procedure to problem 15, we enter the data as follows:

MTB > Set C_1
DATA > 72 89 48 65 86 56 75 39 78 98 64 82
DATA > 68 87 56 76 94 73 84 45 67 87 87 76
DATA > 80 78 64 70 93 78 65 48 69 86 92 85
DATA > 75 92 58 62 85 87 69 56 59 95 48 79
DATA > END
MTB > Set C_2
DATA > 1 1 1 1 1 1 1 1 1 1 1 1
DATA > 2 2 2 2 2 2 2 2 2 2 2 2
DATA > 3 3 3 3 3 3 3 3 3 3 3 3
DATA > 4 4 4 4 4 4 4 4 4 4 4 4
DATA > END
MTB > Set C_3
DATA > 1 2 3 4 5 6 7 8 9 10 11 12
DATA > END

From the Non-parametric menu select FRIEDMAN and enter C_1 for the RESPONSE variable and C_2 for TREATMENT, and C_3 for BLOCKS.

The MINITAB output for this example is given by the Table below:

```
* NOTE * Text found in data line.
MTB  > SET C3
DATA > 1 2 3 4 5 6 7 8 9 10 11 12
DATA > END
MTB  > SET C3
DATA > 1 2 3 4 5 6 7 8 9 10 11 12
DATA > 1 2 3 4 5 6 7 8 9 10 11 12
DATA > 1 2 3 4 5 6 7 8 9 10 11 12
DATA > 1 2 3 4 5 6 7 8 9 10 11 12
DATA > END
MTB  > Friedman C1 C2 C3.
```

Friedman Test: C1 versus C2, C3

```
Friedman test for C1 by C2 blocked by C3

S = 1.10 DF = 3 P = 0.777

                        Est        Sum of
C2          N        Median        Ranks
1          12        72.000         28.0
2          12        75.250         29.0
3          12        78.250         34.0
4          12        73.500         29.0

Grand median = 74.750
```

18.8   References

Berenson, Mark, L., and Levine, David, M., 1989. *Basic Business Statistics.* 4th Edition. Prentice-Hall.

Black, Ken, 2004. *Business Statistics.* 4th Edition. Wiley.

Canavos, George, C., 1984. *Applied Probability and Statistical Methods.* Little, Brown, and company.

Chou, Ya-Lun, 1992. *Statistical analysis for Business and Economics.* Elsevier.

Groebner, David, F., Shannon, Patrick, W., Fry, Phillip, C., and Smith, Kent, D., 2001. *Business Statistics.* 5th Edition. Prentice-Hall.

Hoel, Paul, G., and Jessen, Raymond J., 1982. *Basic Statistics for Business and Economics.* 3rd Edition. Wiley.

Johnson, Robert, 1976. *Elementary Statistics.* 2nd Edition. DUXBURY Press.

Keller, Gerald, and Warreck Brian, 2000. *Statistics for Management and Economics.* Duxbury.

Lapin, Lawrence, L., 1993. *Statistics for Modern Business Decisions.* 6th Edition. Dryden.

Levin, Richard, I., 1978. *Statistics for Management.* Prentice-Hall.

Levin, Richard, F., and Rubin, David, S., 1998. *Statistics for Management.* 7th Edition. Prentice-Hall.

McClave, James, T., Benson, P. George, and Sinchich, Terry, 2001. *Statistics for Business and Economics.* 8th Edition. Prentice Hall.

18.9 PROBLEMS

1. Suppose 26 cola drinkers are randomly sampled to determine whether they prefer diet or regular cola. The random sample contains 8 diet cola drinkers (D) and 18 regular cola drinkers (R). If we assume that the sequence of sampled cola drinkers is given by: $D R R R R R D R R D R R R R R D R D R R R D D D R R$, is this sequence of cola drinkers random or non-random at $\alpha = 0.05$?

2. A researcher is conducting a poll to find out what the "current generation" thinks their opportunity to succeed is relative to that of their parents, and interviewed 64 "current generation" adults, 40 of whom indicated that they have more opportunity to succeed (Y), and 24 said they have less opportunity to succeed (N). If the sequence of their responses is as shown below: $Y Y N Y Y N N Y Y Y N N Y N N Y Y Y Y Y N Y Y Y Y N N Y Y$ $N N N Y Y Y N N Y Y Y Y Y N Y N Y Y Y N N N N Y N N Y Y Y Y Y Y N N N Y Y Y Y$, test, at $\alpha = 0.05$, using the runs test to determine if the sequence of responses is random or not.

3. A sample of 30 observations is listed in the order in which they were observed:
80, 34, 10, 20, 40, 64, 50, 47, 44, 25, 86, 66, 49, 53, 65 77, 28, 28, 55, 74, 81, 90, 67, 53, 38, 71, 72, 73, 75, 78 If the runs-above-and below the median value is applied to this data, can we conclude that the data was randomly generated at $\alpha = 0.01$?

4. A sample of 30 observations is listed in the order in which they were observed:
80, 34, 10, 20, 40, 64, 50, 47, 44, 25, 86, 66, 49, 53, 65 77, 28, 28, 55, 74, 81, 90, 67, 53, 38, 71, 72, 73, 75, 78 If the "runs-up-and-down" test is used can we conclude that the observations in the sample are generated randomly at $\alpha = 0.01$?

5. Suppose a time series data consists of 40 observations, $y_1, y_2, y_3, \ldots, y_{40}$ and for this data set $s_y^2 = \dfrac{1}{n} \sum_{i=1}^{n} (y_i - \bar{y})^2 = 12$ and $\delta^2 = \dfrac{1}{n-1} \sum_{i=1}^{n} (y_{i+1} - y_i)^2 = 6$.

   Using the Von Neumann ratio test, do these results indicate independence among the successive terms of the data at $\alpha = 0.01$?

6. A survey of 200 families with 3 children, selected at random, gave the following results:

Female Births	0	1	2	3
Number of families	35	50	70	45

   Are these data consistent with the hypothesis that male and female births are equal likely at $\alpha = 0.05$ and $\alpha = 0.01$?

7. A firm sells four products and wishes to determine whether sales of these products are distributed uniformly among four classes of customers.

   A random sample of 1000 sales records provides the following observed data:

Customer Group	Product 1	Product 2	Product 3	Product 4	Total
Professionals	85	23	56	36	200
Businessman	153	44	128	75	400
Factory workers	128	26	101	45	300
Farmers	34	7	15	44	100
	400	100	300	200	1000

   Test the hypothesis that customer groups and product distribution are Independent at $\alpha = 0.05$.

8. A random sample of 180 Republicans and 150 Democrats produced the following results on the question of National security. On the basis of this data can we conclude that there is no difference between the 2 political parties on the question of National security at $\alpha = 0.05$ and $\alpha = 0.01$?

	IN FAVOR	OPPOSED	UNDECIDED	TOTALS
REPUBLICANS	90	65	25	180
DEMOCRATS	60	55	35	150
	150	120	60	330

9. Ten thousand (10,000) ovens were examined and 400 of them were found to be defective. If it is known that this brand of ovens is 3 percent defective, is the obtained result in agreement with the stated belief at $\alpha = 0.05$? Use both a Normal test and a χ^2 test.

10. The number of accidents of workers in a plant is observed for a 30-day period and the following information is obtained:

n_a = Number of Accidents	0	1	2	3	4	5
n_d = Number of Days	12	8	6	2	1	1

Is a Poisson distribution of $\hat{\lambda} = 1.17$ a good fit for this data set at $\alpha = 0.05$?

11. The daily demand for a product, for 30 working days, is as follows: 38, 35, 76, 58, 48, 59, 67, 63, 33 ,69, 53, 51, 28, 25, 36, 32, 61, 57, 49, 78, 48, 42, 72, 52, 47, 66, 58, 44, 44, 56

Use the Kolmogorov-Smirnoff Statistic to test the null hypothesis that this data is normally distributed with $\mu = 50$ and $\sigma = 10$ at $\alpha = 0.05$.

12. A production manager conducts an experiment to compare 2 methods of assembling a product. To do so he selects a sample of 10 pairs of workers and assigns the method of assembling the product to them randomly, and obtains the following results (the numbers indicate the average number of units assembled per hour):

Pair number	1	2	3	4	5	6	7	8	9	10
Method 1	15	24	18	17	14	25	19	18	23	27
Method 2	12	21	12	19	18	22	16	18	20	22
d_i = Method 1 − Method 2	+	+	+	−	−	+	+	0	+	+

Question: Are the 2 methods of assembly equally effective at $\alpha = 0.05$?

13. Eleven students were randomly selected from a large statistics class and their grades on two successive examinations were recorded. For the grades indicated below, use the Wilcoxon signed rank test to determine whether the 2 tests are of equal difficulty at $\alpha = 0.05$.

Students	1	2	3	4	5	6	7	8	9	10	11
Test 1	79	94	76	86	65	52	78	82	85	64	85
Test 2	82	85	63	89	59	55	74	81	87	50	73
d_i = Difference = Test 1 − Test 2	−3	9	13	−3	6	−3	4	1	−2	14	12
Rank	4	8	10	4	7	4	6	1	2	11	9
Signed Rank	−4	8	10	−4	7	−4	6	1	−2	11	9

14. In a paired experiment the speed with which items are packed per hour by 2 different systems is observed and is given below:

Pair	1	2	3	4	5	6	7	8	9	10	11	12	13	14	15	16	17	18
System 1	10	11	9	8	15	12	11	13	15	10	13	12	14	13	14	12	14	12
System 2	7	6	12	9	13	7	13	9	8	11	9	8	13	10	8	7	7	12
d_i = System 1– System 2	3	5	–3	–1	2	5	–2	4	7	–1	4	4	1	3	6	5	7	0
Signed Rank of $|d_i|$	7	13	–7	–2	4.5	13	–4.5	10	16.5	–2	10	10	2	7	15	13	16.5	X

Can we accept the hypothesis: H_0: $F(x) = G(x)$ (*i.e.*, the 2 systems pack items with the same speed) at $\alpha = 0.05$ using the Wilcoxon signed rank-test?

15. Twelve students were randomly selected from a large undergraduate class and their scores on the four examinations given to the class during the semester is shown below:

Student	Exam 1	Exam 2	Exam 3	Exam 4
1	72 (2)	68 (1)	80 (4)	75 (3)
2	89 (3)	87 (2)	78 (1)	92 (4)
3	48 (1)	56 (2)	64 (4)	58 (3)
4	65 (2)	76 (4)	70 (3)	62 (1)
5	86 (2)	94 (4)	93 (3)	85 (1)
6	56 (1)	73 (2)	78 (3)	87 (4)
7	75 (3)	84 (4)	65 (1)	69 (2)
8	39 (1)	45 (2)	48 (3)	56 (4)
9	78 (4)	67 (2)	69 (3)	59 (1)
10	98 (4)	87 (2)	86 (1)	95 (3)
11	64 (2)	87 (3)	92 (4)	48 (1)
12	82 (3)	76 (1)	85 (4)	79 (2)

Use the Friedman test to determine whether differences among the four examinations are statistically significant at $\alpha = 0.05$ and $\alpha = 0.01$.

16. On 12 randomly selected days the following number of units of the same product were sold by 2 competitors, A and B.

Days	1	2	3	4	5	6	7	8	9	10	11	12
A	42	58	47	39	41	56	61	36	38	46	43	51
B	63	57	48	59	64	52	65	60	37	66	68	49

Using the Wald-Wolfowitz test can the null hypothesis that the samples come from identical distributions be rejected at $\alpha = 0.05$.

17. The following information represents the daily number of finished units for two production workers, A and B, over a five-day period.

A	47	49	50	52	53	$n_1 = 5$
B	46	48	55	56	58	$n_2 = 5$

Use the Mann-Whitney U statistic to test the null hypothesis that these samples come from identical distributions, at $\alpha = 0.05$.

18. A marketing research firm is interested in comparing consumer acceptance of two new products, A and B. Twelve randomly selected consumers were asked to rate their acceptance of product A using a scale from 1 (strongly dislike) to 5 (strongly like). An equal number of consumers rated product B. The following results were obtained:

Product A	1	2	5	5	4	3	5	4	4	3	5	2	$n_1 = 12$
Product B	2	2	1	1	3	1	2	2	4	3	1	3	$n_2 = 12$

Use the Mann-Whitney U statistic to determine whether the null hypothesis that these random samples come from populations with identical distributions can be accepted at $\alpha = 0.05$ and $\alpha = 0.01$?

19. To determine whether the distributions of 3 makes of gasoline are identically distributed (as far as the number of miles traveled per gallon is concerned) the following data was obtained. Apply the Kruskal-Wallis H test, at $\alpha = 0.05$, and $\alpha = 0.01$, to determine whether these 3 gasolines are identically distributed.

Type I		Type II		Type III	
7.7	(2)	8.7	(4)	10.7	(14)
6.8	(1)	9.2	(7)	9.8	(9.5)
8.5	(3)	10.5	(13)	12.5	(20)
9.0	(6)	9.8	(9.5)	11.4	(18.5)
11.0	(17)	11.4	(18.5)	10.8	(15)
8.9	(5)	12.6	(21)	13.5	(23)
10.1	(12)	10.9	(16)	14.1	(24)
9.5	(8)	9.9	(11)	12.7	(22)
$T_I = 2 + 1 + 3 + 6 + 17 + 5 +$ $+ 12 + 8$ $= 54$ $n_1 = 8$		$T_{II} = 4 + 7 + 13 + 9.5 +$ $+ 18.5 + 21 + 16 + 11$ $= 100$ $n_2 = 8$		$T_{III} = 14 + 9.5 + 20 + 18.5$ $+ 15 + 23 + 24 + 22$ $= 146$ $n_3 = 8$	

20. Two judges rated the talent performance of the ten semifinalists in a recent Miss America Pageant, using the scale 1 (worst) to 10 (best). The following results were obtained:

Semifinalists	1	2	3	4	5	6	7	8	9	10
Judge 1	4	6	5	10	3	7	9	1	8	2
Judge 2	7	1	4	6	8	2	3	9	10	5

Compute the Spearman rank correlation coefficient and comment on whether a relationship is apparent.

21. A survey is conducted by a large company to determine if its workers commit some type of office theft. If 13 randomly selected employees were asked the question: "Do you think your co-workers commit some kind of theft" and 5 of them say yes (Y) and 8 say no (N), does the following sequence of their responses: N N N N Y Y Y N N N N Y Y, represent a random sample, at $\alpha = 0.05$? (Hint: Use the small sample runs test).

22. A machine produces parts that are either Good (G) or Defective (D). A quality control individual randomly selects 50 of the parts produced in a particular day and examines them one at a time, in the order in which they were made. The result is 28 good parts and 22 defective parts. The sequence of good parts (G) and defective parts (D) is shown below:

G G D D G G G G G D D D G G D D D D G G G G D D

G G D D D D G G G G D D D D D G G G G G G G G D D D

At $\alpha = 0.05$, is the sequence of good and defective parts shown above randomly produced? (*Hint*: Use the large sample runs test with $R = 14$).

23. Suppose we have a sample of 30 observations and wish to use the "runs above and below the median" method to test: H_0: the data is randomly generated against H_1: The data is not randomly generated. If there are 10 runs above and below the sample median, is H_0 rejected or not rejected at $\alpha = 0.01$

24. Suppose we have a sample of 30 observations and wish to use the "runs up and down" method to test: H_0: The data is randomly generated against H_1: The data is not randomly generated. If the number of runs of "+"s and "−"s signs is 10, is H_0: rejected or not rejected at $\alpha = 0.01$?

25. Suppose that a time series data consists of 50 observations$(y_1, y_2, \ldots, y_{50})$ and for this set of data we have obtained: $\hat{s}_y^2 = \dfrac{1}{n}\sum_{i-1}^{n}(y_i - \overline{y})^2 = 10$

    and $\delta^2 = \dfrac{1}{n-1}\sum_{i=1}^{n}(y_{i+1} - y_i)^2 = 22$.

    Using the Von Neamann ratio test, do these results indicate independence among the successive terms of the data at $\alpha = 0.05$?

26. It is believed that there are two times as many automobile accidents on Saturdays and Sundays as on any other day of the week. If 100 accidents are chosen randomly and the observed number of accidents according to the days of the week is as shown:

Monday	Tuesday	Wednesday	Thursday	Friday	Saturday	Sunday
5	9	8	10	11	27	30

   Do these results support the above stated belief at $\alpha = 0.05$? $\alpha = 0.01$?

27. A sample of 100 small machine parts was taken from products produced by 3 different operators to determine if they produce the same quality parts (where quality is determined by some specified criteria), and the following results were observed.

Observed Output			
Operator			
Quality	1	2	3	Totals
---	---	---	---	---
Good	30	27	23	80
Average	8	6	6	20
Totals	38	33	29	100

   Is the H_0 hypothesis: Quality of output is independent of operator rejected or not rejected at $\alpha = 0.05$? $\alpha = 0.01$?

28. A market research firm wishes to determine if the number of responses to a mailed questionnaire would increase if a $1 bill is enclosed. Three hundred questionnaires, 150 of them with and 150 without the dollar, were mailed out and the following number of responses/non-responses were obtained:

	Responded	Did not Respond	Totals
Dollar included	100	50	150
Dollar not included	80	70	150
Totals	180	120	300

Is the number of responses related to the inclusion of the dollar at $\alpha = 0.05$? $\alpha = 0.01$?

29. For the purpose of comparing two manufacturing processes, 100 units were selected from the output of the 2 processes and the observed results are tabulated below:

Process	Good	Defective	Total
P1	94	6	100
P2	90	10	100
Totals	184	16	200

Are the 2 processes the same at $\alpha = 0.05$ and $\alpha = 0.01$?

30. The records of 100 randomly selected accounts are examined for errors, and the following results were obtained:

Number of errors	0	1	2	3	4
Number of Accounts	32	40	25	2	1

Does this information support the claim that the errors are distributed according to the Poisson distribution with parameter $\hat{\lambda} = 1$ at $\alpha = 0.05$?

31. Consider the following data, representing the lengths of time (in minutes) for 50 customers to complete their banking transactions at a local bank:

2.3, 0.2, 2.9, 0.4, 2.8, 2.4, 4.4, 5.8, 2.8, 3.3, 3.3, 9.7, 2.5, 5.6, 9.5, 1.8, 4.7, 0.7, 6.2, 1.2, 7.8, 0.8, 0.9, 0.4, 1.3, 3.1, 3.7, 7.2, 1.6, 1.9, 2.4, 4.6, 3.8, 1.5, 2.7, 0.4, 1.3, 1.1, 5.5, 3.4, 4.2, 1.2, 0.5, 6.8, 5.2, 6.3, 7.6, 1.4, 0.5, 1.4

Use the Kolmogorov-Smirnov statistic to test the hypothesis that the data above are not exponentially distributed with $\theta = 3.2$ at $\alpha = 0.01$.

32. Fifteen pairs of plots are planted with 2 varieties of corn and the observed yields are as recorded below.

Pair	1	2	3	4	5	6	7	8	9	10	11	12	13	14	15
Variety 1	120	128	136	138	125	130	135	148	150	130	130	128	120	135	124
Variety 2	118	134	150	133	135	140	142	132	125	135	120	118	130	138	126

Does this information lead us to accept the H_0 hypothesis that the mean yields of corn varieties are equal, at $\alpha = 0.05$, when using the sign test?

33. The following data are the results of planting corn with 2 different types of fertilizer on eight pairs of plots:

Pair	1	2	3	4	5	6	7	8
A	164	165	158	149	170	155	154	162
B	150	143	152	160	151	145	148	134
$d_i = A - B$	14	22	6	−11	19	10	6	28
Signed Rank of $|d_i|$	5	7	1.5	−4	6	3	1.5	8

Can we accept H_0: The corn yields are the same for each fertilizer, at $\alpha = 0.05$, using the Wilcoxon signed rank test?

34. An analyst wants to determine whether there is a difference in the cost per mile of airfares in the United States between 1980 and 2000 for various cities. Seventeen cities were randomly selected and the corresponding costs are listed below:

City	1	2	3	4	5	6	7	8	9	10	11	12	13	14	15	16	17
1980	20.2	19.5	18.6	20.9	19.9	18.6	19.6	23.2	21.8	20.3	19.2	19.5	18.7	17.7	21.6	22.4	20.8
2000	22.8	12.7	14.1	16.1	25.2	20.2	14.9	21.3	18.7	20.9	22.6	16.9	20.6	18.5	23.4	21.3	17.4

Can we accept H_0: There is no difference in the cost per mile between 1980 and 2000 at $\alpha = 0.05$, using the Wilcoxon signed rank test?

35. A market research company wants to determine brand preference for televisions, among 3 manufacturers. As part of the study, the research company randomly selects 8 potential television buyers, shows them each of the 3 brands, and asks them to rank the televisions from 1 to 3, with the results showing below:

Individual	1	2	3	4	5	6	7	8
Brand A	3	1	3	2	3	1	3	2
Brand B	1	3	2	3	2	2	1	1
Brand C	2	2	1	1	1	3	2	3

Use the Friedman test at $\alpha = 0.05$ and $\alpha = 0.01$ to determine if there are any significant differences between the rankings of these brands.

36. Weekly family income was randomly obtained at 2 different cities and produced the following results:

City X: 75, 90, 100, 120, 130, 148, 155, 165, 170, 200

City Y: 127, 135, 145, 158, 167, 180, 195, 198, 205, 210

Using the Wald-Wolfowitz test, can the null hypothesis that the samples come from identical distributions be rejected at $\alpha = 0.05$?

37. A two year study was conducted to determine whether there is a difference in the number of colds experienced by smokers and nonsmokers. The random sample selected consisted of 14 nonsmokers and 12 smokers and the recorded data represent the number of colds observed during the two-year study period:

Nonsmokers	1	0	2	7	3	1	2	2	4	3	5	0	2	1
Smokers	4	2	6	5	8	10	8	7	6	4	9	3		

Use the Mann-Whitney U statistic to determine whether there is reason to believe that these random samples come from populations with different distributions, at $\alpha = 0.05$?

38. Use the Mann-Whitney U test and the following data to determine whether there is a significant difference between the values of group 1 and group 2, at $\alpha = 0.05$.

Group 1	15	17	26	11	18	21	13	29	$n_1 = 8$
Group 2	23	14	24	13	22	23	18	21	$n_2 = 8$

39. To test the claim that there is no significant difference in the amount of customer's initial deposits when they open savings accounts according to geographic region in the USA, an analyst selects savings and loan offices of equal size from 4 regions of

the United States, and located in areas having similar economic and population characteristic. The following data represent the dollar amounts of adult customers selected randomly:

Region 1		Region 2		Region 3		Region 4	
$ 1200	(23)	$ 22	(5)	$ 675	(15)	$ 1075	(21)
450	(12)	950	(19)	500	(13)	1050	(20)
110	(2)	100	(1)	1100	(22)	750	(17)
800	(18)	350	(9)	310	(7)	180	(3)
375	(10)	275	(6)	660	(14)	330	(8)
200	(4)					680	(16)
						425	(11)
$n_1 = 6$		$n_2 = 5$		$n_3 = 5$		$n_4 = 7$	
$T_1 = 23 + 12 + 2 + 18$		$T_2 = 5 + 19 + 1$		$T_3 = 15 + 13 + 22 + 7$		$T_4 = 21 + 20 + 17 + 3 + 8$	
$+ 10 + 4 = 69$		$+ 9 + 6 = 40$		$+ 14 = 71$		$+ 16 + 11 = 96$	

Use the Kruskal-Wallis H test to test the claim in H_0 that there is no significant difference in the initial amount of deposit because of geographic region, at $\alpha = 0.05$.

40. Compute Spearman's rank correlation for the following variables to determine the degree of association between the 2 variables, and then test H_0: $\rho_s = 0$ vs H_1: $\rho_s \neq 0$ at $\alpha = 0.05$.

X values	23 (3)	41 (10.5)	37 (8)	29 (6)	25 (4)	17 (1)	33 (7)	41 (10.5)	40 (9)	28 (5)	19 (2)
Y values	201 (2)	259 (11)	234 (7)	240 (8)	231 (6)	209 (3)	229 (5)	246 (9)	248 (10)	227 (4)	200 (1)

SOLUTION

1. We have $n(R) = 18$, $n(D) = 8$, and $N = n(R) + n(D) = 26$, and the hypotheses being tested are:

a) H_0: The observations are generated randomly.

vs

H_1: The observations are not generated randomly.

b) $\alpha = 0.05$

c) Use the small sample runs test because both $n_1 = n(R) = 18 \leq 20$ and $n_2 = n(D) = 8 \leq 20$.

d) When $n_1 = n(R) = 18$ and $n_2 = n(8) = 8$, we obtain from Table 18.2 and $\alpha = 0.025$:

Lower Tail = 7

Upper Tail = 17

e) The observed number of runs is $R = 12$, as can be verified by the given sample in the problem statement.

f) Since $7 < R = 12 < 17$, H_0 is not rejected, and we conclude that the data are randomly generated.

Using $D = 1$, and $R = 2$, the MINITAB output for this example is shown below:

```
MTB > set c1
DATA > 1 2 2 2 2 2 1 2 2 1 2 2 2 2 1 2 1 2 2 2 1 1 1 2 2 2
DATA > end
MTB > Runs C1.
```

Runs Test: *C1*

```
C1

K = 1.6923

The observed number of runs = 12
The expected number of runs = 12.0769
18 Observations above K 8 below
* N Small — The following approximation may be invalid.
              The test is significant at 0.9710.
              Cannot reject at alpha = 0.05.
```

Comparing the MINITAB solution to the hand solution of this problem, we see that the two solutions are identical ($R = 12$ in both solutions, and H_0 is not rejected).

2. We have $n(Y) = 40$ and $n(N) = 24$, and $N = n(Y) + n(N) = 64$, and the hypotheses being tested are:

a) H_0: The observations are generated randomly,

vs

H_1: The observations are not generated randomly

b) $\alpha = 0.05$

c) Because $n_1 = n(Y) = 40 \geq 20$ and $n_2 = n(N) = 24 \geq 20$, use the large sample runs test, and the test statistic is $Z^* = \dfrac{R - E(R)}{\sigma(R)}$ where $R =$ observed number of runs = 27 (from the given observations)

$$E(R) = \mu_R = \frac{2n_1 n_2}{n_1 + n_2} + 1 = \frac{2(40)(24)}{40 + 24} + 1$$

$$= \frac{2}{64}(960) + 1 = 30 + 1 = 31$$

and $\sigma_R = \sqrt{\dfrac{2n_1 n_2 (2n_1 n_2 - n_1 - n_2)}{(n_1 + n_2)^2 (n_1 + n_2 - 1)}}$

$$= \sqrt{\frac{2(40)(24)[2(40)(24) - 40 - 24]}{(64)^2 (64 - 1)}}$$

$$= \sqrt{\frac{(1920)(1856)}{(64)^2(63)}} = \sqrt{\frac{870}{63}} = \sqrt{\frac{(30)(29)}{63}} = \sqrt{13.8095} = 3.7161$$

d) For $\alpha = 0.05$, the rejection region is:

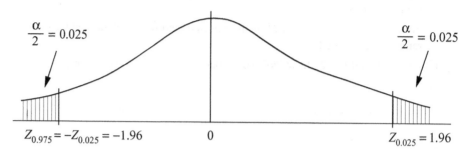

$\dfrac{\alpha}{2} = 0.025$

$\dfrac{\alpha}{2} = 0.025$

$Z_{0.975} = -Z_{0.025} = -1.96$ 0 $Z_{0.025} = 1.96$

e) Then $Z^* = \dfrac{27 - 31}{3.7161} = \dfrac{-4}{3.7161} = -1.076$

f) Since Z^* falls outside of the rejection region, we do not reject H_0

g) We conclude that the observations are generated randomly.
Using $Y = 1$, and $N = 2$, the MINITAB output for this example is shown below:

```
MTB >   set C1
DATA > 1 1 2 1 1 2 2 1 1 1 2 2 1 2 2 1 1 1 1
       1 2 1 1 1 1 2 2 1 1 2 2 2 1 1 1 1 2 2
       1 1 1 1 2 1 2 1 1 1 2 2 2 1 2 2 1 1 1
       1 1 2 2 1 1 1 1
DATA > end
MTB > Runs C1.
```

Runs Test: C1

```
C1
K = 1.3750

The observed number of runs = 27
The expected number of runs = 31.0000
24 Observations above K 40 below
     The test is significant at 0.2818
     Cannot reject at alpha = 0.05
```

Comparing the MINITAB solution to the hand solution of this problem, we see that the two solutions are identical ($R = 27$ in both solutions, and H_0 is not rejected).

3. Ranking the data, we obtain:

90, 86, 81, 80, 78, 77, 75, 74, 73, 72, 71, 67, 66, 65, 64, 55, 53, 53, 50, 49, 47, 44, 40, 38, 34, 28, 28, 25, 20,10.

Then the location of the median is $= \dfrac{n + 1}{2} = \dfrac{30 + 1}{2} = 15.5$, and the value of

the median $= \dfrac{V_{15} + V_{16}}{2} = \dfrac{64 + 55}{2} = \dfrac{119}{2} = 59.5$

Comparing the given data set against the value of the median, we obtain:

$a - bbbb - a - bbbb - aa - bb - aa - bbb - aaaa - bb - aaaaa$
The number of runs $R_1 = 11$ and $n = 30$

Then, $E(R_1) = \dfrac{n+2}{2} = \dfrac{30+2}{2} = \dfrac{32}{2} = 16$, and

$$\sigma(R_r) = \sqrt{\dfrac{n(n-2)}{4(n-1)}} = \sqrt{\dfrac{30(28)}{4(29)}} = \sqrt{\dfrac{30(7)}{29}}$$

$$= \sqrt{7.2413} = 2.69,$$

and $Z^* = \dfrac{R_1 - E(R_1)}{\sigma(R_1)} = \dfrac{11-16}{2.69} = \dfrac{-5}{2.69} = -1.859$

Since we are testing: H_0: the data is randomly generated vs H_1: the data is not randomly generated, and the rejection region is:

Rejection Region $< -Z_{0.005} = -2.58$ or Rejection Region $> Z_{0.005} = 2.58$, H_0 cannot be rejected. Therefore, we conclude that this data is randomly generated.

The MINITAB output for this example is shown below:

```
MTB >  set c1
DATA > 80,  34,  10,  20,  40,  64,  50,  47,  44,  25,  86,  66,
       49,  53,  65,  77,  28,  28,  55,  74,  81,  90,  67,  53,
       38,  71,  72,  73,  75,  78
DATA > end
MTB > Runs C1.
```

Runs Test: C1

```
C1
K=56.4333
The observed number of runs = 11
The expected number of runs = 16.0000
15 Observations above K 15 below
    The test is significant at  0.0632
    Cannot reject at alpha = 0.05
```

Comparing the MINITAB solution to the hand solution of this problem, we see that the two solutions are identical ($R = 11$ in both solutions, and H_0 is not rejected).

4. The sequence of $+$'s and $-$'s signs are:

$-, -, +, +, +, -, -, +, +, +, -, +, +, +, +, -, 0, +, +, +, +, -, -, -, +, +, +, +, +$

The number of runs is $R_2 = 10$ but, since 2 successive observations are equal (28,28), their difference is 0, and the sample size should be reduced by 1, or $n = 30 - 1 = 29$.

Then, $E(R_2) = \dfrac{1}{3}(2n - 1) = \dfrac{1}{3}[2 \times 29 - 1] = \dfrac{1}{3}[58 - 1] = \dfrac{57}{3} = 19$

$$\sigma(R_2) = \sqrt{\dfrac{1}{90}(16n - 29)} = \sqrt{\dfrac{1}{90}[16 \times 29 - 29]}$$

$$= \sqrt{\dfrac{29}{90}(16 - 1)} = \sqrt{\dfrac{29}{90}(15)} = \sqrt{\dfrac{435}{90}} = 2.2$$

and $Z^* = \dfrac{R_2 - E(R_2)}{\sigma(R_2)} = \dfrac{10 - 19}{2.2} = -\dfrac{9}{2.2} = -4.09$

Since $Z^* = -4.09 < -Z_{\alpha/2} = -2.58$, H_0 is rejected, and we conclude that the observations are not randomly generated.

This is a surprising result because Problem 18.4 is the same as problem 18.3 which was solved by the "runs above and below the median" test and H_0 was not rejected. We would expect that the 2 methods should have produced the same results.

5. For $\delta^2 = 6$ and $s_y^2 = 12$, we obtain $K = \dfrac{\delta^2}{s_y^2} = \dfrac{6}{12} = 0.5$,

   and from Table 18.3, when $n = 40$ and $\alpha = 0.01$, $k = 1.3266$ and $k' = 2.7760$. Since $K < k = 1.3266$, the successive terms are not independent but they are positively correlated.

6. If $p(f) = p(m) = p = {}^1/_2$, the probabilities of $p(f = 0)$, $p(f = 1)$, $p(f = 2)$, and $p(f = 3)$ are obtained from the

   Binomial $p(n = 3, p = 1/2, X) = \dfrac{3!}{X!(3 - X)!}\dfrac{1}{8}$,

   since $p^x(1 - p)^{3-x} = \left(\dfrac{1}{2}\right)^x \left(\dfrac{1}{2}\right)^{3-x} = \left(\dfrac{1}{2}\right)^3 = \dfrac{1}{8}$.

   These probabilities are equal to: $p(f = X = 0) = 1/8$,
   $p(f = X = 1) = 3/8$, $p(f = X = 2) = 3/8$, and $p(f = X = 3) = 1/8$.
   Then we construct the following table

   to derive the value of $X_\delta^2 = \displaystyle\sum_{i=1}^{k} \dfrac{(o_i - e_i)^2}{e_i}$.

Female Births	Observed Frequencies (o_i)	Expected Frequencies (e_i)	$(o_i - e_i)^2 / e_i$
0	35	$200\,(1/8) = 25$	$(35 - 25)^2/25 = \dfrac{100}{25} = 4$
1	50	$200\,(3/8) = 75$	$(50 - 75)^2/75 = \dfrac{25 \times 25}{3 \times 25} = \dfrac{25}{3}$
2	70	$200\,(3/8) = 75$	$(70 - 75)^2/75 = \dfrac{5 \times 5}{75} = \dfrac{1}{3}$
3	45	$200\,(1/8) = 25$	$(45 - 25)^2/25 = \dfrac{20 \times 20}{25} = 16$
			$X_{\delta=k-1}^2 = \displaystyle\sum_{i=1}^{k} \dfrac{(o_i - e_i)^2}{e_i} = 20 + \dfrac{26}{3} = 28.67$

Since $\chi_{4-1}^2 = \chi_3^2 = 28.67$ and $\chi_3^2 = (\alpha = 0.05) = 7.815$ and $\chi_3^2 (\alpha = 0.01) = 11.345$, and $\chi_3^2 = 28.67 > \chi_3^2 (0.05)$ and $\chi_3^2 = 28.67 > \chi_3^2 (0.01)$, we reject the hypothesis that male and female births are equal likely at both $\alpha = 0.05$ and $\alpha = 0.01$.

7. The Expected product distribution is calculated as follows:
   For Row 1:

   a) Professionals & product $1 = \dfrac{200}{1,000}(400) = 80$

   b) Professionals & product $2 = \dfrac{200}{1,000}(100) = 20$

   c) Professionals & product $3 = \dfrac{200}{1,000}(300) = 60$

   d) Professionals & product $4 = \dfrac{200}{1,000}(200) = 40$

   To calculate the Expected Product distribution for Rows 2, 3 and 4, the corresponding ratios are 400/1000, 300/1000, and 100/1000 respectively.

Then the Table of the Expected Frequencies becomes:

Customer Group	Product				Total
	1	2	3	4	
Professionals	80	20	60	40	200
Businessman	160	40	120	80	400
Factory workers	120	30	90	60	300
Farmers	40	10	30	20	100
Totals	400	100	300	200	1000

Then, $\chi^2_\delta = \chi^2_{(r-1)(0-1)} = \chi^2_{3 \times 3} = \chi^2_9 = \dfrac{(85 - 80)^2}{80} + \dfrac{(23 - 20)^2}{20}$

$$+ \frac{(56 - 60)^2}{60} + \frac{(36 - 40)^2}{40} + \frac{(153 - 160)^2}{160}$$

$$+ \frac{(44 - 40)^2}{40} + \frac{(128 - 120)^2}{120} + \frac{(75 - 80)^2}{80}$$

$$+ \frac{(128 - 120)^2}{120} + \frac{(26 - 30)^2}{30} + \frac{(101 - 90)^2}{90}$$

$$+ \frac{(45 - 60)^2}{60} + \frac{(34 - 40)^2}{40} + \frac{(7 - 10)^2}{10} + \frac{(15 - 30)^2}{30} + \frac{(44 - 20)^2}{20}$$

$$= \left(\frac{25}{80} + \frac{9}{20} + \frac{16}{60} + \frac{16}{40} \right) + \left(\frac{49}{160} + \frac{16}{40} + \frac{64}{120} + \frac{25}{80} \right)$$

$$+ \left(\frac{64}{120} + \frac{16}{30} + \frac{121}{90} + \frac{225}{60} \right) + \left(\frac{36}{40} + \frac{9}{10} + \frac{225}{30} + \frac{576}{20} \right)$$

$$= 1.446 + 1.552 + 6.16 + 38.1 = 47.258$$

Since $\chi^2_9 (\alpha = 0.05) = 16.919$ and $\chi^2_9 = 47.258 > \chi^2_9 (0.05)$, we reject H$_0$ and conclude that customer group and product sales are not Independent.

8. We first find the Expected frequencies from:

$$\frac{180}{330}(150) = 81.82, \frac{180}{330}(120) = 65.45, \frac{180}{330}(60) = 32.73,$$

$$\frac{150}{330}(150) = 68.18, \frac{150}{330}(120) = 54.55, \frac{150}{330}(60) = 27.27;$$

Then we calculate $\chi^2_{(r-1)(0-1)} = \chi^2_{(2-1)(3-1)} = \chi^2_2 = \dfrac{(90 - 81.82)^2}{81.82}$

$$+ \frac{(65 - 65.45)^2}{65.45} + \frac{(25 - 32.73)^2}{32.73} + \frac{(60 - 68.18)^2}{68.18}$$

$$+ \frac{(55 - 54.55)^2}{54.55} + \frac{(35 - 27.27)^2}{27.27} = 0.8178 + 0.0031$$

$$+ 1.8256 + 0.9814 + 0.0037 + 2.192 = 5.82$$

Since $\chi^2_2(\alpha = 0.05) = 5.991$ and $\chi^2_2 (\alpha = 0.01) = 9.210$, and $\chi^2_2 = 5.82 < 5.991$ and $\chi^2_2 < 9.210$, H$_0$: The 2 samples come from the same population is not rejected, at both α values. Therefore there is no significant difference between the 2 political parties as far as national security is concerned (Homogeneity is not rejected).

9. The sample proportional defective $p = \dfrac{400}{10,000} = 0.04$, and σ_p is equal to:

$$\sigma_p = \sqrt{\frac{\pi(1 - \pi)}{n}} = \sqrt{\frac{0.03(0.97)}{10,000}} \doteq 0.0017. \text{ Then using the normal distribution to}$$

test the hypothesis:

$H_0: \pi = 0.03$ vs $H_1 \neq 0.03$, we obtain: $Z^* = \dfrac{p - \pi}{\sigma(p)} = \dfrac{0.04 - 0.03}{0.0017} = \dfrac{0.01}{0.0017}$

$= 5.882$, and since $Z^* > Z_{\alpha/2} = 1.96$, H_0 is rejected.

To use the chi-square, we use equation (18.15) because $\delta = 1$ and obtain:

$$\chi_1^{*2} = \sum_{i=1}^{2} \frac{\left(|o_i - e_i| - \dfrac{1}{2}\right)^2}{e_i} = \frac{(|400 - 300| - 0.5)^2}{300} + \frac{(|9,600 - 9,700| - 0.5)^2}{9,700},$$

since $p = 0.04$ and $np = 1,000(0.04) = 400$ defective and $10,000 - 400 = 9,600$, good items (observed) while the corresponding expected values are: $n\pi = 10,000(0.03) = 300$ and $10,000 - n\pi = 10,000 - 300 = 9,700$.

Then, $\chi_1^{*2} = \dfrac{(99.5)^2}{300} + \dfrac{(99.5)^2}{9,700} = 33.0008 + 1.0206 = 34.0214.$

Since $\chi_1^{*2}(0.975) = 0.001$ and $\chi_1^2(0.025) = 5.024$, and $\chi_1^{*2} > \chi_1^2(0.025)$, H_0 is, again, rejected.

10. From the given data we have:

$$\hat{\lambda} = \frac{\displaystyle\sum_{i=0}^{5}(n_a\, n_d)_i}{\displaystyle\sum_{i=1}^{5} n_{d_i}}$$

$$= \frac{(0 \times 12) + (1 \times 8) + (2 \times 6) + (3 \times 2) + (4 \times 1) + (5 \times 1)}{12 + 8 + 6 + 2 + 1 + 1}$$

$$= \frac{8 + 12 + 6 + 4 + 5}{30} = \frac{35}{30} = \frac{7}{6} = 1.17,$$

and the Poisson distribution is: $P(x, 1.17) = \dfrac{e^{-1.17}(1.17)^x}{x!}$ for $x = 0, 1, 2 \ldots,$

and $p(x = 0) = 0.31037$, $p(x = 1) = 0.36313$, $p(x = 2) = 0.21243$, $p(x = 3) = 0.08285$, $p(x = 4) = 0.024233$, and $p(x = 5) = 0.00567$

# of Accidents	Observed o_i	Expected (e_i) $= 30\left[\dfrac{e^{-1.17}(1.17)^x}{x!}\right]$	$\dfrac{(o_i - e_i)^2}{e_i}$
0	12	$30(0.31037) = 9.311$	0.7766
1	8	$30(0.36313) = 10.894$	0.7688
2	6	$30(0.21243) = 6.373$	0.0218
3	2	$30(0.08285) = 2.4855$	0.0948
4	1	$30(0.024233) = 0.727$	0.1025
5	1	$30(0.00567) = 0.170$	4.0524
			$\chi_4^{*2} = \displaystyle\sum_{i=0}^{5} \dfrac{(o_i - e_i)^2}{e_i} = 5.8169$

Since $\delta = k - 1 - m = 6 - 1 - 1 = 4$, $\chi_\delta^2(\alpha = 0.05) = 9.488$,

and $\chi_4^{*2} = 5.8169 < \chi_4^2(0.05)$, H_0: The data is Poisson distributed, is not rejected, and we conclude that the Poisson distribution with $\hat{\lambda} = 1.17$ is a good fit.

APPENDICES & TABLES

A Elements of Set Theory

Sets and set algebra are extensively used both in business and the sciences, because they provide a means with which to communicate important concepts and ideas. Students of business administration use sets in the study of probability, statistics, programming, optimization, etc. The material included in this appendix is the basic coverage of sets and set algebra needed in the discussion of probability and statistics. It includes some basic definitions, the most important operations in the algebra of sets (with an elementary discussion of Venn diagrams) and an example demonstrating the basic set operations and the use of sets in defining the probability of occurrence of an event in a stochasitic experiment.

A.1   Definitions

1. **Set** is defined as a collection of objects which we wish to study. These objects must be *well defined* (*i.e.*, it must be clear whether or not an object belongs to the set), *distinct* (*i.e.*, we must be able to distinguish between the objects and no object may appear more than once), and the *order of appearance* of the objects in the set is not important. A set may be *finite* or *infinite*, depending on whether the number of objects that belong to the set can be counted or not.
2. **Elements of a set** are the objects that belong to the set.
3. **Subset of a set** is a small portion of a set. It may include no elements, one, two or more elements, up to the total number of elements in the set.
4. **Proper subset** is a subset, defined in a set, whose number of elements is at least one less than the number of elements in the defining set. When the subset contains exactly the number of elements of the defining set, the set and the subset are equal to each other.
5. **Equality of sets**   Two sets (set 1 and set 2) are said to be equal if every element of set 1 is also an element of set 2 and vice versa.
6. **Universal Set** is a set which contains all the elements we wish to consider in our study. The Universal set is represented either by the capital letter U of the English alphabet or the capital letter S of the English alphabet.
7. **Null Set**   In contrast to the universal set which contains all the elements under consideration, the null is a set that has no elements. It is represented by φ (the lower case Greek letter phi) or by a set of empty brackets ({ }).
8. **Notation used in specifying sets, membership of elements in sets and in describing a set** Customarily sets are designated by capital letters of the English alphabet, while elements belonging to a set are usually represented by lower case letters of the English alphabet. For example the set consisting of the vowels of the English alphabet can be represented by:

$$V = \{a, e, i, o, u, (y)\}$$

Note the capital letter V representing the set in question, the set of brackets within which the elements appear separated by commas and the parenthesis around y which here indicates that y sometimes is considered a vowel and sometimes not. This method of describing a set is called "the Listing Method". There is another method, called the "Rule Method" or "descriptive method" which involves the use of a defining property to determine if an object belongs to a set. The format of the descriptive method, in specifying the set of the vowels of the English alphabet, is shown below:

$$V = \{x/x \text{ is a vowel of the English alphabet}\}$$

In words this specification reads: "V is the set of all elements x, such that x is a vowel of the English alphabet.

To indicate that an element belings or does not belong to a set, we use the notation:

$a \, \varepsilon \, V$ which reads: "the element a belongs to the set V"

$b \, \not\varepsilon \, V$ which reads: "the element b does not belong to the set V"

9. **Number of Possible Subsets in a set with n element**

Suppose a given set has n elements, where $n = 0, 1, 2 \ldots$ How many subsets (proper and otherwise) can be defined in this set? Using the definitions of sets and subsets discussed above, we can easily conclude that:

a) The number of subsets in a set with 0 elements is 1

b) The number of subsets in a set with 1 elements is 2

c) The number of subsets in a set with 2 elements is 4

d) The number of subsets in a set with 3 elements is 8

....

e) The number of subsets in a set with n elements is 2^n

This general expression can be verified for the specific values of n given above by substituting $n = 0, 1, 2, 3$ in the expression 2^n.

Then, the number of proper subsets is equal to $2^n - 1$ because there is only one subset which is equal to the given set.

10. **Counting the number of Elements in a set**

If y is considered a vowel of the English alphabet, then the set V above consists of 6 elements. This is represented in set notation by writing $n(V) = 6$. As another example let U be the set that contains all the possible numbers which show up when a fair die is rolled repeatedly. Since the possible outcomes of this experiment are the numbers 1, 2, 3, 4, 5, and 6, the set U can be specified as: $U = \{1, 2, 3, 4, 5, 6\}$ and $n(U) = 6$.

If we are interested, say, in the event that the number which shows up is even, then we are led to define another set E which contains only even numbers, namely:

$$E = \{2, 4, 6\} \text{ and } n(E) = 3$$

In the major application of sets to probability theory we may be interested in the probability of the event that an even number shows up. As is discussed in chapter 4 the probability of the event E is defined by:

$$P(E) = \frac{n(E)}{n(U)} = \frac{3}{6} = 0.5 \quad \text{(for a fair coin)}$$

A.2   Set Algebra

Set algebra consists of a number of set operations which allow us to combine sets and produce new sets.

These set operations are best illustrated by means of "Venn" diagrams so named after the English logician of the 19th century.

A Venn diagram uses a large rectangle to represent the universal set, while subsets of the universal set are represented by circles or ellipsoids within the rectangle of the universal set. The use of Venn diagram allows for much needed visibility with sets and their operations. The set operations discussed below and illustrated by Venn diagram are Complementation, Intersection, Union, Exclusive Union and Difference. To facilitate the discussion of these set operations let us assume that a universal set U is given with number of elements $n(U)$, and let us define in U subsets A and B with $n(A)$ and $n(B)$ elements respectively.

1. **Complementation**
   The complement of a set A is another set $\overline{A}$ whose elements are all the elements that belong to the Universal set U but not to set A.

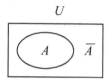

   Clearly $n(A) + n(\overline{A}) = n(U)$
   Dividing this equation by $n(U)$, we obtain: $p(A) + p(\overline{A}) = 1$,
   since $P(A) = n(A)/n(U)$ and $P(\overline{A}) = n(\overline{A})/n(U)$.

2. **Intersection**
   The intersection of two sets A and B is another set, represented by $A \cap B$, whose elements are the elements that sets A and B have in common. If there are no common elements, then the intersection is the empty (null) set. Clearly if set $B = U$, then $A \cap U = A$, while if $B = \overline{A}$, then $A \cap \overline{A} = \varnothing$.

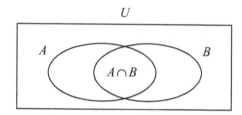

   Two (or more) sets that have no common elements are called "Mutually exclusive" or "disjoint".

3. **Union**
   The Union of 2 sets A and B is another set, represented by $A \cup B$, whose elements are the elements that belong either to set A or to set B or to both sets A and B. The Union of sets A and B is shown in the Venn diagram below and is equal to:

   $$A \cup B = (A \cap \overline{B}) + (A \cap B) + (\overline{A} \cap B)$$

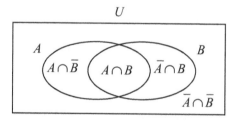

   Clearly from the Venn diagram:
   $n(A \cap \overline{B}) + n(A \cap B) + n(\overline{A} \cap B) + n(\overline{A} \cap \overline{B}) = n(U)$,
   and by dividing through by $n(U)$ we obtain:
   $p(A \cap \overline{B}) + p(A \cap B) + p(\overline{A} \cap B) + p(\overline{A} \cap \overline{B}) = 1$

If we let $B = U$, then $A \cup (U) = U$ while if $B = \overline{A}$, then $A \cup \overline{A} = U$.
Also, if $B = \varnothing$ (empty set), then $A \cup \varnothing = A$.

4. **Exclusive Union**

The exclusive union of 2 sets A and B is another set, represented by $A \underline{\cup} B$, whose elements are the elements that belong to A or to B but not to both. Clearly, $A \underline{\cup} B = (A \cap \overline{B}) + (\overline{A} \cap B)$

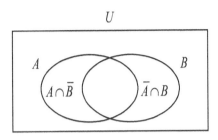

5. **Difference**

The difference of 2 sets A and B is another set, represented by $A-B$, whose elements are the elements in A but not in B.

Similarly, $B-A$ is a set that consists of all the elements in B which are not also in A. Clearly, from the Venn diagram, we have the relationships:

$$A - B = A \cap \overline{B}$$

and

$$B - A = \overline{A} \cap B,$$

from which it can be seen that $A - B \neq B - A$

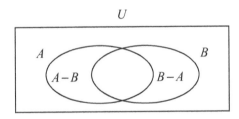

6. Another important set operation is the "Cartesian Product" of two sets, which is another set, represented by $A \times B$, whose elements are all the possible ordered pairs (*i.e.* two numbers which together designate a single point and such that one component is always first, the other always the second) such that $a \, \varepsilon \, A$ and $b \, \varepsilon \, B$.

For example, if $A = \{a_1, a_2, a_3\}$ and $B = \{b_1, b_2\}$, then:

$$A \times B = \{(a_1, b_1), (a_1, b_2), (a_2, b_1), (a_2, b_2), (a_3, b_1), (a_3, b_1)\}$$

The Cartesian Product is useful in Combinational analysis because it keeps track of all the possible combinations of the values of the two sets. It can be extended to 3 or more sets by first finding the Cartesian Product of A and B (as shown above) and then, considering $A \times B$ as a single set, finding the Cartesian Product of it with another set C, etc.

A.3 An Example

Let $U = \{1, 2, 3, 4, 5, 6, 7, 8, 9\}$ be the Universal set and define $A = \{1, 2, 3, 4, 5\}$ and $B = \{4, 5, 6, 7, 8\}$ on the Universal set U.

Then $\overline{A} = U - A = \{6, 7, 8, 9\}$

$A - B = A \cap \overline{B} = \{1, 2, 3\}$

$B - A = \overline{A} \cap B = \{6, 7, 8\}$

$A \cup B = \{1, 2, 3, 4, 5, 6, 7, 8\}$

$A \cap B = \{4, 5\}$

B Elements of Differential and Integral Calculus

Many important quantitative models are based on a branch of mathematics called "differential and Integral Calculus", which traces its roots to problems posed by the Greek philosophers and Geometers some 2500 years ago. The solution techniques needed for these problems, however, became available only after the work by Newton and Leibnitz in the beginning of the 18th century.

In this Appendix we will apply "Differential Calculus" to Optimization problems of functions of one and two independent variables, while "Integral Calculus" is applied to the determination of the "Areas of non-regular shapes" (where a "regular" shape is one of the following: rectangle, square, triangle, circle, trapezoid) and in the calculation of probabilities of events of continuous Random Variables.

B.1   Differential Calculus

■ Basic Definitions

1. **A function** $y = f(x)$ is a mathematical relationship in which the values of a single dependent variable (y) are determined from the values of one (or more) independent variable (x). A function consists of ordered pairs in which each element of the domain (*i.e.*, the permissible values of the independent variable x) is associated with one and only one element in the range (*i.e.*, the permissible values of the dependent variable y).

   A function may be linear ($y = a + bx$) or non-linear ($y = a + bx + cx^2$ or $y = K e^{cx}$ or $y = \ln x$, etc).

   In either case we wish to determine the "slope of the function". For a linear function the slope is determined directly from the "Rate of Change" of the function, which is the "change in the value of the dependent variable divided by the change in the value of the independent variable", or in terms of Mathematics:

$$\textbf{Rate of Change} \text{ of function } y = f(x)$$

$$\text{ROC} = [f(x + \Delta x) - f(x)]/\Delta x \tag{B1}$$

   For non-linear functions, the Rate of change is not sufficient to define the slope of the function. What is needed is the "derivative" of the function which requires, for its definition, the concepts of: "Limit of a Function" and "Continuity of a function in an interval and at a point."

2. **Limit of a Function** If, in the function $y = f(x)$, y approaches some fixed value L, as x approaches the value a, then we say that "L = Limit of y as x approaches a" or, mathematically speaking:

$$\text{Lim } y = \lim_{x \to a} f(x) = L \text{ or, simply: } \lim_{x \to a} f(x) = L \tag{B2}$$

Example 1

Find the limiting value of y as $x \to \infty$ in the function

$$y = f(x) = 1 + \left(\frac{1}{2}\right)^x$$

Allowing x to vary, we obtain the following ordered pairs of values:

x	0	1	2	3	$\cdots$
y	2	1.5	1.25	1.125	$\cdots$

Clearly, as x increases without limit, y decreases but it approaches the value of 1, even though y never actually becomes equal to 1.

In this case we say: $\lim\limits_{x \to \infty} \left[1 + \left(\dfrac{1}{2} \right)^x \right] = 1$

■ ■ ■

Note: In this example, the a and L in the above definitions are respectively: $a = \infty$ and $L = 1$.

3. **Continuity**
   - A function $y = f(x)$ is continuous in an interval from $x = b$ to $x = c$, if the function has no breaks or jumps in the interval.
   - A function $y = f(x)$ is continuous at a point $x = a$, if:

   a) $f(a)$ is defined (*i.e.*, the domain of x includes the point of $x = a$)
   b) The limit $L = \lim f(x)$ exists

   $$x \to a$$

   c) The limit L exists and is equal to $f(a)$ as x approaches a either from left or right. Using mathematical notation we write:

   $$\text{Lim } f(x) = L = f(a)$$
   $$x \to a$$

Example 2

Specify whether the function $y = f(x) = x^2$ ($0 \leq x < \infty$) is continuous (or not) at $x = a = 6$.

Since:

$f(6) = 36$ is defined (because $x = 6$ is in the interval of definition of x)
$\lim (x^2) = 36$
$x \to 6$

and   C) $\lim (x^2) = 36 = f(6)$,
        $x \to 6$

the function $y = x^2$ ($0 \leq x < \infty$) is continuous at $x = 6$.

■ ■ ■

4. **Derivative of a Function** The derivative of a function $y = f(x)$ is another function, represented by $y' = dy/dx = f'(x)$, where $f'(x)$ can be obtained from the given function $f(x)$ from the expression:

$$f'(x) = \lim_{\Delta x \to 0} \{ [f(x + \Delta x) - f(x)]/\Delta x \} \tag{B3}$$

The derivative of a function gives the slope of the function at a given value of the independent variable. If a function is discontinuous, it has no slope for those values of the independent variable in the interval of discontinuity. But continuity alone is not sufficient for a function to have a derivative at a given point. The mathematical requirement that must be met for a derivative to exist at a given point is defined in terms of the derivative formula, and it states:

$$\lim_{\Delta x \to 0} \{ [f(x + \Delta x) - f(x)]/\Delta x \} = \lim_{\Delta x \to 0} \{ [f(x + \Delta x) - f(x)]/\Delta x \}$$

(from the left)   (from the right)   (B4)

Example 3

Let $y = 2x$; find $f'(x)$

Given $y = f(x) = 2x$

Then $y + \Delta y = f(x + \Delta x) = 2(x + \Delta x) = 2x + 2\Delta x$,

and $f(x + \Delta x) - f(x) = [2x + 2\Delta x] - [2x] = 2\Delta x$

Therefore $f'(x) = \lim_{\Delta x \to 0} \{[f(x + \Delta x) - f(x)]/\Delta x\} = \lim_{\Delta x \to 0} [(2\Delta x)/\Delta x] = 2$

This value of 2 is the slope of the function $y = f(x) = 2x$ for all values of x.

■ ■ ■

Example 4

Let $y = f(x) = \begin{cases} 1 + 2x & \text{for } x \leq 1 \\ 5 - 2x & \text{for } x \geq 1 \end{cases}$

Since $f(1) = 3$, this function is continuous at $x = 1$

However $\lim_{\Delta x \to 0} \{[f(x + \Delta x) - f(x)]/\Delta x\} = -2$

as $x = 1$ is approached from the right,

and $\lim_{\Delta x \to 0} \{[f(x + \Delta x) - f(x)]/\Delta x\} = 2$,

as $x = 1$ is approached from the left

Since these two limits are not the same, the function

$y = f(x) = \begin{cases} 1 + 2x & \text{for } x \leq 1 \\ 5 - 2x & \text{for } x \geq 1 \end{cases}$

does not have a derivative at $x = 1$; but it does have a derivative at any other value of x.

■ ■ ■

■ Rules for Determining Derivatives

When particular functional forms are substituted in the defining derivative formula(B3), specific derivative rules are obtained. The most important of these are the following:

1. If $y = f(x) = c$ (where c is a constant value); then $f'(x) = 0$ (B5)
2. If $y = f(x) = x$; then $f'(x) = 1$ (B6)
3. If $y = f(x) = x^n$; then $f'(x) = nx^{n-1}$ (B7)
4. If $y = f(x) = cg(x)$; then $f'(x) = c\,g'(x)$ (B8)

5. If $y = f(x) = g(x) \pm h(x)$; then $f'(x) = g'(x) \pm h'(x)$ (B9)

6. If $y = f(x) = g(x)h(x)$; then $f'(x) = g(x)\,h'(x) + g'(x)h(x)$ (B10)

7. If $y = f(x) = h(x)/g(x)$; then $f'(x) = [g(x)\,h'(x) - h(x)g'(x)]/[g(x)]^2$ (B11)

8. If $y = f[g(x)] = f(u)$ and $u = g(x)$; then $dy/dx = (dy/dx)(du/dx)$
   (CHAIN RULE) (B12)

9. If $y = f(x) = [h(x)]^n$; then $f'(x) = n[h(x)]^{n-1}\,h'(x)$ (B13)

10. If $y = \log_b u$ and $u = f(x)$; then: $dy/dx = (1/u\,(\log_b e)\,(du/dx)$ (B14)

11. If $y = [f(x)]^{g(x)}$; then: $dy/dx = [f(x)]^{g(x)} \{[f'(x)/f(x)]g(x) + g'(x)\ln f(x)\}$ (B15)

12. If $y = b^u$ and $u = f(x)$; then $dy/dx = b^u\,(\ln b)\,(du/dx)$ (B16)

Note: If $b = e$, then $\log_b e = \log_e e = \ln e = 1$

■ Optimization Methodology of a function of a single Variable

Suppose we are given a function $y = f(x)$ $(c \le x \le d)$ for which $f'(x)$ and $f''(x)$ ($f''(x)$ is the derivative of $f'(x)$ or the second derivative of $f(x)$) can be found using the methods discussed above. Now we wish to determine the values of x at which this function assumes maximum and/or minimum values.

Maximum and minimum values are jointly known as optimal values. We distinguish between LOCAL and ABSOLUTE optimal values, using the following definitions:

1. **Local Optima**
   A function $y = f(x)$ is said to reach a "Local maximum" at a value $x = a$ (where $c < a < d$), if $y(a) > y(x)$ for any point x in the neighborhood of a.

   A function $y = f(x)$ is said to reach a "Local minimum" at a value $x = b$ (where $c < b < d$), if $y(b) < y(x)$ for any point x in the neighborhood of b.

2. **Absolute Optima**
   a) A function $y = f(x)$ is said to reach an "Absolute Maximum" at a value $x = g$, if $y(g) > y(x)$ for any x in the domain of x.
   b) A function $y = f(x)$ is said to reach an "Absolute Minimum" at a value $x = h$, if $y(h) < y(x)$ for any x in the domain of x.

   A function can attain a LOCAL OPTIMUM only at an interior point (*i.e.*, a point which is not an end point of an interval). LOCAL OPTIMA are determined from first and second derivatives as is discussed below under "Optimization Methodology". If the end points of the domain of a variable (independent) are defined, then ABSOLUTE optimum values are defined (otherwise they are not defined). ABSOLUTE OPTIMA can occur at either interior or end points, and they are found as follows:
   a) Evaluate the given function at the end points (If $c \le x \le d$ the end points are defined; otherwise they are not!)
   b) Find all the local optima (in accordance with the procedure given below) and evaluate the given function at the Local Optima points.
   c) Compare the results.
   d) Select Absolute Maximum (the highest value in the comparison) or Absolute Minimum (the lowest value in the comparison).

3. **Optimization Methodology**
   Given a function $y = f(x)$ which is to be optimized:
   Find $f'(x)$
   Set $f'(x) = 0$ and solve for x to find the "critical" points at which local optima occur (Let this $x_j = x_j^*$)

Find $f''(x)$

Evaluate $f''(x)$ for each critical point found above. Then:

a) If $f''(x_j^*) > 0$, the critical point is a local minimum

b) If $f''(x_j^*) < 0$, the critical point is a local maximum

c) If $f''(x_j^*) = 0$, the critical point is a "Point of Inflection"

Inflection points are neither maxima nor minima points but are points which mark the transition from a positive to negative or negative to positive direction.

Example 5

Find all local and absolute maxima and minima for the function:

$$f(x) = -x^3/3 + 5x^2 - 6x + 10 \qquad \text{for} \quad 0 \le x \le 20$$

$$f(0) = 10$$

$$f(20) = -\frac{2330}{3} = -776.67$$

$$f'(x) = -x^2 + 10x - 6$$

Let $f'(x) = 0$ and solve for x to obtain the critical values at which local optima occur;

Using the Quadratic Solution Formula (where the assumed Quadratic equation is: $y = ax^2 = bx = c$):

$$x_{1,2} = \frac{-b \pm \sqrt{b^2 - 4ac}}{2a},$$

for the Quadratic equation: $-x^2 + 10x - 6 = 0$ (with $a = -1$, $b = 10$, and $c = -6$), or $x^2 - 10x + 6 = 0$ (by multiplying the above equation by (-1)) with $a = 1$, $b = -10$, and $c = 6$, we obtain:

$$x = \left[10 + \sqrt{100 - 4(1)(6)}\right]/2(1) = (10 + \sqrt{76})/2$$

$$= (10 + 8.72)/2$$

$$= 18.72/2 = 9.36$$

and

$$x_2 = (10 - 8.72)/2 = 0.64$$

$$f''(x) = -2x + 10$$

$$f''(9.36) = -8.72 < 0 \qquad \text{(Local Maximum at } x = 9.36)$$

$$f''(0.64) = +8.72 > 0 \qquad \text{(Local Minimum at } x = 0.64)$$

$$f(9.36) = 118.55$$

$$f(0.64) = 8.12$$

Summary

$$f(0) = +10$$

$$f(0.64) = +8.12 \quad \leftarrow \quad \text{Local Minimum}$$

$$f(9.36) = +118.55 \quad \leftarrow \quad \text{Local \& Absolute Maximum}$$

$$f(20) = -776.67 \quad \leftarrow \quad \text{Absolute Minimum}$$

■ ■ ■

■ Optimization Methodology of a function of two Variables

Given $y = f(x_1, x_2)$; then let:

$fx_1 = $ First partial derivative of given function with respect to x_1;

or
$$\partial y / \partial x_1 = \lim \left\{ [f(x_1 + \Delta x_1, x_2) - f(x_1, x_2)] / \Delta x_1 \right\} \qquad \text{(B17)}$$
$$\Delta x_1 \to 0$$

$fx_2 = $ First partial derivative of given function with respect to x_2;

or
$$\partial y / \partial x_2 = \lim \left\{ [f(x_1, x_2 + \Delta x_2) - f(x_1, x_2)] / \Delta x_2 \right\} \qquad \text{(B18)}$$
$$\Delta x_2 \to 0$$

In a similar manner we can define:

$fx_1x_1 = \partial^2 y / \partial x_1^2 = $ second partial derivative of given function with respective to x_1

$fx_2x_2 = \partial^2 y / \partial x_2^2 = $ second partial derivative of given function with respective to x_2

$fx_1x_2 = fx_2x_1 = \partial^2 y / \partial x_1 \partial x_2 = \partial^2 y / \partial x_2 \partial x_1 = $ Cross partial derivative

Then, the optimization of a function of two variables proceeds as follows:

Find fx_1 and fx_2
Set $fx_1 = 0$ and $fx_2 = 0$ and solve simultaneously to find the critical point; call it:

(x_1^*, x_2^*). It is possible for a function to have one or more critical points.
A critical point (x_1^*, x_2^*) corresponds to a **possible** minimum if:
$fx_1x_1 > 0$ and $fx_2x_2 > 0$ when evaluated at the critical point in question.
A critical point (x_1^*, x_2^*) corresponds to a **possible** maximum if:
$fx_1x_1 < 0$ and $fx_2x_2 < 0$ when evaluated at the critical point in question.

Additional Requirement

But, the second derivative conditions stated above are not sufficient to guarantee an optimum value for a function of two independent variables in all directions (they are sufficient along the principal axes, however). The following additional requirement is needed with the associated interpretation;

We let
$$D = (fx_1x_1)(fx_2x_2) - (fx_1x_2)^2, \qquad \text{(B19)}$$

and evaluate D at each of the critical points.

If $D > 0$, the critical point is either a Maximum or Minimum point, depending on the tentative conclusion reached by the second derivative test.

If $D = 0$, the test is inconclusive. We must evaluate the function at the critical point, and at points in the neighborhood of the critical point and then, by comparison, determine the type of optimality that exists at the critical point in question.

If $D < 0$, the function has a "Saddle Point" at the critical point (which is neither a maximum nor a minimum but it is a maximum in one pair of axes and a minimum in another pair of axes).

For functions of more than two independent variables determining the optimality of the function is more difficult because additional conditions are needed. We will not consider such functions here.

Example 6

Determine the optimality of the function $z = f(x, y) = 2x^3 - 2xy + y^2$

Then

$$\left.\begin{array}{l} fx = 6x^2 - 2y \\ fy = -2x + 2y \end{array}\right\} \text{ and } \left.\begin{array}{l} fx = 0 \\ fy = 0 \end{array}\right\} \text{ or } \left.\begin{array}{l} 6x^2 - 2y = 0 \\ -2x + 2y = 0 \end{array}\right\} \text{ or }$$

$(x_1^* = 0, y_1^* = 0)$ ← critical point 1

$(x_2^* = 1/3, y_2^* = 1/3)$ ← critical point 2

and $fxx = 12x; fyy = 2; fxy = fyx = -2$

Examine critical point 1 $(x_1^* = 0, y_1^* = 0)$

Since $fxx = 12x = 0$, when evaluated at $x_1^* = 0$ and $y_1^* = 0, fyy = 2$, and $fxy = fyx = -2$, the value of D is:

$$D = (fxx)(fyy) - (fxy)^2 = (0)(2) - (-2)^2 = -4 < 0$$

Since $D < 0$, the function $= f(x, y) = 2x^3 - 2xy + y^2$ has a saddle point at the critical point $x = x_1^* = 0$ and $y = y_1^* = 0$.

Now Examine critical point 2$(x_2^* = 1/3, y_2^* = 1/3)$

Since $fxx = 12x = 12 (1/3) = 4$, when evaluated at the critical point, $fyy = 2$, and $fxy = fyx = -2$, the value of D is:

$$D = (fxx)(fyy) - (fxy)^2 = (4)(2) - (-2)^2 = 8 - 4 = 4 > 0$$

Since both the second derivatives $fxx = 12x$ and $fyy = 2$ are positive, when evaluated at the critical point $(x_2^* = 1/3, y_2^* = 1/3)$, the function $z = f(x, y)$ $z = f(x, y) = 2x^3 - 2xy + y^2$ has a possible minimum at the $(x_2^* = 1/3, y_2^* = 1/3)$ critical point. The fact that $D > 0$, when evaluated at the critical point, makes it definite that this function has a minimum at the critical point.

■ ■ ■

■ Integral Calculus

1. Areas of Regular and Irregular Shapes

The area of regular shapes (*i.e.*, the area of rectangles, squares, circles, triangles, and trapezoids) can be found from the well-known formulas of plain geometry, namely:

Area of rectangle $A_1 = xy$ (sides x and y)

Area of square $A_2 = x^2$ (side x)

Area of circle $A_3 = \pi r^2$ (radius r)

Area of triangle $A_4 = \dfrac{1}{2} bh$ (base b and height h)

Area of trapezoid $A_5 = \dfrac{1}{2} (b_1 + b_2)h$ (bases b_1 and b_2, and height h)

However, no such formulas are available to find the areas of "irregular" shapes, such as the area formed under a non-linear function and above the x-axis, and between the x-values $x_1 = a$ and $x_2 = b$. However, we can still find such areas approximately, by subdividing the area into small rectangles and then calculating the sum of the areas of the rectangles. The procedure for performing such calculations consists of the following steps:

  a) Divide the distance from a to b into n small equal intervals and treat each such interval (Δx) as the base of the rectangle. The value of $\Delta x = (b - a)/n$.

The height of the rectangle is given by the value of the function at the midpoint of each rectangle base, $f(x_i)$.

The approximate area (since the area of each rectangle is given by $f(x_i)(\Delta x)$) is given by:

$$A = f(x_1)\Delta x + f(x_2)\Delta x + \cdots + f(x_n)\Delta x = \sum_{i=1}^{n} f(x_i)\Delta x \qquad \text{(B20)}$$

The accuracy of the approximation depends on the number of rectangles in the interval from a to b. As the number of rectangles increases (*i.e.*, as $\Delta x \to 0$ or $n \to \infty$) the approximation becomes more accurate.

The exact area is given by the limiting value of the sum of a number of terms, when the number of terms increases infinitely as the value of each term approaches zero, namely:

$$A = \lim_{n \to \infty} \sum_{i=1}^{n} f(x_i)\Delta x \qquad \text{(B21)}$$

This limiting value, which is always a numerical value, is called the "Definite integral" of the function $f(x)$ for the interval a to b, and is represented by:

$$A = \int_{a}^{b} f(x)\, dx = \lim_{n \to \infty} \sum_{i=1}^{n} f(x_i)\, \Delta x \qquad \text{(B22)}$$

■ ■ ■

Example 7

Find the area under the curve $y = f(x) = x$, from $x = a = 0$ to $x = b = 2$.

Geometrically: The resulting shape is a right triangle with base $b = 2$ and height $h = 2$; therefore, the area $= \dfrac{1}{2}$ (base)(height) or $A = \dfrac{1}{2}(2)(2) = 2$

Using the limiting summation method

1. $\Delta x = (b - a)/n = (2 - 0)/n = 2/n$
2. To find $f(x_i)$, we note the following:

$$x_1 = a + \Delta x = 0 + \Delta x = \Delta x$$

$$x_2 = x_1 + \Delta x = \Delta x + \Delta x = 2\Delta x$$

$$.$$
$$.$$
$$.$$

$$x_i = x_{i-1} + \Delta x = i\Delta x$$

Then, since $y = f(x) = x$, $f(x_i) = (i\Delta x) = i\Delta x = i(2/n)$

3. Therefore:

$$A = \lim_{n\to\infty} f(x_i)\,\Delta x = \lim_{n\to\infty} \sum_{i=1}^{n} [i(2/n)]\,[2/n]$$

$$= \lim_{n\to\infty} (4/n^2)\left(\sum_{i=1}^{n} i\right)$$

But: $\sum_{i=1}^{n} i = n(n+1)/2$ (See equation (D13) of Appendix D on Elements of Summation Theory)

Then

$$A = \lim_{n\to\infty} (4/n^2)[n(n+1)/2] = \lim_{n\to\infty} (2(n+1)/n)$$

$$= \lim_{n\to\infty} 2(1 + 1/n) = 2(1 + 0) = 2$$

Note that this is the same result we obtained using the Geometric method. This example was purposely selected to allow the comparisons of the result of the limiting summation method against the geometric result. Now that we have done so, we have gained the confidence that this method works for any $f(x)$, regardless of how complex, even though we may not be able to verify the result geometrically.

In what follows, we will first relate the definite integral to the "indefinite integral" of the function $f(x)$ and then, using the "Fundamental theorem" of Integral Calculus, we will calculate the definite integral value from its indefinite integral.

■ ■ ■

■ Relationship Between Integral and Differential Calculus

To determine the value of the definite integral of a function, without using the limiting summation method, we must introduce two additional concepts, namely: a) the Indefinite Integral and b) the Fundamental Theorem of Integral Calculus.

The Indefinite Integral of a function $f(x)$ is another function $g(x)$, provided $g'(x) = f(x)$;
or, using the integral notation introduced above, we write:
$\int f(x)\,dx = g(x)$ provided $g'(x) = f(x)$

Because of this relationship, integration is sometimes thought of as the "reverse process of differentiation", and the term "anti-derivative" is often used synonymously with the term "indefinite integral".

Example 8

Determine the indefinite integral of $f(x) = x$

We write: $\int x\,dx = g(x) + c = \dfrac{1}{2}x^2 + c$ where c is any constant;

$g(x) + c = \dfrac{1}{2}x^2 + c$ is clearly the indefinite integral of $f(x) = x$

because $g'(x) = x = f(x)$ for any value of c. (Since the derivative of any constant $= 0$)

The constant value of c illustrates that the indefinite integral is an entire family of functions. The constant c is called the "constant of Integration", and it can be evaluated only if additional information, known as "Initial Conditions", is given. In the example above, for instance, if it is known that $g(6) + c = 20$, then $20 = \dfrac{1}{2}(6)^2 + c$, from which $c = 2$.

The Fundamental Theorem of Integral Calculus relates the concepts of the definite integral (which is a numerical value) and the indefinite integral (which is a function) and states that: "The value of the definite integral of $f(x)$ between a and b is given by the indefinite integral $g(x)$, evaluated at the upper limit (b) minus the indefinite integral evaluated at the lower limit of integration (a)".

In mathematical terms we write:

$$\int_a^b f(x)dx = g(x) + c \Big|_a^b = [g(b) + c] - [g(a) + c] = g(b) - g(a) \qquad \text{(B23)}$$

Clearly the constant of integration is eliminated by the subtraction. Therefore, it is not necessary to include it when evaluating a definite integral, but it **must** be included with the indefinite integral.

■ ■ ■

Example 9

Find the definite integral of the function $f(x) = x$ from $x = 0$ to $x = 2$, using the Indefinite Integral concept:

$$\int_{a=0}^{b=2} f(x)dx = \int_0^2 xdx = g(x) + c = \frac{1}{2}x^2 + c \Big|_0^2 = \left[\frac{1}{2}(2)^2 + c\right] - \left[\frac{1}{2}(0)^2 + c\right]$$

$$= 2 + c - 0 - c = 2, \text{ as before.}$$

We list below 3 basic properties of Definite Integrals:

$$\int_a^c f(x)dx = \int_a^b f(x)dx + \int_b^c f(x)dx, \text{ where } a < b < c \qquad \text{(B24)}$$

$$\int_a^a f(x)dx = 0 \qquad \text{(B25)}$$

$$\int_a^b f(x)dx = -\int_b^a f(x)dx \qquad \text{(B26)}$$

■ ■ ■

■ Methods of Integration

It is apparent from what we have said above that integration is more complicated than differentiation. The usual problem in integration is to find the definite integral of a given function $f(x)$, in the interval $x = a$ to $x = b$, i.e., we need to find $\int_a^b f(x)dx$.

Since the value of the definite integral is usually found from the indefinite integral by using the Fundamental Theorem of Integral Calculus, the Methods of integration discussed below concentrate on finding $g(x)$. Of course, the value of the definite integral can also be found directly by using the Limiting Summation Method as discussed earlier.

It should be stated that there are some functions, the most important of which is the normal probability density function of a continuous random variable x (we discuss this extensively in chapters 5 and 6), given by:

$$f(x) = \left(\frac{1}{\sqrt{2\pi}} \cdot \frac{1}{\sigma}\right) Exp[-(x - \mu)^2/2\sigma^2], \quad -\infty < x < \infty \qquad \text{(B27)}$$

Note : $Exp[-(x - \mu)^2/2\sigma^2] = e^{-\frac{1}{2\sigma^2}(x-\mu)^2}$

which cannot be integrated by any known method in "closed" form; *i.e.*, we cannot find a function $g(x)$, such that $g'(x) = f(x)$. The definite integral of such functions is found by numerical integration techniques (which are similar to the Limiting Summation Method discussed earlier) using digital computers to find results accurate to any degree of accuracy we wish, and then list these results in tables. Such tables are usually found in many statistics texts, such as the tables given in the tables section of this book (Part IX Appendices & Tables).

Another way of finding $g(x)$, for a given $f(x)$, is to use extensive "Tables of Integration", usually found in books called "Mathematical Tables", in which the $g(x)$ is listed for many functions $f(x)$.

However, for functions $f(x)$ usually encountered in Probability and Statistics and Business Applications, the following three methods should prove sufficient to solve most such problems.

1. **"Rules of Integration" Method**

This method consists of a number of basic rules which list the required $g(x)$ for the given $f(x)$. No formal proof of these individual rules are needed because it is obvious that $g'(x) = f(x)$ and, therefore, $g(x)$ is the required result. To use this method, we must identify our function with one of the functions given, and then extract the corresponding $g(x)$. For more complicated functions this may not be possible and we will have to use other methods, such as the "Integration by Substitution" or "Integration by Parts" methods, discussed later.

In the formulas that follow k, c, and b are any three constants except that b cannot equal to 0 or 1. Then:

a) If $f(x) = k$ then $g(x) = kx + c$ .... (B28)

b) If $f(x) = x$ $g(x) = \dfrac{1}{2}x^2 + c$ .... (B29)

c) If $f(x) = x^n$ $g(x) = x^{n+1}/(n + 1) + c$ .... (B30)
(for $n \neq 1$)

d) If $f(x) = k\,f_1(x)$ $g(x) = k g_1(x)$ .... (B31)

e) If $f(x) = f_1(x) \pm f_2(x)$ $g(x) = g_1(x) \pm g_2(x)$ .... (B32)

f) If $f(x) = b^{kx}$ $g(x) = [b^{kx}/k(\ln b)] + c$ .... (B33)

g) If $f(x) = \log_b(kx)$ $g(x) = x \log_b(kx) - x\log_b e + c$ .... (B34)

h) If $f(x) = \log_e(kx) = \ln(kx)$ $g(x) = x\ln(kn) - x + c$ .... (B35)

i) If $f(x) = 1/x$ $g(x) = \ln x + c$ .... (B36)

(for $n = -1$; see rule 3 above)

Note: e is the base of the Naperian (or Natural) logarithms, and $e \approx 2.718281828 \dots$

2. **"Integration By Substitution" Method**

This method of integration is based on the following formulas:

$$\int u^n du = [(u^{n+1})/n + 1] + c \qquad \text{for } n + 1 \neq 0 \qquad (B37)$$

$$\int \frac{du}{u} = \ln u + c \qquad \text{for } n = -1 \qquad (B38)$$

$$\int e^u du = e^u + c,$$

(B39)

which are generalizations of the "Rules of Integration" formulas (3), (6) (where b is replaced by e), and (9) respectively, and where u is a function of x. When $u = x$ these formulas reduce to the corresponding formulas of the "Rules of Integration" method.

The method consists of identifying a function of x under the integral and calling it u (*i.e.*, substitute u for a function of x), identifying the value of n, and then make sure that the derivative of what we called u is equal to the du. If in our problem the derivative of u is not exactly du but differs from it only by a constant multiplier, make proper adjustments by multiplying and dividing the expression by the needed constant (one inside the integral sign, the other outside), thus matching the above formulas and, then, obtaining an answer to our problem.

The following examples illustrate the method:

Example 10

Integrate: $\int (4x^3 + 5)^2 (3x^2)\, dx = \int f(x)dx$, where: $f(x) = (4x^3 + 5)^2(3x^2)$

Let $u = 4x^3 + 5$ and $n = 2$

Then $du = 12x^2 dx$

Examining the factors inside the integral sign we see that after the u substitution is made, the remaining factor of $3x^2 dx$ is not equal to du (which is equal to $12x^2\, dx$) but could be made equal to du by multiplying if by 4. If we do this, however, the value of the integral increases by a factor 4. To prevent this from happening, we need to multiply the entire integral by the factor $\dfrac{1}{4}$ thus preserving the identity.

Then we have:

$$\int (4x^3 + 5)^2\, (3x^2 dx) = \frac{1}{4} \int (4x^3 + 5)^2\, [4(3x^2 dx)] = \frac{1}{4} \int u^2 du$$

Therefore, applying formula (B37) above to the last expression, we get:

$$\frac{1}{4} \int u^2\, du = \frac{1}{4}(u^3/3) + c = (1/12)(u^3) + c$$

However, $u = 4x^3 + 5$
Therefore, the final result is:

$$\int (4x^3 + 5)^2\, (3x^2\, dx) = (1/12)(4x^3 + 5)^3 + c = g(x) + c$$

Clearly, this is the correct result because

$$\frac{d}{dx}[g(x) + c] = g'(x) = f(x) = (3/12)(4x^3 + 5)^2(12x^2) = (4x^2 + 5)^2(3x^2)$$

Note: The dx in the original problem is part of the problem statement.

▪▪▪

Example 11

Integrate $\int 2xdx/(x^2 + 3) = \int f(x)dx$, where $f(x) = \dfrac{2x}{(x^2 + 3)}$

Let $u = x^2 + 3$

Then $du = 2xdx$

Since we have an exact match, because $\dfrac{2xdx}{x^2 + 3} = \dfrac{du}{u}$,

the result, using formula (B38) above, is:

$\int 2xdx/(x^2 + 3) = \int du/u = \ln u + c = \ln (x^2 + 3) + c = g(x) + c$

■ ■ ■

Example 12

Integrate $\int e^{x^2+9} (xdx) = \int f(x)dx$, where: $f(x) = e^{x^2+9}x$

Let $u = x^2 + 9$
Then: $du = 2xdx$

Obviously, we need to multiply (xdx) by 2 in order to provide the needed $du = 2xdx$ for the chosen $u = x^2 + 9$. But, in order to preserve the correct value of the integral, the entire integral needs to be multiplied by the factor $\dfrac{1}{2}$.

$$\text{Therefore: } \int e^{x^2+9} (xdx) = \frac{1}{2} \int e^{x^2+9} (2xdx) = \frac{1}{2} \int e^u du$$

Applying formula (B39) above to this last integral, we obtain:

$$\int e^{x^2+9} (xdx) = \frac{1}{2} \int e^u \, du = \frac{1}{2} e^u + c = \frac{1}{2} e^{x^2+9} + c = g(x) + c$$

3. "Integration By Parts" Method
   This method of integration is based on the formula:

$$\int udv = uv - \int vdu, \tag{B40}$$

   where u and v are functions of x. This formula is obtained from the product rule of differentiation, namely:

$$d(uv) = udv + vdu \tag{B41}$$

   By integrating both sides of equation (B41), we obtain:

$$\int d(uv) = \int udv + \int vdu \tag{B42}$$

   or

$$uv = \int udv + \int vdu, \tag{B43}$$

   from which we obtain equation (B40) when equation (B43) is solved for $\int udv$.

   The method consists of determining what to call u and dv in the given problem. The product of the two choices has to equal the expression inside the integral sign. If the determination has been made correctly, $\int vdu$ will be easier to integrate than $\int udv$. If, on the other hand,

$\int vdu$ is more complex than the original (given) function, we made "bad choices". In such a case, we should go back and reverse our choices. To help with the choices of u and dv, we offer the following suggestions:

Whenever there are functions of the form $\int x^n e^u dx$, $\int x^n \cos u dx$ or $\int x^n \sin u dx$,

let $u = x^n$ and $dv =$ the rest of the expression. Since the application of the method requires the derivative of u (to find du) and the integral of dv (to find v), these choices will help simplify the integration.

If the given function is of the form $\int e^x \cos x dx$, it makes no difference what you call u and what you call dv. The degree of difficulty is the same. However, in this case, the integration has to be done twice and the value of the integral is found by solving for it (the integral) algebraically.

■ ■ ■

Example 13

Integrate $\int xe^{-x}dx$ by parts (*i.e.*, by using the formula:

$$\int udv = uv - \int vdu$$

According to suggestion (1) above, we let $u = x$ and $dv = e^{-x}dx$. Since the right-hand side (RHS) of the "integration by parts" formula requires u, v and du we must differentiate u (to find du) and integrate dv (to find v).

By application of the appropriate differentiation and integration rules we find:

$$du = dx \text{ and } v = \int dv = \int e^{-x}dx = -e^{-x}$$

By substituting u, v and du in the RHS of the "integration by parts" formula, we obtain:

$$\int xe^{-x}dx = (x)(-e^{-x}) - \int (-e^{-x})(dx) = -xe^{-x} + \int e^{-x}dx$$

Clearly this last integral is easier to evaluate than the given integral $\int xe^{-x}dx$, because the factor x has been eliminated through differentiation. Then, from "integration rule" #6 (with $b = e$) we obtain: $\int e^{-x}dx = -e^{-x}$ and the overall result now becomes:

$$\int xe^{-x}dx = -xe^{-x} - e^{-x} + c = -e^{-x}(x + 1) + c = g(x) + c$$

Clearly $g(x)$ is the correct result because $g'(x) = f(x)$.

Note: If, instead of the above choices for u and dv, we had let $u = e^{-x}$ and $dv = xdx$ then: $du = -e^{-x}dx$ and $v = x^2/2$.

Application of the "integration by parts" formula would result in:

$$\int xe^{-x}dx = (e^{-x})(x^2/2) - \int (x^2/2)(-e^{-x}dx) = \frac{1}{2}x^2e^{-x} + \frac{1}{2}\int x^2e^{-x}dx$$

which is more complicated than the starting expression. Clearly these later choices represent "bad choices" for u and dv.

■■■

Example 14

Integrate: $\int x \ln x dx = \int \ln x \, x dx$

Let $u = \ln x$ and $dv = xdx$. Then $du = (1/x)dx$ and $v = \int xdx = x^2/2$

Substituting these into the "integration by parts" formula, we obtain:

$$\int x \ln x dx = \int \ln x(x dx) = (\ln x)(x^2/2) - \int (x^2/2)(dx/x)$$

$$= \frac{1}{2}x^2 \ln x - \frac{1}{2}\int xdx = (\frac{1}{2})x^2\ln x - (\frac{1}{4})x^2 + c = g(x) + c$$

Since it can be shown that $g'(x) = f(x) = x \ln x$, the result is correct.

■ Application of Integral Calculus in Probability Calculations

In Chapters 5 and 7 of this text, we introduced continuous random variables whose distribution of values is described in terms of their density functions, $f(x)$, which are similar to the functions we have been discussing above but with the added requirement that the area under these probability density functions, in their interval of definition, must be equal to one, a condition imposed on all probability functions by one of the **Axioms** (*i.e.*, basic assumptions which require no proof for their validity) of Probability. The question, then, is: Given a random variable x, with a density function, $f(x)$, how do we make sure that the total probability under the density function is equal to 1? How do we find probabilities of events whose probability of occurrence is less than one? The answer to these and similar other questions is: By Integration!

The elements of probability theory were discussed in Chapter 4. What we wish to demonstrate here is how integral calculus can be used in probability calculations. The method consists of finding the indefinite integral of the given probability function and then evaluate it, in accordance with the Fundamental Theorem of integral calculus, to find the probability of the event of interest.

In general, if X is a random variable, and $f(x)$ is the probability density function of X, where $a \leq X \leq b$, then the probability that the random variable X is between the values of $X = x_1 = c$ and $X = x_2 = d$ (where $a \leq c \leq d \leq b$), can be written as:

$$p(c \leq X \leq d) = \int_c^d f(x)dx = g(x)]_c^d = g(d) - g(c), \tag{B44}$$

where $g(x)$ is the indefinite integral of $f(x)$ (*i.e.*, $g'(x) = f(x)$).

If none of the methods of integration, discussed above, can be used to find the indefinite integral $g(x)$, for the given function $f(x)$, (one such example is the $f(x)$ associated with a normally distributed random variable defined by equation (B27)), the method above cannot be used. To find probabilities of events for such functions numerical methods must be used (similar to the "Limiting Summation" method) and the results are tabulated in tables which are usually found in all statistical texts.

Below we give an example which, in addition to the calculation of the probability of a desired event for a given random variable with a known form of a density function $f(x)$, demonstrates other useful calculations usually associated with continuous random variables.

Example 15

Let X be a continuous random variable, with $f(x) = Ax^{-1/2}$ in the interval $0 \leq x \leq 16$ and $f(x) = 0$ for all other values of x.

1. Find the value of A for which $f(x)$ is a proper probability function
2. Find the Cumulative Density Function of $X = \text{CDF}(X)$
3. Find the Expected (Average) value of $X = E(X)$
4. Find $E(X^2)$
5. Find the Variance of $X = V(X)$
6. Find the Standard Deviation of $X = \sigma(X)$
7. Find $P(4 \leq x \leq 9)$

Solutions:

1. For any density function $f(x)$ to be a proper probability function, we must have:

$$\int_a^b f(x)dx = 1 \qquad \text{(B45)}$$

For the given function: $f(x) = \begin{cases} Ax^{-1/2} & 0 \leq x \leq 16 \\ 0 & \text{for all other } x \end{cases}$ and

this implies that: $\displaystyle\int_0^{16} Ax^{-1/2}dx = 1$

Using "Rule of Integration" #4, we can write the Left-Hand Side (LHS) of the above equation as:

$$\int_0^{16} Ax^{-1/2}dx = A\int_0^{16} x^{-1/2}dx$$

$$= A\left[\left(x^{-1/2+1}\right)\middle/\left(-\frac{1}{2}+1\right)\right]\Big|_0^{16}, \text{ by using "Rule of integration" #3}$$

$$= 2Ax^{1/2}\Big|_0^{16}$$

$$= 2A(16^{1/2} - 0^{1/2}) = 2A(4 - 0)$$

$$= 2A(4)$$

$$= 8A$$

Since the LHS of the equation is equal to $8A$, if the total area under the given function is to be equal to 1, we must have: $8A = 1$, or $A = 1/8$

Therefore, if $A = 1/8$, the density function $f(x) = 1/8x^{-1/2}$, in the interval: $0 \leq x \leq 16$, is proper and can be used for probability calculations.

2. **By definition** $\quad \text{CDF}(X) = \int_a^x f(x)dx$ $\qquad\qquad$ (B46)

$$= 1/8 \int_0^x x^{-1/2}dx$$

$$= (1/8)(x^{1/2}/\frac{1}{2})\Big|_0^x = \frac{1}{4}x^{1/2}\Big|_0^x$$

$$= \frac{1}{4}(x^{1/2} - 0^{1/2}) = \frac{1}{4}x^{1/2}$$

Clearly, if $x = 0$, CDF(0) = 0, while if $x = 16$, CDF(16) = 1. These are two of the defining properties of CDF(X).

3. **By definition** $\quad E(X) = \int_\alpha^b xf(x)dx$ $\qquad\qquad$ (B47)

$$= \int_0^{16} x(1/8x^{-1/2}) = 1/8 \int_0^{16} x^{1/2}dx$$

$$= (1/8)\big[(x^{3/2}/(3/2))\big]\Big|_0^{16} = \big[(1/8)/(2/3)\big](x^{3/2})\Big|_0^{16}$$

$$= (1/12)(16^{3/2} - 0^{3/2}) = 1/12\big[(4^2)^{3/2} - 0\big]$$

$$= \frac{1}{12}\big[4^3 - 0\big]$$

$$= (1/12)(4^3) = \frac{(16 \times 4)}{(3 \times 4)} = 16/3 = 5.33\dots$$

4. **By definition** $\quad E(X^2) = \int_a^b x^2 f(x)dx$ $\qquad\qquad$ (B48)

$$= \int_0^{16} x^2\big[1/8x^{-1/2}\big]dx = 1/8 \int_0^{16} x^{3/2}dx$$

$$E(X^2) = \big[(1/8)(x^{5/2}/(5/2))\big]\Big|_0^{16} = (1/8)(2/5)x^{5/2}\Big|_0^{16}$$

$$= \frac{2}{40}x^{5/2} = (1/20)[(4^2)^{5/2} - 0] = (1/20)\,(4^5)$$

$$= (16)(16)(4)\,/\,(4)(5) = 256\,/\,5$$

$$= 51.2$$

5. **By definition** $\quad V(X) = E(X^2) - \big[E(X)\big]^2$ $\qquad\qquad$ (B49)

$$= 256/5 - (16/3)^2 = 256/5 - 256/9$$

$$= 256(1/5 - 1/9) = 256((9 - 5)/45)$$

$$= 256(4/45)$$

$$\approx 22.8$$

6. **By definition** $\sigma(X) = \sqrt{V(X)}$ (B50)

$$= \sqrt{22.8}$$

$$= 4.77$$

7. **By definition** $P(c \leq X \leq d) = \int_{c}^{d} f(x)dx$ (B51)

$$P(4 \leq X \leq 9) = \int_{4}^{9} 1/8x^{-1/2}dx = \frac{1}{8}\int_{4}^{9} x^{-1/2}dx = \frac{1}{8}\left[\frac{x^{1/2}}{1/2}\right]_{4}^{9}$$

$$= \frac{1}{4}(9^{1/2} - 4^{1/2}) = \frac{1}{4}(3 - 2) = \frac{1}{4}$$

$$= 0.25$$

Therefore, the random variable X, having the probability density function $f(x) = 1/8x^{-1/2}$, in the interval $0 \leq x \leq 16$, has a probability of 0.25 of falling in the interval $4 \leq x \leq 9$.

C

Solutions of Systems of Linear Equations Using Matrix Algebra

Problem: Given a set of n linear equation in $n = 3$ here unknowns;

$$a_{11}x_1 + a_{12}x_2 + a_{13}x_3 = b_1$$
$$a_{21}x_1 + a_{22}x_2 + a_{23}x_3 = b_2 \qquad \text{(C1)}$$
$$a_{31}x_1 + a_{32}x_2 + a_{33}x_3 = b_3$$

or

$$\begin{bmatrix} a_{11}\,a_{12}\,a_{13} \\ a_{21}\,a_{22}\,a_{23} \\ a_{31}\,a_{32}\,a_{33} \end{bmatrix} \begin{bmatrix} x_1 \\ x_2 \\ x_3 \end{bmatrix} = \begin{bmatrix} b_1 \\ b_2 \\ b_3 \end{bmatrix} \qquad \text{(C2)}$$

or $$AX = B \qquad \text{(C3)}$$

Solve for the Unknowns X_1, X_2, X_3.

Solutions
■ Algebraic

Solve one of the equations of set (C1) for one of the unknowns, in terms of the others (for example, solve equation 1 for x_1 to obtain: $x_1 = 1/a_{11}(b_1 - a_{12}x_2 - a_{13}x_3)$), and then substitute for x_1 in the other 2 equations.

After simplification, by combining similar terms, we now have 2 equations in 2 unknowns. Continue the process until one variable is completely solved for. Then go back and, using this solved variable, find the values of the other variables.

Example 1

Solve Algebraically the System of Equations

$$2x_1 + 3x_2 - 4x_3 = 9 \qquad (1)$$

$$3x_1 - 2x_2 + 3x_3 = -15 \qquad (2)$$

$$x_1 + 4x_2 - 2x_3 = 12 \qquad (3)$$

Solution Solve equation (3) for x_1 to obtain

$$x_1 = 12 - 4x_2 + 2x_3 \qquad (4)$$

Now substitute (4) into (1) and (2) to obtain

$$2(12 - 4x_2 + 2x_3) + 3x_2 - 4x_3 = 9 \qquad (1)'$$
and $$3(12 - 4x_2 + 2x_3) - 2x_2 + 3x_3 = -15 \qquad (2)'$$

By simplifying (1)' and (2)', by combining similar terms, we obtain

$$-5x_2 + 0x_3 = -15 \qquad (1)''$$
and $$-14x_2 + 9x_3 = -51 \qquad (2)''$$

Then, from (1)'' we obtain $x_2 = 3$, and by substituting this value into (2)'', we obtain

$$x_3 = \frac{1}{9}[-51 + 14x_2] = \frac{1}{9}[-51 + 14(3)] = \frac{1}{9}[-51 + 42] = \frac{1}{9}(-9) = -1$$

When the values of $x_2 = 3$ and $x_3 = -1$ are substituted into equation (4) above, we obtain

$$x_1 = 12 - 4(3) + 2(-1) = 12 - 12 - 2 = -2,$$

and the solution to this system of equation is $x_1 = -2$, $x_2 = 3$, and $x_3 = -1$.

■ ■ ■

■ Matrix Solutions

1. **The Available Matrix Solutions**
   a) **The Gaussian Elimination Method**
      i) Form the Augmented Matrix A/B from set (C2) above.
      ii) Apply Row Operations (see section 4 below) to A/B to transform the coefficient matrix A to I.
      iii) When $A = I$, the solution is read off in the B position of the A/B matrix.

Example 2

Solve the problem of example 1, using the Gauss Elimination method.

Solution The augmented matrix A/B is $A/B = \begin{pmatrix} 2 & 3 & -4 & 9 \\ 3 & -2 & 3 & -15 \\ 1 & 4 & -2 & 12 \end{pmatrix} \begin{matrix} R_1 \\ R_2 \\ R_3 \end{matrix}$

Now apply Row Operations to Matrix A/B

Interchange rows R_1 and R_3 in A/B above to obtain

$$A/B_1 = \begin{pmatrix} 1 & 4 & -2 & 12 \\ 3 & -2 & 3 & -15 \\ 2 & 3 & -4 & 9 \end{pmatrix} \begin{matrix} R_1 \\ R_2 \\ R_3 \end{matrix}$$

Now multiply R_1 by -3 and add to R_2, and multiply Row R_1 by -2 and add to R_3 to obtain

$$A/B_{2,3} = \begin{pmatrix} 1 & 4 & -2 & 12 \\ 0 & -14 & 9 & -51 \\ 0 & -5 & 0 & -15 \end{pmatrix} \begin{matrix} R_1 \\ R_2 \\ R_3 \end{matrix}$$

Interchange Rows R_2 and R_3 to obtain $A/B_4 = \begin{pmatrix} 1 & 4 & -2 & 12 \\ 0 & -5 & 0 & -15 \\ 0 & -14 & 9 & -51 \end{pmatrix} \begin{matrix} R_1 \\ R_2 \\ R_3 \end{matrix}$

Multiply R_2 by $\left(-\dfrac{1}{5}\right)$ to obtain $A/B_5 = \begin{pmatrix} 1 & 4 & -2 & 12 \\ 0 & 1 & 0 & 3 \\ 0 & -14 & 9 & -51 \end{pmatrix} \begin{matrix} R_1 \\ R_2 \\ R_3 \end{matrix}$

Now multiply R_2 by -4 and add to R_1, and multiply R_2 by $(+14)$ and add to R_3 to obtain

$$A/B_6 = \begin{pmatrix} 1 & 0 & -2 & 0 \\ 0 & 1 & 0 & 3 \\ 0 & 0 & 9 & -9 \end{pmatrix} \begin{matrix} R_1 \\ R_2 \\ R_3 \end{matrix}$$

Multiply R_3 by $(1/9)$ to obtain $A/B_7 = \begin{pmatrix} 1 & 0 & -2 & 0 \\ 0 & 1 & 0 & 3 \\ 0 & 0 & 1 & -1 \end{pmatrix} \begin{matrix} R_1 \\ R_2 \\ R_3 \end{matrix}$

Now multiply R_3 by $(+2)$ and add to R_1 to obtain $A/B_8 = \begin{pmatrix} 1 & 0 & 0 & -2 \\ 0 & 1 & 0 & 3 \\ 0 & 0 & 1 & -1 \end{pmatrix} \begin{matrix} R_1 \\ R_2 \\ R_3 \end{matrix}$

The solution is $x_1 = -2$, $x_2 = 3$, and $x_3 = -1$, and this is the same solution, which was obtained using the Algebraic Method (See Example 1).

■ ■ ■

b) **"Inverse" Method**
  i) Form the Augmented Matrix A/I.
  ii) Transform (through Row operations, see section 4 below) the Augmented Matrix A/I to I/A^{-1}.
  iii) Pre-Multiply the matrix equation (C3), *i.e.*, $AX = B$, by A^{-1}.
  iv) Then the solution is:

$$X = A^{-1}B \tag{C4}$$

Example 3

Solve the problem of example 1, by first finding the Inverse of matrix A.

Solution The Augmented matrix $A/I = \begin{pmatrix} 2 & 3 & -4 & 1 & 0 & 0 \\ 3 & -2 & 3 & 0 & 1 & 0 \\ 1 & 4 & -2 & 0 & 0 & 0 \end{pmatrix} \begin{matrix} R_1 \\ R_2, \\ R_3 \end{matrix}$

Applying the same sequence of Row Operations to the Augmented matrix A/I, as we applied to the Augmented Matrix A/B of Example 2, we obtain

$$A/I_8 = \begin{pmatrix} 1 & 0 & 0 & \dfrac{8}{45} & \dfrac{10}{45} & -\dfrac{1}{45} \\ 0 & 1 & 0 & -\dfrac{9}{45} & \dfrac{0}{45} & \dfrac{18}{45} \\ 0 & 0 & 1 & -\dfrac{14}{45} & \dfrac{5}{45} & \dfrac{13}{45} \end{pmatrix} \begin{matrix} R_1 \\ R_2 \\ R_3 \end{matrix}$$

from which we obtain:

$$A^{-1} = \begin{pmatrix} 8/15 & 10/45 & -1/45 \\ -9/45 & 0/45 & 18/45 \\ -14/45 & 5/45 & 13/45 \end{pmatrix} = \frac{1}{45}\begin{pmatrix} 8 & 10 & -1 \\ -9 & 0 & 18 \\ -14 & 5 & 13 \end{pmatrix},$$

and the solution is:

$$x = \begin{pmatrix} x_1 \\ x_2 \\ x_3 \end{pmatrix} = A^{-1}B = \frac{1}{45}\begin{pmatrix} 8 & 10 & -1 \\ -9 & 0 & 18 \\ -14 & 5 & 13 \end{pmatrix}\begin{pmatrix} 9 \\ -15 \\ 12 \end{pmatrix} = \begin{pmatrix} -2 \\ 3 \\ -1 \end{pmatrix},$$

from which we obtain the same solution: $x_1 = -2$, $x_2 = 3$, and $x_3 = -1$.

■■■

c) Cramer's Rule

This method bypasses the calculation of the Inverse, BUT requires the calculation of $(n + 1)$ determinants. Then the solution for variable x_j is given as the ratio of the 2 Determinants:

$$x_j = |A_j|/|A| \qquad (C5)$$

where A_j = The Matrix formed from matrix A by replacing the j-th column of A with the R.H.S. Vector B.

Note: The value of the determinants of matrices A_j and A (i.e., $|A_j|$ and $|A|$) are to be found using the methods discussed in (2a), (2b), or (2c) below.

Example 4

Solve the problem of example 1, using Cramer's rule.

Solution To use Cramer's rule we need to find the determinant of the 4 matrices

$$A = \begin{pmatrix} 2 & 3 & -4 \\ 3 & -2 & 3 \\ 1 & 4 & -2 \end{pmatrix}, A_1 = \begin{pmatrix} 9 & 3 & -4 \\ -15 & -2 & 3 \\ 12 & 4 & -2 \end{pmatrix},$$

$$A_2 = \begin{bmatrix} 2 & 9 & -4 \\ 3 & -15 & 3 \\ 1 & 12 & -2 \end{bmatrix} \quad \text{and} \quad A_3 = \begin{bmatrix} 2 & 3 & 9 \\ 3 & -2 & -15 \\ 1 & 4 & 12 \end{bmatrix}$$

Then, using equation (C12), we find:

$$\begin{aligned} \text{Det } A = |A| &= [(2)(-2)(-2) + (3)(4)(-4) + (1)(3)(3)] - [(1)(-2)(-4) \\ &\quad + (2)(4)(3) + (-2)(3)(3)] \\ &= [8 - 48 + 9] - [8 + 24 - 18] = [-31] - [14] \\ &= -31 - 14 = -45 \end{aligned}$$

$$
\begin{aligned}
\text{Det } A_1 = |A_1| &= [(9)(-2)(-2) + (-15)(4)(-4) + (12)(3)(3)] \\
&\quad -[(12)(-2)(-4) + (9)(4)(3) + (-15)(3)(-2)] \\
&= [36 + 240 + 108] - [96 + 108 + 90] \\
&= [384] - [294] = 90
\end{aligned}
$$

$$
\begin{aligned}
\text{Det } A_2 = |A_2| &= [(2)(-15)(-2) + (3)(12)(-4) + (1)(9)(3)] \\
&\quad -[(1)(-15)(-4) + (2)(12)(3) + (3)(9)(-2)] \\
&= [60 - 144 + 27] - [60 + 72 - 54] = [-57] - [78] \\
&= -57 - 78 = -135
\end{aligned}
$$

$$
\begin{aligned}
\text{Det } A_3 = |A_3| &= [(2)(-2)(12) + (3)(4)(9) + (1)(3)(-15)] \\
&\quad - [(1)(-2)(9) + (2)(4)(-15) + (3)(3)(12)] \\
&= [-48 + 108 - 45] - [-18 - 120 + 108] \\
&= [15] - [-30] = 15 + 30 = 45
\end{aligned}
$$

Therefore, the solutions for x_1, x_2, and x_3 are according to equation (C5):

$$
x_1 = \frac{|A_1|}{|A|} = \frac{90}{-45} = -2, \; x_2 = \frac{|A_2|}{|A|} = \frac{-135}{-45} = +3,
$$

and

$$
x_3 = \frac{|A_3|}{|A|} = \frac{45}{-45} = -1,
$$
and these solutions are the same as those obtained by using the other methods to solve the same problem.

■ ■ ■

d) **Finding the Inverse by the "ADJOINT" Matrix Method**

i) Find the cofactor $A_{ij} = (-1)^{i+j} \times$ (Minor of a_{ij}) for each element a_{ij} (C6)

   (see (2c) below).

ii) Form the cofactor matrix A: $\text{Cof} A = \begin{pmatrix} A_{11} & A_{12} & \cdots & A_{1n} \\ A_{21} & A_{22} & \cdots & A_{2n} \\ \multicolumn{4}{c}{\dotfill} \\ A_{n1} & A_{n2} & \cdots & A_{nn} \end{pmatrix} \Bigg]$ (C7)

iii) Form the "Adjoint" Matrix $\text{Adj} A = (\text{C of } A)^t$ (C8)

iv) Find the Inverse: $A^{-1} = \dfrac{1}{|A|} (\text{Adj} A)$,   (C9)

   where $|A| = $ Determinant of Matrix A

v) Then $X = A^{-1}B$ (C10)

Example 5 Solve the problem of example 1, using the "Adjoint" Matrix Method to first find the Inverse of Matrix A, then $X = A^{-1}B$.

Solution We will use equation (C6) and matrix $A = \begin{pmatrix} 2 & 3 & -4 \\ 3 & -2 & 3 \\ 1 & 4 & -2 \end{pmatrix}$

to find the COFACTOR Matrix $A = \text{C of } A$, given by equation (C7). We obtain

$$A_{11} = (-1)^{1+1} \det \begin{pmatrix} -2 & 3 \\ 4 & -2 \end{pmatrix} = (1)[4 - 12] = -8$$

$$A_{12} = (-1)^{1+2} \det \begin{pmatrix} 3 & 3 \\ 1 & -2 \end{pmatrix} = (-1)[-6 - 3] = (-1)(-9) = 9$$

$$A_{13} = (-1)^{1+3} \det \begin{pmatrix} 3 & -2 \\ 1 & 4 \end{pmatrix} = (+1)[12 + 2] = (+1)(14) = 14$$

$$A_{21} = (-1)^{2+1} \det \begin{pmatrix} 3 & -4 \\ 4 & -2 \end{pmatrix} = (-1)[-6 + 16] = (-1)(10) = -10$$

$$A_{22} = (-1)^{2+2} \det \begin{pmatrix} 2 & -4 \\ 1 & -2 \end{pmatrix} = (+1)[-4 + 4] = (1)(0) = 0$$

$$A_{23} = (-1)^{2+3} \det \begin{pmatrix} 2 & 3 \\ 1 & 4 \end{pmatrix} = (-1)[8 - 3] = (-1)(5) = -5$$

$$A_{31} = (-1)^{3+1} \det \begin{pmatrix} 3 & -4 \\ -2 & 3 \end{pmatrix} = (1)[9 - 8] = (1)(1) = 1$$

$$A_{32} = (-1)^{3+2} \det \begin{pmatrix} 2 & -4 \\ 3 & 3 \end{pmatrix} = (-1)[6 + 12] = (-1)(18) = -18$$

$$A_{33} = (-1)^{3+3} \det \begin{pmatrix} 2 & 3 \\ 3 & -2 \end{pmatrix} = (1)[-4 - 9] = (1)(-13) = -13$$

Then, the cofactor matrix A is given by:

$$\text{Cof } A = \begin{pmatrix} A_{11} & A_{12} & A_{13} \\ A_{21} & A_{22} & A_{23} \\ A_{31} & A_{32} & A_{33} \end{pmatrix} = \begin{pmatrix} -8 & 9 & 14 \\ -10 & 0 & -5 \\ 1 & -18 & -13 \end{pmatrix}$$

Note: The Transposed of a given Matrix A is another matrix, represented by A^t, which is obtained from matrix A by interchanging Rows and Columns. Applying this definition to the cofactor matrix $A = \text{Cof } A$ above, we obtain $(\text{Cof } A)^t$ which is, by definition, the "Adjoint" Matrix A. Therefore:

$$\text{Adj} A = (\text{Cof } A)^t = \begin{pmatrix} -8 & -10 & 1 \\ 9 & 0 & -18 \\ 14 & -5 & -13 \end{pmatrix}$$

Since we have already found the determinant of Matrix A ($\det A = |A| = -45$; see Cramer's rule solution) the Inverse of Matrix A, using the "Adjoint" Matrix Method, is given by equation (C9), and is equal to:

$$A^{-1} = \frac{1}{|A|}(\text{Adj} A) = \frac{1}{-45} \begin{bmatrix} -8 & -10 & 1 \\ 9 & 0 & -18 \\ 14 & -5 & -13 \end{bmatrix} = \frac{1}{45} \begin{bmatrix} 8 & 10 & -1 \\ -9 & 0 & 18 \\ -14 & 5 & 13 \end{bmatrix},$$

and we see that the Inverse of Matrix A, A^{-1}, obtained by the Adjoint Matrix Method is the same as the one obtained using the Gauss Elimination Method and the Augmented Matrix A/I, as it should be because the INVERSE, when it exists, is UNIQUE, and does not depend on the method used to find it. Then the solution is:

$$X = \begin{pmatrix} x_1 \\ x_2 \\ x_3 \end{pmatrix} = A^{-1}B = \frac{1}{45} \begin{bmatrix} 8 & 10 & -1 \\ -9 & 0 & 18 \\ -14 & 5 & 13 \end{bmatrix} \begin{bmatrix} 9 \\ -15 \\ 12 \end{bmatrix} = \begin{bmatrix} -2 \\ 3 \\ -1 \end{bmatrix},$$

and $x_1 = -2$, $x_2 = 3$, and $x_3 = -1$, as before.

Note: In the two methods above (*i.e.*, *c*) and *d*)), the solution depends on the determinant of the coefficient Matrix A (*i.e.*, $|A|$), which is obtained as shown below.

■ ■ ■

2. **The Determinant of a Square Matrix A**
    The determinant is a characteristic value associated with Square Matrices. The range of its value can be conveniently divided into 3 regions namely:

    $$|A| > 0, |A| = 0, \text{ or } |A| < 0.$$

    Depending on the size of the square matrix, the determinant $|A|$ can be found as follows
    a) Determinant of a 2 × 2 Matrix A

    If $A = \begin{pmatrix} a_{11} & a_{12} \\ a_{21} & a_{22} \end{pmatrix}$, then det $A = |A| = a_{11}a_{22} - a_{12}a_{21}$ \hfill (C11)

    b) Determinant of a 3 × 3 Matrix A

    If $A = \begin{pmatrix} a_{11} & a_{12} & a_{13} \\ a_{21} & a_{22} & a_{23} \\ a_{31} & a_{32} & a_{33} \end{pmatrix}$,

    then

    $$|A| = (a_{11}a_{22}a_{33} + a_{21}a_{32}a_{13} + a_{31}a_{12}a_{23})$$
    $$- (a_{31}a_{22}a_{13} + a_{11}a_{32}a_{23} + a_{33}a_{21}a_{12}) \tag{C12}$$

    c) **Determinant of an n × n matrix A (Cofactor Expansion Method)**
       i)   Find the minor of element a_{ij} of matrix A. It is equal to the Determinant of the submatrix formed by deleting the *ith* row & *jth* column.
       ii) Then, the Cofactor of $a_{ij} = A_{ij} = (-1)^{i+j} \times$ (Minor of element a_{ij})
       iii) Multiply the cofactors of *any row* or *any column* by the corresponding elements of that row or column in Matrix A.
       iv) The sum of these products is the determinant of the matrix. Example
            $$|A| = a_{11}A_{11} + a_{12}A_{12} + a_{13}A_{13} \tag{C13}$$
            (using the 1ˢᵗ Row of a 3 × 3 Matrix)

Note: If $|A| = 0$, the Matrix A is called singular, A^{-1} does not exist, and no solution is possible.

Example 6

Find the determinant of Matrix A of example 1, where

$$A = \begin{pmatrix} 2 & 3 & -4 \\ 3 & -2 & 3 \\ 1 & 4 & -2 \end{pmatrix},$$

using the COFACTOR EXPANSION method.

Solution To solve this problem, we first need to find the Cofactor Matrix A (*i.e.*, Cof (A)), which was found in example 5 previously, and is given by:

$$\text{Cof } A = \begin{pmatrix} -8 & 9 & 14 \\ -10 & 0 & -5 \\ 1 & 18 & -13 \end{pmatrix}$$

Then to find the Determinant of Matrix A, we use an expansion about any row or column of Matrix A, as follows: det $A = |A| = (2)(-8) + 3(9) + (-4)(14) = -16 + 27 - 56 = -45$, which is obtained by multiplying each element of Row 1 of Matrix A by the corresponding element of the C of A Matrix, and summing the products.

We can similarly obtain det $A = |A|$ about any other row or column of A and the result will always be the same because the Determinant is unique.

For example, expanding about column 3 of A, we obtain: det $A = |A| = (-4)(14) + (3)(-5) + (-2)(-13) = -56 - 15 + 26 = -45$, and both of these results are identical to the value obtained for det $A = |A|$, using equation (C12), which is a special formula applicable only when the given Matrix A is 3×3, while the Cofactor Expansion Method can be applied to any $n \times n$ Matrix A.

■ ■ ■

d) **Properties of Determinants**
  i) The work needed to find $|A|$ is reduced considerably if the Row or Column selected for the Cofactor Expansion has many zeros.
  ii) The determinant of A and its transpose (A^t) are equal.
  iii) If all a_{ij} in any row or column are $= 0$, $|A| = 0$.
  iv) If the elements of any 2 rows (or columns) are equal or proportional, then $|A| = 0$.
  v) If the elements of any row are multiplied by K, then the determinant is also multiplied by K.
  vi) The Determinant of the Identity Matrix $|I| = 1$.
  vii) Any non-zero multiple of one row may be added to any other row, without changing the value of the determinant.
  viii) Interchanging any two rows of a matrix, changes the sign BUT NOT the value of the Determinant.

3. **The Rank of a Matrix**
   The rank of a matrix is the number of Linearly Independent rows (or columns) in the matrix.

a) **Methods of Obtaining the Rank of a Matrix**

i) Use Row Operations to obtain zeros in as many rows as possible. The number of rows that cannot be reduced to zero is the Rank of the matrix.

ii) Determine the order (*i.e.*, the size or dimensionality) of the largest square submatrix whose determinant $\neq 0$.

A) If A is square & $|A| \neq 0$, $r(A)$ = Number of rows of A.

B) If A is NOT square (or if A is square but $|A| = 0$), r(A) is equal to the size of the largest Square submatrix in A whose Determinant $\neq 0$.

C) If there is NO square submatrix in A with Det $\neq 0$, r(A) = 0.

b) The Rank of a System (r(S)) of Equations ($AX = B$)

i) $r(S) = r(A/B)$ (C14)
(*i.e.*, the Rank of the System is equal to the Rank of the Augmented matrix A/B)

ii) $r(A/B)$ can be found by one of the above two methods.

c) **Rules for Determining Consistency & Number of Solutions based on RANK**

i) Determine $r(A)$, $r(A/B)$, and n = number of variables in $AX = B$

ii) If $r(A/B) = r(A)$, the System of Equations is consistent, and solutions exist. We write: $r(S) = r(A/B) = r(A)$ (C15)

iii) If $r(S) = r(A/B) = n$ (number of variables), the system has a UNIQUE SOLUTION.   (C16)

If $r(S) = r(A/B)$, but it is not equal to the value of n, the system has INFINITE SOLUTIONS.   (C17)

Example 7

For the problem of example 1, Determine the Rank of Matrix A, the Rank of the System, and state whether this system is INCONSISTENT or CONSISTENT and, if CONSISTENT, state whether the system has a UNIQUE solution, or an INFINITE number of solutions.

Solution For the system of equations of example 1, we have:

$$A = \begin{pmatrix} 2 & 3 & -4 \\ 3 & -2 & 3 \\ 1 & 4 & -2 \end{pmatrix} \quad \text{and} \quad A/B = \begin{pmatrix} 2 & 3 & -4 & 9 \\ 3 & -2 & 3 & -15 \\ 1 & 4 & -2 & 12 \end{pmatrix}$$

Since Matrix A is a 3×3 square matrix and det $A = |A| = -45 \neq 0$, the rank of Matrix $A = r(A) = 3$. The Rank of the system is given by the Rank of the A/B Matrix, whose dimensionality is 3×4. Since A/B is not a Square Matrix, the largest square submatrix in it is 3×3 (Actually there are 4 such 3×3 submatrices in A/B, one of which is A whose Determinant $\neq 0$). Since there is a 3×3 submatrix in A/B, whose Determinant $\neq 0$, $r(A/B) = 3$. But, if $r(A) = r(A/B)$ the System of equations are consistent, and this means that solutions exist. However, since $r(A) = r(A/B) = n = 3$, this system of equations has a unique solution, given by:

$x_1 = -2$, $x_2 = 3$, and $x_3 = -1$, as was demonstrated in examples 1 through 5.

■ ■ ■

4. **Row Operations**

   The matrix solution methods (a) and (b) are based on the application of Row Operations to the Augmented Matrices A/B and A/I.

   The Row Operations usually used are the following three:

   a) If 2 rows of an augmented matrix are interchanged the solution to the system of Matrix equations $AX = B$ does not change.

   b) If a row of an augmented matrix is multiplied by a non-zero constant, the solution to the system of matrix equations $AX = B$ does not change.

   c) If a row of any augmented matrix is multiplied by a non-zero constant and this result is added to another row, the solution to the system of matrix equations $AX = B$ does not change.

D Elements of Summation Theory

D.1 The Summation Operator Σ

Let $x_1, x_2, \ldots, x_n$ represent the values obtained in a sample. Often we require the sum of these numbers, namely $x_1 + x_2 + \cdots + x_n$, because we are interested in the average, or mean value, of these numbers. On other occasions we require the sum of the squares of the sample observations, namely $x_1^2 + x_2^2 + \cdots + x_n^2$, to find the variance. Expressions such as these can be simplified by the introduction of the "summation operator", Σ, which is the capital sigma letter of the Greek alphabet. Symbols, such as the Σ, which tell us to carry out an operation (the operation here is addition) are called operators.

To obtain the sum of the sample observations we write:

$$\sum_{i=1}^{n} x_i = x_1 + x_2 + \cdots + x_n \tag{D1}$$

while the sum of the squares can be represented as

$$\sum_{i=1}^{n} x_i^2 = x_1^2 + x_2^2 + \cdots + x_n^2 \tag{D2}$$

The letter i, which is a subscript to the variable x and also appears below the Σ, is called the "index of summation". The value of i appearing below the Σ is called the "initial value" of the index, while the value appearing on top of Σ represents the "ending value" of the index. The index itself can assume all the consecutive integer values between its initial value and ending value (*i.e.*, $1 \leq i \leq n$ here). The quantity to the right of Σ (*i.e.*, x_i in (D1) and x_i^2 in (D2)) is referred as the "argument" of the summation.

The summation operator, Σ, directs us to do the following:

1. Assign to the index of summation its initial value.
2. Substitute this value in the argument of the summation and write the result down.

   For example, in the expression $\sum_{i=1}^{n} x_i^2$, the summation index i is assigned the value of 1, and this value is substituted in the argument x_i^2 to produce x_1^2. If the argument does not include the index i, it remains constant as the index of summation changes.
3. The summation operator, Σ, now provides the $+$ sign, and the value of the index of summation is incremented by 1 (*i.e.*, $i = 1 + 1 = 2$ now) and the process is repeated until after i is assigned the "ending value" (*i.e.*, until $i = n$), when the process terminates. Note that in the expanded form of the summation notation the first entry is the argument evaluated at the initial value of the summation index while the last entry is the argument evaluated at the ending index value. The in-between entries represent the argument evaluated at successive integer values of the summation index between the initial and ending values. There is nothing unique about choosing i as the index. Any other letter of the alphabet, but usually i, j, k, can be chosen as summation indeces.

D.2 Summation Theorems

The summation notation is used very extensively in statistics now, and a number of theorems have evolved because of this use, which make the application of the summation operator much easier. These theorems are basically restatements of operational results and can be proved by correctly applying the summation operator. For the sake of clarity and simplification we classify these theorems as "single summation" and "Double Summation" theorems, depending on whether a single or double summation indeces are involved.

■ Single Summation Theorems

These theorems involve only a single index of summation, varying from an initial index value to an ending value, and a single Σ. The most important of these theorems are:

1. $\displaystyle\sum_{i=1}^{n} c = \underbrace{c + c + \cdots + c}_{n\ terms} = nc$ (where c is a constant) $\hspace{2cm}$ (D3)

> In words, this rule states that the summation of a constant is equal to the product of the constant and the number of terms in the summation.

2. $\displaystyle\sum_{i=1}^{n} cx_i = cx_1 + cx_2 + \cdots + cx_n = c(x_1 + x_2 + \cdots + x_n) = c\sum_{i=1}^{n} x_i$ $\hspace{1cm}$ (D4)

> or in words: The summation of the products of a constant c by an observation x_i is the product of the constant and the summation of the observations.

3. $\displaystyle\sum_{i=1}^{n}(x_i - y_i + z_i) = (x_1 - y_1 + z_1) + (x_2 - y_2 + z_2) + \cdots + (x_n - y_n + z_n)$

$$= (x_1 + x_2 + \cdots + x_n) - (y_1 + y_2 + \cdots + y_n)$$

$$+ (z_1 + z_2 + \cdots + z_n) = \sum_{i=1}^{n} x_i - \sum_{i=1}^{n} y_i + \sum_{i=1}^{n} z_i$$

$$= \sum_{i=1}^{n} x_i - \sum_{i=1}^{n} y_i + \sum_{i=1}^{n} z_i \hspace{2cm} \text{(D5)}$$

> or in words: The summation of a sum or difference of observations of two or more variables, associated with an individual sum, is the sum or difference of the individual summations.

■ Double Summation Theorems

These theorems involve two indeces of summation (i and j for example) and two summation signs Σ. While the "single summation theorems" generate rules, which make the summation of single arrays of numbers easier, the "Double Summation Theorems" make the summation of "Tables of Values" easier. A "Table of values" usually consists of several rows (one or more) and several columns (one or more). It is constructive to think of the index i as counting the number of rows in the table while j counts the number of columns in the same table. To demonstrate the validity of these theorems one applies the rules of the summation operator to one of the summation signs holding the other summation index constant, thus reducing the double summation to a single summation. The rules are then applied again to the remaining summation sign to complete the evaluation of the summation.

Before we state the most important of these theorems and demonstrate their validity, let us illustrate the computations involved in a double summation.

Suppose we were asked to evaluate the double summation:

$$\sum_{i=1}^{n}\sum_{j=1}^{m} x_{ij} \hspace{2cm} \text{(D6)}$$

By holding i fixed and applying the rules of the summation operator to the inner summation sign with summation index j we can re-write the given double summation as:

$$\sum_{i=1}^{n}\sum_{j=1}^{m} x_{ij} = \sum_{i=1}^{n}(x_{i1} + x_{i2} + \cdots + x_{im}) \hspace{2cm} \text{(D7)}$$

Applying now the rules of the summation operator to this last result we can write the original double summation as:

$$\sum_{i=1}^{n}\sum_{j=1}^{m}x_{ij} = \sum_{i=1}^{n}(x_{i1} + x_{i2} + \cdots + x_{im}) = \begin{Bmatrix} x_{11} + x_{12} + \cdots + x_{1m} \\ x_{21} + x_{22} + \cdots + x_{2m} \\ \cdots\cdots\cdots\cdots\cdots\cdots\cdots \\ x_{n1} + x_{n2} + \cdots + x_{nm} \end{Bmatrix} \quad \text{(D8)}$$

Three of the most important double summation theorems correspond to the three single summation theorems discussed above and they are:

1. $\displaystyle\sum_{i=1}^{n}\sum_{j=1}^{m}c = \sum_{i=1}^{n}(c + c + \cdots + c) = \sum_{i=1}^{n}(mc)$

$$= mc + mc + \cdots + mc = n(mc) = nmc \quad \text{(D9)}$$

2. $\displaystyle\sum_{i=1}^{n}\sum_{j=1}^{n}cx_{ij} = c\sum_{i=1}^{n}\sum_{j=1}^{m}x_{ij}$ \hspace{3cm} (D10)

3. $\displaystyle\sum_{i=1}^{n}\sum_{j=1}^{m}(x_{ij} - y_{ij} + z_{ij}) = \sum_{i=1}^{n}\sum_{j=1}^{m}x_{ij} - \sum_{i=1}^{n}\sum_{j=1}^{m}y_{ij} + \sum_{i=1}^{n}\sum_{j=1}^{m}z_{ij}$ \hspace{1cm} (D11)

We state below a fourth theorem which states that the order of evaluation of the multiple indeces of summation is not important and the result of the summation remains the same regardless of which index is evaluated first, namely:

4. $\displaystyle\sum_{i=1}^{n}\sum_{j=1}^{m}x_{ij} = \sum_{j=1}^{m}\sum_{i=1}^{n}x_{ij}$ \hspace{3cm} (D12)

Note that many more such theorems (rules) can be stated for both single and double summations, but we felt that only a few are needed to illustrate the concepts involved.

D.3   Some Useful Summation Formulas

Applying the rules of the summation operators to the following three summations, we obtain the "closed-form" expressions:

1. $\displaystyle\sum_{i=1}^{n}i = 1 + 2 + \cdots + n = \frac{n(n + 1)}{2}$ \hspace{3cm} (D13)

2. $\displaystyle\sum_{i=1}^{n}i^2 = 1^2 + 2^2 + \ldots + n^2 = \frac{n(n + 1)(2n + 1)}{6}$ \hspace{2cm} (D14)

3. $\displaystyle\sum_{i=1}^{n}i^3 = 1^3 + 2^3 + \ldots + n^3 = \left[\frac{n(n + 1)}{2}\right]^2$ \hspace{2cm} (D15)

These formulas, which are most frequently encountered in the evaluation of the definite integral of a function $f(x)$ by the limiting value of an infinite summation

$(i.e., \displaystyle\int_{a}^{b}f(x)dx = \lim\sum_{i=1}^{n}f(x_i)\Delta x)$, tell us that the values of the summation in the left can be easily obtained by the "closed-form" expressions in the corresponding right-hand side (*RHS*), for any value of *n*.

Another set of useful summation formulas can be obtained by applying the rules of the summation operator to the following summations:

4. $\displaystyle\sum_{i=0}^{n} \frac{1}{i!} = \frac{1}{0!} + \frac{1}{1!} + \frac{1}{2!} + \cdots + \frac{1}{n!}$ (D16)

and $\displaystyle\lim_{n\to\infty} \sum_{i=0}^{n} \frac{1}{i!} = e$ (D17)

where *e* is the base of the Naperian or natural logarithms.

5. $\displaystyle\sum_{i=0}^{n} \frac{x^i}{i} = 1 + x + \frac{x^2}{2!} + \frac{x^3}{3!} + \cdots + \frac{x^n}{n!}$ (D18)

and $\displaystyle\lim_{n\to\infty} \sum_{i=0}^{n} \frac{x^i}{i!} = e^x$ (D19)

6. $\displaystyle\sum_{k=0}^{n} (-1)^k \frac{x^{2k+1}}{2^{k+1}!} = x - \frac{x^3}{3!} + \frac{x^5}{5!} - \frac{x^7}{7!} + \cdots$ (D20)

and $\displaystyle\lim_{n\to\infty} \sum_{k=0}^{n} (-1)^k \frac{x^{2k+1}}{2k+1!} = \sin x \quad (\text{all } x)$ (D21)

7. $\displaystyle\sum_{k=0}^{n} (-1)^k \frac{x^{2k}}{2^k!} = 1 - \frac{x^2}{2!} + \frac{x^4}{4!} - \frac{x^6}{6!} + \cdots$ (D22)

and $\displaystyle\lim_{n\to\infty} \sum_{k=0}^{n} (-1)^k \frac{x^{2k}}{2k!} = \cos x \quad (\text{all } x)$ (D23)

The summation (4) above can be evaluated by a computer to obtain as accurate value for *e* as one may desire. The summations (5), (6), and (7) can similarly be evaluated by a computer to obtain expressions for e^x, sin *x* and cos *x* to any accuracy we wish by simply including more terms in the corresponding summations (*i.e.*, by increasing the value of *n*). In these last three summations it is necessary to specify the value of *x*, something not needed in summation (4) above.

E

Statistical Symbols and the Greek Alphabet

It is accepted practice in Statistics to use letters of the English alphabet (both Capital and Lower Case) to represent random variables (X, Y, Z) and sample measures ($\bar{x}$, $\hat{s}^2$, $\hat{s}$), respectively.

Similarly, letters of the Greek alphabet (both capital and lower case) are used to represent certain mathematical operations (Π is used to represent multiplication and Σ summation, for example) and population's parameters ($\mu =$ population mean, $\sigma^2 =$ population variance, $\sigma =$ population standard deviation, $\rho =$ population correlation, for example), respectively.

Below, in the hope of simplifying its use, we offer a list of the letters of the Greek alphabet, along with their Greek name, and their English equivalent.

■ Greek Alphabet

Greek Letter	Greek Name	English Equivalent	Greek Letter	Greek Name	English Equivalent
A α	Alpha	a	N ν	Nu	n
B β	Beta	b	Ξ ξ	Xi	x
Γ γ	Gamma	g	O o	Omicron	$\breve{o}$
Δ δ	Delta	d	Π π	Pi	p
E ε	Epsilon	$\breve{e}$	P ρ	Rho	r
Z ζ	Zeta	z	Σ σ s	Sigma	s
H η	Eta	$\bar{e}$	T τ	Tau	t
Θ θ ϑ	Theta	th	Y υ	Upsilon	u
I ι	Iota	i	Φ ϕ φ	Phi	ph
K κ	Kappa	k	X χ	Chi	ch
Λ λ	Lambda	l	Ψ ψ	Psi	ps
M μ	Mu	m	Ω ω	Omega	$\bar{o}$

F Sampling and Sampling Techniques

In order to obtain the values of the characteristics of a population, we need to measure these characteristics, and this can happen by either a census study (in which the characteristic(s) of interest are measured in every element of the population), or a sampling study (in which the characteristics of interest are measured in only a portion of the elements of the population). Therefore, sampling is the process of learning about a population on the basis of a sample drawn from the population of interest.

In this Appendix we will discuss the following topics:

1. Reasons for Sampling
2. The theoretical basis for sampling
3. Basic concepts of sampling
4. Sampling Techniques available
   a) Random Sampling Techniques
   b) Nonrandom Sampling Techniques

■ Reasons for Sampling

In general a sample is less expensive to obtain than having to conduct a full census study, but there are more specific reasons for choosing a sampling study over a census study, such as the following:

1. The population under investigation may be infinite and sampling is the only reasonable procedure. But, even if the population is finite, it may include a very large number of elements and the complete enumeration of such a population is practically impossible. The costs of locating, visiting, and interviewing the elements of the population in either case would be prohibitive.
2. The measurement of a population often requires the destruction of the elements in it (as, for example, when we are trying to find the life expectancy of light bulbs), and sampling can save the product.
3. Sampling can provide results more quickly, if it is a matter of urgency to have the results available as early as possible.
4. There comes a point in every study beyond which the increased information from additional observations is not worth the additional cost increases.

Note: The main reasons to take a Census, instead of conducting a sampling study, are:

1. To obtain results with great accuracy, and
2. To eliminate the possibility that (by chance) a randomly selected sample might not be representative of the entire population. (**Example:** A random selection of voters in New York State could yield mostly upstate voters when in fact most of the voters are in New York City.)

■ The theoretical basis for Sampling

The theory of sampling, which makes it possible for us to infer the characteristics of an entire population from the evidence obtained from a small sample, is based on the permanent characteristics of "mass data" which is usually summarized by the phrase **"Unity in Diversity"**, which claims that the variation from unit to unit in a population is due to the fact that the many forces which act upon the elementary units of a population, affect these units differently (for example siblings, although similar in many respects, may differ from each other in personality, habits, intelligence, etc.) But these differences between the elements of a population are within a well defined limit (for example human height has an average of about 5'8", but the maximum height doesn't exceed 8'). These facts, that is: that the populations have characteristic properties and the elements of the population have variations on these characteristics within well defined limits, make it possible to select a small random sample that can be used to infer from it the characteristics of the entire population.

Another important property of the data is **"Uniformity"**, which states that the independent forces which act on the elements of a population and produce variability among the elements, also act in such a way that they tend to generate equal values above and below some central value (for example grades in University classes show some *A* and *F* grades but most of the grades are *C*). We can summarize by saying that the individual elements of a population tend to vary from each other (within limits) and at the same time conform to each other (according to some standard). Therefore, both **Diversity** and **Uniformity** are present in the data.

Because of Diversity, if a number of random samples are taken, the sample will differ (within limits) from each other but they are also similar to each other (because of Uniformity, if a large sample is selected, its characteristics will differ very little from the characteristics of the entire population). Uniformity refers to the tendency of the measurable characteristics to cluster around some central value, usually measured by an average, which becomes more stable as the number of observations in the sample increase. The individual observations differ from this central value in some definite pattern (distribution).

The basic reason that large amounts of data tend to exhibit less fluctuation is a tendency of small units of data to cancel each other out. If a small sample has one large observation in it, that values will force the sample mean to go up. But in a large sample such a large observation is likely to be balanced out by a small observation, so that the sample mean is not affected very much by either (large or small) extreme observation. Another way to explain the stability of averages is to consider the "sampling" effect in large samples according to which a few unusual observations do not very much affect the mean because there are so many other and more typical observations which "swamp" the unusual and extreme observations. But this is not the case in small samples (where the opportunity to "swamp" the extreme observations by the more typical observations is not as great) so that averages based on small samples have a greater variability than averages based on large samples. It is this increased stability of an average, as the sample size n increases, that makes is possible to calculate the size of the sample, to make certain that the average possesses the desired amount of stability (or a small standard error).

■ Basic Concepts of Sampling

For sampling to be properly understood and applied it is important to understand the meaning of the following concepts:

1. **Target Population** is the population we intend to sample.
2. **Frame or Sampled Population or Working Population:** If the Target population is not readily available for sufficient samples to be drawn from it, it is important that an adequate working population be found from which the needed samples are to be drawn. But, if the Frame is sufficiently different from the Target population, the inferences drawn are valid only for the Frame and not the Target population.
3. **A sample** is a subset of the population, which is expected to be representative of the entire population, and which is to be used to make inferences about the entire population. It is important to distinguish random samples from judgment samples. In a random sample every unit of the population has the same probability of being selected into the sample. In addition, for a random sample the sampling error can be measured and controlled, using probability theory.

   In contrast, a judgment sample, is selected according to personal judgment, which is used to decide which elements are representative of the entire population and should be included in the sample.

The size of the sample can vary from one element to all the elements of the population and depends on the variability of the population and the degree of accuracy required.

When a sample contains all the elements of the population, it is a Census sample.

4. **Statistical Errors:** An error in a statistic (or estimator) is the difference between the value of the statistic (or estimator, $\hat{\theta}$) and the corresponding population parameter (θ),

or in equation form
$$\text{error} = \hat{\theta} - \theta, \tag{F1}$$

depending on the causes that produce them, are classified as **non-sampling** and **sampling** errors.

a) **Non-sampling errors** include biases and mistakes. A bias exists when the value of a sample statistic (such as $\bar{x}$, $\hat{s}^2$, etc.) shows a tendency to deviate in one direction from the value of a parameter (*i.e.*, the sample results tend to be always higher or lower from the parameter and cannot be cancelled out by averaging). Factors which cause biases include the use of an estimator which is known from theory to be a biased estimator, careless definition of the Target population, imperfect selection of the Frame, and others.

The main source of mistakes is the carelessness of processing generated data (either in recording them or in their computations).

b) **Sampling errors** occur because a partial observation of the population is made (it should be zero for a census study). The sampling error then is equal to the difference between the sample result and the result of a census, when both are obtained using the same procedures. Sampling errors tend to cancel each other out when averaged. This is equivalent to saying that the Expected Value of the sample statistic (or estimator) is equal to the corresponding population parameter, or, in

equation form:
$$E(\hat{\theta}) = \theta \tag{F2}$$

If $E(\hat{\theta}) = \theta$, the statistic $\hat{\theta}$ is said to be an **unbiased estimator** of the parameter θ.

For example, since $E(\bar{x}) = \mu$ and $E(\hat{s}^2) = \sigma^2$, the estimators $\bar{x}$ and $\hat{s}^2$ are unbiased estimators of the population parameters μ and σ^2, respectively. But, since $E(\hat{s}) \neq \sigma$, $\hat{s}$ is a biased estimator of the population parameter σ, where bias is defined as the difference between the expected value of an estimator and the value of the corresponding population parameter, or in equation form:
$$\text{bias} = E(\hat{\theta}) - \theta \tag{F3}$$

The bias is equal to zero for an unbiased estimator (because $E(\hat{\theta}) = \theta$) but different than zero for a biased estimator. When $\hat{\theta} = \hat{s}$ and $\theta = \sigma$, the bias $= E(\hat{s}) - \sigma \neq 0$. The total error of a statistical study is defined as the square root of the sum of the squares of the sampling and non-sampling errors, or in equation from:

$$\text{Total error} = e_T = \sqrt{(Sampling\ error)^2 + (Non\text{-}sampling\ error)^2}$$
$$= \sqrt{e_s^2 + e_{NS}^2} \tag{F4}$$

and one of the major concerns in a statistical study is to make the total error as small as possible. Non-sampling errors can be kept small by taking care to properly define the Target and working (Frame) population, and this is usually possible for small samples. But small samples tend to have large sampling errors. Therefore, it is important to choose the size of the sample carefully, to keep the total error to a minimum, because the smaller the standard error, the greater the precision or reliability of the estimate.

5. **Efficiency of Sampling Techniques**

A sampling technique is **efficient**, if the desired results are obtained at the lowest possible cost, and one sampling technique is more efficient than another if it produces the same accuracy at lower cost or better accuracy at the same cost.

In random sampling accuracy can be obtained because the standard error can be computed, and accuracy can be increased to any level by increasing the sample size. But the accuracy of a single random sample is inversely proportional to the square root of the sample size, as can be seen by the formula for the standard error of the sample mean $\sigma(\overline{x}) = \dfrac{\sigma}{\sqrt{n}}$, where σ is the population standard deviation and n is the sample size. Therefore, if we want to double the accuracy (*i.e.*, if we want to reduce $\sigma(\overline{x})$ by a factor of 2) we must increase the sample size by a factor of 4. But we should always remember that additional accuracy means extra cost, and we should always try to balance accuracy against cost.

■ Sampling Techniques Available

The two main types of sampling are random and non-random. The term random sample describes the process used to select the sample and, since randomness can enter a sampling process in many ways, random samples can be of many kinds. We will discuss the following four (4) basic random sampling techniques, in which every unit of the population has the same probability of being selected into the sample:

1. Simple random sampling
2. Stratified random sampling
3. Systematic random sampling
4. Cluster (or Area) random sampling

Each of these techniques offer advantages and disadvantages, some techniques are simpler to use, some are less costly, and others have a greater ability to reduce the sampling error.

In non-random sampling the units of the population do not have the same probability of being selected into the sample. A non-random sample is selected without the use of randomization but is based on other considerations, such as expert judgment and/or convenience. But it is important to remember that non-random sampling is subject to sampling error, even though there is no way of measuring this sampling error.

Some of the more important non-random sampling techniques are:

1. Convenience sampling
2. Judgment sampling
3. Quota sampling
4. Snowball sampling

■ Random Sampling Techniques

1. **Simple Random Sampling**

Simple random sampling can be considered as the basis for the other random sampling techniques, and can be defined in the following 3 but equivalent ways:

a) When a sample of size n is drawn from a population with N elements, all n items are selected independently of one another, and all N items of the population have the same chance of being selected for inclusion in the sample.

The term "independently" here means the following:
- When sampling "with replacement", the selection of an item in one draw has no influence on the probability of selection in any other draw.
- When sampling "without replacement", the selection of one item in one draw has no influence on the probability of selection in any other draw, except that the same item cannot be drawn twice.

b) When a sample of size n is drawn from a population with N elements, at each selection, all remaining items in the population have the same chance of being drawn.

If sampling is made with replacement, each item has a probability of $1/N$ of being drawn at each selection. If sampling is made without replacement, the probability of selection of each item remaining in the population is: at the first draw $1/N$, at the second draw $1/(N - 1)$, at the third draw $1/(N - 2)$, etc.

c) All the possible samples of size n are equally likely to be selected. If sampling is made with replacement, each possible sample has the probability of $1/N^n$ of occurring. If sampling is made without replacement, each possible sample has a probability of $1/{_N}P_n$ of occurring,

where
$$_N P_n = \frac{N!}{(N - n)!}$$
(F5)

and $_N P_n$ is the number of permutations of N items selected n at a time.

If any of the above 3 methods of describing a simple random sample is true, the other 2 are also true. Simple random sampling is a practical procedure of selecting a sample of size n, from a Population with N items, if the value of N is not very large, and if the sampling units can be found easily and inexpensively. The desire to obtain greater efficiency and have a random sample when it is not practical to use the simple random sampling techniques directly are the main reasons for using other kinds of random sampling. But, it should be remembered, that every random sampling technique uses simple random sampling somehow.

2. **Stratified Random Sampling**

Here, in an attempt to obtain a more efficient sample than can be produced by a simple random procedure, the population is divided into non-overlapping subpopulations called strata, and then a simple random sample is extracted from each of the subpopulations. The main reason for using stratified random sampling is that it has the potential for reducing the sampling error. Strata selection is usually based on available information. Internally, strata should be relatively homogeneous, but externally, to increase the benefits of stratification, the strata should differ as much as possible.

Stratification is often done by using demographic variables such as: gender, religion, race, education, economic status, and age. If we have 2 levels for gender, 4 for religion, 3 for race, 4 for education, 3 for economic status, and 3 for age, then there are: $2 \times 4 \times 3 \times 4 \times 3 \times 3 = 864$ strata. A proportionate stratified random sample occurs when the percentage of the sample taken from each stratum is proportionate to the percentage that each stratum has within the whole population. For example, if a population is divided into strata and their respective sizes are 5, 10, 15, 20, 20, and 30 percent of the population, and a sample of 1000 is to be drawn, then the desired proportional sample will be obtained in the following manner:

Select from stratus 1: 1000(0.05) = 50 items

Select from stratus 2: 1000(0.10) = 100 items

Select from stratus 3: $1000(0.15) = 150$ items

Select from stratus 4: $1000(0.20) = 200$ items

Select from stratus 5: $1000(0.20) = 200$ items

Select from stratus 6: $1000(0.30) = 300$ items

Size of the entire sample $= 1000$ items

Obviously, proportional stratification yields an appropriate sample. This procedure is satisfactory if there is no great difference in variation from stratum to stratum. But if the standard deviations differ substantially in the strata, in order to obtain a more efficient procedure, it is necessary to select more samples from strata with very large variations, and fewer samples from strata with small variations.

Whenever the proportions of the strata in the sample are different from the proportions of the strata in the population, **disproportionate** stratified random sample occurs.

The accuracy of the estimators in a stratified sampling can be obtained provided the sample is sufficiently large. As an absolute minimum, two observations must be selected from each stratum, to make sure that the variance of each stratum can be calculated.

3. **Systematic Random Sample**

To obtain a systematic random sample of size n from a population with N items, we first determine the sampling cycle, which is defined by:

$$k = \frac{N}{n}, \tag{F6}$$

where $N =$ population size, $n =$ sample size, and $k =$ size of interval for selection.

Next, a number is selected at random from the first sampling interval which serves as the starting point. If this number is b (where $b \leq k$), then the sample with size n would have as its elements the sampling units (which have previously been numbered 1 through N) with numbers corresponding to: $b, b + k, b + 2k, b + 3k, \ldots$

A systematic sample is not a simple random sample because the sampling units selected are not independent, and with systematic sampling only k samples of size n can possibly be selected because each of the remaining $_NC_{n-k}$ samples has a zero probability of being drawn. Systematic sampling has the advantage of simplicity because it is easy to select every kth item from a list. However a problem with systematic sampling can occur if the population has hidden periodicities, and the selected items coincide with these periodicities. In such cases the sample will not be representative of the entire population.

4. **Cluster (or Area) Sampling**

In this sampling technique the population is divided into non-overlapping areas, or clusters, which tend to be, internally, heterogeneous. Often clusters are naturally occurring groups of the population and are already identified (such as States, or Standard Metropolitan Statistical Areas). Then a sample of clusters is drawn to represent the population, and then individual elements are randomly selected from the clusters to form the sample of size n.

In cluster sampling it is desirable to have in the same cluster elementary units which are very different from each other (for example, rich and poor people living in the same neighborhood in a city) and differences between clusters as small as possible. These requirements are very difficult to meet simultaneously because, in most populations, similar elementary units tend to cluster together.

This difficulty causes cluster sampling to have a greater standard error that statistified sampling has, for the same number of elementary units in the sample. But, because the cost per elementary unit is lower in cluster sampling than in stratified sampling, more elementary units can be included in cluster sampling for the same or lower cost. Therefore it is possible to have a larger cluster sample that can produce the same accuracy, with lower cost, than a simple or stratified random sample.

When all of the elements of the drawn cluster are selected into the sample, the process is known as **single-stage sampling**. When only a sample of elements is selected from the drawn clusters, the process is known as **two-stage sampling**. At both stages a simple random sample is chosen. When the clusters (or primary units) are geographic areas, the process is known as **area sampling**. Two of the most important advantages of cluster sampling are convenience and cost. This is so because clusters are usually convenient to obtain, and the cost/element is usually lower than in stratified sampling because of lower locating element costs. But cluster sampling also has disadvantages, particularly if the elements of a cluster are similar. In such cases the efficiency of cluster sampling may be less than the efficiency of simple random sampling. In the extreme case, when all the elements of a cluster are the same, sampling from the cluster is equivalent to obtaining a single unit from the cluster.

■ Lot Acceptance Sampling Techniques

The 4 random sampling techniques discussed previously are jointly referred to as **single sampling** techniques because each technique generates a single sample from which an estimate is made or a hypothesis is tested.

But the choice between accepting or rejecting the quality of incoming material can often be made without using the entire sample, as when the following rule is used to accept or reject the incoming lot: "Take a random sample of 100 from the lot. If there are 5 or more defective elements in the sample, reject the lot. If less than 5 defective items are in the sample, accept the lot". It is possible that in such a test we may find 5 defective in the first 10 items examined. It is therefore unnecessary to examine the other 90 items because the lot has already been rejected. Such a possibility, leads to **double sampling**, a procedure in which a small sample is examined first and a decision is made to accept or reject the lot, or take a second sample, using a decision rule like the one below:

"Select and examine a random sample of 30 items. If 2 or less defective items are found, accept the lot. If 4 or more defective items are found, reject the lot. If 3 defective items are found, take a second sample of 60 items (the total now is 100). If the total number of defectives in the combined lot is 4 or less, accept the lot, if more than 4, reject the lot".

The benefit of such a plan is that costs are substantially reduced, especially if the sampling/testing process is destructive. Thus, double sampling is less expensive than single sampling, Triple sampling is less expensive than double sampling, etc. This observation leads to **multiple sampling**, a procedure that utilizes a series of small samples in which the cumulative number of defectives is compared against an "accept" or "reject" criterion, after each sample is drawn, until a decision can be made.

A logical extension to multiple sampling is **sequential sampling** in which one item is observed at a time, deciding after each observation whether to accept, or reject the lot, or to continue sampling. This technique is appropriate for inspecting products which are very expensive and whose testing leads in their destruction.

■ Non-Random Sampling Techniques

These techniques select element from a population without using a randomization process. Because chance is not used to select the items of the sample, these techniques are not desirable for use in collecting data to be analyzed by the inferential statistics methods discussed in this text, and the sampling error cannot be determined objectively for these techniques, of which we discuss the following four: Convenience Sampling, Judgment Sampling, Quota Sampling, and Snowball Sampling.

1. **Convenience Sampling**
   In this technique the elements for the sample are selected for the convenience of the analyst, who chooses elements that are readily available and willing to participate in the study. Here the sample is less variable than the population because the extreme elements are not readily available, and the analyst selects most of his/her elements from the middle of the population.

2. **Judgment Sampling**
   In this technique the elements of the sample are chosen by the analyst who believes that by exercising his own judgment he/she can select a representative sample and, thus save time and money. But it is still the judgment of one individual, and there is no guarantee that his/her judgment is better than another individual's judgment. A problem that is associated with judgment sampling is the fact that the analyst usually makes errors of judgment in one direction which tend to introduce biases in the sample. Also, in judgment sampling, it is not possible to calculate the probability that an element is going to be selected for the sample, and the sampling error cannot be determined because the selection is non-random.

3. **Quota Sampling**
   The first stage of this techniques is similar to stratified sampling because certain population subgroups, such as age, gender, or geographic region are used as strata.
   But then the analyst uses non-random sampling methods (such as convenience or judgment sampling) to select data from each stratum, until the desired quota (*i.e.*, number of samples) is obtained. Usually quotas are based on the proportions of the subclasses in the entire population. Quota sampling is less expensive than most random techniques because it is essentially a convenience technique with the analyst performing his/her selection where the quota can be obtained quickly. But we should remember that it is a non-random technique.

4. **Snowball Sampling**
   In this technique subjects are selected for inclusion in the sample by referrals from other subjects which have participated in the study, who identify other subjects who, in their judgment, fit the profile of subjects wanted for the study. This results in lower cost, and subjects can be obtained efficiently, when the subjects are difficult to locate. This is the main advantage of this technique while its main disadvantage is the fact that this is a non-random technique.

PROBLEMS

1. A population consists of the numbers: 0, 1, and 2. From this population a random sample of 2 is drawn, with replacement.

   a) Find the expected value, $\mu = E(X)$, and variance, $\sigma^2 = V(X)$ of this population.

   b) Obtain the possible samples, and, $\bar{x}$, $\hat{s}^2$ and $\hat{s}$, for each sample.

   c) What are the sampling distributions of $\bar{x}$ and $\hat{s}^2$?

   d) Obtain $E(\bar{x})$ and $V(\bar{x})$. Is $\bar{x}$ an unbiased estimator of μ?

   e) Obtain $E(\hat{s}^2)$ and $V(\hat{s}^2)$. Is $\hat{s}^2$ an unbiased estimator of σ^2?

   f) What is the sampling distribution of $\hat{s}$. Find $E(\hat{s})$ and $V(\hat{s})$. Compare $E(\hat{s})$ to
   $\sigma = \sqrt{\sigma^2}$ of the population. Is $\hat{s}$ an unbiased estimator of σ?

2. Redo problem 1 but this time the random sample of 2 is drawn without replacement. Are $\bar{x}$, $\hat{s}^2$, and $\hat{s}$ unbiased estimators of the population parameters μ, σ^2, and σ, respectively?

3. A population consists of 6 type written pages, labeled: A, B, C, D, E, and F and the number of errors on these pages are, respectively: 3, 4, 4, 5, 6, 8.

   a) A random sample of 3 pages is selected from this population, without replacement. What are the possible samples and their respective sample means?

   b) Find the sampling distribution of $\bar{x}$ and calculate $E(\bar{x})$ and $V(\bar{x})$

4. Suppose a systematic sample of 3 is selected from the population of problem (3)

   a) What are the two possible samples and their respective sample means?

   b) Obtain the sampling distribution of $\bar{x}$

   c) Calculate $E(\bar{x})$, $V(\bar{x})$, and $\sigma(\bar{x})$

5. Use the population of problem (3) and assume that items A, B, C and D constitute stratum 1, while items E and F constitute stratum 2.

   a) What are the 12 possible stratified random samples of size 3, each of which includes two items from stratum 1 and one item from stratum 2? What are their respective sample means?

   b) Obtain the sampling distribution of $\bar{x}$

   c) Calculate $E(\bar{x})$, $V(\bar{x})$, and $\sigma(\bar{x})$

   d) Which variance of $\bar{x}$, $V(\bar{x})$, of problems (3), (4), (5) is smaller? Which sampling design produces the largest variance in the sampling distribution of the mean?

SOLUTIONS

1. a) If we let X be the random variable representing the population, with values 0, 1, 2, then the $PMF(X)$ is given by:

X	P(X)	XP(X)	X² P(X)
0	1/3	0	0
1	1/3	1/3	1/3
2	1/3	2/3	4/3
	$\Sigma P(x_i) = 1$	$E(X) = \Sigma x_i P(x_i) = 1$	$E(X^2) = \Sigma x_i^2 P(x_i) = 5/3$

Therefore, $\mu = E(X) = 1$, and $\sigma^2 = V(X) = E(X^2) - [E(X)]^2 = \dfrac{5}{3} - (1)^2$

$$= \frac{5}{3} - 1 = \frac{5-3}{3} = \frac{2}{3}, \text{ and } \sigma = \sqrt{V(X)} = \sqrt{2/3} = 0.816$$

b)

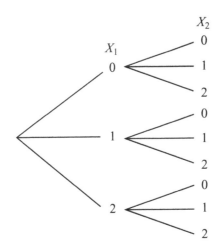

Outcomes $X_1, \ X_2$	$\bar{x} = \dfrac{X_1 + X_2}{2}$	$\hat{s}^{*2} = \dfrac{(X_2 - X_1)^2}{2}$	$\hat{s} = \sqrt{\hat{s}^2}$
0, 0	0	0	0
0, 1	0.5	0.5	$\sqrt{0.5} = \sqrt{2}/2$
0, 2	1	2	$\sqrt{2}$
1, 0	0.5	0.5	$\sqrt{0.5} = \sqrt{2}/2$
1, 1	1	0	0
1, 2	1.5	0.5	$\sqrt{0.5} = \sqrt{2}/2$
2, 0	1	2	$\sqrt{2}$
2, 1	1.5	0.5	$\sqrt{0.5} = \sqrt{2}/2$
2, 2	2	0	0

*The formula for the unbiased sample variance, $\hat{s}^2$, becomes when $n = 2$:

$$\hat{s}^2 = \frac{n(x_1^2 + x_2^2 + \cdots + x_n^2) - (x_1 + x_2 + \cdots + x_n)^2}{n(n - 1)}$$

$$= \frac{2(x_1^2 + x_2^2) - (x_1 + x_2)^2}{2(1)} = \frac{(x_2 - x_1)^2}{2}$$

c) The sampling distributions for $\bar{x}$ and $\hat{s}^2$, and $\hat{s}$ are:

$\bar{x}$	$P(\bar{x})$
0	1/9
0.5	2/9
1	3/9
1.5	2/9
2	1/9

$\hat{s}^2$	$P(\hat{s}^2)$
0	3/9
0.5	4/9
2	2/9

$\hat{s}^2$	$P(\hat{s})$
0	3/9
$0.5 = \dfrac{\sqrt{2}}{2}$	4/9
$\sqrt{2}$	2/9

d) $E(\overline{x}) = \sum \overline{x}_i P(\overline{x}_i) = 0(1/9) + 0.5(2/9) + 1(3/9) + 1.5(2/9) + 2(19)$
   $= 0 + 1/9 + 3/9 + 3/9 + 2/9 = 9/9 = 1$

$E(\overline{x}^2) = \sum \overline{x}_i^2 P(\overline{x}_i) = (0)^2(1/9) + (0.5)^2(2/9) + (1)^2(3/9) + (1.5)^2(2/9) + 2^2(1/9)$

$= 0 + 0.5/9 + 3/9 + 2.25/9 + 4/9 = \dfrac{9.75}{9} = \dfrac{975}{900} = \dfrac{39}{36} = \dfrac{13}{12}$,

and $V(\overline{x}) = E(\overline{x})^2 - [E(\overline{x})]^2 = \dfrac{13}{12} - (1)^2 = \dfrac{13}{12} - 1 = \dfrac{(13-12)}{12} = \dfrac{1}{12}$

Since $E(\overline{x}) = \mu = 1$ of the population, $\overline{x}$ is an unbiased estimator of μ

e) $E(\hat{s}^2) = \sum \hat{s}_i^2 \, P(\hat{s}_i^2) = (0)(3/9) + (0.5)(4/9) + (2)(2/9)$
   $= 0 + 2/9 + 4/9 = 6/9 = 2/3$

$E[(\hat{s}^2)]^2 = \sum (\hat{s}_i^2)^2 \, P(\hat{s}_i^2) = (0)^2(3/9) + (0.5)^2(4/9) + (2)^2(2/9)$

$= 0 + 1/9 + 8/9 = 1$, and

$V(\hat{s}^2) = E\left[(\hat{s}^2)\right]^2 - \left[E(\hat{s}^2)\right]^2 = 1 - \left(\dfrac{2}{3}\right)^2 = 1 - \dfrac{4}{9} = \dfrac{9-4}{9} = \dfrac{5}{9}$

Since $E(\hat{s}^2) = \sigma^2 = 2/3$ of the population, $\hat{s}^2$ is an unbiased estimator of the population variance σ^2.

f) The sampling distribution of $\hat{s}$ is given in part (3) above. Then:

$E(\hat{s}) = \sum \hat{s}_i P(\hat{s}_i) = (0)(3/9) + \left(\sqrt{2}/2\right)(4/9) + \left(\sqrt{2}\right)(2/9)$

$= 0 + 2\sqrt{2}/9 + 2\sqrt{2}/9 = 4\sqrt{2}/9$,

and $E(\hat{s})^2 = \sum \left(\hat{s}_i\right)^2 P(\hat{s}_i) = (0)^2(3/9) + \left(\sqrt{2}/2\right)^2(4/9) + \left(\sqrt{2}\right)^2(2/9)$

$= 0 + 2/9 + 4/9 = 6/9 = 2/3$,   and

$V(\hat{s}) = E(\hat{s}^2) - \left[(E(\hat{s})\right]^2 = \dfrac{2}{3} - \left[\dfrac{4\sqrt{2}}{9}\right]^2 = \dfrac{2}{3} - \dfrac{16(2)}{81} = \dfrac{2}{3} - \dfrac{32}{81}$

$= \dfrac{2(27) - 32}{81} = \dfrac{54 - 32}{81} = \dfrac{54 - 32}{81} = \dfrac{22}{81} = 0.2716$ and $\sigma \, (\hat{s}^2) = 0.52116$

Since $E(\hat{s}) \approx \dfrac{4\sqrt{2}}{9} \approx 0.6285$ and $\sigma = \sqrt{2/3} = 0.8165$, and $E(\hat{s}) \neq \sigma$, $E(\hat{s})$

is not an unbiased estimator of σ, but a biased estimator, even thought $\hat{s}^2$ is an unbiased estimator of σ^2 (because $E(\hat{s}^2) = \sigma^2$).

2. a) As in problem F1, $\mu = E(X) = 1, \sigma^2 = V(X) = \dfrac{2}{3}$,

and $\sigma = \sqrt{V(X)} = \sqrt{2/3} = 0.816$

b)

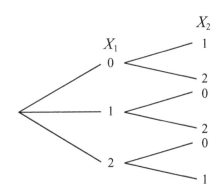

Outcomes X_1, X_2	$\bar{x} = \dfrac{X_1 + X_2}{2}$	$\hat{s}^2 = \dfrac{(X_2 - X_1)^2}{2}$	$\hat{s} = \sqrt{\hat{s}^2}$
0, 1	0.5	0.5	$\sqrt{0.5} = \sqrt{2}/2$
0, 2	1	2	$\sqrt{2}$
1, 0	0.5	0.5	$\sqrt{0.5} = \sqrt{2}/2$
1, 2	1.5	0.5	$\sqrt{0.5} = \sqrt{2}/2$
2, 0	1	2	$\sqrt{2}$
2, 1	1.5	0.5	$\sqrt{0.5} = \sqrt{2}/2$

c) The sampling distributions of $\bar{x}$ and $\hat{s}^2$, and $\hat{s}$ are:

$\bar{x}$	$P(\bar{x})$
0.5	2/6
1	2/6
1.5	2/6

$\hat{s}^2$	$P(\hat{s}^2)$
0.5	4/6
2	2/6

$\hat{s}$	$P(\hat{s})$
$\dfrac{\sqrt{2}}{2}$	4/6
$\sqrt{2}$	2/6

d) $E(\bar{x}) = \Sigma \bar{x}_i P(\bar{x}_i) = (0.5)(2/6) + (1)(2/6) + (1.5)(2/6)$

$\qquad = 1/6 + 2/6 + 3/6 = 6/6 = 1$

$E\left(\bar{x}^2\right) = \Sigma \bar{x}_i^2 P(\bar{x}_i) = (0.5)^2(2/6) + (1)^2(2/6) + (1.5)^2(2/6) = 0.5/6 + 2/6$

$\qquad + 4.5/6 = 7/6,$ and

$V(\bar{x}) = E(\bar{x})^2 - [E(\bar{x})]^2 = \dfrac{7}{6} - (1)^2 = \dfrac{7}{6} - 1 = \dfrac{(7-6)}{6} = \dfrac{1}{6}$

Since $E(\bar{x}) = 1 = \mu = E(X)$ of the population, $\bar{x}$ is an unbiased estimator of μ.

e) $E(\hat{s}^2) = \Sigma \hat{s}_i^2 P(\hat{s}_i^2) = (0.5)(4/6) + (2)(2/6) = 2/6 + 4/6 = 6/6 = 1$

$E[(\hat{s}^2)]^2 = \Sigma (\hat{s}_i^2)^2 P(\hat{s}_i^2) = (0.5)^2(4/6) + (2)^2(2/6)$

$\qquad = 1/6 + 8/6 = 9/6 = 3/2 = 1.5,$ and

$V(\hat{s}^2) = E\left[(\hat{s}^2)\right]^2 - \left[E(\hat{s}^2)\right]^2 = \dfrac{3}{2} - 1 = \dfrac{(3-2)}{2} = \dfrac{1}{2} = 0.5$

Since $E(\hat{s}^2) = 1 \neq \sigma^2 = V(X) = 2/3$, $\hat{s}^2$ is not an unbiased estimator of σ^2.

f) The sampling distribution of $\hat{s}$ is given in part (3) above. Then:

$$E(\hat{s}) = \left(\sqrt{2}/2\right)(4/6) + \left(\sqrt{2}\right)(2/6) = \sqrt{2}/3 + \sqrt{2}/3 = \frac{2\sqrt{2}}{3}$$

$$= \frac{2.828427125}{3} = 0.94281$$

$$E(\hat{s})^2 = \Sigma(\hat{s}_i)^2 P(\hat{s}_i) = \left(\sqrt{2}/2\right)^2 (4/6) + \left(\sqrt{2}\right)^2(2/6) = 2/6 + 4/6 = 6/6 = 1$$

Since $E(\hat{s}) = 0.94281 \neq \sigma = 0.816$ of the population, $\hat{s}$ is not an unbiased estimator for σ.

Clearly in this case, in which the random sample of 2 was drawn without replacement from the population: 0, 1, 2;

$\bar{x}$ is an unbiased estimator of μ

$\hat{s}^2$ is a biased estimator of σ^2 (it was unbiased for samples with replacement)

$\hat{s}$ is a biased estimator of σ (it was also biased for samples with replacement)

3. a) Since the samples are drawn without replacement, there are: $N = \dfrac{6!}{3! \ 3!} = 20$ of

them and they are the following (as can be verified by drawing a tree diagram and discarding repetitions), and their respective samples and $\bar{x}$'s are (to find the corresponding $\bar{x}$ the sum of the errors of the 3 elements in each sample are divided by 3):

Sample	$\bar{x}$
ABC	11/3
ABD	12/3
ABE	13/3
ABF	15/3
ACD	12/3
ACE	13/3
ACF	15/3
ADE	14/3
ADF	16/3
AEF	17/3
BCD	13/3
BCE	14/3
BCF	16/3
BDE	15/3
BDF	17/3
BEF	18/3
CDE	15/3
CDF	17/3
CEF	18/3
DEF	19/3

b) Since all these samples are equally likely, the sampling distribution of $\bar{x}$ is:

$\bar{x}$	$\frac{11}{3}$	$\frac{12}{3}$	$\frac{13}{3}$	$\frac{14}{3}$	$\frac{15}{3}$	$\frac{16}{3}$	$\frac{17}{3}$	$\frac{18}{3}$	$\frac{19}{3}$
$P(\bar{x})$	$\frac{1}{20}$	$\frac{2}{20}$	$\frac{3}{20}$	$\frac{2}{20}$	$\frac{4}{20}$	$\frac{2}{20}$	$\frac{3}{20}$	$\frac{2}{20}$	$\frac{1}{20}$
$\bar{x}P(\bar{x})$	$\frac{11}{60}$	$\frac{24}{60}$	$\frac{39}{60}$	$\frac{28}{60}$	$\frac{60}{60}$	$\frac{32}{60}$	$\frac{51}{60}$	$\frac{36}{60}$	$\frac{19}{60}$
$\bar{x}^2P(\bar{x})$	$\frac{121}{180}$	$\frac{288}{180}$	$\frac{507}{180}$	$\frac{392}{180}$	$\frac{900}{180}$	$\frac{512}{180}$	$\frac{867}{180}$	$\frac{648}{180}$	$\frac{361}{180}$

and $\Sigma \bar{x}P(\bar{x}) = 300/60 = 5 = E(\bar{x})$,

while $E(\bar{x})^2 = \Sigma \bar{x}_i^2 P(\bar{x}) = 4596/180 = 25.5333$

Therefore, $V(\bar{x}) = E(\bar{x})^2 - [E(\bar{x})]^2 = 25.5333 - 5^2 = 25.5333 - 25 = 0.5333$,

and $\sigma(\bar{x}) = 0.7303$

4. a) Since $N = 6$ and $n = 3$, $k = N/n = 6/3 = 2 = $ size of interval of selection, there can be only 2 possible samples of size 3 from a population of 6. These samples are ACE and BDF, and their $\bar{x}$'s are:

$$\bar{x}_{ACE} = \frac{3 + 4 + 6}{3} = \frac{13}{3}, \text{ and} \qquad \bar{x}_{BDF} = \frac{4 + 5 + 8}{3} = \frac{17}{3}$$

b) Then, the sampling distribution of $\bar{x}$ is:

$\bar{x}$	$P(\bar{x})$	$\bar{x}P(\bar{x})$	$\bar{x}^2P(\bar{x})$
13/3	1/2	13/6	169/18
17/3	1/2	17/6	289/18
	$\Sigma P(\bar{x}_1) = 1$	$E(\bar{x}) = \Sigma \bar{x}_i P(\bar{x}_i)$ $= \dfrac{30}{6} = 5$	$E(\bar{x}^2) = \Sigma \bar{x}_i^2 P(\bar{x}_i)$ $= \dfrac{458}{18} = 25.4444$

c) Therefore $E(\bar{x}) = 5$, $V(\bar{x}) = E(\bar{x}^2) - [E(\bar{x})]^2 = 25.4444 - 5^2 = 0.4444$,

and $\sigma(\bar{x}) = \sqrt{V(\bar{x})} = 0.6667$

5. a) There are six possible samples of size 2 from stratum 1 $\left(\dfrac{4!}{2! \ 2!} = 6 \right)$ and they are:

AB, AC, AD, BC, BD, and CD, and since each of them is combined with one sample from stratum 2 (E or F), there are all together 12 possible samples, as shown below, together with the sample mean for each sample.

Sample	$\bar{x}$
ABE	13/3
ABF	15/3
ACE	13/3
ACF	15/3
ADE	14/3
ADF	16/3
BCE	14/3
BCF	16/3
BDE	15/3
BDF	17/3
CDE	15/3
CDF	17/3

b) The sampling distribution of $\bar{x}$ is:

x	13/3	14/3	15/3	16/3	17/3
$P(\bar{x})$	2/12	2/12	4/12	2/12	2/12

c) $E(\bar{x}) = \Sigma \bar{x}_i P(\bar{x}_i) = \left(\dfrac{13}{3}\right)\left(\dfrac{2}{12}\right) + \left(\dfrac{14}{3}\right)\left(\dfrac{2}{12}\right) + \left(\dfrac{15}{3}\right)\left(\dfrac{4}{12}\right)$

$$+ \left(\dfrac{16}{3}\right)\left(\dfrac{2}{12}\right) + \left(\dfrac{17}{3}\right)\left(\dfrac{2}{12}\right) = \dfrac{90}{18} = 5$$

$E(\bar{x})^2 = \Sigma \bar{x}_i^2 P(\bar{x}_i) = \left(\dfrac{13}{3}\right)^2\left(\dfrac{1}{6}\right) + \left(\dfrac{14}{3}\right)^2\left(\dfrac{1}{6}\right)$

$$+ \left(\dfrac{15}{3}\right)^2\left(\dfrac{2}{6}\right) + \left(\dfrac{16}{3}\right)^2\left(\dfrac{1}{6}\right) + \left(\dfrac{17}{3}\right)^2\left(\dfrac{1}{6}\right) = \dfrac{1360}{54} = 25.18518$$

$V(\bar{x}) = E(\bar{x}^2) - [(E(\bar{x}))]^2 = 25.185185 - 5^2$

$\qquad = 0.185185,$ and $\sigma(\bar{x}) = 0.43033$

d) $V(\bar{x}) = 0.5333$ for problem (3), $V(\bar{x}) = 0.4444$ for problem (4), and
$V(\bar{x}) = 0.185185$ for problem (5).

Tables

Table 1 The Standardized Normal Distribution

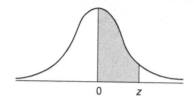

Entry represents area under the standardized normal distribution from the mean to Z

Z	.00	.01	.02	.03	.04	.05	.06	.07	.08	.09
0.0	.0000	.0040	.0080	.0120	.0160	.0199	.0239	.0279	.0319	.0359
0.1	.0398	.0438	.0478	.0517	.0557	.0596	.0636	.0675	.0714	.0753
0.2	.0793	.0832	.0871	.0910	.0948	.0987	.1026	.1064	.1103	.1141
0.3	.1179	.1217	.1255	.1293	.1331	.1368	.1406	.1443	.1480	.1517
0.4	.1554	.1591	.1628	.1664	.1700	.1736	.1772	.1808	.1844	.1879
0.5	.1915	.1950	.1985	.2019	.2054	.2088	.2123	.2157	.2190	.2224
0.6	.2257	.2291	.2324	.2357	.2389	.2422	.2454	.2486	.2518	.2549
0.7	.2580	.2612	.2642	.2673	.2704	.2734	.2764	.2794	.2823	.2852
0.8	.2881	.2910	.2939	.2967	.2995	.3023	.3051	.3078	.3106	.3133
0.9	.3159	.3186	.3212	.3238	.3264	.3289	.3315	.3340	.3365	.3389
1.0	.3413	.3438	.3461	.3485	.3508	.3531	.3554	.3577	.3599	.3621
1.1	.3643	.3665	.3686	.3708	.3729	.3749	.3770	.3790	.3810	.3830
1.2	.3849	.3869	.3888	.3907	.3925	.3944	.3962	.3980	.3997	.4015
1.3	.4032	.4049	.4066	.4082	.4099	.4115	.4131	.4147	.4162	.4177
1.4	.4192	.4207	.4222	.4236	.4251	.4265	.4279	.4292	.4306	.4319
1.5	.4332	.4345	.4357	.4370	.4382	.4394	.4406	.4418	.4429	.4441
1.6	.4452	.4463	.4474	.4484	.4495	.4505	.4515	.4525	.4535	.4545
1.7	.4554	.4564	.4573	.4582	.4591	.4599	.4608	.4616	.4625	.4633
1.8	.4641	.4649	.4656	.4664	.4671	.4678	.4686	.4693	.4699	.4706
1.9	.4713	.4719	.4726	.4732	.4738	.4744	.4750	.4756	.4761	.4767
2.0	.4772	.4778	.4783	.4788	.4793	.4798	.4803	.4808	.4812	.4817
2.1	.4821	.4826	.4830	.4834	.4838	.4842	.4846	.4850	.4854	.4857
2.2	.4861	.4864	.4868	.4871	.4875	.4878	.4881	.4884	.4887	.4890
2.3	.4893	.4896	.4898	.4901	.4904	.4906	.4909	.4911	.4913	.4916
2.4	.4918	.4920	.4922	.4925	.4927	.4929	.4931	.4932	.4934	.4936
2.5	.4938	.4940	.4941	.4943	.4945	.4946	.4948	.4949	.4951	.4952
2.6	.4953	.4955	.4956	.4957	.4959	.4960	.4961	.4962	.4963	.4964
2.7	.4965	.4966	.4967	.4968	.4969	.4970	.4971	.4972	.4973	.4974
2.8	.4974	.4975	.4976	.4977	.4977	.4978	.4979	.4979	.4980	.4981
2.9	.4981	.4982	.4962	.4983	.4984	.4984	.4985	.4985	.4986	.4986
3.0	.49865	.49869	.49874	.49878	.49882	.49886	.49889	.49893	.49897	.49900
3.1	.49903	.49906	.49910	.49913	.49916	.49918	.49921	.49924	.49926	.49929
3.2	.49931	.49934	.49936	.49938	.49940	.49942	.49944	.49946	.49948	.49950
3.3	.49952	.49953	.49955	.49957	.49958	.49960	.49961	.49962	.49964	.49965
3.4	.49966	.49968	.49969	.49970	.49971	.49972	.49973	.49974	.49975	.49976
3.5	.49977	.49978	.49978	.49979	.49980	.49981	.49981	.49982	.49983	.49983
3.6	.49984	.49985	.49985	.49986	.49986	.49987	.49987	.49988	.49988	.49989
3.7	.49989	.49990	.49990	.49990	.49991	.49991	.49992	.49992	.49992	.49992
3.8	.49993	.49993	.49993	.49994	.49994	.49994	.49994	.49995	.49995	.49995
3.9	.49995	.49995	.49996	.49996	.49996	.49996	.49996	.49996	.49997	.49997

Table 2 Critical Values of *t*

For a particular number of degrees of freedom,
entry represents the critical value of t
corresponding to a specified upper tail area α

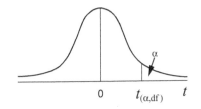

$$0 \quad t_{(\alpha, df)} \quad t$$

Degrees of Freedom	Upper Tail Areas					
	.25	.10	.05	.025	.01	.005
1	1.0000	3.0777	6.3138	12.7062	31.8207	63.6574
2	0.8165	1.8856	2.9200	4.3027	6.9546	9.9248
3	0.7649	1.6377	2.3534	3.1824	4.5407	5.8409
4	0.7407	1.5332	2.1318	2.7764	3.7469	4.6041
5	0.7267	1.4759	2.0150	2.5706	3.3649	4.0322
6	0.7176	1.4396	1.9432	2.4469	3.1427	3.7074
7	0.7111	1.4149	1.8946	2.3646	2.9900	3.4995
8	0.7064	1.3964	1.8595	2.3080	2.8965	3.3554
9	0.7027	1.3830	1.8331	2.2622	2.8214	3.2498
10	0.6998	1.3722	1.8125	2.2281	2.7638	3.1693
11	0.6974	1.3634	1.7959	2.2010	2.7181	3.1050
12	0.6956	1.3562	1.7823	2.1788	2.6810	3.0545
13	0.6938	1.3502	1.7709	2.1604	2.6503	3.0123
14	0.6924	1.3450	1.7613	2.1448	2.6245	2.9768
15	0.6912	1.3406	1.7531	2.1315	2.6025	2.9467
16	0.6901	1.3368	1.7459	2.1199	2.5836	2.9208
17	0.6892	1.3334	1.7396	2.1098	2.5669	2.8982
18	0.6884	1.3304	1.7341	2.1009	2.5524	2.8784
19	0.6876	1.3277	1.7291	2.0930	2.5395	2.8609
20	0.6870	1.3253	1.7247	2.0880	2.5280	2.8453
21	0.6864	1.3232	1.7207	2.0796	2.5177	2.8314
22	0.6858	1.3212	1.7171	2.0739	2.5083	2.8188
23	0.6853	1.3195	1.7139	2.0687	2.4999	2.8073
24	0.6648	1.3178	1.7109	2.0539	2.4922	2.7969
25	0.6844	1.3163	1.7081	2.0595	2.4851	2.7874
26	0.6840	1.3150	1.7056	2.0555	2.4786	2.7787
27	0.6837	1.3137	1.7033	2.0518	2.4727	2.7707
28	0.6834	1.3125	1.7011	2.0484	2.4671	2.7633
29	0.6830	1.3114	1.6991	2.0452	2.4620	2.7564
30	0.6828	1.3104	1.6973	2.0423	2.4573	2.7500
31	0.6825	1.3095	1.6955	2.0395	2.4528	2.7440
32	0.6822	1.3086	1.6939	2.0359	2.4487	2.7385
33	0.6820	1.3077	1.6924	2.0345	2.4448	2.7333
34	0.6818	1.3070	1.6909	2.0322	2.4411	2.7284
35	0.6816	1.3062	1.6896	2.0301	2.4377	2.7238

Reprinted from *Basic Business Statistics: Concepts and Applications*, Fifth Edition by Mark L. Berenson and David M. Levine (1992), Prentice Hall, Inc.

Table 2 Critical Values of *t* (continued)

Degrees of Freedom	Upper Tail Areas					
	.25	.10	.05	.025	.01	.005
36	0.6814	1.3055	1.6883	2.0281	2.4346	2.7195
37	0.6812	1.3049	1.6871	2.0262	2.4314	2.7154
38	0.6810	1.3042	1.6860	2.0244	2.4286	2.7116
39	0.6808	1.3036	1.6849	2.0227	2.4258	2.7079
40	0.6807	1.3031	1.6839	2.0211	2.4233	2.7045
41	0.6805	1.3025	1.6829	2.0196	2.4208	2.7012
42	0.6804	1.3020	1.6820	2.0181	2.4185	2.6981
43	0.6802	1.3016	1.6811	2.0167	2.4163	2.6951
44	0.6801	1.3011	1.6802	2.0154	2.4141	2.6923
45	0.6800	1.3006	1.6794	2.0141	2.4121	2.6896
46	0.6799	1.3002	1.6787	2.0129	2.4102	2.6870
47	0.6797	1.2998	1.6779	2.0117	2.4083	2.6846
48	0.6796	1.2994	1.6772	2.0106	2.4066	2.6822
49	0.6795	1.2991	1.6756	2.0096	2.4049	2.6800
50	0.6794	1.2987	1.6759	2.0086	2.4033	2.6778
51	0.6793	1.2984	1.6753	2.0076	2.4017	2.6757
52	0.6792	1.2980	1.6747	2.0066	2.4002	2.6737
53	0.6791	1.2977	1.6741	2.0057	2.3988	2.6718
54	0.6791	1.2974	1.6736	2.0049	2.3974	2.6700
55	0.6790	1.2971	1.6730	2.0040	2.3961	2.6682
56	0.6789	1.2969	1.6726	2.0032	2.3948	2.6665
57	0.6788	1.2966	1.6720	2.0025	2.3936	2.6649
58	0.6787	1.2963	1.6716	2.0017	2.3924	2.6633
59	0.6787	1.2961	1.6711	2.0010	2.3912	2.6618
60	0.6786	1.2958	1.6706	2.0003	2.3901	2.6603
61	0.6785	1.2955	1.6702	1.9996	2.3890	2.6589
62	0.6785	1.2954	1.6698	1.9990	2.3880	2.6575
63	0.6784	1.2961	1.6694	1.9983	2.3870	2.6561
64	0.6783	1.2949	1.6690	1.9977	2.3860	2.6549
65	0.6783	1.2947	1.6686	1.9971	2.3851	2.6536
66	0.6782	1.2945	1.6683	1.9966	2.3842	2.6524
67	0.6782	1.2943	1.6679	1.9960	2.3833	2.6512
68	0.6781	1.2941	1.6676	1.9955	2.3824	2.6501
69	0.6781	1.2939	1.6672	1.9949	2.3816	2.6490
70	0.6780	1.2938	1.6669	1.9944	2.3808	2.6479
71	0.6780	1.2936	1.6666	1.9939	2.3800	2.6469
72	0.6779	1.2934	1.6663	1.9936	2.3793	2.6459
73	0.6779	1.2933	1.6660	1.9930	2.3785	2.6449
74	0.6778	1.4931	1.6657	1.9925	2.3778	2.6439
75	0.6778	1.2929	1.6654	1.9921	2.3771	2.6430

Table 2 Critical Values of *t* (continued)

Degrees of Freedom	Upper Tail Areas					
	.25	*.10*	*.05*	*.025*	*.01*	*.005*
76	0.6777	1.2928	1.6652	1.9917	2.3764	2.6421
77	0.6777	1.2926	1.6649	1.9913	2.3758	2.6412
78	0.6776	1.2925	1.6646	1.9908	2.3751	2.6403
79	0.6776	1.2924	1.6644	1.9905	2.3745	2.6395
80	0.6776	1.2922	1.6641	1.9901	2.3739	2.6387
81	0.6776	1.2921	1.6639	1.9897	2.3733	2.6379
82	0.6775	1.2920	1.6636	1.9893	2.3727	2.6371
83	0.6775	1.2918	1.6634	1.9890	2.3721	2.6364
84	0.6774	1.2917	1.6632	1.9886	2.3716	2.6356
85	0.6774	1.2916	1.6630	1.9883	2.3710	2.6349
86	0.6774	1.2915	1.6628	1.9879	2.3705	2.6342
87	0.6773	1.2914	1.6626	1.9876	2.3700	2.6335
88	0.6773	1.2912	1.6624	1.9873	2.3695	2.6329
89	0.6773	1.2911	1.6622	1.9870	2.3690	2.6322
90	0.6772	1.2910	1.6620	1.9867	2.3685	2.6316
91	0.6772	1.2909	1.6618	1.9864	2.3680	2.6309
92	0.6772	1.2908	1.6616	1.9861	2.3675	2.6303
93	0.6771	1.2907	1.6614	1.9858	2.3671	2.6297
94	0.6771	1.2906	1.6612	1.9856	2.3667	2.6291
95	0.6771	1.2905	1.6611	1.9853	2.3662	2.6285
96	0.6771	1.2904	1.6609	1.9850	2.3658	2.6280
97	0.6770	1.2903	1.6607	1.9847	2.3654	2.6275
98	0.6770	1.2902	1.6606	1.9845	2.3650	2.6268
99	0.6770	1.2902	1.6604	1.9842	2.3646	2.6264
100	0.6770	1.2901	1.6602	1.9840	2.3642	2.6259
110	0.6767	1.2893	1.6586	1.9818	2.3607	2.6213
120	0.6765	1.2886	1.6577	1.9799	2.3578	2.6174
130	0.6764	1.2881	1.6567	1.9784	2.3554	2.6142
140	0.6762	1.2876	1.6558	1.9771	2.3533	2.6114
150	0.6761	1.2872	1.6551	1.9759	2.3515	2.6090
∞	0.6745	1.2816	1.6449	1.9600	2.3263	2.5758

Table 3 Critical Values of χ^2

For a particular number of degrees of freedom, entry represents the critical value of χ^2 corresponding to a specified upper tail area (α).

For larger values of degrees of freedom (df) the expression $Z = \sqrt{2\chi^2} - \sqrt{2(df)} - 1$ may be used and the resulting upper tail area can be obtained from the table of the standardized normal distribution (Table 1).

Degrees of Freedom	Upper Tail Aress (α)											
	.995	.99	.975	.95	.90	.75	.25	.10	.05	.025	.01	.005
1			0.001	0.004	0.016	0.102	1.323	2.706	3.841	5.024	6.635	7.879
2	0.010	0.020	0.051	0.103	0.211	0.575	2.773	4.605	5.991	7.378	9.210	10.597
3	0.072	0.115	0.216	0.352	0.584	1.213	4.108	6.251	7.815	9.348	11.345	12.838
4	0.207	0.297	0.484	0.711	1.064	1.923	5.385	7.779	9.488	11.143	13.277	14.860
5	0.412	0.554	0.831	1.145	1.610	2.675	6.626	9.236	11.071	12.833	15.086	16.750
6	0.676	0.872	1.237	1.635	2.204	3.455	7.841	10.645	12.592	14.449	16.812	18.548
7	0.989	1.239	1.690	2.167	2.833	4.255	9.037	12.017	14.067	16.013	18.475	20.278
8	1.344	1.646	2.180	2.733	3.490	5.071	10.219	13.362	15.507	17.535	20.090	21.955
9	1.735	2.088	2.700	3.325	4.168	5.899	11.389	14.684	16.916	19.023	21.666	23.589
10	2.156	2.558	3.247	3.940	4.865	6.737	12.549	15.987	18.307	20.483	23.209	25.188
11	2.603	3.053	3.186	4.575	5.578	7.584	13.701	17.275	19.675	21.920	24.725	26.757
12	3.074	3.571	4.404	5.226	6.304	8.438	14.845	18.549	21.026	23.337	26.217	28.299
13	3.565	4.107	5.009	5.892	7.042	9.299	15.984	19.812	22.362	24.736	27.688	29.819
14	4.075	4.660	5.629	6.571	7.790	10.165	17.117	21.064	23.685	26.119	29.141	31.319
15	4.601	5.229	6.262	7.261	8.547	11.037	18.245	22.307	24.996	27.488	30.578	32.801
16	5.142	5.812	6.908	7.962	9.312	11.912	19.369	23.542	26.296	28.845	32.000	34.267
17	5.697	6.408	7.564	8.672	10.085	12.792	20.489	24.769	27.587	30.191	33.409	35.718
18	6.265	7.015	8.231	9.390	10.865	13.675	21.605	25.989	28.869	31.526	34.805	37.156
19	6.844	7.633	8.907	10.117	11.651	14.562	22.718	27.204	30.144	32.852	36.191	38.582
20	7.434	8.260	9.591	10.851	12.443	15.452	23.828	28.412	31.410	34.170	37.566	39.997
21	8.034	8.897	10.283	11.591	13.240	16.344	24.935	29.615	32.671	35.479	38.932	41.401
22	8.643	9.542	10.982	12.338	14.042	17.240	26.039	30.813	33.924	36.781	40.289	42.796
23	9.260	10.196	11.689	13.091	14.848	18.137	27.141	32.007	35.172	38.076	41.638	44.181
24	9.886	10.856	12.401	13.848	15.659	19.037	28.241	33.196	36.415	39.364	42.980	45.559
25	10.520	11.524	13.120	14.611	16.473	19.939	29.339	34.382	37.652	40.646	44.314	46.928
26	11.160	12.198	13.844	15.379	17.292	20.843	30.435	35.563	38.885	41.923	45.642	48.290
27	11.808	12.879	14.573	16.151	18.114	21.749	31.528	36.741	40.113	43.194	46.963	49.645
28	12.461	13.565	15.308	16.928	18.939	22.657	32.620	37.916	41.337	44.461	48.278	50.993
29	13.121	14.257	16.047	17.708	19.768	23.567	33.711	39.087	42.557	45.722	49.588	52.336
30	13.787	14.954	16.791	18.493	20.599	24.478	34.800	40.256	43.773	46.979	50.892	53.672

Table 4 The F Distribution

Upper 10% points

α = 0.1

S1\S2	1	2	3	4	5	6	7	8	9	10	12	15	20	24	30	40	60	120	∞
1	39.86	49.50	53.59	55.83	57.24	58.20	58.91	59.44	59.86	60.19	60.71	61.22	61.74	62.00	62.26	62.53	62.79	62.06	62.33
2	8.53	9.00	9.15	9.24	9.29	9.33	9.35	9.37	9.38	9.39	9.41	9.42	9.44	9.45	9.46	9.47	9.47	9.48	9.49
3	5.54	5.46	5.39	5.34	5.31	5.28	5.27	5.25	5.24	5.23	5.22	5.20	5.18	5.18	5.17	5.16	5.15	5.14	5.13
4	4.54	4.32	4.19	4.11	4.05	4.01	3.98	3.95	3.94	3.92	3.90	3.87	3.84	3.83	3.82	3.80	3.79	3.78	3.76
5	4.06	3.78	3.62	3.52	3.45	3.40	3.37	3.34	3.32	3.30	3.27	3.24	3.21	3.19	3.17	3.16	3.14	3.12	3.10
6	3.78	3.46	3.29	3.18	3.11	3.05	3.01	2.98	2.96	2.94	2.90	2.87	2.84	2.82	2.80	2.78	2.76	2.74	2.72
7	3.59	3.26	3.07	2.96	2.88	2.83	2.78	2.75	2.72	2.70	2.67	2.63	2.59	2.58	2.56	2.54	2.51	2.49	2.47
8	3.46	3.11	2.92	2.81	2.73	2.67	2.62	2.59	2.56	2.54	2.50	2.46	2.42	2.40	2.38	2.36	2.34	2.32	2.29
9	3.36	3.01	2.81	2.69	2.61	2.55	2.51	2.47	2.44	2.42	2.38	2.34	2.30	2.28	2.25	2.23	2.21	2.18	2.16
10	3.29	2.92	2.73	2.61	2.52	2.46	2.41	2.38	2.35	2.32	2.28	2.24	2.20	2.18	2.16	2.13	2.11	2.08	2.06
11	3.23	2.86	2.66	2.54	2.45	2.39	2.34	2.30	2.27	2.25	2.21	2.17	2.12	2.10	2.08	2.05	2.03	2.00	1.97
12	3.18	2.81	2.61	2.48	2.39	2.33	2.28	2.24	2.21	2.19	2.15	2.10	2.06	2.04	2.01	1.99	1.96	1.93	1.90
13	3.14	2.76	2.56	2.43	2.35	2.28	2.23	2.20	2.16	2.14	2.10	2.05	2.01	1.98	1.96	1.93	1.90	1.88	1.85
14	3.10	2.73	2.52	2.39	2.31	2.24	2.19	2.15	2.12	2.10	2.05	2.01	1.96	1.94	1.91	1.89	1.86	1.83	1.80
15	3.07	2.70	2.49	2.36	2.27	2.21	2.16	2.12	2.09	2.06	2.02	1.97	1.92	1.90	1.87	1.85	1.82	1.79	1.76
16	3.05	2.67	2.46	2.33	2.24	2.18	2.13	2.09	2.06	2.03	1.99	1.94	1.89	1.87	1.84	1.81	1.78	1.75	1.72
17	3.03	2.64	2.44	2.31	2.22	2.15	2.10	2.06	2.03	2.00	1.96	1.91	1.86	1.84	1.81	1.78	1.75	1.72	1.69
18	3.01	2.62	2.42	2.29	2.20	2.13	2.08	2.04	2.00	1.98	1.93	1.89	1.84	1.81	1.78	1.75	1.72	1.69	1.66
19	2.99	2.61	2.40	2.27	2.18	2.11	2.06	2.02	1.98	1.96	1.91	1.86	1.81	1.79	1.76	1.73	1.70	1.67	1.63
20	2.97	2.59	2.38	2.25	2.16	2.09	2.04	2.00	1.96	1.94	1.89	1.84	1.79	1.77	1.74	1.71	1.68	1.64	1.61
21	2.96	2.57	2.36	2.23	2.14	2.08	2.02	1.98	1.95	1.92	1.87	1.83	1.78	1.75	1.72	1.69	1.66	1.62	1.59
22	2.95	2.56	2.35	2.22	2.13	2.06	2.01	1.97	1.93	1.90	1.86	1.81	1.76	1.73	1.70	1.67	1.64	1.60	1.57
23	2.94	2.55	2.34	2.21	2.11	2.05	1.99	1.95	1.92	1.89	1.84	1.80	1.74	1.72	1.69	1.66	1.62	1.59	1.55
24	2.93	2.54	2.33	2.19	2.10	2.04	1.98	1.94	1.91	1.88	1.83	1.78	1.73	1.70	1.67	1.64	1.61	1.57	1.53
25	2.92	2.53	2.32	2.18	2.09	2.02	1.97	1.93	1.89	1.87	1.82	1.77	1.72	1.69	1.66	1.63	1.59	1.56	1.52
26	2.91	2.52	2.31	2.17	2.08	2.01	1.96	1.92	1.88	1.86	1.81	1.76	1.71	1.68	1.65	1.61	1.58	1.54	1.50
27	2.90	2.51	2.30	2.17	2.07	2.00	1.95	1.91	1.87	1.85	1.80	1.75	1.70	1.67	1.64	1.60	1.57	1.53	1.49
28	2.89	2.50	2.29	2.16	2.06	2.00	1.94	1.90	1.87	1.84	1.79	1.74	1.69	1.66	1.63	1.59	1.56	1.52	1.48
29	2.89	2.50	2.28	2.15	2.06	1.99	1.93	1.89	1.86	1.83	1.78	1.73	1.68	1.65	1.62	1.58	1.55	1.51	1.47
30	2.88	2.49	2.28	2.14	2.05	1.98	1.93	1.88	1.85	1.82	1.77	1.72	1.67	1.64	1.61	1.57	1.54	1.50	1.46
40	2.84	2.44	2.23	2.09	2.00	1.93	1.87	1.83	1.79	1.76	1.71	1.66	1.61	1.57	1.54	1.51	1.47	1.42	1.38
60	2.79	2.39	2.16	2.04	1.95	1.87	1.82	1.77	1.74	1.71	1.66	1.60	1.54	1.51	1.48	1.44	1.40	1.35	1.29
120	2.75	2.35	2.13	1.99	1.90	1.82	1.77	1.72	1.68	1.65	1.60	1.55	1.48	1.45	1.41	1.37	1.32	1.26	1.19
∞	2.71	2.30	2.08	1.94	1.85	1.77	1.72	1.67	1.63	1.60	1.55	1.49	1.42	1.38	1.34	1.30	1.24	1.17	1.00

From E.S. Pearson and H. O. Hartley *Biometrika Tables for Statisticians*, Volume I, Table 18.

Table 5 Critical Values of F

For a particular combination of numerator and denominator degrees of freedom, entry represents the critical values of F corresponding to a specified upper tail area (α)

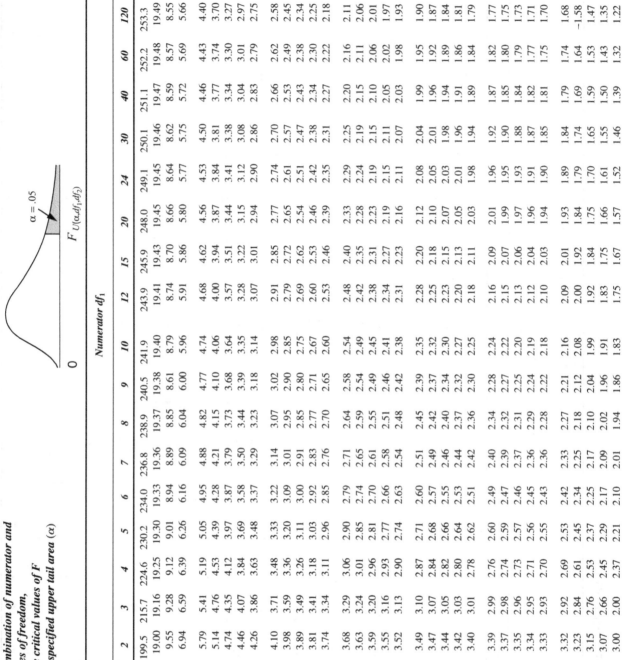

Denominator df_2	Numerator df_1																		
	1	2	3	4	5	6	7	8	9	10	12	15	20	24	30	40	60	120	∞
1	161.4	199.5	215.7	224.6	230.2	234.0	236.8	238.9	240.5	241.9	243.9	245.9	248.0	249.1	250.1	251.1	252.2	253.3	254.3
2	18.51	19.00	19.16	19.25	19.30	19.33	19.36	19.37	19.38	19.40	19.41	19.43	19.45	19.45	19.46	19.47	19.48	19.49	19.50
3	10.13	9.55	9.28	9.12	9.01	8.94	8.89	8.85	8.61	8.79	8.74	8.70	8.66	8.64	8.62	8.59	8.57	8.55	8.53
4	7.71	6.94	6.59	6.39	6.26	6.16	6.09	6.04	6.00	5.96	5.91	5.86	5.80	5.77	5.75	5.72	5.69	5.66	5.63
5	6.61	5.79	5.41	5.19	5.05	4.95	4.88	4.82	4.77	4.74	4.68	4.62	4.56	4.53	4.50	4.46	4.43	4.40	4.36
6	5.99	5.14	4.76	4.53	4.39	4.28	4.21	4.15	4.10	4.06	4.00	3.94	3.87	3.84	3.81	3.77	3.74	3.70	3.67
7	5.59	4.74	4.35	4.12	3.97	3.87	3.79	3.73	3.68	3.64	3.57	3.51	3.44	3.41	3.38	3.34	3.30	3.27	3.23
8	5.32	4.46	4.07	3.84	3.69	3.58	3.50	3.44	3.39	3.35	3.28	3.22	3.15	3.12	3.08	3.04	3.01	2.97	2.93
9	5.12	4.26	3.86	3.63	3.48	3.37	3.29	3.23	3.18	3.14	3.07	3.01	2.94	2.90	2.86	2.83	2.79	2.75	2.71
10	4.95	4.10	3.71	3.48	3.33	3.22	3.14	3.07	3.02	2.98	2.91	2.85	2.77	2.74	2.70	2.66	2.62	2.58	2.54
11	4.84	3.98	3.59	3.36	3.20	3.09	3.01	2.95	2.90	2.85	2.79	2.72	2.65	2.61	2.57	2.53	2.49	2.45	2.40
12	4.75	3.89	3.49	3.26	3.11	3.00	2.91	2.85	2.80	2.75	2.69	2.62	2.54	2.51	2.47	2.43	2.38	2.34	2.30
13	4.67	3.81	3.41	3.18	3.03	2.92	2.83	2.77	2.71	2.67	2.60	2.53	2.46	2.42	2.38	2.34	2.30	2.25	2.21
14	4.60	3.74	3.34	3.11	2.96	2.85	2.76	2.70	2.65	2.60	2.53	2.46	2.39	2.35	2.31	2.27	2.22	2.18	2.13
15	4.54	3.68	3.29	3.06	2.90	2.79	2.71	2.64	2.59	2.54	2.48	2.40	2.33	2.29	2.25	2.20	2.16	2.11	2.07
16	4.49	3.63	3.24	3.01	2.85	2.74	2.65	2.59	2.54	2.49	2.42	2.35	2.28	2.24	2.19	2.15	2.11	2.06	2.01
17	4.45	3.59	3.20	2.96	2.81	2.70	2.61	2.55	2.49	2.45	2.38	2.31	2.23	2.19	2.15	2.10	2.06	2.01	1.96
18	4.41	3.55	3.16	2.93	2.77	2.66	2.58	2.51	2.46	2.41	2.34	2.27	2.19	2.15	2.11	2.05	2.02	1.97	1.92
19	4.38	3.52	3.13	2.90	2.74	2.63	2.54	2.48	2.42	2.38	2.31	2.23	2.16	2.11	2.07	2.03	1.98	1.93	1.88
20	4.35	3.49	3.10	2.87	2.71	2.60	2.51	2.45	2.39	2.35	2.28	2.20	2.12	2.08	2.04	1.99	1.95	1.90	1.84
21	4.32	3.47	3.07	2.84	2.68	2.57	2.49	2.42	2.37	2.32	2.25	2.18	2.10	2.05	2.01	1.96	1.92	1.87	1.81
22	4.30	3.44	3.05	2.82	2.66	2.55	2.46	2.40	2.34	2.30	2.23	2.15	2.07	2.03	1.98	1.94	1.89	1.84	1.78
23	4.28	3.42	3.03	2.80	2.64	2.53	2.44	2.37	2.32	2.27	2.20	2.13	2.05	2.01	1.96	1.91	1.86	1.81	1.76
24	4.26	3.40	3.01	2.78	2.62	2.51	2.42	2.36	2.30	2.25	2.18	2.11	2.03	1.98	1.94	1.89	1.84	1.79	1.73
25	4.24	3.39	2.99	2.76	2.60	2.49	2.40	2.34	2.28	2.24	2.16	2.09	2.01	1.96	1.92	1.87	1.82	1.77	1.71
26	4.23	3.37	2.98	2.74	2.59	2.47	2.39	2.32	2.27	2.22	2.15	2.07	1.99	1.95	1.90	1.85	1.80	1.75	1.69
27	4.21	3.35	2.96	2.73	2.57	2.46	2.37	2.31	2.25	2.20	2.13	2.06	1.97	1.93	1.88	1.84	1.79	1.73	1.67
28	4.20	3.34	2.95	2.71	2.56	2.45	2.36	2.29	2.24	2.19	2.12	2.04	1.96	1.91	1.87	1.82	1.77	1.71	1.65
29	4.18	3.33	2.93	2.70	2.55	2.43	2.35	2.28	2.22	2.18	2.10	2.03	1.94	1.90	1.85	1.81	1.75	1.70	1.64
30	4.17	3.32	2.92	2.69	2.53	2.42	2.33	2.27	2.21	2.16	2.09	2.01	1.93	1.89	1.84	1.79	1.74	1.68	1.62
40	4.08	3.23	2.84	2.61	2.45	2.34	2.25	2.18	2.12	2.08	2.00	1.92	1.84	1.79	1.74	1.69	1.64	-1.58	1.51
60	4.00	3.15	2.76	2.53	2.37	2.25	2.17	2.10	2.04	1.99	1.92	1.84	1.75	1.70	1.65	1.59	1.53	1.47	1.39
120	3.92	3.07	2.66	2.45	2.29	2.17	2.09	2.02	1.96	1.91	1.83	1.75	1.66	1.61	1.55	1.50	1.43	1.35	1.25
∞	3.84	3.00	2.00	2.37	2.21	2.10	2.01	1.94	1.86	1.83	1.75	1.67	1.57	1.52	1.46	1.39	1.32	1.22	1.00

Table 5 Critical Values of F (Continued)

$\alpha = .025$

$0 \qquad F_{U(\alpha,\,df_1,\,df_2)}$

Numerator df_1

Denominator df_2	1	2	3	4	5	6	7	8	9	10	12	15	20	24	30	40	60	120	∞
1	647.8	799.5	864.2	899.6	921.8	937.1	948.2	956.7	963.3	968.6	976.7	984.9	993.1	997.2	1001	1006	1010	1014	1018
2	38.51	39.00	39.17	39.26	39.30	39.33	39.36	39.37	39.39	39.40	39.41	39.43	39.45	39.46	39.46	39.47	39.48	39.49	39.50
3	17.44	16.04	15.44	15.10	14.88	14.73	14.62	14.54	14.47	14.42	14.34	14.25	14.17	14.12	14.08	14.04	13.99	13.95	13.90
4	12.22	10.65	9.98	9.60	9.36	9.20	9.07	8.98	8.90	8.84	8.75	8.66	8.56	8.51	8.46	8.41	8.36	8.31	8.26
5	10.01	8.43	7.76	7.39	7.15	6.98	6.85	6.76	6.68	6.62	6.52	6.43	6.33	6.28	6.23	6.18	6.12	6.07	6.02
6	8.81	7.26	6.60	6.23	5.99	5.82	5.70	5.60	5.52	5.46	5.37	5.27	5.17	5.12	5.07	5.01	4.96	4.90	4.85
7	8.07	6.54	5.89	5.52	5.29	5.12	4.99	4.90	4.82	4.76	4.67	4.57	4.47	4.42	4.36	4.31	4.25	4.20	4.14
8	7.57	6.06	5.42	5.05	4.82	4.65	4.53	4.43	4.36	4.30	4.20	4.10	4.00	3.95	3.89	3.84	3.78	3.73	3.67
9	7.21	5.71	5.08	4.72	4.48	4.32	4.20	4.10	4.03	3.96	3.87	3.77	3.67	3.61	3.56	3.51	3.45	3.39	3.33
10	6.94	5.46	4.83	4.47	4.24	4.07	3.95	3.85	3.78	3.72	3.62	3.52	3.42	3.37	3.31	3.26	3.20	3.14	3.08
11	6.72	5.26	4.63	4.28	4.04	3.88	3.76	3.66	3.59	3.53	3.43	3.33	3.23	3.17	3.12	3.06	3.00	2.94	2.88
12	6.55	5.10	4.47	4.12	3.89	3.73	3.61	3.51	3.44	3.37	3.28	3.18	3.07	3.02	2.96	2.91	2.85	2.79	2.72
13	6.41	4.97	4.36	4.00	3.77	3.60	3.48	3.39	3.31	3.25	3.15	3.05	2.95	2.89	2.84	2.78	2.72	2.66	2.60
14	6.30	4.86	4.24	3.89	3.66	3.50	3.38	3.29	3.21	3.15	3.05	2.95	2.84	2.79	2.73	2.67	2.61	2.55	2.49
15	6.20	4.77	4.15	3.80	3.58	3.41	3.29	3.20	3.12	3.06	2.96	2.86	2.76	2.70	2.64	2.59	2.52	2.46	2.40
16	6.12	4.69	4.08	3.73	3.50	3.34	3.22	3.12	3.05	2.99	2.89	2.79	2.68	2.63	2.57	2.51	2.45	2.38	2.32
17	6.04	4.62	4.01	3.66	3.44	3.28	3.16	3.06	2.98	2.92	2.82	2.72	2.62	2.56	2.50	2.44	2.38	2.32	2.25
18	5.98	4.56	3.95	3.61	3.38	3.22	3.10	3.01	2.93	2.87	2.77	2.67	2.56	2.50	2.44	2.38	2.32	2.26	2.19
19	5.92	4.51	3.90	3.56	3.33	3.17	3.05	2.96	2.88	2.82	2.72	2.62	2.51	2.45	2.39	2.33	2.27	2.20	2.13
20	5.87	4.46	3.86	3.51	3.29	3.13	3.01	2.91	2.84	2.77	2.68	2.57	2.46	2.41	2.35	2.29	2.22	2.16	2.09
21	5.83	4.42	3.82	3.48	3.25	3.09	2.97	2.87	2.80	2.73	2.64	2.53	2.42	2.37	2.31	2.25	2.18	2.11	2.04
22	5.79	4.38	3.78	3.44	3.22	3.05	2.93	2.84	2.76	2.70	2.60	2.50	2.39	2.33	2.27	2.21	2.14	2.08	2.00
23	5.75	4.35	3.75	3.41	3.18	3.02	2.90	2.81	2.73	2.67	2.57	2.47	2.36	2.30	2.24	2.18	2.11	2.04	1.97
24	5.72	4.32	3.72	3.38	3.15	2.99	2.87	2.78	2.70	2.64	2.54	2.44	2.33	2.27	2.21	2.15	2.08	2.01	1.94
25	5.69	4.29	3.69	3.35	3.13	2.97	2.85	2.75	2.68	2.61	2.51	2.41	2.30	2.24	2.18	2.12	2.05	1.98	1.91
26	5.65	4.27	3.67	3.33	3.10	2.94	2.82	2.73	2.65	2.59	2.49	2.39	2.28	2.22	2.16	2.09	2.03	1.95	1.88
27	5.63	4.24	3.65	3.31	3.08	2.92	2.80	2.71	2.63	2.57	2.47	2.36	2.25	2.19	2.13	2.07	2.00	1.93	1.85
28	5.61	4.22	3.63	3.29	3.06	2.90	2.78	2.69	2.61	2.55	2.45	2.34	2.23	2.17	2.11	2.05	1.98	1.91	1.83
29	5.59	4.20	3.61	3.27	3.04	2.88	2.76	2.67	2.59	2.53	2.43	2.32	2.21	2.15	2.09	2.03	1.96	1.89	1.81
30	5.57	4.18	3.58	3.25	3.03	2.87	2.75	2.65	2.57	2.51	2.41	2.31	2.20	2.14	2.07	2.01	1.94	1.87	1.79
40	5.42	4.05	3.46	3.13	2.90	2.74	2.62	2.53	2.45	2.39	2.29	2.18	2.07	2.01	1.94	1.88	1.80	1.72	1.64
60	5.28	3.93	3.34	3.01	2.79	2.63	2.51	2.41	2.33	2.27	2.17	2.06	1.94	1.88	1.82	1.74	1.67	1.58	1.48
120	5.15	3.80	3.23	2.89	2.67	2.52	2.39	2.30	2.22	2.16	2.05	1.94	1.82	1.76	1.69	1.61	1.53	1.43	1.31
∞	5.02	3.69	3.12	2.79	2.57	2.41	2.29	2.19	2.11	2.05	1.94	1.83	1.71	1.64	1.57	1.48	1.39	1.27	1.00

Table 5 Critical Values of F (Continued)

$\alpha = .01$

$F_{U(\alpha, df_1, df_2)}$

Denominator

df_2	Numerator df_1																		
	1	2	3	4	5	6	7	8	9	10	12	15	20	24	30	40	60	120	∞
1	4052	4999.5	5403	5625	5764	5859	5928	5982	6022	6056	6106	6157	6209	6235	6261	6287	6313	6339	6366
2	98.50	99.00	99.17	99.25	99.30	99.33	99.36	99.37	99.39	99.40	99.42	99.43	99.45	99.46	99.47	99.47	99.48	99.49	99.50
3	34.12	30.82	29.46	28.71	28.24	27.91	27.67	27.49	27.35	27.23	27.05	26.87	26.69	26.60	26.50	26.41	26.32	26.22	26.13
4	21.20	18.00	16.69	15.98	15.52	15.21	14.98	14.80	14.66	14.55	14.37	14.20	14.02	13.93	13.84	13.75	13.65	13.56	13.46
5	16.26	13.27	12.06	11.39	10.97	10.67	10.46	10.29	10.16	10.05	9.89	9.72	9.55	9.47	9.38	9.29	9.20	9.11	9.02
6	13.75	10.92	9.78	9.15	8.75	8.47	8.26	8.10	7.98	7.87	7.72	7.56	7.40	7.31	7.23	7.14	7.06	6.97	6.88
7	12.25	9.55	8.45	7.85	7.46	7.19	6.99	6.84	6.72	6.62	6.47	6.31	6.16	6.07	5.99	5.91	5.82	5.74	5.65
8	11.26	8.65	7.59	7.01	6.63	6.37	6.18	6.03	5.91	5.81	5.67	5.52	5.36	5.28	5.20	5.12	5.03	4.95	4.86
9	10.56	8.02	6.99	6.42	6.06	5.80	5.61	5.47	5.35	5.26	5.11	4.96	4.81	4.73	4.65	4.57	4.48	4.40	4.31
10	10.04	7.56	6.55	5.99	5.64	5.39	5.20	5.06	4.94	4.85	4.71	4.56	4.41	4.33	4.25	4.17	4.08	4.00	3.91
11	9.65	7.21	6.22	5.67	5.32	5.07	4.89	4.74	4.63	4.54	4.40	4.25	4.10	4.02	3.94	3.86	3.78	3.69	3.60
12	9.33	6.93	5.95	5.41	5.06	4.82	4.64	4.50	4.39	4.30	4.16	4.01	3.86	3.78	3.70	3.62	3.54	3.45	3.36
13	9.07	6.70	5.74	5.21	4.86	4.62	4.44	4.30	4.19	4.10	3.96	3.82	3.66	3.59	3.51	3.43	3.34	3.25	3.17
14	8.86	6.51	5.56	5.04	4.69	4.46	4.28	4.14	4.03	3.94	3.80	3.66	3.51	3.43	3.35	3.27	3.18	3.09	3.00
15	8.68	6.36	5.42	4.89	4.56	4.32	4.14	4.00	3.89	3.80	3.67	3.52	3.37	3.29	3.21	3.13	3.05	2.96	2.87
16	8.53	6.23	5.29	4.77	4.44	4.20	4.03	3.89	3.78	3.69	3.55	3.41	3.26	3.18	3.10	3.02	2.93	2.84	2.75
17	8.40	6.11	5.18	4.67	4.34	4.10	3.93	3.79	3.68	3.59	3.46	3.31	3.16	3.08	3.00	2.92	2.83	2.75	2.65
18	8.29	6.01	5.09	4.58	4.25	4.01	3.84	3.71	3.60	3.51	3.37	3.23	3.08	3.00	2.92	2.84	2.75	2.66	2.57
19	8.18	5.93	5.01	4.50	4.17	3.94	3.77	3.63	3.52	3.43	3.30	3.15	3.00	2.92	2.84	2.76	2.67	2.58	2.49
20	8.10	5.85	4.94	4.43	4.10	3.87	3.70	3.56	3.46	3.37	3.23	3.09	2.94	2.86	2.78	2.69	2.61	2.52	2.42
21	8.02	5.78	4.87	4.37	4.04	3.81	3.64	3.51	3.40	3.31	3.17	3.03	2.88	2.80	2.72	2.64	2.55	2.46	2.36
22	7.95	5.72	4.82	4.31	3.99	3.76	3.59	3.45	3.35	3.26	3.12	2.98	2.83	2.75	2.67	2.58	2.50	2.40	2.31
23	7.88	5.66	4.76	4.26	3.94	3.71	3.54	3.41	3.30	3.21	3.07	2.93	2.78	2.70	2.62	2.54	2.45	2.35	2.26
24	7.82	5.61	4.72	4.22	3.90	3.67	3.50	3.36	3.26	3.17	3.03	2.89	2.74	2.66	2.58	2.49	2.40	2.31	2.21
25	7.77	5.57	4.68	4.18	3.85	3.63	3.46	3.32	3.22	3.13	2.99	2.85	2.70	2.62	2.54	2.45	2.36	2.27	2.17
26	7.72	5.53	4.64	4.14	3.82	3.59	3.42	3.29	3.18	3.09	2.96	2.81	2.66	2.58	2.50	2.42	2.33	2.23	2.13
27	7.68	5.49	4.60	4.11	3.78	3.56	3.39	3.26	3.16	3.06	2.93	2.78	2.63	2.55	2.47	2.38	2.29	2.20	2.10
28	7.64	5.45	4.57	4.07	3.75	3.53	3.36	3.23	3.12	3.03	2.90	2.75	2.60	2.52	2.44	2.35	2.26	2.17	2.06
29	7.60	5.42	4.54	4.04	3.73	3.50	3.33	3.20	3.09	3.00	2.87	2.73	2.57	2.49	2.41	2.33	2.23	2.14	2.03
30	7.56	5.39	4.51	4.02	3.70	3.47	3.30	3.17	3.07	2.98	2.84	2.70	2.55	2.47	2.39	2.30	2.21	2.11	2.01
40	7.31	5.18	4.31	3.83	3.51	3.29	3.12	2.99	2.89	2.80	2.66	2.52	2.37	2.29	2.20	2.11	2.02	1.92	1.80
60	7.08	4.98	4.13	3.65	3.34	3.12	2.95	2.82	2.72	2.63	2.50	2.35	2.20	2.12	2.03	1.94	1.84	1.73	1.60
120	6.85	4.79	3.95	3.48	3.17	2.96	2.79	2.66	2.56	2.47	2.34	2.19	2.03	1.95	1.86	1.76	1.66	1.53	1.38
∞	6.63	4.61	3.78	3.32	3.02	2.80	2.64	2.51	2.41	2.32	2.18	2.04	1.88	1.79	1.70	1.59	1.47	1.32	1.00

Table 5 Critical Values of *F* (*Continued*)

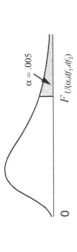

$\alpha = .005$

$F_{U(\alpha, df_1, df_2)}$

Denominator df_2	Numerator df_1																		
	1	*2*	*3*	*4*	*5*	*6*	*7*	*8*	*9*	*10*	*12*	*15*	*20*	*24*	*30*	*40*	*60*	*120*	∞
1	16211	20000	21615	22500	23056	23437	23715	23925	24091	24224	24426	24630	24836	24940	25044	25148	25253	25359	25465
2	198.5	199.0	199.2	199.2	199.3	199.3	199.4	199.4	199.4	199.4	199.4	199.4	199.4	199.5	199.5	199.5	199.5	199.5	199.5
3	55.55	49.80	47.47	46.19	45.39	44.84	44.43	44.13	43.88	43.69	43.39	43.08	42.78	42.62	42.47	42.31	42.15	41.99	41.83
4	31.33	26.28	24.26	23.15	22.46	21.97	21.62	21.35	21.14	20.97	20.70	20.44	20.17	20.03	19.89	19.75	19.61	19.47	19.32
5	22.78	18.31	16.53	15.56	14.94	14.51	14.20	13.96	13.77	13.62	13.38	13.15	12.90	12.78	12.66	12.53	12.40	12.27	12.14
6	18.63	14.54	12.92	12.03	11.46	11.07	10.79	10.57	10.39	10.25	10.03	9.81	9.59	9.47	9.36	9.24	9.12	9.00	8.88
7	16.24	12.40	10.88	10.05	9.52	9.16	8.89	8.68	8.51	8.38	8.18	7.97	7.75	7.65	7.53	7.42	7.31	7.19	7.08
8	14.69	11.04	9.60	8.61	8.30	7.95	7.69	7.50	7.34	7.21	7.01	6.81	6.61	6.50	6.40	6.29	6.18	6.06	5.95
9	13.61	10.11	8.72	7.96	7.47	7.13	6.88	6.69	6.54	6.42	6.23	6.03	5.83	5.73	5.62	5.52	5.41	5.30	5.19
10	12.83	9.43	8.08	7.34	6.87	6.54	6.30	6.12	5.97	5.85	5.66	5.47	5.27	5.17	5.07	4.97	4.86	4.75	4.64
11	12.23	8.91	7.60	6.88	6.42	6.10	5.86	5.68	5.54	5.42	5.24	5.05	4.86	4.76	4.65	4.55	4.44	4.34	4.23
12	11.75	8.51	7.23	6.52	6.07	5.76	5.52	5.35	5.20	5.09	4.91	4.72	4.53	4.43	4.33	4.23	4.12	4.01	3.90
13	11.37	8.19	6.93	6.23	5.79	5.48	5.25	5.08	4.94	4.82	4.64	4.46	4.27	4.17	4.07	3.97	3.87	3.76	3.65
14	11.06	7.92	6.68	6.00	5.56	5.26	5.03	4.86	4.72	4.60	4.43	4.25	4.06	3.96	3.86	3.76	3.66	3.55	3.44
15	10.80	7.70	6.48	5.80	5.37	5.07	4.85	4.67	4.54	4.42	4.25	4.07	3.88	3.79	3.69	3.58	3.48	3.37	3.26
16	10.58	7.51	6.30	5.64	5.21	4.91	4.69	4.52	4.38	4.27	4.10	3.92	3.73	3.64	3.54	3.44	3.33	3.22	3.11
17	10.38	7.35	6.16	5.50	5.07	4.78	4.56	4.39	4.25	4.14	3.97	3.79	3.61	3.51	3.41	3.31	3.21	3.10	2.98
18	10.22	7.21	6.03	5.37	4.96	4.66	4.44	4.28	4.14	4.03	3.86	3.68	3.50	3.40	3.30	3.20	3.10	2.99	2.87
19	10.07	7.09	5.92	5.27	4.85	4.56	4.34	4.18	4.04	3.93	3.76	3.59	3.40	3.31	3.21	3.11	3.00	2.89	2.78
20	9.94	6.99	5.82	5.17	4.76	4.47	4.26	4.09	3.96	3.85	3.68	3.50	3.32	3.22	3.12	3.02	2.92	2.81	2.69
21	9.83	6.89	5.73	5.09	4.68	4.39	4.18	4.01	3.88	3.77	3.60	3.43	3.24	3.15	3.05	2.95	2.84	2.73	2.61
22	9.73	6.81	5.65	5.02	4.61	4.32	4.11	3.94	3.81	3.70	3.54	3.35	3.18	3.08	2.98	2.88	2.77	2.68	2.55
23	9.83	6.73	5.58	4.95	4.54	4.26	4.05	3.88	3.75	3.64	3.47	3.30	3.12	3.02	2.92	2.82	2.71	2.60	2.48
24	9.55	6.66	5.52	4.89	4.49	4.20	3.99	3.83	3.69	3.59	3.42	3.25	3.06	2.97	2.87	2.77	2.66	2.55	2.43
25	9.48	6.60	5.46	4.84	4.43	4.15	3.94	3.78	3.64	3.54	3.37	3.20	3.01	2.92	2.82	2.72	2.61	2.50	2.38
26	9.41	6.54	5.41	4.79	4.38	4.10	3.89	3.73	3.60	3.49	3.33	3.15	2.97	2.87	2.77	2.67	2.56	2.45	2.33
27	9.34	6.49	5.36	4.74	4.34	4.06	3.85	3.69	3.56	3.45	3.28	3.11	2.93	2.83	2.73	2.63	2.52	2.41	2.29
28	9.28	6.44	5.32	4.70	4.30	4.02	3.81	3.65	3.52	3.41	3.25	3.07	2.89	2.79	2.69	2.59	2.48	2.37	2.25
29	9.23	6.40	5.28	4.66	4.26	3.98	3.77	3.61	3.48	3.38	3.21	3.04	2.86	2.76	2.66	2.56	2.45	2.33	2.21
30	9.18	6.35	5.24	4.62	4.23	3.95	3.74	3.58	3.45	3.34	3.18	3.01	2.82	2.73	2.63	2.52	2.42	2.30	2.18
40	8.83	6.07	4.96	4.37	3.99	3.71	3.51	3.35	3.22	3.12	2.95	2.78	2.60	2.50	2.40	2.30	2.18	2.06	1.93
60	8.49	5.78	4.73	4.14	3.76	3.49	3.29	3.13	3.01	2.90	2.74	2.57	2.39	2.29	2.19	2.08	1.98	1.83	1.69
120	8.18	5.54	4.50	3.92	3.55	3.28	3.09	2.93	2.81	2.71	2.54	2.37	2.19	2.09	1.98	1.87	1.75	1.61	1.43
∞	7.88	5.30	4.28	3.72	3.35	3.09	2.90	2.74	2.62	2.52	2.36	2.19	2.00	1.90	1.79	1.67	1.53	1.36	1.00

Source: Reprinted from E. S. Pearson and H. O. Hartley, eds., Biometrika Tables for Statisticians, 3d ed., 1966, by permission of the Biometrika Trustees.

Table 6 The Cumulative Binomial Distribution*

n	r	p = .10	p = .20	p = .25	p = .30	p = .40	p = .50
5	0	.59049	.32768	.23730	.16807	.07776	.03125
	1	.91854	.73728	.63281	.52822	.33696	.18750
	2	.99144	.94208	.89648	.83692	.68256	.50000
	3	.99954	.99328	.98437	.96922	.91296	.81250
	4	.99999	.99968	.99902	.99757	.98976	.96875
	5	1.00000	1.00000	1.00000	1.00000	1.00000	1.00000
10	0	.34868	.10737	.05631	.02825	.00605	.00098
	1	.73610	.37581	.24403	.14931	.04636	.01074
	2	.92981	.67780	.52559	.38278	.16729	.05469
	3	.98720	.87913	.77588	.64961	.38228	.17187
	4	.99837	.96721	.92187	.84973	.63310	.37695
	5	.99985	.99363	.98027	.95265	.83376	.62305
	6	.99999	.99914	.99649	.98941	.94524	.82812
	7	1.00000	.99992	.99958	.99841	.98771	.94531
	8		1.00000	.99997	.99986	.99832	.98926
	9			1.00000	.99999	.99990	.99902
	10				1.00000	1.00000	1.00000
15	0	.20589	.03518	.01336	.00475	.00047	.00003
	1	.54904	.16713	.08018	.03527	.00517	.00049
	2	.81594	.39802	.23609	.12683	.02711	.00369
	3	.94444	.64816	.46129	.29687	.09050	.01758
	4	.98728	.83577	.68649	.51549	.21728	.05923
	5	.99775	.93895	.85163	.72162	.40322	.15088
	6	.99969	.98194	.94338	.86886	.60981	.30362
	7	.99997	.99576	.98270	.94999	.78690	.50000
	8	1.00000	.99921	.99581	.98476	.90495	.69638
	9		.99989	.99921	.99635	.96617	.84912
	10		.99999	.99988	.99933	.99065	.94077
	11		1.00000	.99999	.99991	.99807	.98242
	12			1.00000	.99999	.99972	.99631
	13				1.00000	.99997	.99951
	14					1.00000	.99997
	15						1.00000
20	0	.12158	.01153	.00317	.00080	.00004	.00000
	1	.39175	.06918	.02431	.00764	.00052	.00002
	2	.67693	.20608	.09126	.03548	.00361	.00020
	3	.86705	.41145	.22516	.10709	.01596	.00129
	4	.95683	.62965	.41484	.23751	.05095	.00591
	5	.98875	.80421	.61717	.41637	.12560	.02069
	6	.99761	.91331	.78578	.60801	.25001	.05766
	7	.99958	.96786	.89819	.77227	.41589	.13159
	8	.99994	.99002	.95907	.88667	.59560	.25172
	9	.99999	.99741	.98614	.95204	.75534	.41190
	10	1.00000	.99944	.99606	.98286	.87248	.58810
	11		.99990	.99906	.99486	.94347	.74828
	12		.99998	.99982	.99872	.97897	.86841
	13		1.00000	.99997	.99974	.99353	.94234

Table 6 The Cumulative Binomial Distribution (Continued)

n	r	p = .10	p = .20	p = .25	p = .30	p = .40	p = .50
20	14			1.00000	.99996	.99839	.97931
	15				.99999	.99968	.99409
	16				1.00000	.99995	.99871
	17					.99999	.99980
	18					1.00000	.99998
	19						1.00000
25	0	.07179	.00378	.00075	.00013	.00000	.00000
	1	.27121	.02739	.00702	.00157	.00005	.00000
	2	.53709	.09823	.03211	.00896	.00043	.00001
	3	.76359	.23399	.09621	.03324	.00237	.00008
	4	.90201	.42067	.21374	.09047	.00947	.00046
	5	.96660	.61669	.37828	.19349	.02936	.00204
	6	.99052	.78004	.56110	.34065	.07357	.02164
	7	.99774	.89088	.72651	.51185	.15355	.05388
	8	.99954	.95323	.85056	.67693	.27353	.11476
	9	.99992	.98267	.92867	.81056	.42462	.21218
	10	.99999	.99445	.97033	.90220	.58577	.34502
	11	1.00000	.99846	.98027	.95575	.73228	.50000
	12		.99963	.99663	.98253	.84623	.65498
	13		.99992	.99908	.99401	.92220	.78782
	14		.99999	.99979	.99822	.96561	.88524
	15		1.00000	.99996	.99955	.98683	.94612
	16			.99999	.99990	.99567	.97836
	17			1.00000	.99998	.99879	.99268
	18				1.00000	.99972	.99796
	19					.99995	.99954
	20					.99999	.99992
	21					1.00000	.99999
	22						1.00000
	23						
50	0	.00515	.00001	.00000	.00000		
	1	.03379	.00019	.00001	.00000		
	2	.11173	.00129	.00009	.00000		
	3	.25029	.00566	.00050	.00003		
	4	.43120	.01850	.00211	.00017		
	5	.61612	.04803	.00705	.00072	.00000	
	6	.77023	.10340	.01939	.00249	.00001	
	7	.87785	.19041	.04526	.00726	.00006	
	8	.94213	.30733	.09160	.01825	.00023	
	9	.97546	.44374	.16368	.04023	.00076	.00000
	10	.99065	.58356	.26220	.07885	.00220	.00001
	11	.99678	.71067	.38162	.13904	.00569	.00005
	12	.99900	.81394	.51099	.22287	.01325	.00015
	13	.99971	.88941	.63704	.32788	.02799	.00047
	14	.99993	.93928	.74808	.44683	.05396	.00130
	15	.99998	.96920	.83692	.56918	.09550	.00330
	16	1.00000	.98556	.90169	.68388	.15609	.00767
	17		.99374	.94488	.78219	.23688	.01642

Table 6 The Cumulative Binomial Distribution (*Continued*)

n	r	p = .10	p = .20	p = .25	p = .30	p = .40	p = .50
50	18		.99749	.97127	.85944	.33561	.03245
	19		.99907	.98608	.91520	.44648	.05946
	20		.99968	.99374	.95224	.56103	.10132
	21		.99990	.99738	.97491	.67014	.16112
	22		.99997	.99898	.98772	.76602	.23994
	23		.99999	.99963	.99441	.84383	.33591
	24		1.00000	.99988	.99763	.90219	.44386
	25			.99996	.99907	.94266	.55614
	26			.99999	.99966	.96859	.66409
	27			1.00000	.99988	.98397	.76006
	28				.99996	.99238	.83888
	29				.99999	.99664	.89868
	30				1.00000	.99863	.94054
	31					.99948	.96755
	32					.99982	.98358
	33					.99994	.99233
	34					.99998	.99670
	35					1.00000	.99870
	36						.99953
	37						.99985
	38						.99995
	39						.99999
	40						1.00000
100	0	.00003					
	1	.00032					
	2	.00194					
	3	.00784					
	4	.02371	.00000				
	5	.05758	.00002				
	6	.11716	.00008				
	7	.20605	.00028	.00000			
	8	.32087	.00086	.00001			
	9	.45129	.00233	.00004			
	10	.58316	.00570	.00014	.00000		
	11	.70303	.01257	.00039	.00001		
	12	.80182	.02533	.00103	.00002		
	13	.87612	.04691	.00246	.00006		
	14	.92743	.08044	.00542	.00016		
	15	.96011	.12851	.01108	.00040		
	16	.97940	.19234	.02111	.00097		
	17	.98999	.27119	.03763	.00216		
	18	.99542	.36209	.06301	.00452	.00000	
	19	.99802	.46016	.09953	.00889	.00001	
	20	.99919	.55946	.14883	.01646	.00002	
	21	.99969	.65403	.21144	.02883	.00004	
	22	.99989	.73893	.28637	.04787	.00011	
	23	.99996	.81091	.37018	.07553	.00025	
	24	.99999	.86865	.46167	.11357	.00056	
	25	1.00000	.91252	.55347	.16313	.00119	

Table 6 The Cumulative Binomial Distribution (*Continued*)

n	r	p = .10	p = .20	p = .25	p = .30	p = .40	p = .50
100	26		.94417	.64174	.22440	.00240	
	27		.96585	.72238	.29637	.00460	.00000
	28		.97998	.79246	.37678	.00843	.00001
	29		.98875	.85046	.46234	.01478	.00002
	30		.99394	.89621	.54912	.02478	.00004
	31		.99687	.93065	.63311	.03985	.00009
	32		.99845	.95540	.71072	.06150	.00020
	33		.99926	.97241	.77926	.09125	.00044
	34		.99966	.98357	.83714	.13034	.00089
	35		.99985	.99059	.88392	.17947	.00176
	36		.99994	.99482	.92012	.23861	.00332
	37		.99998	.99725	.94695	.30681	.00602
	38		.99999	.99860	.96602	.38219	.01049
	39		1.00000	.99931	.97901	.46028	.01760
	40			.99968	.98750	.54329	.02844
	41			.99985	.99283	.62253	.04431
	42			.99994	.99603	.69674	.06661
	43			.99997	.99789	.76347	.09667
	44			.99999	.99891	.82110	.13563
	45			1.00000	.99946	.86891	.18410
	46				.99974	.90702	.24206
	47				.99988	.93621	.30865
	48				.99995	.95770	.38218
	49				.99998	.97290	.46021
	50				.99999	.98324	.53979
	51				1.00000	.98999	.61782
	52					.99424	.69135
	53					.99680	.79794
	54					.99829	.81590
	55					.99912	.86437
	56					.99956	.90333
	57					.99979	.93339
	58					.99990	.95569
	59					.99996	.97156
	60					.99998	.98240
	61					.99999	.98951
	62					1.00000	.99398
	63						.99668
	64						.99824
	65						.99911
	66						.99956
	67						.99980
	68						.99991
	69						.99996
	70						.99998
	71						.99999
	72						1.00000

From *Poisson's Binomial Exponential Limit* by E. C. Molina © 1942. Reprinted by permission of Van Nostrand Company.

Table 7 The Cumulative Poisson Distribution

r	λ = .1	λ = .2	λ = .3	λ = .4	λ = .5
0	.90484	.81873	.74082	.67032	.60653
1	.99532	.98248	.96306	.93845	.90980
2	.99985	.99885	.99640	.99207	.98561
3	1.00000	.99994	.99973	.99922	.99825
4		1.00000	.99998	.99994	.99983
5			1.00000	1.00000	.99999
6					1.0000

r	λ = .6	λ = .7	λ = .8	λ = .9	λ = 1.0
0	.54881	.49658	.44933	.40657	.36788
1	.87810	.84419	.80879	.77248	.73576
2	.97688	.96586	.95258	.93714	.91970
3	.99664	.99425	.99092	.98654	.98101
4	.99961	.99921	.99859	.99766	.99634
5	.99996	.99991	.99982	.99966	.99941
6	1.00000	.99999	.99998	.99996	.99992
7		1.00000	1.00000	1.00000	.99999
8					1.00000

r	λ = 2	λ = 3	λ = 4	λ = 5	λ = 6
0	.13534	.04979	.01832	.00674	.00248
1	.40601	.19915	.09158	.04043	.01735
2	.67668	.42319	.23810	.12465	.06197
3	.85712	.64723	.43347	.26503	.15120
4	.94735	.81526	.62884	.44049	.28506
5	.98344	.91608	.78513	.61596	.44568
6	.99547	.96649	.88933	.76218	.60630
7	.99890	98810	94887	.86663	.74398
8	.99976	.99620	.97864	.93191	.84724
9	.99995	.99890	.99187	.96817	.91608
10	.99999	.99971	.99716	.98630	.95738
11	1.00000	.99993	.99908	.99455	.97991
12		.99998	.99973	.99798	.99117
13		1.00000	.99992	.99930	.99637
14			.99998	.99977	.99860
15			1.00000	.99993	.99949
16				.99998	.99982
17				1.00000	99994
18					.99998
19					1.00000

Table 7 The Cumulative Poisson Distribution (*Continued*)

r	λ = 7	λ = 8	λ = 9	λ = 10
0	.00091	.00033	.00012	.00004
1	.00730	.00302	.00123	.00050
2	.02964	.01375	.00623	.00277
3	.08176	.04238	.02123	.01034
4	.17299	.09963	.05496	.02925
5	.30071	.19124	.11569	.06709
6	.44971	.31337	.20678	.13014
7	.59871	.45296	.32390	.22022
8	.72909	.59255	.45565	.33282
9	.83050	.71662	.58741	.45793
10	.90148	.81589	.70599	.58304
11	.94665	.88808	.80301	.69678
12	.97300	.93620	.87577	.79156
13	.98719	.96582	.92615	.86446
14	.99428	.98274	.95853	.91654
15	.99759	.99177	.97796	.95126
16	.99904	.99628	.98889	.97296
17	.99964	.99841	.99468	.98572
18	.99987	.99935	.99757	.99281
19	.99996	.99975	.99894	.99655
20	.99999	.99991	.99956	.99841
21	1.00000	.99997	.99982	.99930
22		.99999	.99993	.99970
23		1.00000	.99998	.99988
24			.99999	.99995
25			1.00000	.99998
26				.99999
27				1.00000

From *Poisson's Binomial Exponential Limit* by E. C. Molina © 1942. Reprinted by permission of Van Nostrand Reinhold Company.

Index